GEOMETRY

WITH APPLICATIONS AND PROBLEM SOLVING

GEOMETRY

WITH APPLICATIONS AND PROBLEM SOLVING

STANLEY R. CLEMENS
PHARES G. O'DAFFER
THOMAS J. COONEY

ADDISON-WESLEY PUBLISHING COMPANY

MENLO PARK, CALIFORNIA · READING, MASSACHUSETTS ·
LONDON · AMSTERDAM · DON MILLS, ONTARIO · SYDNEY

Photograph Credits

Computer Generated Geometry

1. Ramtek Corporation
2. NASA/Jet Propulsion Laboratory
3. National Center for Atmospheric Research/High Altitude Observatory/NCAR SMM/C/T: Solar Maximum Mission (NASA/GSFC funded) coronagraph/Polarimeter Experiment
4. Ramtek Corporation/NASA/Jet Propulsion Laboratory
5. Brookhaven National Laboratory/New York University Medical Center
6. Lawrence Livermore National Laboratory
7. Matrix Instruments Inc.
8. Matrix Instruments Inc.
9. Matrix Instruments Inc.

The Geometry of a Silicon Chip

1. Intel Corporation
2. Intel Corporation
3. National Semiconductor Corporation
4. Bell Laboratories
5. National Semiconductor Corporation
6. National Semiconductor Corporation
7. Intel Corporation
8. Intel Corporation
9. Intel Corporation
10. Bell Laboratories

Careers in Computers

1. NCR Corporation
2. Alex Cameron/Tandem Computers, Inc.
3. Alex Cameron/Tandem Computers, Inc.
4. Prime Computer, Inc.
5. Bell Helicopter/Textron

Geometry and Computers in Industry

1. General Motors Corporation
2. TRW, Inc.
3. California Computer Products, Inc. (CalComp).
4. Anacomp, Inc.
5. Tandy Corporation—TRS-80™. TRS-80 is a trademark of the Radio Shack Division of Tandy Corporation.
6. Sperry-Univac, a Division of Sperry Corporation
7. Lawrence Livermore National Laboratory
8. Engineered Systems, Inc., Omaha, Neb.
9. Alex Cameron/Tandem Computers, Inc.
10. National Semiconductor Corporation
11. Alex Cameron/Tandem Computers, Inc.
12. Copyright Peter Menzel
13. Trilog

Cover photo acknowledgement: © 1981 Jim Anderson/Woodfin Camp & Associates

ISBN 0-201-20343-X

BCDEFGHIJKL-VH-8987654

About the Authors

Stanley R. Clemens is Associate Professor of Mathematics at Illinois State University. He received the B.A. and M.A. degrees from Bluffton College and Indiana University respectively, and the Ph.D. degree in mathematics from the University of North Carolina. Dr. Clemens' geometry writings include several journal articles as well as *Laboratory Investigations in Geometry* and *Geometry: An Investigative Approach,* both published by Addison-Wesley.

Phares G. O'Daffer is Professor of Mathematics at Illinois State University. He received the B.A. and M.A. degrees in mathematics from Illinois State University, and the Ph.D. degree in mathematics education from the University of Illinois. Formerly a high school teacher, Dr. O'Daffer is the author or co-author of numerous articles and textbooks, including *Experiences With Geometry, Laboratory Investigations in Geometry,* and *Geometry: An Investigative Approach,* all published by Addison-Wesley. He has also served as president of the Illinois Council of Teachers of Mathematics.

Thomas J. Cooney is Professor of Mathematics Education at the University of Georgia. A former high school geometry teacher, he received the B.A. and M.A. degrees from the University of Toledo and the Ph.D. degree in mathematics education from the University of Illinois. Dr. Cooney has written several articles and textbooks in mathematics education, and he has served as president of the School Science and Mathematics Association.

Full-Color Photo Sections

Our collection of full-color photographs emphasizes two important themes of the 1980's. First, computers are valuable tools that will influence our lives greatly. Second, geometry is important and prominent in computer use.

The first collection of photos has two parts. These follow page 148.

Computer Generated Geometry
The Geometry of a Silicon Chip

The second collection focuses on careers where geometry and mathematics are important. These follow page 468.

Careers in Computers
Geometry and Computers in Industry

Preface

Geometry With Applications and Problem Solving is a new text for high school geometry. It emphasizes the strong relationship that exists between geometric content and geometric applications in the physical world. The authors built the text on the following ideas:

Geometry grows from observations of simple things and common relationships. In this book you will see theorems—basic conclusions—motivated by a physical problem, and then applied to that problem to provide a solution. Most lessons are structured around such theorems, yet provide instances of the relationship under discussion and opportunities to provide inductive reasoning.

Proof-writing skills must be developed by beginning with the simplest of situations. You will begin building your proof skills with problems that are short, simple, and involve a single concept. These lead gradually to more complex proofs in later chapters.

Geometry students should develop skills in critical thinking, logical reasoning, and problem solving. Problem solving is a prominent strand in this text. Activities and problem solving occur in each problem set. These opportunities to experiment and apply inductive reasoning skills are important to your creative development.

The study of geometry must not be isolated from the world or from other areas of mathematics. You will find special interest pages on these topics: Problem-Solving Techniques, Algebra Reviews, Geometry in Our World (applications of geometry to careers, computer graphics and hobbies), and a first chapter that provides a preview. It shows examples of geometry in the world, how to use geometry to solve problems, and geometry in recreational situations.

Other features have been designed to help make this text useful in your study of geometry:

- The language is brief but precise. Illustrations and photographs are numerous.
- Exercises are grouped into A, B, and C levels, leading from simple numerical problems to challenging proofs.
- Answers are given for most odd-numbered problems.
- List of symbols, glossary of geometric terms, and lists of theorems and postulates are in the back of the book.
- Chapter Reviews prepare you for Chapter Tests.
- Complete coverage of geometric theorems is provided, permitting you to proceed with confidence to other math courses.

You will find *Geometry with Applications and Problem Solving* success oriented but also challenging. When you complete the course you should find that the physical world is more understandable and that the geometric skills you have developed are useful in your problem-solving activities.

Stanley R. Clemens
Phares G. O'Daffer
Thomas J. Cooney

Contents

3 Triangles and Congruence 82

4 Proving Theorems Using Basic Properties 128

5 Parallel Lines and Planes 168

9 Similarity 302

10 Circles 340

11 Area and Perimeter 392

12 Solids 432

13 Transformations and Symmetry 474

14 Coordinate Geometry 502

Using Geometry—A Preview

Visualizing Geometric Figures in Nature

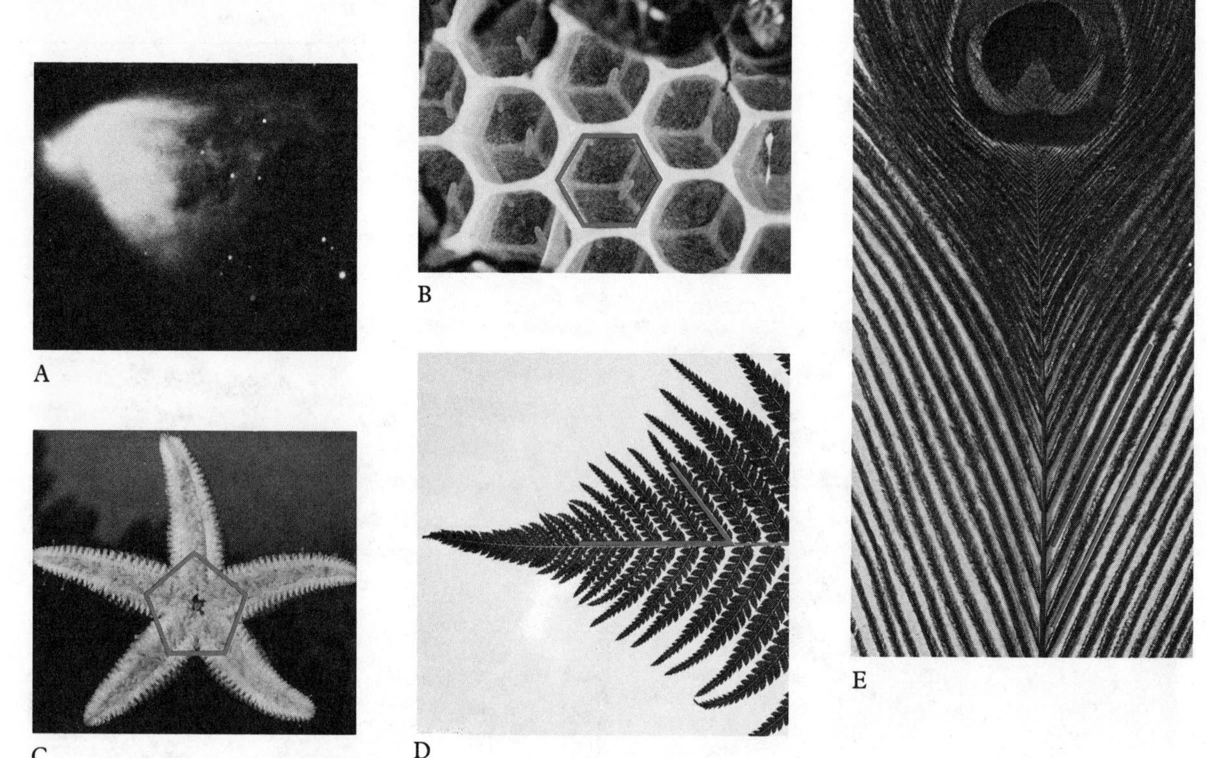

It is possible that the world of nature provided humans with their first notions of geometry. There are many examples of geometric shapes in the physical world. Over the centuries, people began to classify the shapes. They gave them names and created definitions in order to describe the things they saw.

1. Name at least one geometric figure suggested by each picture.
2. Triangles, quadrilaterals, pentagons, and hexagons are examples of geometric figures called polygons. Write the letter of each picture that suggests a polygon and name the polygon suggested.
3. We often look for relationships between two or more geometric figures. We say three points are collinear (lie on one line), two lines are parallel (do not meet), or two angles are congruent (are the same size). Write the letter of each picture that suggests a relationship and name the relationship suggested.
4. Describe at least one natural object not shown here that suggests a geometric figure or relationship.

Observing Geometric Figures in Our World

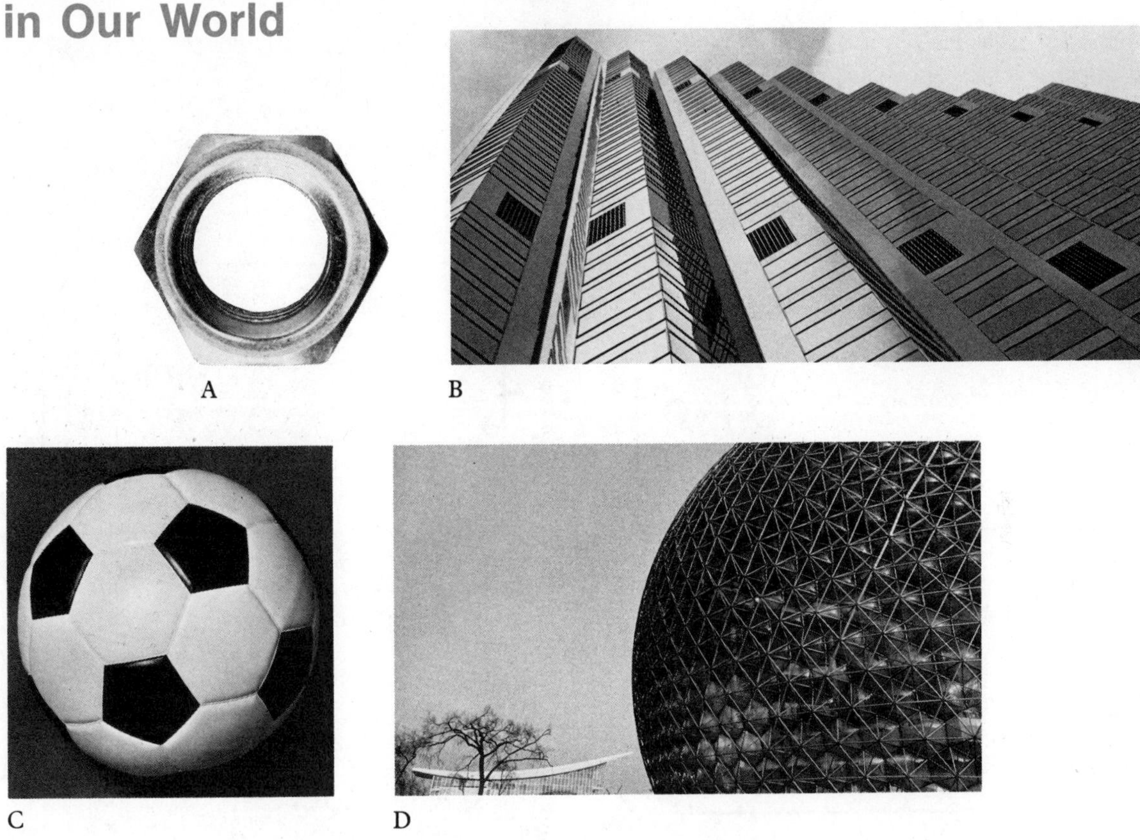

A B

C D

Throughout the ages humans have used the simple geometric shapes suggested by nature as the basis for the creation of interesting and useful objects. Because these objects are all around us, we can realize the importance of being able to talk about them. To describe our environment as we communicate with others, we need a language of geometry.

1. Name at least one geometric figure or relationship suggested by each picture.
2. As illustrated by the soccer ball, the world of sports is rich with examples of geometric figures. Give some other examples of "geometry in sports."
3. As illustrated by the geodesic dome, the world of design and architecture relies heavily on geometric figures. Find examples of "geometry in architecture" or "geometry in design" in your community, or in magazines or reference books.
4. Start a scrapbook (using photos you take or pictures from magazines) on "Geometry in Our World."

Using Geometry to Solve Problems

The study of geometry provides many useful techniques for solving problems. Relationships between geometric ideas, called theorems, are the basis for these techniques. Each of the problems below is solved using one or more theorems you will study in this geometry book.

Problem 1

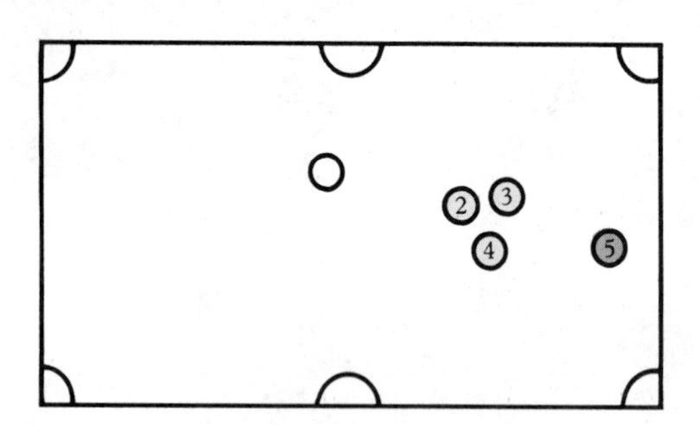

At what point on the wall do you shoot the white ball so as to bank and hit the red ball?

Solution

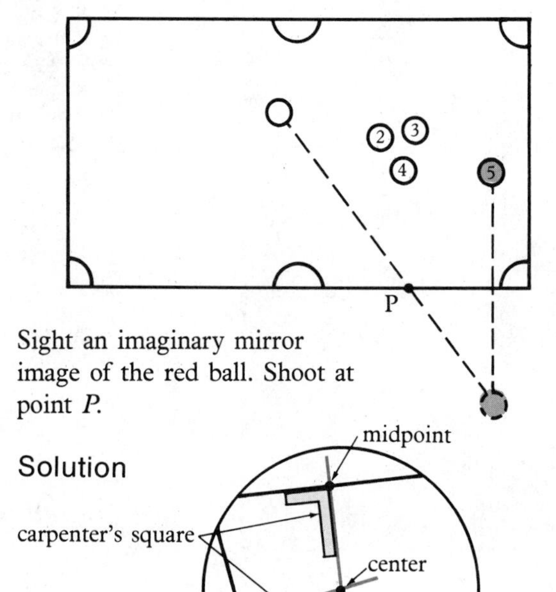

Sight an imaginary mirror image of the red ball. Shoot at point *P*.

Problem 2

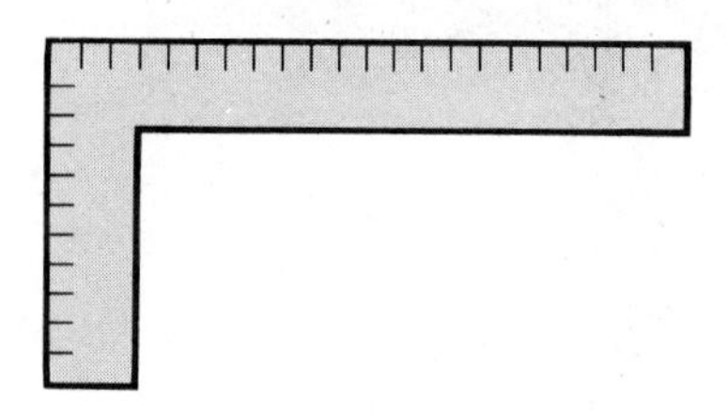

Use a carpenter's square or other object with a "square corner" to find the center of a large circular table top so that a base may be attached.

Solution

The red lines go through the midpoint of the two chords of the circle.

1. Trace this "pool table" and draw an accurate diagram showing the point at which the white ball must hit a wall to bank and strike the red ball.

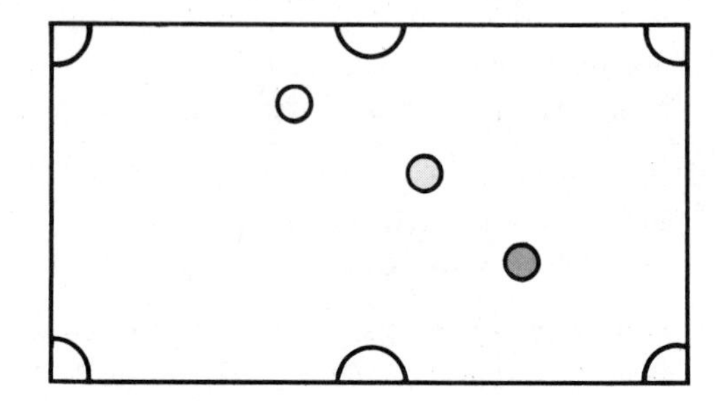

2. Draw around a circular object to produce a circle on your paper. Use a method similar to the one above to find the center of the circle.

Problem 3

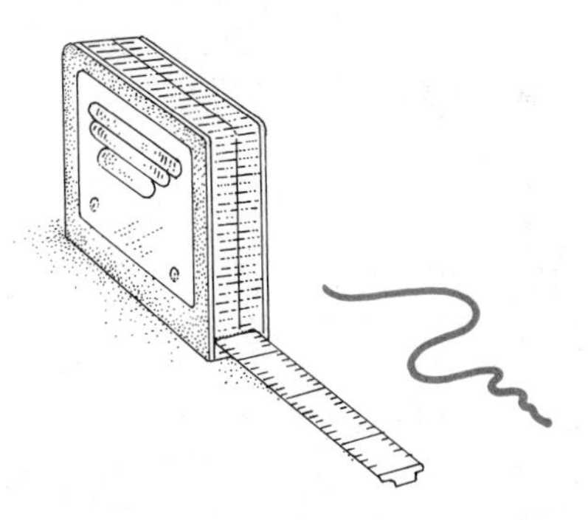

You have only string and a measuring tape. How can you mark off a square corner for a playing field?

Solution

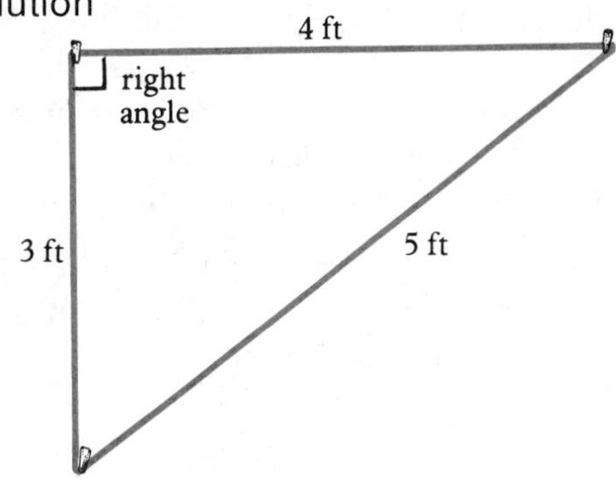

Knot the string at 3-, 4-, and 5-foot intervals and lay it out as shown.

Problem 4

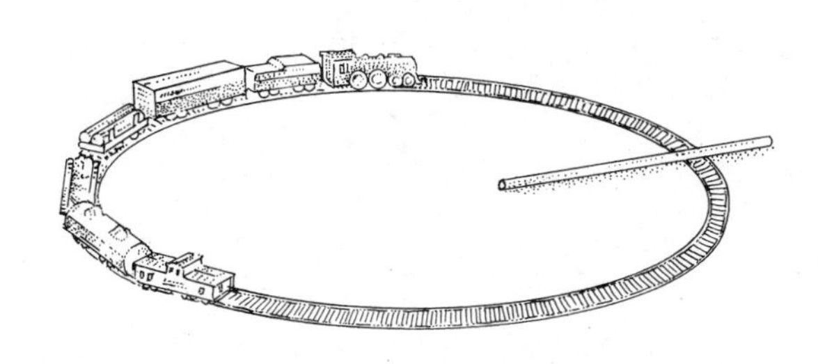

How can you quickly divide a small dowel stick into five equal lengths to make fence posts for a model train layout?

Solution

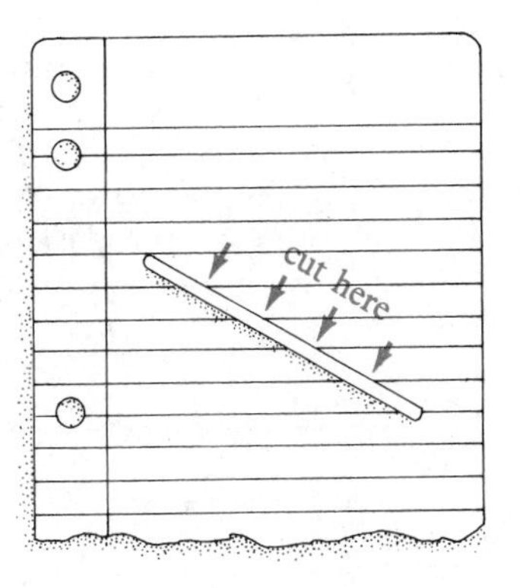

Lay the dowel across notebook paper. Mark at the lines as shown.

1. Use these segments and your compass to construct a right angle.

3 cm

4 cm

5 cm

2. Make a knotted string with 3-, 4-, and 5-decimeter segments and use it to lay off a right angle corner.
3. Cut a strip of cardboard and use the method of Problem 4 to divide the cardboard into seven equal length pieces.
4. Find a different way to accurately divide a strip of cardboard into five equal pieces.

Using Geometry for Recreation

Many ideas of geometry can be a source of humor. Other geometric puzzles can be interesting and challenging recreation. We hope you can have some fun with geometry!

Look at these "Geomotoons."

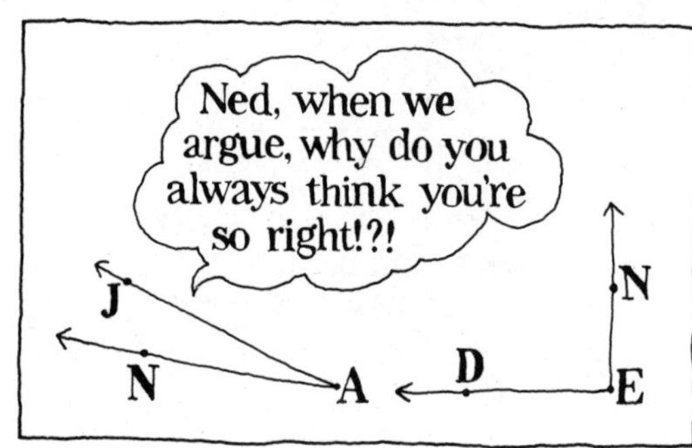

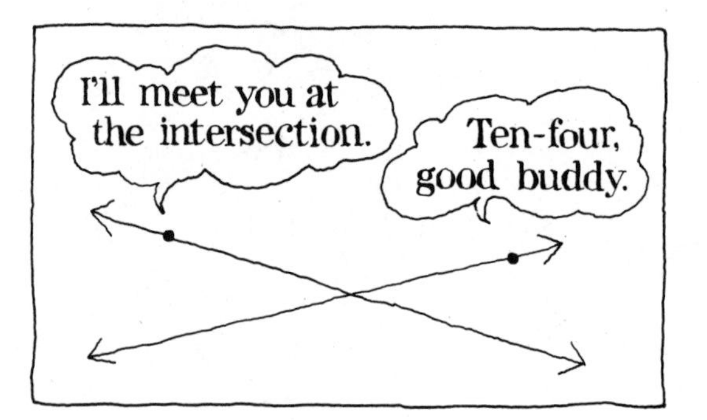

"Geodoodles" are also fun.

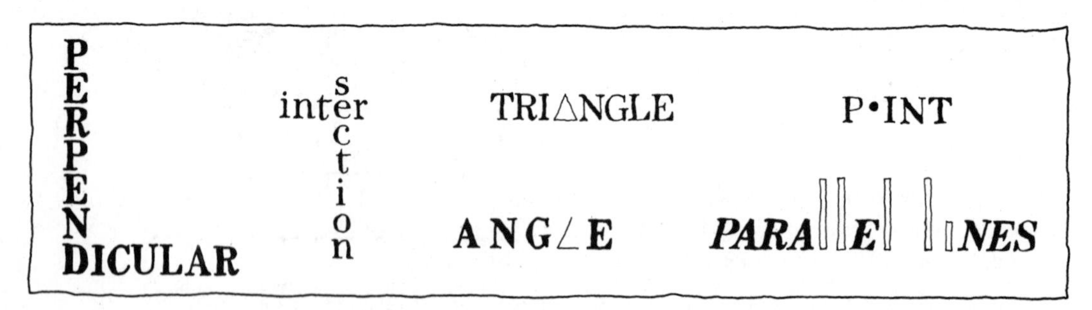

1. Create a "Geomotoon" of your own.
2. Design a "Geodoodle" of your own. You may wish to use words such as "right angle," "line," "circle," "bisect," or "square."

Try the TANGRAM Puzzle

Trace this square and cut it into seven pieces as shown. You now have the seven pieces of the famous Chinese Tangram Puzzle, which is claimed to be at least 4000 years old.

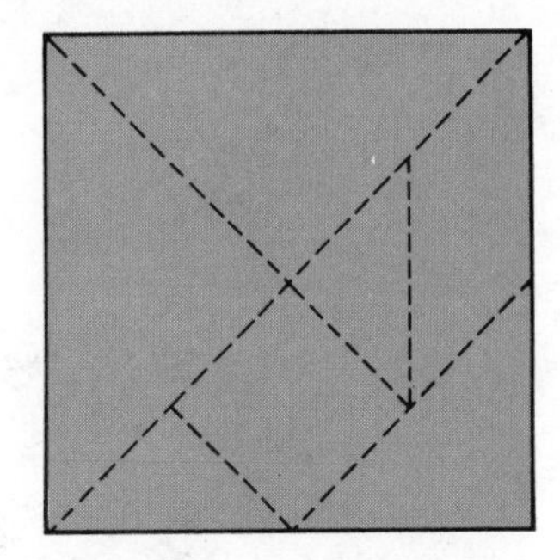

Puzzle 1

Can you place all seven tangram pieces together to form a shape like the one below?

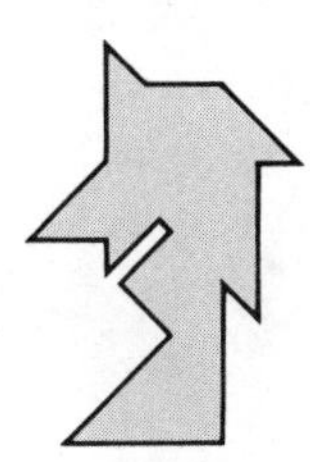

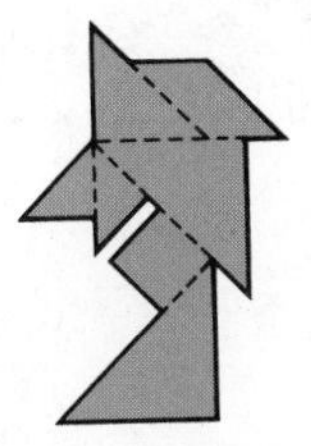

Solution

Can you place all seven tangram pieces together to form shapes like the ones below? In some cases, hints are given by the inclusion of some of the dotted lines. Draw pictures to show your solutions.

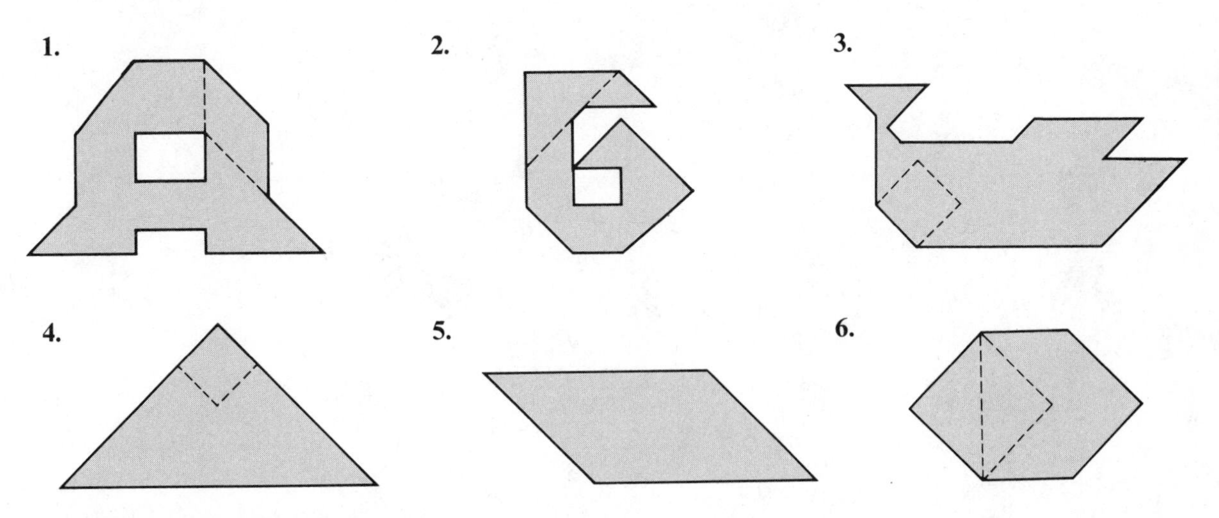

7. Make a figure of your own with the seven tangram pieces. Give your puzzle to a friend to solve.

CHAPTER 1

Definitions and Constructions

1–1 Point, Line, Plane, and Space

How would you describe a point? a line? a plane? space? These four ideas are very important in the study of geometry. Yet we will not define point, line, and plane. Instead, we will look at objects that suggest these ideas.

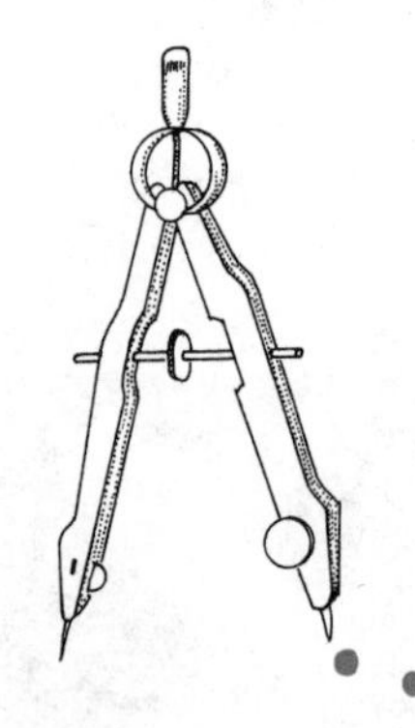

A point as a part of a physical object

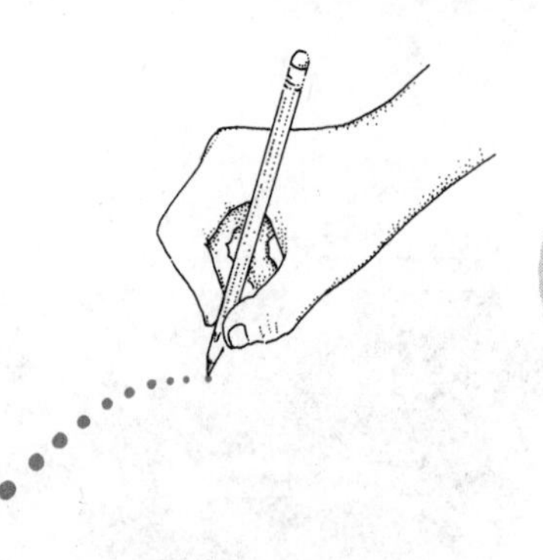

A point as the smallest dot you can draw

POINT
location, no length, width or height

A point is an idea, or abstraction. Since a point cannot be defined using simpler terms, it is an undefined term.

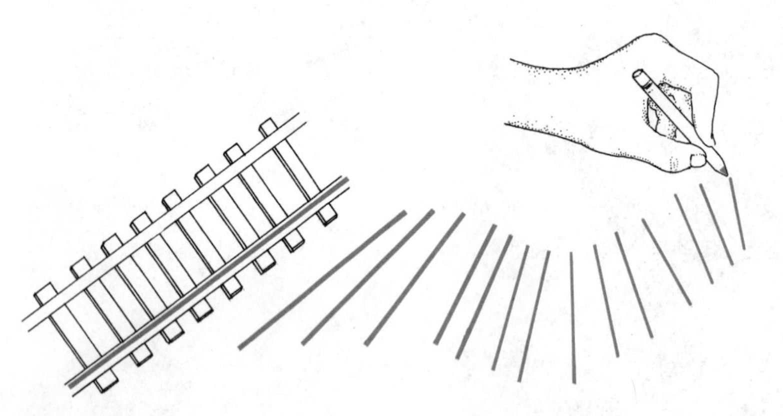

A line as part of a physical situation

A line as the thinnest streak you can draw

LINE
unlimited length, straight, no thickness, no endpoints

A line is an idea or abstraction. Since a line cannot be defined using simpler terms it is an undefined term.

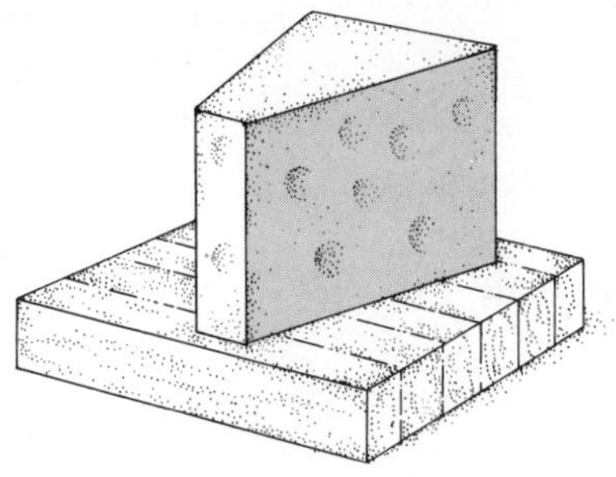

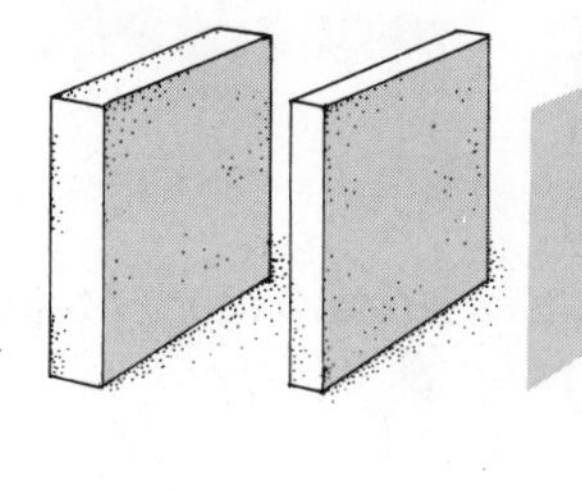

PLANE
no boundary, continues in all directions, flat, no thickness

A plane as a part of a physical object

A plane as the thinnest slice you can cut

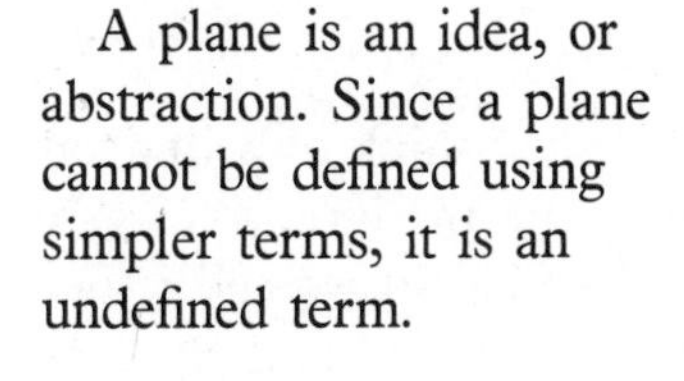

A plane is an idea, or abstraction. Since a plane cannot be defined using simpler terms, it is an undefined term.

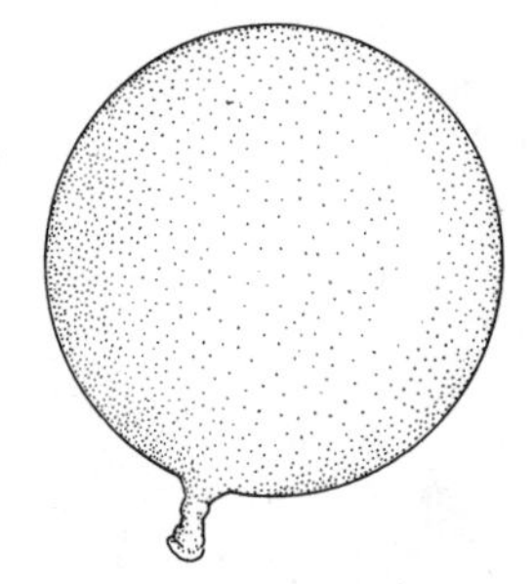

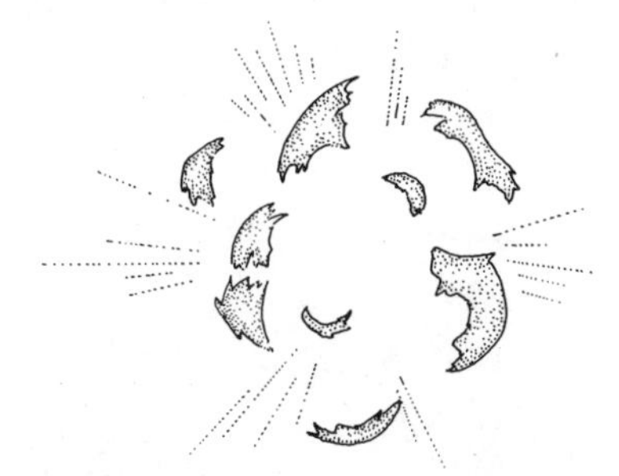

SPACE
no boundary, length, width, and height

Points on, inside, and outside the balloon

Space as that which remains after the balloon has been removed

Space is an idea, or abstraction.

Definition 1–1
Space is the set of all points.

EXERCISES

1. Indicate whether the red portion of each of these figures suggests point, line, plane, or space.

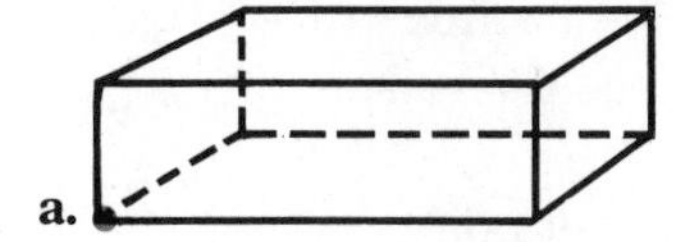

a.

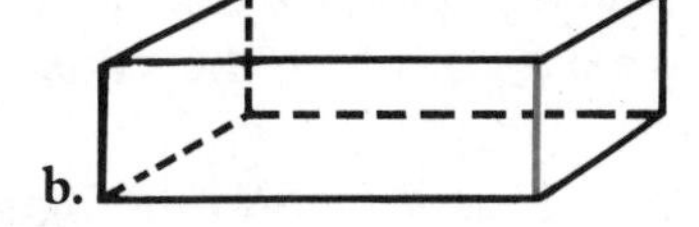

b.

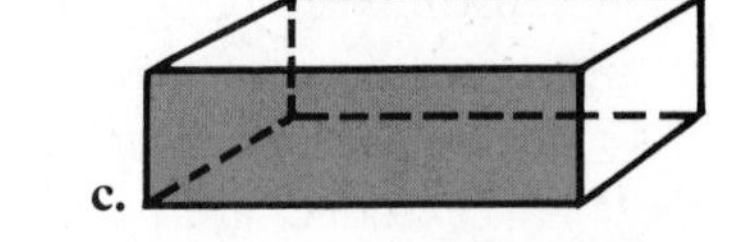

c.

2. Name five objects that are shaped so that part of them suggests the idea of point. Identify the specific part of each object.
3. Name three objects or physical situations that illustrate the idea of a line or part of a line.
4. Name five objects that are shaped so that part of them suggests the idea of plane. Identify the specific part of each object.
5. Name three objects, like the balloon, that can be used to suggest the idea of space.

1–2 Relations Among Points, Lines, and Planes

We draw dots on paper to represent points. Capital letters beside them name the points. We call them *point A, point B,* and *point C.*

We can think of a line as a set of points. By labeling a pair of points, we can name the line in terms of two points. For example, points A and B are on the line, so we call it *line AB*. We assume that only one line goes through both A and B. Another way of saying this is, *Two points determine a line.* Sometimes a line is labeled by using one small letter. Here line AB can also be called *line* ℓ.

We write: $\overleftrightarrow{AB}$

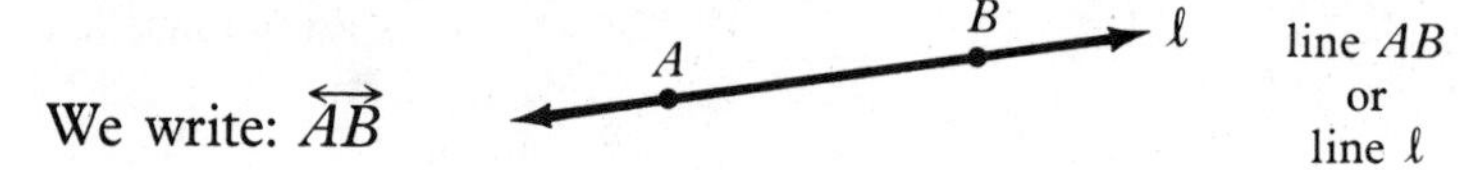

line AB
or
line ℓ

A plane can also be thought of as a set of points. A plane is named either by placing a single letter by the plane or by naming a set of three points on the plane that are not all on one line. We say *plane N* or *plane ABC.*

Points A, B, and C are on plane N.

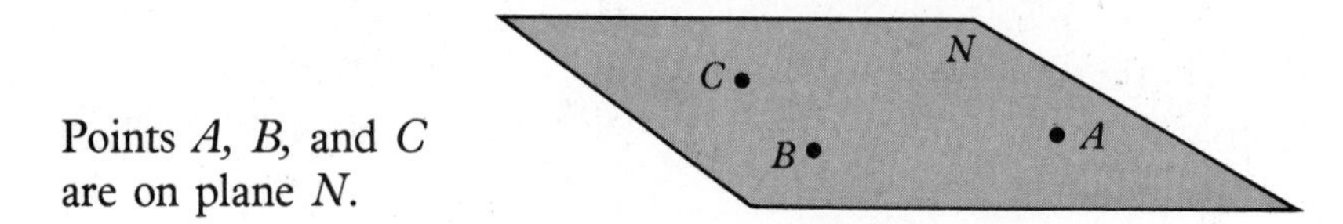

We assume that only one plane contains the three points. We say that three points not all on one line determine a plane.

When thinking of line ℓ as a set of points, we can say point A *is on* line ℓ and point A *is an element of* line ℓ to describe the same situation. We can also say *line* ℓ *contains point A*.

If A, B, and C are points on line ℓ, as shown in the figure, we say point B is *between* points A and C. If A, B, and C are not all on the same line, we do not use *between* to describe their relationship.

Point B is between points A and C.

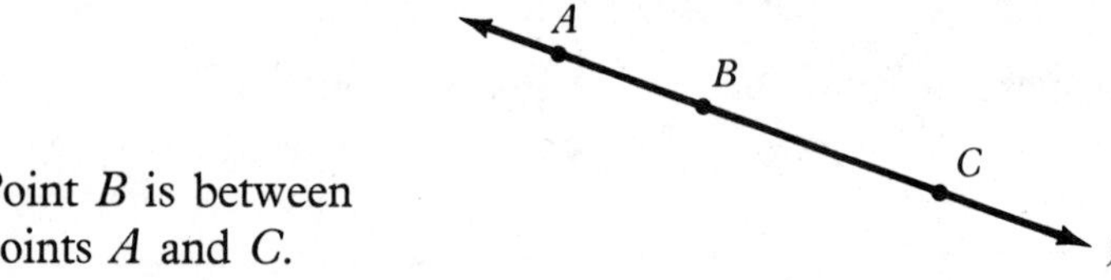

Some of the basic relationships for points and lines in a plane are described below using models, symbols, and definitions.

Physical Model, Figure	Description, Symbol	Definition

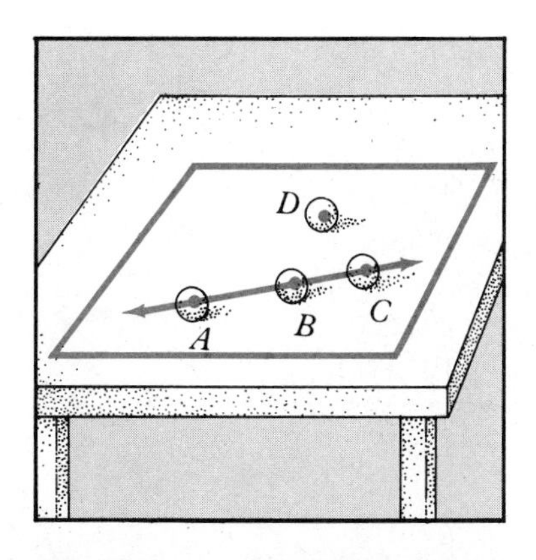

A, B, and C are *collinear.* A, D, and C are *noncollinear.* A, B, C, and D all lie in the same plane. They are *coplanar* points. Points not all in the same plane are *noncoplanar* points.

Definition 1-2

Collinear points are points that lie on the same line.

Definition 1-3

Coplanar points are points that all lie in one plane.

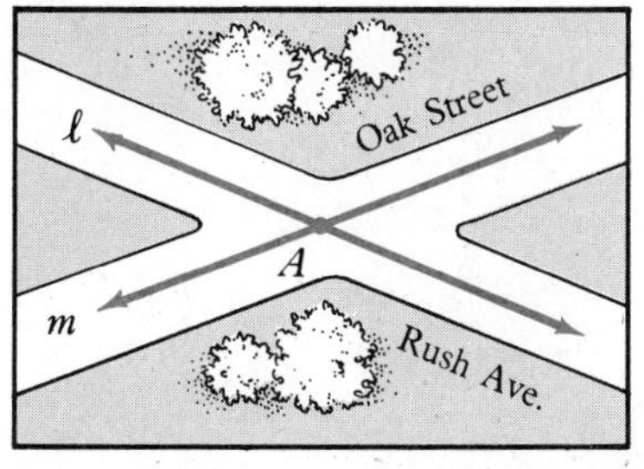

Lines ℓ and m *intersect* at point A.

Definition 1-4

Intersecting lines are two lines with a point in common.

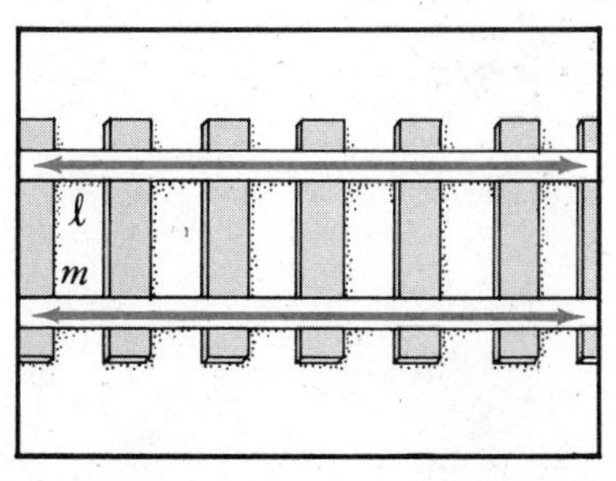

Lines ℓ and m do not have a common point. ℓ is *parallel* to m.
We write: $\ell \parallel m$

Definition 1-5

Parallel lines are lines in the same plane that do not intersect.

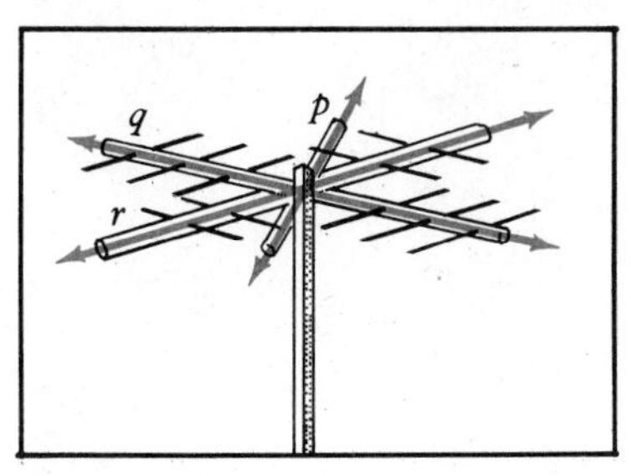

Lines p, q, and r have exactly one point in common. They are *concurrent lines.*

Definition 1-6

Concurrent lines are three or more coplanar lines that have a point in common.

EXERCISES

A.

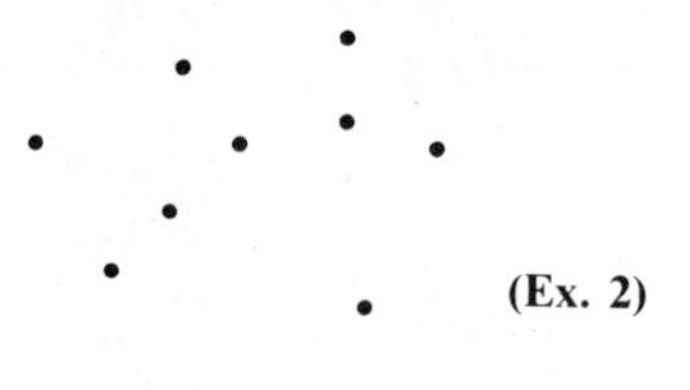
(Ex. 2)

1. Draw three points that are collinear.
2. Trace the set of dots shown and use a straightedge to draw a line through sets of three or more collinear points.

Exercises 3, 4, and 5 refer to the figure on the right.

3. Name sets of three collinear points.
4. Name sets of three noncollinear points.
5. Name four points, no three of which are collinear.

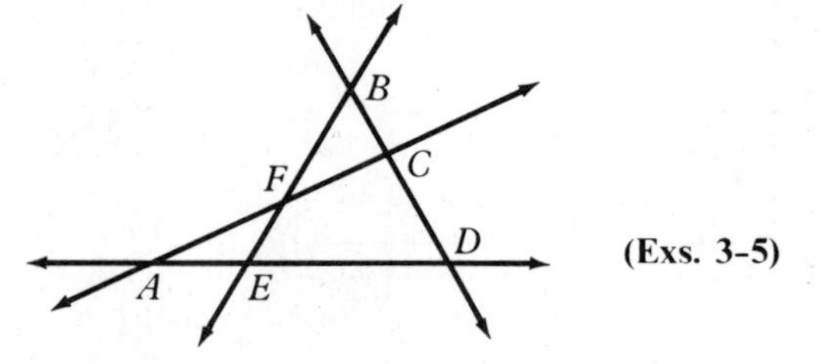

(Exs. 3-5)

Exercises 6–8 refer to the figure on the right. (If lines appear to be parallel, you may assume that they are.)

6. List three pairs of intersecting lines.
7. List three concurrent lines.
8. List all pairs of parallel lines.
9. Draw four concurrent lines.

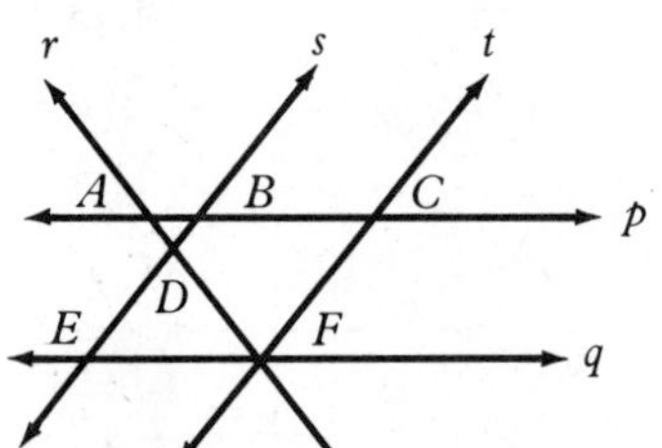

(Exs. 6–8)

Activity

Curve-stitching designs or *string sculpture* is the creation of interesting designs made entirely with straight lines of string or thread. The designs can be very simple or quite complex.

To get an idea how a *string design* is made, trace the angle below and mark it as shown. Use a fine point pen or pencil and connect points with the same number.

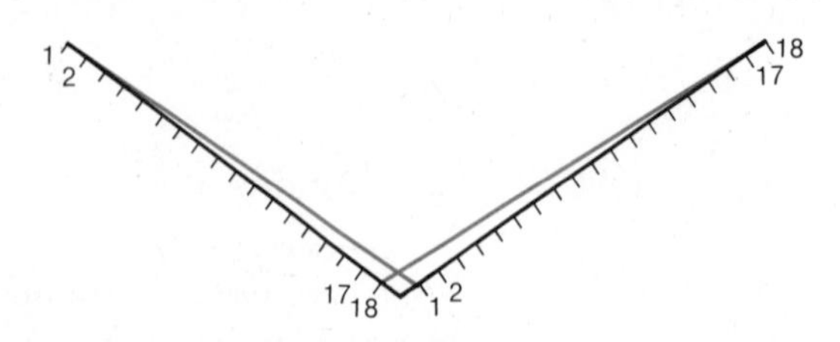

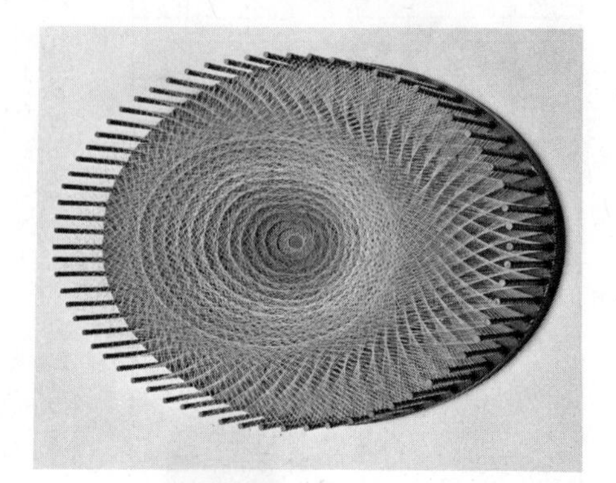

B.

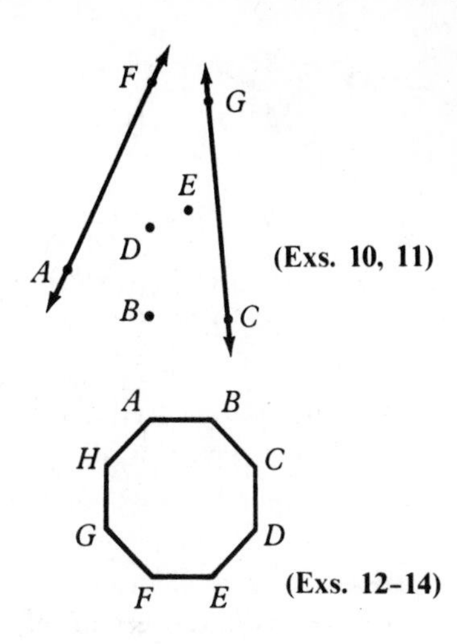

(Exs. 10, 11)

(Exs. 12–14)

10. It is important to notice that three points may be collinear even though the lines may not be drawn. Name sets of three collinear points in this figure.

11. There is a line through each pair of points even though it may not have been drawn. Name two such lines in this figure.

12. Name three different lines which, if drawn, would be parallel to $\overleftrightarrow{BC}$.

13. Name three different lines which, if drawn, would be parallel to $\overleftrightarrow{EF}$.

14. Name four lines connecting labeled points that are concurrent at the center of the figure.

15. Points *A, B, C,* and *D* on this cube are coplanar. How many different sets of four coplanar points on the cube can you list?

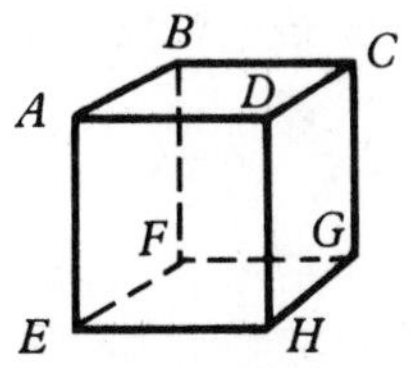

16. Lines are often used to describe (or model) physical reality. Would you use parallel lines, concurrent lines, or collinear points to describe or draw each case?

a. Starting a fire with a magnifying glass

b. Light coming from a flashlight

c. Using a refracting telescope

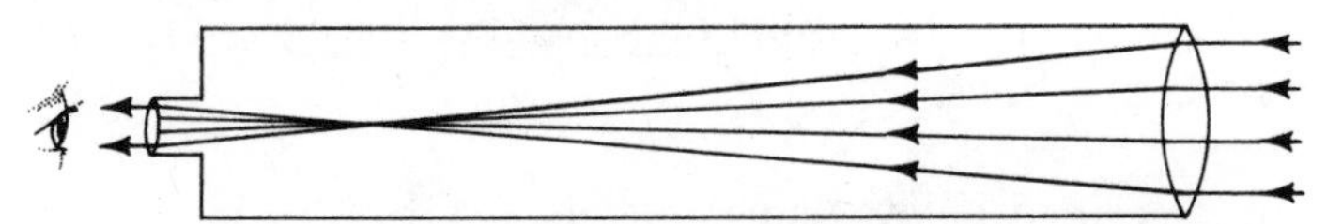

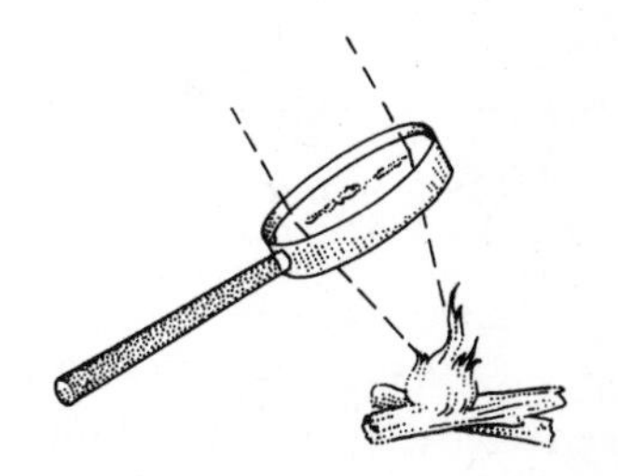

17. Can four lines be drawn so that they intersect in one point? Two points? Three points? Four points? Five points? Six points? More than 6 points? Show drawings for each.

PROBLEM SOLVING

How many lines do six points determine if one line is drawn through each pair of points?

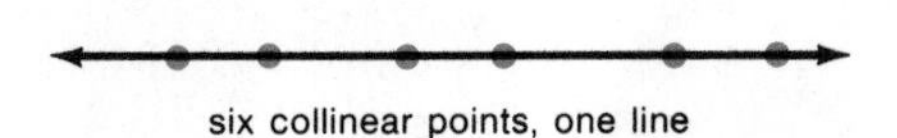

six collinear points, one line

Experiment! See if six points can be arranged to determine six lines. Arrange six points to determine seven lines, eight lines, nine lines, . . . 14 lines.

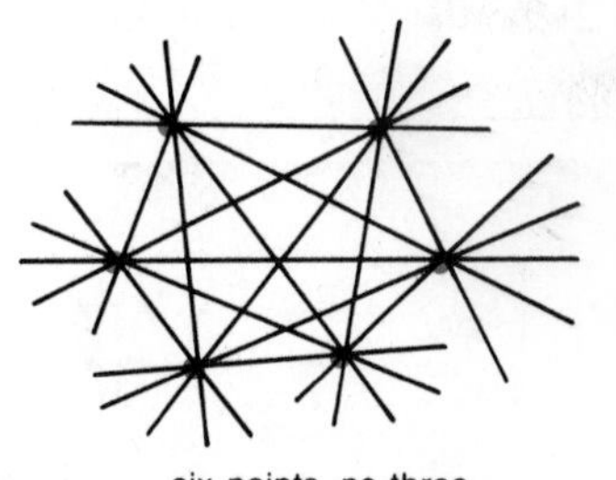

six points, no three collinear, fifteen lines

1–3 Some Basic Geometric Figures

Since lines, planes, and space are thought of as *sets of points* it is useful to define geometric figures in terms of sets and points. A *plane figure* is a figure with all points in one plane, but not all on one line. A *space figure* has points not all in a single plane.

First, we review some basic ideas about sets.

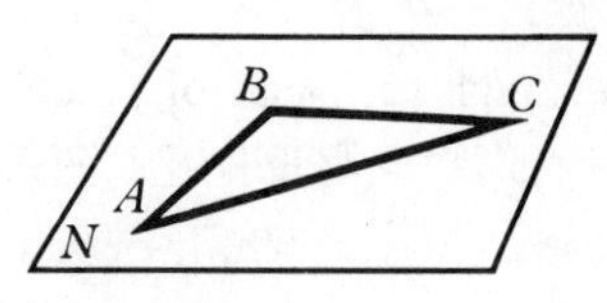

A triangle is a plane figure.

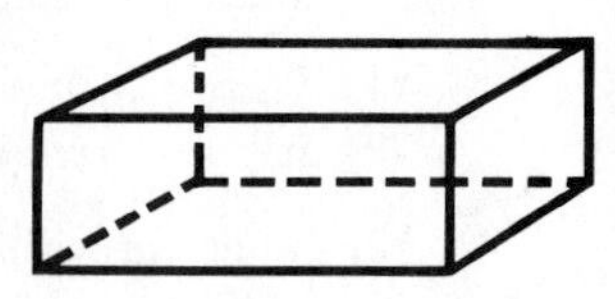

A box is a space figure.

Subset. If every element of a first set is also in a second set, the first set is a *subset* of the second.

Example

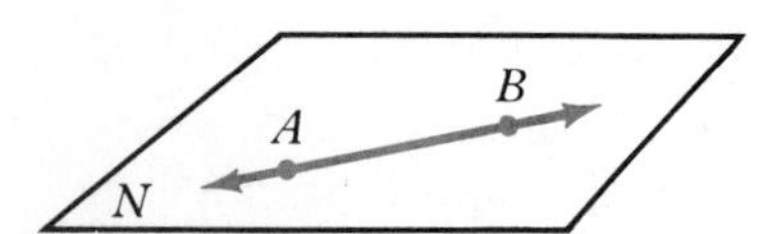

Line AB is a *subset* of plane N.

Union. The *union* of two or more sets is a set that contains all the elements of these sets.

Example

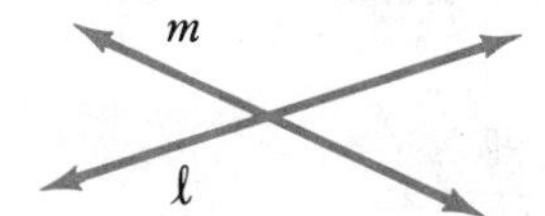

The *union* of lines ℓ and m consists of all the points on these two lines.

Intersection. The *intersection* of two sets is the set that contains those elements common to both sets.

Example

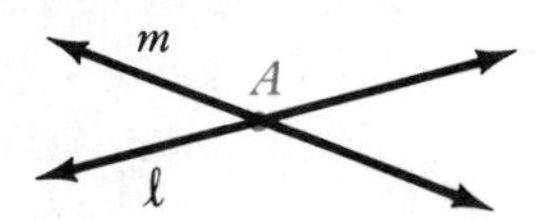

The intersection of line ℓ and line m is the point A.

Some basic geometric figures are described below using models, symbols, and definitions.

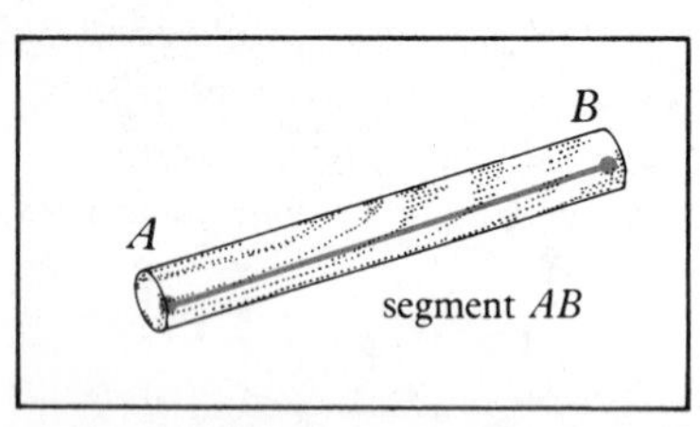

A and B are endpoints.

We write: $\overline{AB}$

Definition 1-7

A **segment,** $\overline{AB}$, is the set of points A and B and all the points between A and B.

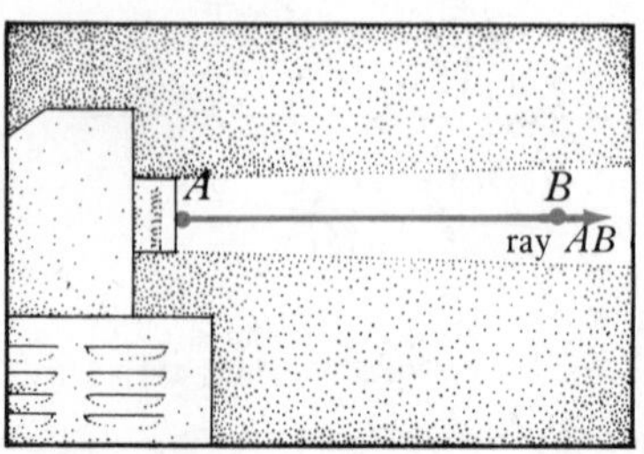

A is the endpoint.

We write: $\overrightarrow{AB}$

Definition 1-8

A **ray,** $\overrightarrow{AB}$, is a subset of a line that contains a given point A and all points on the same side of A as B.

Physical Model, Figure	Description, Symbol	Definition

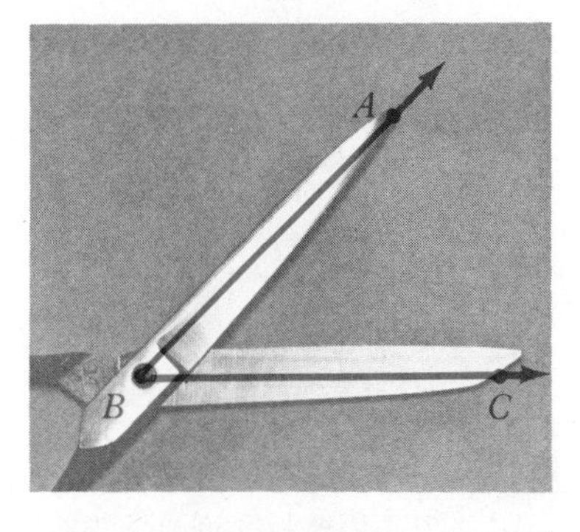

B is the *vertex*. $\overrightarrow{BA}$ and $\overrightarrow{BC}$ are the sides. The interior of $\angle ABC$ is the intersection of the points on A's side of $\overleftrightarrow{BC}$ with the points on C's side of $\overleftrightarrow{AB}$.

Definition 1-9

An **angle** is the union of two noncollinear rays which have the same endpoint.

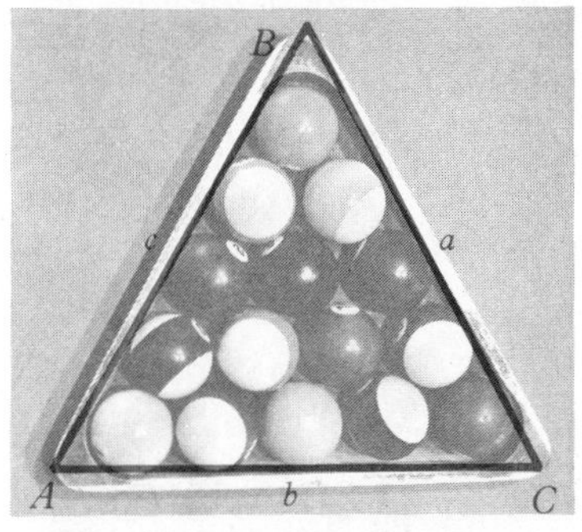

A, B, and C are vertices. $\overline{AB}$, $\overline{BC}$, and $\overline{AC}$ are sides.

We write: $\triangle ABC$

Definition 1-10

A **triangle** is the union of three segments determined by three noncollinear points.

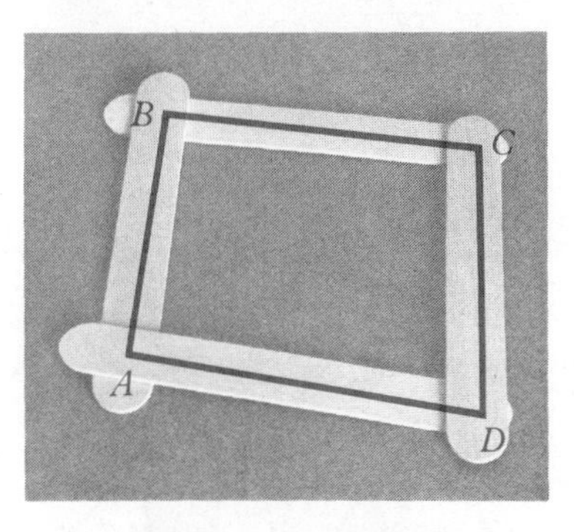

A, B, C, and D are *vertices*. $\overline{AB}$, $\overline{BC}$, $\overline{CD}$, and $\overline{AD}$ are *sides*.

We write: quadrilateral $ABCD$

Definition 1-11

A **quadrilateral** is the union of four segments determined by four points, no three of which are collinear. The segments intersect only at their endpoints.

Points A and B are on the circle. Point O is the center of the circle. $\overline{AB}$ is a *diameter* of the circle. $\overline{OB}$ is a *radius* of the circle.

We say: circle O
We write: $\odot O$

Definition 1-12

A **circle** is the set of all points in a plane that are a fixed distance from a given point in the plane.

EXERCISES

A.

Make six drawings of the line shown. Shade heavily each of the following figures, one on each drawing.

1. $\overline{BC}$ **2.** $\overrightarrow{BD}$ **3.** $\overrightarrow{CA}$ **4.** $\overline{AD}$ **5.** $\overleftrightarrow{BC}$ **6.** $\overrightarrow{DB}$

A B C D

(Exs. 1-6)

Draw and label an appropriate figure for each exercise 7–12.

7. $\angle ABC$ **8.** $\angle XYZ$ **9.** $\triangle DEF$ **10.** $\angle A$ **11.** $\overrightarrow{BA}$ **12.** $\overline{CD}$

In exercises 13–15 choose the two symbols that name the same angle.

13. $\angle ABC$, $\angle CAB$, $\angle CBA$

14. $\angle CAB$, $\angle BAC$, $\angle CBA$

15. $\angle ACB$, $\angle CAB$, $\angle BCA$

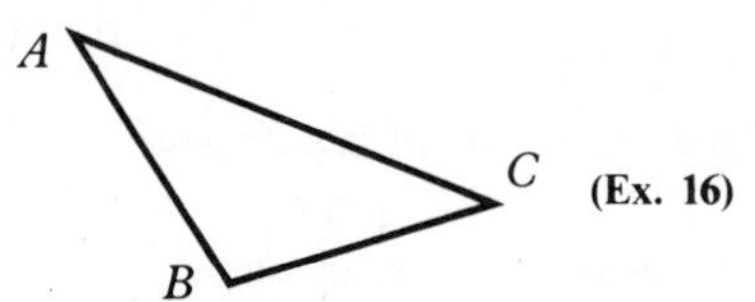

(Exs. 13-15)

16. $\triangle ABC$ and $\triangle BAC$ are two names for the triangle shown. There are four other names for this triangle. How many of them can you write?

A B C

(Ex. 16)

17. Use a compass to draw a circle. Label the center, a radius, and a diameter of the circle. Write the name of the circle.

18. Choose points A, B, C, and D on the circle and draw quadrilateral $ABCD$.

Activity

To make this design draw a circle. Then, with compass opening equal to the radius and with compass tip placed at equal intervals around the circle, draw the arcs.

Complete a design like this. Then make and color some other designs, using both circles and segments, that involve the procedure described above. You may wish to have a ruler-compass design contest.

19. Name with symbols the four lines drawn in this figure. Name a line that has not been drawn.

20. Name eight segments which have been drawn. Name several which have not been drawn.

In exercises 21–24, choose the two symbols which name the same set in the figure.

21. $\overleftrightarrow{AB}$, $\overrightarrow{AB}$, p 22. $\overrightarrow{AE}$, $\overrightarrow{AC}$, q

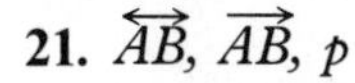

23. $\overrightarrow{BC}$, $\overrightarrow{CB}$, $\overrightarrow{BD}$ 24. $\overline{BC}$, $\overline{BD}$, $\overline{DB}$

(Exs. 19–25)

25. Name six different angles in the figure.

26. Trace and cut out two triangles like $\triangle DEF$. Put them together to form as many different shaped quadrilaterals as you can.

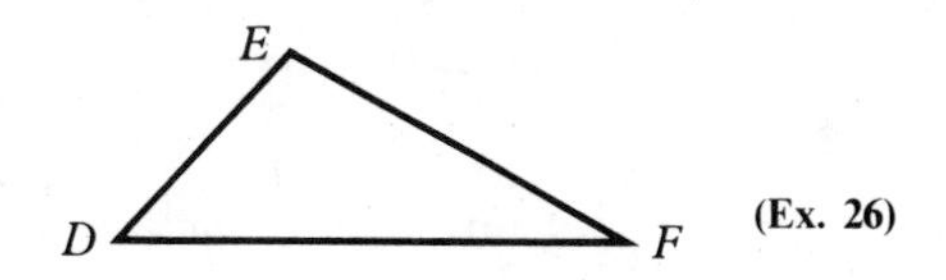

(Ex. 26)

27. Does $\overline{CD}$ name the same segment as $\overline{DC}$? Why?

28. Does $\overrightarrow{CD}$ name the same ray as $\overrightarrow{DC}$? Why?

C.

29. Begin with three points as shown in the figure. Draw $\angle BAC$, $\angle ABC$, and $\angle ACB$. Does the resulting figure consist of three lines or three segments? Is it a triangle? Why or why not?

30. Name at least eight triangles in this figure.

31. Trace the figure. Then draw one more segment that will add exactly three more triangles.

32. Name at least eight quadrilaterals in this figure.

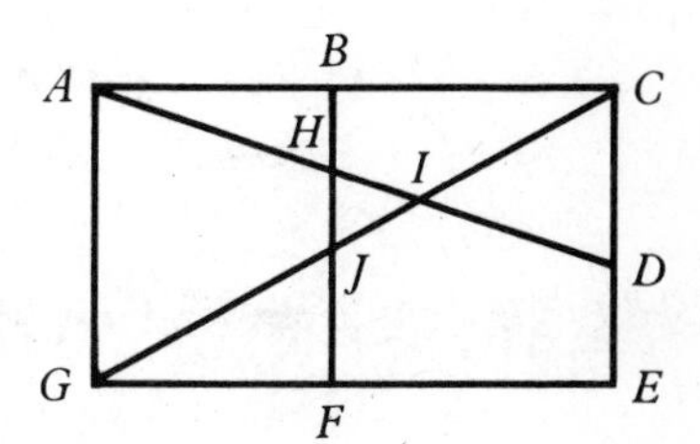

PROBLEM SOLVING

How can you glue six toothpicks together to form four triangles?

(*Hint:* Regardless of the size of the toothpicks, you will need to use plenty of space!)

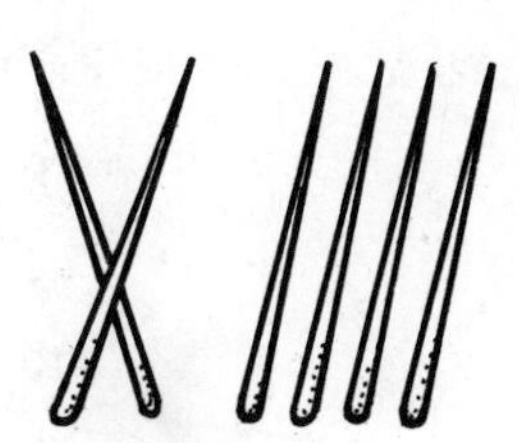

1-4 Segments and Angles—Congruence and Measurement

The man shown here is going to saw a board so that it will be 0.5 meters in length and will have an angled edge of 45°. First he has to measure.

Details of the basic properties of segment and angle measure will be presented on pages 72–73.

Length measure assigns a real number to each segment.

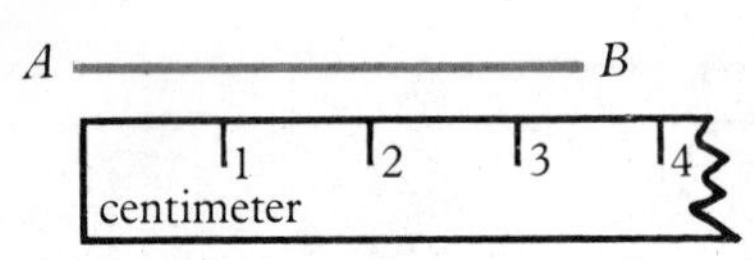

The *length* of $\overline{AB}$ is 3.5 cm.

We write: $AB = 3.5$

We have a special way to describe two segments that are the same length.

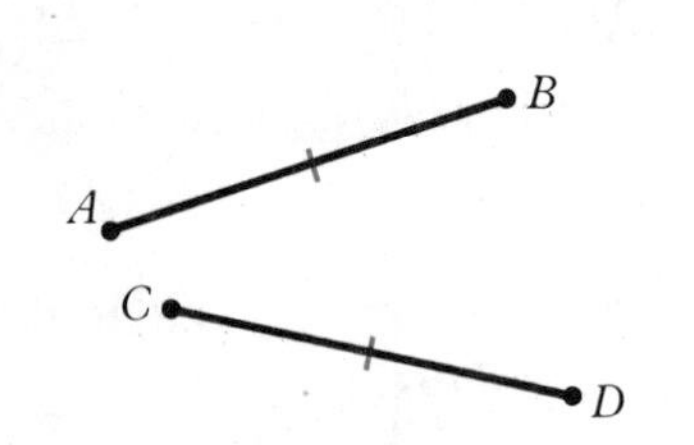

We say: $\overline{AB}$ is congruent to $\overline{CD}$.

We write: $\overline{AB} \cong \overline{CD}$

We sometimes mark each segment to show that they are congruent.

Definition 1-13

Two **segments** are **congruent** if they have the same length.

Angle measure assigns a real number between 0 and 180 to each angle.

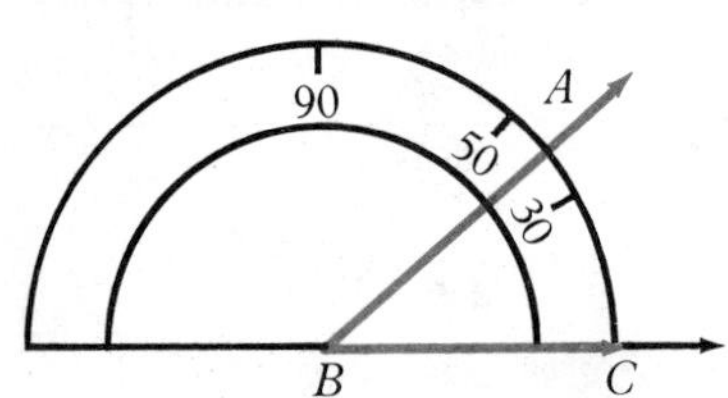

The *degree measure* of $\angle ABC$ is 40.

We write: $m\angle ABC = 40$

We sometimes write that $\angle ABC$ has a measure of 40°.

We have a special way to describe two angles that have the same measure.

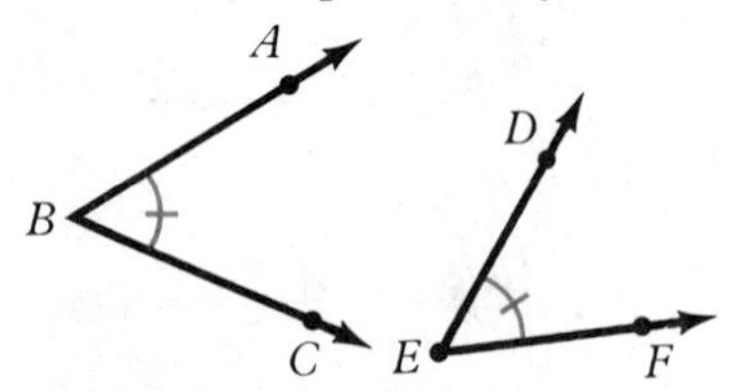

We say: $\angle ABC$ is congruent to $\angle DEF$.

We write: $\angle ABC \cong \angle DEF$

Definition 1-14

Two **angles** are **congruent** if they have the same measure.

A draftsman uses a variety of tools and drawing techniques to draw accurate plans for building projects. In geometry we will learn to use two tools—the unmarked ruler and the compass—to make special types of drawings called *constructions*. The two constructions described below use the idea of congruence defined on page 20.

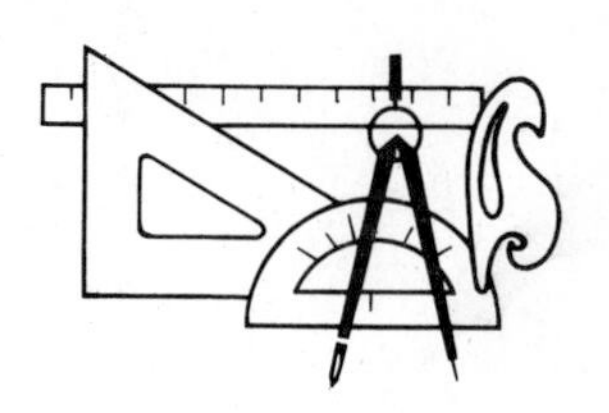

Construction 1. Construct a segment congruent to a given segment. (Copy a segment.)

1. Open your compass the length of the given segment.

A B

Given segment

2. Draw a ray longer than the given segment.

3. Use the same compass to mark a copy of the segment on the ray.

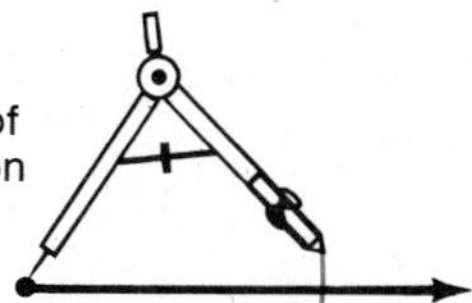

Construction 2. Construct an angle congruent to a given angle. (Copy an angle.)

1. Draw an arc intersecting both rays of the given angle.

Given angle

2. Draw a ray to serve as one side of the copy.

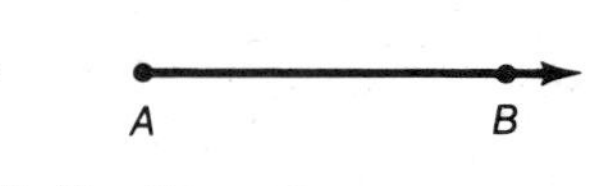

3. With the same compass opening as in (1), draw an arc crossing the ray.

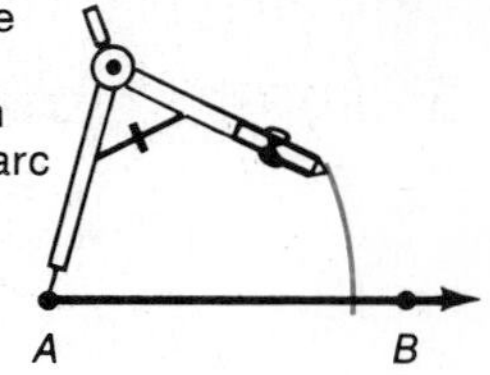

4. Open your compass to measure the opening of the given angle.

Given angle

5. Use the same opening as in (4) and draw an arc as shown.

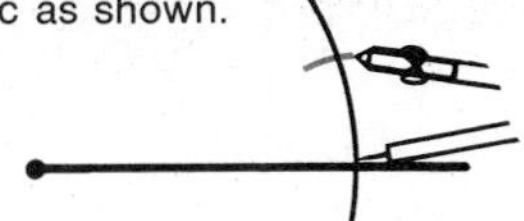

6. Draw the second side to complete the copy of the given angle.

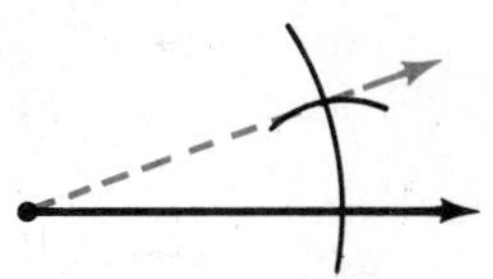

The three different types of angles are defined below. Use Construction 2 to construct angles congruent to each angle shown.

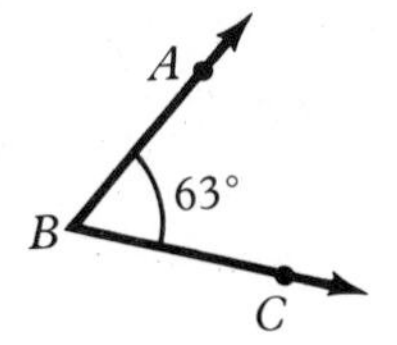

Definition 1-15

An **acute angle** is an angle with measure less than 90°.

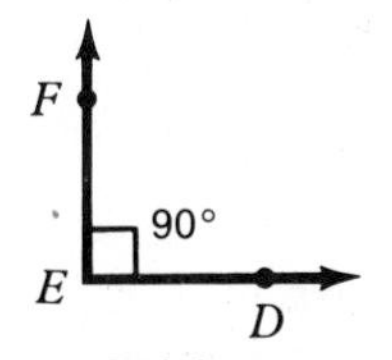

Definition 1-16

A **right angle** is an angle with measure of 90°.

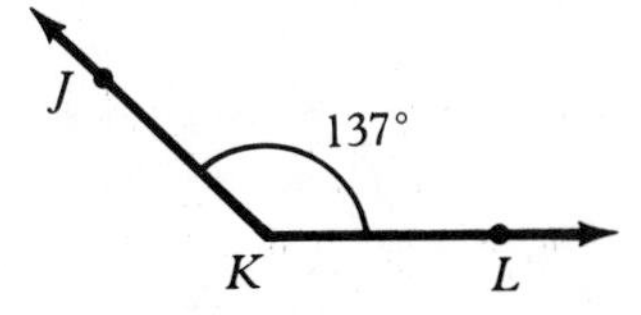

Definition 1-17

An **obtuse angle** is an angle with measure greater than 90°.

EXERCISES

A.

1. Use your centimeter ruler to find the length of this segment. $AB = \underline{?}$

2. Draw segments with the following lengths. Use an unmarked ruler and a compass to construct segments congruent to each segment you draw.
   $CD = 8$ cm $EF = 5.6$ cm $GH = 7.5$ cm

3. Write a statement using $\cong$ or $\ncong$ (not congruent) for the three sets of segments shown.

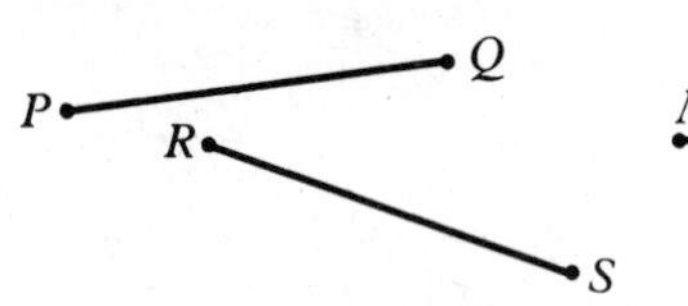

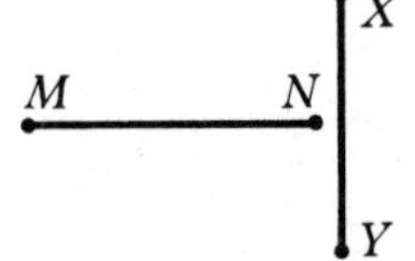

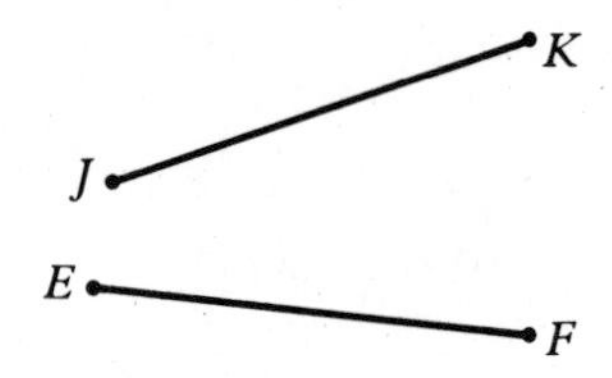

Trace these angles on your paper. Use your protractor to find their measures. Extend the sides if necessary.

4.

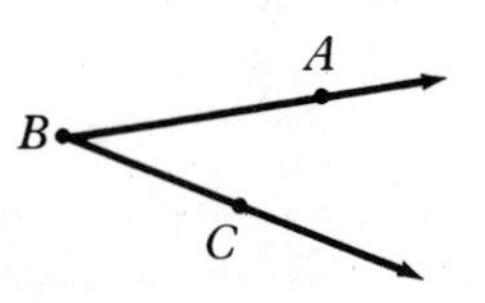

$m\angle ABC = \underline{?}$

5.

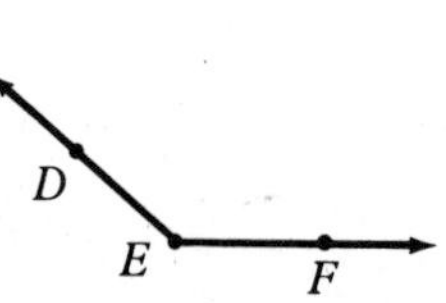

$m\angle DEF = \underline{?}$

6.

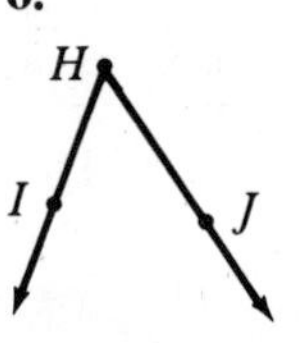

$m\angle IHJ = \underline{?}$

7.

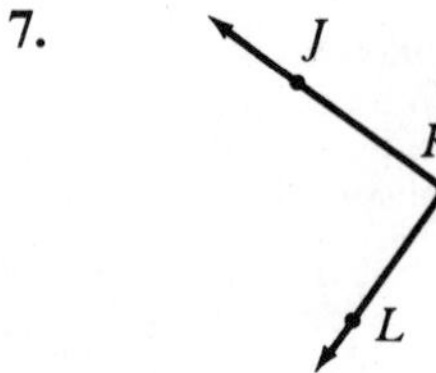

$m\angle JKL = \underline{?}$

8. Classify the angles in exercises 4–7 as acute, right, or obtuse.

9. Use an unmarked ruler and a compass to construct angles congruent to each of the angles in exercises 4–7.

Activity

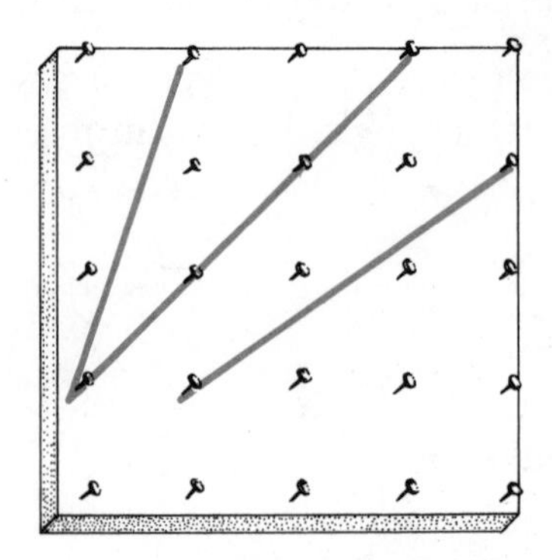

Begin with a 5 × 5 square array of dots. Two dots are endpoints of a segment. Two segments with a common endpoint determine an angle.

a. How many different lengths of segments can be drawn on a 5 × 5 square array?

b. How many different sizes of angles can be drawn on a 5 × 5 square array?

B.

10. Name four right angles in the figure.

11. Name four acute angles.

12. Name four obtuse angles.

Segments of lengths a and b are shown.

13. Construct a segment of length $2a$.

14. Construct a segment of length $a + b$.

15. Construct a segment of length $b - a$.

Angles with measures x and y are shown.

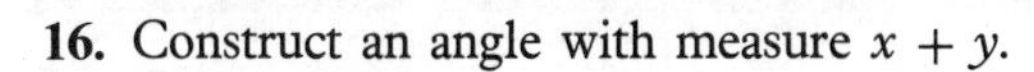

16. Construct an angle with measure $x + y$.

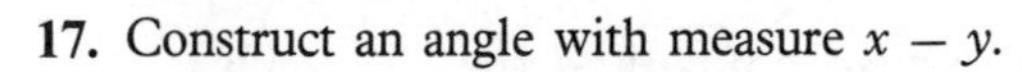

17. Construct an angle with measure $x - y$.

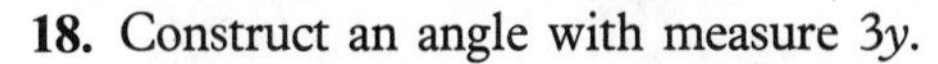

18. Construct an angle with measure $3y$.

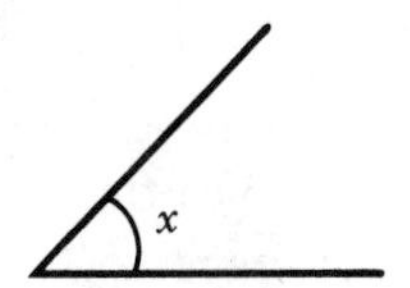

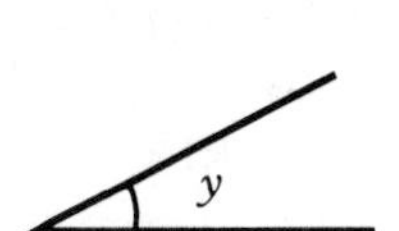

19. A plane is flying in a southeasterly direction. Through how many degrees does it turn when it changes course to South-South West?

C. 

20. Construct $\triangle ABC$ with side $\overline{AB}$ and angles A and B.

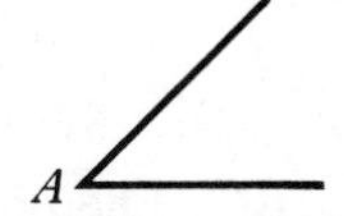

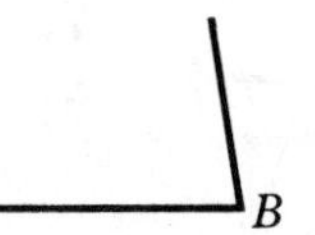

21. Follow these instructions to divide segment $\overline{AB}$ into three congruent segments.

    a. Draw a ray from point A and mark off three congruent segments on it.

    b. Draw $\overline{EB}$.

    c. Use Construction 2 to copy $\angle AEB$ at D and again at C.

    d. The sides of the copied angles divide $\overline{AB}$ into three congruent segments.

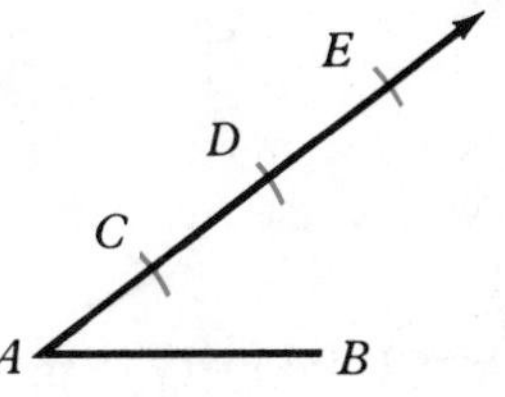

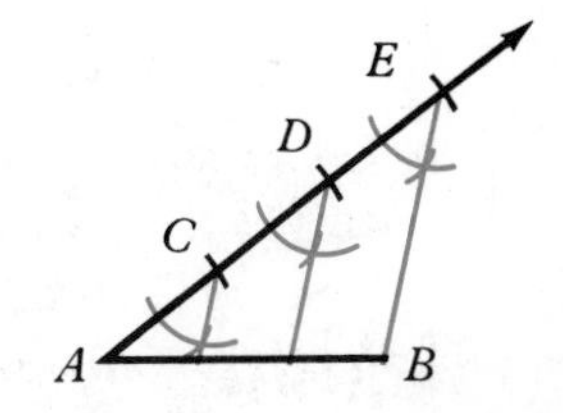

PROBLEM SOLVING

A farmer wishes to separate these 11 sheep by building eleven pens with exactly four straight fences. How can this be done? (The fences may cross.)

1–5 Segment and Angle Bisectors

In a baseball diamond, second base is the same distance from both foul lines. Home plate, first base, second base, and third base are at the corners of a square. Is the pitcher's mound at the point midway between

a. home plate and second base?

b. first base and third base?

c. neither of these?

Laying out a baseball diamond involves the ideas defined below and the construction procedures described on page 25.

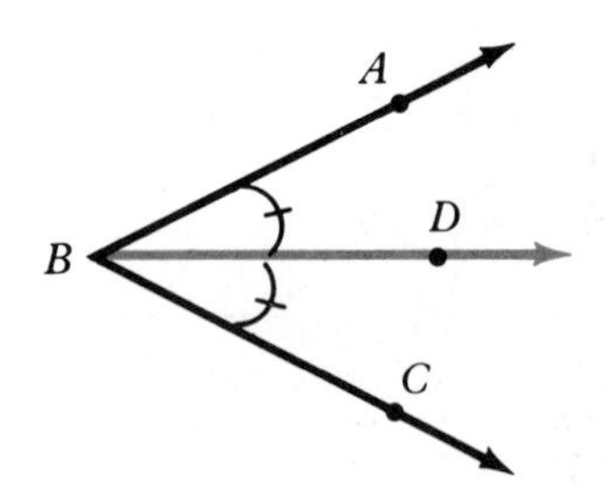

Ray BD is the *bisector* of $\angle ABC$. The points on $\overrightarrow{BD}$ are equal in distance from the sides of $\angle ABC$.

Definition 1–18

The **bisector of an angle** ABC is a ray BD in the interior of $\angle ABC$ such that $\angle ABD \cong \angle DBC$

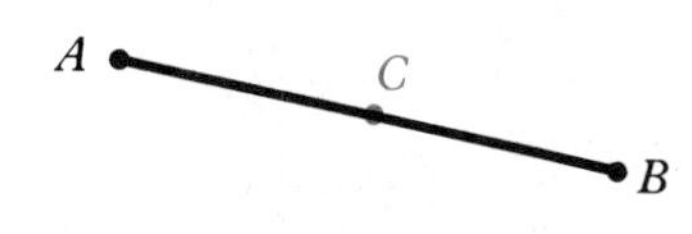

Point C is the *midpoint* of $\overline{AB}$.

Definition 1–19

The **midpoint of a segment** is a point C between A and B such that $\overline{AC} \cong \overline{CB}$.

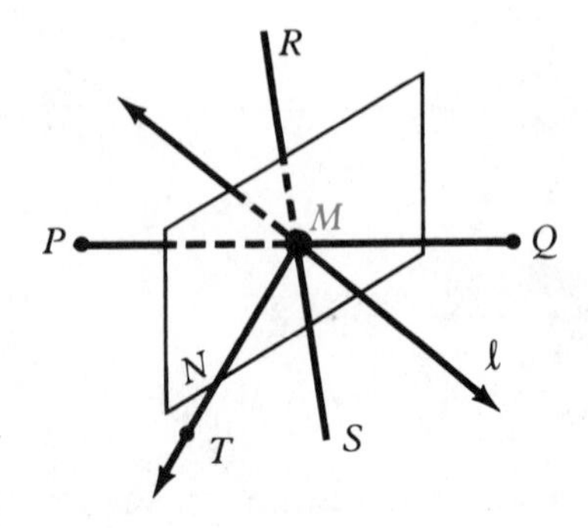

$\overline{RS}$, $\overrightarrow{MT}$, line ℓ, and plane N all intersect $\overline{PQ}$ at the midpoint M, and are bisectors of $\overline{PQ}$.

Definition 1–20

A **bisector of a segment** is any point, segment, ray, line, or plane that contains the midpoint of the segment.

Methods for bisecting an angle and a segment are given below.

Construction 3. Bisect an angle.

1. Given angle *ABC*.

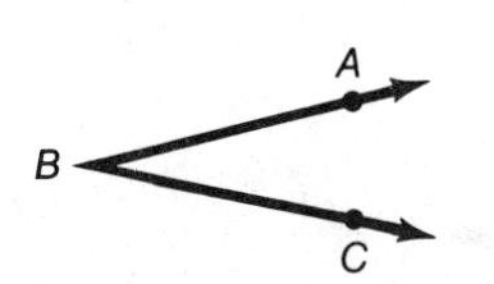

2. With *B* as center, draw an arc that intersects both sides of the angle, at *F* and *G*.

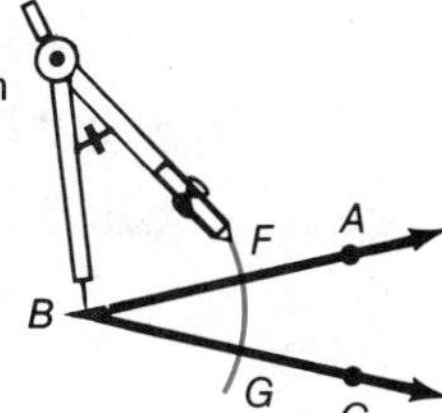

3. With *F* as center, draw an arc in the interior of the angle.

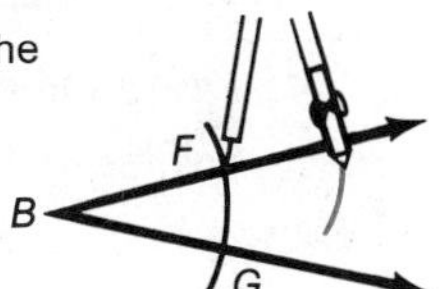

4. With *G* as center, and the same opening as in (3) draw an arc that crosses the first arc.

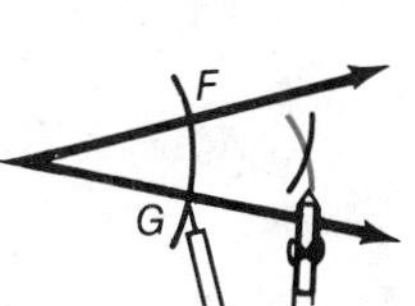

5. Connect *B* and the point of arc intersection to produce the bisector of the angle.

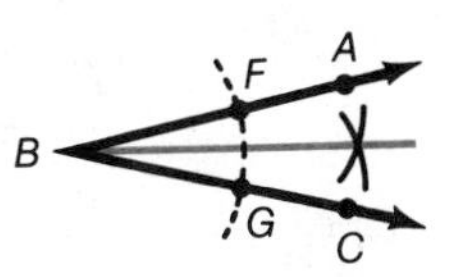

Construction 4. Bisect a segment.

1. Given line segment $\overline{AB}$.

A B

2. With *A* as center and opening greater than half of *AB*, draw a semicircular arc.

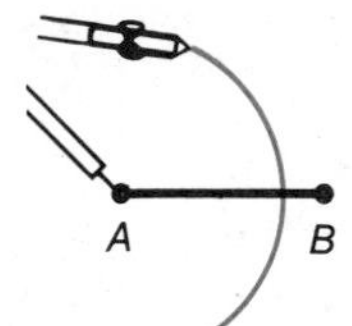

3. With *B* as center and the same opening as in (2), draw a semicircular arc that intersects the first arc.

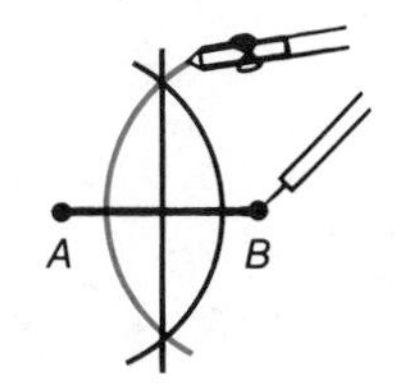

4. Connect the two points of intersection to complete the construction of the bisector of $\overline{AB}$.

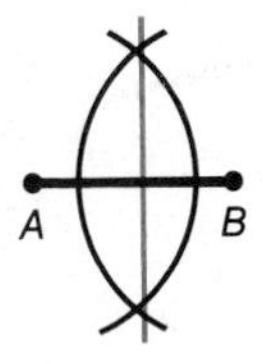

This diagram shows how bisecting an angle helps to lay out a baseball diamond. Notice that the pitcher's mound is on the angle bisector 60 feet 6 inches from home plate. It is not on a line from first to third base. Also, it is not at the midpoint of the line from home to second base.

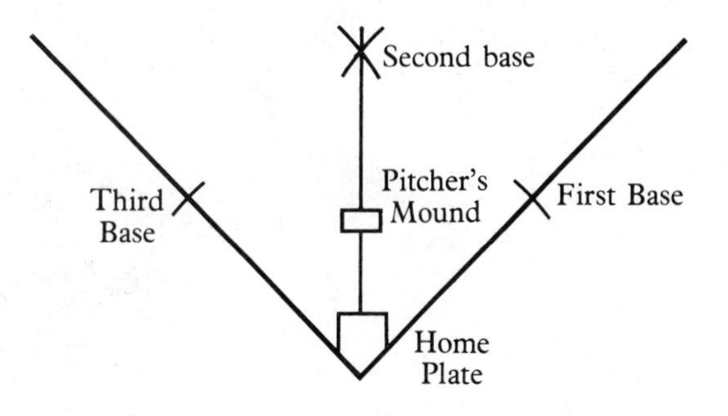

EXERCISES

A. 

1. Draw a segment $\overline{AB}$. Bisect $\overline{AB}$.
2. Draw a segment $\overline{AB}$. Construct a point N such that $AN = \frac{1}{4}AB$.
3. What other fractions of $\overline{AB}$ can you construct?
4. Draw angles the approximate sizes of angles A, B, and C. Construct the angle bisectors.

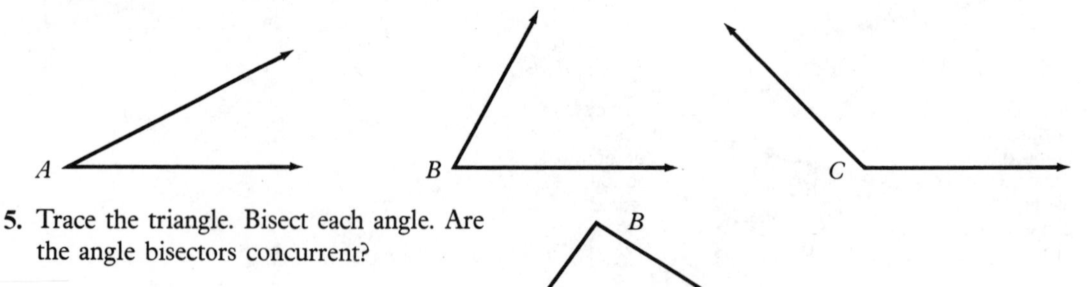

5. Trace the triangle. Bisect each angle. Are the angle bisectors concurrent?

B

A

C

6. The bisector of $\angle XYZ$ is $\overrightarrow{YT}$. Write the names of the congruent angles that are formed.

Activity

To construct these designs, you need to bisect angles.

1. Construct one of these designs and color it.
2. Use a compass and straightedge to construct a design of your own which requires angle bisection.

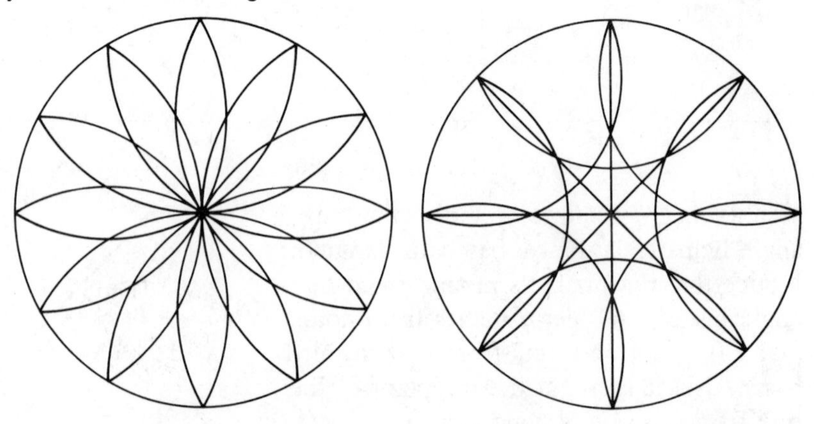

B.

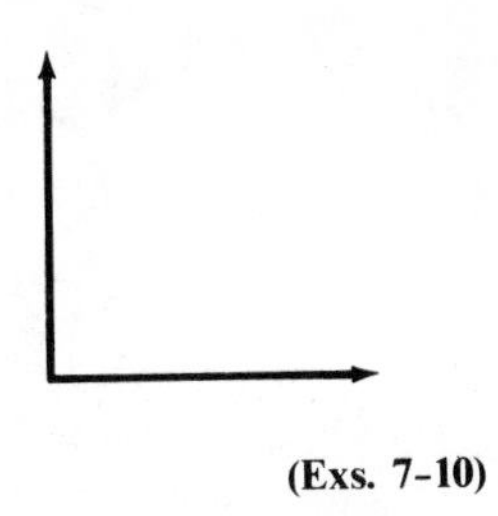

(Exs. 7-10)

Use constructions to complete exercises 7–10. You may copy right angle ABC if you wish. Do not use a protractor.

7. Construct a 45° angle. **8.** Construct a $22\frac{1}{2}$° angle.

9. Construct a 135° angle. **10.** Construct a $67\frac{1}{2}$° angle.

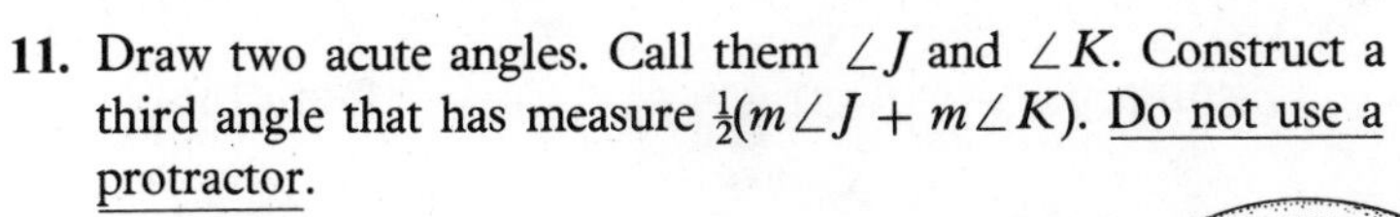

11. Draw two acute angles. Call them $\angle J$ and $\angle K$. Construct a third angle that has measure $\frac{1}{2}(m\angle J + m\angle K)$. Do not use a protractor.

12. Draw the four directions found on a compass. Use a straightedge and compass to construct a line pointing in the direction North-North East.

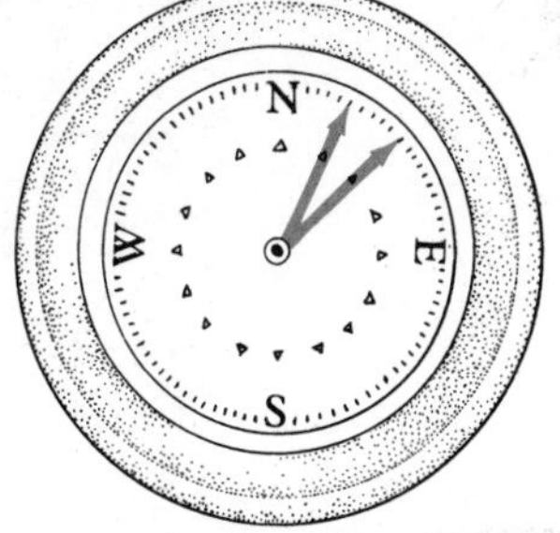

C.

13. Construct a $112\frac{1}{2}$° angle. **14.** Construct an $82\frac{1}{2}$° angle.

15. Construct a $157\frac{1}{2}$° angle. **16.** Construct a $97\frac{1}{2}$° angle.

17. In the diagram, $\overrightarrow{BF}$ bisects $\angle EBG$, $m\angle ABC = 90$, $m\angle ABE = 20$, $m\angle GBC = 24$. What is $m\angle ABF$?

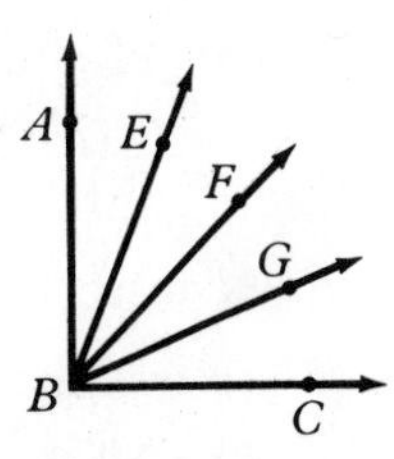

18. Construct a segment with length $4CD - \frac{1}{2}AB$.

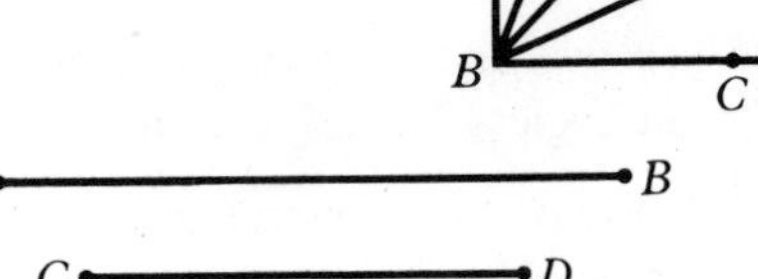

PROBLEM SOLVING

A *rusty compass* is one that is stuck and always has the same opening.

A *collapsible compass* is one that springs back together as soon as it is lifted from the paper.

1. Bisect $\overline{AB}$ using:

A ——— B

a. a collapsible compass

b. a rusty compass with opening from C to D.

2. Bisect an angle using:

a. a collapsible compass **b.** a rusty compass.

1–6 Perpendicular Lines and Planes

There are many examples of perpendicular lines and planes in our everyday life. We use some of these examples in the following definitions.

Physical Model	Figure, Description	Definition
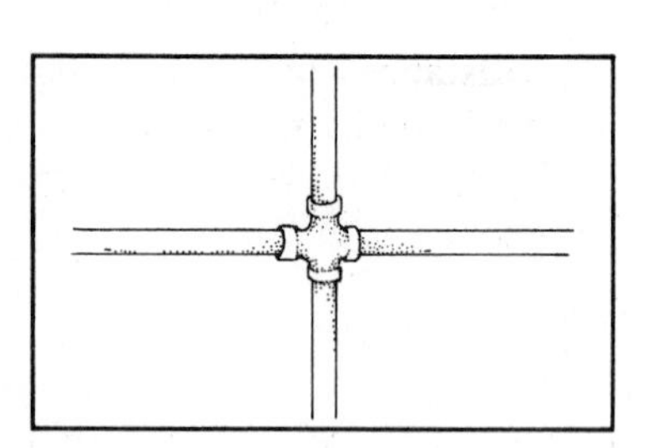	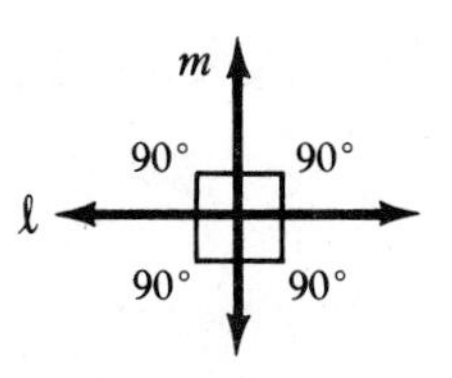 ℓ is perpendicular to m. We write: $\ell \perp m$	**Definition 1–21** Two lines are **perpendicular** if they intersect to form congruent right angles.

On the basis of simple statements that can be proved, we will interpret this definition of perpendicular to include these ideas:

1. When two lines are perpendicular, all angles formed are 90° angles (right angles), and they are congruent.
2. When two lines intersect to form one, two, or three 90° angles (right angles), the lines form four right angles and are perpendicular.
3. When two lines intersect to form a pair of congruent angles with a common side, the lines are perpendicular.

Physical Model	Figure, Description	Definition
	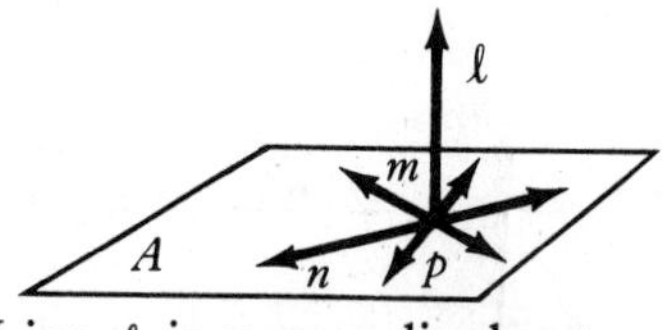 Line ℓ is perpendicular to lines m, n, p, etc., so line ℓ is perpendicular to plane A.	**Definition 1–22** A **line is perpendicular to a plane** if it is perpendicular to each line in the plane that intersects the line.
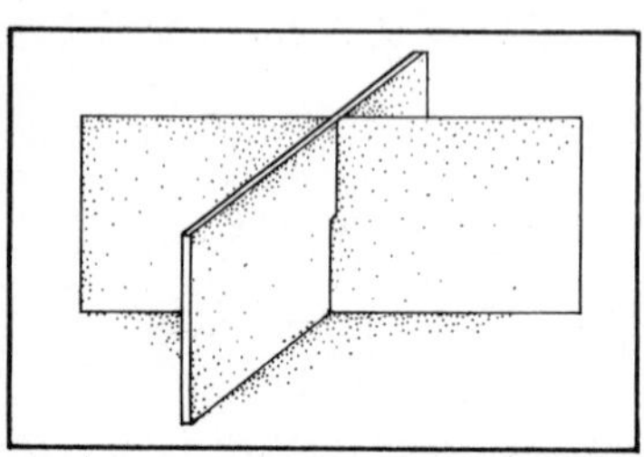	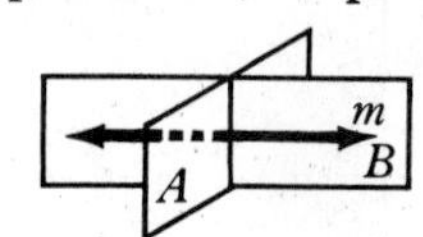 Line m in plane B is perpendicular to plane A, so plane B is perpendicular to plane A.	**Definition 1–23** Two **planes are perpendicular** if there is a line in one plane that is perpendicular to the other plane.

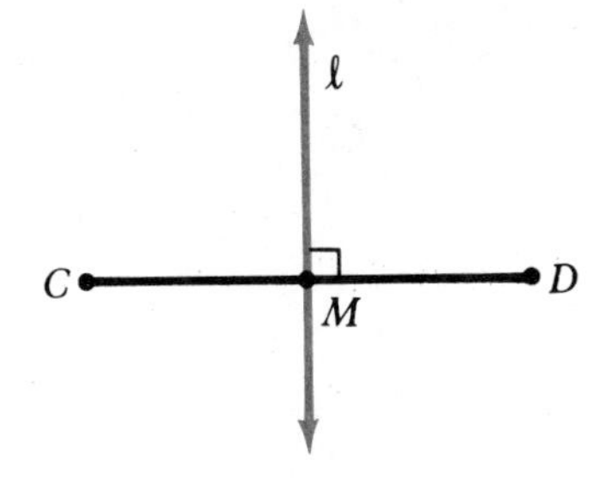

ℓ is the perpendicular bisector of $\overline{CD}$.

Definition 1–24

The **perpendicular bisector of a segment** is a line perpendicular to the segment and which contains its midpoint.

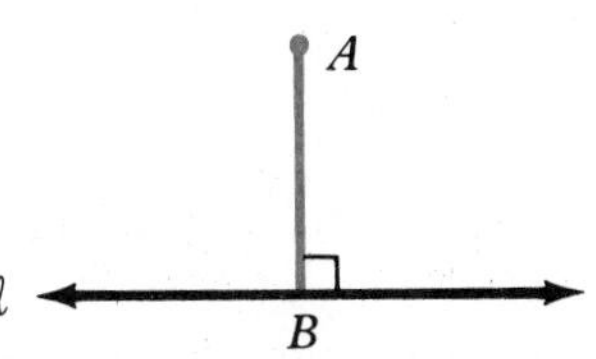

AB is the distance from point A to line ℓ.

Definition 1–25

The **distance from a point to a line** is the length of the segment drawn from the point perpendicular to the line.

In Construction 4, we actually constructed the perpendicular bisector of a segment. Here are two more important constructions that involve perpendicular lines.

Construction 5. Construct a perpendicular to a line through a given point on the line.

1. Given a line ℓ and a point P on ℓ.

2. Draw arcs on each side of P.

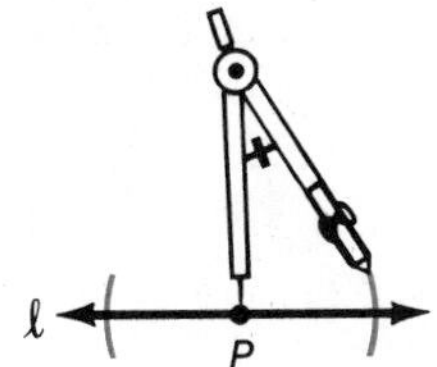

3. Draw crossing arcs above line ℓ.

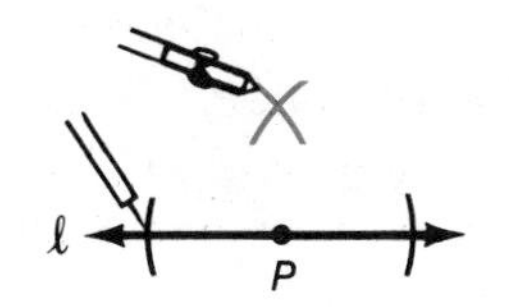

4. Draw the perpendicular to line ℓ through P.

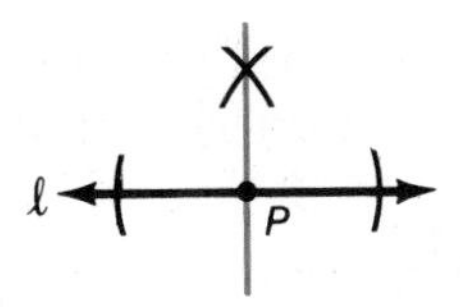

Construction 6. Construct a perpendicular to a line through a given point not on the line.

1. Given a line ℓ and a point P not on ℓ.

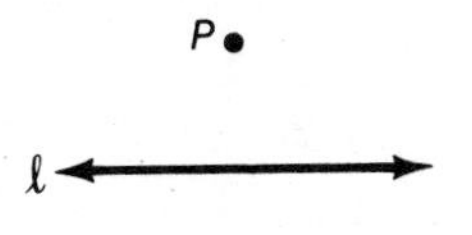

2. Draw two arcs cutting line ℓ.

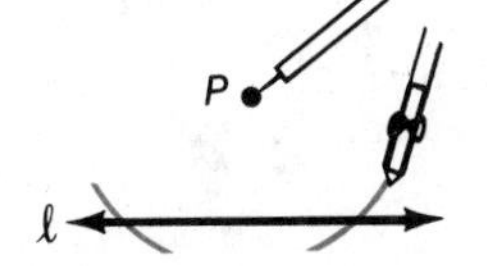

3. Draw two crossing arcs below line ℓ.

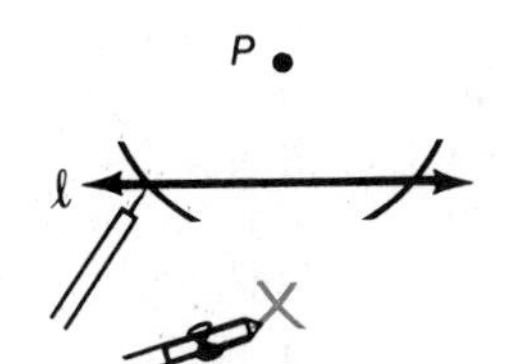

4. Draw the perpendicular to line ℓ through P.

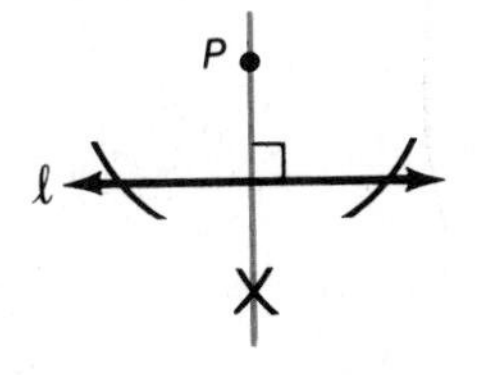

EXERCISES

A.

1. $\angle 1 \cong \angle 2$. What can you conclude about lines j and k?

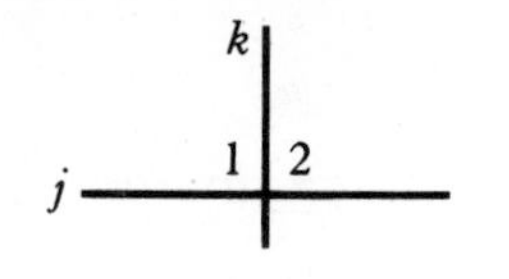

2. $m\angle 3$ is 90. What can you conclude about lines m and n and angles 1, 2, and 4.

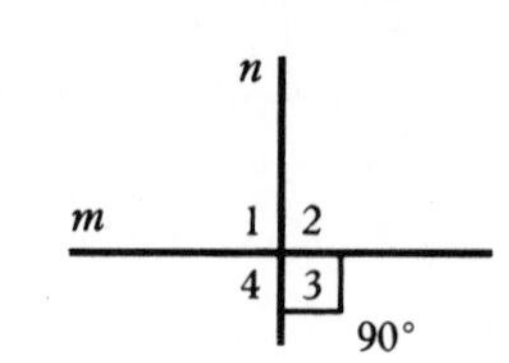

3. Draw a segment $\overline{PQ}$. Construct the perpendicular bisector of $\overline{PQ}$.

4. Draw a line ℓ. Construct a line perpendicular to ℓ that contains point A on ℓ.

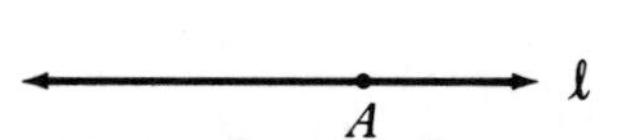

5. Draw a line m and a point P not on m. Construct a line perpendicular to m through P.

6. Name four lines that are perpendicular to plane $ABCD$.

7. Name four pairs of perpendicular planes.

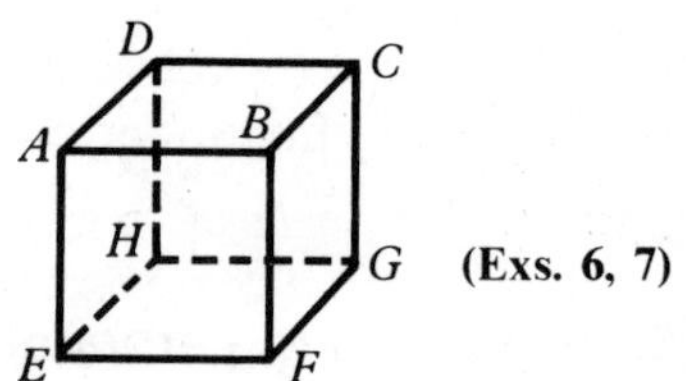

(Exs. 6, 7)

8. Line r is perpendicular to plane Z. What does this tell you about lines r, m, and n?

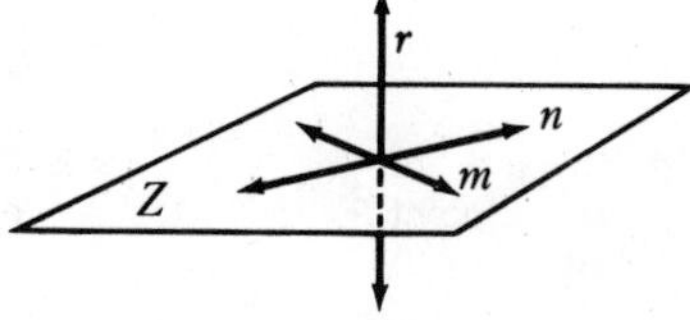

B.

9. Construct a rectangle with sides congruent to $\overline{AB}$ and $\overline{CD}$.

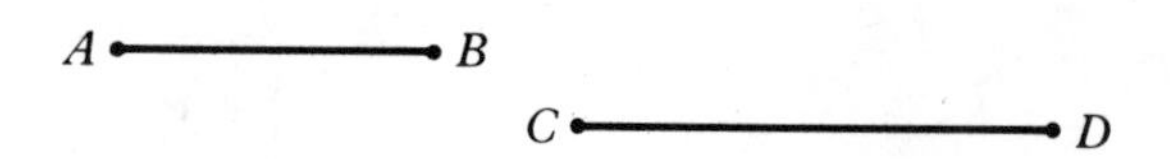

Activity

These directions show how to use a MIRA or a sheet of colored plastic to construct a perpendicular to a line through a point not on the line. (Construction 6) Show how to do Constructions 3, 4, and 5 in this chapter using the MIRA or plastic.

Place the MIRA with the drawing edge next to P in such a way that the visual image of the half of line ℓ in front of the MIRA is exactly on the half of line ℓ that is behind the MIRA. Draw along the drawing edge to produce the perpendicular to line ℓ through point P.

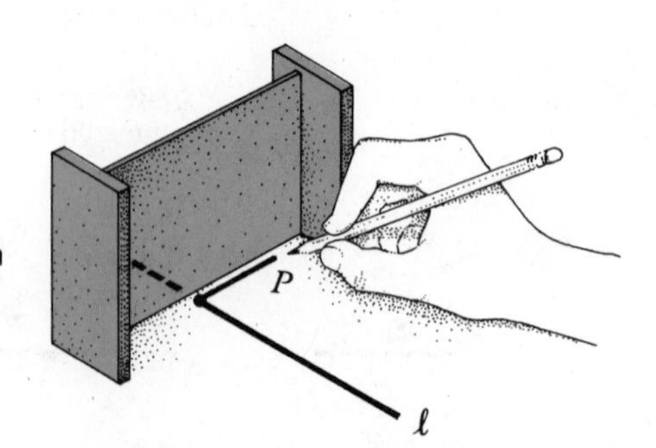

10. Construct a triangle with a 45° angle and sides congruent to segments $\overline{PQ}$ and $\overline{RS}$. (No protractors please!)

11. Apply Construction 5 to construct a square with side AB.

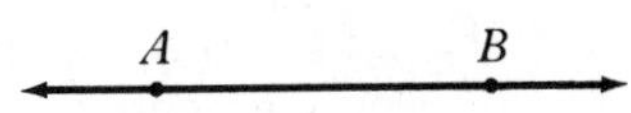

12. Draw a triangle ABC. Apply Construction 6 to construct a point D on $\overline{BC}$ so that $\overline{AD}$ is perpendicular to $\overline{BC}$.

13. Is plane X perpendicular to plane Y? According to the definition of perpendicular planes, what information is needed to be sure that the planes are perpendicular?

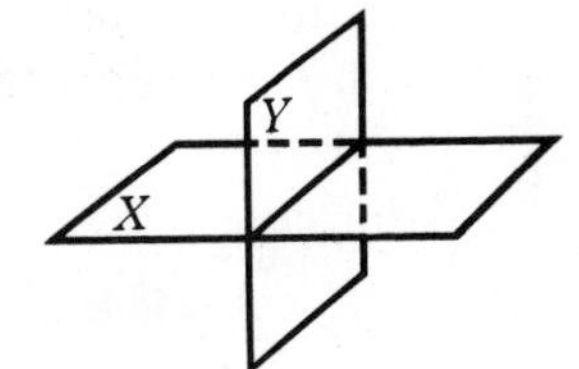

C.

14. Two cities need additional water. They decide to build a water treatment plant along a nearby river and pipe water from the plant to each city. Each city will pay the cost of laying the pipe from the plant to its city. The plant should be located an equal distance from the two cities. Trace the map shown and determine through construction the point where the plant should be located under this proposal.

15. Another proposal for the water treatment plant location in Exercise 14 calls for the cities to share the cost of the entire pipeline equally. Under this plan the total length of the pipeline should be kept to a minimum. Where should the treatment plant be located? Trace the map and construct the desired location of the plant.

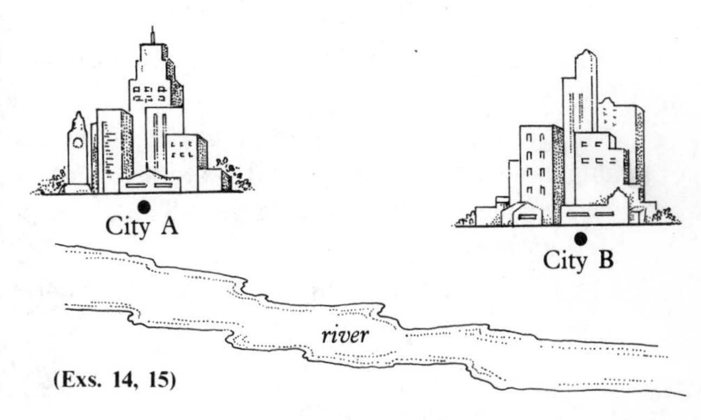

(Exs. 14, 15)

PROBLEM SOLVING

Shown are four identical cubes from each of which one or more small, also identical cubes have been removed.

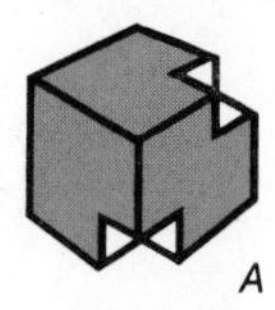
A

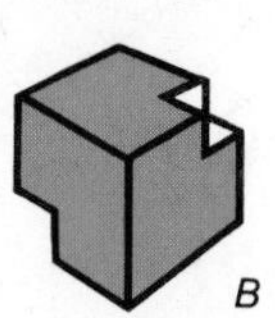
B

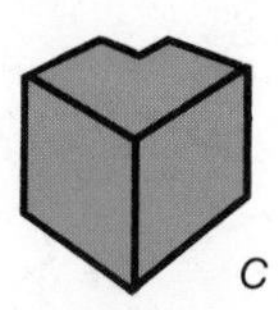
C

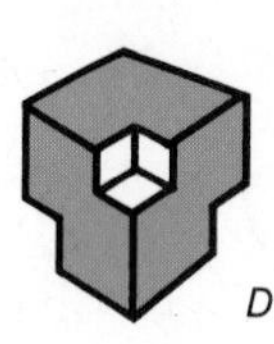
D

Compare each pair of figures: A & B, A & C, A & D, B & C, B & D, and C & D. Which one pair could be the same (depending upon the hidden back corner)?

1–7 Polygons

Geometric figures made up of straight line segments are common in the world. Such figures are called *polygons*.

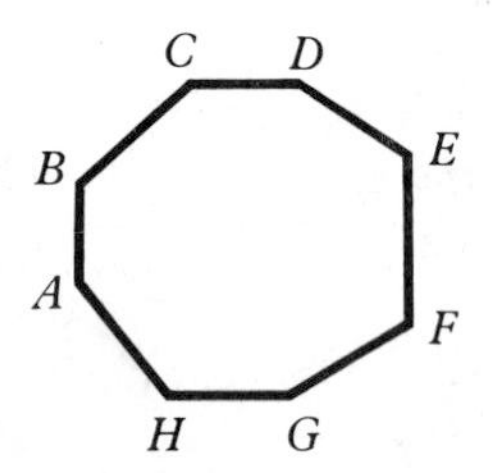

This polygon has eight sides. Points *A, B, C, D, E, F, G,* and *H* are its vertices. Each segment of the polygon is called a side.

We write: polygon *ABCDEFGH*

Definition 1-26

A **polygon** is the union of segments meeting only at endpoints such that (1) at most two segments meet at one point, and (2) each segment meets exactly two other segments.

Polygons are named by the number of their sides. For example, triangle—3 sides; quadrilateral—4 sides; pentagon—5 sides; hexagon—6 sides; heptagon—7 sides; octagon—8 sides. A polygon with *n* sides can be called an **n-gon.**

The following definitions give more information about polygons.

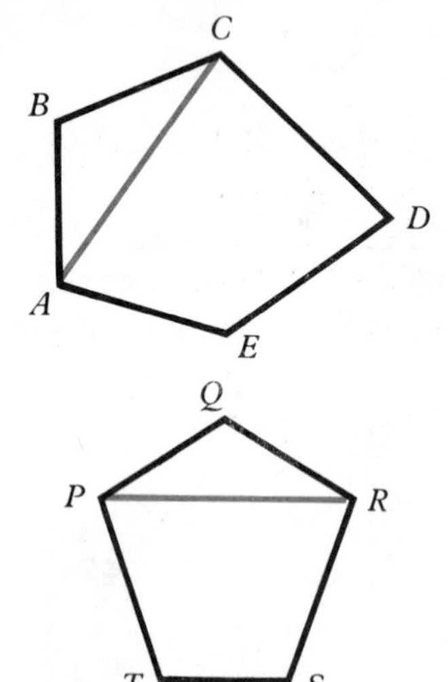

The end points of $\overline{AC}$ are non-consecutive vertices of polygon *ABCDE*. $\overline{AC}$ is one of the *diagonals* of the polygon.

Definition 1-27

A **diagonal of a polygon** is a segment joining any two nonconsecutive vertices of the polygon.

Every diagonal of this polygon, like $\overline{PR}$, is in the interior of the polygon. *PQRST* is a convex polygon.

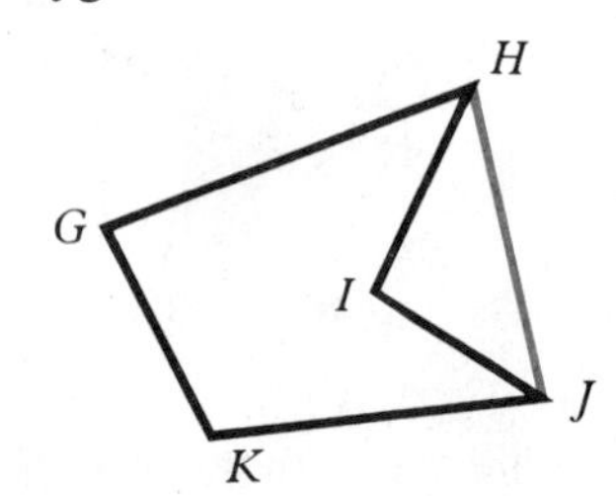

At least one of the diagonals of this polygon is not in its interior. *GHIJK* is not a convex polygon.

Definition 1-28

A **polygon** is **convex** if all of the diagonals of the polygon are in the interior of the polygon.

Triangles with congruent sides have special names.

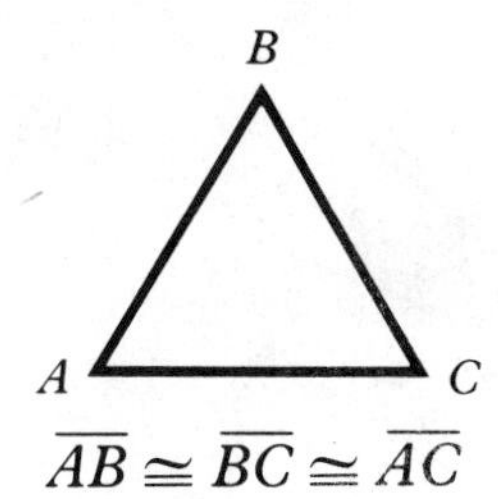

$\overline{AB} \cong \overline{BC} \cong \overline{AC}$

Definition 1-29

An **equilateral triangle** is a triangle with all sides congruent to one another.

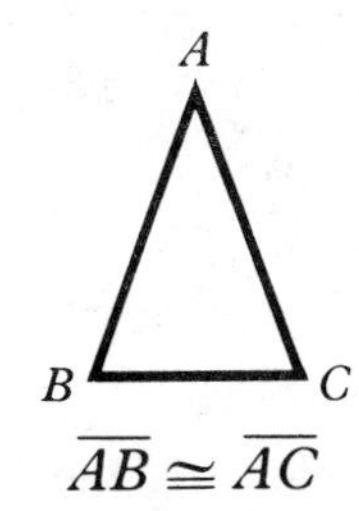

$\overline{AB} \cong \overline{AC}$

$\angle A$ is called the *vertex angle.* $\angle B$ and $\angle C$ are called *base angles.*

Definition 1-30

An **isosceles triangle** is a triangle with two sides congruent to one another.

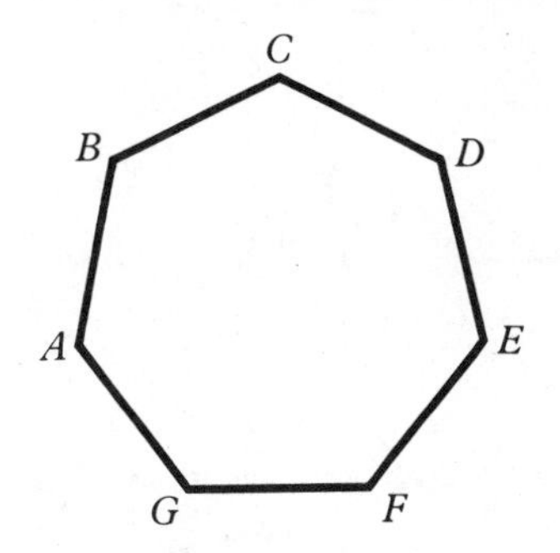

Some polygons have properties that make them *regular polygons.*

All sides are equal in length. All angles are equal in measure.

Definition 1-31

A **regular polygon** is a polygon with all sides congruent to each other and all angles congruent to each other.

$ABCDEFG$ is a regular polygon.

EXERCISES

A.

In exercises 1–4 select the figure that is not a polygon. Explain why it is not a polygon.

1.

a.

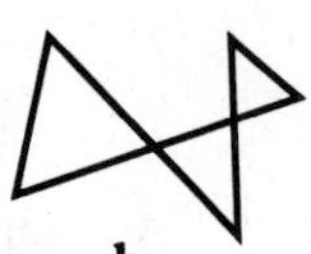
b.

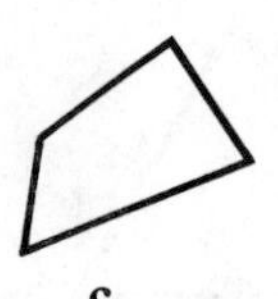
c.

2.

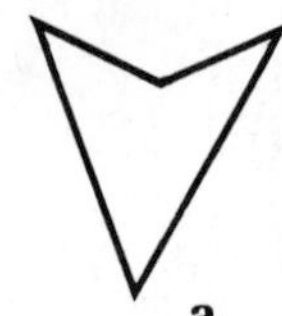
a.

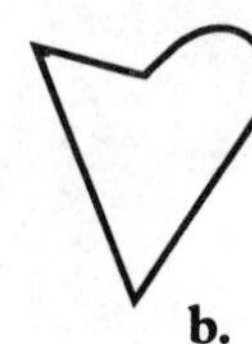
b.

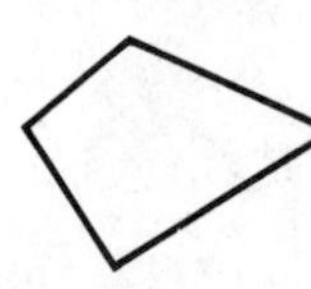
c.

3.

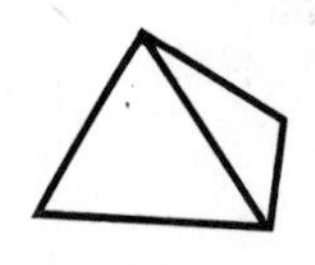
a.

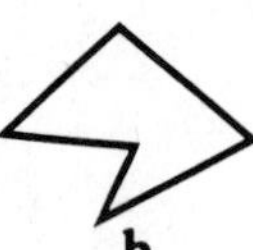
b.

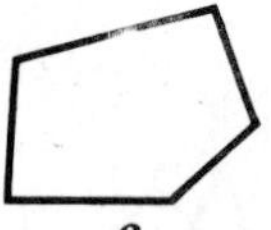
c.

4.

a.

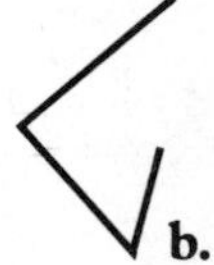
b.

c.

5. Which figures above are convex polygons? For example, figure 1c is a convex polygon.

6. Draw a convex octagon. Draw a diagonal of this figure.

7. Draw a non-convex octagon.

8. Identify each triangle as equilateral, isosceles, or neither. Use a ruler.

a. b. c.

9. Which of these polygons are regular polygons?

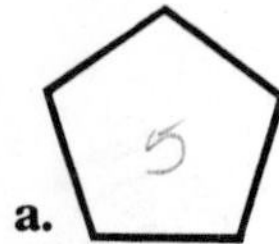

a.

b.

c.

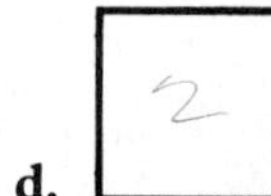
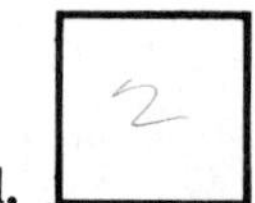
d.

(Exs. 9, 10)

10. Draw as many diagonals as possible for each polygon.

Activity

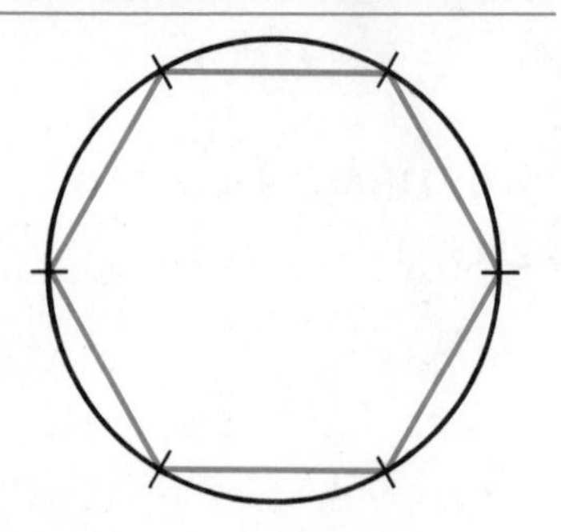

The compass and straightedge construction method described in the activity on page 18 can be used to construct a regular hexagon.

Combine this method with bisecting angles and constructing perpendicular bisectors to construct:

a. a regular 12-gon
b. a regular octagon
c. a regular 16-gon.

B.

11. *ABCDE* is a regular pentagon. Name as many isosceles triangles as you can. (If a triangle looks isosceles, you may assume that it is.)

12. Some letters of the alphabet can be drawn as a polygon, and others cannot. Draw as many polygons in the shape of letters of the alphabet as you can.

13. An open-faced wrench has parallel edges. What do you know about the number of edges on a nut that this wrench fits?

14. The valve stem on the top of a fire hydrant is usually in the shape of a regular pentagon rather than the usual shape of a regular hexagon. Why do you think this is done?

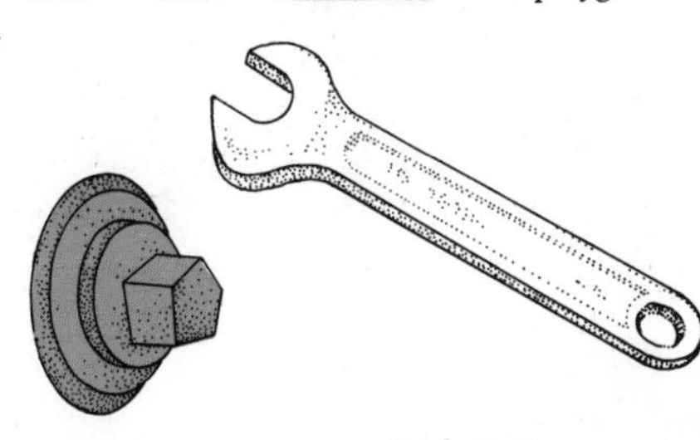

C.

15. The figure on the right includes examples of all polygons from 3-gons to 10-gons. Find and name an example of each.

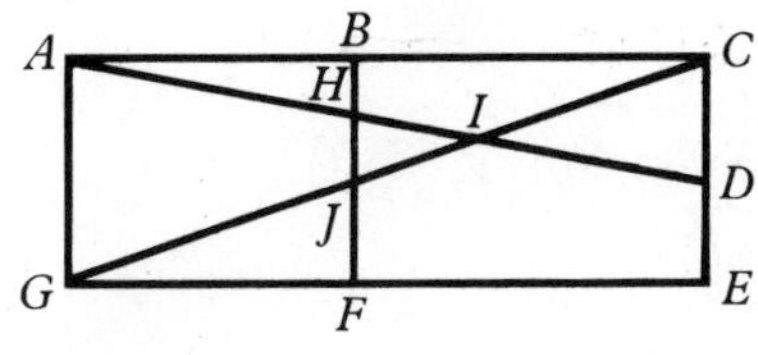

16. Use a protractor and a ruler to draw an octagon with sides of five different lengths all of whose vertex angles measure 135°.

PROBLEM SOLVING

Erastosthenes (275 B.C.) calculated the distance around the earth using an ingenious method. He assumed the rays from the sun to be parallel and found that when the sun was directly overhead in Alexandria, its rays made an angle of $7\frac{1}{5}°$ with a vertical pole 500 miles away in Syene. He assumed the central angle *a* to be $7\frac{1}{5}°$ also. He reasoned that the ratio of central angle *a* to 500 miles would be equal to the ratio of the total number of degrees in a circle to the complete distance around the earth. Can you set up the proportion and find the distance?

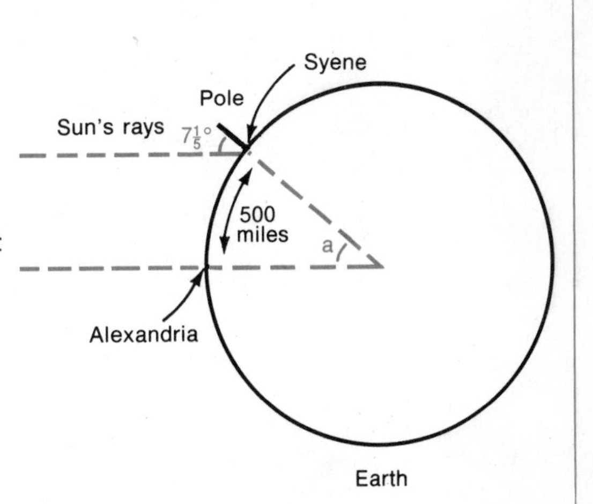

Important Ideas—Chapter 1

Terms

Point (p. 10)
Line (p. 10)
Plane (p. 11)
Space (p. 11)
Collinear points (p. 13)
Coplanar (p. 13)
Intersecting lines (p. 13)
Parallel lines (p. 13)
Concurrent lines (p. 13)
Segment (p. 16)
Ray (p. 16)
Angle (p. 17)
Triangle (p. 17)
Quadrilateral (p. 17)
Circle (p. 17)
Congruent segment (p. 20)
Congruent angle (p. 20)
Acute angle (p. 21)
Right angle (p. 21)
Obtuse angle (p. 21)
Bisector of an angle (p. 24)
Midpoint of a segment (p. 24)
Bisector of a segment (p. 24)
Perpendicular lines (p. 28)
Line perpendicular to a plane (p. 28)
Perpendicular planes (p. 28)
Perpendicular bisector (p. 29)
Distance from a point to a line (p. 29)
Convex polygon (p. 32)
Diagonal of a polygon (p. 32)
Convex polygon (p. 32)
Equilateral triangle (p. 33)
Isosceles triangle (p. 33)
Regular polygon (p. 33)

Constructions

Copy a segment (p. 21)
Copy an angle (p. 21)
Bisect an angle (p. 25)
Bisect a segment (p. 25)
Construct a perpendicular to a line through a given point on the line (p. 29)
Construct a perpendicular to a line through a given point not on the line (p. 29)

Chapter 1—Review

1. Name objects that illustrate the following:

   a. point **b.** plane **c.** parallel lines

   d. intersecting lines **e.** polygon

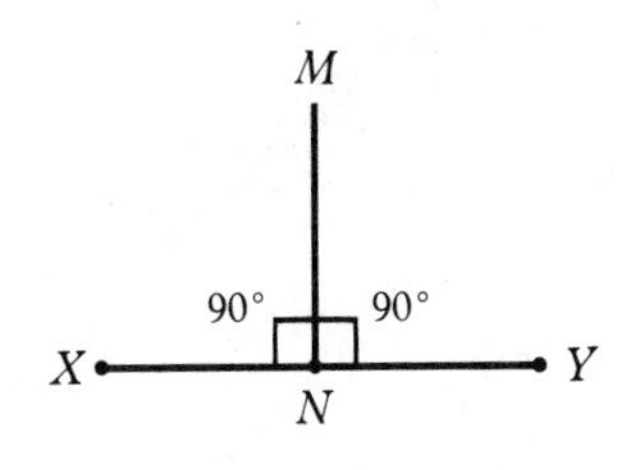

2. Mark the following as true or false.

   a. A laser beam is a better example of a line than a ray.

   b. $\overline{MN}$ is not perpendicular to $\overleftrightarrow{XY}$ since only two right angles are formed.

   c. Point C is on $\overrightarrow{AB}$.

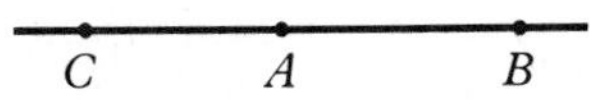

   d. Point C is on $\overleftrightarrow{AB}$.

   e. A radius is a ray.

   f. Two segments are congruent if they have the same length.

3. How many endpoints does a line have? a ray? a segment?

4. Is $\overline{AB}$ the same as $\overline{BA}$? Why or why not?

5. Construct a 135° angle.

6. Draw an obtuse angle and construct its bisector. Are the resulting angles acute, right, or obtuse?

7. Draw a triangle ABC. (Make it fairly large.) Construct the midpoint of each of the three sides.

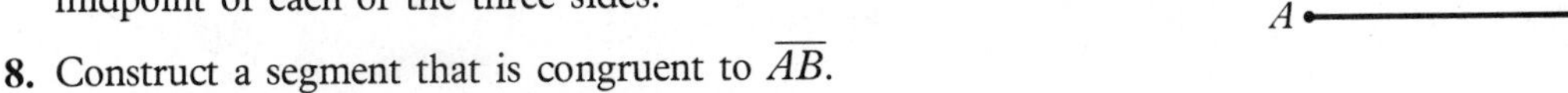

8. Construct a segment that is congruent to $\overline{AB}$.

9. Construct a segment that has length $\frac{1}{4}AB$.

10. Copy $\overline{CD}$ and P on your paper. Construct the line through P perpendicular to $\overline{CD}$.

In exercises 11–14 use the figure of a cube to identify the following:

11. Two parallel planes.

12. A line perpendicular to plane $EFHG$.

13. A line parallel to plane $CDEF$ but not perpendicular to plane $ABCD$.

14. The intersection of plane $BCEG$ and plane $BCFH$.

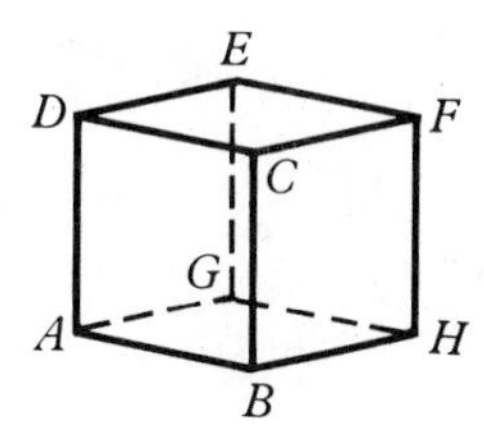

Chapter 1—Test

1. Name objects that illustrate the following:

   a. line b. concurrent lines c. perpendicular lines

   d. regular polygon e. space.

2. Mark the following as true or false.

   a. Two points are always collinear.

   b. If two angles are congruent then they are both right.

   c. Point D is on $\overrightarrow{AB}$.

   d. Point D is on $\overleftrightarrow{AC}$.

   e. A diameter of a circle is a line.

   f. An isosceles triangle must have three congruent sides.

3. Is $\overrightarrow{AB}$ the same as $\overrightarrow{BA}$? Why or why not?

4. If two lines are parallel, how many points do they have in common?

5. Draw a non-convex quadrilateral.

6. Draw a triangle ABC. Construct the angle bisector of each angle.

7. Construct an angle that is congruent to $\angle ABC$.

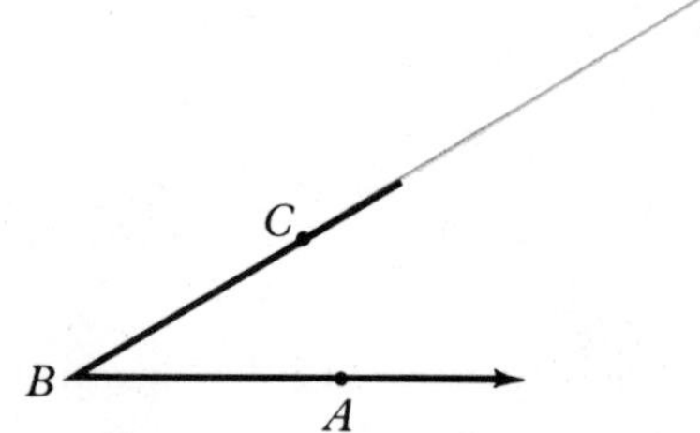

8. Without using a protractor, construct four right angles with a common vertex.

9. Construct a segment congruent to $\overline{AB}$.

10. Construct the midpoint of $\overline{AB}$.

(Exs. 9, 10)

In exercises 11–14 use the figure of a cube to identify the following:

11. A line parallel to plane $ABHG$.

12. A plane perpendicular to $\overleftrightarrow{EG}$.

13. A line that is not parallel and also not perpendicular to any face of the cube.

14. The intersection of plane $ADFH$ and plane $CDEF$.

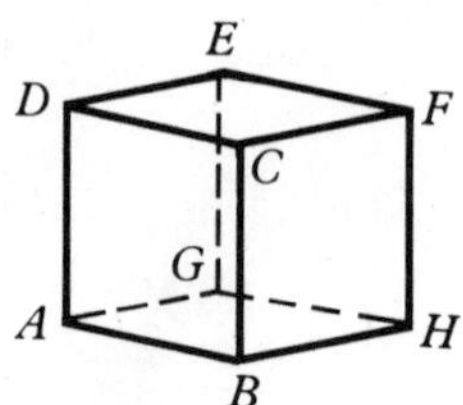

Draw a Diagram

Problems can be fun to solve if you know ways to tackle them. There are several techniques for solving mathematical problems. One of these is to draw a diagram.

Example

On ray $\overrightarrow{AB}$, $AC = 5$ and $AB = 2$. Find BC. To help us solve the problem, we will draw a diagram.

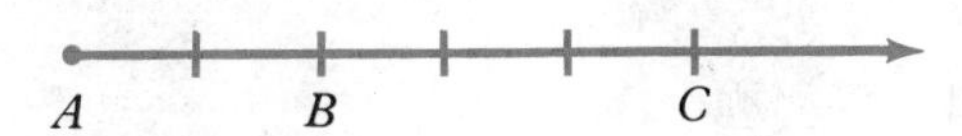

From the diagram, we see that $BC = 3$.

PROBLEMS

Draw diagrams and then solve the following problems.

1. On ray $\overrightarrow{NP}$, $NP = 4$ and $PM = 6$. Find NM.
2. On ray $\overrightarrow{XY}$, $XY = 15$ and $YZ = 6$. Find ZX.
3. How many posts are needed to fence a rectangular field if the posts are to be 5 feet apart and the field is 20 feet by 30 feet?
4. Suppose a bug crawls up a pole two inches in two minutes, then down one inch in one minute, then up two inches in two minutes, and so on. At this rate, how long would it take the bug to climb a height of 10 inches?
5. A stairway has 10 steps, each one foot wide and one foot high. An ant starts at the bottom of the first step and travels straight up the stairway. How far had the ant traveled when it reached the top of the last step?
6. A city high school set up a cross country course through the streets of the city. From the starting point the runners ran 4 blocks east, then 6 blocks north, then 2 blocks west, then 2 blocks south, then 5 blocks west, then 3 blocks north, then 2 blocks west, then 8 blocks south, and 5 blocks east to the finish line. State the direction and the number of blocks from the starting point to the finishing point.

Geometry In Our World

Interior Design: Tessellations

An interior designer encounters examples of geometry when selecting fabric designs, floorcoverings, and wallpaper. Often a geometric concept called a *tessellation* is used in a design. A tessellation is an arrangement of polygons such that no polygons overlap and there are no gaps.

The kitchen shown here has a floor covering and tiled counters that are examples of tessellations.

1 Which polygons will tessellate (or *tile*) a flat surface?

By laying tracing paper over a square and repeatedly tracing it, you can show a "tiling" (or tessellation) of squares. Other tessellations are shown in the picture. Show on your tracing paper a portion of a tessellation using each figure below for which it is possible. Which two figures below *cannot* be used in a tessellation?

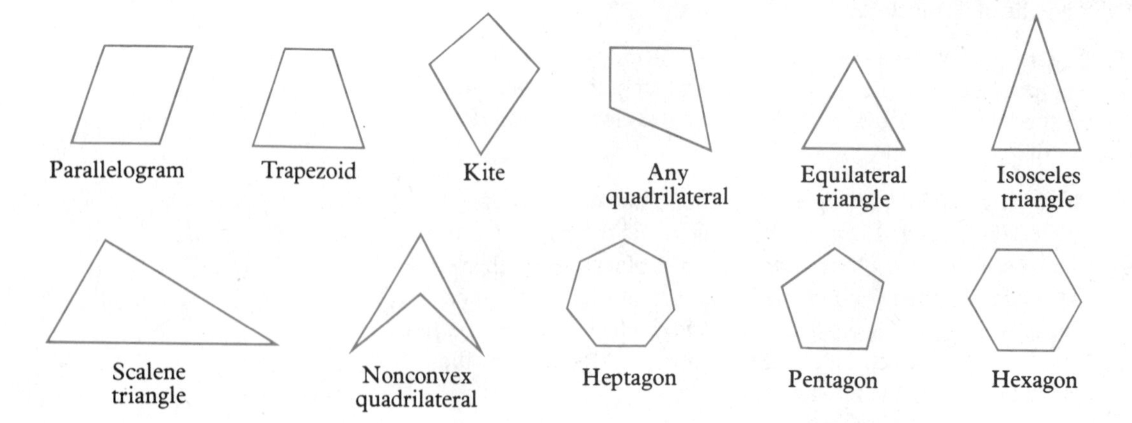

2 Which combinations of regular polygons will tessellate a flat surface?

Interesting floor patterns can be produced by forming tessellations that combine some of the regular polygons pictured below. The pattern shown here has a *square,* a *hexagon,* and a *dodecagon* surrounding each point. It is named using the numbers (4, 6, 12). These numbers show the number of sides of the figures used and the exact order of their arrangement around the point.

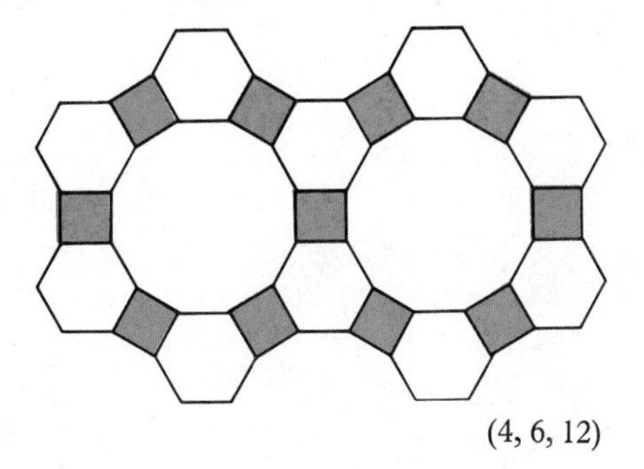

(4, 6, 12)

Trace the figures pictured here to show on your tracing paper a portion of each of the following tessellations. Color each in an interesting way!

(4, 8, 8) (3, 4, 6, 4) (3, 6, 3, 6) (3, 3, 3, 4, 4) (3, 12, 12)

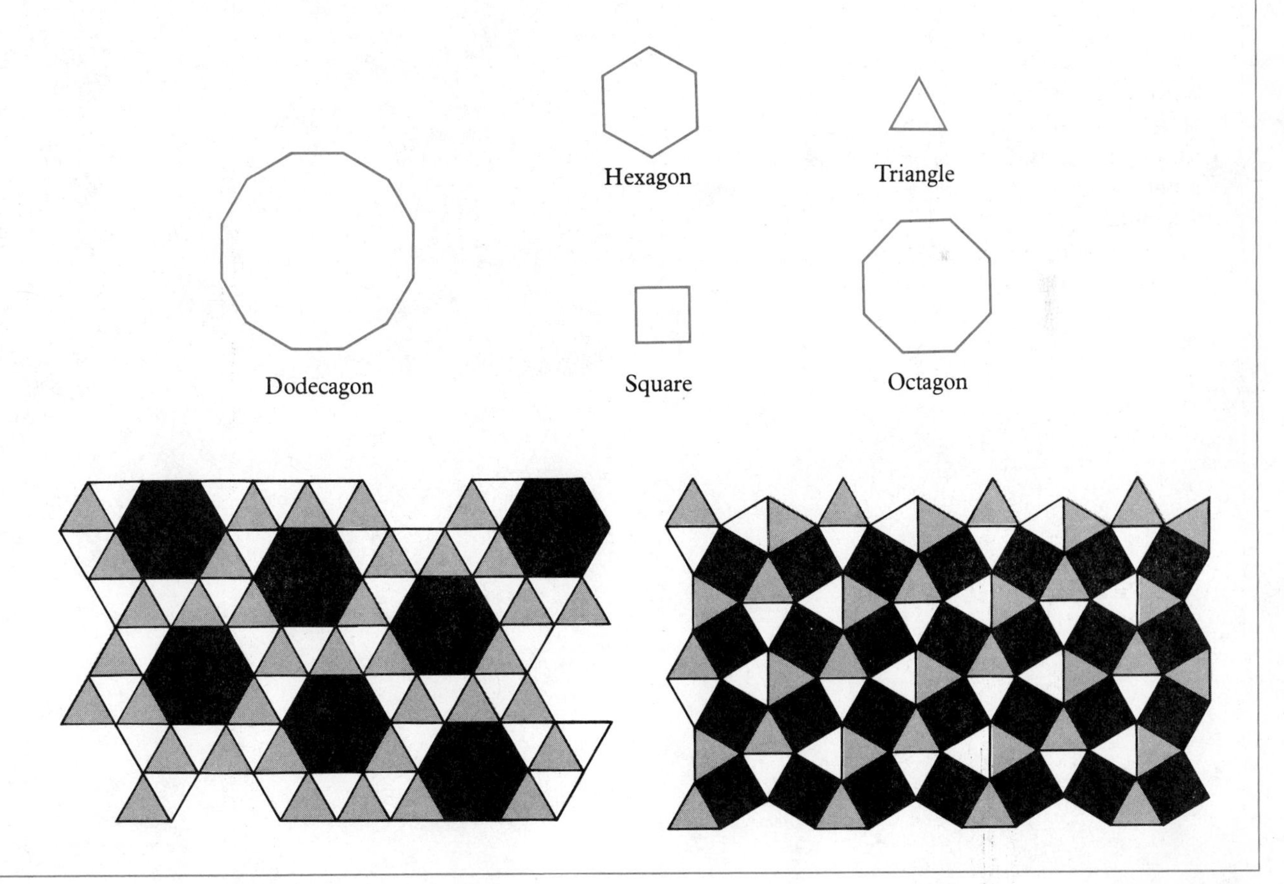

CHAPTER 2

Reasoning in Geometry

2–1 The Process of Inductive Reasoning

B.C. by permission of Johnny Hart and Field Enterprises, Inc.

Reasoning is a process of drawing conclusions from information. Sometimes people draw conclusions based on their observations. After watching an event give the same results several times in succession, a person often concludes that the event will always have the same outcome. This kind of reasoning is called *inductive reasoning*. We shall call a conclusion arrived at through inductive reasoning a *generalization*.

The three examples that follow show how inductive reasoning can be used in geometry.

Example 1 Suppose someone has cut three different shaped triangles from a piece of paper.

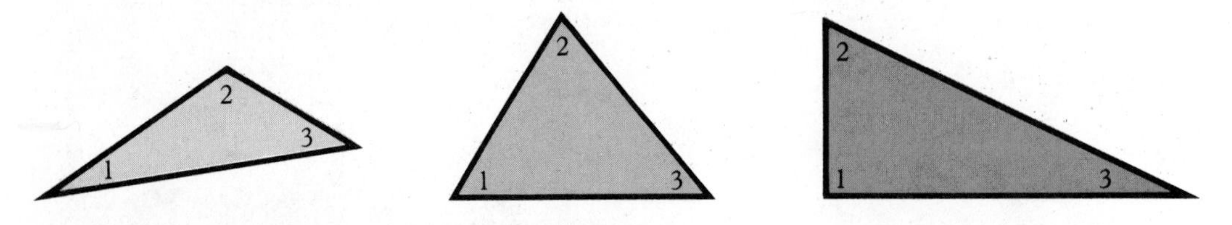

The corners of each of the triangles have been cut off and fitted together as shown below.

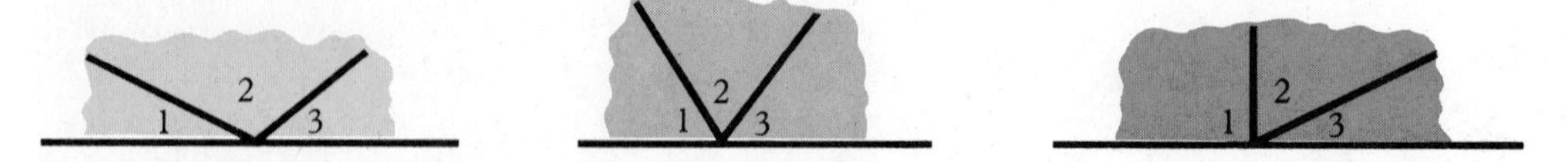

What do you observe about the sum of the angle measures? Do you think this will be true for all triangles?

Complete this generalization:

The sum of the measures of the three angles of a triangle is _?_.

Example 2 Suppose someone has measured all three sides of three different triangles.

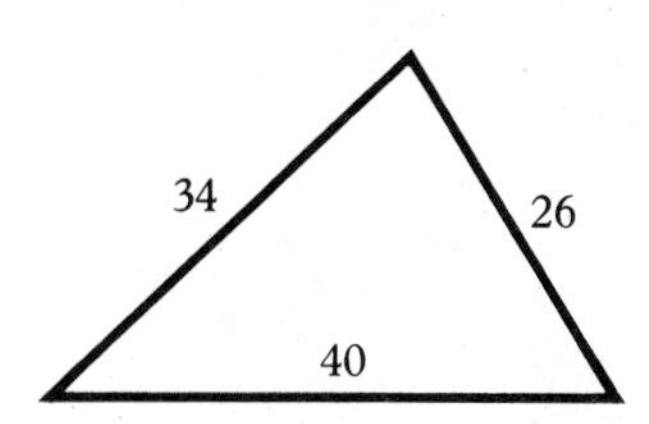

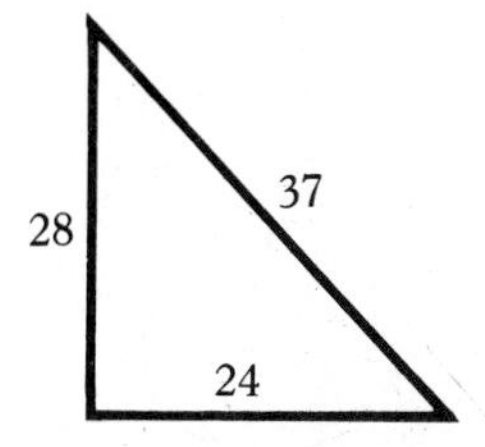

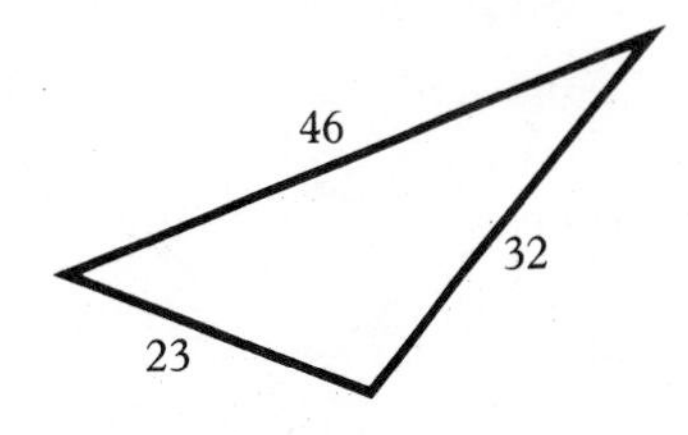

In these triangles the sum of the lengths of two sides is greater than the length of the third side. Do you think this will be true for all triangles?

Complete this generalization:

The sum of the lengths of two sides of a triangle is _?_ the length of the third side.

Example 3 Suppose someone constructs the angle bisectors of each angle of three different triangles.

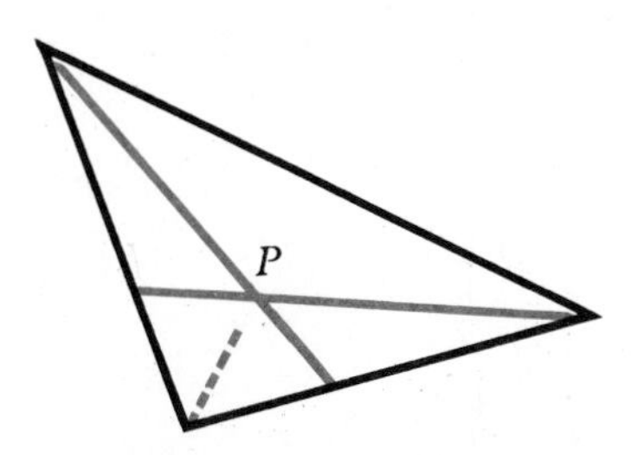

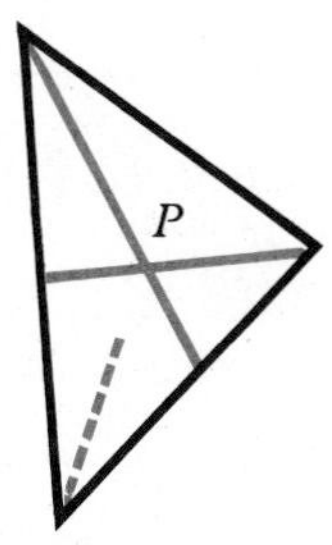

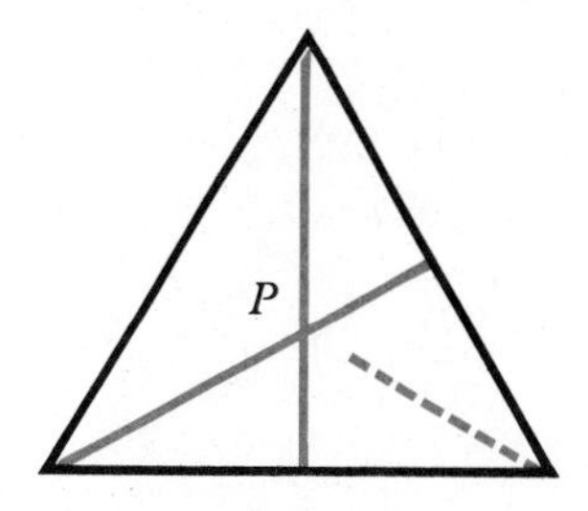

In each triangle will all three angle bisectors meet in point *P*?

Do you think this will be true for all triangles?

Complete this generalization:

The angle bisectors of a triangle _?_ at a point _?_ (inside, on, outside) the triangle.

The process of inductive reasoning may be described as stated here.

Inductive Reasoning

Step 1 You observe that a property is true for every case you check.

Step 2 Since the property is true for all cases checked, you conclude that the property is true for all other cases also and state a generalization.

EXERCISES

A.

Complete the generalization in exercises 1 and 2.

1. **Case 1** **Case 2** **Case 3**

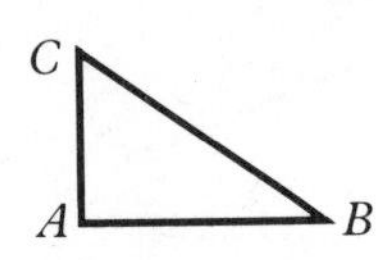

$\angle A$ is a right angle

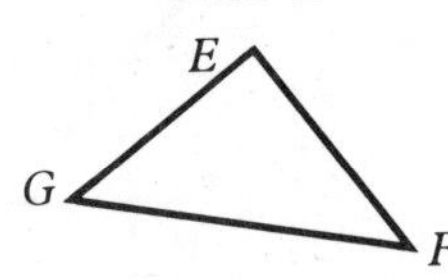

$\angle E$ is a right angle

$\angle Y$ is a right angle

In each case, which side of the triangle is longest?

Generalization: In a right triangle, the side opposite the right angle is _?_ side.

2. **Case 1** **Case 2** **Case 3**

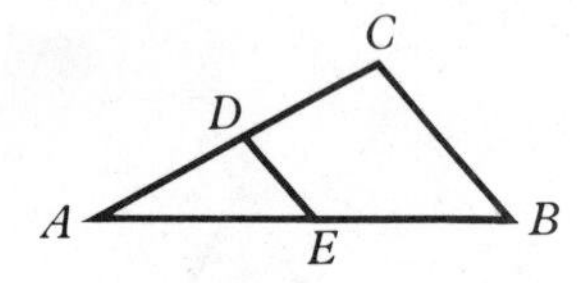

D and E are midpoints

How does DE compare with CB?

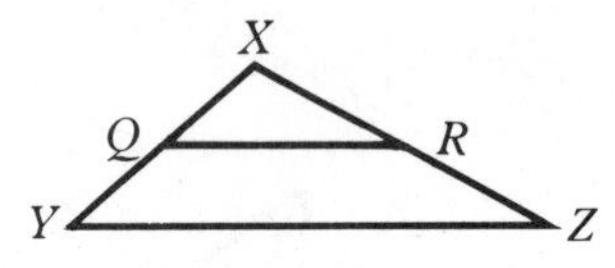

Q and R are midpoints

How does QR compare with YZ?

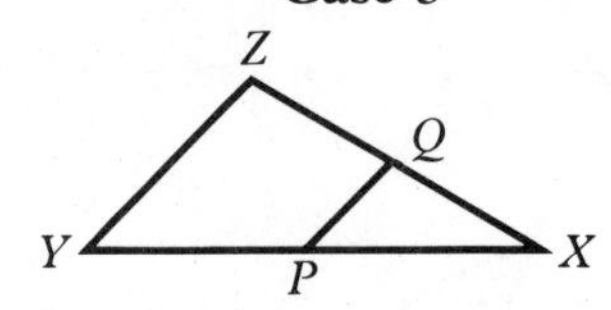

P and Q are midpoints

How does PQ compare with YZ?

Generalization: The measure of a line segment joining the midpoints of two sides of a triangle is _?_ the third side.

Activity

All chords determined by a set of points on a circle divide the interior of the circle into regions.

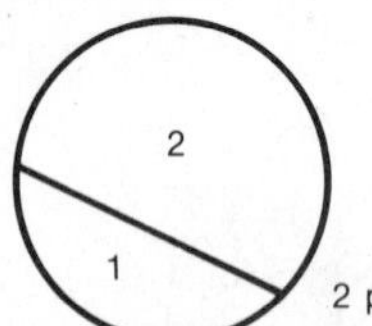

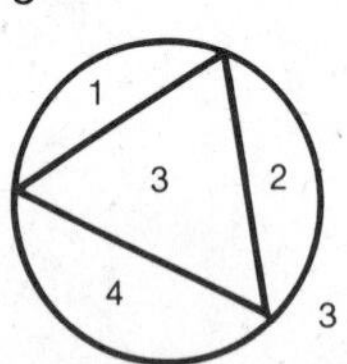

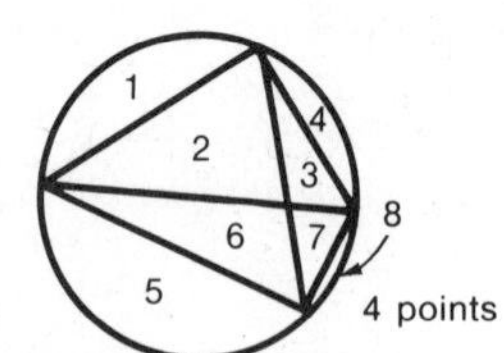

Number of Points	Maximum Number of Regions
1	0
2	2
3	4
4	8
5	—
6	—
7	—

1. Study the pattern in the table and predict the number of regions for 5, 6, and 7 points.
2. Check your prediction by drawing large figures (circles at least 20 cm in diameter) for your classroom bulletin board showing the maximum number of regions for 5, 6, and 7 points.

B.

3. Each triangle below is an equilateral triangle. Measure the angles. (Trace and extend the sides if necessary.) Copy and complete the generalization.

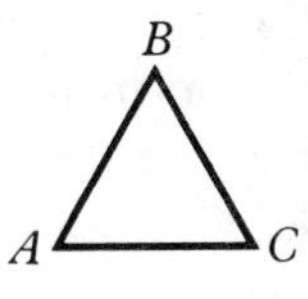

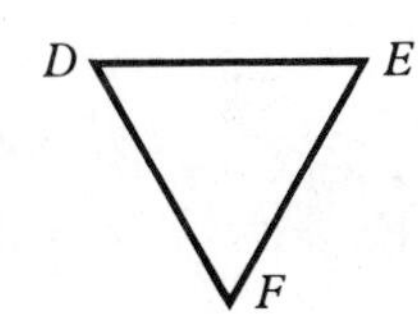

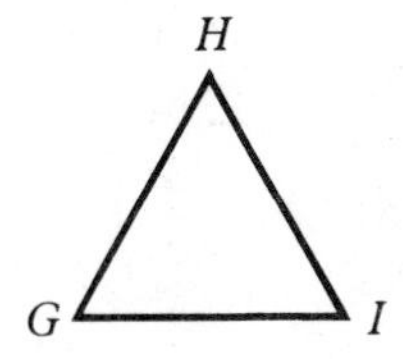

Generalization: If a triangle is an equilateral triangle, then it has _?_ angles.

4. Each triangle below has two congruent sides. Trace the isosceles triangles and bisect the angles formed by the congruent sides. Observe the relationship between the bisector and the opposite side.

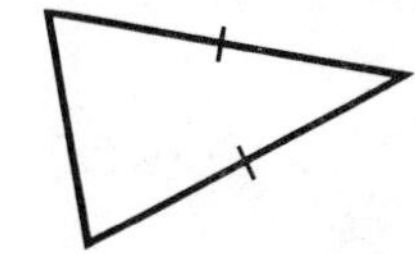

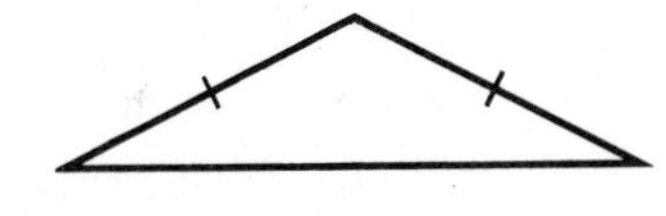

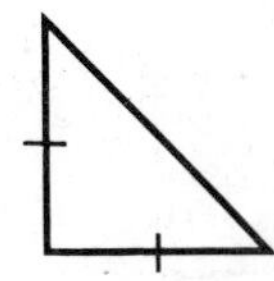

Generalization: In a triangle with two congruent sides, the bisector of the angle formed by the congruent sides is _?_ to the third side.

C.

5. Trace $\triangle ABC$ with $AB = BC = AC$. Choose a point P inside the triangle and construct the perpendiculars from P to the sides of the triangle. Measure h, a, b, and c to the nearest mm. Try as many cases with different points P as needed to state a generalization.

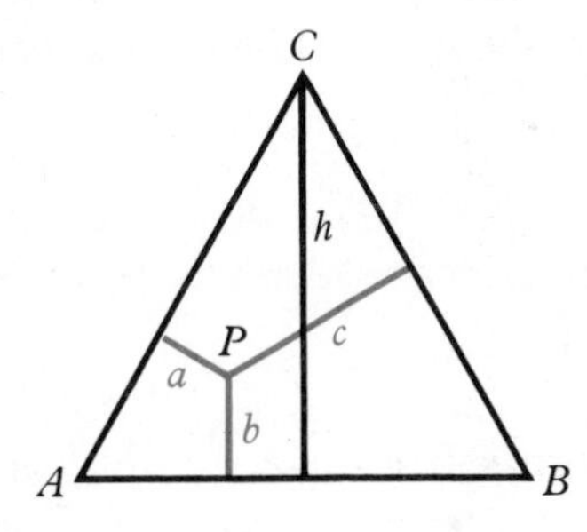

PROBLEM SOLVING

The four toothpicks are arranged to represent a glass with a penny inside.

Move *exactly two* toothpicks so that a glass of the same size is formed and the penny (unmoved) is outside the glass.

2–2 False Generalizations and Counterexamples

This cartoon illustrates a situation in which a generalization, thought to be true, was dramatically shown to be false!

To show that a generalization is false, we often give a *counterexample*. The following three situations show how a counterexample exposes a false generalization.

Example 1

False Generalization: If a quadrilateral has four congruent sides, it has four congruent angles.

Comment: To show that the generalization is false, we must provide a quadrilateral with four congruent sides which does *not* have four congruent angles.

Counterexample: Figure $EFGH$ has all sides congruent but $\angle E$ is not congruent to $\angle F$.

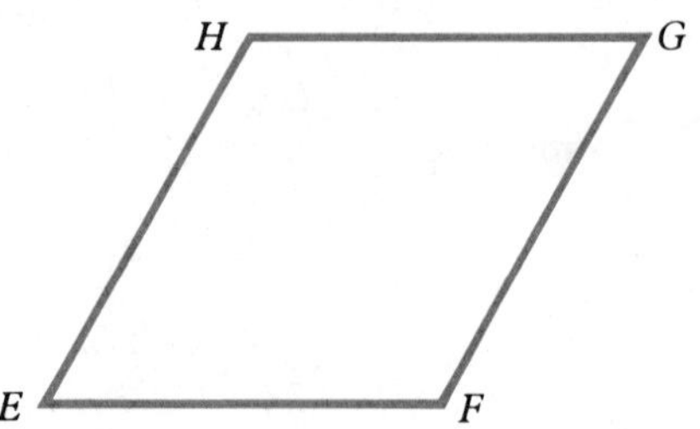

Example 2

False Generalization: If a quadrilateral has a pair of parallel sides, it has a pair of congruent sides.

Comment: To show that the generalization is false, we must produce a quadrilateral with a pair of parallel sides which does *not* have a pair of congruent sides.

Counterexample: Figure *ABCD* has $\overline{BC} \parallel \overline{AD}$ but no two sides are congruent.

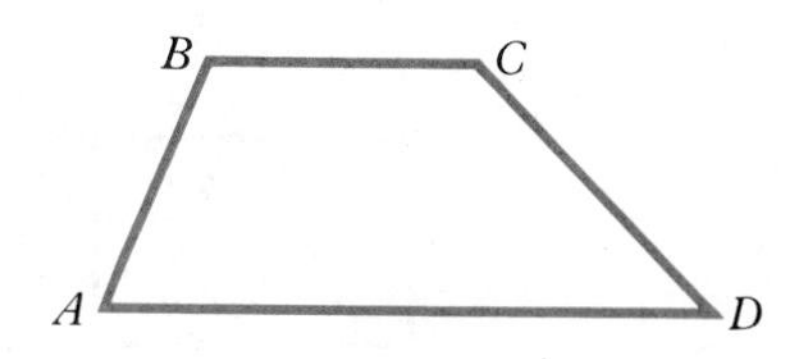

Example 3

False Generalization: If a triangle has a right angle, it has two congruent sides.

Comment: To show that the generalization is false, we must produce a triangle with a right angle which does *not* have two congruent sides.

Counterexample: Figure *TOM* has a right angle ($\angle O$) but all three sides have different lengths.

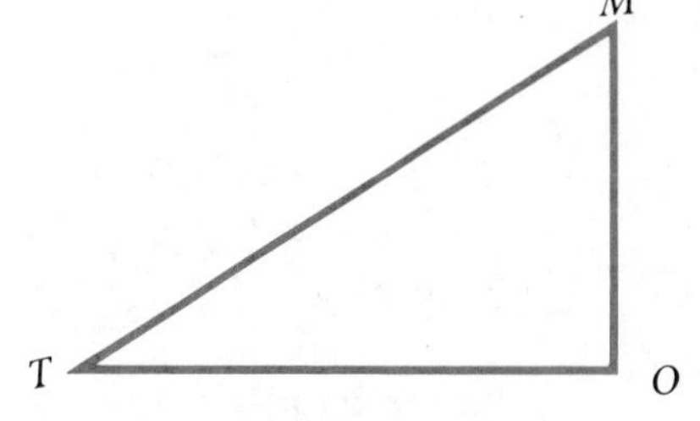

A counterexample can now be described as shown here.

Definition 2-1

A **counterexample** is a single example that shows a generalization to be false.

Example 4

This figure is a counterexample for the following false generalization.

If two lines intersect, then they form right angles.

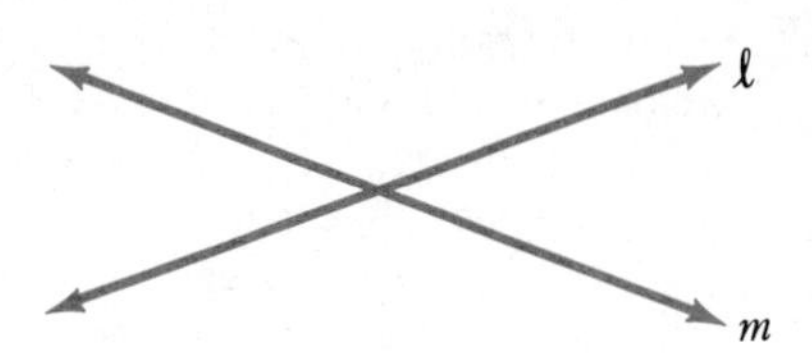

EXERCISES

A.

For exercises 1 and 2, a generalization based on the cases presented is given. Indicate whether you think the generalization is true or false. If it is false, give a counterexample.

1.

Case 1	**Case 2**	**Case 3**	**Case 4**
$\overline{AB} \parallel \overline{DC}$	$\overline{EF} \parallel \overline{HG}$	$\overline{MN} \parallel \overline{PO}$	$\overline{RS} \parallel \overline{UT}$

Generalization: All quadrilaterals have a pair of parallel sides.

2.

Case 1

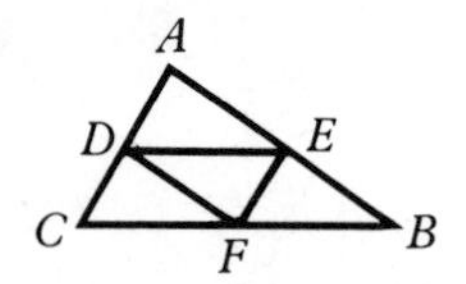

D, *E*, *F* are midpoints

Perimeter of $\triangle ABC$ is twice perimeter of $\triangle DEF$.

Case 2

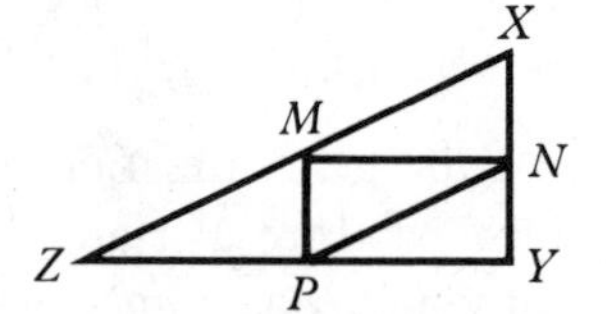

M, *N*, *P* are midpoints

Perimeter of $\triangle XYZ$ is twice perimeter of $\triangle MNP$.

Case 3

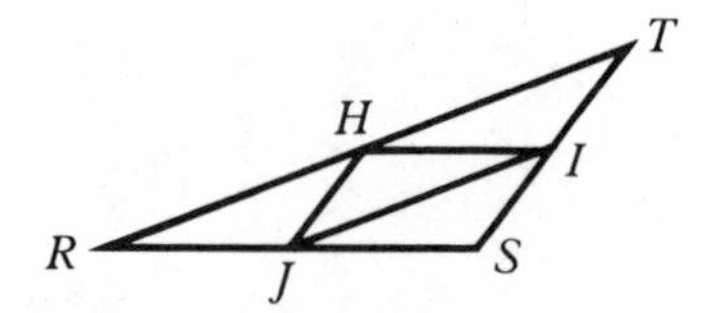

H, *I*, *J* are midpoints

Perimeter of $\triangle RST$ is twice perimeter of $\triangle HIJ$.

Generalization: The perimeter of a triangle is twice the perimeter of the triangle formed by joining the midpoints of its sides.

Activity

Counterexamples play an important role in science. One purpose of space exploration programs is to confirm or disprove theories scientists have formed. Voyager's view of Saturn's rings gave surprising results. Before the Voyager space flights astronomers held many theories concerning Saturn's rings. Were any new findings counterexamples of any of these theories?

Bring to class or describe articles from science magazines or newspapers which support your views.

B.

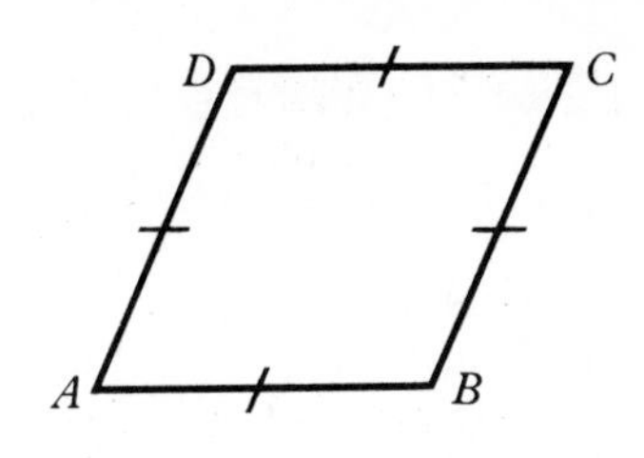

3. For which of the following statements would figure $ABCD$ be a counterexample?
   a. When all sides of a quadrilateral are equal in length, all angles are equal in measure.
   b. When all angles of a quadrilateral are equal in measure, all sides are equal in length.
   c. When one pair of sides of a quadrilateral is congruent, a second pair of sides is also congruent.

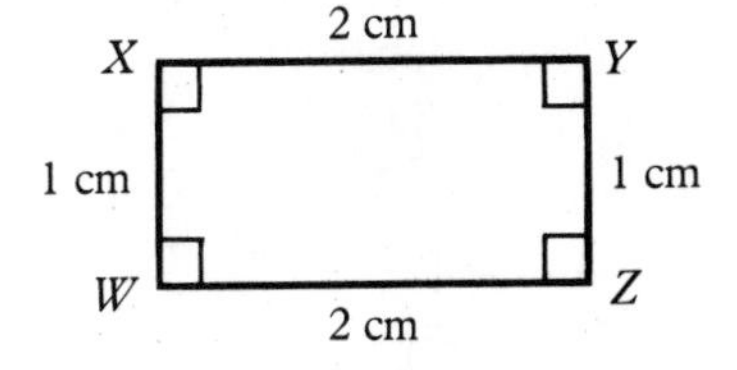

4. For which of the following statements is polygon $WXYZ$ a counterexample?
   a. A polygon with congruent sides is a regular polygon.
   b. A polygon with congruent angles is a regular polygon.
   c. A quadrilateral with congruent angles is a convex quadrilateral.

C.

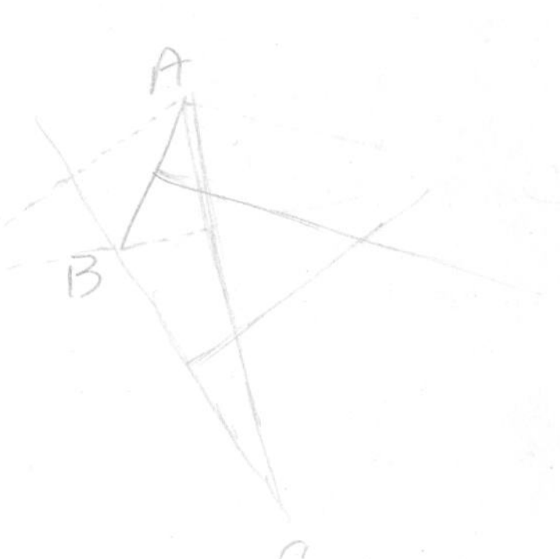

In exercises 5 and 6 indicate whether the statement is true or false. If false, give a counterexample.

5. Given any $\triangle ABC$ the perpendicular bisector of $\overline{AB}$ intersects the perpendicular bisector of $\overline{BC}$ at a point inside the triangle.
6. Given any $\triangle ABC$, the line through A perpendicular to $\overleftrightarrow{BC}$ and the line through B perpendicular to $\overleftrightarrow{AC}$ intersect at a point inside the triangle.

PROBLEM SOLVING

This array of numbers, called *Pascal's triangle,* is named after the French mathematician Blaise Pascal (1623–1662).

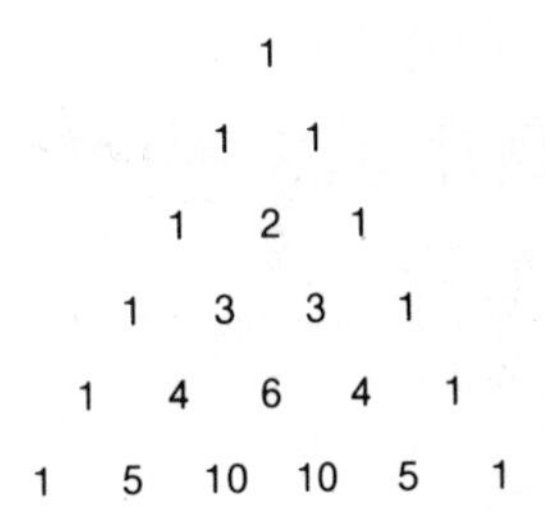

1. Observe the relationship between each number and the numbers nearest it in the row above. Copy the array and complete at least three more rows.
2. Find the sum of the numbers in each row. State a generalization about these sums.
3. Find the polynomials for $(a + b)^2$, $(a + b)^3$, and $(a + b)^4$. List the coefficients of the terms in each polynomial. State a generalization about how this pattern relates to Pascal's Triangle.

2-3 Developing Geometry Using Deductive Reasoning

So far in our study, we have looked for objects in our world that suggest geometric ideas. We have chosen the most basic ideas—point, line, and plane—and called them **undefined terms**.

Using the undefined terms, we have provided **definitions** to describe other geometric figures, such as triangles, segments, and angles. We have also defined relationships, such as congruent, parallel, and perpendicular.

We then used **inductive reasoning** to discover some generalizations about these figures. In the process of making these discoveries, we looked for counterexamples that would disprove the generalizations.

We are now ready to take the next step. We need a method for proving that our discovered generalizations are true for all cases. The method we will use is called **deductive reasoning**. We will study about deductive reasoning in the next few sections.

The process of deductive reasoning requires that we accept a few basic generalizations without proof. These generalizations are called **postulates**.

All other generalizations that can be proved to be true using definitions, postulates, and the logic of deductive reasoning are called **theorems**.

Finally, we use the theorems we have proved to help us solve problems in everyday life.

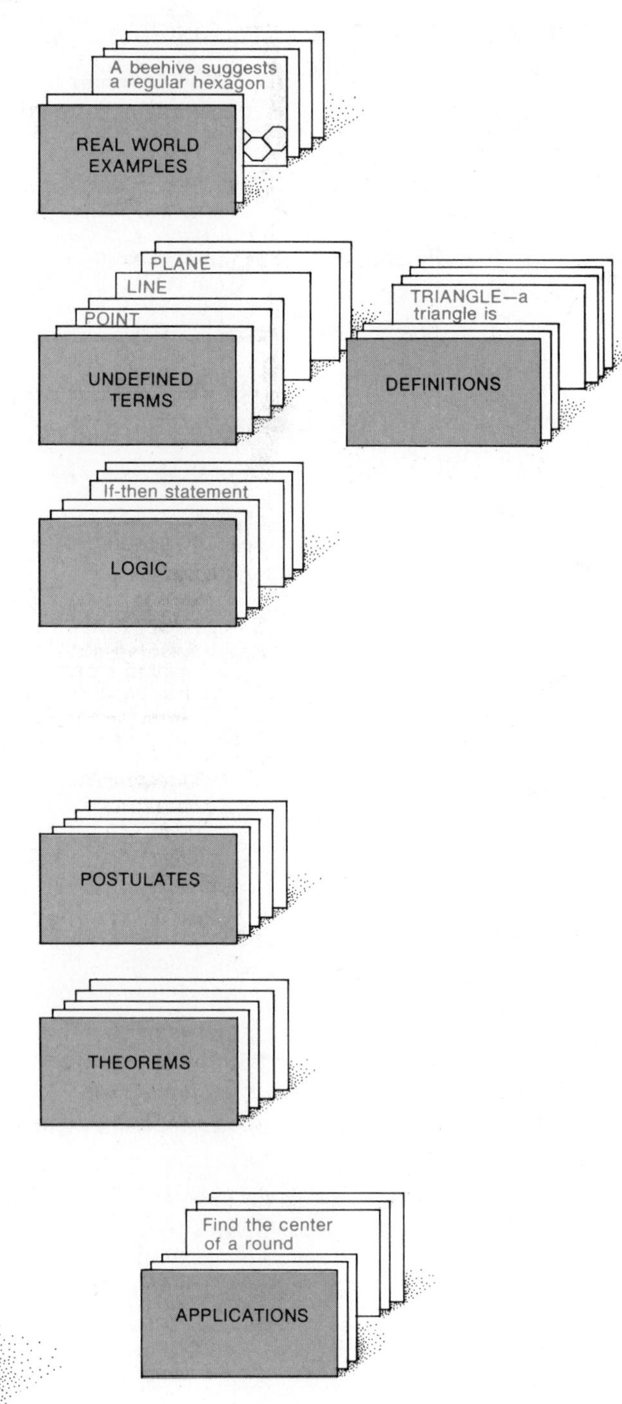

In the previous sections of this chapter we have used inductive reasoning to discover generalizations. Now we will explore logic and deductive reasoning and their role in the proof of theorems. The process of deductive reasoning involves three steps.

We outline these three steps for this theorem:

If two sides of a triangle are congruent,
then the two opposite angles are congruent.

Deductive Reasoning

Step 1 Start with the given conditions (the hypothesis).

Step 2 Use logic and definitions, postulates, or previously proved theorems to justify a series of statements or steps which lead to the desired result.

Step 3 Assert the result (the conclusion).

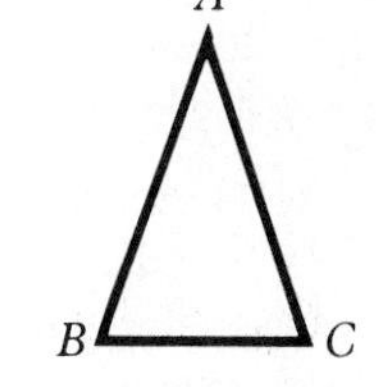

Given: $\triangle ABC$ is a triangle with $\overline{AB} \cong \overline{AC}$.

The statements leading to the conclusion are not included here. In this chapter you will learn some reasoning patterns that will help you select, sequence, and give reasons for appropriate statements.

Therefore, $\angle B$ and $\angle C$ are congruent.

After we use logic to supply the correct statements in Step 2 of the sample proof above, we will have proved this theorem:

If *two sides of a triangle are congruent,*
hypothesis

then *the two opposite angles are congruent.*
conclusion

EXERCISES

A.

1. Webster's New Collegiate Dictionary gives this "definition" of a plane: A plane is a flat or level surface.

   List three words in the "definition" that should also be understood and for which one could try to write a definition.

2. Write a definition for one of the three terms in exercise 1. List any words in your definition that might also need to be defined.

3. Do you think the term *plane* should be selected as an undefined term? Explain.

4. Write a definition of *space* using the undefined terms set and point.

5. Write a statement that you think is a theorem in geometry.

Activity

One objective of a geometry course is to provide practice in logical reasoning in everyday life. In our daily lives we sometimes draw conclusions with little or no supporting evidence.

Accept this story as an accurate depiction of an event that actually happened:

Little Jack Horner sat in a corner
  eating his Christmas pie.
He put in his thumb, pulled out a plum
  and said "What a good boy am I."

Which of these conclusions have you accepted (perhaps without being aware of it) about this story?

1. Jack was eating a plum pie.
2. It was Christmas day.
3. Jack felt he was a "good boy" because he pulled out the plum.
4. Jack was sitting in the corner because he was being punished.
5. Jack was a child.

Now reread the story. Which of these conclusions are accurate, based only on the information given in the story?

B.

In exercises 6-9, the given information and a conclusion based on deductive reasoning are stated. The statements leading from the hypothesis to the conclusion are omitted. State the theorem that was proved.

6. Given: Lines ℓ and m form a linear pair of angles, $\angle 1$ and $\angle 2$. $\angle 1 \cong \angle 2$

$\vdots$

Therefore, $\ell \perp m$.

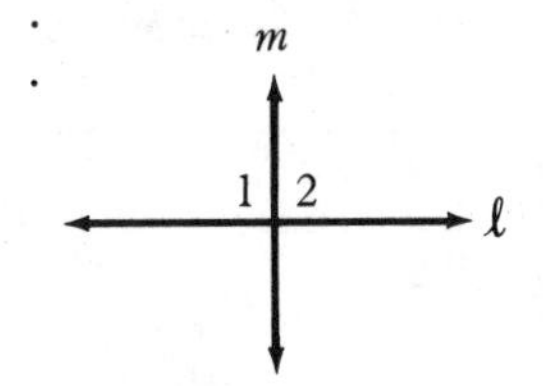

7. Given: $\angle 1$ and $\angle 3$ are vertical angles.

$\vdots$

Therefore, $\angle 1 \cong \angle 3$.

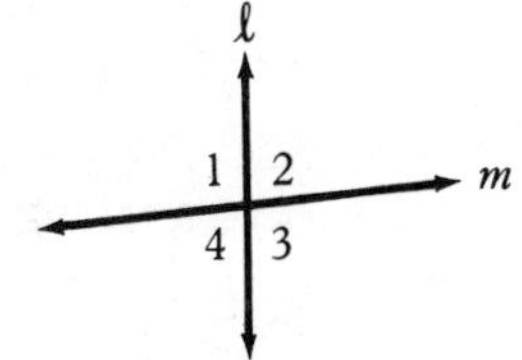

8. Given: In isosceles $\triangle ABC$ with $\overline{AB} \cong \overline{AC}$, $\overline{AD}$ bisects $\angle A$.

$\vdots$

Therefore, $\overline{CD} \cong \overline{DB}$.

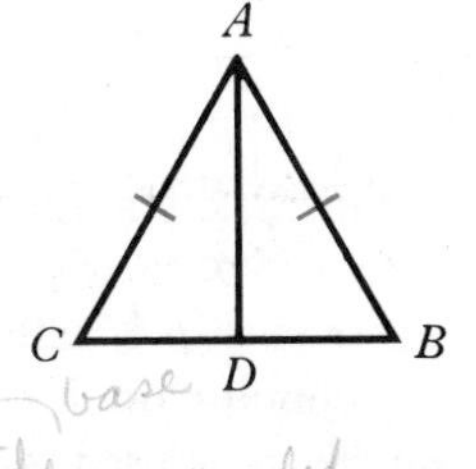

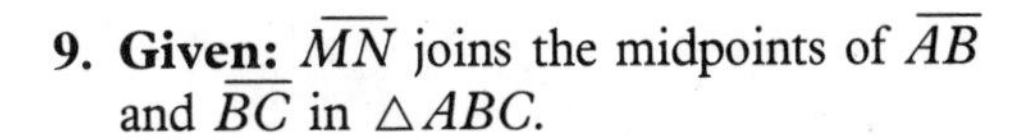

9. Given: $\overline{MN}$ joins the midpoints of $\overline{AB}$ and $\overline{BC}$ in $\triangle ABC$.

$\vdots$

Therefore, $\overleftrightarrow{MN} \parallel \overleftrightarrow{AC}$.

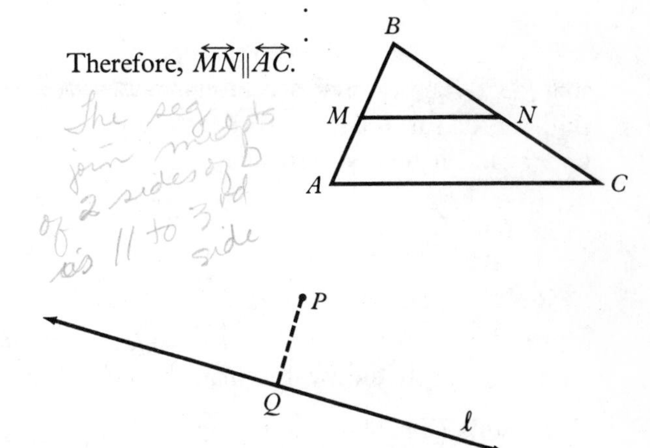

C.

10. Write a logical argument to convince a friend that the shortest distance from a point P to a line ℓ is the length of $\overline{PQ}$ where Q is on ℓ and ℓ is perpendicular to $\overline{PQ}$.

PROBLEM SOLVING

Three ambassadors, all from different countries, paid \$30 for a suite of rooms at a hotel. Each contributed \$10. The clerk later realized that only \$25 should be charged, and gave the bellhop \$5 to return to them. The bellhop reasoned that their language differences might make it difficult for them to decide how to split up the \$5 refund, so the bellhop kept \$2 and returned \$3 to the ambassadors.

Each had paid \$10, minus the \$1 refund, or \$9 for the room. $\$9 \times 3 = \$27$. \$27 plus the \$2 kept by the bellhop amounts to \$29! The original charge, however, was \$30. What happened to the other \$1?

2-4 Types of If-Then Statements

This cartoon illustrates a type of statement that is important in deductive reasoning. The examples below show statements in the "if-then" form.

If p, then q.

If it snows today, then we will ski.
If an isosceles triangle has a 60° angle, then it is an equilateral triangle.
If Lucy does not laugh, then Snoopy is sad.

Definition 2-2 describes this type of statement. The examples below present some skills needed in order to work with and understand if-then statements.

Definition 2-2

An **if-then statement** is a statement of the form—if p, then q—where p and q are simple statements. p is called the **hypothesis**. q is called the **conclusion**. The symbol $p \rightarrow q$ (read p *implies* q) is used to represent an if-then statement.

Example 1 *Given an if-then statement, state the hypothesis and conclusion.*
If the weatherman says it will rain today, then we will not play tennis.

Hypothesis (p): The weatherman says that it will rain today.
Conclusion (q): We will not play tennis.

Example 2 *Given the hypothesis and conclusion, write the if-then statement.*

Hypothesis (p): Figure $ABCD$ is a square.
Conclusion (q): It has four congruent sides.
If-then ($p \rightarrow q$): If figure $ABCD$ is a square, then it has four congruent sides.

Example 3 *Given a statement in another form, write it as an if-then statement.*

The temperature is below 0°C when it snows.
If-then ($p \rightarrow q$): If it snows, then the temperature is below 0°C.

To learn more about the process of deductive reasoning we first must be able to decide whether an if-then statement—like the one shown here—is true. (Is it true? Explain.)

Now consider the following example. Suppose a teacher makes the if-then statement below. For which of the cases do you feel you were treated unfairly and the teacher didn't tell the truth? Your answer to this question will help you see when an if-then statement is false.

If you get A's on all Geometry tests, then you will get an A in the course.

Case 1 You get A's on all tests. (hypothesis true) — You get an A in the course. (conclusion true)

Case 2 You get A's on all tests. (hypothesis true) — You don't get an A in the course. (conclusion false)

Case 3 You don't get A's on all tests. (hypothesis false) — You get an A in the course. (conclusion true)

Case 4 You don't get A's on all tests. (hypothesis false) — You don't get an A in the course. (conclusion false)

The only time you were treated unfairly is in Case 2.

The results of the example above are summarized in the descriptions of true and false if-then statements given here.

> An if-then statement is true if whenever the hypothesis is true, the conclusion is also true. Or, saying it another way, an if-then statement is false only when the hypothesis is true and the conclusion is false.

EXERCISES

A.

In exercises 1–8, first state the hypothesis (p) and the conclusion (q) of the if-then statement. Then decide whether or not the statement is true.

1. If Jana is 15 years old, then Jana is too young to vote in United States elections.
2. If a ball is tossed up, then it will come down.
3. If some apples are red, then horses have four legs.
4. If Rodney bought a pear, then Rodney bought a vegetable.
5. If two lines intersect, then those two lines are not parallel.
6. If three lines are concurrent, then the lines are parallel.
7. If $\triangle ABC$ is isosceles, then $\triangle ABC$ is equilateral.
8. If $\triangle ABC$ is equilateral, then $\triangle ABC$ is isosceles.

In exercises 9–14 write if-then statements ($p \rightarrow q$) with the given hypothesis (p) and conclusion (q).

9. Hypothesis (p): A man lives in Denver.
   Conclusion (q): He lives in Colorado.
10. Hypothesis (p): Two lines intersect to form right angles.
    Conclusion (q): The lines are perpendicular.
11. Hypothesis (p): Two lines are perpendicular.
    Conclusion (q): They intersect to form congruent right angles.
12. Hypothesis (p): A number is prime.
    Conclusion (q): The number has exactly two divisors.
13. p: Two lines are parallel.
    q: They do not intersect.
14. p: Two angles are congruent.
    q: They have the same measure.

Activity

Find statements from magazines or newspapers that involve if-then statements or statements that can be rewritten as if-then statements without changing the meaning. Discuss each statement and the logic behind it.

B.

In exercises 15–24, identify the hypothesis and conclusion and rewrite the statement in if-then form without changing its meaning.

15. A number is even if it ends in 2.

16. Two lines are perpendicular if they meet at right angles.

17. An equiangular triangle must be equilateral.

18. A number is odd whenever it ends in 5.

19. Do as I say and you will be rich.

20. You will improve provided that you work hard.

21. A triangle is isosceles whenever two of its angles are congruent.

22. A line which bisects a segment contains the midpoint of the segment.

23. B is the midpoint of $\overline{AC}$ provided that $\overline{AB} \cong \overline{BC}$.

24. All triangles are polygons.

C.

25. Write as many if-then statements as you can that have the same meaning as the statements in this advertisement from the Nowork Company.

> Join Nowork Company and make a fast buck. Work for Nowork and get promoted fast. We hire only smart people who are too dumb to know they are smart. Nowork assures you excellent training at no pay. You will like working for Nowork Company. We hire any human. We fire any human.

26. Write a true if-then statement (if a, then b), and then rewrite it in each of these forms: b if a; a only if b; a is all that is needed to insure b; b must be true in order for a to be true. Which do you think are true?

PROBLEM SOLVING

Four adults and two children must cross a river in a canoe that will hold only one adult or two children at one time. It will not carry one adult and one child. Explain how the six people can get across the river. What is the least number of times the canoe must cross?

2–5 Converse, Inverse, and Contrapositive

If we begin with a true if-then statement, we can form three types of related statements called the *converse*, the *inverse*, and the *contrapositive* of the original statement. Each type is described below and is compared with the original if-then statement.

$\sim p$ means "not p."

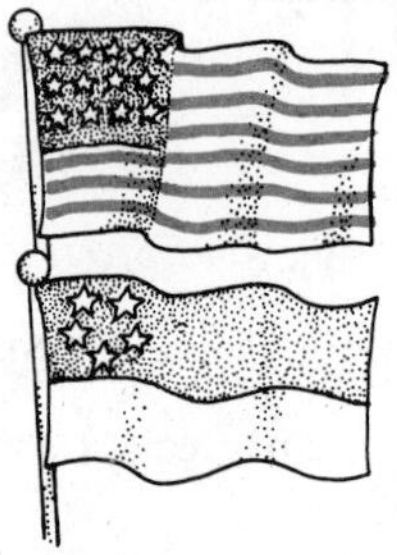

Statement: $p \rightarrow q$ — If a flag is the U.S. flag, then it has stars.

Converse of the statement: $q \rightarrow p$ — If a flag has stars, then it is the U.S. flag.

When an if-then statement $p \rightarrow q$ is true, we *should not assume* that its converse $q \rightarrow p$ is necessarily true.

Statement: $p \rightarrow q$ — If a vehicle is an airplane, then the vehicle is built to fly.

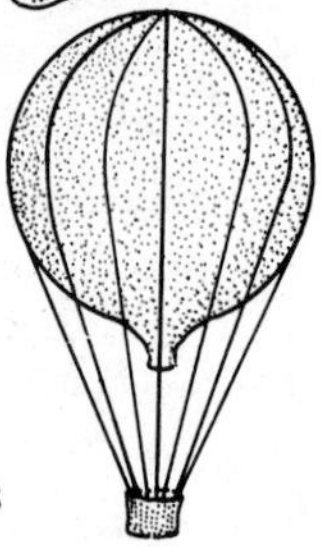

Inverse of the statement: $\sim p \rightarrow \sim q$ — If a vehicle is not an airplane, then the vehicle is not built to fly.

When an if-then statement $p \rightarrow q$ is true, we *should not assume* that its inverse $\sim p \rightarrow \sim q$ is necessarily true.

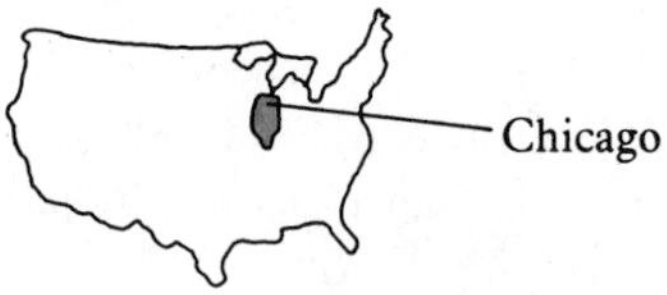

Statement: $p \rightarrow q$ — If you live in Chicago, then you live in Illinois.

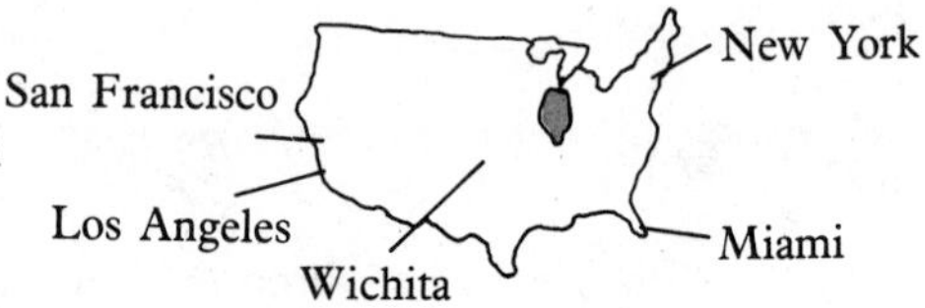

Contrapositive of the statement: $\sim q \rightarrow \sim p$ — If you do not live in Illinois, then you do not live in Chicago.

When an if-then statement $p \rightarrow q$ is true we *can assume* that its contrapositive $\sim q \rightarrow \sim p$ is also true.

We summarize these results as follows:

$p \to q$	given statement	If p, then q	true (assumed)
$q \to p$	converse	If q, then p	not necessarily true
$\sim p \to \sim q$	inverse	If not p, then not q	not necessarily true
$\sim q \to \sim p$	contrapositive	If not q, then not p	always true

When a given statement and its converse are both true we can combine the two statements into one statement by using the phrase *if and only if.*

Statement:
$p \to q$ If today is Tuesday, then tomorrow is Wednesday.

Converse of the statement: If tomorrow is Wednesday, then today is Tuesday.
$q \to p$

if and only if statement: Today is Tuesday if and only if tomorrow is Wednesday.
$p \leftrightarrow q$

Every definition can be stated using an *if and only if* statement. For example, consider this definition.

An equilateral triangle is a triangle with all sides congruent to one another.

It can be restated like this.

A figure is an equilateral triangle if and only if it is a triangle with all sides congruent to one another.

The restatement actually combines two true statements:

1. If a triangle is equilateral, then it has all sides congruent.
2. If a triangle has all sides congruent, then it is equilateral.

We summarize this idea as follows:

p if and only if q means the same thing as *if p, then q* **and** *if q, then p.* When this statement is true we say p and q are *equivalent statements.*

EXERCISES

A.

For exercises 1-4, write the *converse* of each statement. Rewrite statements in if-then form if necessary. For which exercises are the statement and converse both true?

1. If a person is swimming, then that person is wet.

2. If two lines are perpendicular, then they intersect.

3. If a person is poor, then that person doesn't have much money.

4. If $a \cdot b = 0$, then $a = 0$ or $b = 0$.

For exercises 5-8 write the *inverse* of each statement.

5. If a person steals, then the person is dishonest.

6. If a figure is a triangle, then it is a polygon.

7. Any team that wins four World Series games wins the series.

8. Two planes are parallel if they do not intersect.

For exercises 9-12 write the *contrapositive* of each statement.

9. If you drive a car legally, then you are 16 years old or older.

10. All right angles are congruent.

11. We will win the championship if we win the game tonight.

12. If a triangle is equilateral, then it is equiangular.

Activity

Let's Analyze an Ad

(1) If you want to feel your very best, take one ABC tablet each day. (2) People who take ABC vitamins care about their health. You owe it to those close to you to take care of yourself. Start taking ABC today!

When we hear statements like (1) we often erroneously assume the *converse*. "If you take an ABC tablet daily, then you'll feel your very best." When we hear statements like (2) we often erroneously assume the *inverse:* "If I don't take ABC vitamins, then I don't care about my health."

Copy a TV or magazine ad. What are some possible erroneous assumptions you might make?

B.

In exercises 13–18 write two simple statements that are equivalent.

13. A triangle is equilateral if and only if it is equiangular.

14. An angle is a right angle if and only if its measure is 90°.

15. Two lines in a plane are parallel if and only if they have no points in common.

16. A quadrilateral is a rectangle if and only if it has four right angles.

17. A quadrilateral is a parallelogram if and only if it has two pairs of parallel sides.

18. Two angles are complementary if and only if the sum of their measures is 90°.

C.

19. Write the converse, inverse, and contrapositive of these sentences of the form $p \rightarrow q$.

Make a chart like the following and then mark each entry true or false.

	Statement	Converse	Inverse	Contrapositive
If I live in Atlanta, I live in Georgia.	T	F	F	T
If a number is positive, then it is greater than 6.	F	T	T	F
If two segments have the same length, then they are congruent.	T	T	T	T
If a figure is a regular polygon, then all sides are congruent.	T	F	F	T

PROBLEM SOLVING

Two women, Alice and Carol, and two men, Brian and David, are athletes. One is a swimmer, a second is a skater, a third is a gymnast, and a fourth is a tennis player. One day they were seated around a square table:

1. The swimmer sat on Alice's left.
2. The gymnast sat across from Brian.
3. Carol and David sat next to each other.
4. A woman sat on the skater's left.

Who is the tennis player?

2-6 Patterns of Reasoning

We will now study several patterns of reasoning. They will be used often when you prove theorems. Study the cartoon and discussion below.

The first pattern of reasoning we will study begins with a true if-then statement. The hypothesis is established as true. We can then conclude that the conclusion is also true.

$p \rightarrow q$ is true.	If anyone mentions partridge in a pear tree, then Lucy will scream.
p is given.	Charlie says "partridge in a pear tree."
Conclude that q is true.	Therefore, Lucy screams.

The above example illustrates a pattern of reasoning called *affirming the hypothesis.* It is based on establishing that the hypothesis of a true if-then statement is also true. It is also named with the latin words *modus ponens.*

Definition 2-3

Affirming the hypothesis is a pattern of reasoning represented as follows:
Whenever $p \rightarrow q$ is true and p is true, we can conclude q is true.

A second pattern of reasoning is the basis for indirect proof which you will use in later chapters. In the cartoon, the pattern is:

$p \rightarrow q$ is true.
$\sim q$ (not q is given).

Conclude that $\sim p$ is true (p is false).

If you really loved me, then you'd stop playing the piano.
Schroeder didn't stop.

Therefore, Schroeder doesn't love Lucy."

This pattern of reasoning is called *denying the conclusion.* It is also named by the latin words *modus tollens.*

Definition 2-4

Denying the conclusion is a pattern of reasoning represented as follows:

Whenever $p \rightarrow q$ is true
and $\sim q$ (q is false).

We conclude: $\sim p$ (p is false).

The next cartoon suggests a third pattern that is used in writing proofs. It ties together a sequence of statements in the proof of a theorem. The pattern is:

$p \rightarrow q$ is true.
$q \rightarrow r$ is true.

Conclude that $p \rightarrow r$ is true.

Charlie Brown's "chain of reasoning":

If you have a broken heart, then the jagged edges poke you in the side.
If the jagged edges poke you in the side, then you can't sleep at night.

Therefore, if you have a broken heart, then you can't sleep at night.

This example illustrates a pattern of reasoning called the chain rule. It provides a way to "link" if-then statements in writing proofs.

Definition 2-5

The **chain rule** is a pattern of reasoning represented as follows:

Whenever $p \rightarrow q$ is true
and $q \rightarrow r$ is true.

We conclude $p \rightarrow r$ is true.

EXERCISES

A.

For exercises 1–6 state the correct conclusion:

1. $p \rightarrow q$: If Julia votes today, she will vote for Fred Friendly.
p: Julia voted today.
Therefore q: ?

2. $p \rightarrow q$: If $\triangle ABC$ is isosceles, then it has two congruent angles.
p: $\triangle ABC$ is isosceles.
Therefore q: ?

3. $p \rightarrow q$: If it snows the temperature is below $0°C$.
$\sim q$: The temperature is at or above $0°C$.
Therefore $\sim p$: ?

4. $p \rightarrow q$: If a figure is an equilateral triangle, then it has all sides congruent and all angles congruent.
$q \rightarrow r$: If a figure has all sides congruent and all angles congruent, then it is a regular polygon.
Therefore $p \rightarrow r$: ?

5. $p \rightarrow q$: If two lines are parallel they have no points in common.
$\sim q$: Lines m and n have a point in common.
Therefore $\sim p$: ?

6. $p \rightarrow q$: Two perpendicular lines intersect.
$q \rightarrow r$: Lines are not parallel if they intersect.
Therefore $p \rightarrow r$: ?

Activity

Consider the following examples of reasoning often found in advertising. Decide if the companies used correct or incorrect reasoning patterns.

1. "Send your money in before October 1 and buy at $\frac{1}{2}$ price." Paula Joseph mailed her order on October 10. The company honored her request. Did the company lie?

2. "Send your money in before December 1 and buy at $\frac{1}{2}$ price." Angelo Silva sent his money on November 24, but the company refused his request. Did the company lie?

3. "This offer is good for people living in the continental United States." Namoonie Nakak lives in the Arctic. The company refused her offer. Was the company justified?

4. "You will be handsome if you use Neato." Jason does not use Neato but he is very handsome. Was the company wrong?

5. See if you can find and identify examples of correct and incorrect reasoning patterns in advertising.

B.

In exercises 7-9 fill in the missing information so that a correct reasoning pattern is given.

7. (Accept) A point on the perpendicular bisector of a segment is equidistant from the endpoints of the segment.
(Given) ?
(Conclusion) Point C is equidistant from the endpoints of $\overline{AB}$.

8. (Accept) All horizontal lines are parallel.
(Given) ?
(Conclusion) $\overleftrightarrow{EF}$ and $\overleftrightarrow{GH}$ are not horizontal lines.

9. (Accept) ?
(Given) $\angle ABC$ has measure greater than $90°$.
(Conclusion) $\angle ABC$ is an obtuse angle.

C.

In exercises 10–11 write the missing statement. (You should be able to do these exercises even if you don't know the meaning of all the terms used.)

10. Theorem: If $ABCD$ is a square, then $ABCD$ is not a kite.
Proof: 1. If $ABCD$ is a square, then $ABCD$ is a rhombus.
2. (missing statement)
3. If $ABCD$ is a parallelogram, then $ABCD$ is not a kite.
Therefore, if $ABCD$ is a square, $ABCD$ is not a kite.

11. Theorem: If $\triangle ABC$ is a right triangle with $\angle C$ a right angle, then $\angle A$ and $\angle B$ are complementary.
Proof: 1. (missing statement)
2. If $m\angle A + m\angle B + m\angle C = 180$ and $m\angle C = 90$, then $m\angle A + m\angle B = 90$.
3. (missing statement)
Therefore, if $\triangle ABC$ is a right triangle with $\angle C$ a right angle, then $\angle A$ and $\angle B$ are complementary.

PROBLEM SOLVING

Three people named Lee, Martinelli, and Nielsen fill the positions of accountant, cashier, and clerk in a department store. If Nielsen is the cashier, Martinelli is the clerk. If Nielsen is the clerk, Martinelli is the accountant. If Martinelli is not the cashier, Lee is the clerk. If Lee is the accountant, Nielsen is the clerk. What is each person's job?

2–7 Postulates in Geometry

The postulates of geometry are very important in the process of deductive reasoning. They can be compared to the rules of a game. In the "game of geometry" we accept the postulates as true and use them to help us prove theorems.

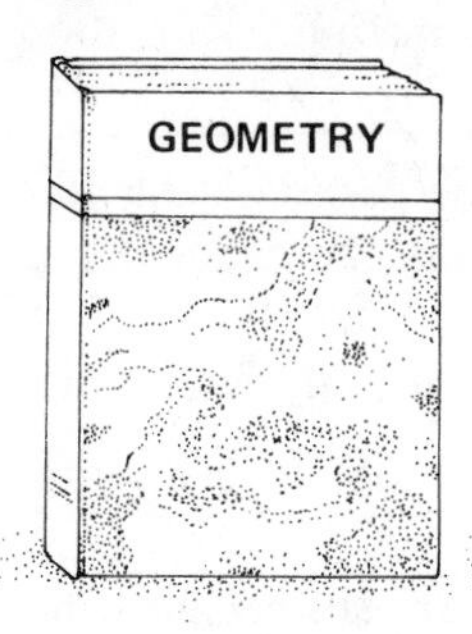

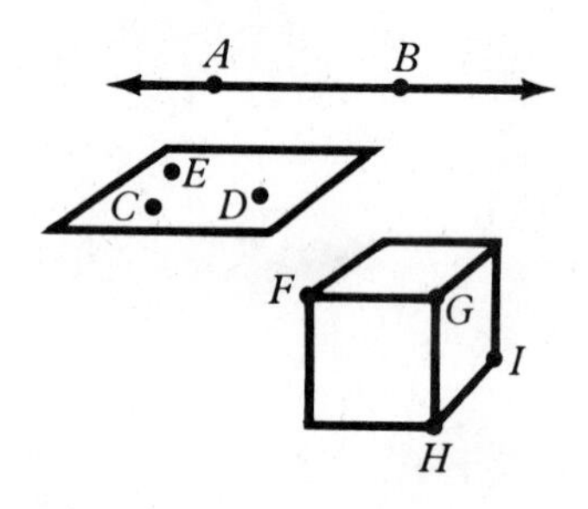

To assure that points exist we accept this postulate. The postulate also gives information about lines and planes.

Points Existence Postulate

Space exists and contains at least four noncoplanar points. A plane contains at least three noncollinear points. A line contains at least two points.

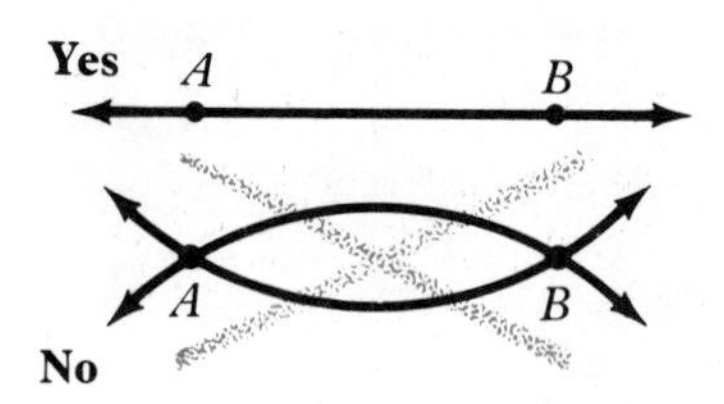

To assure that a line is *straight,* we want one and only one line to contain any two points. We can also say *two points determine a line.*

Point-Line Postulate

Two points are contained in one and only one line.

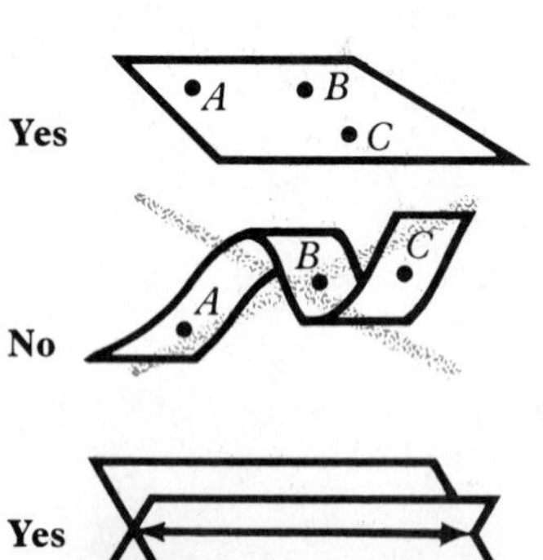

To assure that a plane does not twist and turn in space, we want one and only one plane to contain any three noncollinear points. We can also say *three noncollinear points determine a plane.*

Point-Plane Postulate

Three noncollinear points are contained in one and only one plane.

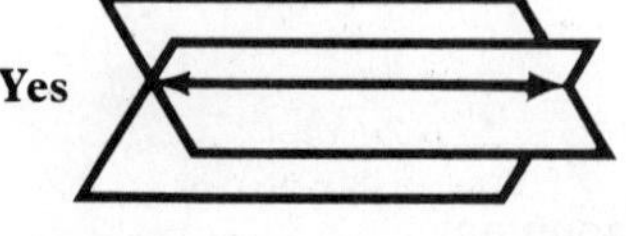

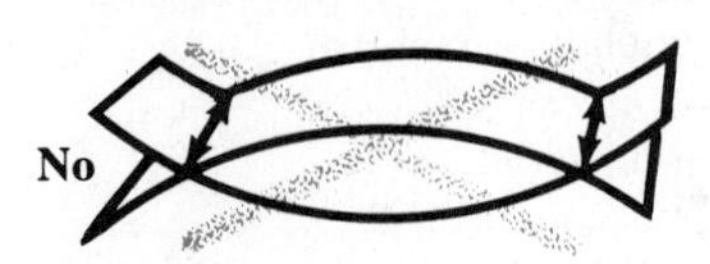

To assure that a plane is straight, we want two planes to intersect in just one line, not two.

Plane Intersection Postulate

If two planes intersect, then they intersect in exactly one line.

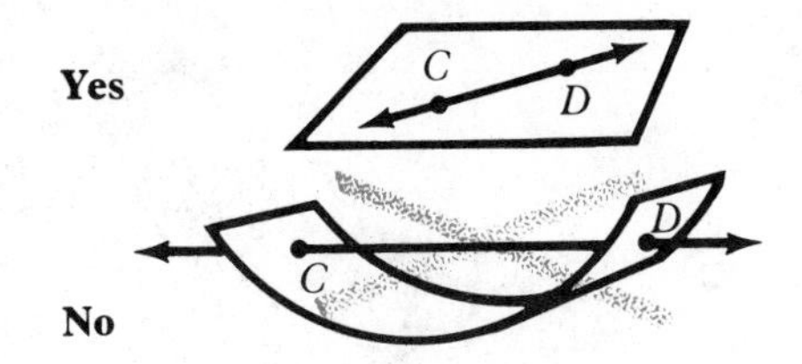

To assure that a plane is flat, we want a plane to contain all points of a line if we know that it contains two points of the line.

Two Points, Line, Plane Postulate

If two points are in a plane, then the line containing them is in the plane.

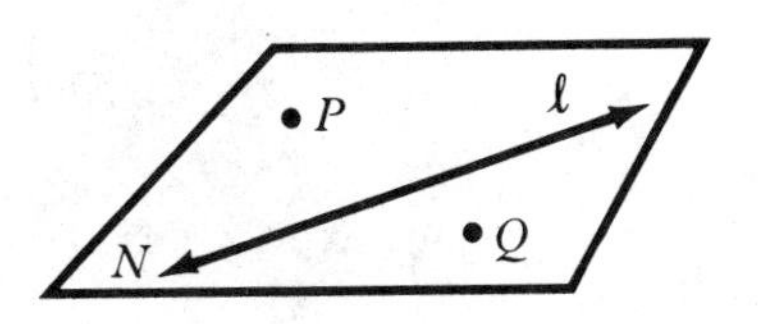

We want a line to separate a plane into two half-planes. We can use this postulate to decide whether two points lie on the same side of a line or on opposite sides of the line.

Plane Separation Postulate

Let N be a plane and ℓ a line in N. The points of the plane not on ℓ form two half-planes such that

a. each half-plane is a convex set.
b. if P is in one half-plane and Q is in the other, then $\overline{PQ}$ intersects ℓ.

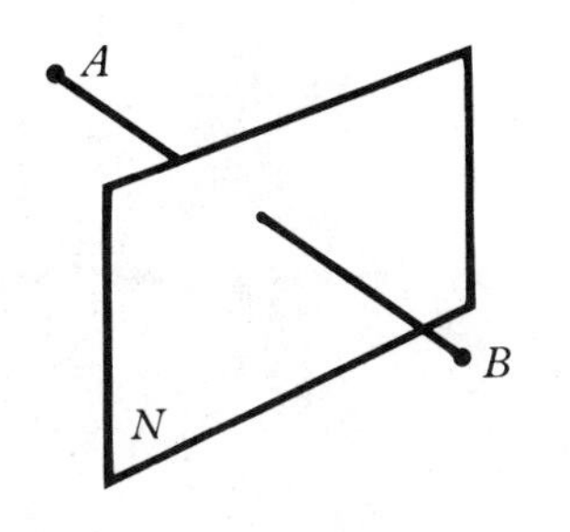

We want a plane to separate space into half-spaces. We can use this postulate to decide whether two points lie on the same side of a plane or on opposite sides of a plane.

Space Separation Postulate

Let N be a plane in space. The points of space not on N form two half-spaces such that

a. each half-space is a convex set.
b. if a point A is in one half-space and B is in the other, $\overline{AB}$ intersects N.

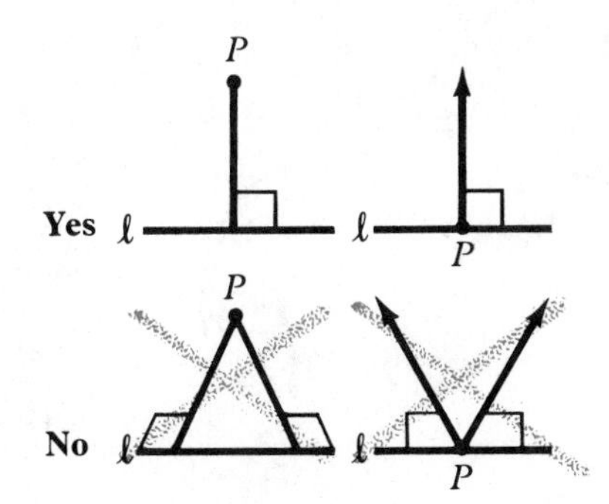

We want to have *only one* line through a given point that is perpendicular to a given line or plane.

Perpendicular Postulate

Given a point and a line in a plane, there is exactly one line through the point perpendicular to the given line. Given a plane in space and a point not in that plane, there is exactly one line through the point perpendicular to the given plane.

These are some of the postulates accepted in geometry. Other important postulates will be presented in the next lesson and in later chapters.

EXERCISES

A.

Complete exercises 1–8 using the words *point, line, plane,* or *space*. Name the postulate that suggests the completed statement.

1. If the two points are in a plane, then the ? that contains them is in the plane.
2. A ? contains at least three noncollinear points.
3. Two points are contained in one and only one ? .
4. If two planes intersect they intersect in exactly one ? .
5. There is exactly one ? through a given point and perpendicular to a given plane.
6. A plane separates ? into two half-spaces.
7. In a plane, there is exactly one ? through a given point and perpendicular to a given line.
8. A line separates a ? into two half-planes.

Activity

Use string and paper clips to make a model for these "postulates." What is the minimum number of pieces of string and paper clips needed to fulfill all the conditions of the postulates?

1. There is at least one piece of string.
2. There are exactly three paper clips on every piece of string.
3. Not all paper clips are on the same string.
4. There is exactly one string through any two paper clips.
5. Any two strings have at least one paper clip in common.

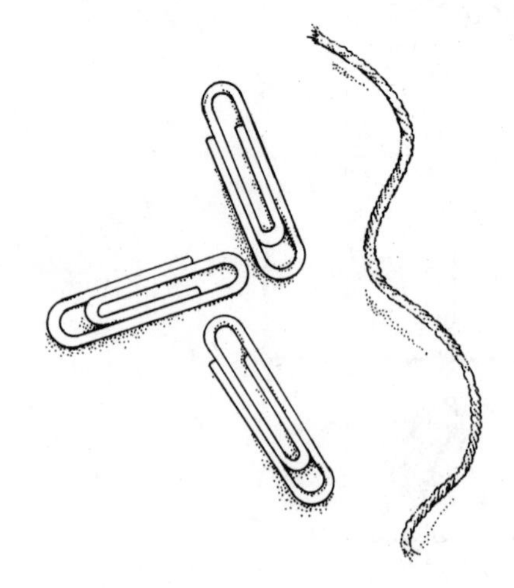

For exercises 9–16, state the postulate that allows you to conclude that the statement is true.

9. Two distinct planes M and N cannot both contain two distinct lines ℓ and m.

10. Two distinct lines ℓ and m cannot both contain two distinct points A and B.

11. Given a point P and a line ℓ in a plane, there cannot be two distinct lines through P and perpendicular to ℓ.

12. If points J and K are in different half-planes determined by a line ℓ, $\overline{JK}$ intersects ℓ.

13. Three noncollinear points A, B, and C cannot all be contained in both of the two distinct planes N and M.

14. If A and B are points in plane M, then $\overleftrightarrow{AB}$ has no points not in plane M.

15. Given a point P and a plane M, there cannot be two lines through P and perpendicular to plane M.

16. Space may contain more, but no less than four noncollinear, noncoplanar points.

17. Photographers and engineers use tripods to mount their cameras and other equipment. Explain why three legs are used instead of four. Which postulate applies to this situation?

18. How many lines can be drawn through four noncollinear points in a plane? Five noncollinear points? Six? n noncollinear points?

19. How many planes are determined by four points, no three of which are collinear?

PROBLEM SOLVING

These 19 points are the corners of four shapes—a square, an envelope with a flap, a box, and an equilateral triangle. (Several edges have been drawn already.) No point is the corner of more than one shape but some points are on the edge of another shape.

Trace this figure and draw in all four shapes.

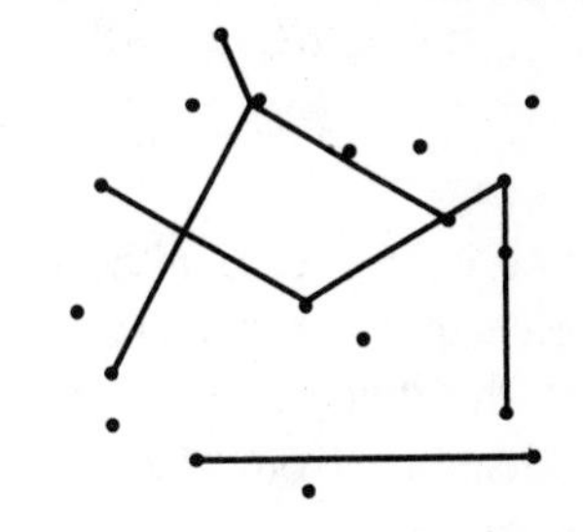

2–8 Some Measurement Postulates

In CB language, the "ten-twenty" (location) in the first picture is the 62 kilometer marker. The location in the second picture, is the 97 kilometer marker. How far has the motorist traveled?

In an earlier chapter (page 20) the idea of measurement of length was introduced intuitively and used freely to form definitions and draw conclusions. Here we look briefly at the postulate on which this idea of length is based.

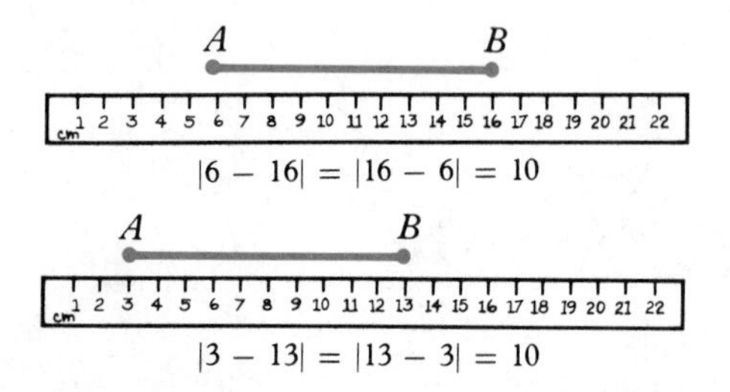

These examples suggest that no matter where the ruler is placed, the length of the segment is the absolute value of the difference of the two numbers matched with the endpoints. The Ruler Postulate includes this idea.

The Ruler Postulate

a. To every pair of points there corresponds a unique positive number called the **distance** between the points.
b. The points on a line can be matched one-to-one with the real numbers so that the distance between any two points is the absolute value of the difference of their associated numbers.

Example 1 Find AB, BC, and AC.

$$AB = |3 - (-2)| = 5$$
$$BC = |18 - 3| = 15$$
$$AC = |-2 - 18| = 20$$

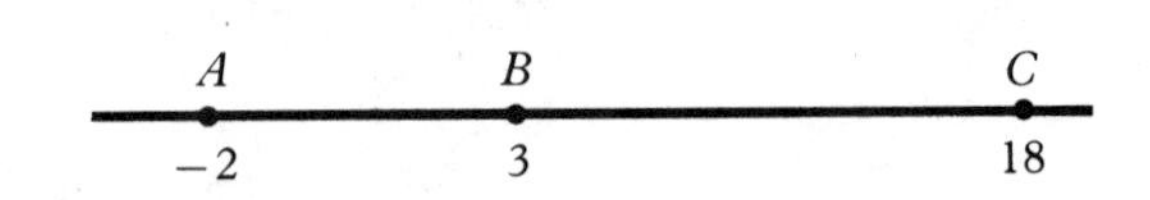

In the example, B is between A and C. Notice that the distance from A to B together with the distance from B to C is the same as the distance from A to C.
We state a definition.

Definition 2–6

Point B is **between** A and C if and only if A, B, and C are collinear and $AB + BC = AC$

A navigator for an airplane checked the course of the airplane (red lines in Figure 1 highlight the course, which is the angle between due north and the plane's line of motion). Later the course was changed as shown in Figure 2. By how many degrees had the course changed?

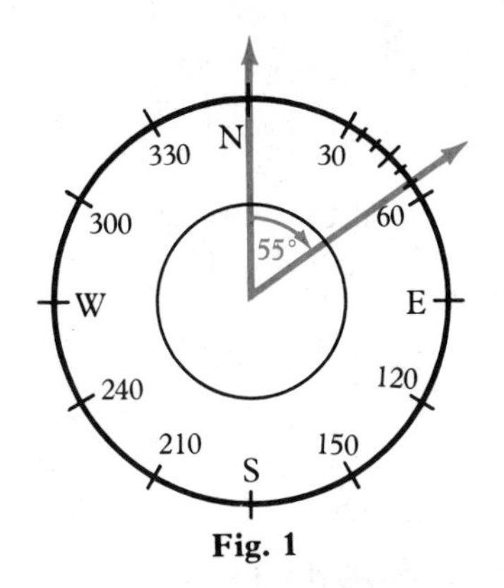

Fig. 1

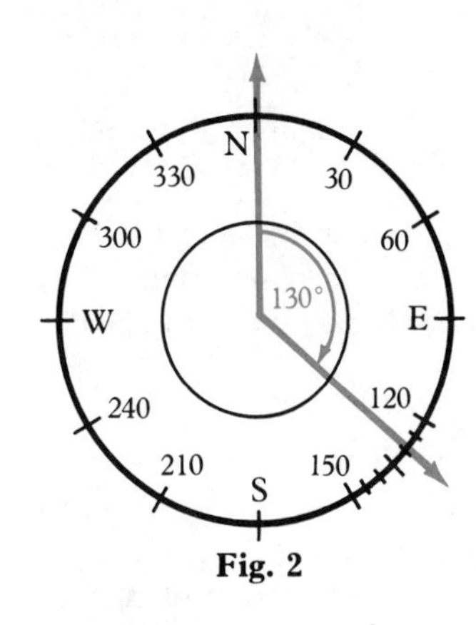

Fig. 2

In the first chapter (page 20) the idea of angle measure was introduced intuitively and used freely to make definitions and draw conclusions. Here we look briefly at the postulate on which this idea is based.

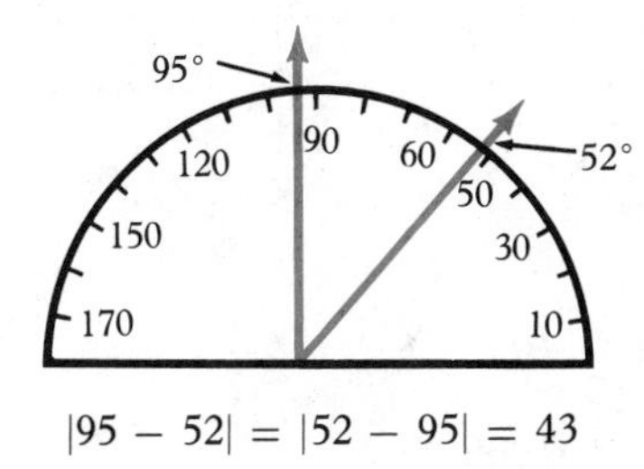

$|95 - 52| = |52 - 95| = 43$

If the protractor is turned so that the rays are matched with different numbers, the absolute value of the difference of the two numbers would be the same. The postulate includes this idea.

The Protractor Postulate

a. To each angle there corresponds a unique real number between 0 and 180 called the measure of the angle.

b. Let P be a point on the edge of half-plane H. Each ray in the half-plane or its edge with vertex P can be matched one-to-one with the real numbers n, $0 < n < 180$, so that the measure of an angle formed by a pair of noncollinear rays with vertex P is the absolute value of the difference of their associated numbers.

Example 2 Find $m\angle ABC$, $m\angle CBD$, and $m\angle ABD$.

$$m\angle ABC = |42 - 20| = 22$$
$$m\angle CBD = |77 - 42| = 35$$
$$m\angle ABD = |77 - 20| = 57$$

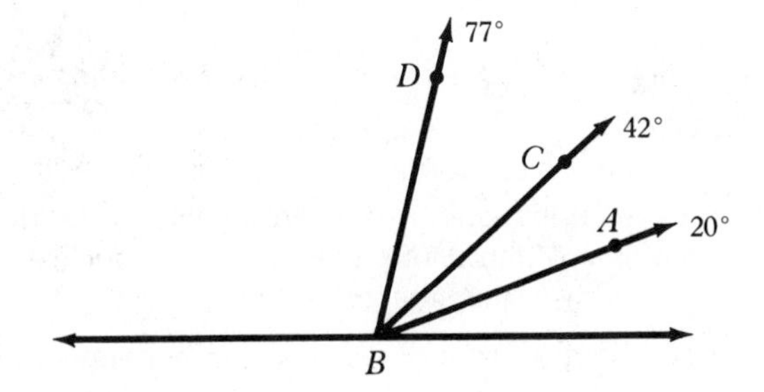

In the example $\overrightarrow{BC}$ is between $\overrightarrow{BA}$ and $\overrightarrow{BD}$. Notice that the measures of $\angle ABC$ and $\angle CBD$ taken together equal the measure of $\angle ABD$. We state a definition.

Definition 2-7

$\overrightarrow{BC}$ is **between** $\overrightarrow{BA}$ and $\overrightarrow{BD}$ if and only if $\overrightarrow{BC}$, $\overrightarrow{BA}$ and $\overrightarrow{BD}$ are coplanar and $m\angle ABC + m\angle CBD = m\angle ABD$.

EXERCISES

A.

A number associated with a point is called the *coordinate of the point.* Find the distance between a pair of points with the coordinates given in exercises 1-12.

1. 5, 2 **2.** 14, 8 **3.** 3, 12 **4.** 17, 0

5. 13, 21 **6.** -5, 13 **7.** 9, -2 **8.** -3, 15

9. -12, 7 **10.** -3, -7 **11.** 0, -8 **12.** -4, -16

Give the measure of each angle in exercises 13-18.

13. $\angle QAS$ **14.** $\angle UAR$

15. $\angle QAV$ **16.** $\angle WAQ$

17. $\angle SAU$ **18.** $\angle VAR$

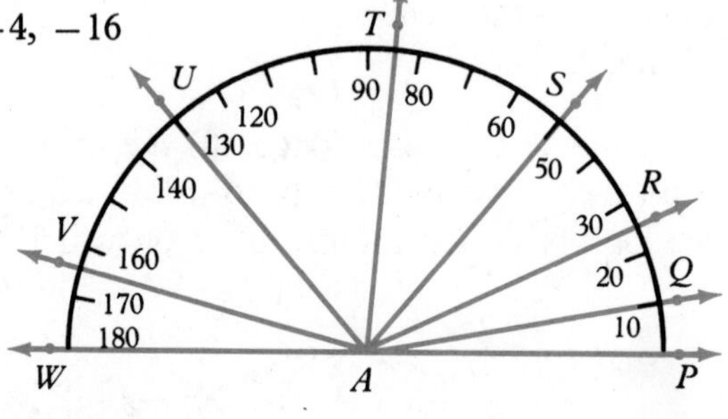

(Exs. 13-18)

B.

The points A, B, and C are collinear. The lengths of certain segments are given. Which point is between the other two?

19. $AC = 4$, $CB = 8$, $AB = 12$

20. $BA = 9$, $BC = 12$, $AC = 3$

21. $CA = 20$, $BA = 11.6$, $CB = 8.4$

22. $AC = 9.3$, $CB = 6.5$, $AB = 15.8$

23. A jacket is going to have three buttonholes four inches apart. A tape measure is placed along the material. The buttonholes are marked by the numbers 7, 11 and 15. Which postulate or definition is being used?

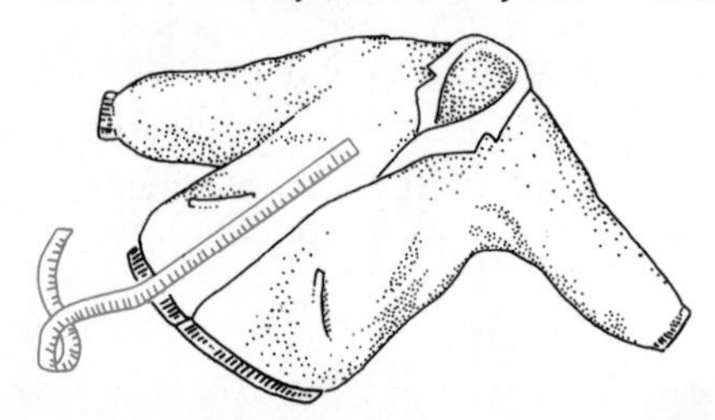

Activity

Estimate the length of these objects to the nearest metric unit indicated. Find the sum of the differences between your estimate and the actual length. The person with the smallest sum wins!

1. Distance around your waist in centimeters (use string)
2. Width of a penny in millimeters
3. Length of room in meters
4. Length of your normal pace in centimeters
5. Height of door in meters

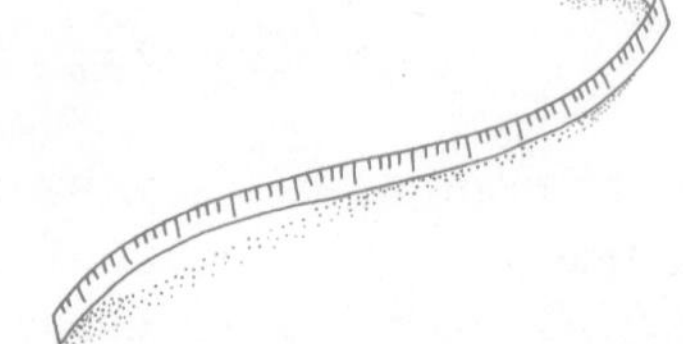

24. Two sides of a picture frame are glued together to form a corner. Each side is cut at a 45° angle. What is the measure of the outside corner? Which postulate or definition is being used?

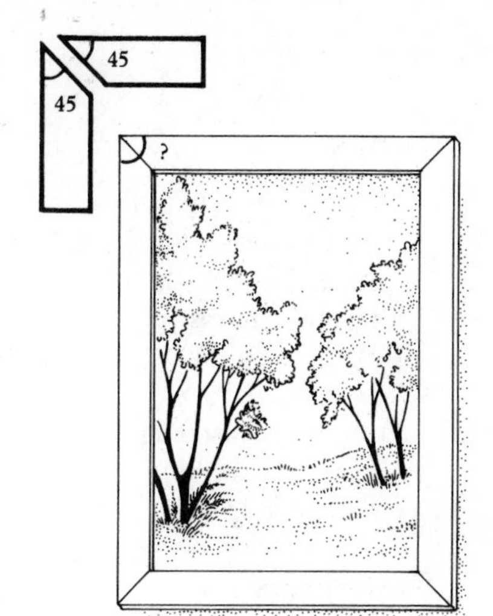

C.

In exercises 25–29, A, B, and C are collinear points with coordinates a, b, and c.

25. If $a < b < c$, $c = 54$, $AC = 26$, and $BC = 19$, find a and b.

26. If $b = -7$, $c = 13$, and A is the midpoint of $\overline{BC}$, find a.

27. If $b = -10$, $c = 4$, and $BA = 28$, find BC and CA. Give two possible answers.

28. If C is between A and B, $BC = 8$, and $CA = 36$, find a, b, and c. Give two possible answers. How many answers are possible?

29. If C is the midpoint of $\overline{AB}$, $c = 14$, and $CB = 10$, give two possible coordinates for A.

Exercises 30–33 refer to an arrangement of rays in the same order as those in the figure.

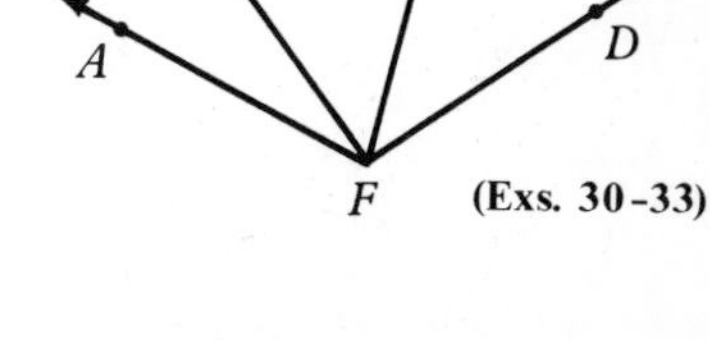

(Exs. 30–33)

30. If $m\angle AFD = 120$ and $m\angle AFC = 2 \cdot m\angle CFD$, find $m\angle AFC$ and $m\angle CFD$.

31. If $m\angle AFC = 3 \cdot m\angle AFB$, $\overrightarrow{FC}$ bisects $\angle AFD$, and $m\angle AFB = 16$, find $m\angle AFD$.

32. If $m\angle AFC = 2 \cdot m\angle CFD$, $m\angle AFB = \frac{1}{2}m\angle CFD$, and $m\angle AFD = 112$, find $m\angle AFB$, $m\angle BFC$, and $m\angle CFD$.

33. If $m\angle BFC = 3 \cdot m\angle AFB$, $m\angle CFD = 4 \cdot m\angle AFB$, and $m\angle AFD = (m\angle AFB)^2 - 240$, find the measure of $\angle AFB$.

PROBLEM SOLVING

A machinist is to make a metal plate like the one shown. The first step is to find the missing dimensions indicated by A, B, C, D, and E. Find them.

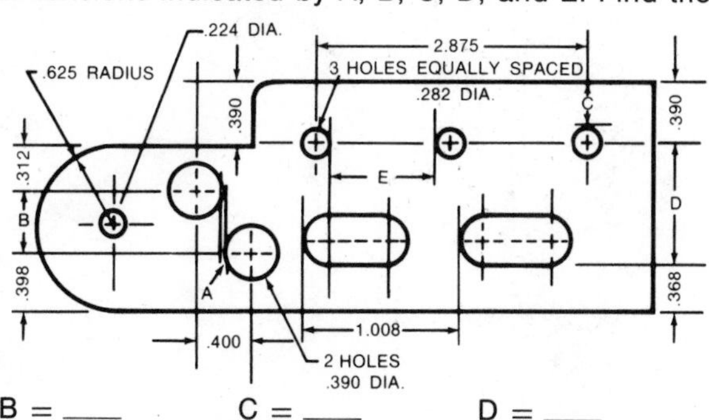

A = ____ B = ____ C = ____ D = ____ E = ____

Important Ideas—Chapter 2

Terms

Generalization (p. 44)
Inductive reasoning (p. 45)
Counterexample (p. 49)
Undefined terms (p. 52)
Postulates (p. 52)
Theorems (p. 52)
Deductive reasoning (p. 53)
Hypothesis (p. 56)
Conclusion (p. 56)
If-then statement (p. 56)
Converse (p. 60)
Inverse (p. 60)
Contrapositive (p. 60)
Affirming the hypothesis (p. 64)
Denying the conclusion (p. 65)
Chain rule (p. 65)
Betweenness of a point (p. 72)
Betweenness of a ray (p. 73)

Postulates

Points Existence Postulate (p. 68)
Point-Line Postulate (p. 68)
Point-Plane Postulate (p. 68)
Plane Intersection Postulate (p. 68)
Two Points, Line, Plane Postulate (p. 69)
Plane Separation Postulate (p. 69)
Space Separation Postulate (p. 69)
Perpendicular Postulate (p. 69)
Ruler Postulate (p. 72)
Protractor Postulate (p. 73)

Chapter 2—Review

1. Complete the generalization below.
$\triangle ABC$ is equilateral.
M, N, O are midpoints.
$\triangle MNO$ is equilateral.

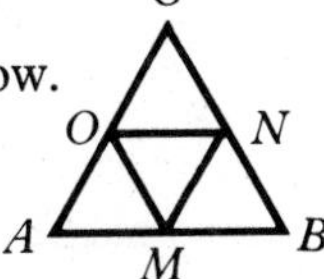

$\triangle EFD$ is equilateral.
R, Q, S are midpoints.
$\triangle RQS$ is equilateral.

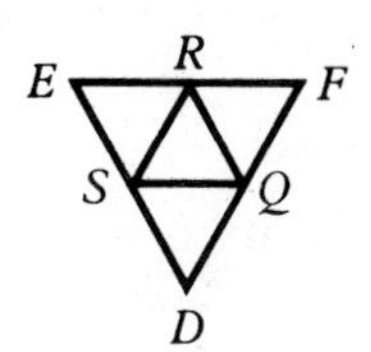

Generalization: The midpoints of an __?__ form the vertices of an __?__.

2. Produce counterexamples for the following false generalizations.
   a. If the diagonals of a quadrilateral are perpendicular, the quadrilateral is a square.
   b. If a quadrilateral has four congruent angles, it has four congruent sides.

3. What is the difference between a theorem and a postulate?

4. True-False
   a. Three points determine a plane.
   b. Given a line ℓ and a point P not on that line, there is only one line containing P that is perpendicular to ℓ.
   c. The intersection of a plane and a line may contain exactly two points.
   d. If A, B, and C are collinear, $AB = 10$ and $BC = 4$ then B is between A and C.

5. If S is between R and T, $ST = 6$, and $RS = 10$, find RT.

6. If $\angle WXY \cong \angle ZXY$, $m\angle WXY = 20$, and $m\angle YXV = 50$, find $m\angle ZXV$.

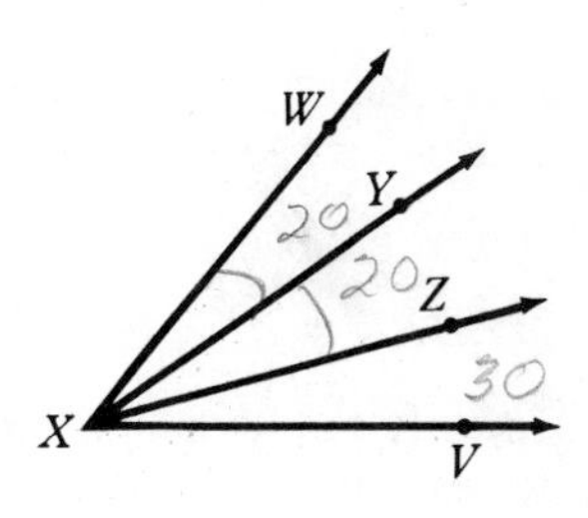

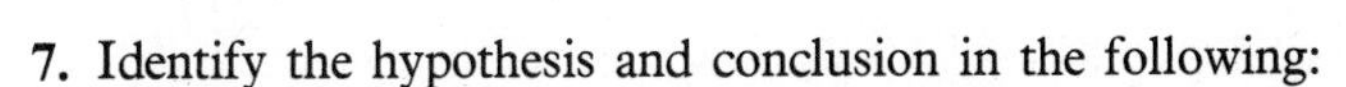

7. Identify the hypothesis and conclusion in the following:
   a. Two lines are parallel if they do not intersect
   b. All squares are rectangles.

8. Consider the statement:
If a figure is a square, it has four right angles.
   a. Write the converse statement.
   b. Write the inverse statement.
   c. Write the contrapositive statement.
   d. Produce counterexamples for a and b.

In exercises 9–10 state a correct conclusion.

9. If a figure is a rectangle, the diagonals are congruent.
$ABCD$ is a rectangle.
Therefore, __?__.

10. If two lines are not in the same plane, they are not parallel.
$\overleftrightarrow{AB} \parallel \overleftrightarrow{CD}$. Therefore, __?__.

Chapter 2—Test

1. Complete the generalization below.

$\triangle ABC$ is isosceles and $\overline{CD}$ bisects $\angle C$.
What is the relationship of $\overline{CD}$ and $\overline{AB}$.

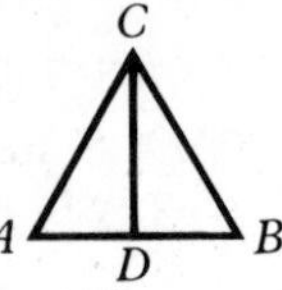

$\triangle XYZ$ is isosceles and $\overline{MZ}$ bisects angle Z.
What is the relationship of $\overline{MZ}$ and $\overline{XY}$?

Generalization: The bisector of the vertex angle of an isosceles triangle is __?__ the base.

2. Produce a counterexample for the following false generalization. There is only one line perpendicular to a given line at a point on that line.

3. What is the purpose of having undefined terms?

4. True-False

a. Two points determine a line.

b. A line separates space into two half-spaces.

c. If two planes intersect, the intersection is a point.

d. If X, Y, and Z are collinear and $XZ + ZY = XY$ then Z is between X and Y.

5. If B is between A and C, $AC = 10$, and $AB = 4$, find BC.

6. Fill in the blanks.

$m\angle ABD +$ __?__ $= m\angle ABC$.

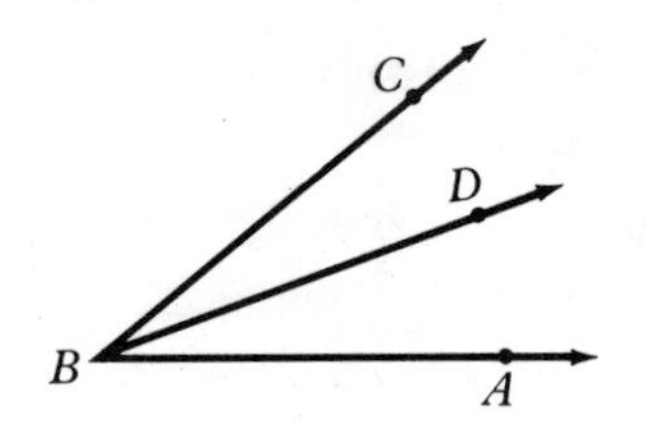

7. Identify the hypothesis and conclusion in the following statements:

a. A triangle is isosceles if it has two congruent sides.

b. All equilateral triangles have three congruent angles.

8. Consider the statement:
If two angles are right angles, they are congruent.

a. Write the converse statement.

b. Write the inverse statement.

c. Write the contrapositive statement.

d. Produce counterexamples to show a and b are false.

In exercises 9–10 state a correct conclusion.

9. If a triangle has three congruent angles, it is equilateral.
$\triangle ABC$ has three congruent angles.
Therefore, __?__.

10. If two angles are right angles (90°), they are congruent.
$\angle A$ is not congruent to $\angle B$.
Therefore, __?__.

Algebra Review

For each problem give the algebraic property illustrated.

A. Associative law (addition and multiplication)
B. Commutative law (addition and multiplication)
C. Distributive law (multiplication over addition)
D. Inverse property (addition and multiplication)
E. Identity property (addition and multiplication)
F. Addition/subtraction of equals
G. Multiplication/division of equals

1. $3 \cdot (7 \cdot 9) = (3 \cdot 7) \cdot 9$

2. If $x = 3$, then $7x = 21$

3. $7 + (-7) = 0$

4. If $x - 2 = 1$, then $x = 3$

5. $x \cdot (a + y) = xa + xy$

6. If $a = b$ then $a + c = b + c$

7. $a + 0 = a$

8. $a \cdot b = b \cdot a$

Solve each equation for x.

9. $x + 3 = 35$

10. $3x = 35$

11. $x - 7 = 19$

12. $\frac{x}{6} = 8$

13. $2x + 9 = 11$

14. $-4x = 8$

15. $10 - x = 42$

16. $\frac{x}{2} + 9 = -5$

17. $3x - 19 = 17$

Solve and graph on a number line.

18. $x > 3$

19. $7 < x$

20. $3x < 15$

21. $x + 1 \geq -17$

22. $x < \frac{4}{5}$

23. $x + 2 \geq 24$

24. $9 - x > 3$

25. $\frac{x}{2} > 10$

26. $3(x + 6) > 12$

Solve each equation.

27. $|x| = 9$

28. $3|x| = 21$

29. $|x + 1| = 4$

30. $|3x| = 21$

31. $|x| - 2 = 35$

32. $|3x + 2| = 17$

33. $|2x + 1| = 13$

34. $|x| - 9 = 25$

35. $3 - |x| = -5$

Evaluate.

36. $\sqrt{25}$

37. $\sqrt{121}$

38. $\sqrt{100 + 69}$

39. $\sqrt{121} + \sqrt{81}$

40. $\sqrt{4^3}$

41. $8\sqrt{9} - 6\sqrt{36}$

Photography: Lenses

Photographers often use different lenses, from wide angle to telephoto, to get the picture they want.

The three photos below are taken from the same position with the same camera. Each photo was taken with a different lens.

Wide angle

Normal

Telephoto

The "normal" lens takes a picture close to what the photographer sees. The "wide angle" lens takes a picture with a broader view of the scene. The telephoto lens actually magnifies the objects.

Photographers must understand the "geometry of photography" to know what each lens does best. We will investigate two ideas: *the focal length* and *the angle of view*.

The focal length is the distance from the lens to the film in the camera when the lens is focused on a distant object. The angle of view is the angle formed by imaginary lines from the edges of the scene to the lens of the camera.

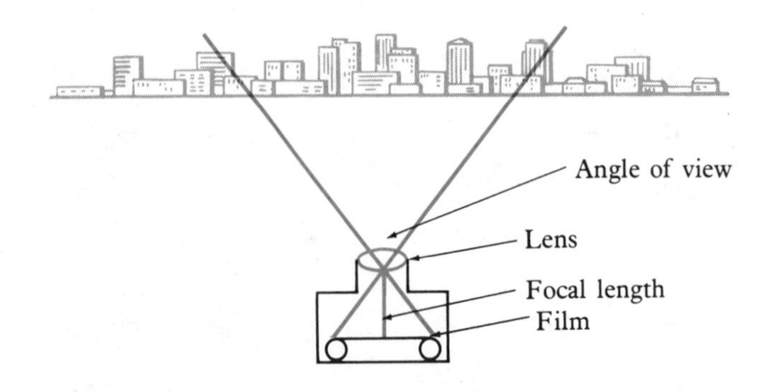

The following diagram illustrates the relationship between focal length and angle of view. The lens of the camera is in the same position in each drawing.

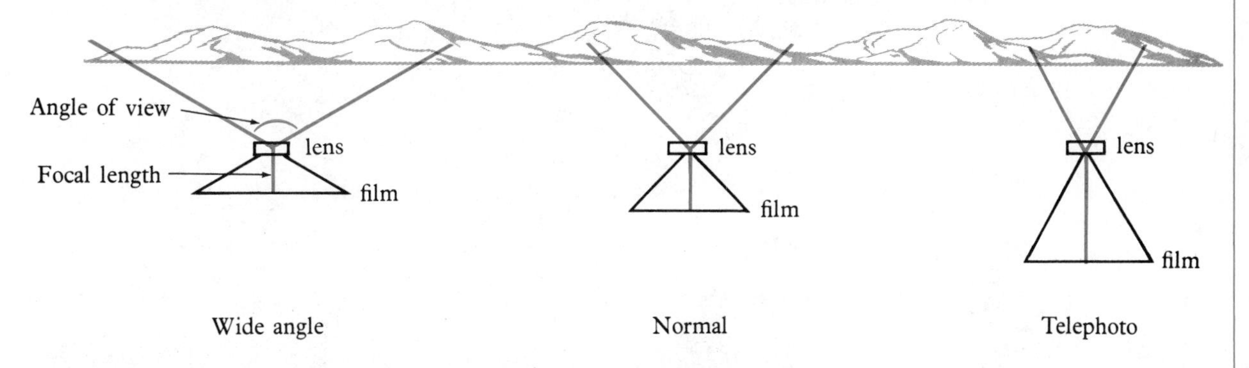

The diagram shows that the shorter the focal length, the larger the angle of view. Wide angle lenses have smaller focal lengths and "see more" of a scene than normal lenses. Telephoto lenses have longer focal lengths and "see less" of the scene than normal lenses.

You can determine the approximate angle of view for a given focal length with the following construction.

Step 1 Draw a segment $\overline{AB}$ with length of 43 mm. This is the length of the diagonal of a picture negative of ordinary film for a widely used camera.

Step 2 Bisect $\overline{AB}$. Call the midpoint C.

Step 3 Construct $\overline{DC} \perp \overline{AB}$, so that $\overline{DC}$ has length equal to the focal length of the lens. (For example, 50 mm)

Step 4 Draw $\overline{DA}$ and $\overline{DB}$.

Step 5 Measure $\angle ADB$ with a protractor to find the approximate angle of view. (For a focal length of 50 mm)

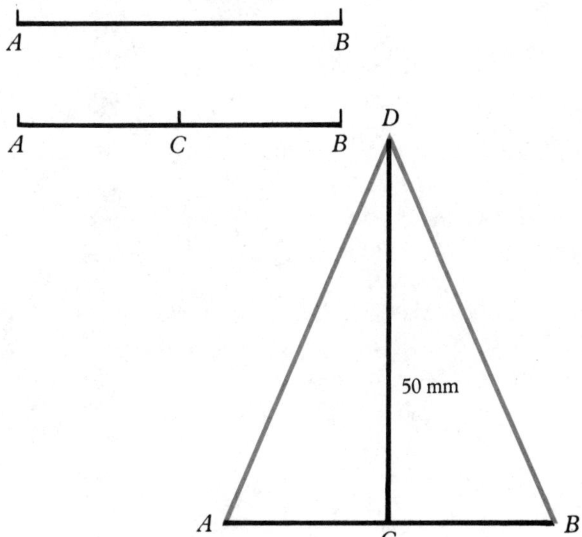

Complete the above construction for each of the following focal lengths.

1. 21 mm **2.** 50 mm **3.** 200 mm

For each focal length, measure to find the angle of view. A lens with focal length of 50 mm has an angle of view about the same as a human eye. This lens is a normal lens. Which focal length is for a wide angle lens? a telephoto lens?

CHAPTER 3

Triangles and Congruence

3–1 Congruent Triangles

Automobiles are manufactured using assembly line production. The parts that are produced must be identical in size and shape so that they can be used in any car on the assembly line. Replacement parts must also be identical. In geometry, figures that have the same size and shape are called congruent.

In geometry we need a useful definition to help us decide when two figures, such as $\triangle ABC$ and $\triangle DEF$, are congruent.

A tracing paper test can be used to show that $\triangle ABC$ is probably congruent to $\triangle DEF$ (based on the pictures shown). This test can help us understand the usual definition of congruence.

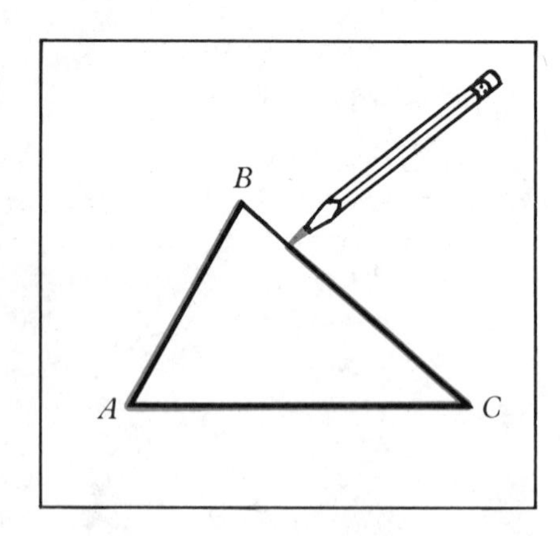

Trace $\triangle ABC$.

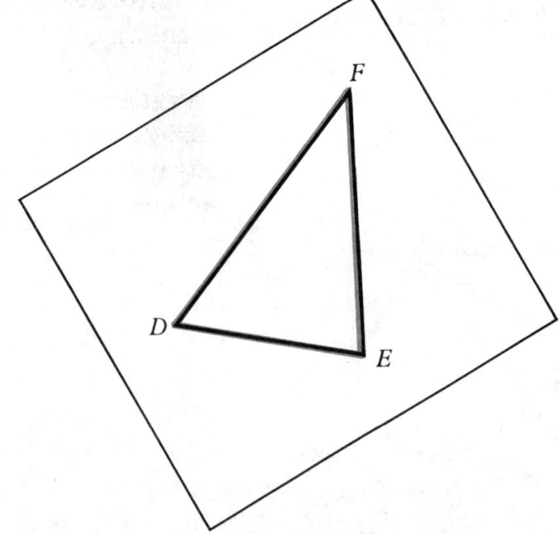

If you can slide, turn, or flip over the paper so the tracing fits on $\triangle DEF$, the triangles are probably congruent.

Consider the tracing test again. If we highlight each vertex with a special symbol we see that the vertices of the two triangles correspond as shown. The angle correspondence is also determined.

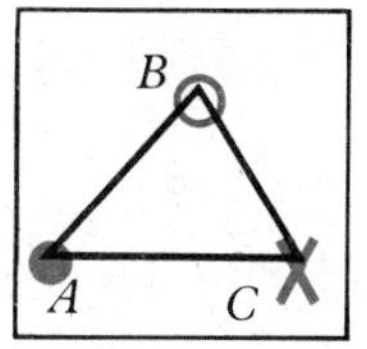

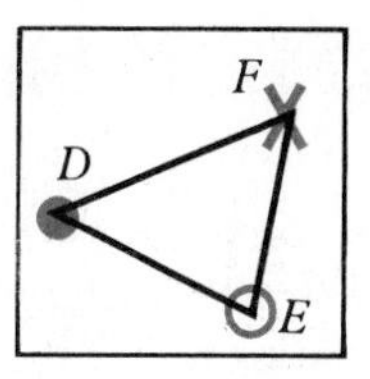

$A \leftrightarrow D$
$B \leftrightarrow E$
$C \leftrightarrow F$

vertex correspondence

$\angle A \leftrightarrow \angle D$
$\angle B \leftrightarrow \angle E$
$\angle C \leftrightarrow \angle F$

angle correspondence

If we highlight each side with a special mark, we see that the sides correspond as shown.

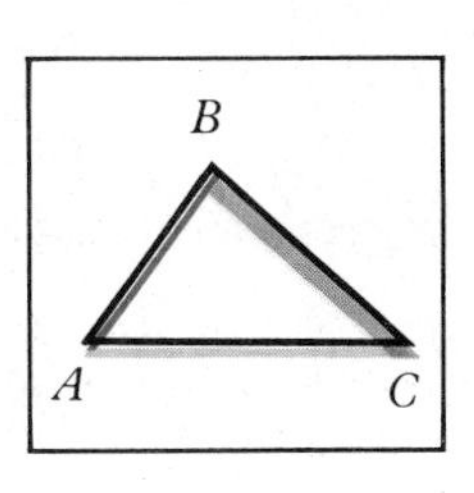

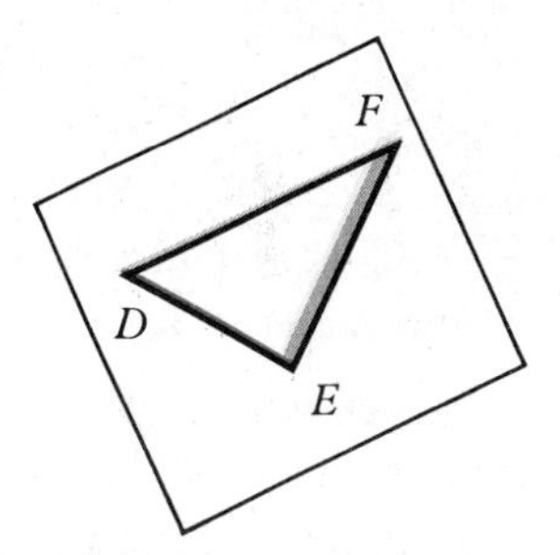

$\overline{AB} \leftrightarrow \overline{DE}$
$\overline{BC} \leftrightarrow \overline{EF}$
$\overline{AC} \leftrightarrow \overline{DF}$

side correspondence

In this tracing test we observe that

$$\overline{AB} \cong \overline{DE} \qquad \angle A \cong \angle D$$
$$\overline{BC} \cong \overline{EF} \qquad \angle B \cong \angle E$$
$$\overline{AC} \cong \overline{DF} \qquad \angle C \cong \angle F$$

Definition 3–1

Two **triangles are congruent** if there is a correspondence between the vertices such that each pair of corresponding sides and angles are congruent. Note that we can define congruence for other figures in a similar manner.

Whenever we can "fit" one triangle onto the other so that all the matching parts are *congruent,* we have a special kind of correspondence called a *congruence.* To show this congruence we write $\triangle ABC \cong \triangle DEF$.

The diagram shows how this statement about the congruent triangles provides specific information about the corresponding parts (angles and sides).

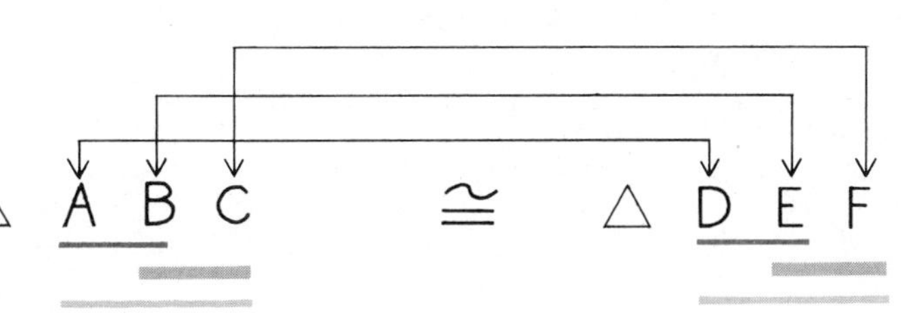

EXERCISES

A.

Which of the following pairs of figures are congruent? (You may want to use tracing paper.)

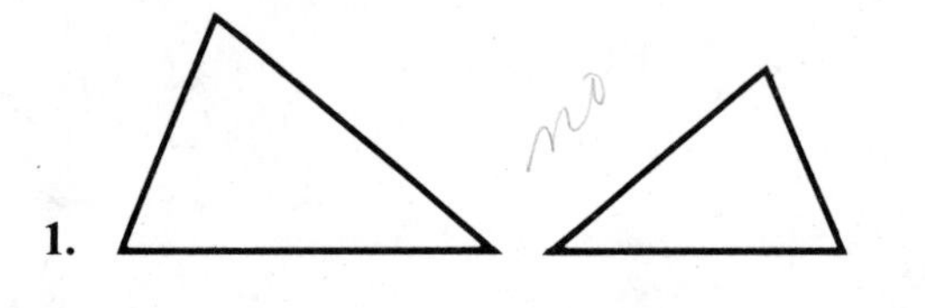

1.

2.

3.

4.

In exercises 5–8 select the correct statement. (Use tracing paper if needed.)

5.

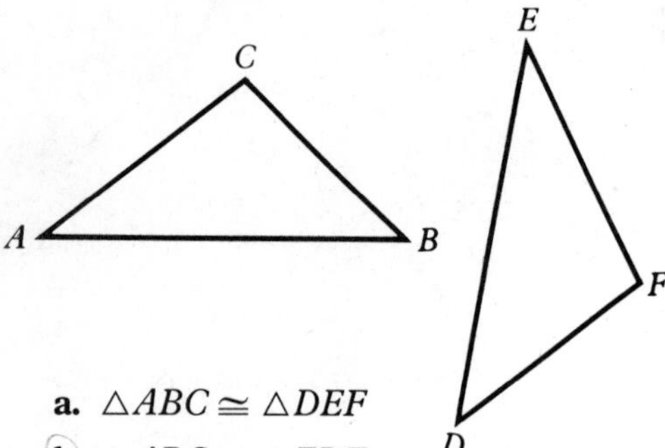

a. $\triangle ABC \cong \triangle DEF$

b. $\triangle ABC \cong \triangle EDF$

c. $\triangle ABC \cong \triangle EFD$

6.

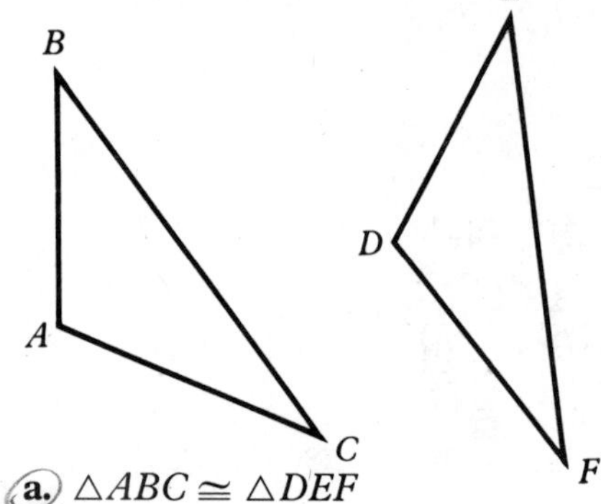

a. $\triangle ABC \cong \triangle DEF$

b. $\triangle ABC \cong \triangle DFE$

c. $\triangle ABC \cong \triangle FED$

7.

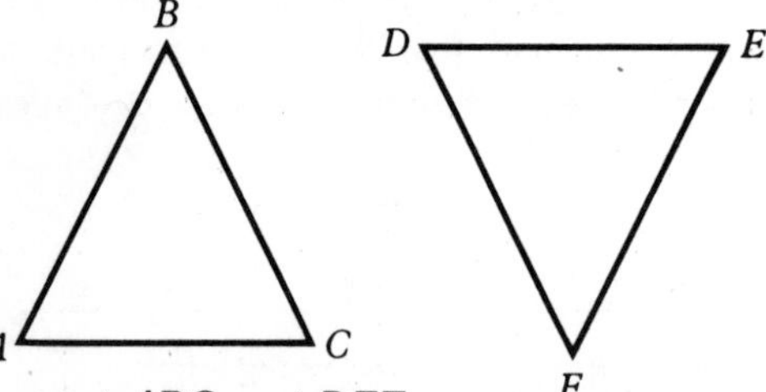

a. $\triangle ABC \cong \triangle DEF$

b. $\triangle ABC \cong \triangle EFD$

c. $\triangle ABC \cong \triangle FDE$

8.

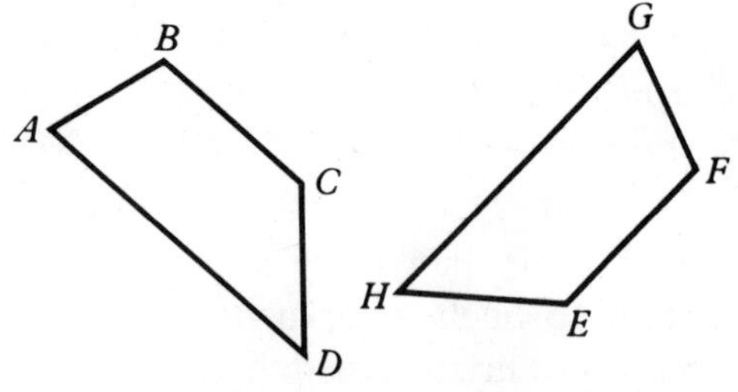

a. $ABCD \cong EFGH$

b. $ABCD \cong FGHE$

c. $ABCD \cong GHEF$

d. $ABCD \cong GFEH$

9. Given that $\triangle ABC \cong \triangle DEF$, select the false statement in each part.
   a. $\overline{AC} \cong \overline{DF}$, $\angle B \cong \angle E$, $\overline{BC} \cong \overline{DE}$, $\angle C \cong \angle F$
   b. $\overline{AB} \cong \overline{ED}$, $\angle A \cong \angle D$, $\angle C \cong \angle F$, $\overline{AB} \cong \overline{EF}$
   c. $\overline{AB} \cong \overline{DE}$, $\overline{BC} \cong \overline{FE}$, $\angle C \cong \angle D$, $\overline{AC} \cong \overline{DF}$

(Ex. 9)

10. Given that $\triangle UVW \cong \triangle XYZ$, complete the congruences for the six pairs of corresponding congruent parts.
    a. $\angle U \cong$ ___?___
    b. $\angle V \cong$ ___?___
    c. $\angle W \cong$ ___?___
    d. $\overline{UV} \cong$ ___?___
    e. $\overline{UW} \cong$ ___?___
    f. $\overline{VW} \cong$ ___?___

(Ex. 10)

11. Given that $\triangle CAT \cong \triangle DOG$, write the congruences for the six pairs of corresponding congruent parts.

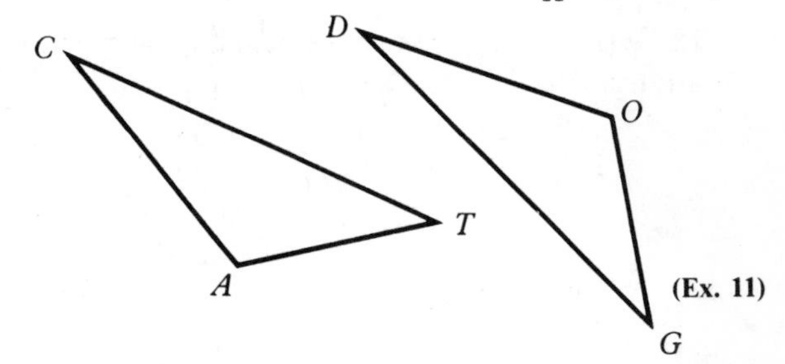

(Ex. 11)

B.

In each of exercises 12 and 13 there are two correct congruence statements. Find them.

12.

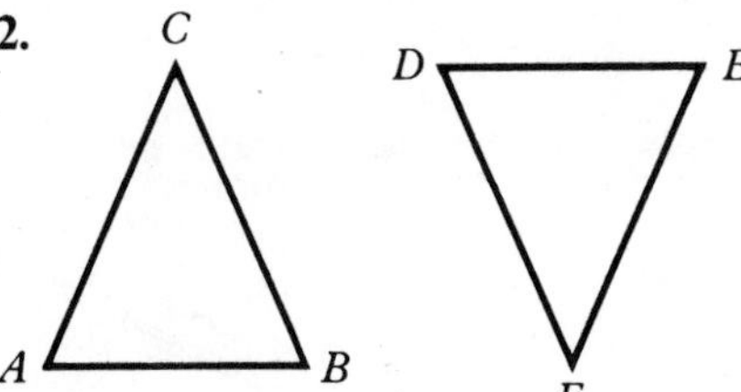

a. $\triangle ABC \cong \triangle DEF$
b. $\triangle ABC \cong \triangle EFD$
c. $\triangle ABC \cong \triangle FDE$
d. $\triangle ABC \cong \triangle EDF$

13.

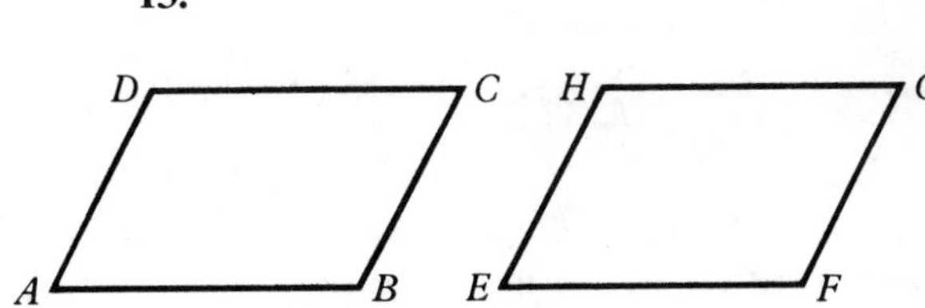

a. $ABCD \cong EFGH$
b. $ABCD \cong FGHE$
c. $ABCD \cong GHEF$
d. $ABCD \cong FEHG$

14. Given that $\triangle PRS \cong \triangle JKL$ write three congruence statements about angles and three congruence statements about sides of the triangles.

15. Given these six congruence statements, complete correctly the statement about congruent triangles.

$$\angle A \cong \angle B \qquad \overline{AP} \cong \overline{BT}$$
$$\angle T \cong \angle P \qquad \overline{AR} \cong \overline{BJ}$$
$$\angle R \cong \angle J \qquad \overline{PR} \cong \overline{TJ}$$
$$\triangle \underline{?\ ?\ ?} \cong \triangle \underline{?\ ?\ ?}$$

16. Given that $\triangle ABC \cong \triangle DEF$, two of the following congruence statements between triangles are also true. Which two?

a. $\triangle BCA \cong \triangle EFD$ **b.** $\triangle ACB \cong \triangle EFD$

c. $\triangle CBA \cong \triangle FDE$ **d.** $\triangle CAB \cong \triangle FDE$

17. When a locksmith cuts a new key three arbitrary points A, B, and C on the surface of the given key correspond to three points A', B', and C' on the new key. How does $\triangle ABC$ relate to $\triangle A'B'C'$?

18. Write a congruence statement for each pair of congruent triangles.

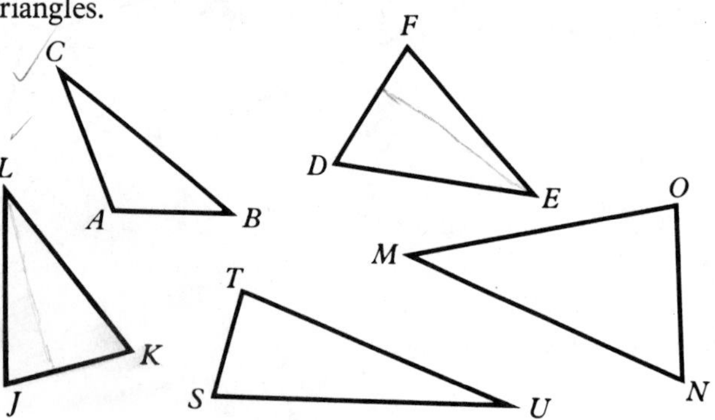

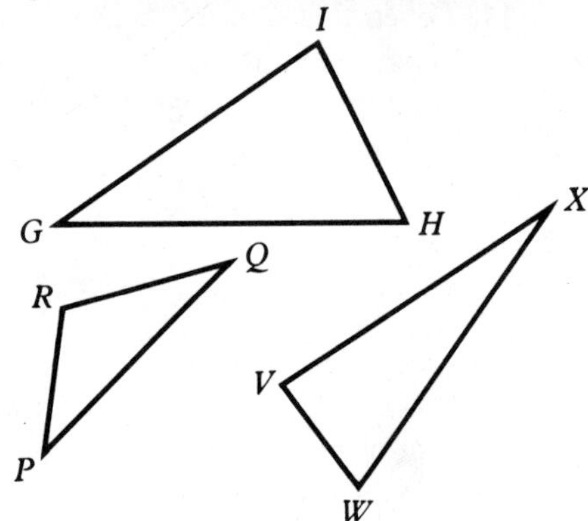

Activity

Every triangle, like $\triangle ABC$, has six parts. There are three sides (a, b, and c) and three angles ($\angle A$, $\angle B$, and $\angle C$).

1. Suppose you are allowed only to open your compass to the lengths of the three sides when needed. Construct a triangle congruent to $\triangle ABC$.
2. Suppose you are allowed only to open your compass to the length of side c, side b, and to copy $\angle A$. Construct a triangle congruent to $\triangle ABC$.
3. How many other combinations of three of the six parts will allow you to construct a triangle congruent to $\triangle ABC$?

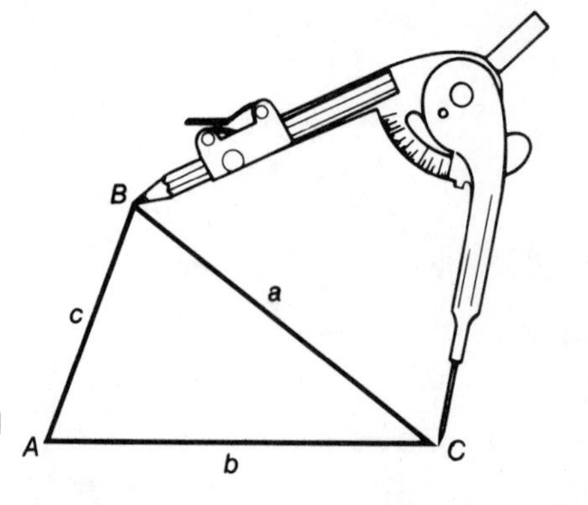

19. If $\triangle ABC$ is an equilateral triangle, we can write $\triangle ABC \cong \triangle BCA$. There are five more congruence statements that can be written. Write them.

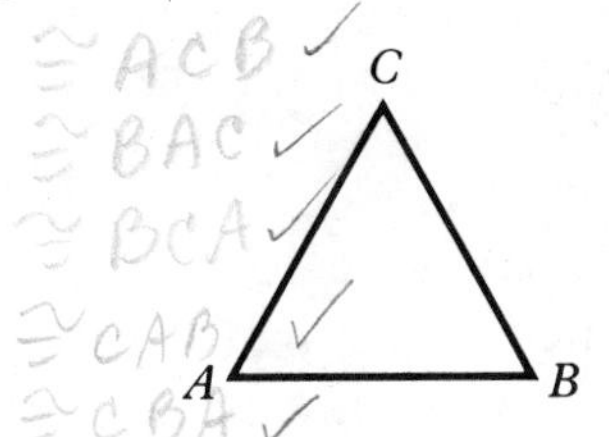

C.

Each figure below contains one or more pairs of congruent triangles. Sometimes the triangles "overlap" each other. Write a correct congruence statement for each pair you find in a figure.

20.

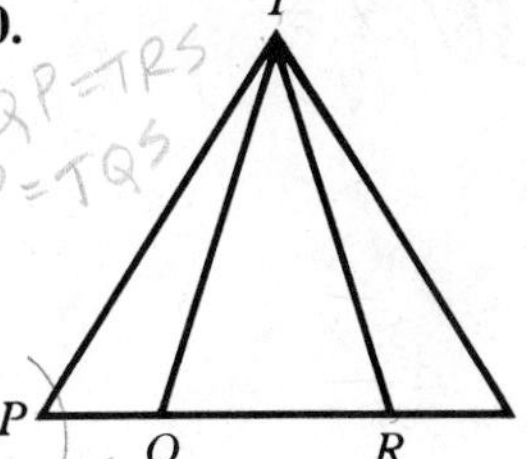

21.

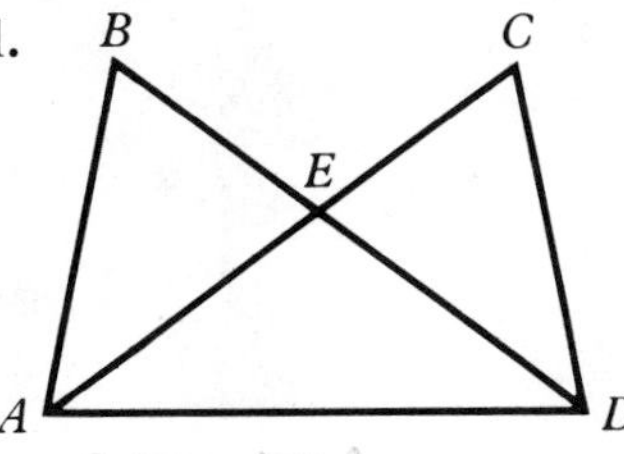

22.

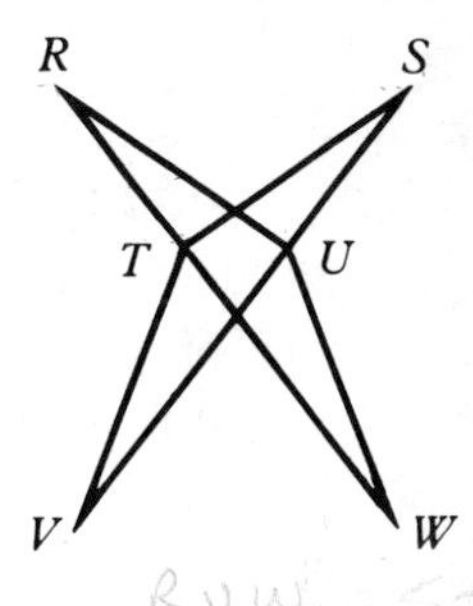

23.

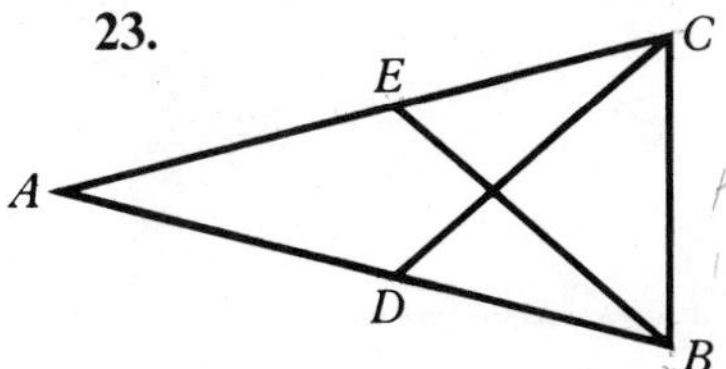

24.

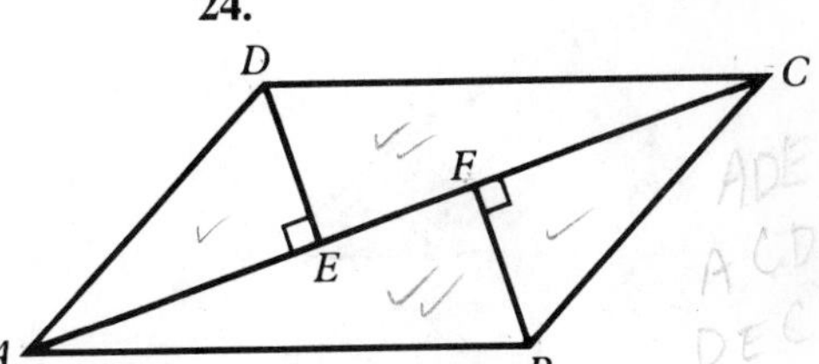

PROBLEM SOLVING

1. Which pairs of figures are identical?

a. 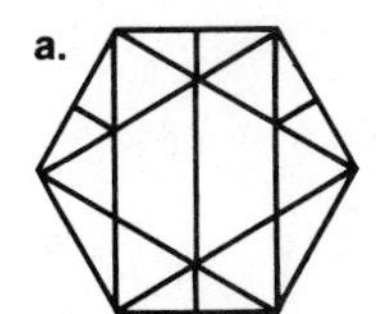

b. 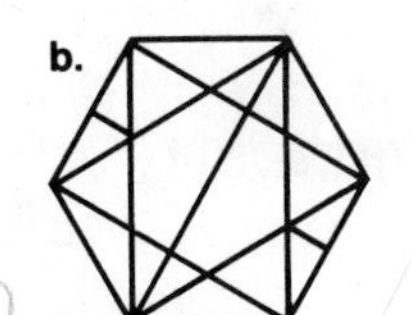

c. 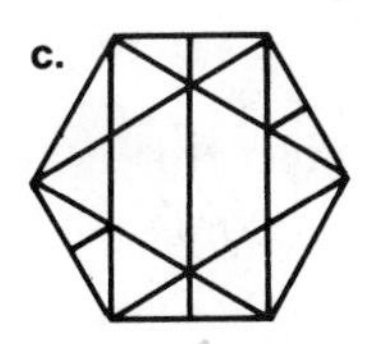

d. 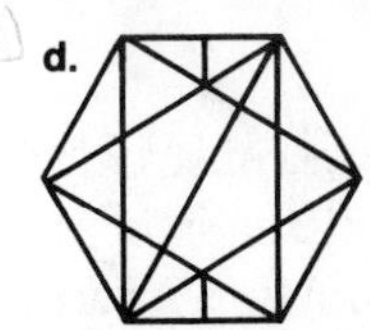

e. 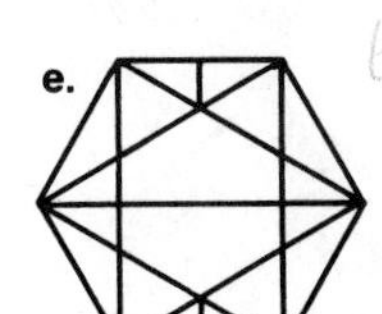

f. 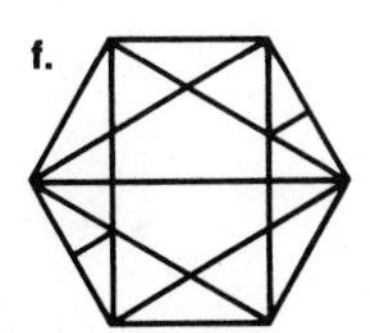

g. 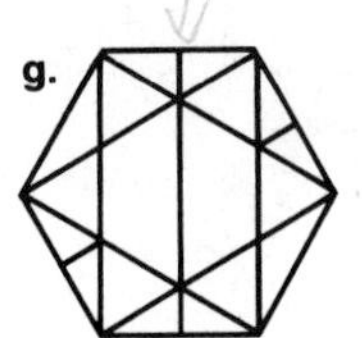

h. 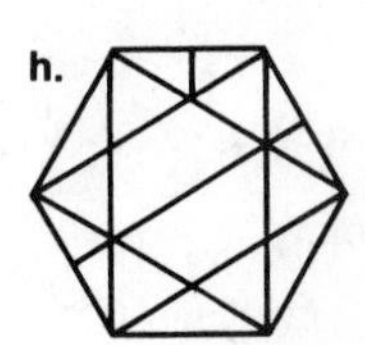

2. Trace figure a and label points where segments intersect. Can you find six pairs of congruent triangles (each involving different sized or shaped triangles) and write the correct congruence statements?

3–2 Congruence Postulates

Suppose a carpet layer needs to repair a carpet with a triangular patch. It is not likely that all three sides and all three angles would be measured in order to cut out the patch. Only a few of these measurements are needed. In this lesson we shall discuss how many and which combinations of the six parts of a triangle (sides a, b, c and angles A, B, C) are needed to determine a particular size and shape of a triangle.

First, we state some ideas that will be useful in our work with congruent triangles.

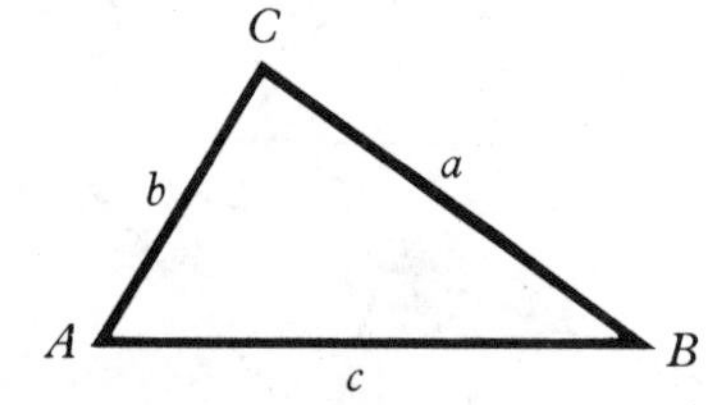

An angle and the side opposite the angle are labeled with the same letter—the angle with a capital letter, and the side with a small letter.

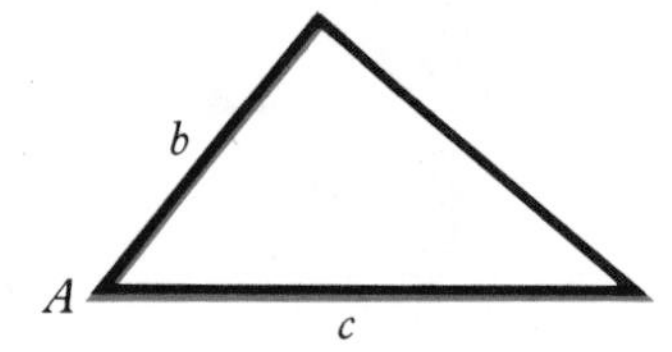

Two sides include an angle if the vertex of the angle is an endpoint of both sides.

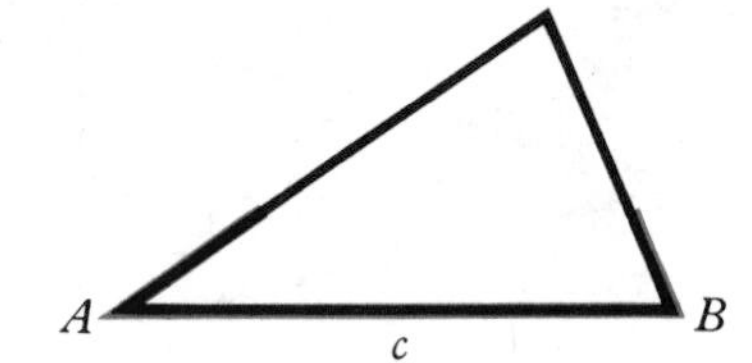

Two angles include a side if the endpoints of the side are vertices of the two angles.

If you construct a triangle given three of the six parts, you find that the size and shape of the triangle is completely determined when you are given the following information.

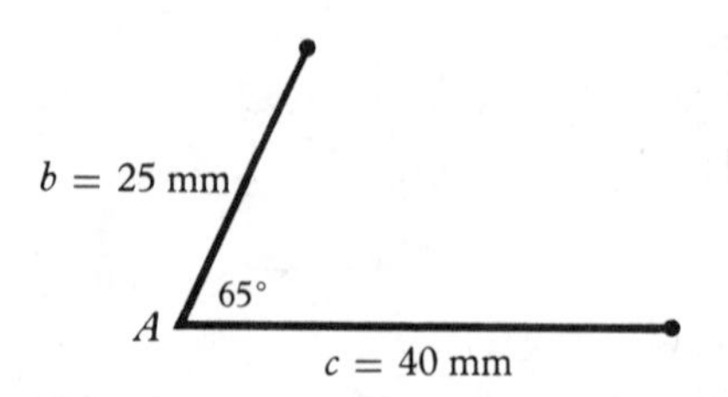

1. Two sides and an included angle.

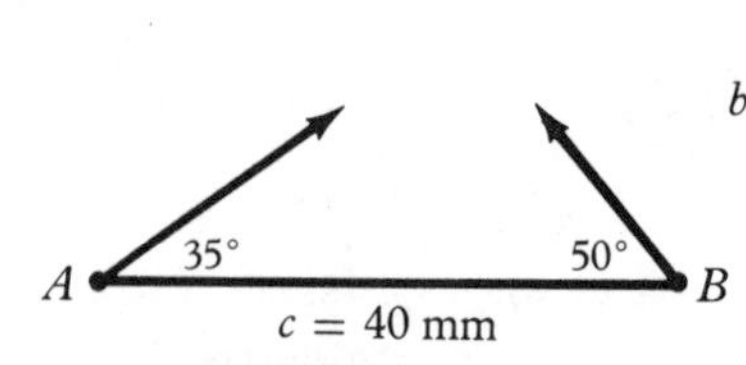

2. Two angles and the included side.

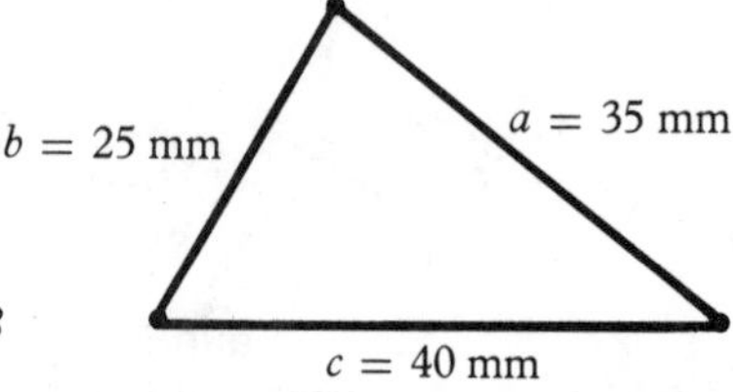

3. Three sides.

From this we obtain the following three congruence postulates.

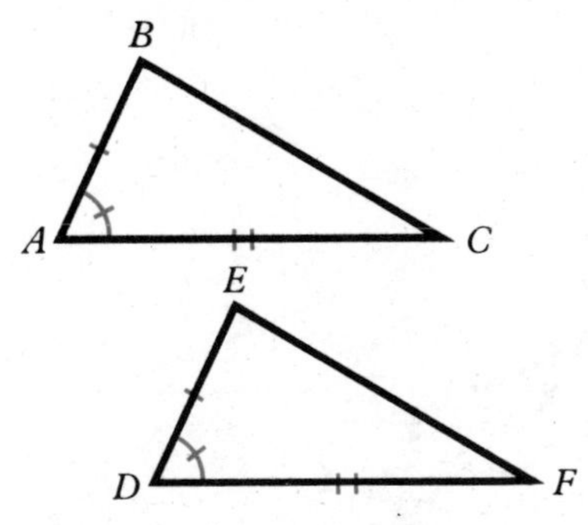

The marks on the triangles indicate which sides and angles are congruent.

We believe that only one triangle can result if two sides and the included angle are given, so we accept this postulate.

SAS Congruence Postulate

If two sides and the included angle of one triangle are congruent respectively to two sides and the included angle of another triangle, then the two triangles are congruent.

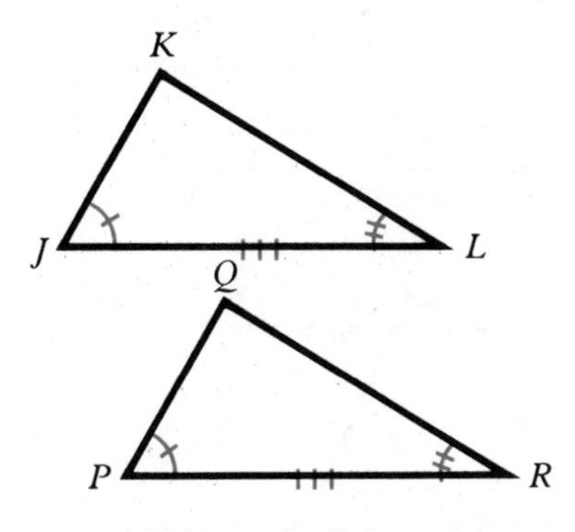

We believe that only one triangle can result if two angles and the included side are given, so we accept this postulate.

ASA Congruence Postulate

If two angles and the included side of one triangle are congruent respectively to two angles and the included side of another triangle, then the two triangles are congruent.

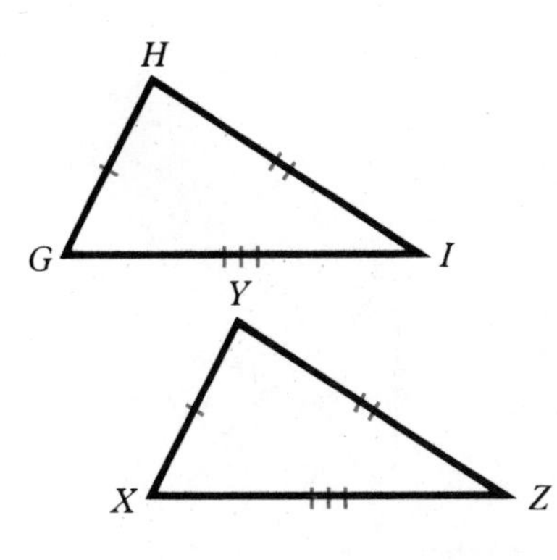

We believe that only one triangle can result if three sides are given, so we accept this postulate.

SSS Congruence Postulate

If all three sides of one triangle are congruent respectively to all three sides of another triangle, then the two triangles are congruent.

The definition of congruent triangles shows six pairs of parts should match. But these three postulates suggest that sometimes we need to check only three of these pairs to be sure we have a congruence. We will use these postulates to prove additional theorems about triangles.

EXERCISES

A.

1. Which of these triangles is not labeled correctly?

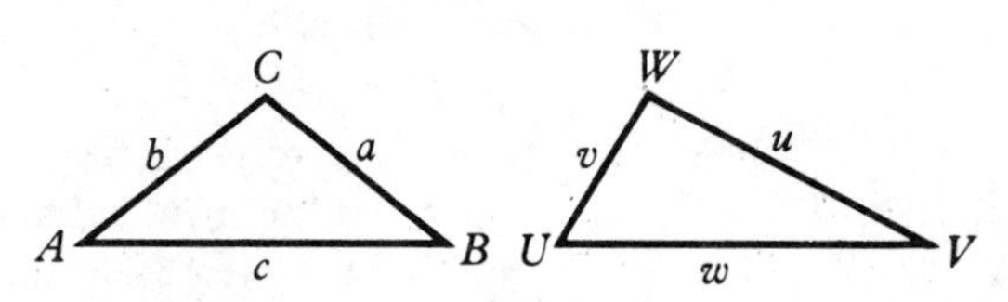

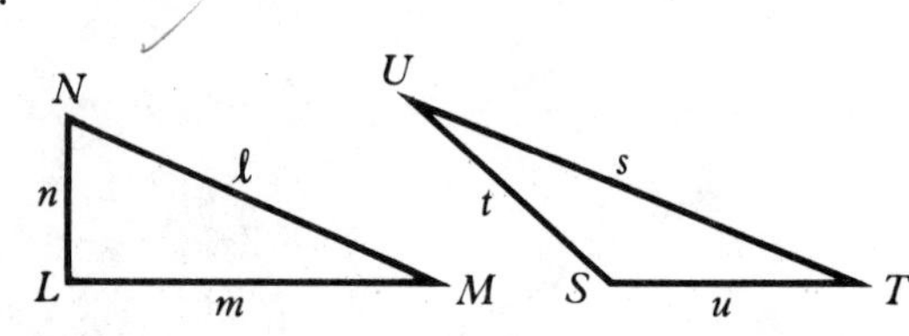

2. Which of these triangles is labeled correctly?

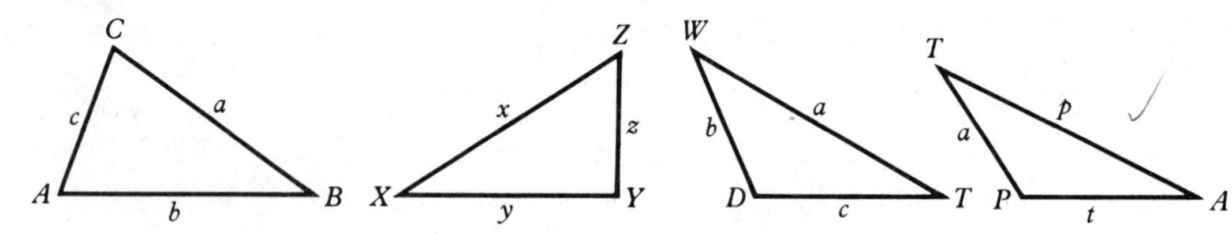

3. Draw a triangle and label its angles and sides using the standard method of labeling.

For each pair of sides (or angles) state the included angle (or side).

4. $\overline{AB}$ and $\overline{AD}$ **5.** $\overline{BD}$ and $\overline{BC}$

6. $\angle A$ and $\angle C$ **7.** $\angle ABD$ and $\angle ADB$

8. $\overline{AD}$ and $\overline{BD}$ **9.** $\overline{BD}$ and $\overline{CD}$

10. $\angle ABC$ and $\angle C$

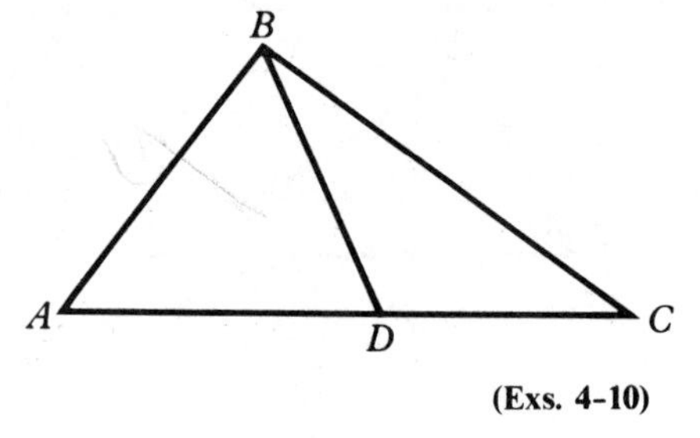

(Exs. 4-10)

By which of the three congruence postulates (SAS, ASA, SSS) are these pairs of triangles congruent? (Assume the congruences are as the markings indicate even though the triangles may not look congruent.)

11.

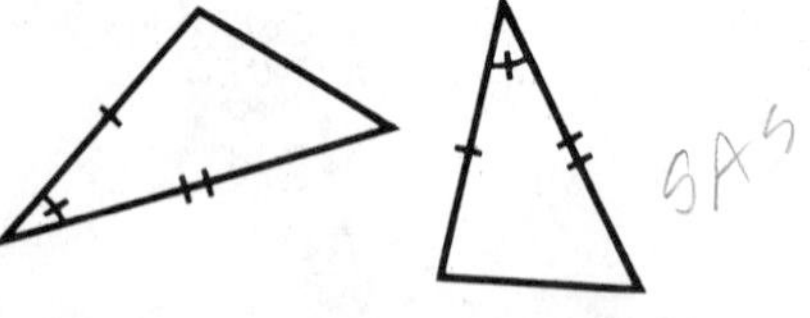

12.

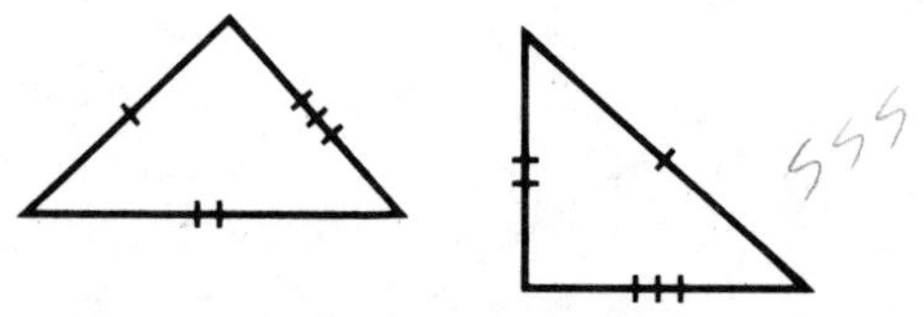

13.

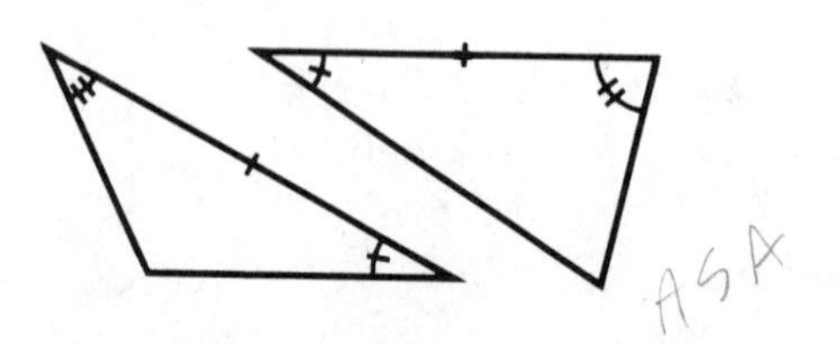

14.

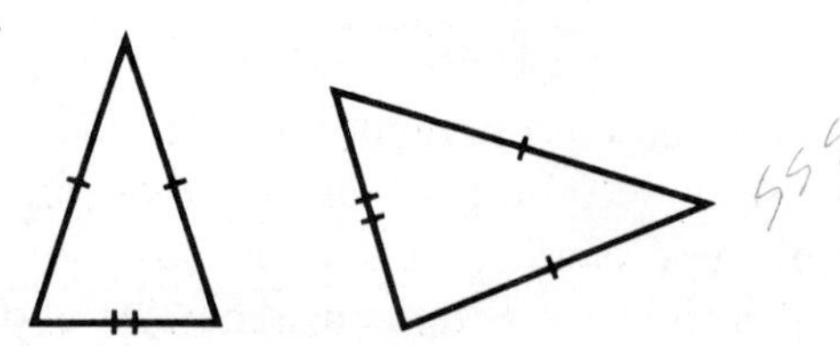

In exercises 15–22 the congruent parts of the triangles are marked. State whether or not there is enough information to decide if the triangles are congruent by the SAS, ASA, or SSS postulate. If they are congruent, state the postulate.

15.

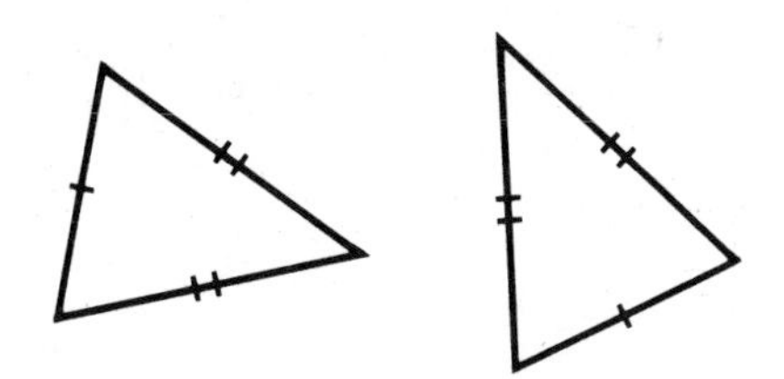

16.

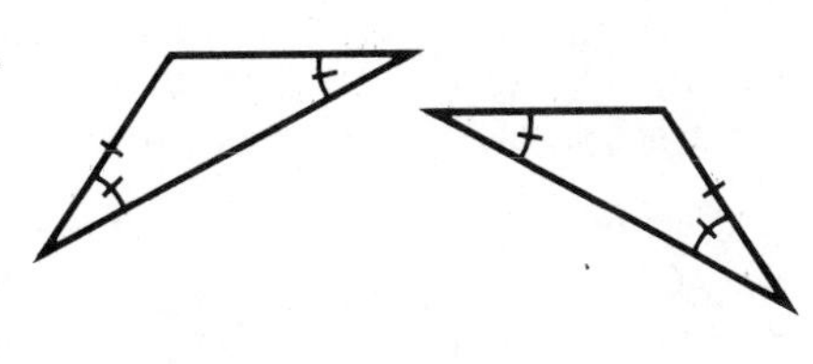

17.

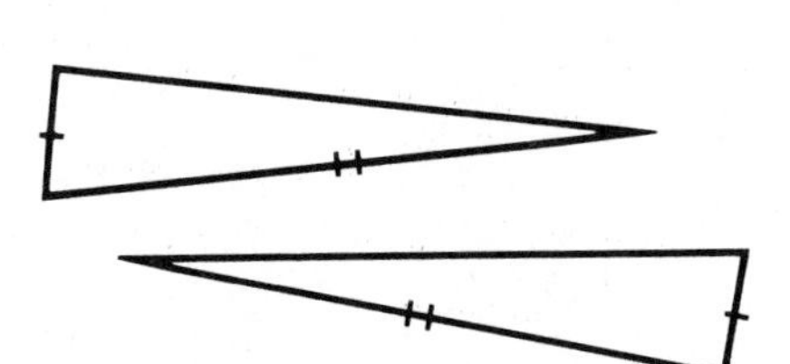

18.

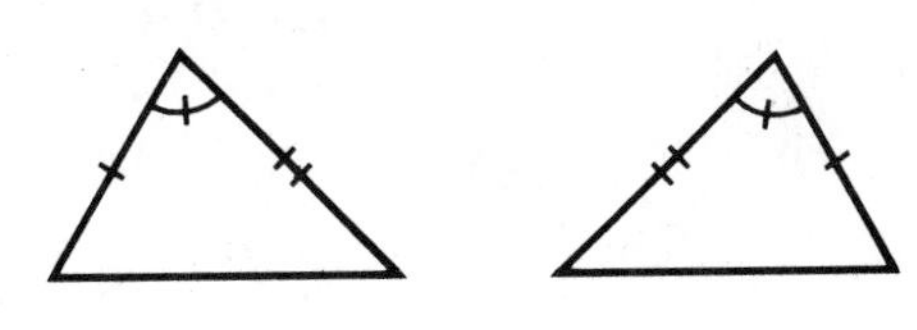

19.

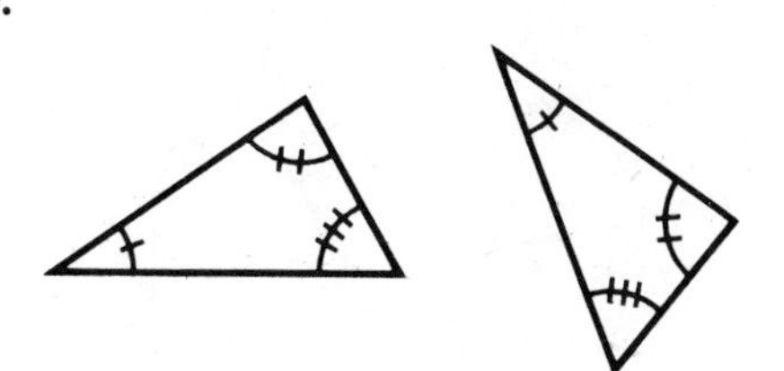

20.

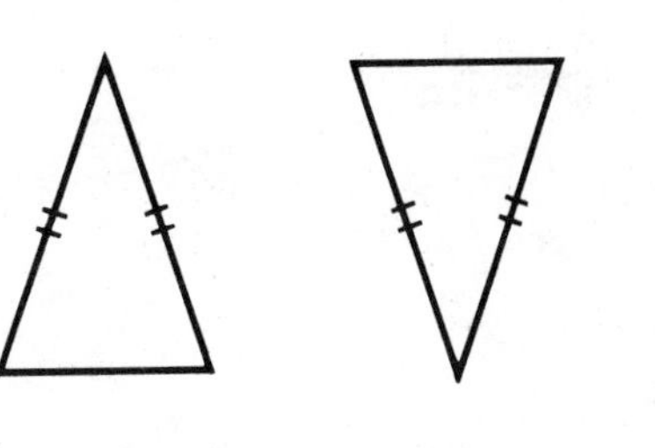

21.

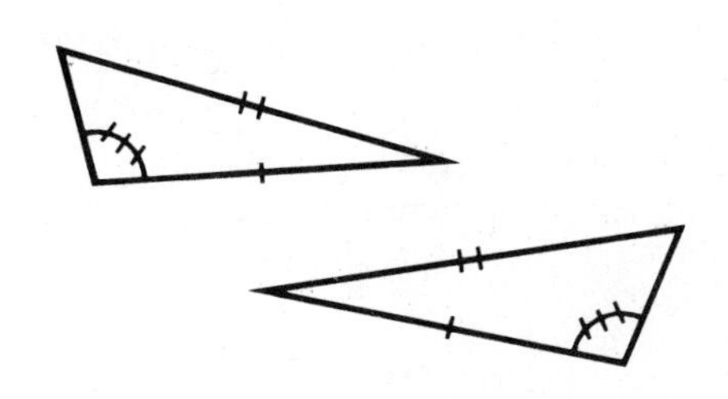

22.

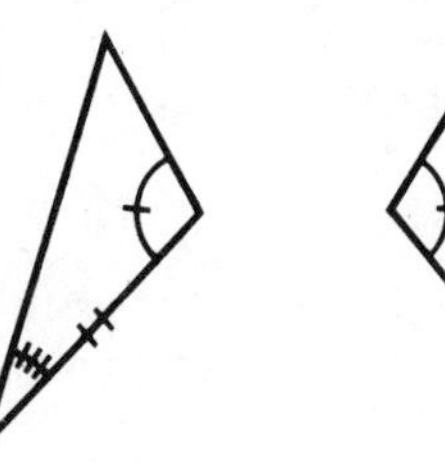

B.

In exercises 23–27 tell whether or not the triangles are congruent. If they are congruent, tell which postulate (SAS, ASA, SSS) can be used to verify this.

23. Given: $\overline{PQ} \cong \overline{XY}$, $\overline{QR} \cong \overline{YZ}$, $\overline{PR} \cong \overline{XZ}$.

24. Given: $\overline{PR} \cong \overline{XZ}$, $\overline{RQ} \cong \overline{ZY}$, $\angle R \cong \angle Z$.

25. Given: $\angle P \cong \angle X$, $\angle R \cong \angle Z$, $\overline{PQ} \cong \overline{XY}$.

26. Given: $\angle Q \cong \angle Y$, $\angle R \cong \angle Z$, $\overline{QR} \cong \overline{YZ}$.

27. Given: $\angle P \cong \angle X$, $\angle Q \cong \angle Y$, $\angle R \cong \angle Z$.

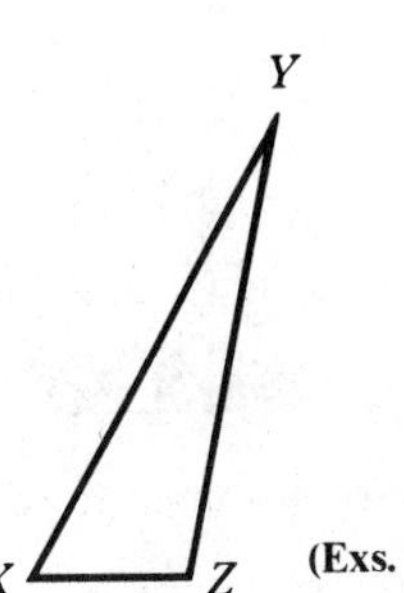

(Exs. 23–27)

28. Use the idea of the SSS postulate to construct a triangle congruent to $\triangle ABC$.

29. Use the idea of the SAS postulate to construct a triangle congruent to $\triangle ABC$.

30. Use the idea of the ASA postulate to construct a triangle congruent to $\triangle ABC$.

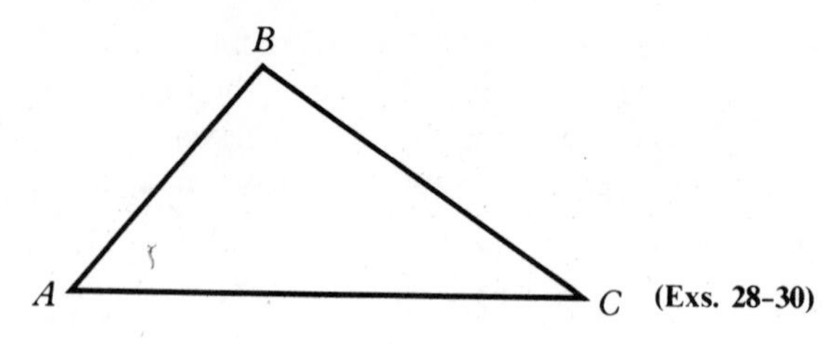

(Exs. 28-30)

31. A team of surveyors want to find the distance AB across a lake. One method requires the construction of a pair of congruent triangles. They select any point C, measure $\angle ACB$, and locate a point D so that $\angle ACD \cong \angle ACB$ and $\overline{CD} \cong \overline{CB}$. Why are $\triangle ACD$ and $\triangle ACB$ congruent? How does this help find the distance across the lake?

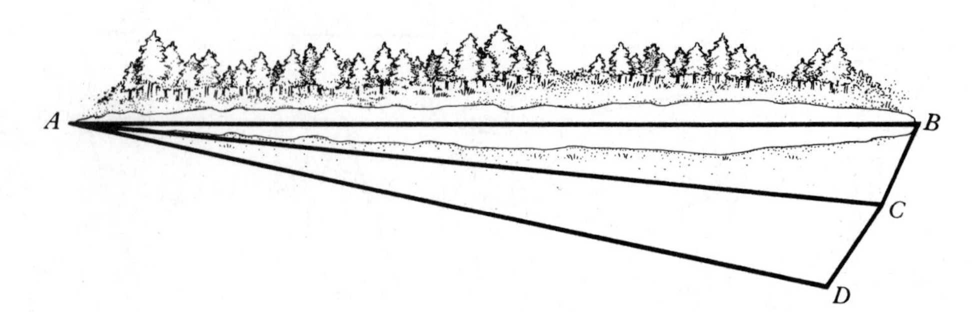

Activity

Make cardboard copies (at least three times the size) of the six pentominoes shown. (A pentominoe is a polygon which bounds five squares on a checker board.)

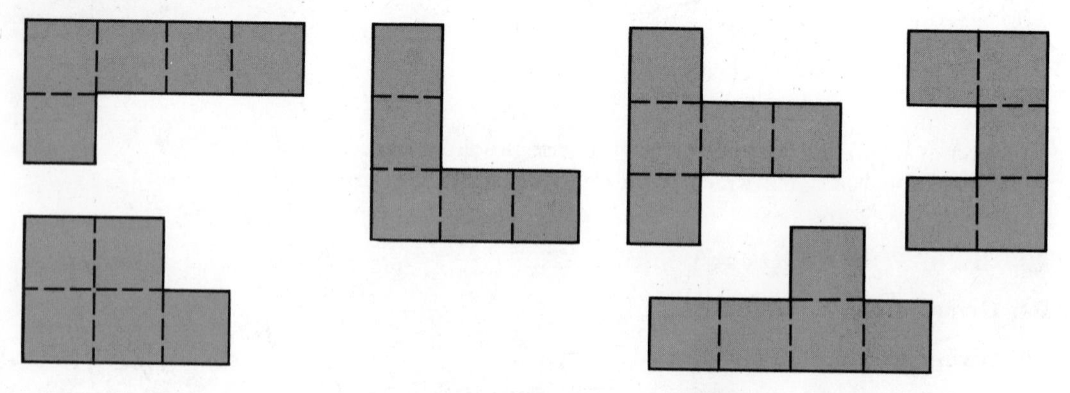

Arrange them to form a pair of rectangles identical in size and shape.

C.

In exercises 32–37 write a congruence statement for each pair of congruent triangles. Also state whether the triangles are congruent by ASA, SAS, or SSS. (Note: Use the idea that a segment is congruent to itself and an angle is congruent to itself.)

32.

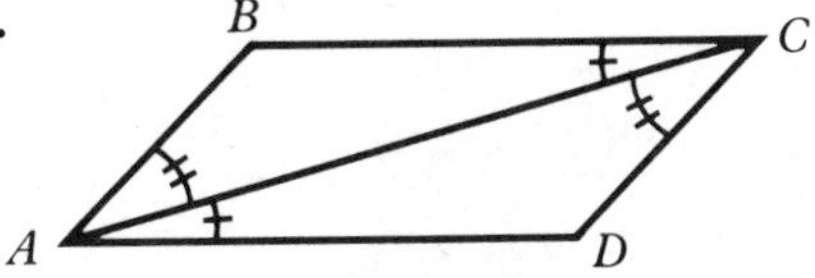

33.

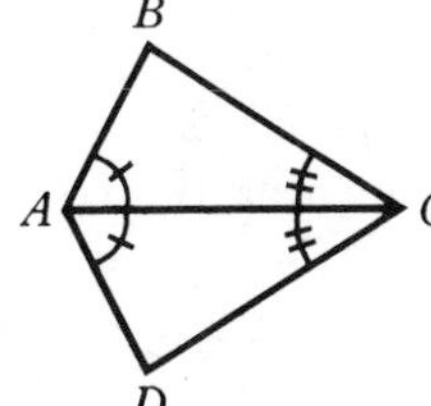

34.

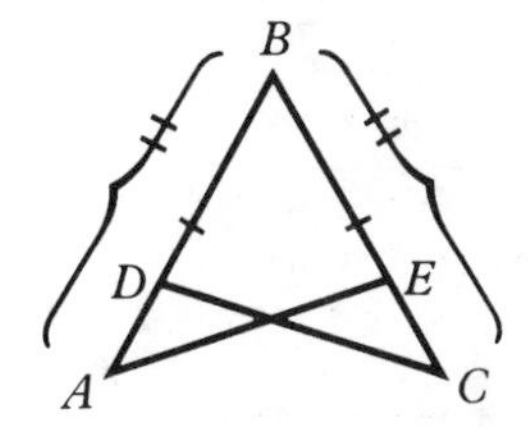

35.

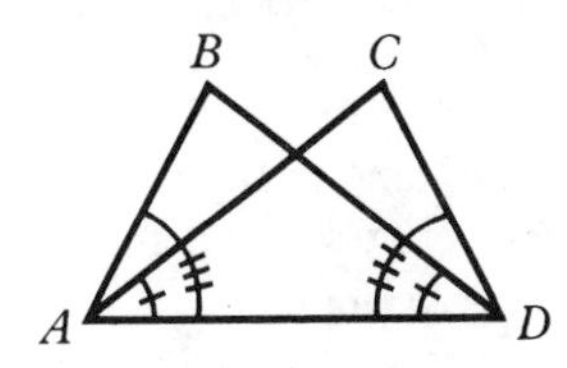

36.

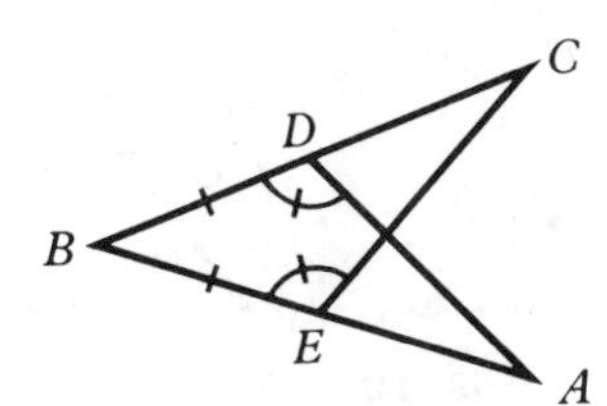

37.

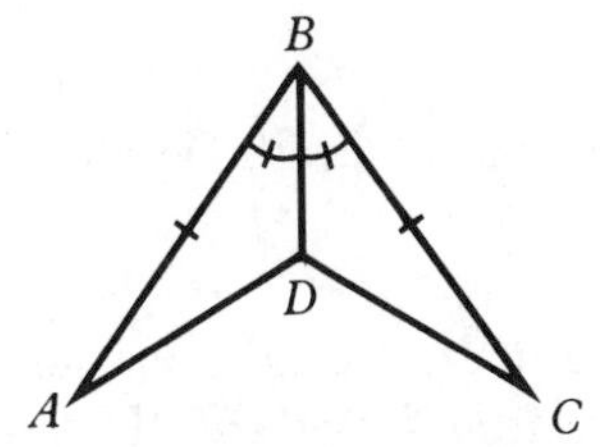

PROBLEM SOLVING

How many ways can a 3 × 3 × 3 cube be positioned in a cube of dimension 4 × 4 × 4? How many 2 × 2 × 2 or 1 × 1 × 1 positions are possible? Complete the table.

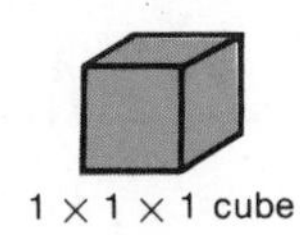
1 × 1 × 1 cube

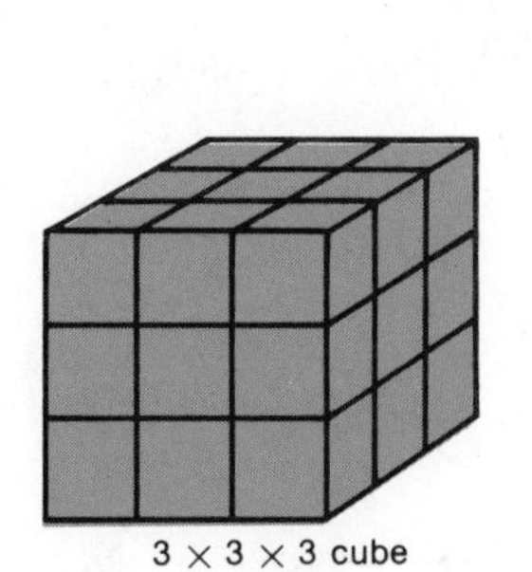
3 × 3 × 3 cube

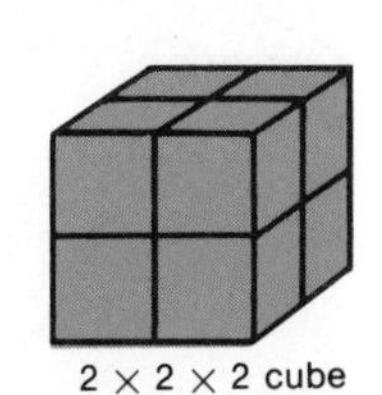
2 × 2 × 2 cube

cube size	number of positions in a 4 × 4 × 4 cube

3–3 Proofs: Using the Congruence Postulates

To prove two triangles congruent, we begin with given information and use *patterns of deductive reasoning* to conclude that they are indeed congruent. Affirming the hypothesis is the pattern most often used, as described below.

REVIEW: Affirming the hypothesis is a pattern of reasoning represented as follows:

Whenever $p \rightarrow q$ is true
and p is affirmed to be true,

---

we can conclude: q is true.

The SSS Postulate has the general form:

If	all three sides of one triangle are congruent respectively to all three sides of another triangle,	then	the two triangles are congruent.
	p		q.

Now we look at a specific application of this statement:

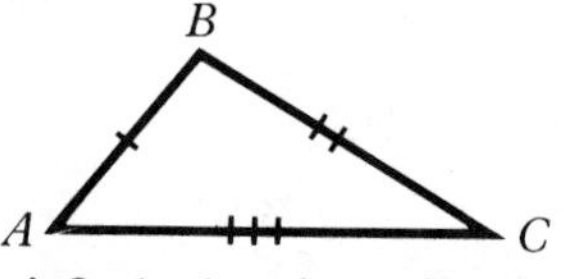

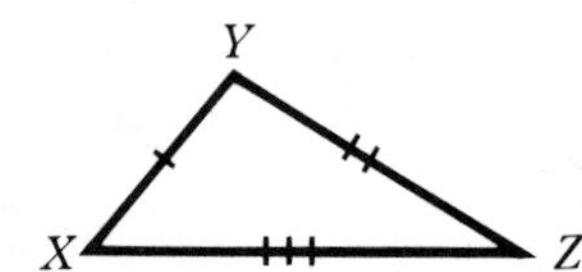

We observe that all conditions stated in p are satisfied, that is, p is true. We have *affirmed the hypothesis.* Therefore we can conclude: q is true. Applying this to our specific case, $\triangle ABC \cong \triangle XYZ$.

It is helpful to organize our thinking by writing the above *proof* in two columns. The left column is used for statements that lead to the desired conclusion. The right column gives reasons why the statements are true.

Given: $\overline{AB} \cong \overline{XY}$
$\overline{BC} \cong \overline{YZ}$
$\overline{AC} \cong \overline{XZ}$

Prove: $\triangle ABC \cong \triangle XYZ$

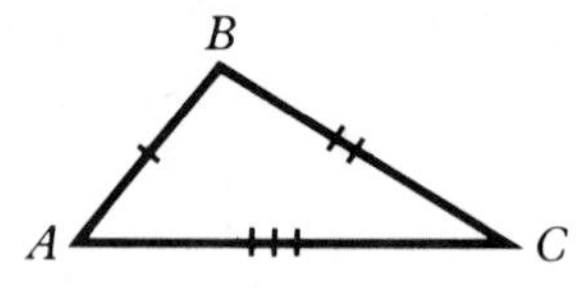

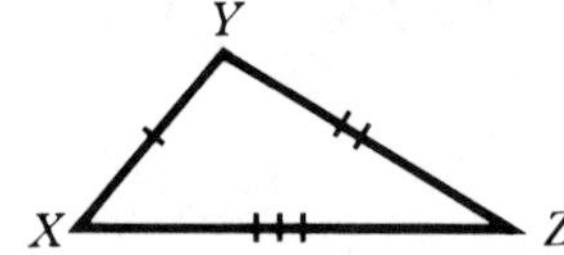

Proof

Statements	Reasons
1. $\overline{AB} \cong \overline{XY}$	1. Given
2. $\overline{BC} \cong \overline{YZ}$	2. Given
3. $\overline{AC} \cong \overline{XZ}$	3. Given
4. $\triangle ABC \cong \triangle XYZ$	4. SSS Congruence Postulate

Here are two more examples of simple proofs that two triangles are congruent. Notice the use of affirming the hypothesis.

Example 1 **Given:** $\overline{AB} \cong \overline{XY}$
$\angle A \cong \angle X$
$\angle B \cong \angle Y$
Prove: $\triangle ABC \cong \triangle XYZ$

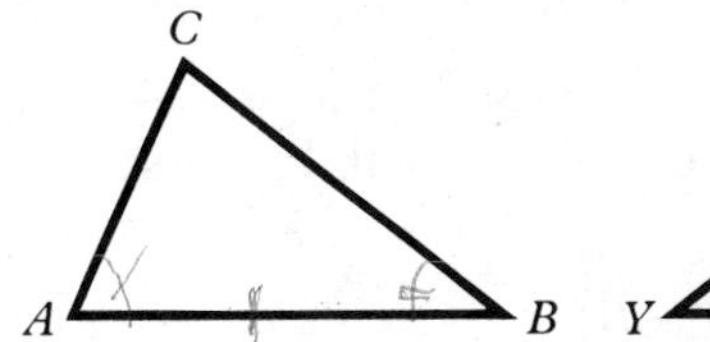

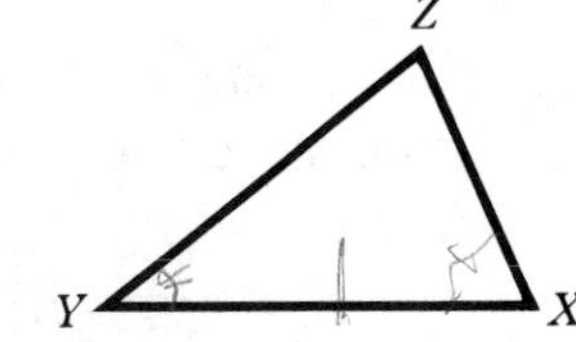

Proof

Statements	Reasons
1. $\overline{AB} \cong \overline{XY}$	1. Given
2. $\angle A \cong \angle X$	2. Given
3. $\angle B \cong \angle Y$	3. Given
4. $\triangle ABC \cong \triangle XYZ$	4. ASA Congruence Postulate

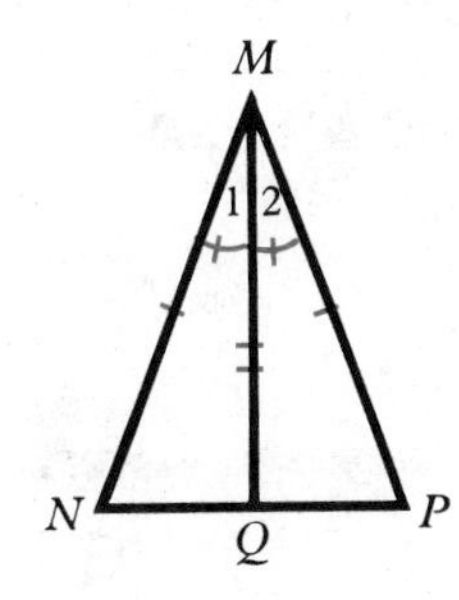

Example 2 **Given:** $\overline{MN} \cong \overline{MP}$
$\angle 1 \cong \angle 2$
Prove: $\triangle MNQ \cong \triangle MPQ$

Proof

Statements	Reasons
1. $\overline{MN} \cong \overline{MP}$	1. Given
2. $\angle 1 \cong \angle 2$	2. Given
3. $\overline{MQ} \cong \overline{MQ}$	3. A segment is congruent to itself.
4. $\triangle MNQ \cong \triangle MPQ$	4. SAS Congruence Postulate

(Note: Sometimes, as in Step 3, a common side of two triangles is involved. The idea that "a segment is congruent to itself" can be used to get a second pair of congruent sides needed to affirm the hypothesis of the SAS congruence postulate. This idea will be discussed further in Chapter 4.)

EXERCISES

A.

Prove the following triangles congruent by writing a two-column proof. Model your proof after the examples on page 97.

1. **Given:** $\overline{AC} \cong \overline{DF}$
   $\overline{AB} \cong \overline{DE}$
   $\angle A \cong \angle D$
   Prove: $\triangle ABC \cong \triangle DEF$
2. **Given:** $\overline{RS} \cong \overline{KL}$
   $\overline{ST} \cong \overline{JK}$
   $\overline{RT} \cong \overline{JL}$
   Prove: $\triangle RST \cong \triangle LKJ$
3. **Given:** $\angle D \cong \angle X$
   $\angle F \cong \angle Z$
   $\overline{DF} \cong \overline{XZ}$
   Prove: $\triangle DEF \cong \triangle XYZ$
4. **Given:** $\overline{AC} \cong \overline{AD}$
   $\overline{AB} \cong \overline{AE}$
   $\overline{BC} \cong \overline{DE}$
   Prove: $\triangle ABC \cong \triangle AED$

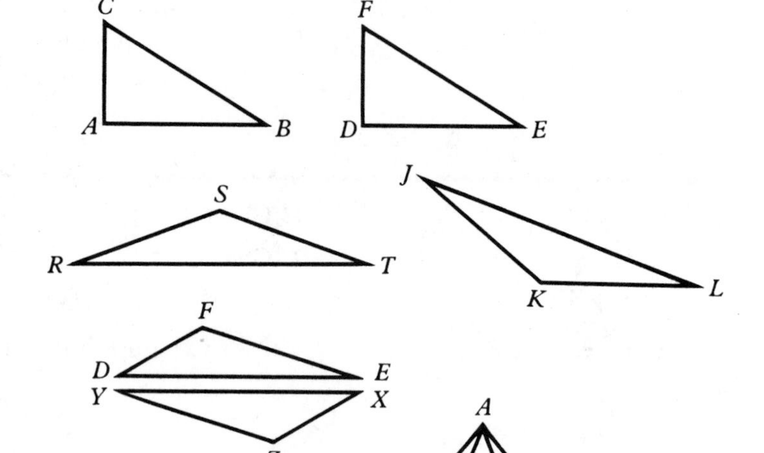

Activity

Make large copies of these pentominoes (figures made of five squares) and arrange them into a pair of rectangles identical in size and shape.

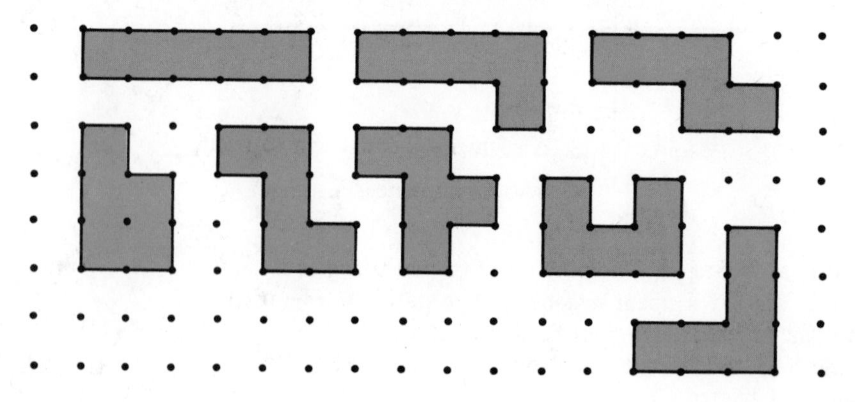

5. Given: $\angle 1 \cong \angle 2$
$\angle 3 \cong \angle 4$
Prove: $\triangle ABD \cong \triangle CDB$

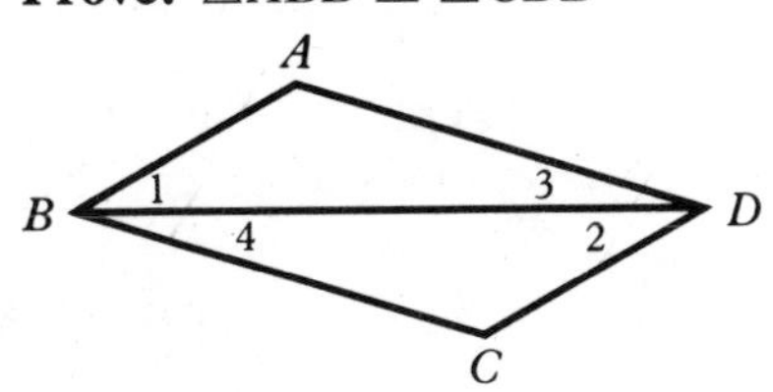

6. Given: $\overline{DE} \cong \overline{DF}$
$\overline{EH} \cong \overline{HF}$
Prove: $\triangle DHE \cong \triangle DHF$

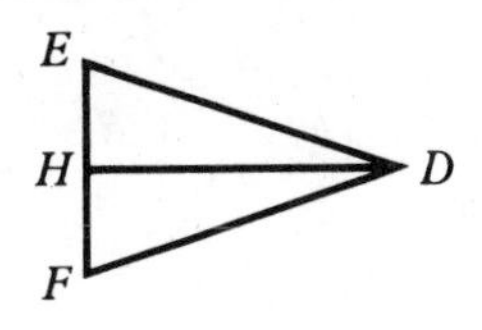

7. Given: $\overline{HI} \cong \overline{KI}$
$\angle 1 \cong \angle 2$
$\overline{JI} \cong \overline{IL}$
Prove: $\triangle HIJ \cong \triangle KIL$

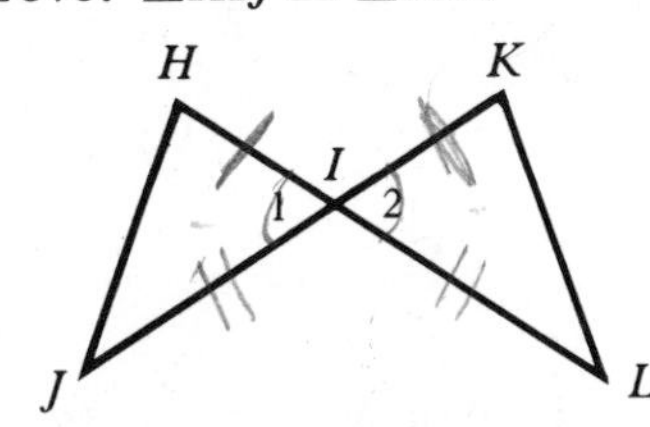

8. Given: $\overline{AB} \cong \overline{CD}$
$\angle 1 \cong \angle 2$
Prove: $\triangle ABD \cong \triangle CDB$

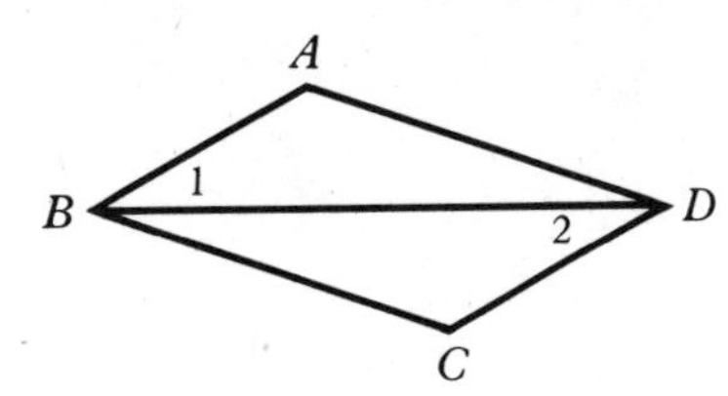

B.

9. Given: $\overline{AC} \cong \overline{BD}$
$\angle A \cong \angle D$
$\angle ACE \cong \angle DBF$
Prove: $\triangle ACE \cong \triangle DBF$

10. Given: $\overline{AC} \cong \overline{BD}$, $\overline{AE} \cong \overline{DF}$
$\angle A \cong \angle D$
Prove: $\triangle CAE \cong \triangle BDF$

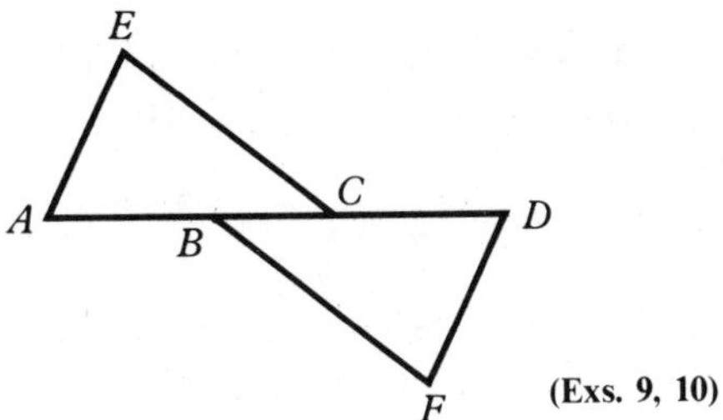

(Exs. 9, 10)

11. Given: $\angle A \cong \angle C$, $\overline{AB} \cong \overline{BC}$
Prove: $\triangle CBE \cong \triangle ABD$

12. Given: $\angle BDA \cong \angle BEC$
$\overline{BD} \cong \overline{BE}$
Prove: $\triangle BDA \cong \triangle BEC$

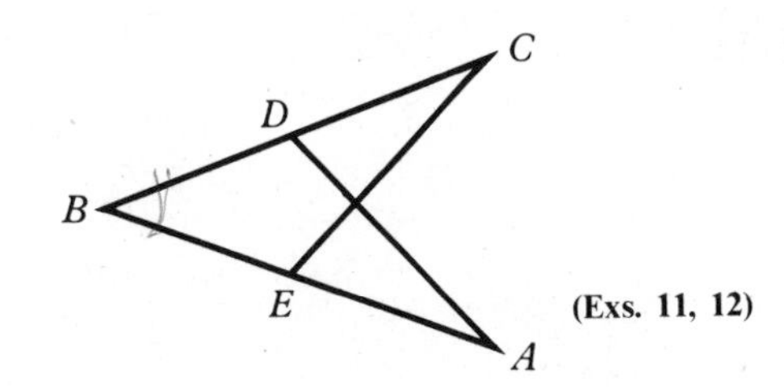

(Exs. 11, 12)

PROBLEM SOLVING

Which of the following patterns do you think can be made into a cube by folding along the edges and taping?

How many other patterns of six squares that will fold to make a cube can you draw?

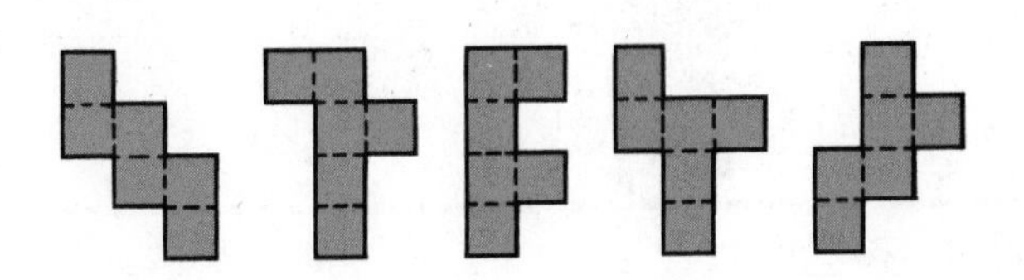

3–4 Proofs: Using Definitions

REVIEW: Two lines are **perpendicular** if they intersect to form congruent right angles.

The definition of perpendicular lines (above) and the definitions of angle bisector, midpoint, segment bisector (p. 24), and perpendicular bisector (p. 29) are often used in making proofs.

Consider the following example of *affirming the hypothesis* (p. 64).

$p \to q$: If a ray bisects an angle,
then the two angles formed are congruent.

p: $\overrightarrow{AC}$ bisects $\angle BAD$.

Therefore conclude q: $\angle 1 \cong \angle 2$

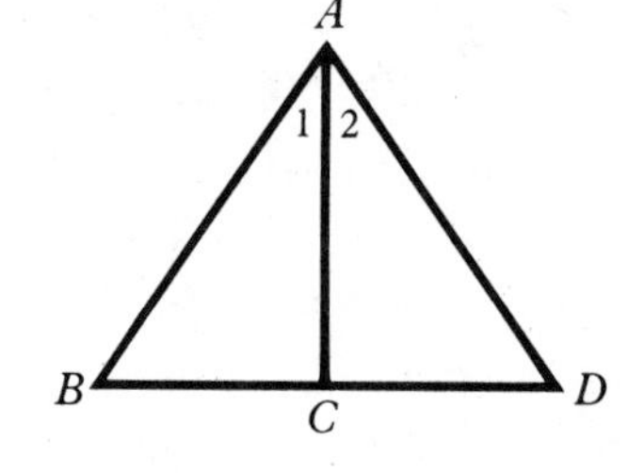

The short proof above is shown below using a two-column arrangement.

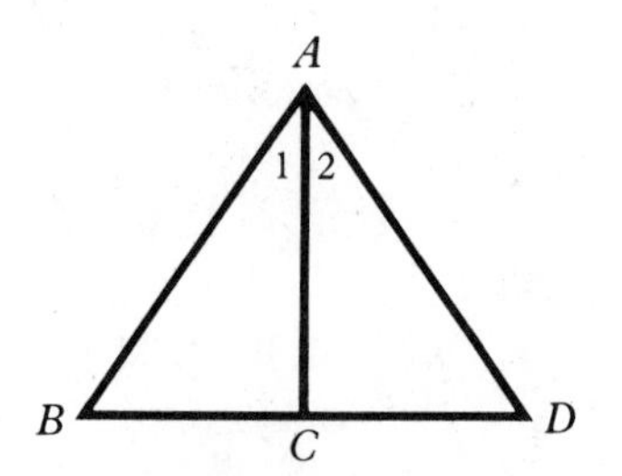

Given: $\overrightarrow{AC}$ bisects $\angle BAD$
Prove: $\angle 1 \cong \angle 2$

Proof

Statements	Reasons
1. $\overrightarrow{AC}$ bisects $\angle BAD$.	**1.** Given
2. $\angle 1 \cong \angle 2$	**2.** Definition of angle bisector

The following short proofs show how the definitions of midpoint, bisector, and perpendicular lines are used. Study each proof.

Example 1

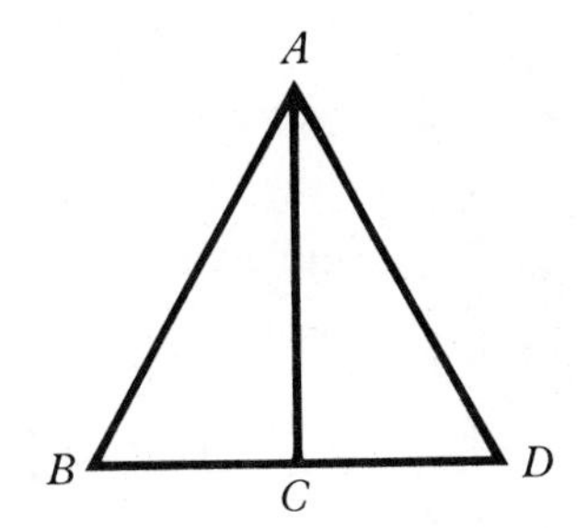

Given: C is the midpoint of $\overline{BD}$.
Prove: $\overline{BC} \cong \overline{CD}$

Proof

Statements	Reasons
1. C is the midpoint of $\overline{BD}$.	**1.** Given
2. $\overline{BC} \cong \overline{CD}$	**2.** Definition of midpoint

Example 2

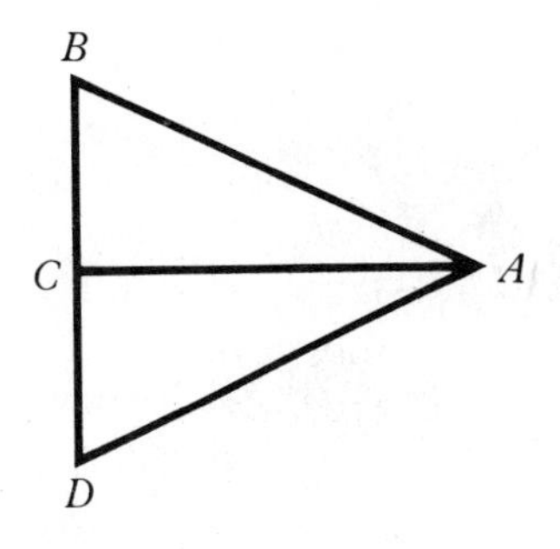

Given: $\overline{AC}$ is the perpendicular bisector of $\overline{BD}$. 
Prove: C is the midpoint of $\overline{BD}$.

Proof

Statements	Reasons
1. $\overline{AC}$ is the perpendicular bisector of $\overline{BD}$.	**1.** Given
2. C is the midpoint of $\overline{BD}$.	**2.** Definition of perpendicular bisector

plus ∠BCA and ∠DCA are rt ∠'s

Example 3

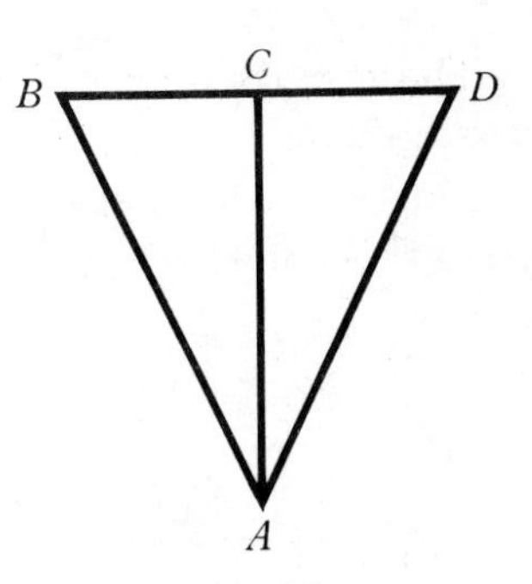

Given: $\overline{AC} \perp \overline{BD}$ 
Prove: $\angle ACD \cong \angle ACB$

Proof

Statements	Reasons
1. $\overline{AC} \perp \overline{BD}$	**1.** Given
2. $\angle ACD \cong \angle ACB$	**2.** Definition of perpendicular lines

∠ACD + ∠ACB are rt ∠'s

All rt ∠'s are ≅

EXERCISES

A.

In exercises 1–8 use one of the definitions reviewed in this section to draw a conclusion from the given.

1. **Given:** $\overline{XM}$ bisects $\angle ZXY$.

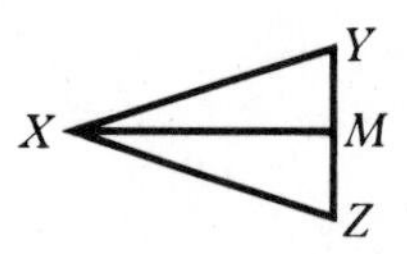

2. **Given:** $\overline{RM} \perp \overline{TU}$

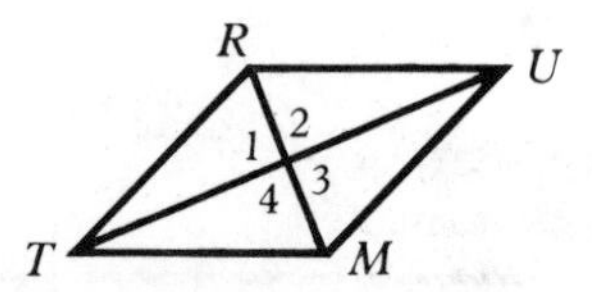

3. **Given:** N is the midpoint of $\overline{AB}$.

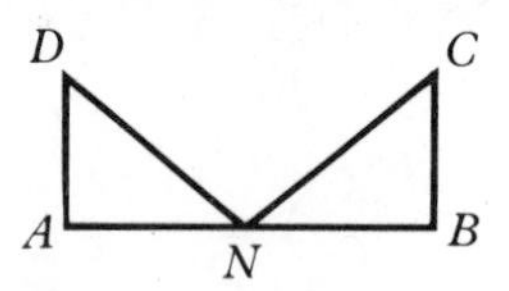

4. **Given:** $\overline{AC}$ and $\overline{BD}$ bisect each other.

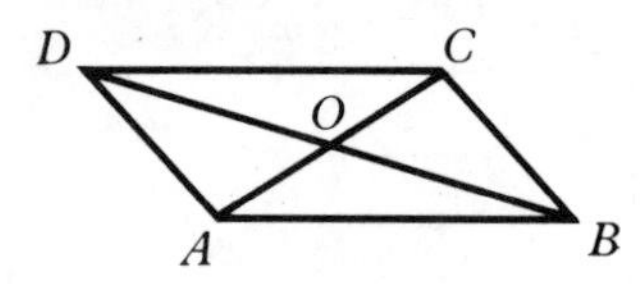

5. **Given:** $\overline{SV}$ is the perpendicular bisector of $\overline{PQ}$.

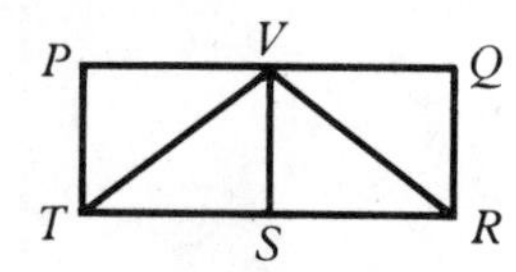

6. **Given:** $\overline{DB}$ bisects $\angle EDF$.

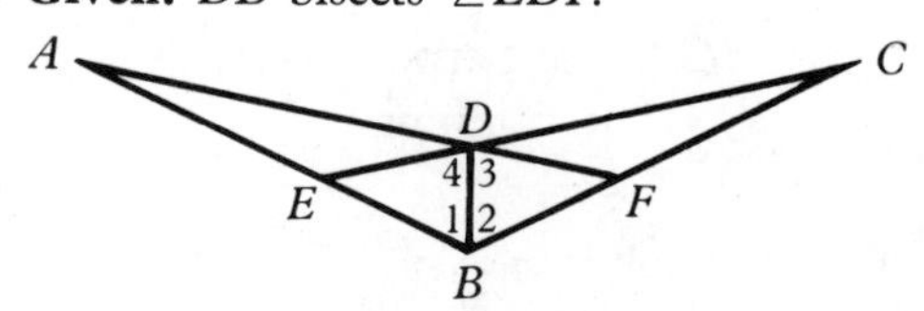

7. **Given:** T is the midpoint of $\overline{QS}$.

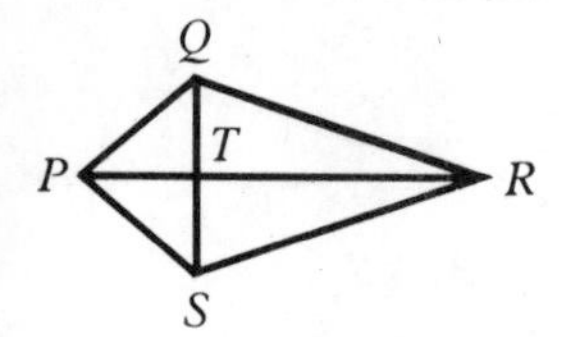

8. **Given:** $\overline{KM}$ is the perpendicular bisector of $\overline{JL}$.

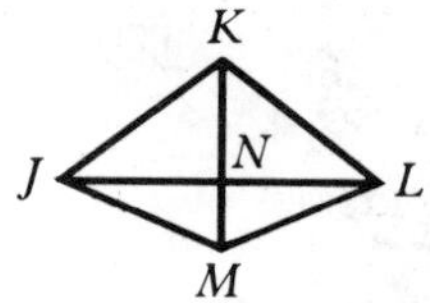

Activity

Make enlarged copies of these ten pentominoes and put them together to form a pair of squares identical in size and shape.

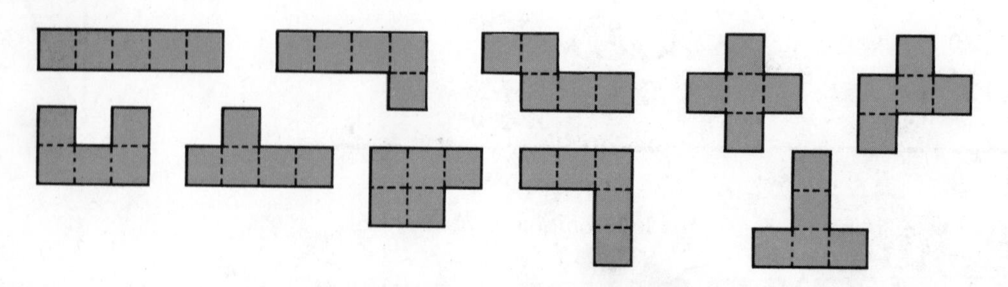

B.

Write a two-column proof for each of exercises 9–14.

9. Given: $\overline{BD}$ bisects $\angle ADC$.
Prove: $\angle ADB \cong \angle BDC$

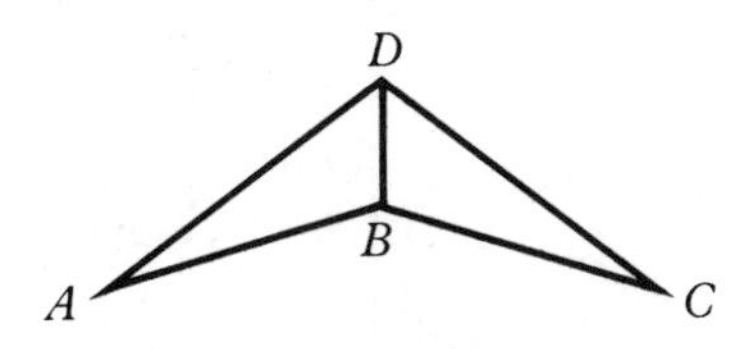

10. Given: $\overline{QS}$ is the perpendicular bisector of $\overline{PR}$.
Prove: S is the midpoint of $\overline{PR}$.

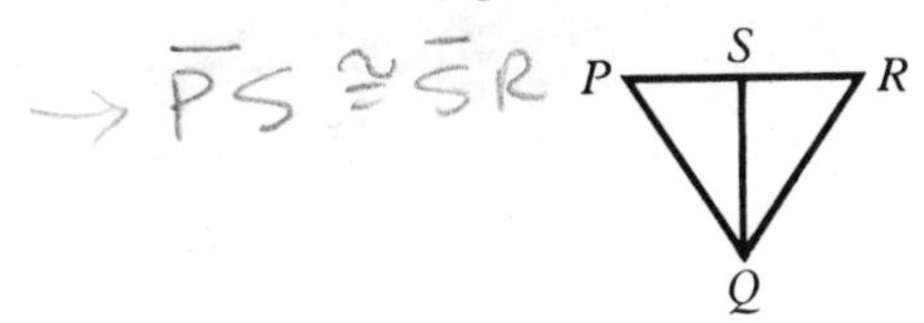

11. Given: M is the midpoint of $\overline{AD}$.
Prove: $\overline{AM} \cong \overline{MD}$

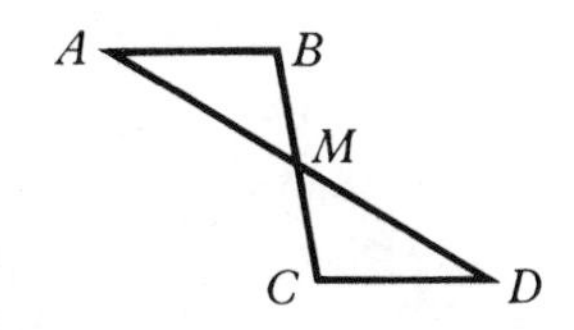

12. Given: $\overline{PR} \perp \overline{QS}$
Prove: $\angle PTQ \cong \angle PTS$

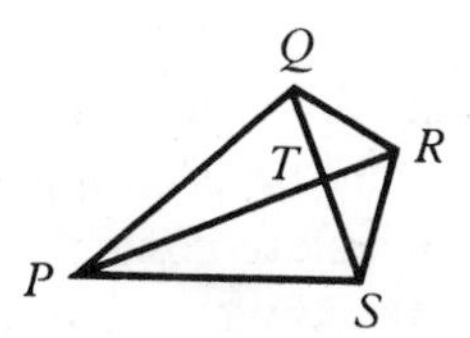

C.

13. Given: $\overline{LQ}$ is the perpendicular bisector of $\overline{JN}$.
Prove: $\overline{JQ} \cong \overline{QN}$

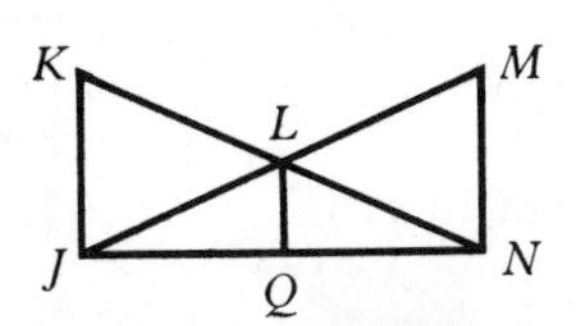

14. Given: $\overline{BD}$ bisects $\overline{AC}$.
Prove: $\overline{AE} \cong \overline{EC}$

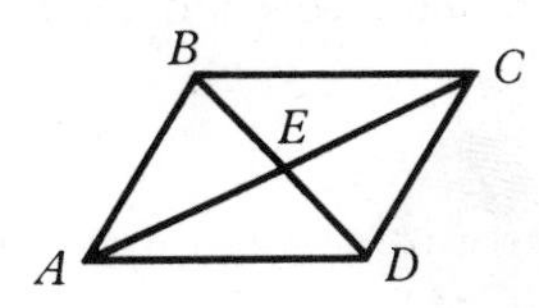

PROBLEM SOLVING

These pictures show four different ways to divide a square into four identical parts.

How many more different ways can you find? Show at least five of them on a geoboard or dot paper.

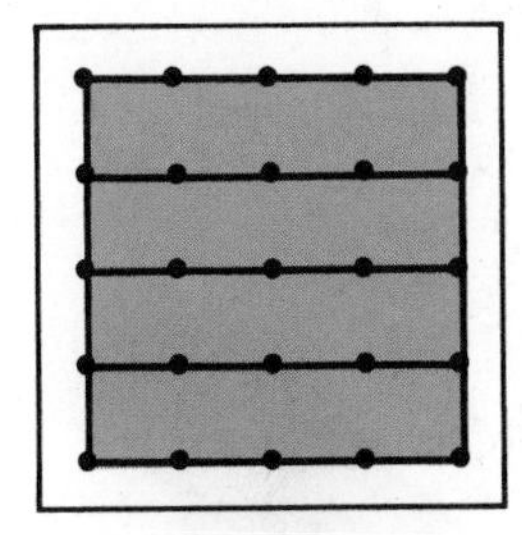
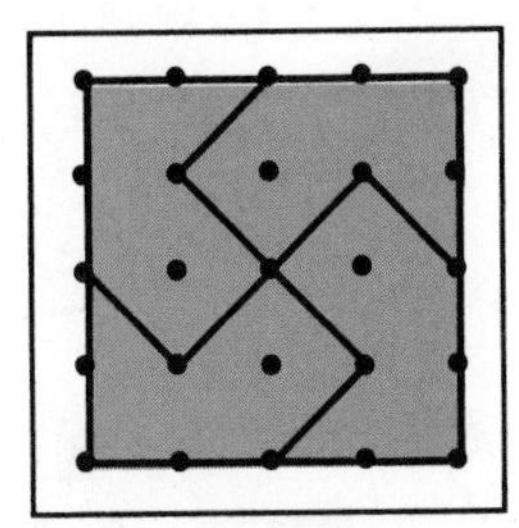
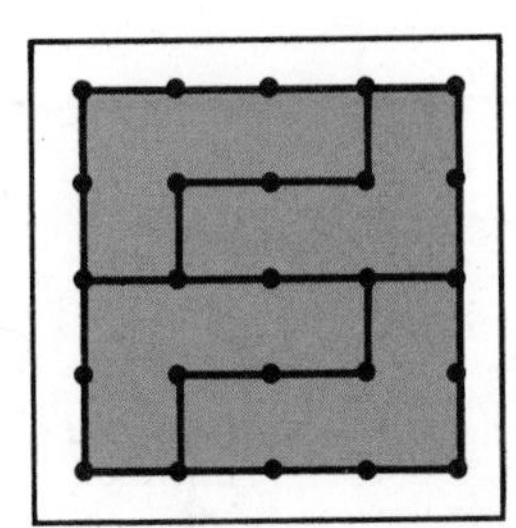
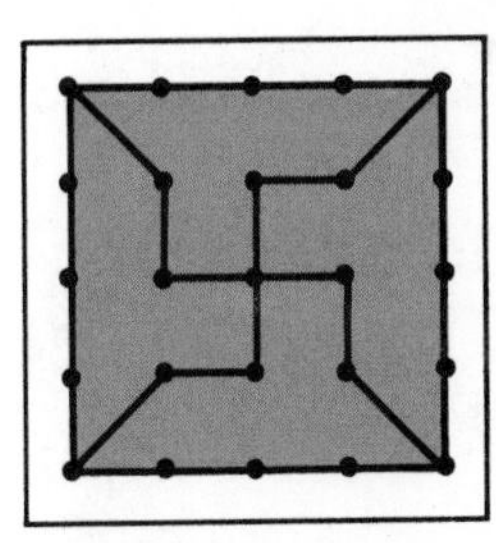

3–5 Proofs: Using Postulates and Definitions

The definitions of angle bisector, segment bisector, perpendicular bisector, and midpoint can be used together with the congruence postulates to prove that two triangles are congruent.

To figure out how to prove that two triangles are congruent, it often helps to analyze the situation by starting with what is to be proved and working backwards. Study this example.

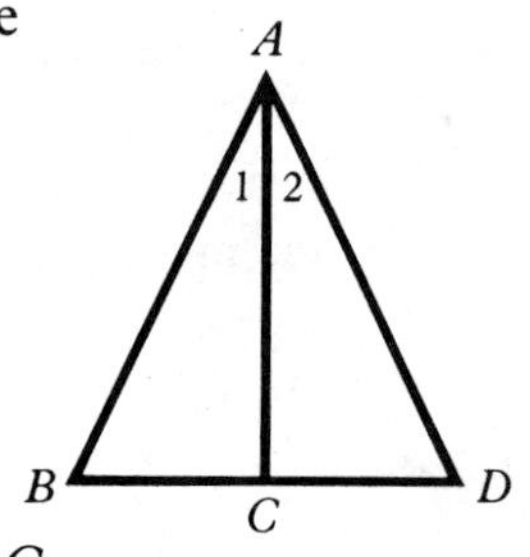

Problem: To prove that two triangles are congruent, as indicated.

Given: $\overline{AB} \cong \overline{AD}$
$\overline{AC}$ bisects $\angle BAD$.
Prove: $\triangle ABC \cong \triangle ADC$

Analysis (how someone might figure out how to do it): "I want to prove that $\triangle ABC \cong \triangle ADC$. I could do this by using the SSS, SAS, or ASA Congruence Postulates. Which one? From the given information, I know that $\overline{AB} \cong \overline{AD}$. If I could show that $\angle 1 \cong \angle 2$ and $\overline{AC} \cong \overline{AC}$, I could use SAS. But $\overline{AC}$ bisects $\angle BAD$, so $\angle 1 \cong \angle 2$. Also, a segment is congruent to itself. I can do it!"

Proof

Statements	Reasons
1. $\overline{AB} \cong \overline{AD}$	**1.** Given
2. $\overline{AC}$ bisects $\angle BAD$.	**2.** Given
3. $\angle 1 \cong \angle 2$	**3.** Why?
4. $\overline{AC} \cong \overline{AC}$	**4.** A segment is congruent to itself.
5. $\triangle ABC \cong \triangle ADC$	**5.** SAS Congruence Postulate

Think through the *analysis* for each proof below. Then complete the proof.

Example 1 **Given:** $\overline{AB} \cong \overline{AD}$
C is the midpoint of $\overline{BD}$.
Prove: $\triangle ABC \cong \triangle ADC$

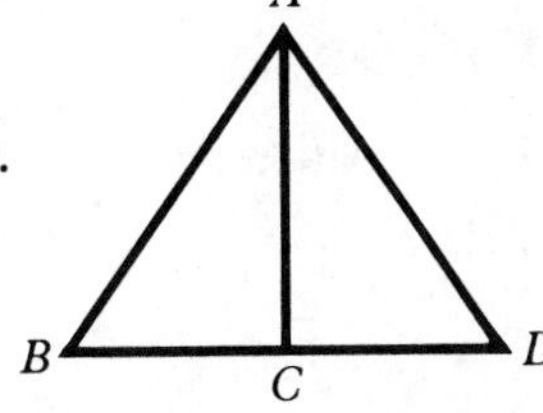

Analysis: "Which congruence postulate should I aim for—ASA, SAS, or SSS? I can prove $\triangle ABC \cong \triangle ADC$ if I can show that three sides of $\triangle ABC$ are congruent respectively to three sides of $\triangle ADC$. I know from the 'given' that $\overline{AB} \cong \overline{AD}$. $\overline{AC} \cong \overline{AC}$, because a segment is congruent to itself. $\overline{BC} \cong \overline{CD}$ if C is a midpoint of $\overline{BD}$. It is! (from the 'given.') I can now write the proof."

Proof

Statements	Reasons
1. $\overline{AB} \cong \overline{AD}$	1. Given
2. C is the midpoint of $\overline{BD}$	2. Given
3. $\overline{BC} \cong \overline{CD}$	3. Why?
4. $\overline{AC} \cong \overline{AC}$	4. A segment is congruent to itself.
5. $\triangle ABC \cong \triangle ADC$	5. Why?

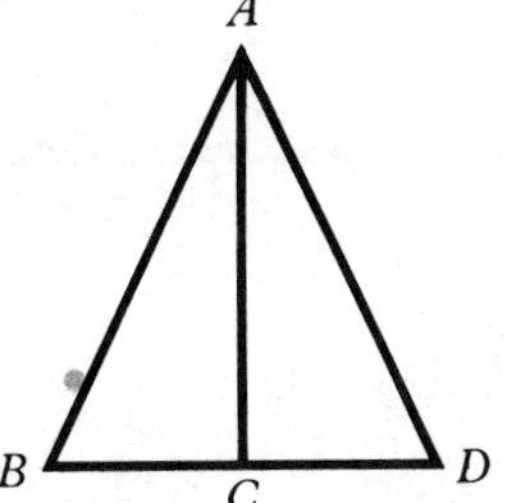

Example 2 **Given:** $\overline{AC}$ is the perpendicular bisector of $\overline{BD}$.
Prove: $\triangle ACB \cong \triangle ACD$

Analysis: "I can prove $\triangle ACB \cong \triangle ACD$ by using one of the congruence postulates. Let's try SAS. I know that $\overline{AC} \cong \overline{AC}$. Since $\overline{AC}$ is the perpendicular bisector of $\overline{BC}$, then $\angle ACB \cong \angle ACD$ and $\overline{BC} \cong \overline{CD}$. I can now write the proof!"

Proof

Statements	Reasons
1. $\overline{AC}$ bisects $\overline{BD}$.	1. Given
2. $\overline{BC} \cong \overline{CD}$	2. Definition of segment bisector
3. $\overline{AC} \perp \overline{BD}$	3. Given
4. $\angle ACB \cong \angle ACD$	4. Why?
5. $\overline{AC} \cong \overline{AC}$	5. Why?
6. $\triangle ACB \cong \triangle ACD$	6. SAS Postulate

EXERCISES

A.

In exercises 1–4 analyze the situation and indicate which of the three congruence postulates (SSS, SAS, or ASA) could be used to prove the triangles congruent.

1. Given: $\overline{AD}$ bisects $\overline{BC}$.
$\overline{AB} \cong \overline{AC}$
Prove: $\triangle ABD \cong \triangle ACD$

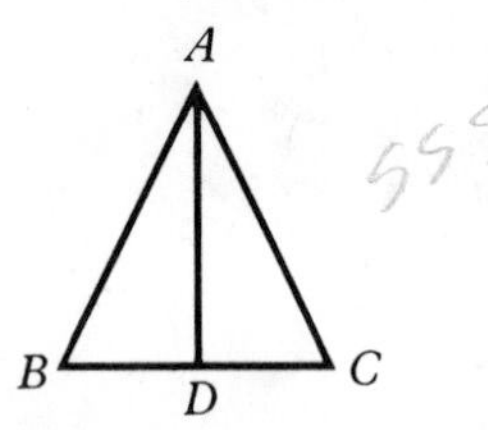

2. Given: $\overline{RT}$ bisects $\angle QRS$.
$\overline{RT}$ bisects $\angle QTS$.
Prove: $\triangle RTQ \cong \triangle RTS$

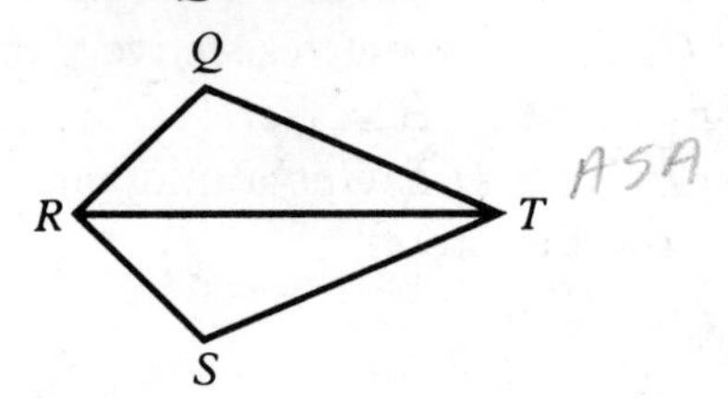

3. Given: $\overline{NP} \perp \overline{MO}$
$\overline{NP}$ bisects $\angle MPO$.
Prove: $\triangle MNP \cong \triangle ONP$

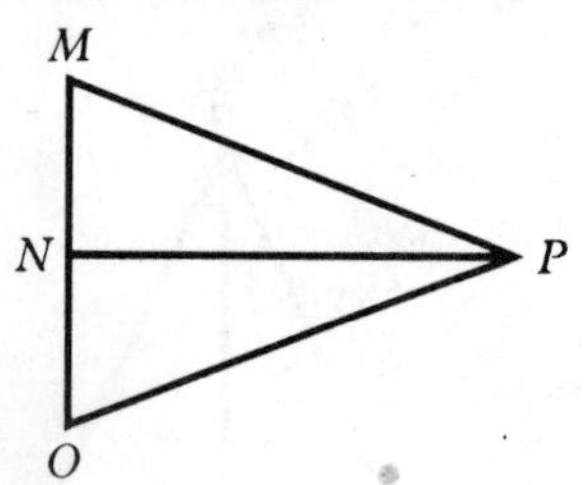

4. Given: $\overline{AE}$ and $\overline{BD}$ bisect each other.
$\angle 1 \cong \angle 2$
Prove: $\triangle ABC \cong \triangle EDC$

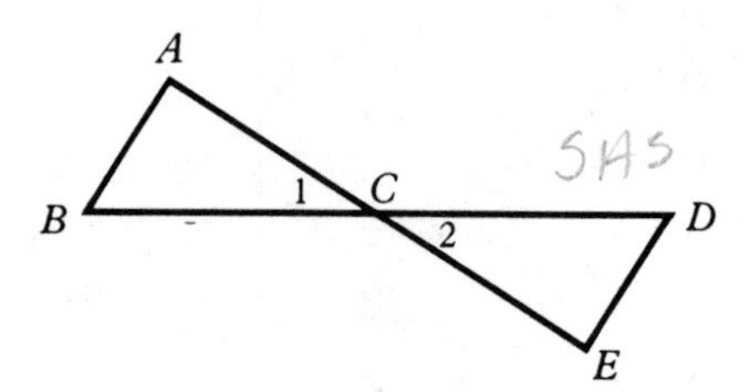

In exercises 5–7, supply the missing statements or reasons.

5. Given: $\overline{AD} \cong \overline{DB}$
$\overline{AB} \perp \overline{DC}$
Prove: $\triangle DAC \cong \triangle DBC$

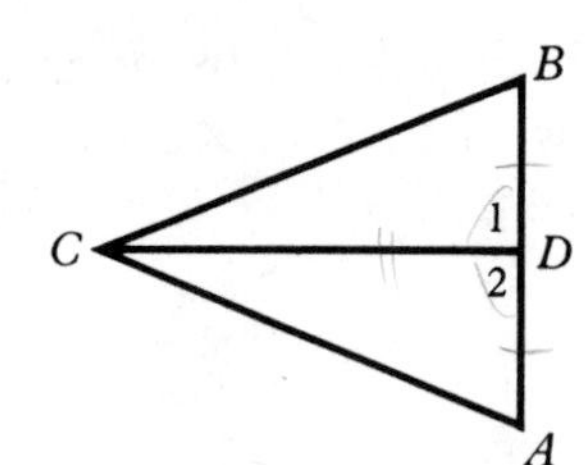

Statements	Reasons
1. $\overline{AD} \cong \overline{DB}$	1. Given
2. $\overline{AB} \perp \overline{DC}$	2. ?
3. $\angle 1 \cong \angle 2$	3. ?
4. ?	4. A segment is congruent to itself.
5. $\triangle DAC \cong \triangle DBC$	5. ?

6. Given: $\overline{AB} \cong \overline{CD}$
$\angle 1 \cong \angle 2$
Prove: $\triangle ABC \cong \triangle CDA$

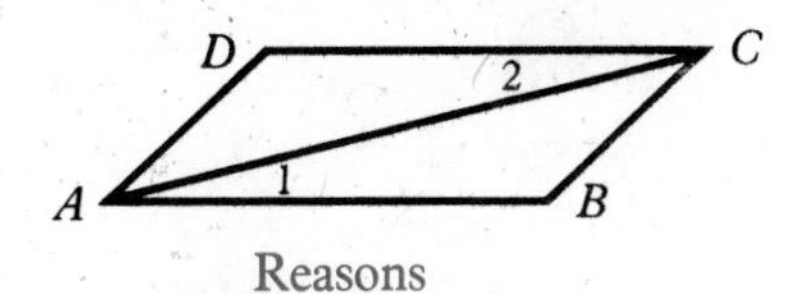

Statements	Reasons
1. $\overline{AB} \cong \overline{CD}$	1. Given
2. $\angle 1 \cong \angle 2$	2. Given
3. ? AC ≅ AC	3. A segment is congruent to itself.
4. $\triangle ABC \cong \triangle CDA$	4. ? SAS

7. Given: $\overline{XM} \perp \overline{YZ}$
$\overline{XM}$ bisects $\angle YXZ$.
Prove: $\triangle XYM \cong \triangle XZM$

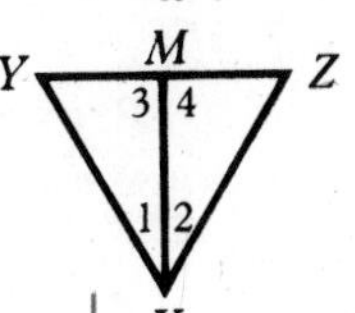

Statements	Reasons
1. $\overline{XM} \perp \overline{YZ}$	1. Given
2. ? ∠3 + ∠4 are rt ∠'s	2. Definition of perpendicular lines
2½ ∠3 ≅ ∠4	2½ All rt ∠'s ≅
3. $\overline{XM}$ bisects $\angle YXZ$	3. ? Given
4. $\angle 1 \cong \angle 2$	4. ? Def of ∠ bisector
5. $\overline{XM} \cong \overline{XM}$	5. ? seg ≅ to itself
6. $\triangle XYM \cong \triangle XZM$	6. ? ASA

B.

In exercises 8–17 prove that the triangles are congruent.

8. Given: $\overline{XM}$ bisects $\angle YXZ$.
$\angle 1 \cong \angle 2$
Prove: $\triangle XMY \cong \triangle XMZ$

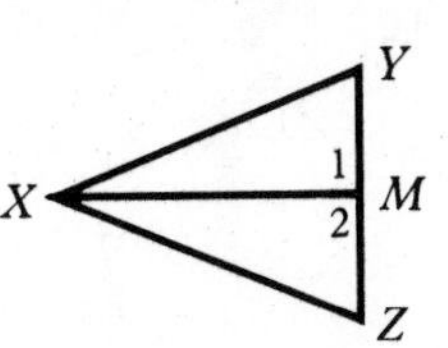

9. Given: $\overline{XM} \perp \overline{YZ}$
$\overline{YM} \cong \overline{MZ}$
Prove: $\triangle XYM \cong \triangle XZM$

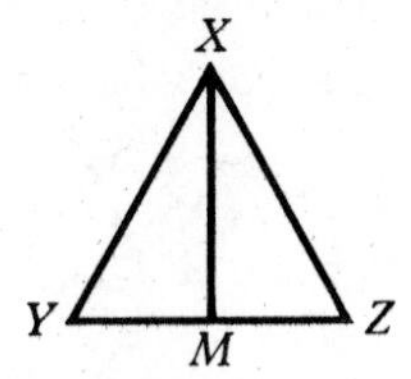

10. Given: $\overline{AC}$ is the bisector of $\angle BAD$.
$\overline{AB} \cong \overline{AD}$
Prove: $\triangle BAC \cong \triangle DAC$

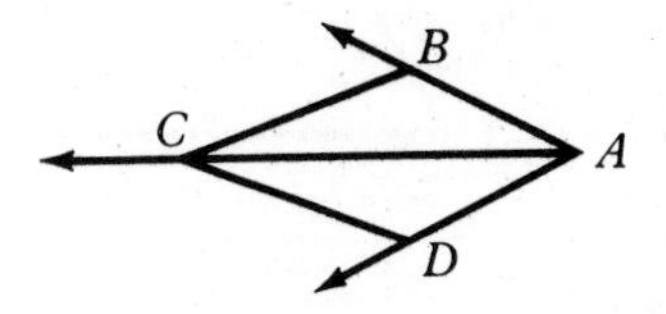

11. Given: $\overline{QM} \cong \overline{QP}$
$\overline{QN}$ bisects $\overline{MP}$.
Prove: $\triangle QNM \cong \triangle QNP$

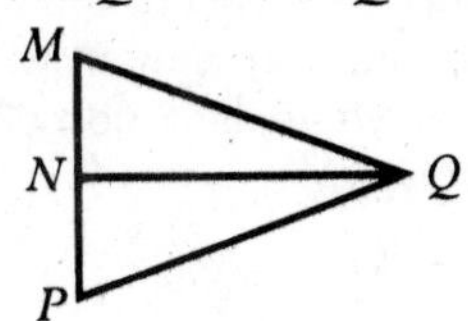

12. **Given:** $\overline{AC}$ bisects $\angle DAB$.
$\overline{AC}$ bisects $\angle DCB$.
Prove: $\triangle ACD \cong \triangle ACB$

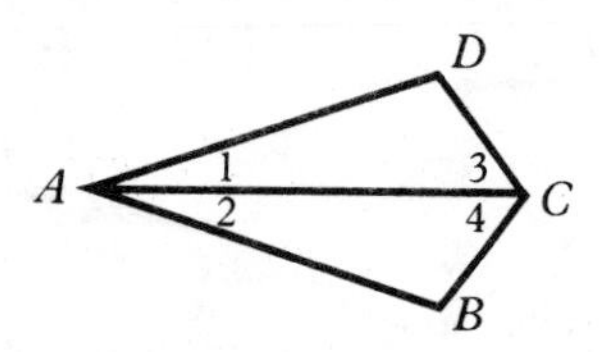

13. **Given:** $\overline{HR} \perp \overline{AE}$
$\overline{AH} \cong \overline{AD}$
$\angle 1 \cong \angle 2$
Prove: $\triangle AHE \cong \triangle ADR$

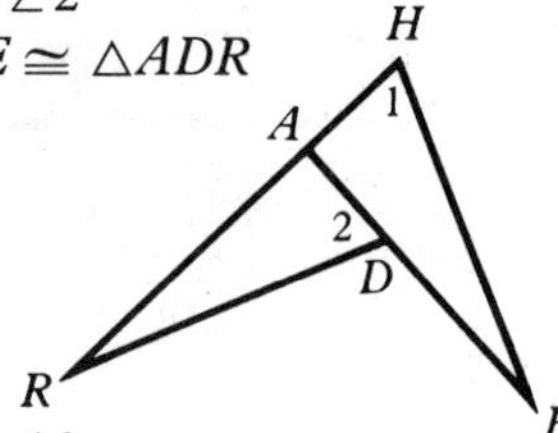

14. **Given:** $\angle 1 \cong \angle 2$
$\overline{XY} \cong \overline{TY}$
$\overline{ZY} \cong \overline{VY}$
Prove: $\triangle XYZ \cong \triangle TYV$

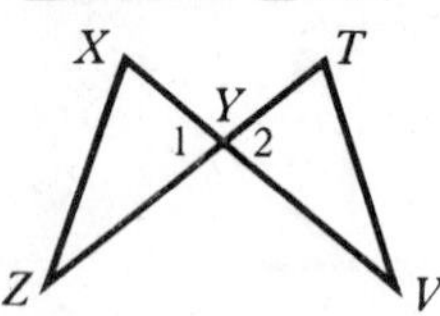

15. **Given:** $\angle 1 \cong \angle 2$
$\angle A \cong \angle E$
N is the midpoint of $\overline{AE}$.
Prove: $\triangle ABN \cong \triangle EDN$

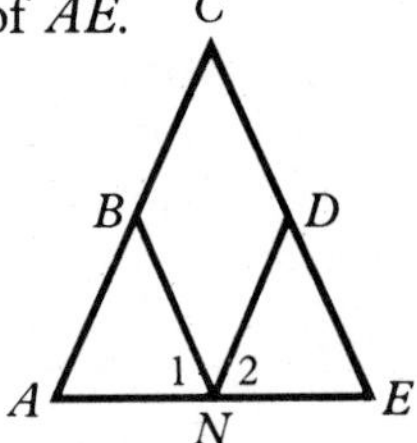

16. **Given:** $\overline{PQ} \cong \overline{SR}$
$\overline{PR}$ bisects $\overline{SQ}$.
$\overline{SQ}$ bisects $\overline{PR}$.
Prove: $\triangle PQT \cong \triangle RST$

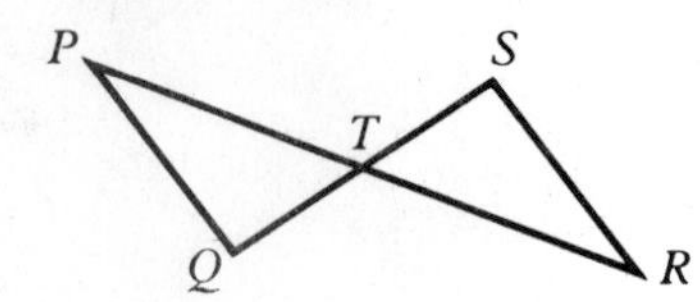

17. **Given:** $\angle E \cong \angle N$
S bisects $\overline{EN}$.
$\overline{EA} \cong \overline{NY}$
Prove: $\triangle EAS \cong \triangle NYS$

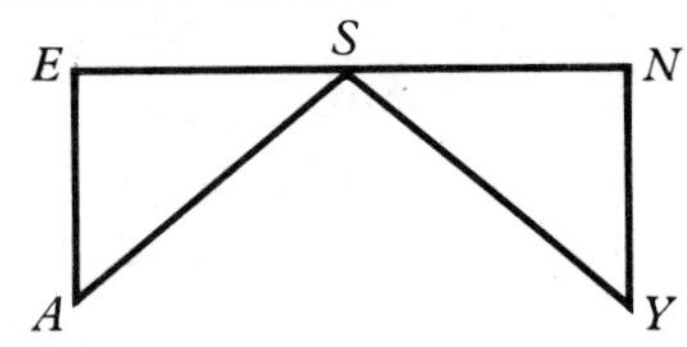

Activity

A *hexiamond* is a polygon which bounds six equilateral triangles.

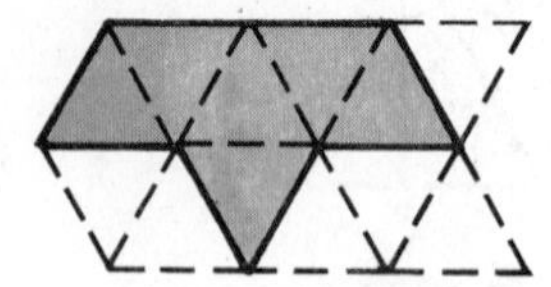

This is a hexiamond.

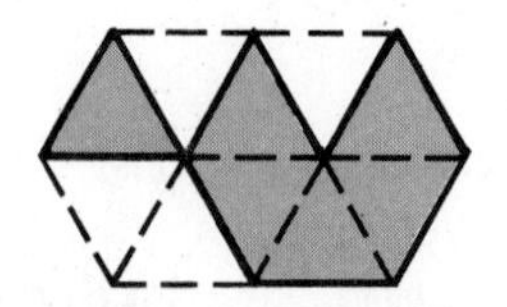

This is not a hexiamond.

Trace and cut six copies of this equilateral triangle from heavy paper or cardboard. Experiment with your six equilateral triangles and discover twelve hexiamonds different in shape. Draw each of these twelve polygons.

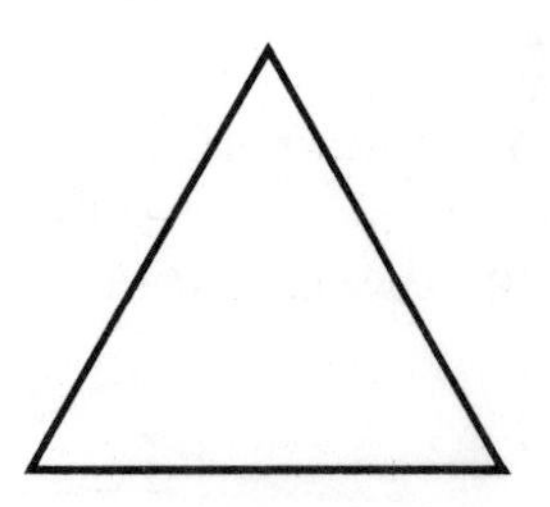

C.

18. Given: $ABCDE$ is a regular pentagon.
Prove: $\triangle AEB \cong \triangle CDB$

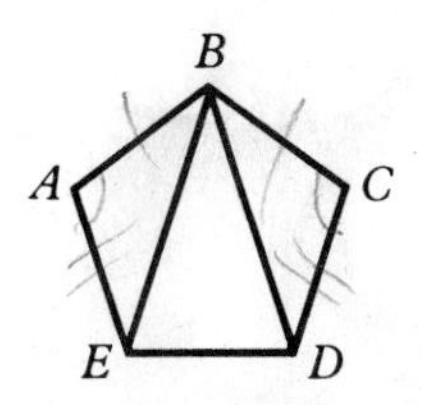

19. Given: $\overline{BF}$ bisects $\angle ABC$.
$ABCDE$ is a regular pentagon.
Prove: $\triangle ABF \cong \triangle CBF$

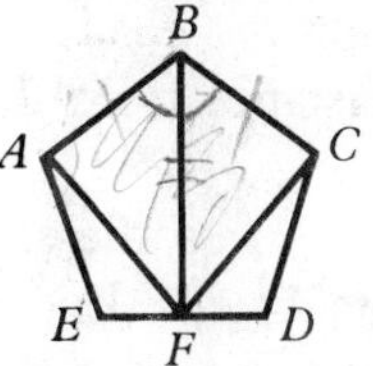

20. Given: $\overline{AB} \cong \overline{AC}$
$\overline{AI}$ bisects $\angle BAC$
Prove: $\triangle AIB \cong \triangle AIC$

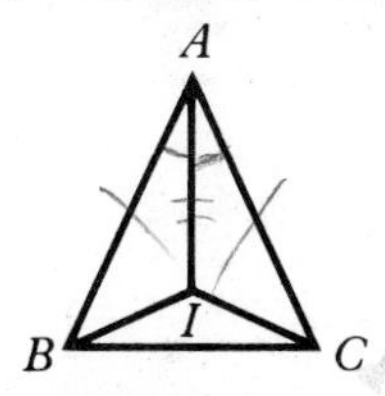

21. Given: $\overline{AB} \cong \overline{BC}$
M is midpoint of $\overline{AC}$
Prove: $\angle A \cong \angle C$

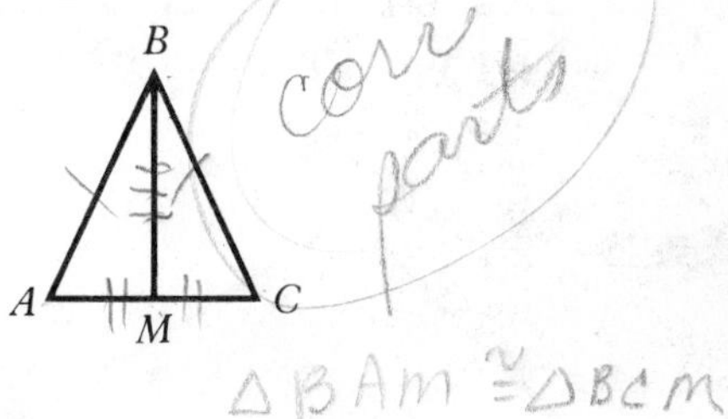

22. Pole $\overline{YZ}$ of a tent is placed perpendicular to level ground. What other conditions must be met to insure that sides $\overline{YW}$ and $\overline{YX}$ are equal in length?

Y
W Z X

PROBLEM SOLVING

The picture shows 13 toothpicks arranged to show six triangles. Which three toothpicks can be removed so that the remaining toothpicks show three triangles?

Can you make a toothpick problem similar to this?

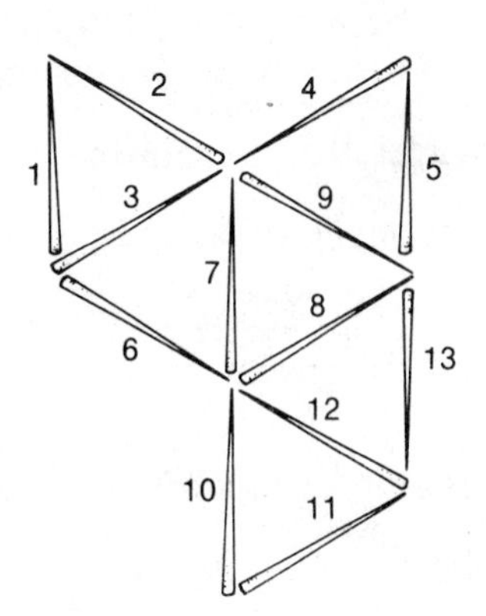

3–6 Proving Segments and Angles Congruent

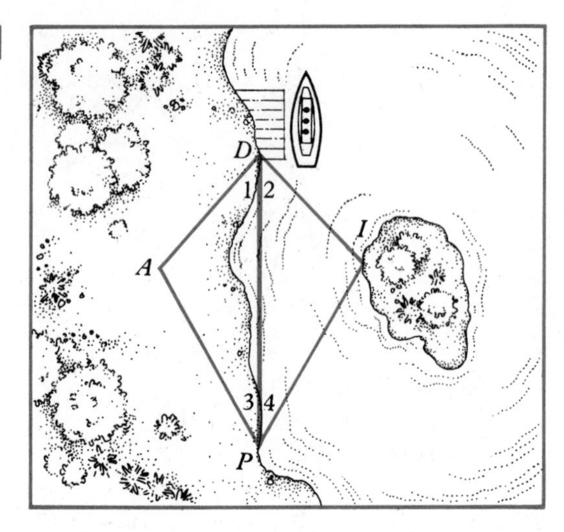

An ingenious geometry student (who was a good swimmer, but not *too* good) used this method to find the distance from the dock to the island:

Pick a second point, P, on the shore. Make $\angle 1 \cong \angle 2$. Make $\angle 3 \cong \angle 4$. Locate, by sight, the intersection point A of the sides of angles 1 and 3. Why is the distance from the dock to the island (DI) the same as DA?

To answer this question, recall the definition of congruent triangles (page 85).

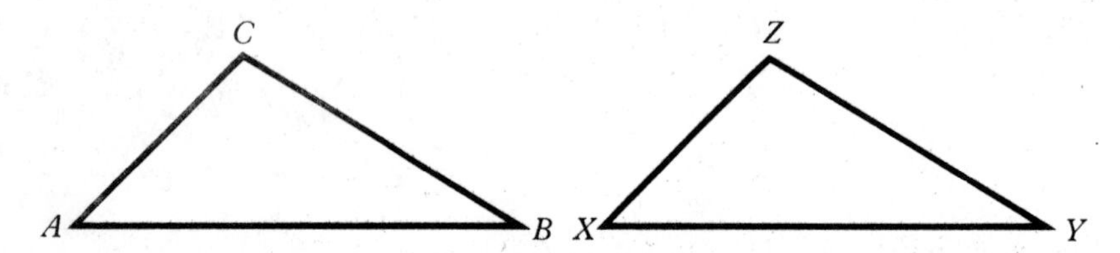

$\triangle ABC \cong \triangle XYZ$ means these six things are true.

$\overline{AB} \cong \overline{XY}$ $\overline{AC} \cong \overline{XZ}$ $\overline{BC} \cong \overline{YZ}$ $\angle A \cong \angle X$ $\angle B \cong \angle Y$ $\angle C \cong \angle Z$

We often prove that a pair of segments or angles are congruent by first proving that a pair of triangles are congruent. We can then use the definition of congruent triangles to conclude that the parts of the triangles that correspond are congruent.

In the dock-island situation above $\triangle DAP \cong \triangle DIP$ by the ASA Postulate. Since $\overline{DA}$ and $\overline{DI}$ are corresponding parts of these triangles, $\overline{DA} \cong \overline{DI}$.

To prove segments or angles congruent, you often can

1. select triangles that contain these segments (or angles);
2. prove the triangles congruent;
3. conclude that the desired corresponding parts of these triangles are congruent.

When writing proofs, we give the following reason for Step 3.

Corresponding Parts of Congruent Triangles are Congruent

Abbreviation: Corresp. parts of $\cong$ $\triangle$s are $\cong$ or **CPCTC**

This procedure is illustrated in the following two examples.

Example 1 **Given:** $\overline{AB} \cong \overline{AD}$, $\angle 1 \cong \angle 2$
Prove: $\overline{BE} \cong \overline{DE}$

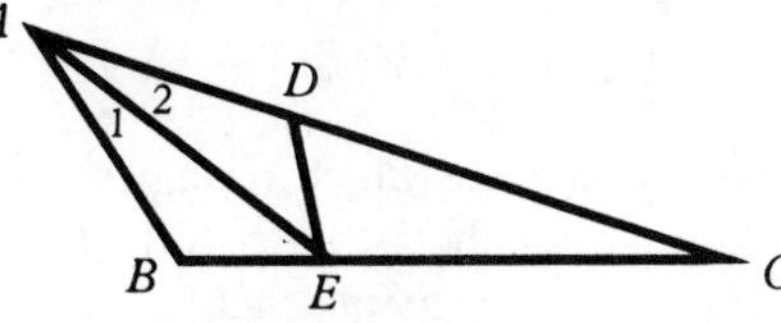

Analysis: "I can prove $\overline{BE} \cong \overline{DE}$ if I can find a pair of congruent triangles that contain these segments. $\triangle ABE$ and $\triangle ADE$ look promising. Which congruence postulate can I use to prove them congruent? Try SAS. Since I know that $\angle 1 \cong \angle 2$, $\overline{AB} \cong \overline{AD}$, and $\overline{AE} \cong \overline{AE}$, I can prove the triangles congruent and conclude that $\overline{BE} \cong \overline{DE}$.

Proof

Statements	Reasons
1. $\overline{AB} \cong \overline{AD}$	**1.** Given
2. $\angle 1 \cong \angle 2$	**2.** Given
3. $\overline{AE} \cong \overline{AE}$	**3.** Why?
4. $\triangle ABE \cong \triangle ADE$	**4.** SAS Postulate
5. $\overline{BE} \cong \overline{DE}$	**5.** Corresp. parts of $\cong$ $\triangle$s are $\cong$.

Example 2 **Given:** $\overline{AC}$ and $\overline{BD}$ bisect each other.
$\angle 1 \cong \angle 2$
Prove: $\angle 3 \cong \angle 4$

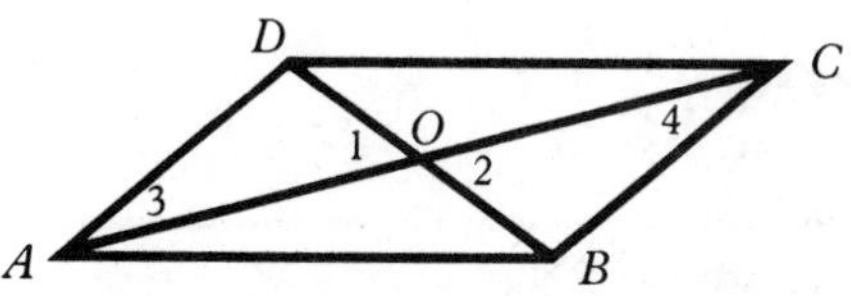

Analysis: "$\angle 3$ and $\angle 4$ are in $\triangle AOD$ and $\triangle BOC$ respectively, and in $\triangle ADC$ and $\triangle ABC$ respectively. From the given information it appears I should prove $\triangle AOD$ congruent to $\triangle COB$. (Why?) Then I can conclude that $\angle 3$ is congruent to $\angle 4$."

Proof

Statements	Reasons
1. $\overline{AC}$ and $\overline{BD}$ bisect each other.	**1.** Given
2. $\overline{AO} \cong \overline{CO}$; $\overline{OB} \cong \overline{OD}$	**2.** Definition of segment bisector
3. $\angle 1 \cong \angle 2$	**3.** Given
4. $\triangle AOD \cong \triangle COB$	**4.** SAS Postulate
5. $\angle 3 \cong \angle 4$	**5.** CPCTC

EXERCISES

A.

In exercises 1–5, indicate which triangles could be proven congruent to establish the indicated fact. (In some cases there may be more than one pair of triangles that are correct.)

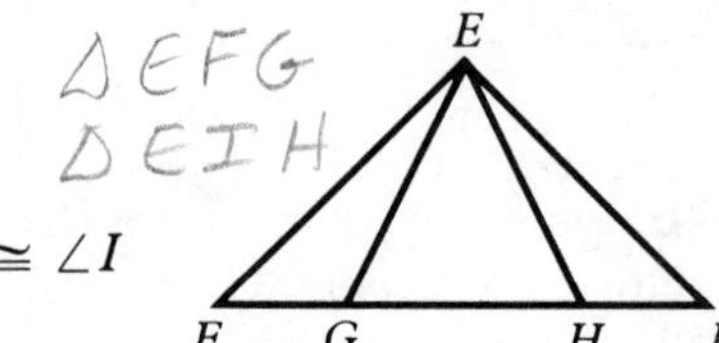

(Exs. 2, 3)

1. Prove: $\overline{AB} \cong \overline{AC}$

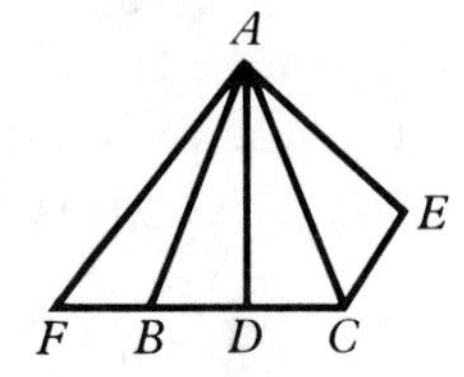

2. Prove: $\angle F \cong \angle I$

3. Prove: $\overline{EG} \cong \overline{EH}$

4. Prove: $\overline{AD} \cong \overline{BC}$

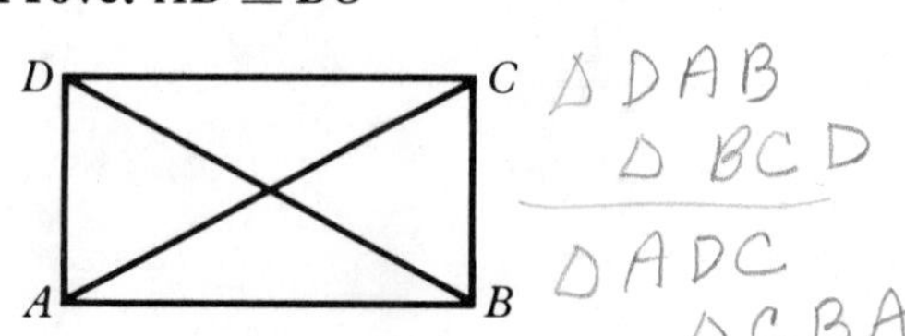

5. Prove: $\overline{JN} \cong \overline{NL}$

In exercises 6–8 provide the missing statements and reasons.

6. Given: $\angle 1 \cong \angle 2$

$\angle 3 \cong \angle 4$

Prove: $\angle A \cong \angle C$

Statements	Reasons
1. $\angle 1 \cong \angle 2$	1. ?
2. ?	2. Given
3. $\overline{DB} \cong \overline{DB}$	3. A segment is congruent to itself.
4. $\triangle ADB \cong \triangle CBD$	4. ?
5. $\angle A \cong \angle C$	5. ?

7. Given: $\overline{MN} \cong \overline{MP}$

$\overline{NO} \cong \overline{OP}$

Prove: $\overline{MO}$ bisects $\angle NMP$.

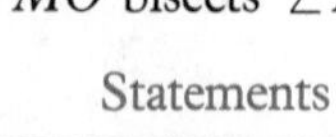

Statements	Reasons
1. $\overline{MN} \cong \overline{MP}$; $\overline{NO} \cong \overline{OP}$	1. ?
2. ?	2. ?
3. $\triangle MNO \cong \triangle MPO$	3. ?
4. ?	4. CPCTC
5. $\overline{MO}$ bisects $\angle NMP$.	5. ?

8. Given: *ABCDEF* is a regular hexagon.
Prove: $\overline{AC} \cong \overline{BF}$

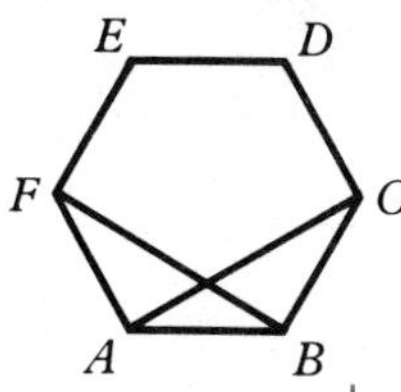

Statements	Reasons
1. *ABCDEF* is a regular hexagon.	1. Given
2. $\overline{AF} \cong \overline{BC}$	2. ?
3. ?	3. A segment is congruent to itself.
4. $\angle FAB \cong \angle ABC$	4. ?
5. $\triangle FAB \cong \triangle CBA$	5. ?
6. ?	6. CPCTC

B.

For the remaining exercises, write complete two-column proofs.

9. Given: $\angle 1 \cong \angle 2$
$\angle 3 \cong \angle 4$
Prove: $\overline{BC} \cong \overline{CD}$

10. Given: $\overline{OA}$, $\overline{OB}$, $\overline{OC}$, $\overline{OD}$ are all congruent.
$\angle 1 \cong \angle 2$
Prove: $\overline{AB} \cong \overline{CD}$

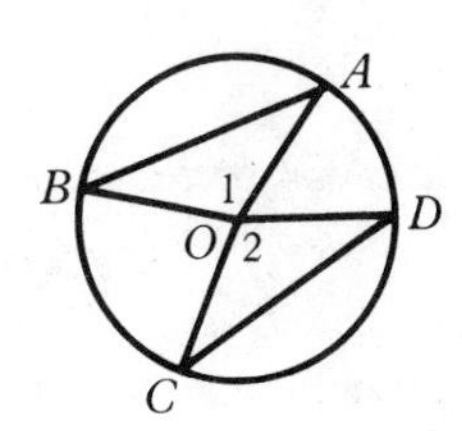

11. Given: *ABCDE* is a regular pentagon.
Prove: $\triangle ADC$ is isosceles.

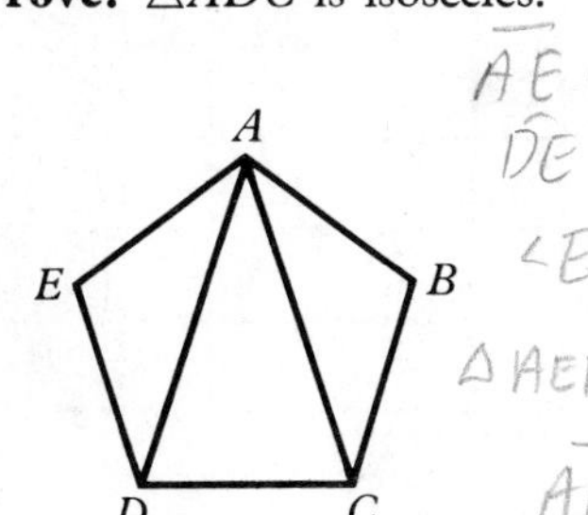

12. Given: $\overline{XO}$ is the perpendicular bisector of $\overline{MP}$.
Prove: $\triangle XMP$ is isosceles.

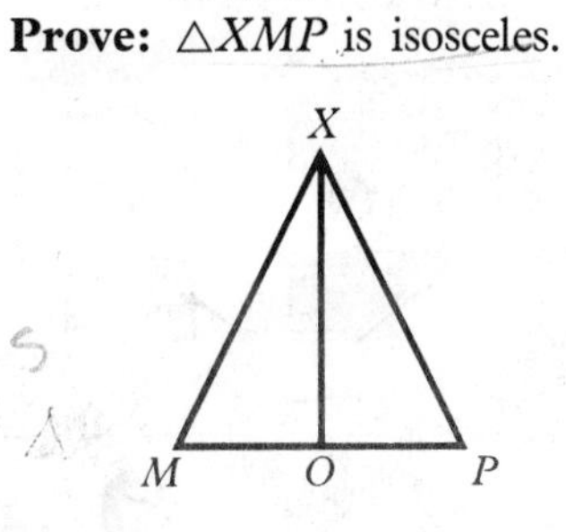

13. Given: $\angle 1 \cong \angle 2$
D bisects $\overline{CE}$.
$\angle C \cong \angle E$
Prove: $\overline{BD} \cong \overline{DF}$

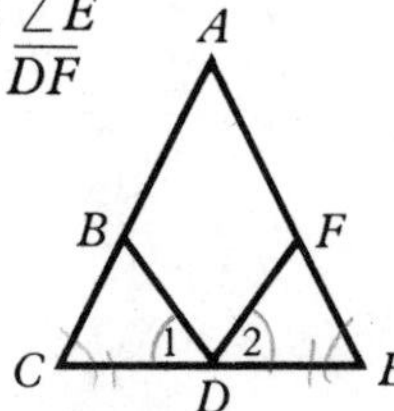

14. Given: $ABCDEFGH$ is a regular octagon.
Prove: $\overline{DF} \cong \overline{GE}$

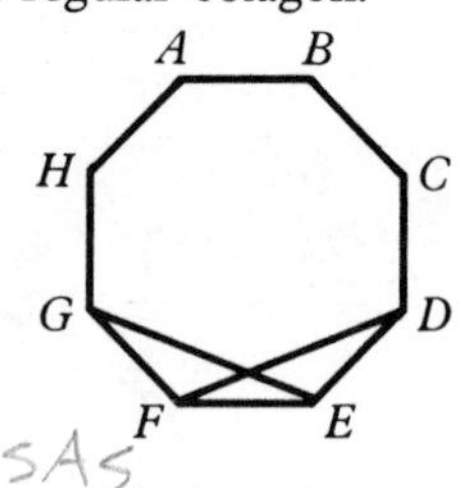

15. In a gym one end of a volleyball net is hung from bolts secured to a wall at P and M. Each point in the plane of the net is an equal distance from the two base lines $\overline{AC}$ and $\overline{BD}$. Why is $\overleftrightarrow{PM}$ perpendicular to $\overline{AB}$?

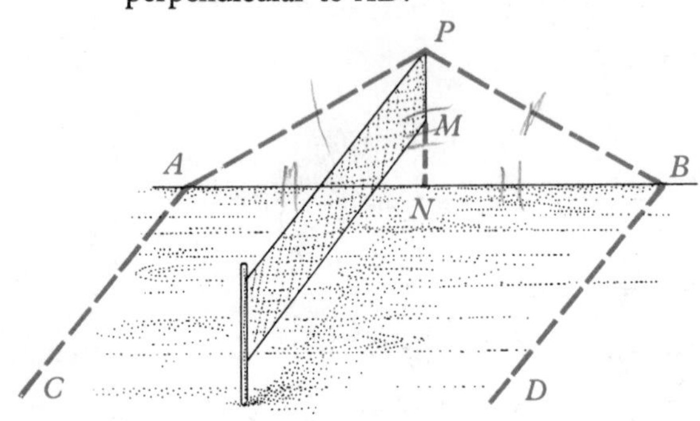

16. Given: $\overline{AD} \cong \overline{BC}$
$\angle 1 \cong \angle 2$
N is the midpoint of $\overline{AB}$.
Prove: $\triangle CND$ is isosceles.

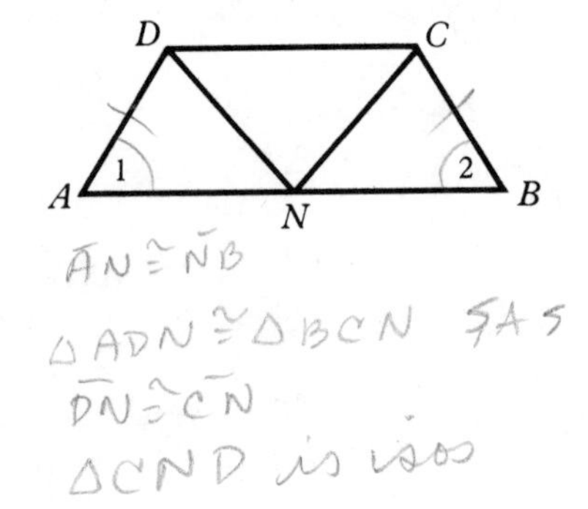

Activity

Make these 12 pentominoe shapes from squares the size of those on a checker board.

Six pentominoe pieces have been arranged so that none of the remaining six pieces will fit on the checker board without overlapping. Do this with a different collection of six pieces.

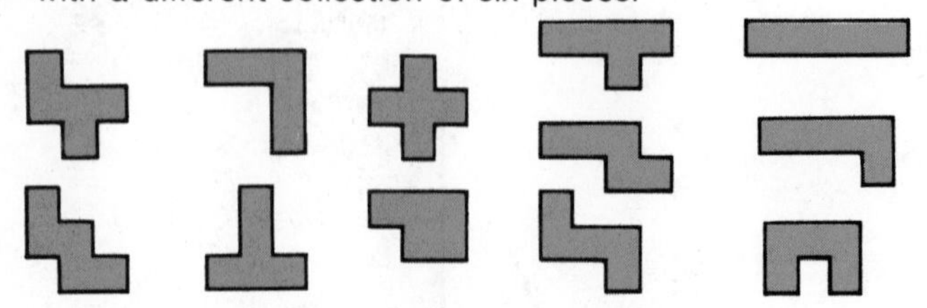

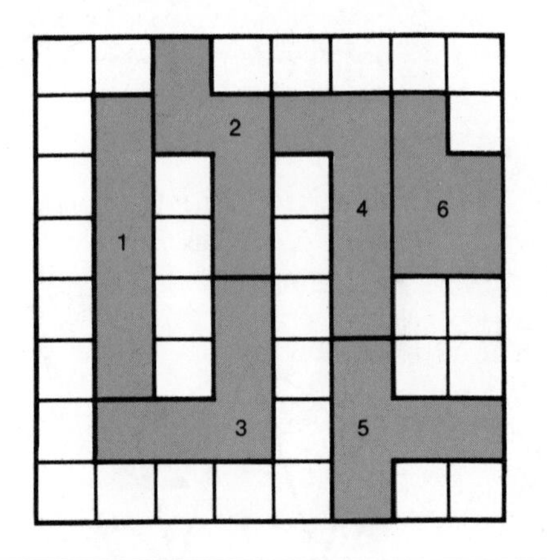

C.

In exercises 17-20 you may also need to prove more than one pair of triangles congruent.

17. Given: *ABCDEF* is a regular hexagon.
Prove: $\angle 1 \cong \angle 2$
(*Hint:* First prove that $\overline{AE} \cong \overline{BD}$.)

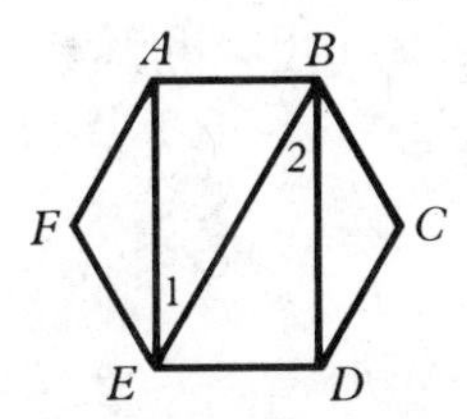

18. Given: $\angle 1 \cong \angle 2$, $\angle 3 \cong \angle 4$
$\angle 5 \cong \angle 6$, $\angle 7 \cong \angle 8$
Prove: $\angle A \cong \angle C$

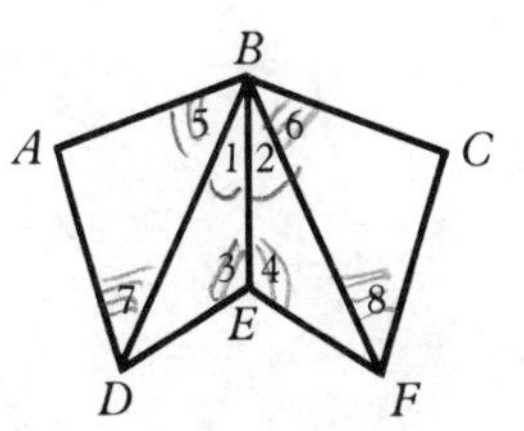

19. Given: *ABCDE* is a regular pentagon.
$\overrightarrow{AG}$ bisects $\angle EAB$ and is the perpendicular bisector of $\overline{DC}$.
Prove: $\triangle BCF \cong \triangle EDF$

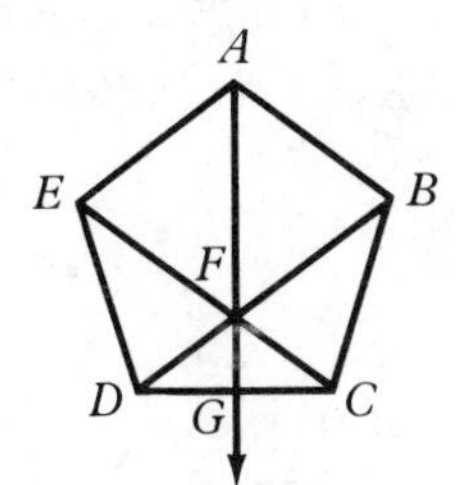

20. Given: *ABCDEFGH* is a regular octagon.
$\overline{AF} \perp \overline{AB}$; $\overline{BG} \perp \overline{GF}$
$\angle 1 \cong \angle 2$
Prove: $\triangle AHI \cong \triangle GHI$

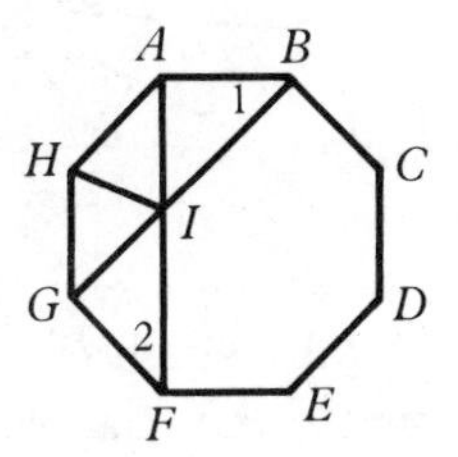

PROBLEM SOLVING

Show how to cut a regular hexagon into 18 congruent kites. A kite is a quadrilateral with exactly two pairs of congruent adjacent sides. (*Hint:* Draw all the diagonals of the hexagon. Then draw six more short segments, strategically located.)

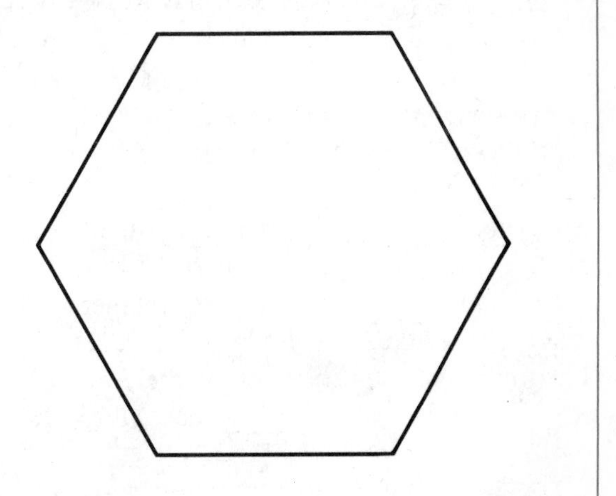

3–7 Proofs: Overlapping Triangles

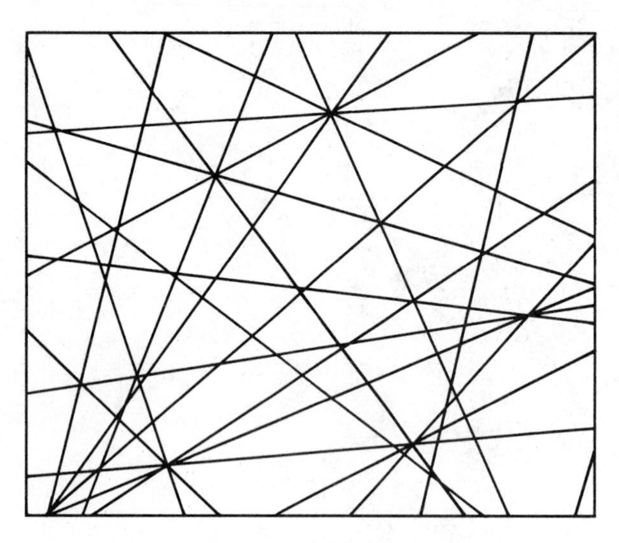

A popular "puzzle problem" requests that you find a pair of congruent equilateral triangles in this figure and trace them on your paper. Can you solve it?

In proofs several triangles in a figure often overlap each other, making it difficult to visualize the triangles that would be the most useful to prove congruent. Sometimes it is helpful to pictorially or mentally separate the triangles to aid in analyzing the proof, as indicated in the example below.

Example 1

Given: $\angle 1 \cong \angle 2$
$\overline{AC} \cong \overline{DF}$
$\angle 3 \cong \angle 4$
Prove: $\overline{EF} \cong \overline{BC}$

Analysis: "I need to choose a pair of triangles that contain $\overline{EF}$ and $\overline{BC}$. How about $\triangle EFH$ and $\triangle BCH$? I can't prove them congruent. Let's try $\triangle EFD$ and $\triangle BCA$! They are congruent because of the ASA postulate and I can conclude that $\overline{EF} \cong \overline{BC}$."

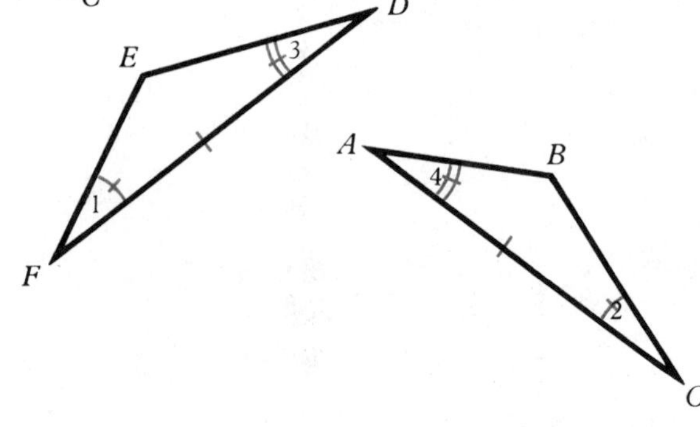

You will be asked to complete this proof as an exercise.

Example 2

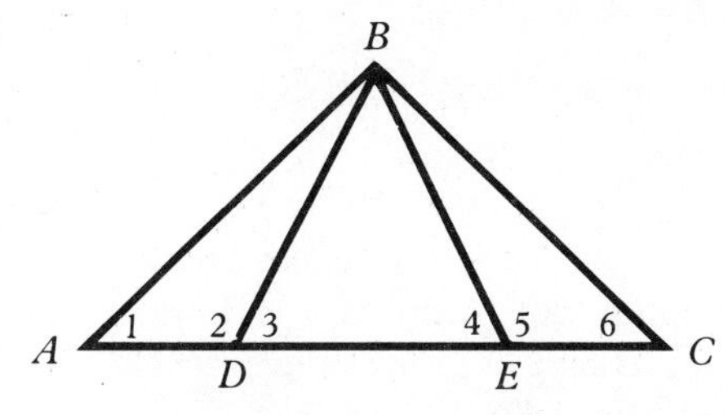

Given: $\angle 1 \cong \angle 6$
$\angle 3 \cong \angle 4$
$\overline{AE} \cong \overline{CD}$
Prove: $\angle ABE \cong \angle CBD$

Analysis: "Overlapping triangles $\triangle ABE$ and $\triangle CBD$ contain two pairs of congruent angles. The included sides are also congruent. I can use ASA to prove it."

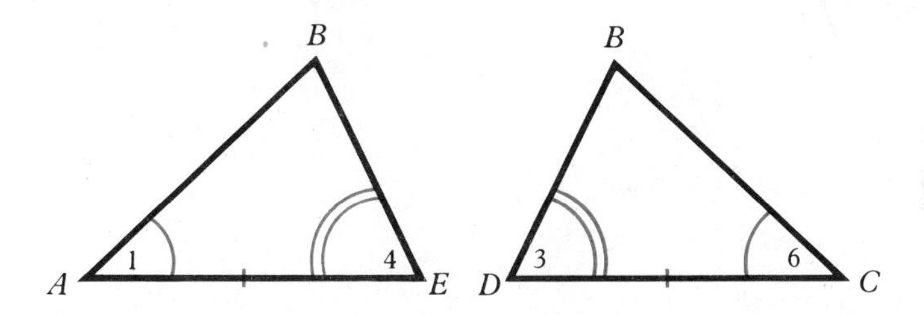

Sometimes it is useful to use colored pencils to outline the overlapping triangles. Study the following example.

Example 3

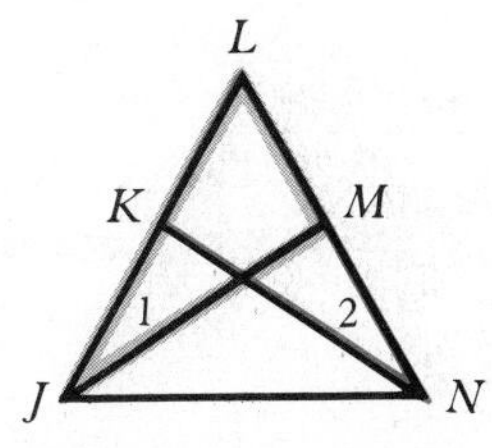

Given: $\triangle LJN$ is isosceles with $\overline{JL} \cong \overline{LN}$.
$\angle 1 \cong \angle 2$
Prove: $\overline{LK} \cong \overline{LM}$

Analysis: "I can prove $\overline{LK} \cong \overline{LM}$ if these segments are corresponding parts of congruent triangles. Let's try $\triangle LKN$ and $\triangle LMJ$. I know that $\angle 1 \cong \angle 2$ and that $\angle JLN$ is congruent to itself. Aha! I know that $\triangle JLN$ is isosceles. So the triangles are congruent by ASA. I can prove it!"

Example 4

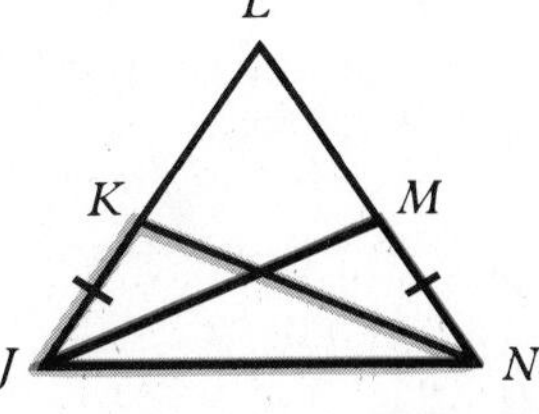

Given: $\overline{JK} \cong \overline{NM}$, $\angle KJN \cong \angle MNJ$
Prove: $\overline{KN} \cong \overline{MJ}$

Analysis: "$\overline{KN}$ and $\overline{MJ}$ are corresponding parts in $\triangle LKN$ and $\triangle LMJ$ just like Example 3. But the given information is part of $\triangle KJN$ and $\triangle MNJ$. Since $\overline{JN}$ is congruent to itself, I can prove $\triangle KJN \cong \triangle MNJ$ by SAS."

EXERCISES

A.

In exercises 1 and 2 name all pairs of triangles (nonoverlapping and overlapping) that appear congruent. Use vertices A and B in one triangle and vertices C and D in the other triangle.

1. 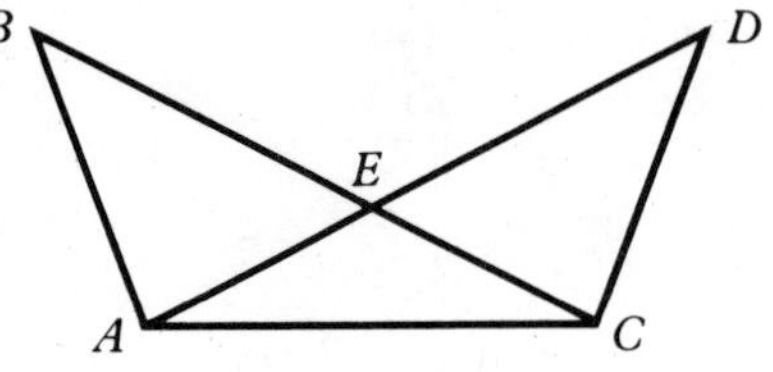

2. 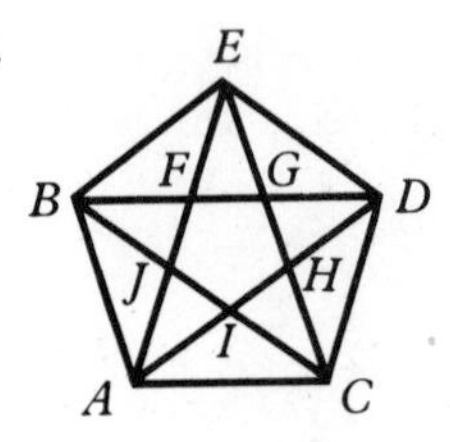

B.

3. Write a complete two-column proof for Example 1.

4. Write a complete two-column proof for Example 3.

For exercises 5–10 write a complete two-column proof.

5. Given: $\overline{BD} \cong \overline{CE}$
$\angle ABC \cong \angle ACB$
Prove: $\overline{BE} \cong \overline{CD}$

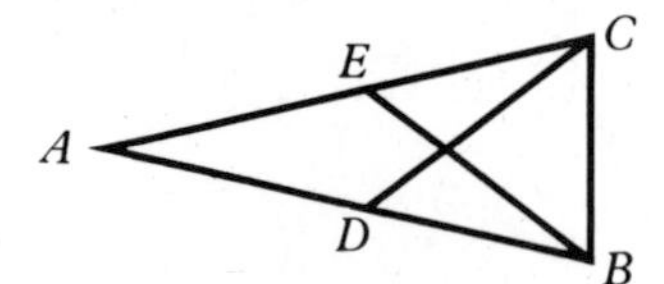

6. Given: $\angle DAB \cong \angle CBA$
$\angle DBA \cong \angle CAB$
Prove: $\overline{AD} \cong \overline{BC}$

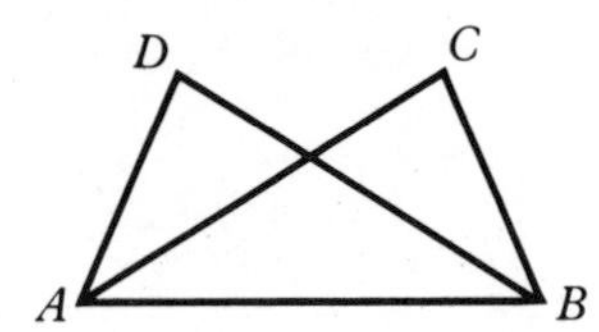

Activity

Triangles are used in scaffolding because they are rigid figures. Three straws pinned together will hold its shape even if picked up and moved around.

Which of the frameworks do you think are rigid? Build models to check your answers.

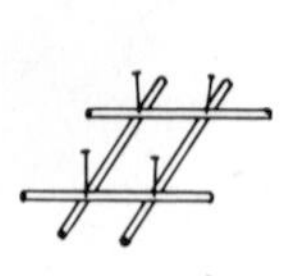

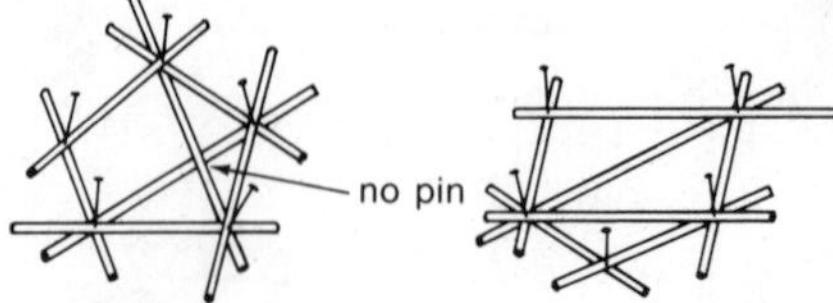

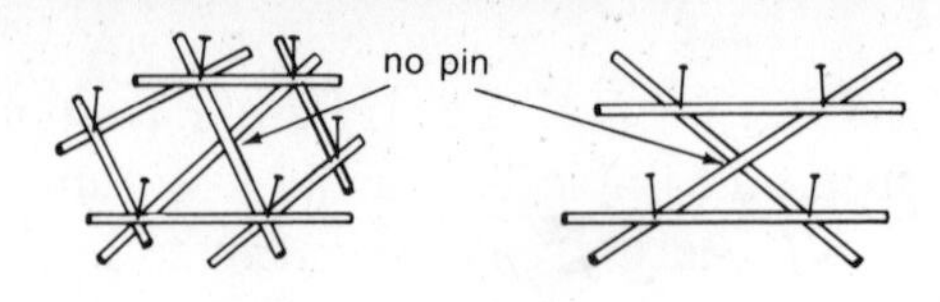

7. Given: $\angle 1 \cong \angle 2$, $\angle 3 \cong \angle 4$
$\overline{AC} \cong \overline{BD}$
Prove: $\overline{AE} \cong \overline{BF}$

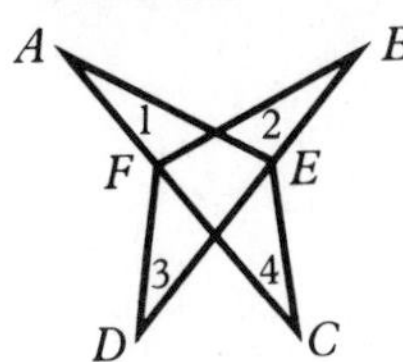

8. Given: $\angle 1 \cong \angle 2$, $\overline{BE} \cong \overline{EC}$
$\angle AEC \cong \angle BED$
Prove: $\overline{AE} \cong \overline{DE}$

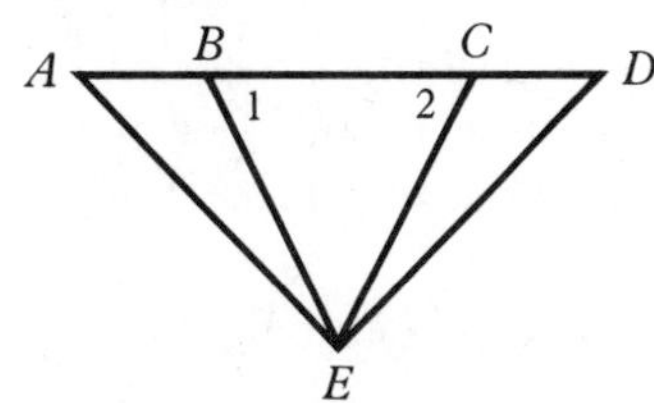

9. Given: $\angle 1 \cong \angle 2$, $\overline{PQ} \cong \overline{RQ}$
$\overline{PV} \cong \overline{TR}$
Prove: $\overline{QT} \cong \overline{QV}$

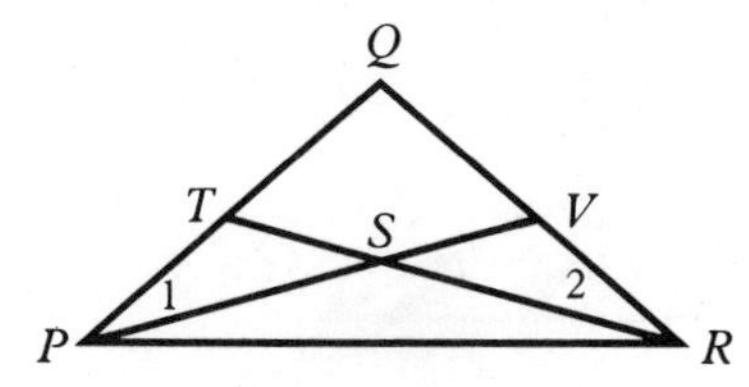

10. Given: Figure $PQRS$ with $\overline{PQ} \cong \overline{RS}$,
$\angle RQP$ and $\angle QRS$ are right angles.
Prove: $\overline{QS} \cong \overline{RP}$

(i.e., the diagonals are congruent.)

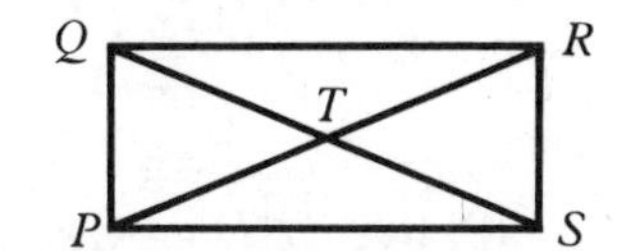

C.

11. Given: $\overline{HF} \perp \overline{BD}$, $\overline{HG} \perp \overline{AC}$
$\overline{HF} \cong \overline{HG}$
Prove: $\overline{AG} \cong \overline{DF}$

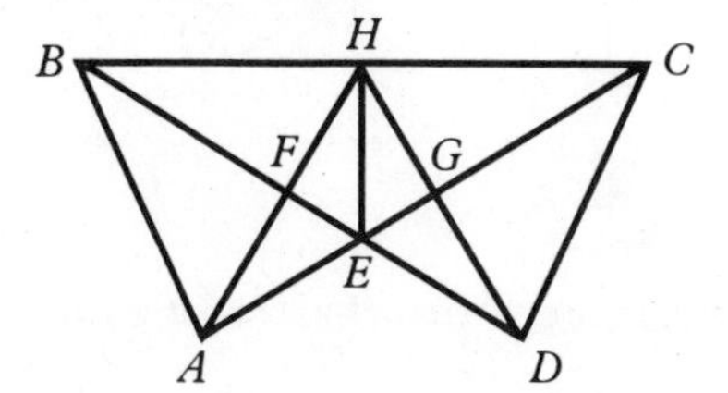

12. Given: Regular pentagon $ABCDE$
Prove: $\overline{AD} \cong \overline{EB}$

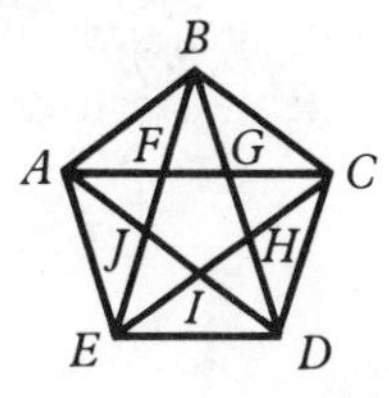

PROBLEM SOLVING

How many different triangles are there in this figure that are congruent to the lettered triangles below?

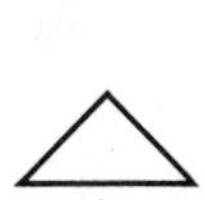
A

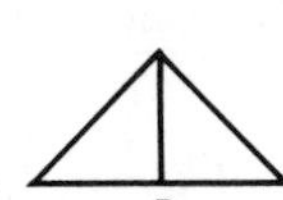
B

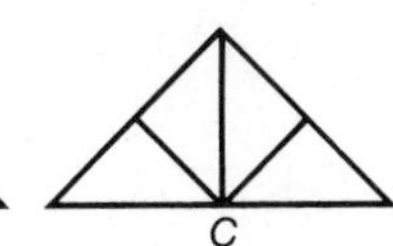
C

D

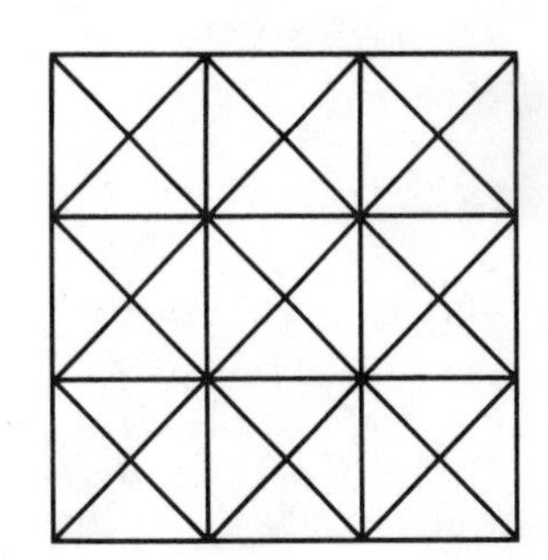

Do you see other types of triangles in the figure? If so, draw them.

3–8 Proofs: Chains of Congruences

To write certain proofs, one pair of triangles must be proven congruent in order to provide the information needed to prove a second pair of triangles congruent.

Study the example below and supply the missing steps.

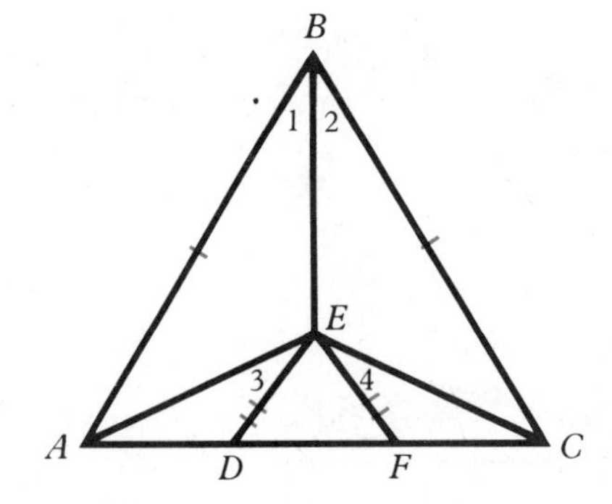

Example **Given:** $\overline{AB} \cong \overline{CB}$
$\overline{ED} \cong \overline{EF}$
$\angle 1 \cong \angle 2$
$\angle 3 \cong \angle 4$
Prove: $\overline{AD} \cong \overline{CF}$

Analysis: "I could prove $\overline{AD} \cong \overline{CF}$ if I could prove $\triangle AED \cong \triangle CEF$. But not enough information is given to prove this. If I knew that $\overline{AE} \cong \overline{CE}$, I could prove these triangles congruent by SAS. But $\overline{AE}$ and $\overline{CE}$ are corresponding parts of $\triangle ABE$ and $\triangle CBE$, and I can prove these triangles congruent. I can do it!"

Proof

Statements	Reasons
1. $\overline{AB} \cong \overline{CB}$	**1.** Given
2. $\angle 1 \cong \angle 2$	**2.** Why?
3. $\overline{BE} \cong \overline{BE}$	**3.** Why?
4. $\triangle ABE \cong \triangle CBE$	**4.** SAS postulate
5. $\overline{AE} \cong \overline{CE}$	**5.** Why?
6. $\angle 3 \cong \angle 4$	**6.** Given
7. $\overline{DE} \cong \overline{FE}$	**7.** Given
8. $\triangle AED \cong \triangle CEF$	**8.** Why?
9. $\overline{AD} \cong \overline{CF}$	**9.** CPCTC

Note that Steps 1–4 prove a pair of triangles congruent. Steps 5–8 use this first congruence to prove a second pair of triangles congruent.

EXERCISES

1. Given: $\angle 1 \cong \angle 2$, $\overline{UR}$ bisects $\overline{QS}$,
$\overline{PU} \cong \overline{TU}$, $\angle PUQ \cong \angle TUS$
Prove: $\triangle QRU \cong \triangle SRU$

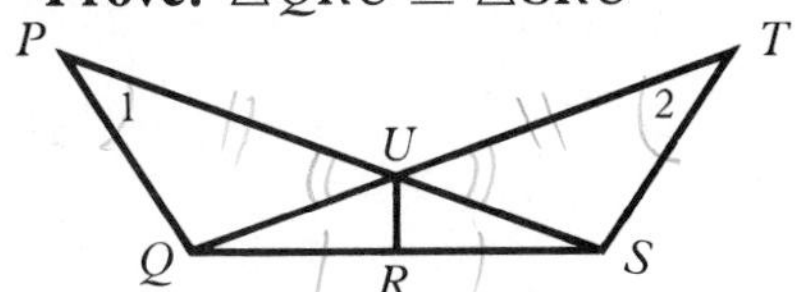

2. Given: $ABCDEF$ is a regular hexagon.
Prove: $\triangle ABD \cong \triangle AFD$

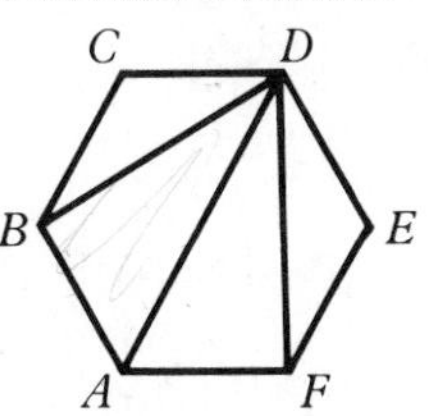

3. Given: $ABCDEFGH$ is a regular octagon.
$\angle 1 \cong \angle 2$
Prove: $\overline{CF} \cong \overline{HE}$

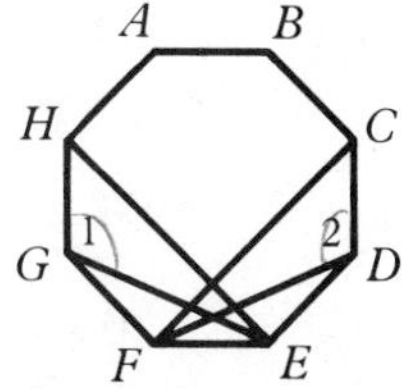

4. Given: $\angle 1 \cong \angle 2$
$\angle AED \cong \angle CFB$
$\overline{AE} \cong \overline{CF}$
Prove: $\overline{AB} \cong \overline{CD}$

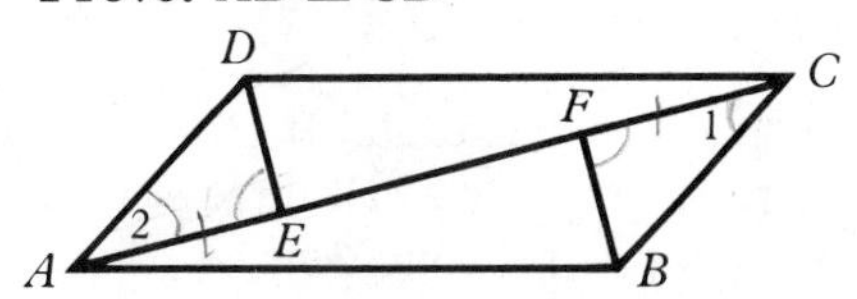

5. Given: $\overline{EH} \cong \overline{BH}$
$\overline{AH} \cong \overline{DH}$
$\overline{AC} \cong \overline{DF}$
$\angle 1 \cong \angle 2$
Prove: $\overline{EF} \cong \overline{BC}$

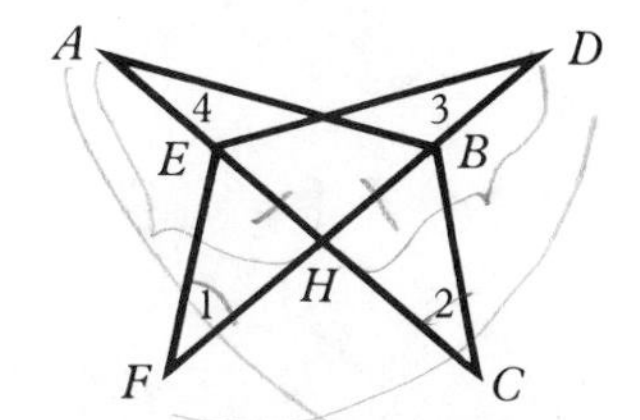

6. Given: $ABCDEFGH$ is a regular octagon.
$\overline{DH}$ bisects $\angle CDE$.
$\angle 1 \cong \angle 2$
Prove: $\triangle BCI \cong \triangle FEI$

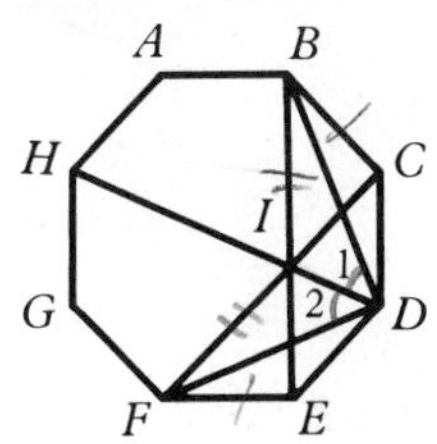

PROBLEM SOLVING

How many ways can you spell "Geometry" with the arrangement shown? Three ways are indicated.

```
                    G
                  G E G
                G E O E G
              G E O M O—E—G—③
        ②—G—E—O M E M O E G
            G E O M—E—T E M O E G
        ①—G—E—O M E T R T E M O E G
          G E O M—E—T—R—Y—R T E M O E G
```

(*Hint:* How many ways can you spell a two-letter word with a similar arrangement? A three-letter word? A four-letter word? Find a pattern.)

Important Ideas—Chapter 3

Terms

Congruent triangles (p. 85)

Postulates

SAS Congruence Postulate. If two sides and the included angle of one triangle are congruent respectively to two sides and the included angle of another triangle, then the two triangles are congruent.

ASA Congruence Postulate. If two angles and the included side of one triangle are congruent respectively to two angles and the included side of another triangle, then the two triangles are congruent.

SSS Congruence Postulate. If all three sides of one triangle are congruent respectively to all three sides of another triangle, then the two triangles are congruent.

Statements

Corresponding parts of congruent triangles are congruent.

Chapter 3—Review

1. Given that $\triangle BAC \cong \triangle QRP$, identify the corresponding sides and angles.
2. In the following cases, state which congruence postulate could be used to prove the triangles congruent.

a.

b.

c.

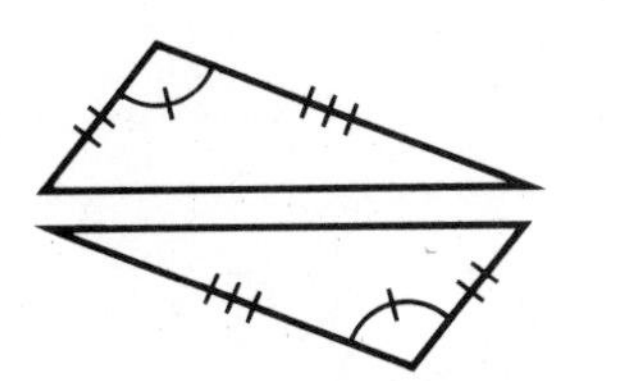

d.

3. In each of the following cases, draw a conclusion based on the given information.

a. Given: $\overline{AB}$ is perpendicular to $\overline{CD}$.

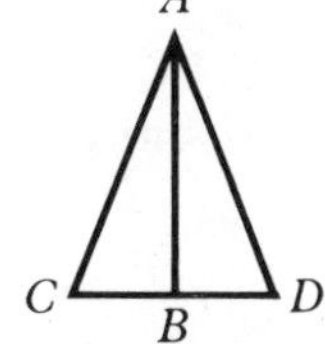

b. Given: E is the midpoint of $\overline{FG}$.

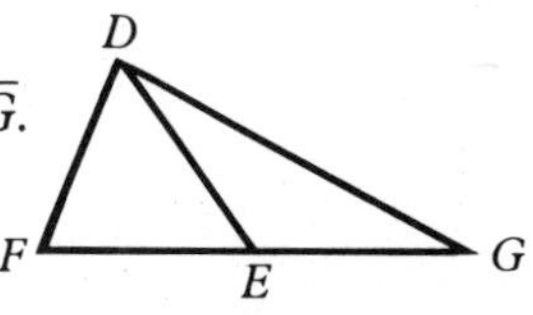

c. Given: $\overline{BD}$ bisects both $\angle B$ and $\angle D$.

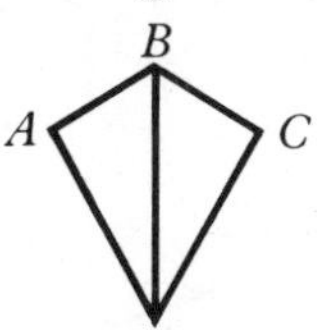

d. Given: $ABCDE$ is a regular pentagon.

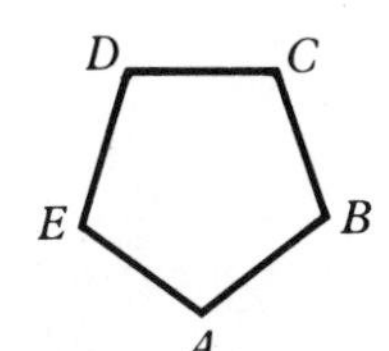

4. **Given:** $\overline{MP}$ bisects $\angle QMN$.
   $\overline{MP}$ bisects $\angle QPN$.
   Prove: a. $\triangle MQP \cong \triangle MNP$
   b. $\angle Q \cong \angle N$

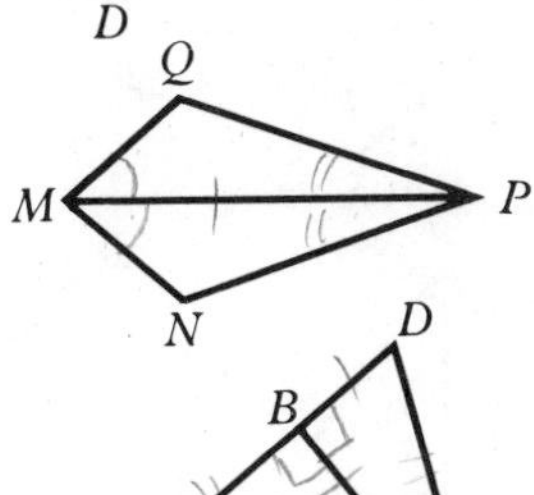

5. **Given:** $\overline{AB} \perp \overline{CD}$
   $\overline{BE} \cong \overline{BD}$
   $\overline{BC} \cong \overline{BA}$
   Prove: $\overline{CE} \cong \overline{AD}$

6. **Given:** $\overline{ZQ} \cong \overline{PY}$
   $\angle Z \cong \angle P$
   $\overline{ZX} \cong \overline{PX}$
   Prove: $\overline{XY} \cong \overline{XQ}$

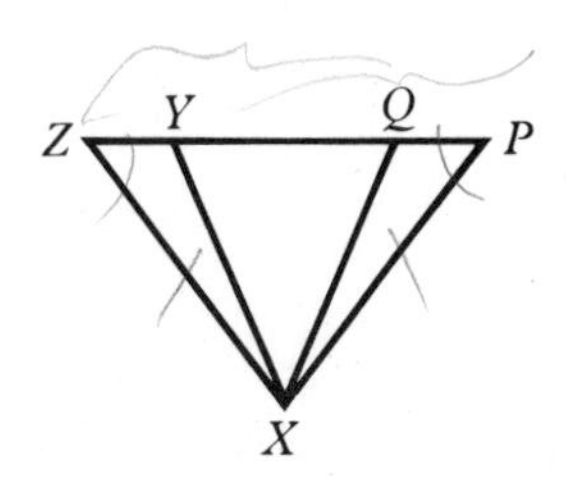

Chapter 3—Test

1. Use the figures to complete the statements.

a. $\triangle ABC \cong$?

b. $\triangle XYZ \cong$?

c. $\triangle FUN \cong$?

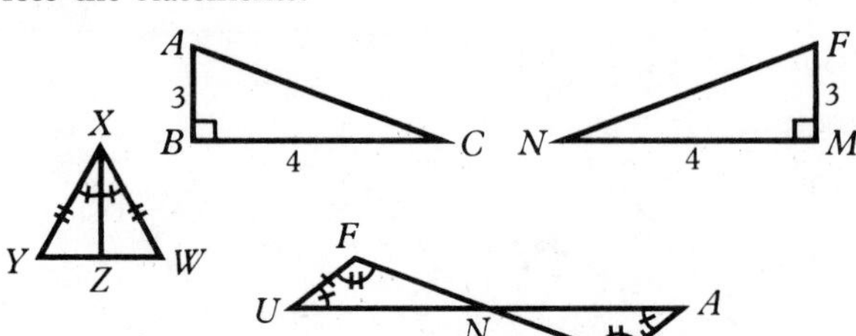

2. In the following cases, draw a conclusion based on the given information.

a. Given: W is the midpoint of $\overline{YZ}$ and $\overline{XV}$.

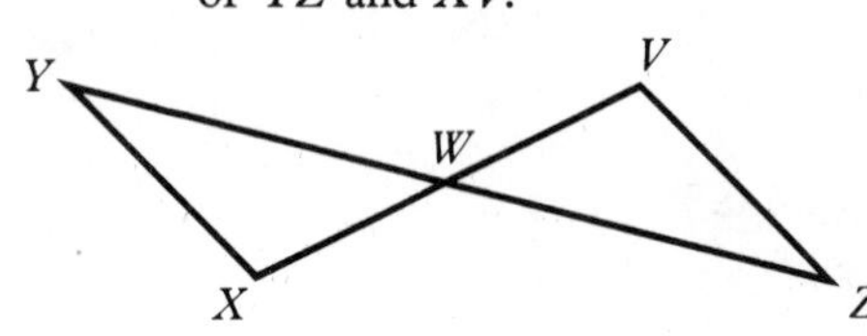

b. Given: $\overline{JI} \perp \overline{HK}$

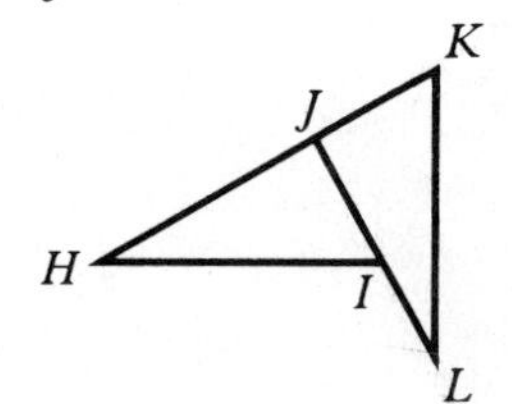

c. Given: $\overline{AC}$ bisects $\angle BAE$

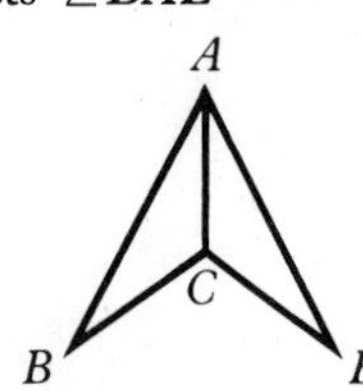

d. Given: $\overline{AC}$ bisects $\overline{BD}$
$\overline{BD}$ bisects $\overline{AC}$

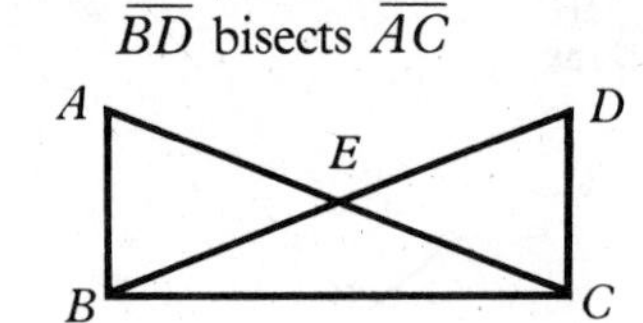

3. Given: $\overline{PA} \cong \overline{SA}$
$\overline{PT} \cong \overline{TS}$

Prove: **a.** $\triangle PAT \cong \triangle SAT$
b. $\angle P \cong \angle S$

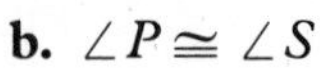

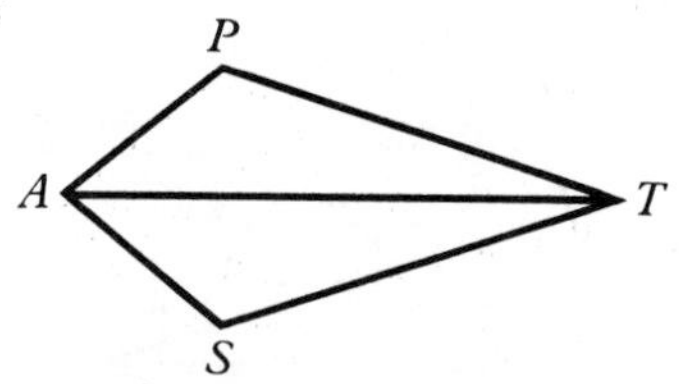

4. Given: $\overline{AD} \perp \overline{BC}$
D is the midpoint of $\overline{BC}$.

Prove: $\overline{AB} \cong \overline{AC}$

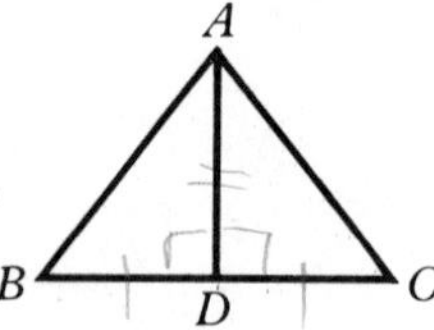

5. Given: $\overline{FE} \cong \overline{FD}$
$\angle E \cong \angle D$

Prove: $\overline{EY} \cong \overline{DR}$

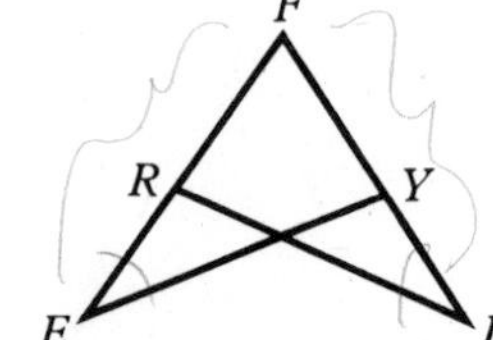

Cumulative Review (Chapters 1–3)

1. Mark the following as true or false.

a. Postulates are statements to be proved.

b. A ray can contain a line.

c. Theorems are proved using deductive reasoning.

2. Draw a triangle ABC so that $\angle B$ is obtuse. Construct a line through B perpendicular to $\overline{AC}$.

In exercises 3 and 4 classify the reasoning as inductive or deductive reasoning.

3. $\angle 1$ and $\angle 2$ are called right angles.
Right angles are congruent.
$\angle 1$ and $\angle 2$ are congruent.

4. $ABCD$ is a square and has perpendicular diagonals.
$EFGH$ is a square and has perpendicular diagonals.
All squares have perpendicular diagonals.

In exercises 5 and 6 state the correct conclusion or write "no conclusion possible."

5. If $\overline{AB} \perp \overline{CD}$ then $\overline{AB}$ and $\overline{CD}$ determine a plane.
$\overline{AB}$ and $\overline{CD}$ determine a plane.
Therefore, _?_.

6. If $ABCD$ is a square, then $\overline{AB} \parallel \overline{CD}$.
$ABCD$ is a square.
Therefore, _?_.

7. Consider the statement,
If two lines are parallel, then they are not perpendicular.

a. Write the converse statement.

b. Write the inverse statement.

c. Write the contrapositive statement.

d. Give counterexamples for the statements which are not true.

8. Given: $\overline{AD} \cong \overline{BC}$, $\overline{AB} \cong \overline{DC}$
Prove: $\triangle ABC \cong \triangle CDA$

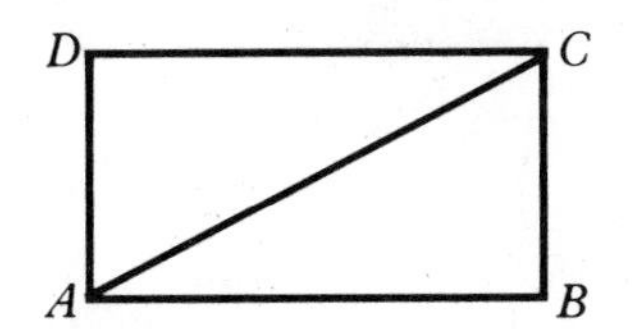

9. Given: $\overline{AB} \cong \overline{AC}$, $\overline{AD}$ bisects $\angle BAC$.
Prove: $\overline{BD} \cong \overline{CD}$.

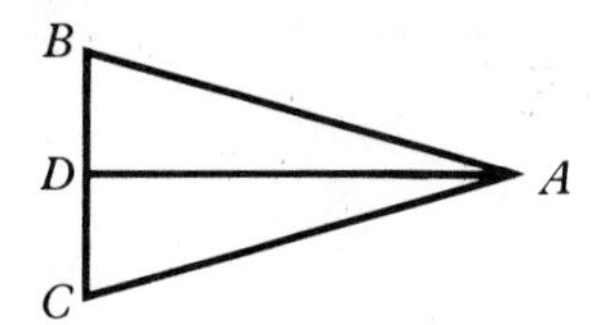

Architecture: Geodesic Domes

The geodesic dome was introduced by R. Buckminster Fuller. His plans for one kind of dome, called a *sun dome*, can be found in the May 1966 issue of *Popular Science*.

Domes of different sizes and shapes have been constructed from a variety of materials. Domes have been used as greenhouses, pool covers, and even houses. Shown below are a dome house in Colorado and a dome that can be set up at a campsite.

Geodesic domes are made as close to portions of spheres as is practical. Two reasons are that the sphere encloses the greatest volume with the least surface, and that it is the strongest shape.

A standard type of dome is based on a solid called an *icosahedron*. Make an icosahedron model using cardboard or straws and yarn from a pattern of 20 equilateral triangles.

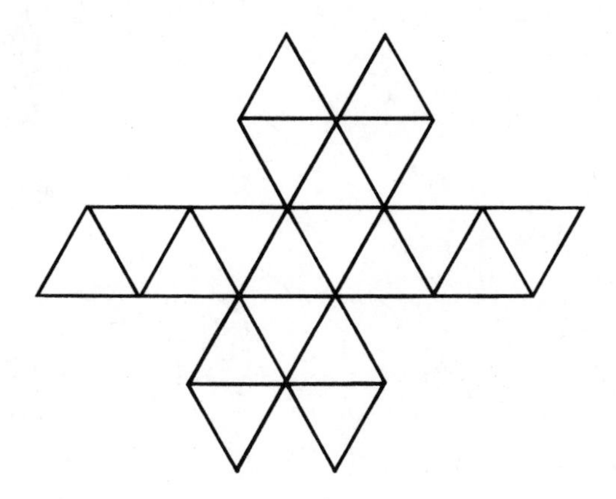

Fig. 1 Pattern for an icosahedron

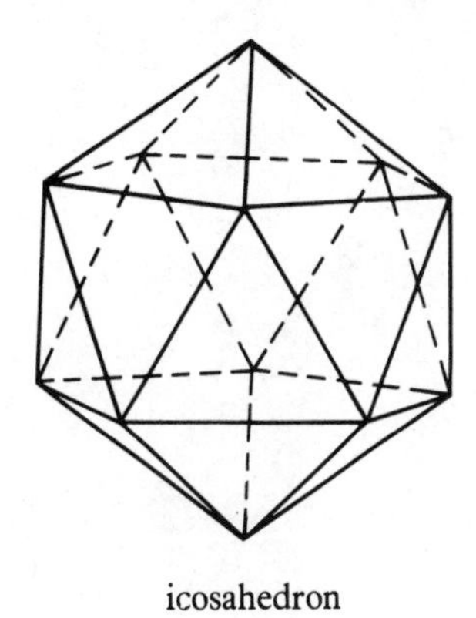

icosahedron

If the bottom five triangles are removed a dome-like structure results.

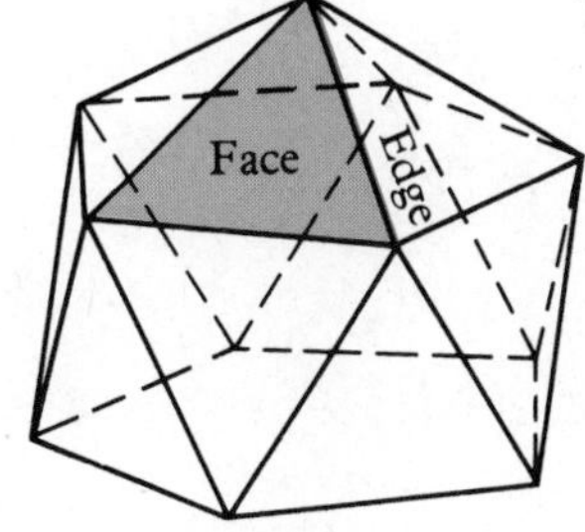

Fig. 2

In an actual dome structure each of the equilateral triangles in Fig. 2 is divided into smaller triangles as shown in Fig. 3. In order for the shape of the dome to be closer to a sphere, pieces used to form the triangles, called *struts,* are made in unequal lengths. Type C struts are slightly longer than type B struts, and type B struts are slightly longer than type A struts.

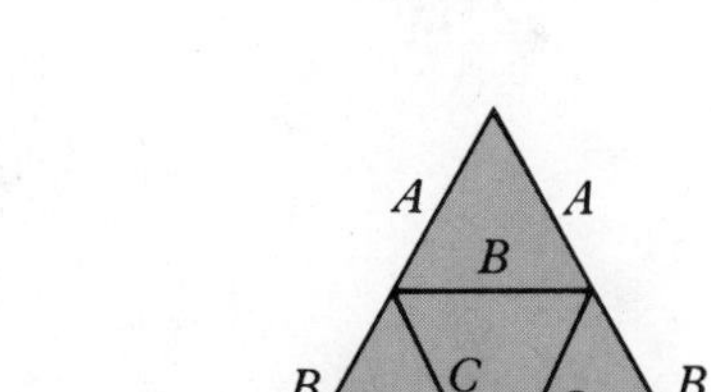

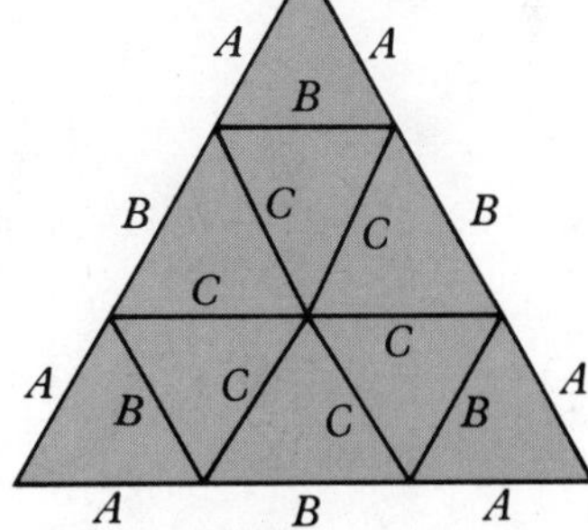

Fig. 3 Face of an icosahedron, divided into 9 triangles

1. How many struts of type A will be needed to complete the dome in Fig. 2? type B? type C?

2. In this dome, how many triangles of sides A, A, B are there? of sides B, C, C?

CHAPTER 4

Proving Theorems Using Basic Properties

4–1 Steps for Proving a Theorem

Notice the similarity between the reflexive property and the statement "dogs are dogs."

REVIEW: Some Number Properties
For any numbers, a, b, and c

1. $a = a$ (Reflexive Property)
2. If $a = b$, then $b = a$. (Symmetric Property)
3. If $a = b$ and $b = c$, then $a = c$. (Transitive Property)

In Chapter 2 we said that a theorem is a generalization that can be proved using definitions, postulates, and the logic of deductive reasoning.

In Chapter 3 we used deductive reasoning to write proofs about congruent triangles.

In this lesson we begin using this reasoning process to prove theorems.

The six-step process for proving a theorem will be illustrated in this lesson with several examples. The first theorem is based upon number properties reviewed above.

The reflexive, symmetric, and transitive properties are also true for segment and angle congruence as summarized in this table.

Steps For Proving a Theorem

Step 1 If the theorem is not in if-then form, rewrite it in this form.

Step 2 Draw and label a diagram to show the conditions of the theorem.

Step 3 Write the "GIVEN" from the hypothesis ("if" part) of the if-then statement.

Step 4 Write the "PROVE" from the conclusion ("then" part) of the if-then statement.

Step 5 Analyze what is to be proved and devise a plan.

Step 6 Write the proof, giving definitions, postulates, or theorems already proved as reasons.

	Reflexive	Symmetric	Transitive
Angle Congruence	$\angle A \cong \angle A$	If $\angle A \cong \angle B$, then $\angle B \cong \angle A$	If $\angle A \cong \angle B$, and $\angle B \cong \angle C$ then $\angle A \cong \angle C$.
Segment Congruence	$\overline{AB} \cong \overline{AB}$	If $\overline{AB} \cong \overline{CD}$, then $\overline{CD} \cong \overline{AB}$.	If $\overline{AB} \cong \overline{CD}$, and $\overline{CD} \cong \overline{EF}$, then $\overline{AB} \cong \overline{EF}$.

This table actually summarizes six generalizations. One of them is stated and proved below. Notice the six steps for proving a theorem.

When $\angle A$ is congruent to $\angle B$, and $\angle B$ is congruent to $\angle C$, it is also true that $\angle A$ is congruent to $\angle C$.

PROOF

Step 1 If $\angle A$ is congruent to $\angle B$ and $\angle B$ is congruent to $\angle C$, then $\angle A$ is congruent to $\angle C$.

Step 2

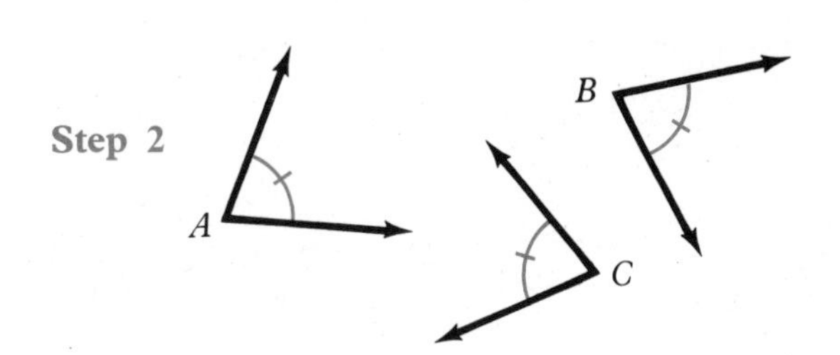

Step 3 Given: $\angle A \cong \angle B$
$\angle B \cong \angle C$

Step 4 Prove: $\angle A \cong \angle C$

Step 5 Devise a plan.
If I interpret each of the GIVEN statements as statements about angle measure, then I could use the transitive property of numbers. And I know that congruent angles do have equal measure by definition of congruent angles.

Step 6

Statements	Reasons
1. $\angle A \cong \angle B$	**1.** Given
2. $m\angle A = m\angle B$	**2.** Definition of congruent angles
3. $\angle B \cong \angle C$	**3.** Given
4. $m\angle B = m\angle C$	**4.** Why?
5. $m\angle A = m\angle C$	**5.** Transitive property of numbers
6. $\angle A \cong \angle C$	**6.** Why?

A similar proof could be given for the other five statements summarized by the chart. We combine all these statements and state the following theorem.

Theorem 4–1 The reflexive, symmetric, and transitive properties hold for angle and segment congruence.

The next two theorems further illustrate the six step process for proving a theorem.

Theorem: If points A, B, C, and D are on a line so that B is the midpoint of $\overline{AC}$ and C is the midpoint of $\overline{BD}$, then $\overline{AB} \cong \overline{CD}$.

PROOF

Step 1 Already done by the statement of the theorem.

Step 2

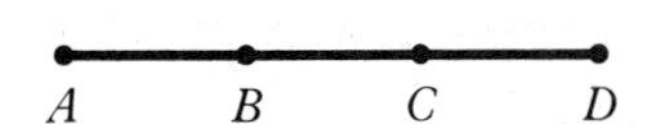

Step 3 **Given:** B is the midpoint of $\overline{AC}$
C is the midpoint of $\overline{BD}$

Step 4 **Prove:** $\overline{AB} \cong \overline{CD}$

Step 5 Devise a plan.

I shall interpret each of the given statements as a statement about segment congruence. Then I shall use the fact that segment congruence satisfies the transitive property.

Step 6

Statements	Reasons
1. B is the midpoint of $\overline{AC}$	1. Given
2. C is the midpoint of $\overline{BD}$	2. Why?
3. $\overline{AB} \cong \overline{BC}$	3. Definition of midpoint
4. $\overline{BC} \cong \overline{CD}$	4. Why?
5. $\overline{AB} \cong \overline{CD}$	5. Transitive property (Theorem 4–1)

The reason in Step 5 is a theorem that has already been proved. We have been using the postulates, definitions, and the given as reasons in proofs up to this point. The proof above shows that theorems already proved are also an important part of the deductive reasoning process.

When you are devising a plan for a proof, review definitions, postulates, and theorems that have already been proved.

Theorem 4–2 In an isosceles triangle the segment from the vertex angle to the midpoint of the opposite side forms a pair of congruent triangles.

The statement of this theorem is complex enough to illustrate the importance of steps 1 and 2 in this six step process.

PROOF

Step 1 If $\triangle ABC$ is an isosceles triangle with $\overline{AB} \cong \overline{AC}$ and if D is the midpoint of $\overline{BC}$, then $\triangle ABD \cong \triangle ACD$.

Step 2

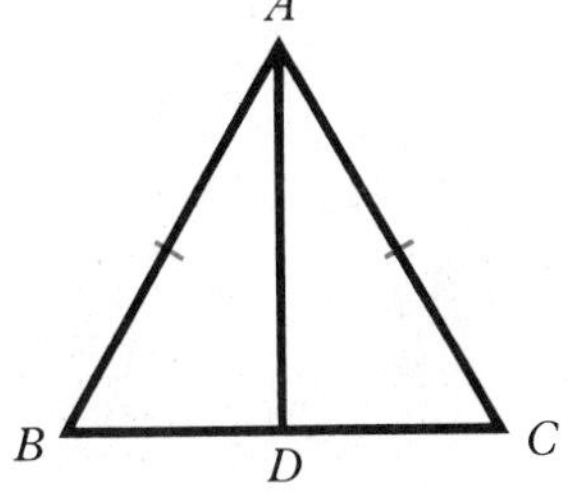

Step 3 **Given:** $\overline{AB} \cong \overline{AC}$
D is the midpoint of $\overline{BC}$.

Step 4 **Prove:** $\triangle ABD \cong \triangle ACD$

Step 5 Devise a plan.
I shall use the given information, the definition of midpoint, and the reflexive property of segment congruence together with the SSS Congruence Postulate.

Step 6

Statements	Reasons
1. $\overline{AB} \cong \overline{AC}$	**1.** Given
2. D is midpoint of $\overline{BC}$	**2.** Given
3. $\overline{BD} \cong \overline{CD}$	**3.** Definition of midpoint
4. $\overline{AD} \cong \overline{AD}$	**4.** Reflexive property of segment congruence (Theorem 4–1)
5. $\triangle ABD \cong \triangle ACD$	**5.** SSS Congruence Postulate

EXERCISES

A.

In exercises 1–3 a theorem is given in if-then form. Draw a picture and state the "Given" and "Prove" using the picture and its labeling. *Do not prove any of the theorems.*

1. Theorem. If $\triangle ABC$ is an isosceles triangle, then $\triangle ABC$ has a pair of congruent angles.

2. Theorem. If points X, Y, Z are midpoints of the sides of $\triangle ABC$, then segments $\overline{XY}$, $\overline{XZ}$, and $\overline{YZ}$ divide $\triangle ABC$ into four congruent triangles.

3. Theorem. If X and Y are the midpoints of two sides of a triangle, then $\overline{XY}$ is equal to one half the length of the third side.

In exercises 4–7, restate the theorem in if-then form, draw a picture, and state the "Given" and "Prove." *Do not attempt to prove the theorems.*

4. An equilateral triangle is an isosceles triangle.

5. Two intersecting lines form two pairs of congruent angles.

6. Two intersecting lines that are not perpendicular form a pair of obtuse angles.

7. An angle bisector of a vertex angle in an equilateral triangle is a perpendicular bisector of a side.

Name the property of segment or angle congruence (reflexive, symmetric, or transitive) illustrated by each statement below.

8. If two segments are congruent, the congruence statement may be written with either segment first.

9. Any segment is congruent to itself.

10. If a first angle is congruent to a second angle and the second angle is congruent to a third angle, then the first angle is congruent to the third angle.

In exercises 11–14 use the "Given" and "Prove" to draw the picture. Then write a general theorem. *Do not prove any of these theorems.*

11. Given: $\triangle ABC$ is an isosceles triangle with $\overline{AB} \cong \overline{AC}$.
Prove: $\angle B \cong \angle C$

12. Given: $\triangle ABC$ with $\angle B \cong \angle C$
Prove: $\triangle ABC$ is an isosceles triangle.

13. Given: $\triangle ABC$ is an equilateral triangle.
Prove: $\angle A \cong \angle B \cong \angle C$

14. Given: $\triangle ABC$ with $\angle A \cong \angle B \cong \angle C$
Prove: $\triangle ABC$ is an equilateral triangle.

B.

15. If $\angle 1 \cong \angle 2$ and $\angle 2 \cong \angle 3$, why is $\angle 1 \cong \angle 3$?

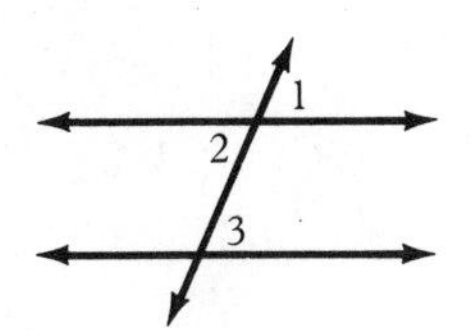

16. If $\overline{AB} \cong \overline{BC}$ and $\overline{BC} \cong \overline{CD}$, why is $\overline{AB} \cong \overline{CD}$?

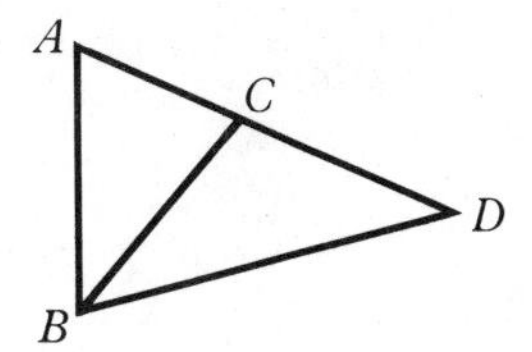

17. If $AB = BC$ and $BC = AC$, why do we know that $\triangle ABC$ is equilateral?

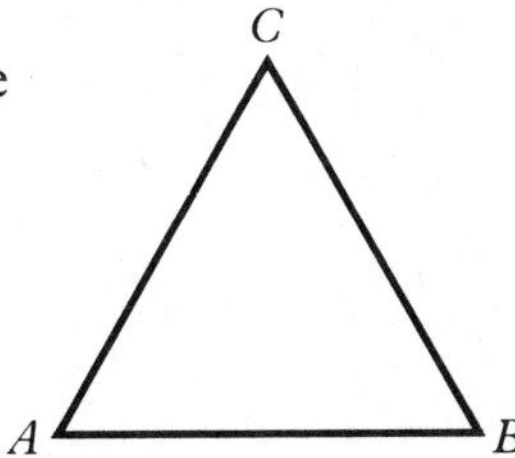

18. If $\overline{AB} \cong \overline{ED}$ and $\overline{ED} \cong \overline{BC}$, how do you know that B is the midpoint of $\overline{AC}$?

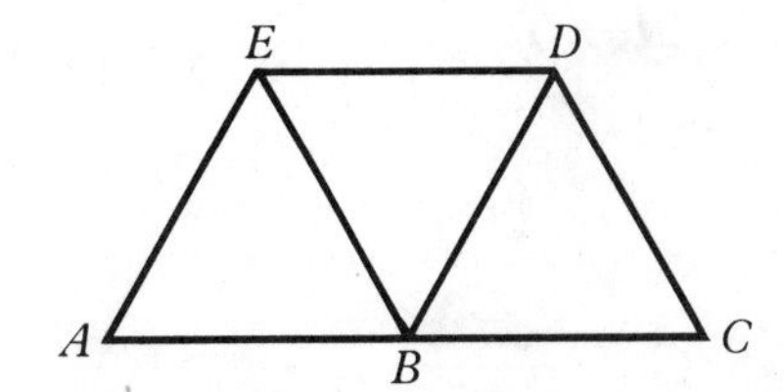

19. In a regular pentagon two diagonals from the same vertex are congruent. For example, $\overline{AC} \cong \overline{AD}$ in the first figure. Use this fact with a transitive property to explain why $\overline{AC}$ and $\overline{BE}$ are congruent in the second figure.

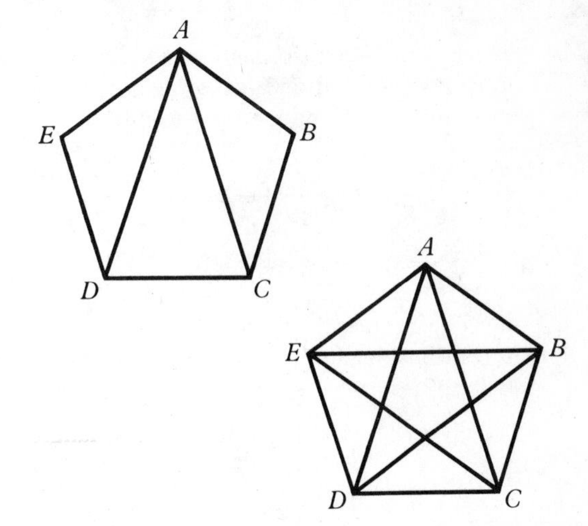

20. A plumber is measuring the length of $\overline{AB}$ in order to cut a piece of pipe of the correct length. The pipe that is cut is called $\overline{CD}$. How does the transitive property for congruence of segments show that the cut pipe $\overline{CD}$ will fit the space $\overline{AB}$? (*Hint:* The tape measure is an important part of the reasoning.)

C.

For exercises 21–22, write a complete two-column proof. Each proof requires the use of one of the congruence properties for segments or angles specified in Theorem 4-1.

21.

Given: $\angle 1 \cong \angle 2$
$\angle 3 \cong \angle 4$
Prove: $\triangle ABD \cong \triangle CDB$

22.

Given: $\overline{BE} \cong \overline{CE}$
$\angle 1 \cong \angle 2$
B is the midpoint of $\overline{AC}$
C is the midpoint of $\overline{BD}$
Prove: $\triangle ABE \cong \triangle DCE$

Activity

These Optical Illusions show why we should rely more on logical reasoning and less on visual information. Answer the questions. Then check by measuring.

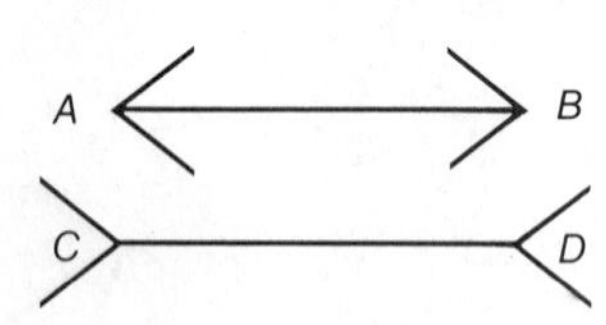

a. Is it further from *A* to *B* or *C* to *D*?

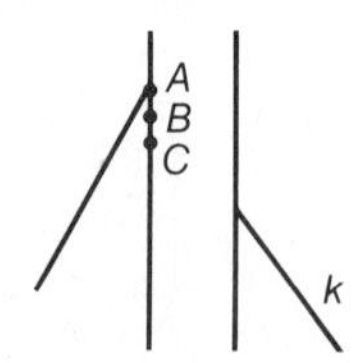

b. Will line *k*, when extended, meet point *A*, point *B*, point *C*, or none of these points?

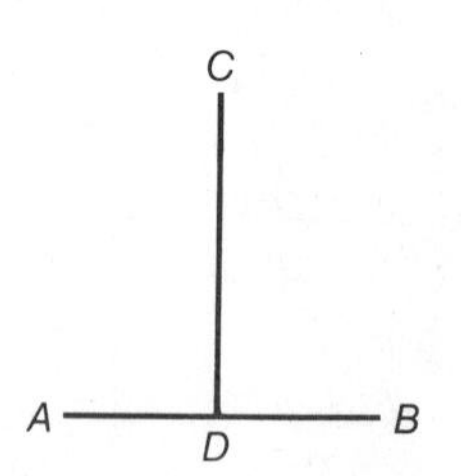

c. Which segment is longer, $\overline{AB}$ or $\overline{CD}$?

Create an optical illusion of your own.

23.

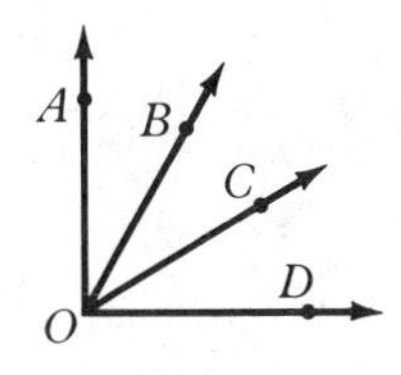

Given: $\overrightarrow{OB}$ bisects $\angle AOC$

$\overrightarrow{OC}$ bisects $\angle BOD$

Prove: $\angle AOB \cong \angle COD$

24.

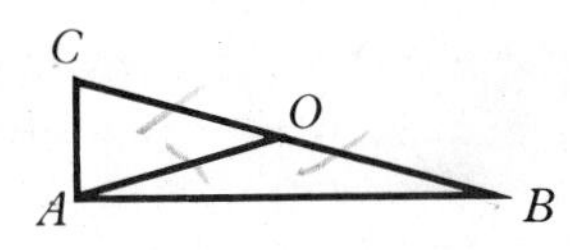

Given: O is midpoint of $\overline{BC}$

$\triangle AOB$ is isosceles with $\overline{OA} \cong \overline{OB}$

Prove: $\triangle AOC$ is isosceles

25.

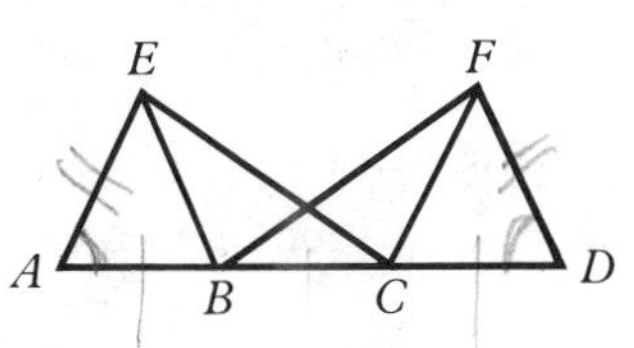

Given: $\triangle ACE \cong \triangle DBF$

B is midpoint of $\overline{AC}$

C is midpoint of $\overline{BD}$

Prove: $\triangle ABE \cong \triangle DCF$

26.

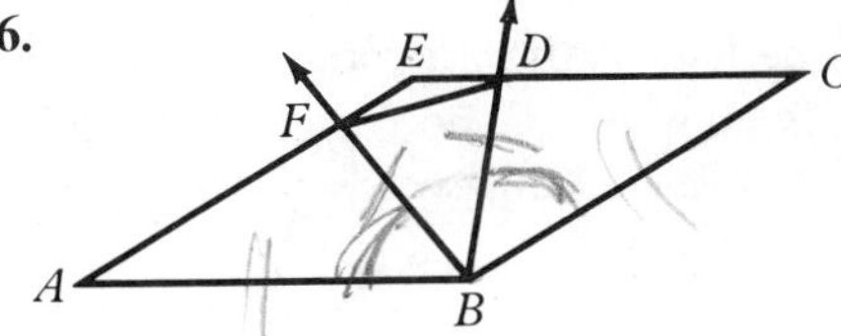

Given: $ABCE$ with $\overline{AB} \cong \overline{BC}$

$\triangle BDF$ is isosceles with $\overline{BF} \cong \overline{BD}$

$\overrightarrow{BF}$ bisects $\angle ABD$ and

$\overrightarrow{BD}$ bisects $\angle CBF$

Prove: $\triangle ABF \cong \triangle CBD$

27. Prove that congruence of triangles satisfies the transitive property.

28. Prove that all right angles are congruent.

PROBLEM SOLVING

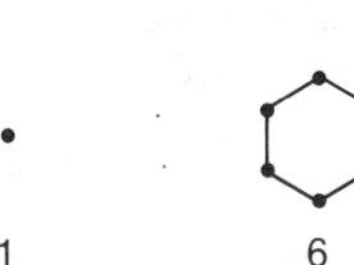

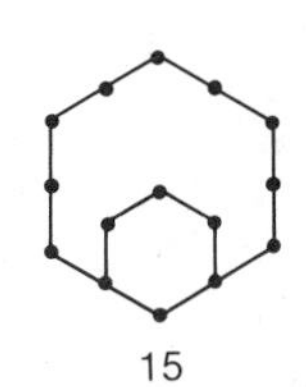

. . .

1 6 15 28

The first four hexagonal numbers are shown above.

a. Give the next 2 hexagonal numbers. Show the dot patterns.

b. Does the formula $n(2n - 1)$ give the nth hexagonal number?

4–2 Using Addition and Subtraction of Equals Property

The properties of numbers on the right review some algebra.

These properties are used in proofs that involve lengths of segments and measures of angles. The two theorems in this lesson illustrate the use of these properties.

In proofs later in the book you will often use these theorems rather than the number properties themselves.

REVIEW: Some Number Properties

Addition of Equals: If $a = b$ and $c = d$, then $a + c = b + d$.
Subtraction of Equals: If $a = b$ and $c = d$, $a > c$, then $a - c = b - d$.
Multiplication of Equals: If $a = b$ and $c = d$, then $a \cdot c = b \cdot d$.
Substitution Principle: If $a = b$, then a may be replaced by b in any equation or inequality.

Theorem 4–3 **Addition of Equal Angles.** If $m\angle APB = m\angle DQE$, $m\angle BPC = m\angle EQF$, $\overrightarrow{PB}$ is between $\overrightarrow{PA}$ and $\overrightarrow{PC}$, and $\overrightarrow{QE}$ is between $\overrightarrow{QD}$ and $\overrightarrow{QF}$, then $m\angle APC = m\angle DQF$.

PROOF

Given: $m\angle APB = m\angle DQE$
$m\angle BPC = m\angle EQF$
Prove: $m\angle APC = m\angle DQF$

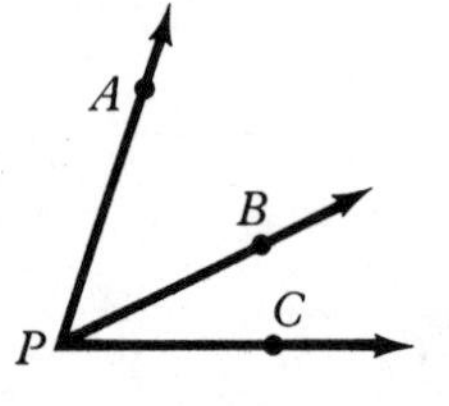

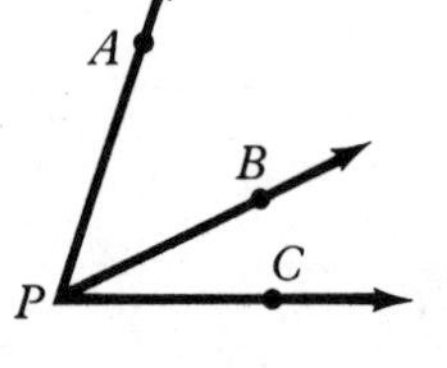
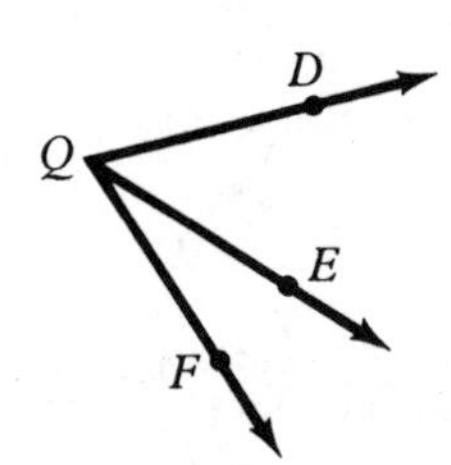

Statements	Reasons
1. $m\angle APB = m\angle DQF$	1. Given
2. $m\angle BPC = m\angle EQF$	2. Given
3. $m\angle APB + m\angle BPC =$ $m\angle DQE + m\angle EQF$	3. Addition of Equals Property
4. $m\angle APB + m\angle BPC = m\angle APC$	4. Definition of between for rays
5. $m\angle DQE + m\angle EQF = m\angle DQF$	5. Why?
6. $m\angle APC = m\angle DQF$	6. Substitution Principle

In general, information telling which rays are between others is not stated in the "Given." It can be taken from the figures. The same is true about points, as illustrated in the next theorem.

Theorem 4–4 **Subtraction of Equal Segments.** If $AC = DF$, $BC = EF$, B is between A and C, and E is between D and F, then $AB = DE$.

Given: $AC = DF$
$BC = EF$
Prove: $AB = DE$

Statements	Reasons
1. $AC = DF$	1. Given
2. $BC = EF$	2. Given
3. $AC = AB + BC$	3. Definition of between for points
4. $DF = DE + EF$	4. Why?
5. $AB + BC = DE + EF$	5. Substitution Principle
6. $AB + BC - BC = DE + EF - EF$	6. Subtraction of Equals Property
7. $AB + BC - BC = AB$	7. Properties of algebra
8. $DE + EF - EF = DE$	8. Why?
9. $AB = DE$	9. Substitution Principle

The next two theorems are stated without proof.

Theorem 4–5 **Addition of Equal Segments.** If $AB = DE$, $BC = EF$, B is between A and C, and E is between D and F, then $AC = DF$.

Theorem 4–6 **Subtraction of Equal Angles.** If $m\angle APC = m\angle DQF$, $m\angle BPC = m\angle EQF$, $\overrightarrow{PB}$ is between $\overrightarrow{PA}$ and $\overrightarrow{PC}$, and $\overrightarrow{QE}$ is between $\overrightarrow{QD}$ and $\overrightarrow{QF}$, then $m\angle APB = m\angle DQE$.

EXERCISES

A.

Are the conclusions for exercises 1-6 justified by the transitive property for equality, the Addition of Equal Angles Theorem, or the Subtraction of Equal Angles Theorem?

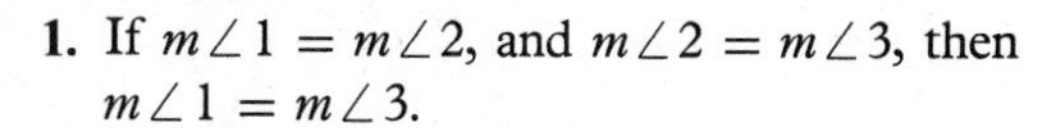

1. If $m\angle 1 = m\angle 2$, and $m\angle 2 = m\angle 3$, then $m\angle 1 = m\angle 3$.
2. If $m\angle COD = m\angle EOF$, then $m\angle COE = m\angle DOF$.
3. If $m\angle BOD = m\angle COE$, then $m\angle BOC = m\angle DOE$.
4. If $m\angle AOC = m\angle DOF$ and $m\angle 1 = m\angle 3$, then $m\angle BOC = m\angle DOE$.

(Exs. 1-6)

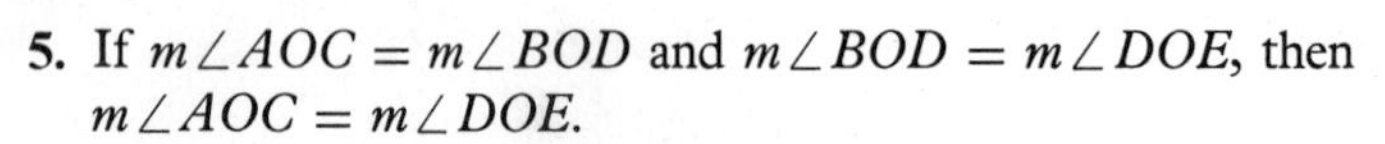

5. If $m\angle AOC = m\angle BOD$ and $m\angle BOD = m\angle DOE$, then $m\angle AOC = m\angle DOE$.
6. If $m\angle AOD = m\angle FOC$ and $m\angle BOD = m\angle EOC$, then $m\angle AOB = m\angle FOE$.

For exercises 7–10, state a property, a theorem, or a combination of them that justifies the given statements.

7. If $BD = CE$, then $BC = DE$.
8. If $AC = DF$, then $AD = CF$.
9. If $BE = DF$, and $DF = AC$, then $CE = AB$.
10. If $AB = EF$ and $BC = DE$, then $AD = CF$.

(Exs. 7–10)

In exercises 11–14 provide all the missing reasons in the proofs.

11. **Given:** $AB = CD$
    Prove: $AC = BD$

Statements	Reasons
1. $AB = CD$	1. Given
2. $BC = BC$	2. ?
3. $AC = BD$	3. ?

12. **Given:** $m\angle AOC = m\angle BOD$
    Prove: $m\angle AOB = m\angle COD$

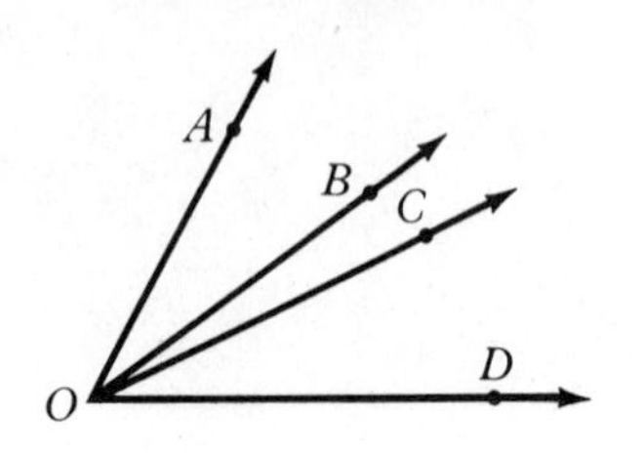

Statements	Reasons
1. $m\angle AOC = m\angle BOD$	1. Given
2. $m\angle BOC = m\angle BOC$	2. ?
3. $m\angle AOB = m\angle COD$	3. ?

13. Given: $AB = CD$
$BD = DE$
Prove: $AC = DE$

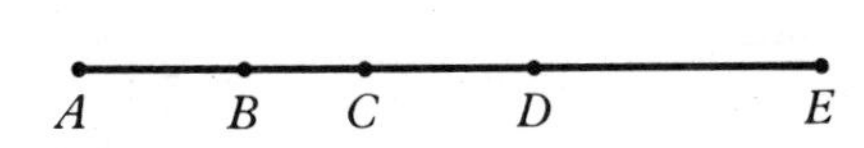

Statements	Reasons
1. $AB = CD$	1. Given
2. $BD = DE$	2. Given
3. $BC = BC$	3. ?
4. $AC = BD$	4. ?
5. $AC = DE$	5. ?

14. Given: $m\angle AOD = m\angle FOC$
$m\angle 3 = m\angle 4$
Prove: $m\angle 1 = m\angle 2$

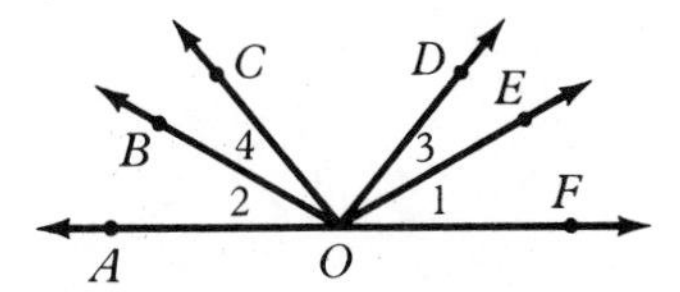

Statements	Reasons
1. $m\angle AOD = m\angle FOC$	1. ?
2. $m\angle COD = m\angle COD$	2. ?
3. $m\angle AOC = m\angle FOD$	3. ?
4. $m\angle 3 = m\angle 4$	4. ?
5. $m\angle 2 = m\angle 1$	5. ?

B.

15. Consider the diagram at the right.

connecting rod bearing
piston
top of piston
0.635 cm
24.32 cm
5.41 cm

a. What is the distance from the center of the connecting rod bearing to the top of the piston?

b. What is the length of the piston?

c. What theorems or postulates support your answers?

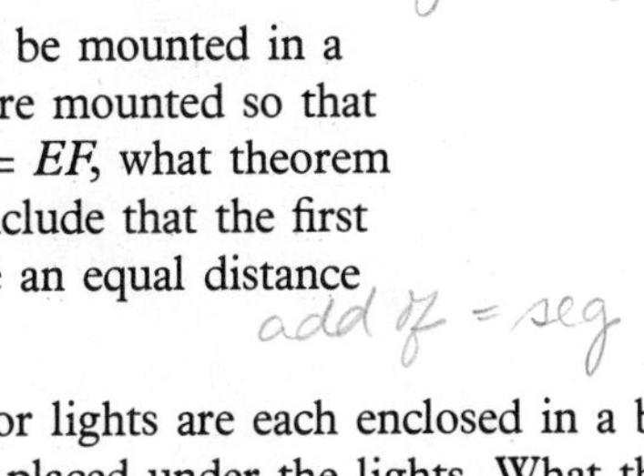

16. Shelf brackets are to be mounted in a book shelf. If they are mounted so that $AB = DE$ and $BC = EF$, what theorem are you using to conclude that the first and third shelves are an equal distance apart at both ends?

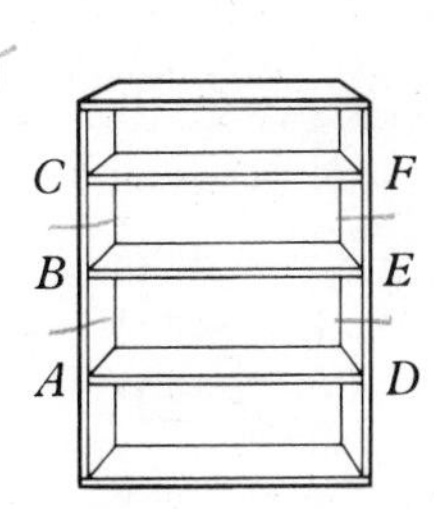

17. Two identical outdoor lights are each enclosed in a box. Two identical wedges are placed under the lights. What theorem assures that the two beams of light form the same angle with the ground?

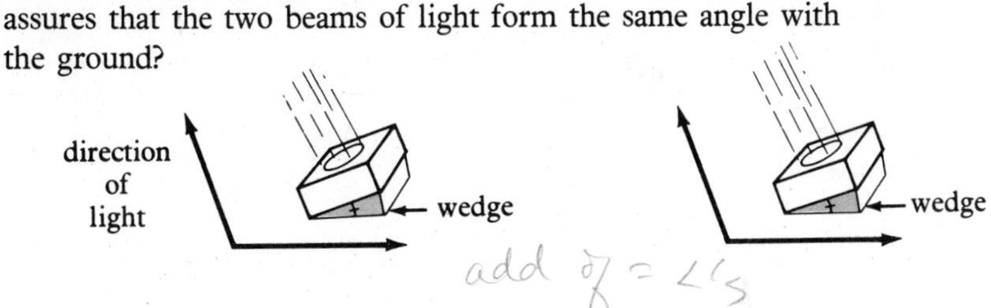

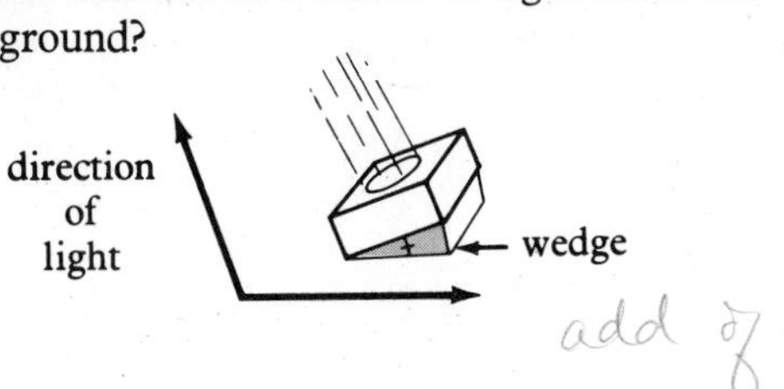

In exercises 18–27 write a complete two-column proof.

18. Given: $\overline{AB} \cong \overline{CD}$
$\angle 1 \cong \angle 2$
$\angle 3 \cong \angle 4$
Prove: $\triangle ACF \cong \triangle DBE$

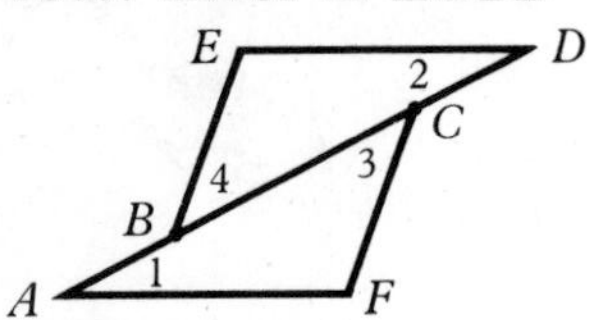

19. Given: $\overline{AE} \cong \overline{DE}$
$\angle 1 \cong \angle 2$
$\angle 3 \cong \angle 4$
Prove: $\overline{AC} \cong \overline{BD}$

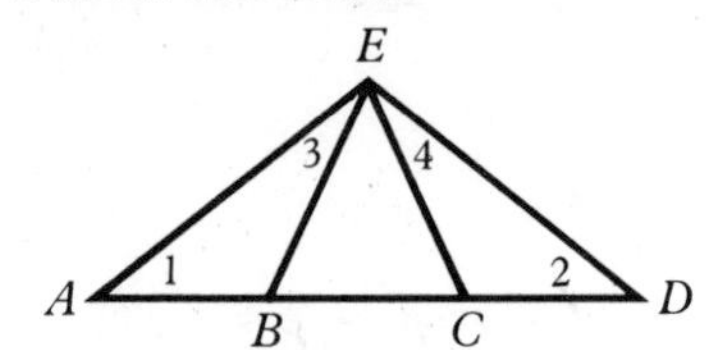

20. Given: $\triangle BFC \cong \triangle DGC$
$\triangle ABC \cong \triangle EDC$
Prove: $\triangle AFC \cong \triangle EGC$

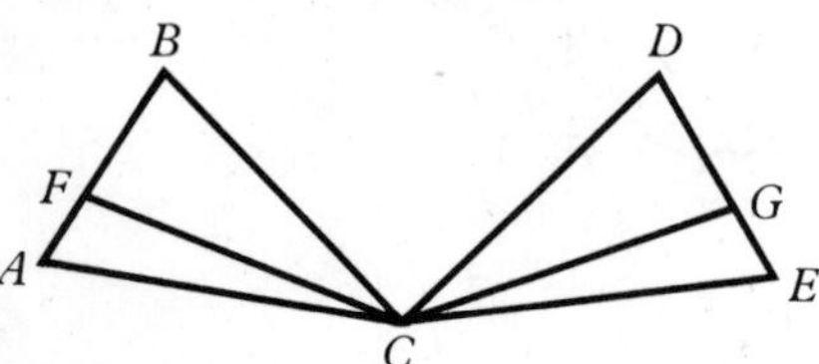

21. Given: B is the midpoint of $\overline{AC}$.
$\angle 1 \cong \angle 2$
$\angle 3 \cong \angle 4$
$\overline{FB} \cong \overline{GB}$
Prove: $\overline{FD} \cong \overline{GE}$

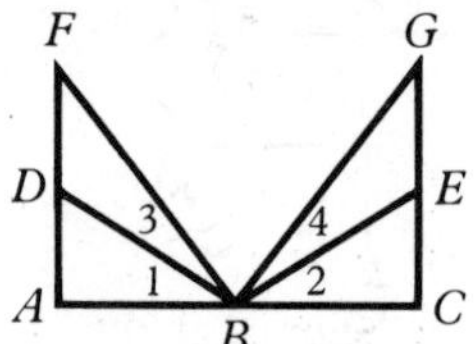

22. Given: B is the midpoint of $\overline{AF}$.
E is the midpoint of $\overline{BC}$.
E is the midpoint of $\overline{DF}$.
$\overline{AB} \cong \overline{CD}$
Prove: $\triangle BEF \cong \triangle CED$

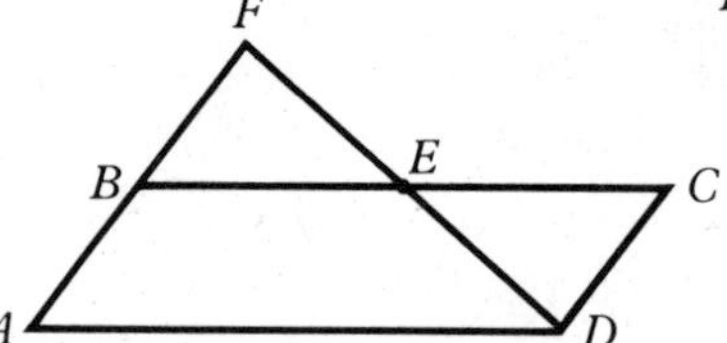

Activity

A set of points that uniquely satisfies a given condition is called a **locus**. The locus of points equidistant from the end points of a line segment is the perpendicular bisector of the segment.

You can demonstrate that this is true by watching the figure traced by a "moving point." Make a special set of 20 cards (8 cm × 13 cm), clip them together, and flip through them with your thumb to see the moving point! To see the perpendicular bisector use a series of cards like these.

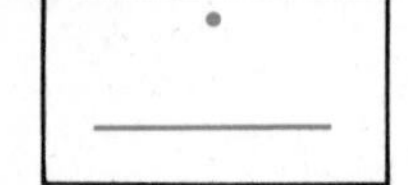 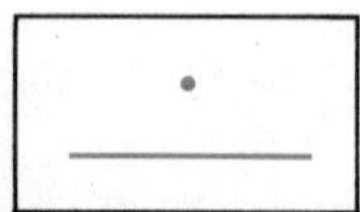 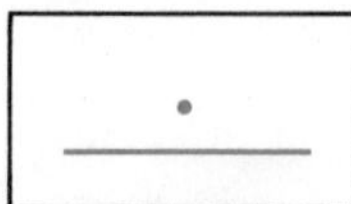 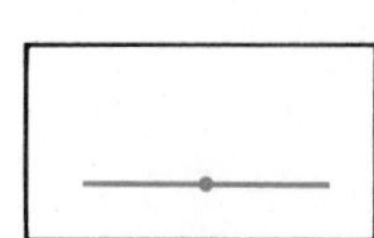 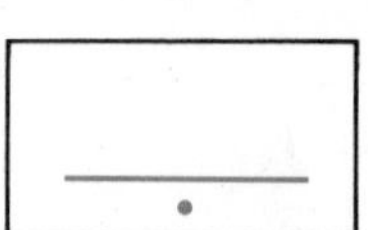

C.

23. Given: C is midpoint of $\overline{AD}$.
$\angle 1 \cong \angle 2$
$\angle 3 \cong \angle 4$
Prove: $\triangle ECG \cong \triangle BCF$

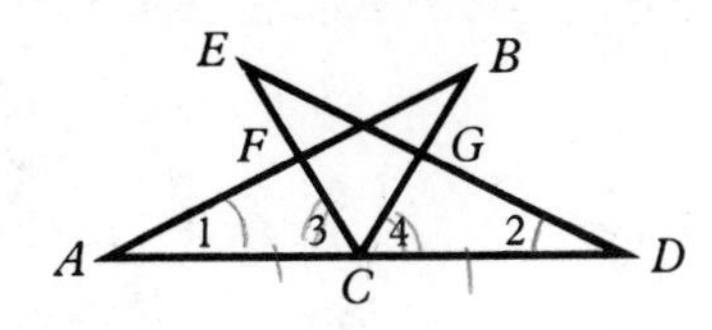

24. Given: $\triangle AEC \cong \triangle DFB$
Prove: $\triangle ABF \cong \triangle DCE$

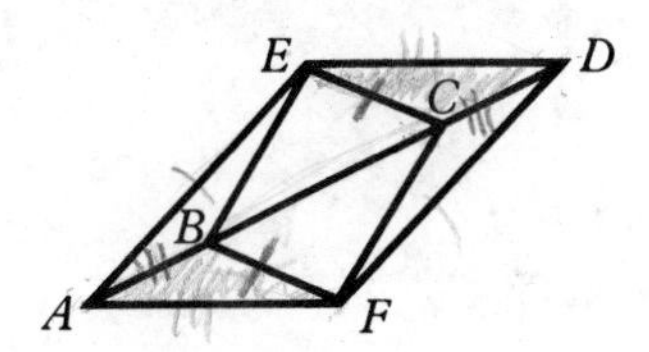

25. Given: $\triangle AEC \cong \triangle DFB$
Prove: $\triangle ABE \cong \triangle DCF$

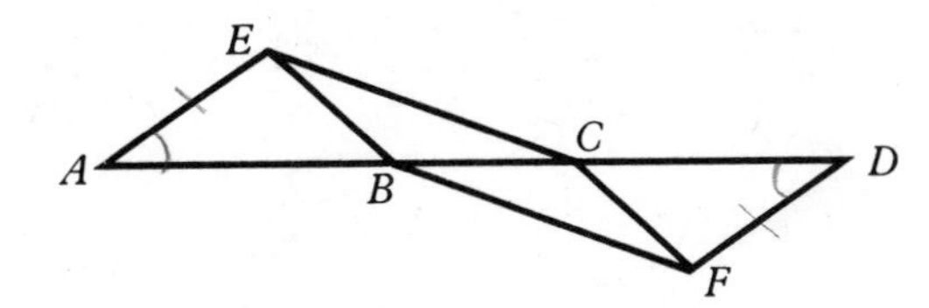

26. Given: $ABCDE$ is a regular pentagon.
$\overline{FE} \cong \overline{GE}$
Prove: $\triangle ABF \cong \triangle DCG$

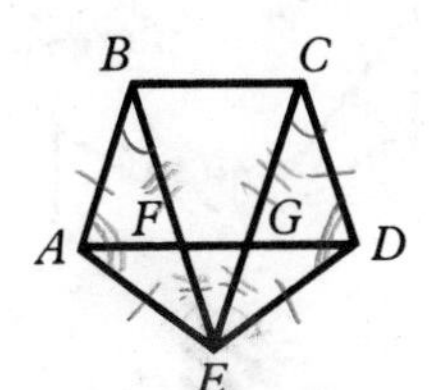

27. Given: $ABCDE$ is a regular pentagon.
$\angle 1 \cong \angle 2$
Prove: $\triangle FGE$ is isosceles

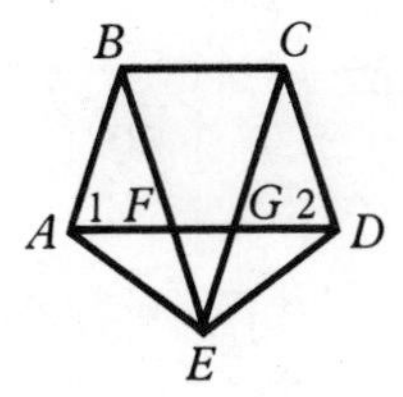

PROBLEM SOLVING

Arrange these nine triangles to form a large triangle so that vertices that touch all have the same symbol.

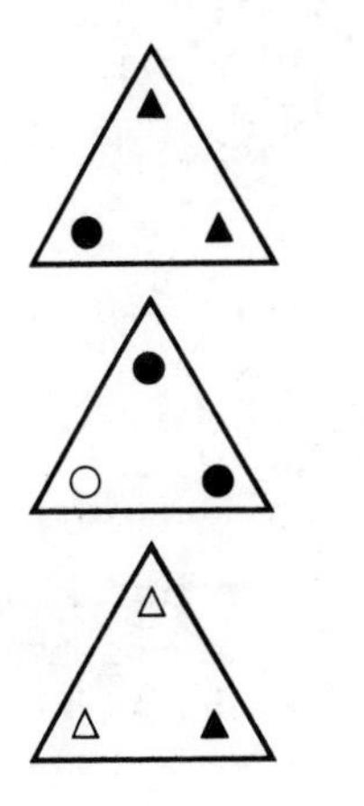
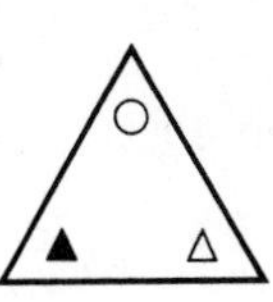
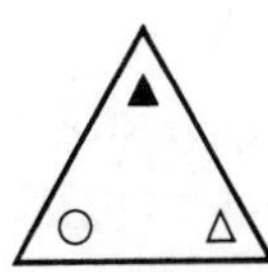

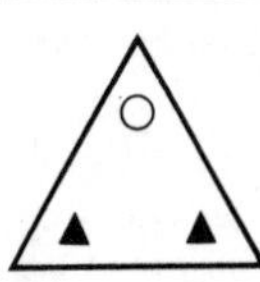

4–3 Proving Theorems—Using Supplements and Complements

Often in the physical world angles occur in pairs whose degree measures have a sum of either 180 or 90. Pairs of this type are studied in this lesson.

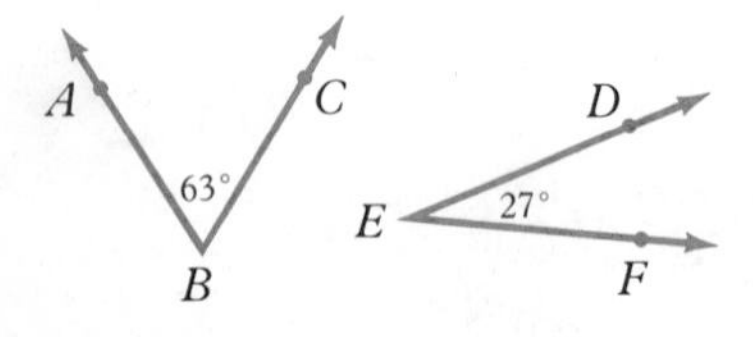

The sum of the measures of $\angle ABC$ and $\angle DEF$ is 90°.

$\angle ABC$ is complementary to $\angle DEF$.
$\angle DEF$ is complementary to $\angle ABC$.

Definition 4–1

Complementary angles are two angles whose measures have a sum of 90°.

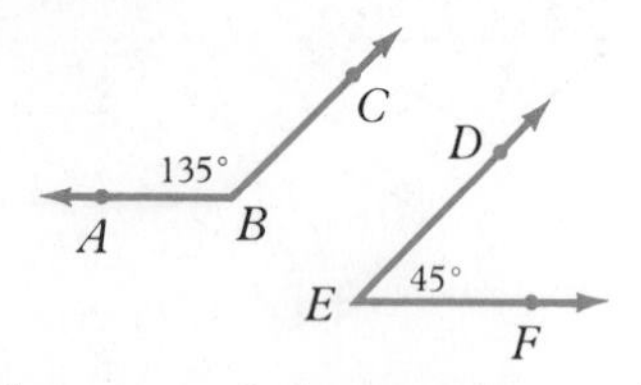

The sum of the measures of $\angle ABC$ and $\angle DEF$ is 180°.

$\angle ABC$ is supplementary to $\angle DEF$.
$\angle DEF$ is supplementary to $\angle ABC$.

Definition 4–2

Supplementary angles are two angles whose measures have a sum of 180°.

Some pairs of angles with a sum of 180° have a common vertex, a common side, and no interior points in common. They are called a linear pair. Find a linear pair of angles in the photograph at the top of the page.

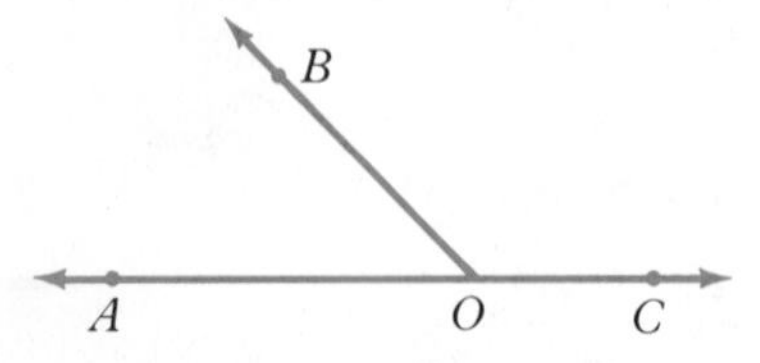

$\angle AOB$ and $\angle BOC$ have a common side, $\overrightarrow{OB}$. The union of the other two sides, $\overrightarrow{OA}$ and $\overrightarrow{OC}$ is a line.

$\angle AOB$ and $\angle BOC$ are a linear pair of angles.

Definition 4–3

A linear pair of angles is a pair of angles with a common side such that the union of the other two sides is a line.

The framework that supports the roof of a house is often assembled separately. This framework is called a roof truss system. One task of a production engineer is to identify all angles of the same size in this roof truss system. Then all boards with congruent angles can be cut at the same time.

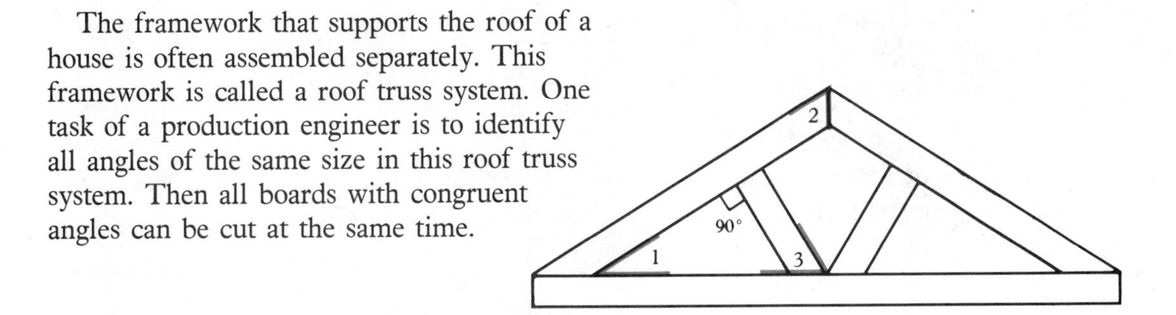

The theorem in this lesson provides information that is useful in determining the size of angles.

Use your protractor to answer these questions about complements.

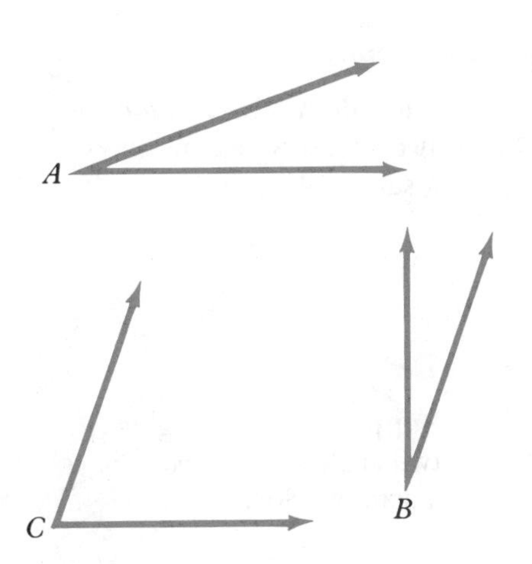

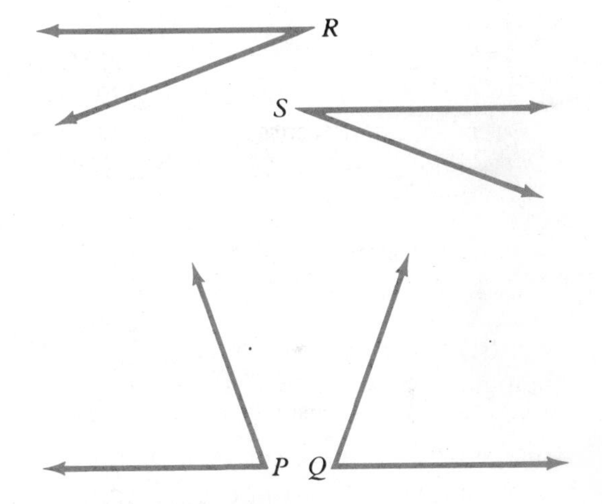

Is $\angle A$ complementary to $\angle C$?
Is $\angle B$ complementary to $\angle C$?
How does $m\angle A$ compare with $m\angle B$?

Is $\angle P$ complementary to $\angle R$?
Is $\angle Q$ complementary to $\angle S$?
How does $m\angle P$ compare with $m\angle Q$?

You may have said that $\angle A$ and $\angle B$ are congruent and $\angle P$ and $\angle Q$ are congruent. Theorem 4–7 summarizes the two situations discussed above.

Theorem 4–7 **Congruent Complements Theorem.** Two angles that are complementary to the same angle (or congruent angles) are congruent.

We shall prove the first part of the Congruent Complements Theorem. The second part will be completed as an exercise.

PROOF

Given: $\angle A$ is complementary to $\angle C$
$\angle B$ is complementary to $\angle C$
Prove: $\angle A \cong \angle B$

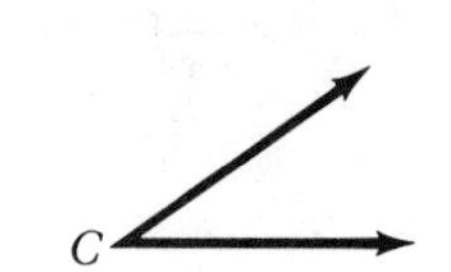

Statements	Reasons
1. $\angle A$ is complementary to $\angle C$	**1.** Given
2. $m\angle A + m\angle C = 90$	**2.** Definition of complementary angles
3. $\angle B$ is complementary to $\angle C$	**3.** Why?
4. $m\angle B + m\angle C = 90$	**4.** Why?
5. $m\angle A + m\angle C = m\angle B + m\angle C$	**5.** Substitution Principle
6. $m\angle A = m\angle B$	**6.** Subtraction of Equals Property
7. $\angle A \cong \angle B$	**7.** Definition of congruent angles

APPLICATION

In a triangle with a 90° angle, the sum of the other two angles is also 90°. Consequently, $\angle 2$ and $\angle 3$ in this roof truss system are both complements of $\angle 1$. By Theorem 4–7 we can conclude that $\angle 2$ and $\angle 3$ have the same measure.

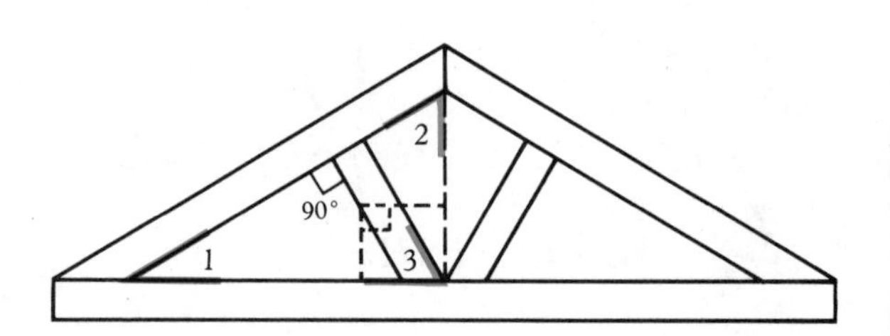

Theorem 4–8 **Congruent Supplements Theorem.** Two angles that are supplementary to the same angle (or to congruent angles) are congruent.

It seems reasonable that two angles that form a linear pair should be supplementary. This fact is accepted as true and called the Linear Pair Postulate.

Linear Pair Postulate

If two angles form a linear pair, the angles are supplementary.

Study each step in the proofs below and supply the missing reasons.

Example 1

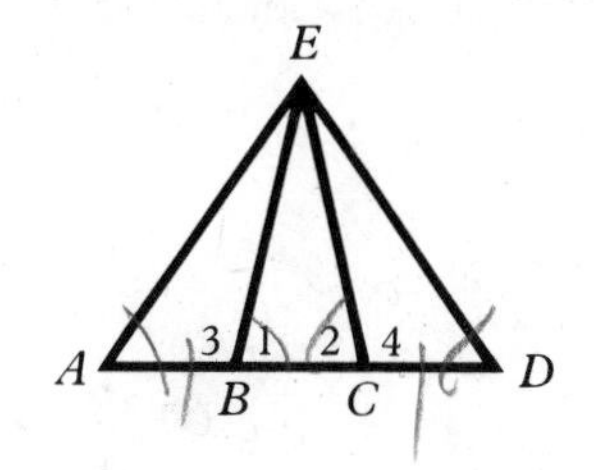

Given: $\angle A \cong \angle D$
$\angle 1 \cong \angle 2$
$\overline{AB} \cong \overline{CD}$
Prove: $\overline{BE} \cong \overline{CE}$

Statements	Reasons
1. $\angle A \cong \angle D$	**1.** Given
2. $\overline{AB} \cong \overline{CD}$	**2.** Why?
3. $\angle 1 \cong \angle 2$	**3.** Why?
4. $\angle 1$ and $\angle 3$ are supplementary	**4.** Linear Pair Postulate
5. $\angle 2$ and $\angle 4$ are supplementary	**5.** Why?
6. $\angle 3 \cong \angle 4$	**6.** Congruent Supplements Theorem
7. $\triangle ABE \cong \triangle DCE$	**7.** Why?
8. $\overline{BE} \cong \overline{CE}$	**8.** CPCTC

Example 2

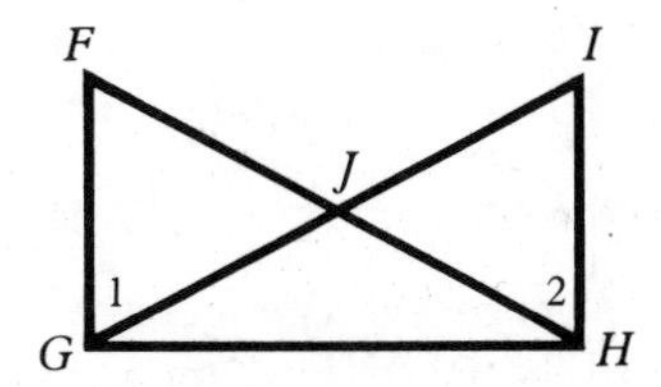

Given: $\angle FGH$ and $\angle IHG$ are right angles.
$\angle 1 \cong \angle 2$
Prove: $\triangle IHG \cong \triangle FGH$

Statements	Reasons
1. $\angle FGH$ and $\angle IHG$ are right angles.	**1.** Given
2. $\angle FGH \cong \angle IHG$	**2.** All right angles are congruent.
3. $m\angle FGH = m\angle IHG = 90$	**3.** Why?
4. $\angle 1 \cong \angle 2$	**4.** Given
5. $\angle 1$ and $\angle IGH$ are complementary.	**5.** Definition of complements
6. $\angle 2$ and $\angle FHG$ are complementary.	**6.** Why?
7. $\angle IGH \cong \angle FHG$	**7.** Congruent Complements Theorem
8. $\overline{GH} \cong \overline{HG}$	**8.** Reflexive property (Segments)
9. $\triangle IHG \cong \triangle FGH$	**9.** Why?

EXERCISES

A.

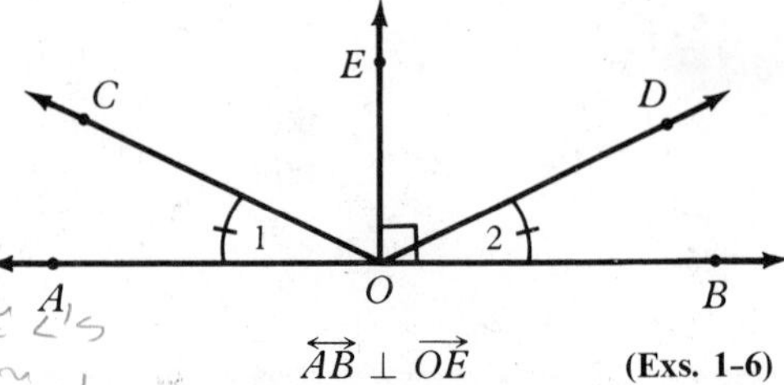

$\overleftrightarrow{AB} \perp \overrightarrow{OE}$
$\angle 1 \cong \angle 2$

(Exs. 1-6)

1. Name a supplement of $\angle 1$.
2. Name a supplement of $\angle COB$.
3. Name a complement of $\angle COE$.
4. Name a complement of $\angle 2$.
5. Why are $\angle COE$ and $\angle DOE$ congruent?

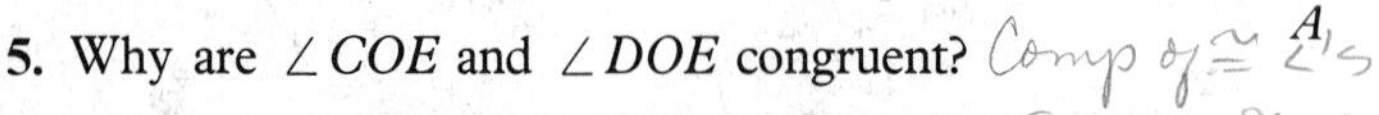

6. Why are $\angle COB$ and $\angle AOD$ congruent?

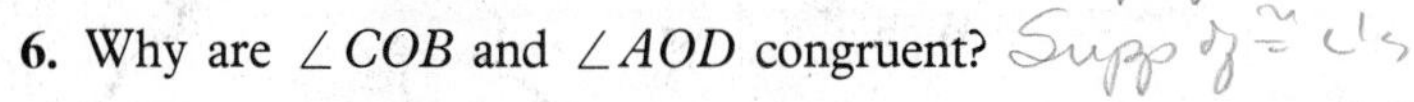

7. Name two angles that are supplements of $\angle COE$.

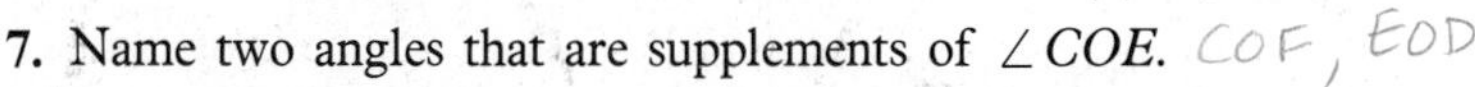

8. Name two angles that are complements of $\angle 3$.
9. Name two angles that are complements of $\angle HOF$.
10. Why are $\angle COE$ and $\angle BOG$ congruent?
11. Why are $\angle AOH$ and $\angle COE$ congruent?

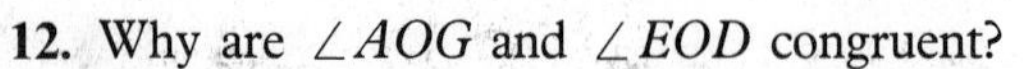

12. Why are $\angle AOG$ and $\angle EOD$ congruent?
13. Why are $\angle 3$ and $\angle AOC$ congruent?

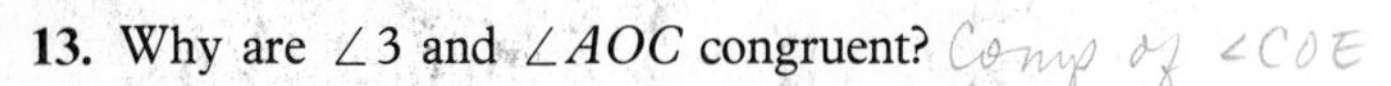

14. Why are $\angle 3$ and $\angle AOD$ supplements?

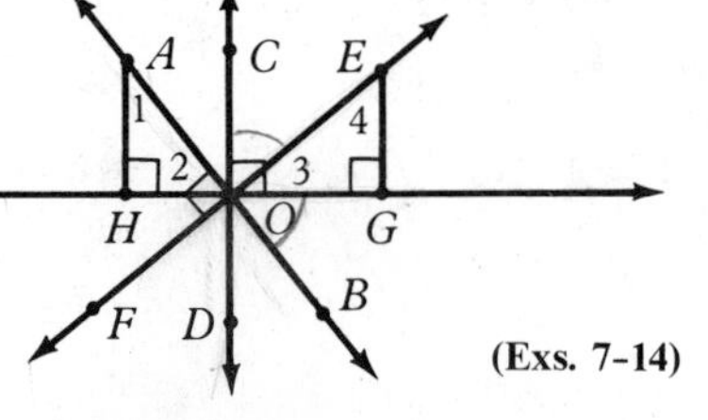

(Exs. 7-14)

$\overleftrightarrow{AB} \perp \overleftrightarrow{EF}$, $\overleftrightarrow{CD} \perp \overleftrightarrow{HG}$
$\overline{AH} \perp \overline{HG}$, $\overline{EG} \perp \overline{HG}$

B.

15. If $m\angle A = x$, then the complement of $\angle A$ has measure _?_.
16. If $m\angle B = x$, then the supplement of $\angle B$ has measure _?_.
17. Two angles are supplementary. The measure of one is four times the measure of the other. Find the measures of the two angles.
18. Two angles are supplementary. The measure of one is 20 less than three times the measure of the other. Find the measures of the two angles.

Activity

Make a set of 20 cards like the ones below. Clip them together, and flip through them to show that the locus of points equidistant from the two sides of an angle is the angle bisector.

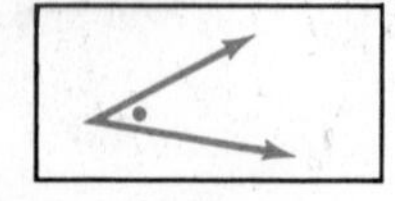
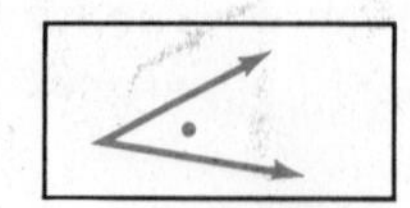
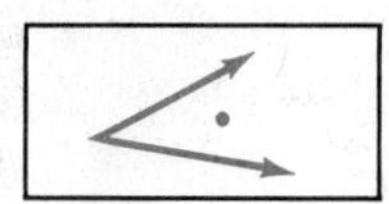
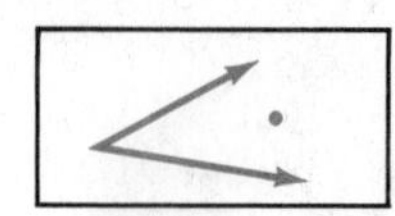
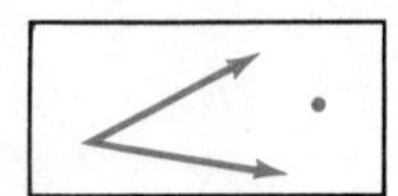

Computer Generated Geometry

Special programs make it increasingly easy to generate geometric diagrams on the computer screen. The geometry of machine parts and other technological devices can be analyzed with an accuracy never before possible. Geometry is revealed in places where it was unsuspected in science, business, and manufacturing. These photos show how simple circular shapes, parallel lines, intersecting lines, and planes work together to make visually exciting electronic artwork.

1 **The geometry of this automobile part is apparent. Engineers can rotate the picture and view it from any angle.**

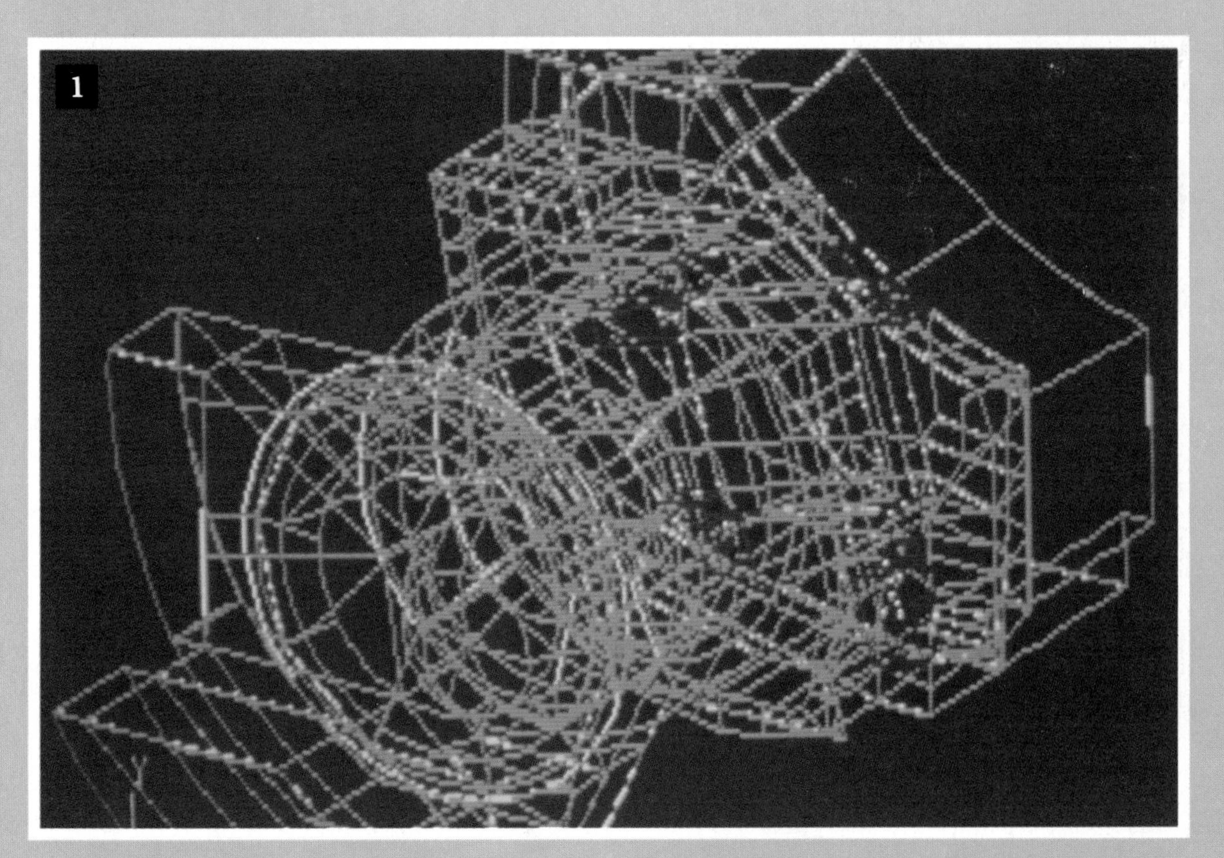

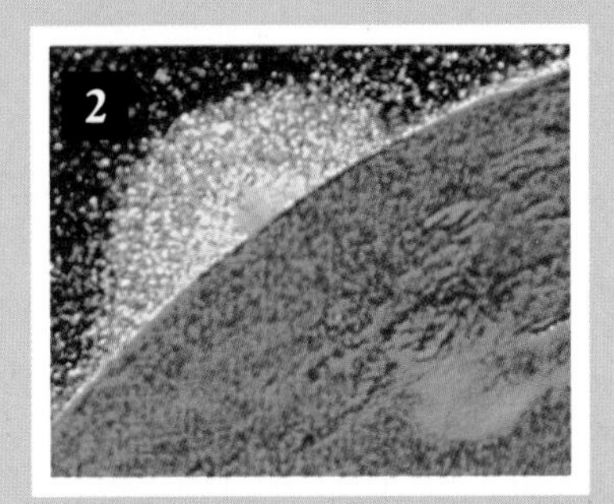

2

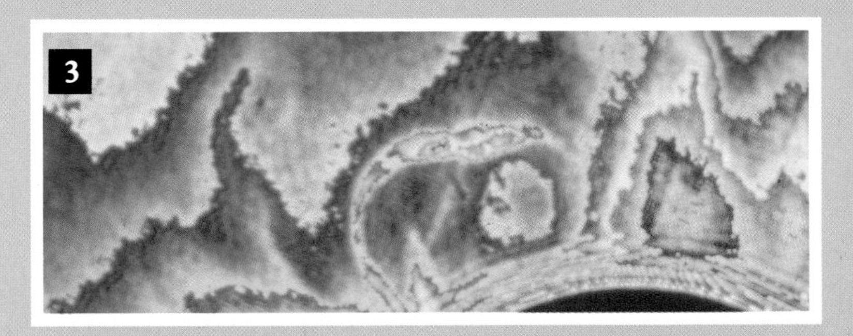

3

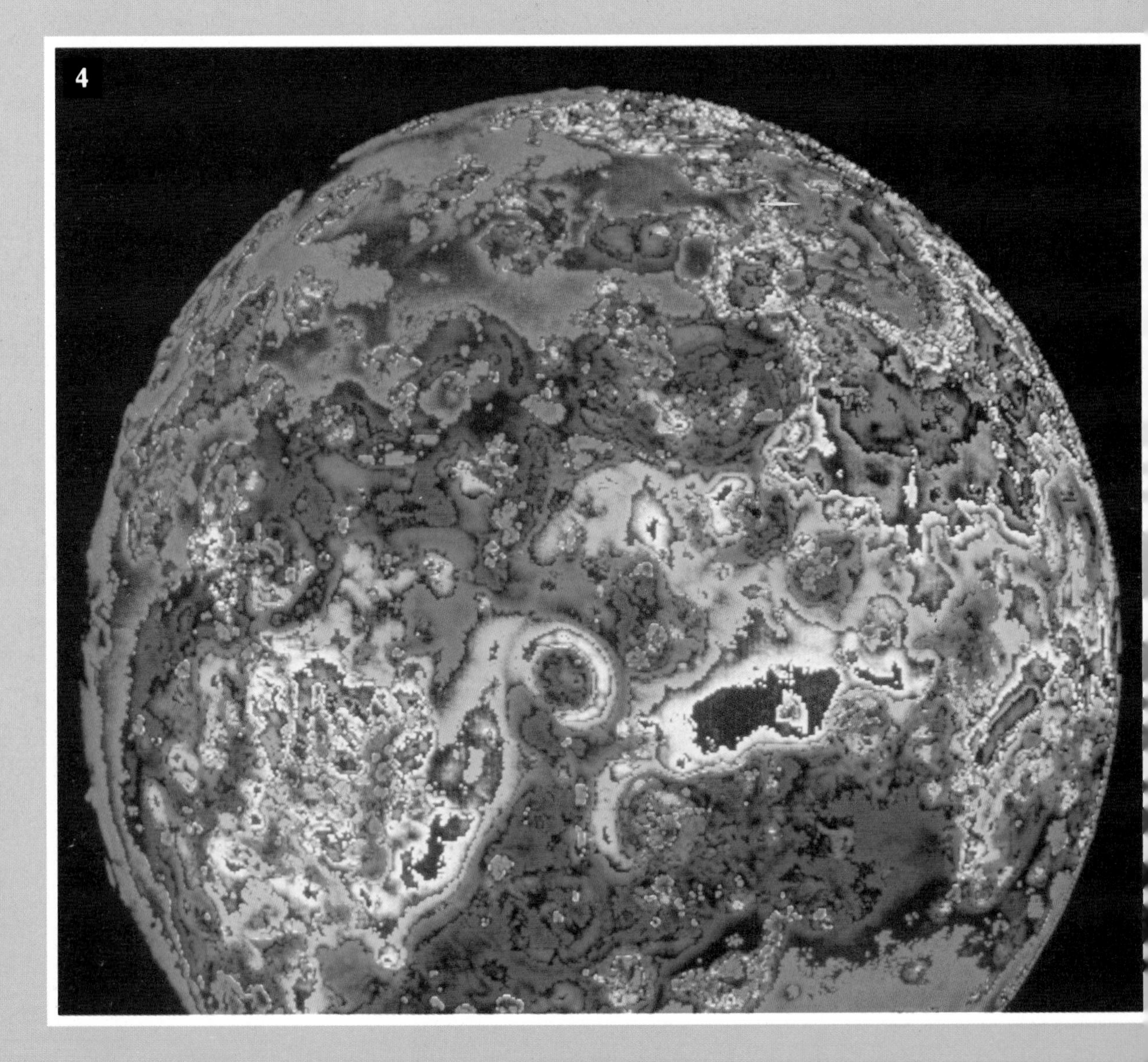

4

2 The curvature shown in this computer-produced drawing of Io, one of Jupiter's moons, can be used to calculate its diameter.

3 Actual colors from this explosion on the sun are translated by computers into this photograph to show differences in temperature.

4 This photo of one of Jupiter's moons was radioed to earth and processed by computer to show its geometry more clearly.

5 A computerized brain scanner provides a "map" permitting researchers to study brain activity. This photo shows a normal human brain.

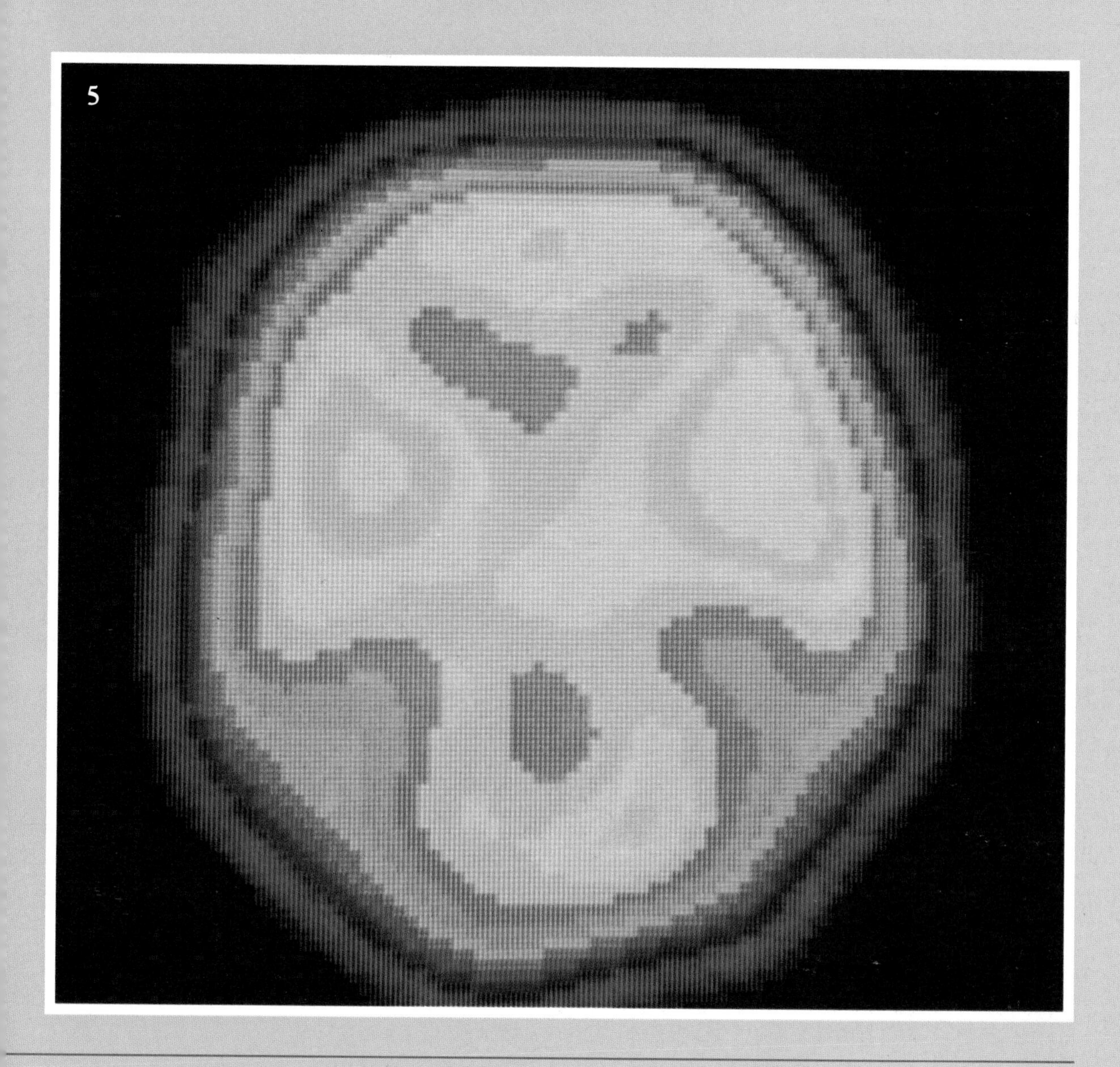

6 An example of abstract design shows the computer's capability.

7 The geometry of these curves is important in analyzing business activity.

8 The surface in this graph looks like a three-dimensional image of a cowboy hat.

9 The graph above is now shown in a two-dimensional countour plot.

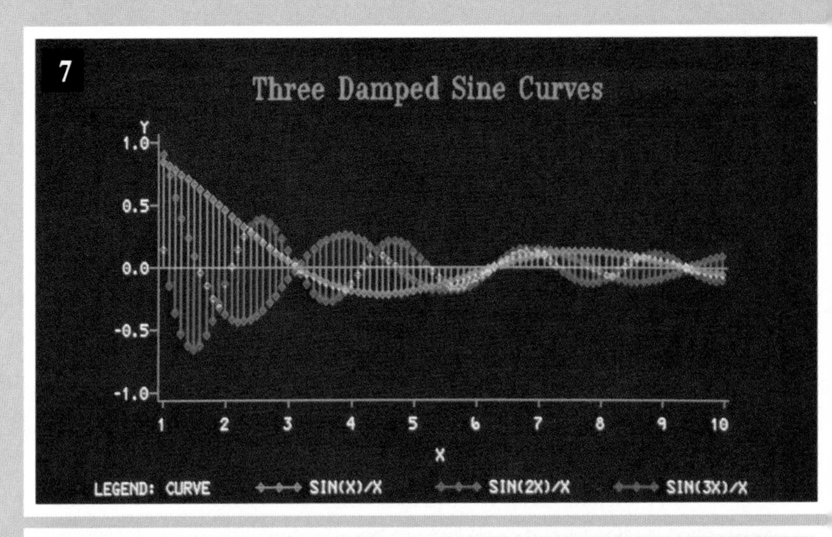

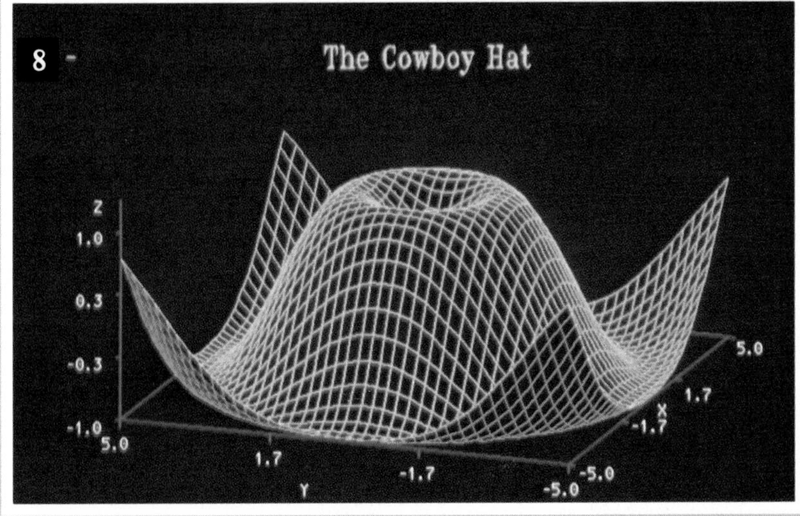

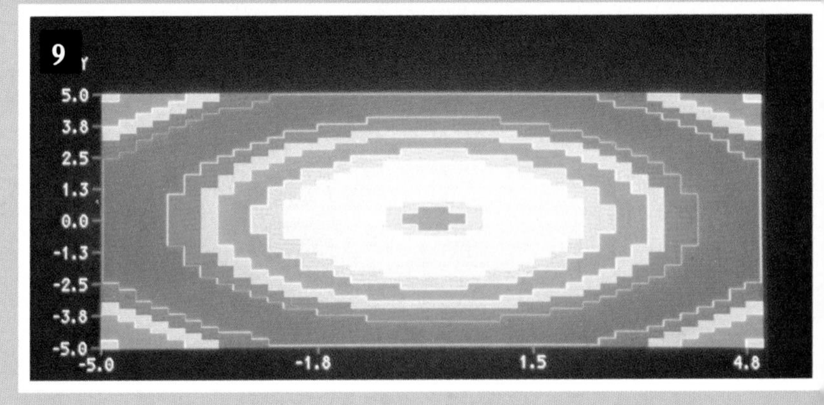

The Geometry of a Silicon Chip

A silicon chip, the heart of a computer, is a miracle of miniaturization. Electrical circuits are drawn by engineers and then photographically reduced 500 times smaller. Then the circuits are reproduced on a sheet of silicon for use inside the computer. In these photos the geometric concepts of congruence, similarity, parallel, and perpendicular are all strikingly apparent.

1 **The gray rectangular piece mounted on this carrier is a silicon chip. Mass-produced chips are identical in their finest detail.**

2 **The size of a chip and its carrier are dramatically illustrated.**

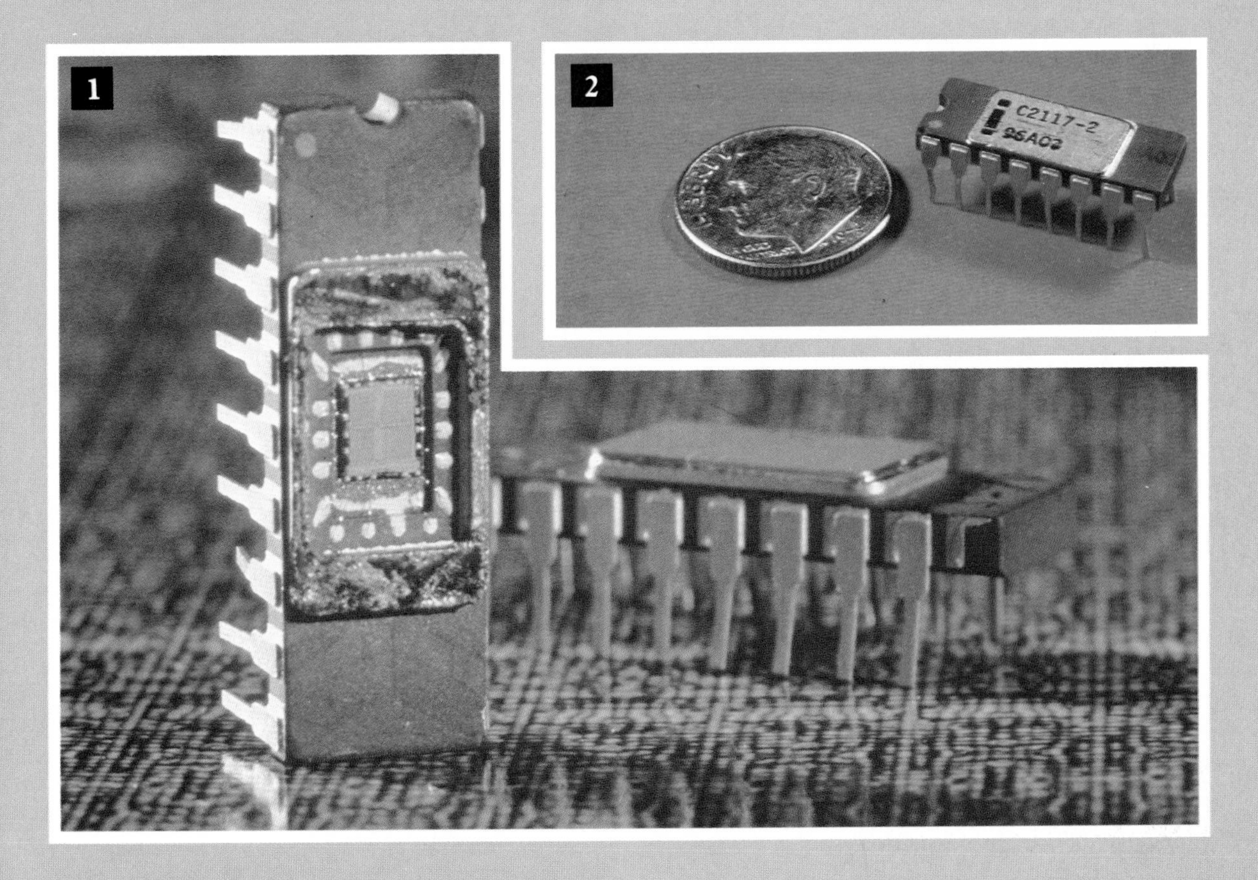

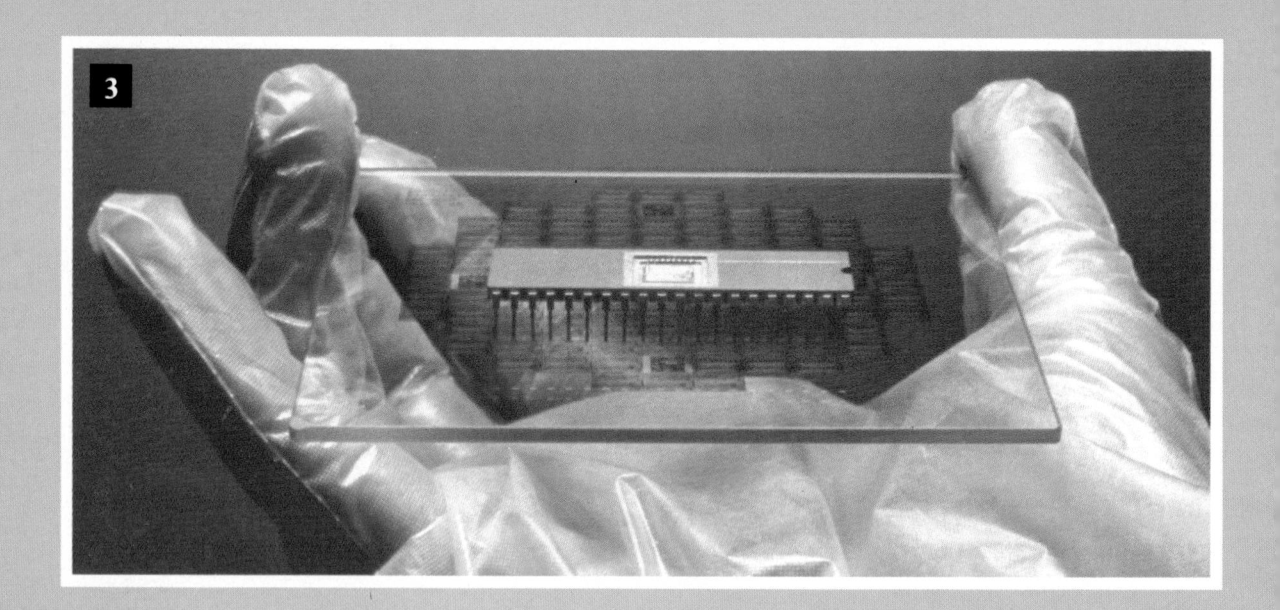
3

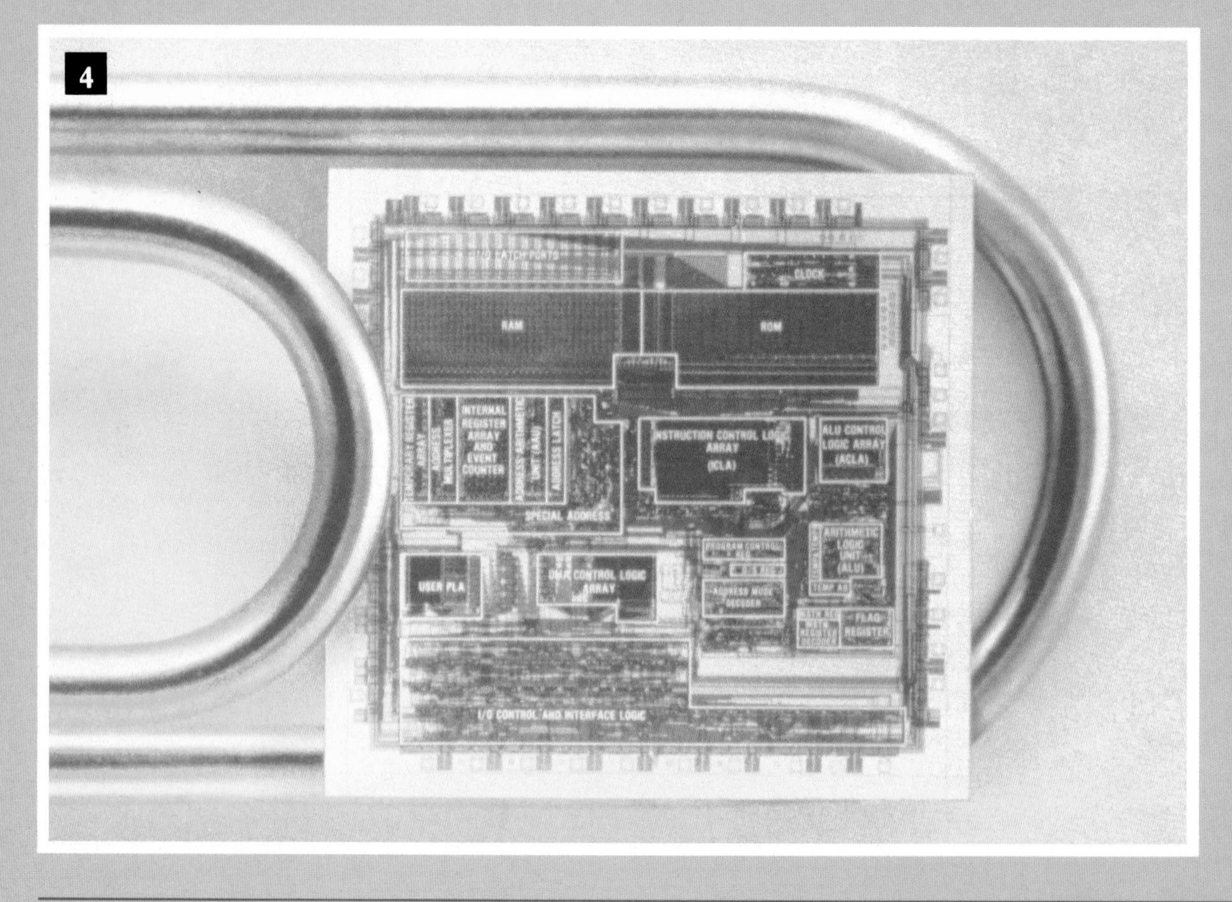
4
CLOCK
RAM
ROM
INTERNAL REGISTER ARRAY AND EVENT COUNTER
ADDRESS LATCH
INSTRUCTION CONTROL LOGIC ARRAY (ICLA)
ALU CONTROL LOGIC ARRAY (ACLA)
SPECIAL ADDRESS
ARITHMETIC LOGIC UNIT (ALU)
USER PLA
DMA CONTROL LOGIC ARRAY
FLAG REGISTER
I/O CONTROL AND INTERFACE LOGIC

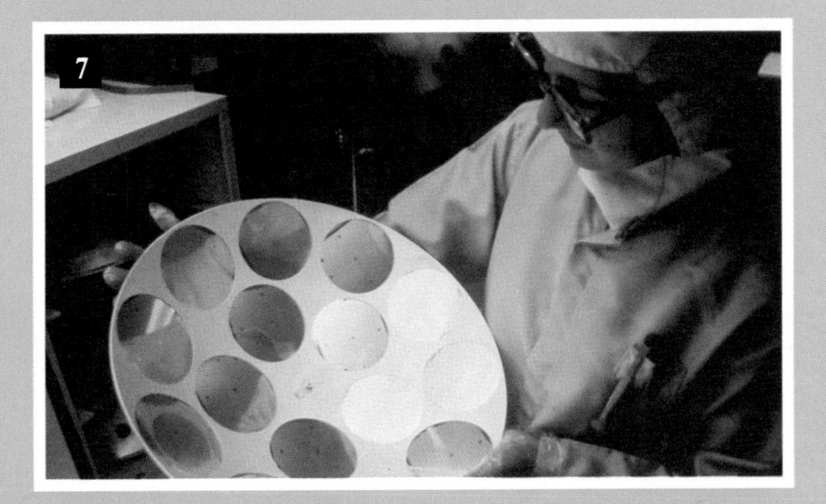

3 This chip and its holder are ready to be plugged into a printed circuit board along with other components to do useful work.

4 Space visualization skills are used in creating chip designs. Component parts are shaped so that they fit together with little wasted space.

5 Difficult space visualization problems must be solved to design such an intricate network.

6 Original drawings as large as 8 feet by 8 feet are made. Notice how polygon shapes are joined with parallel and perpendicular electrical impulse paths.

7 The large diagram is photographically reduced and manufactured onto these disks like a sheet of postage stamps.

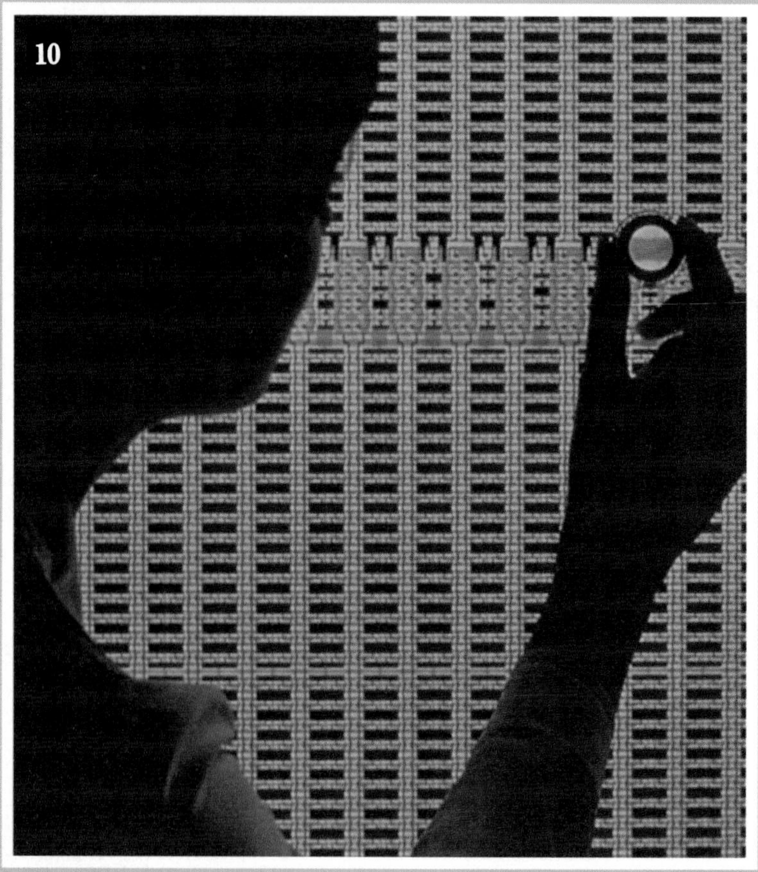

10

8 **A disk of chips is compared to a single chip. Notice that the disk is a tesselation of chips.**

9 **Here, only one layer of circuitry is complete. As many as ten layers may be placed one on top of another to make one chip. The circuit designer has a very interesting geometric puzzle.**

10 **A technician checks circuits before they are reduced. Any flaw must be detected at this stage. Notice the role of symmetry and repeating patterns in circuit design.**

Use Theorems 4-7 and 4-8 in exercises 19-22.

19. Given: $\overline{AD} \cong \overline{CD}$
$\overline{BD} \perp \overline{AC}$
$\angle 1 \cong \angle 2$
Prove: $\triangle ABD \cong \triangle CBD$

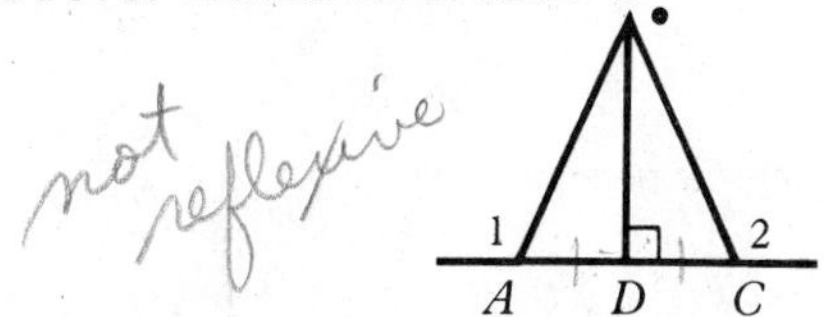

20. Given: $\angle BAX \cong \angle DAX$
$\angle BCY \cong \angle DCY$
Prove: $\overline{BC} \cong \overline{DC}$

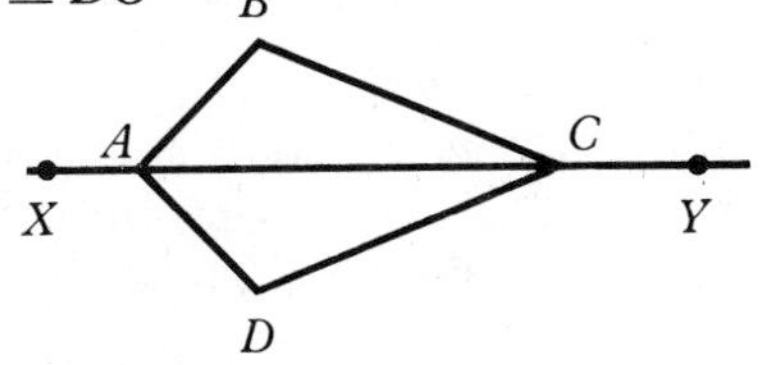

21. Given: $ABCD$ is a quadrilateral with all sides equal in length.
$\angle 1 \cong \angle 2$
W, X, Y, Z are midpoints of the sides.
Prove: $\triangle BWX \cong \triangle DZY$

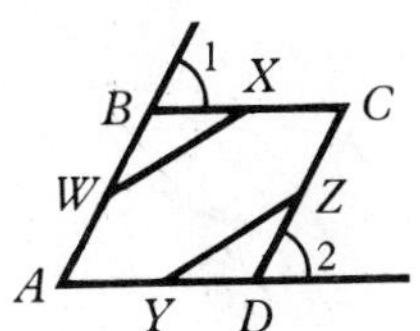

22. Given: $\overline{AC} \perp \overline{AB}$, $\overline{BD} \perp \overline{AB}$
$\angle 1 \cong \angle 2$
Prove: $\overline{AD} \cong \overline{BC}$

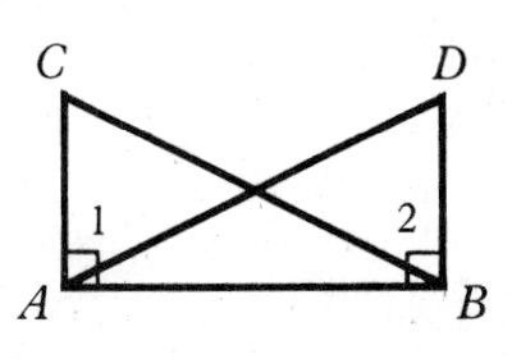

C.

23. Given: $\angle 1 \cong \angle 2$
$\angle 3 \cong \angle 4$
$\overline{BE} \cong \overline{DE}$
$\overline{AB} \perp \overline{BC}$, $\overline{AD} \perp \overline{CD}$
Prove: $\triangle BEC \cong \triangle DEC$

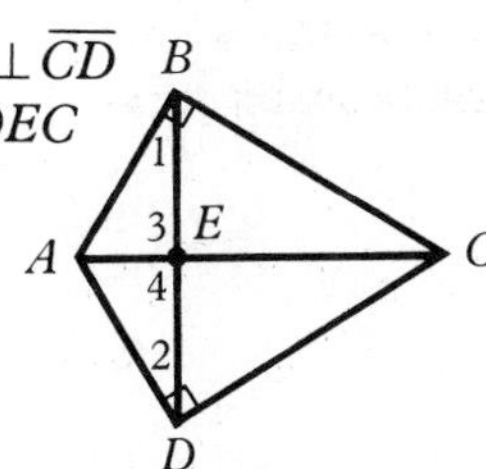

24. Given: $\overline{AB} \perp \overrightarrow{OE}$, O is the midpoint of $\overline{AB}$.
$\angle A \cong \angle B$
$\angle 1 \cong \angle 2$
Prove: $\triangle AOD \cong \triangle BOC$

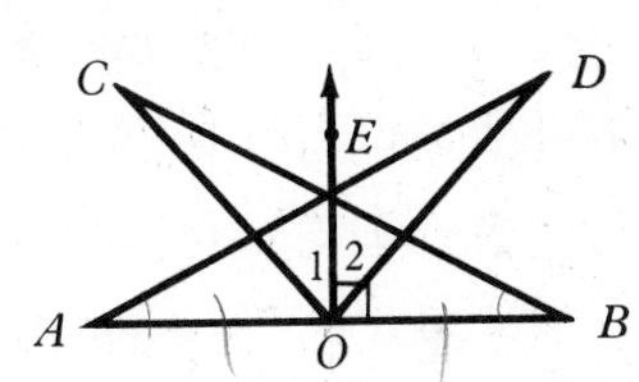

25. Prove the second part of Theorem 4-7.

26. Prove Theorem 4-8.

PROBLEM SOLVING

1. Use a calculator and a "guess and check" method to find two decimals x and y such that $x - y = 1$ and $x \cdot y = 1$.

2. If $\frac{AB}{AC} = \frac{AC}{CB}$ this line is divided into a special ratio called the *golden section*. Show that AB is the same as the number x you found in problem 1.

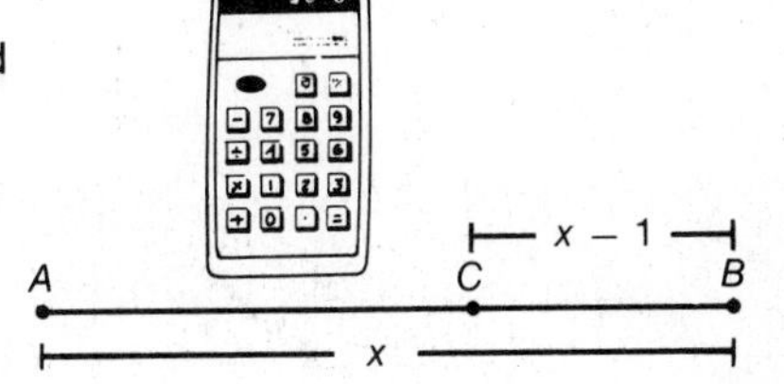

4-4 Proving Theorems—Using Vertical Angles

In this lesson we study pairs of angles formed by a pair of intersecting lines.

The windmill shown here provides many examples of angles formed by intersecting lines. In addition to many linear pairs of angles, there are many pairs of angles that are across from each other. These are called vertical angles. The theorems in this lesson are about the relationships between angles formed by intersecting lines.

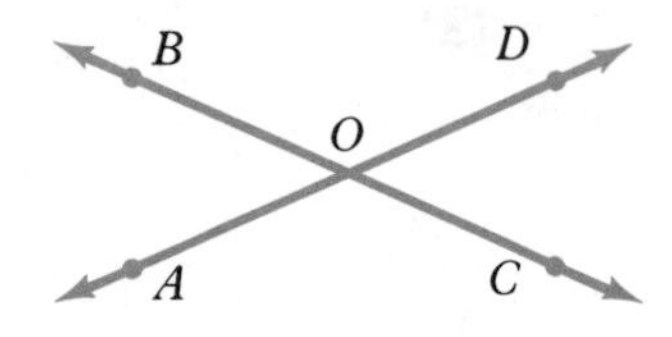

$\overleftrightarrow{BC}$ and $\overleftrightarrow{AD}$ intersect at O.

$\angle AOB$ and $\angle COD$ are vertical angles.

Definition 4-4

Vertical angles are two angles which are formed by two intersecting lines but which are not a linear pair of angles.

Can you convince someone that these five statements are true about the angles formed by the intersecting lines ℓ and m?

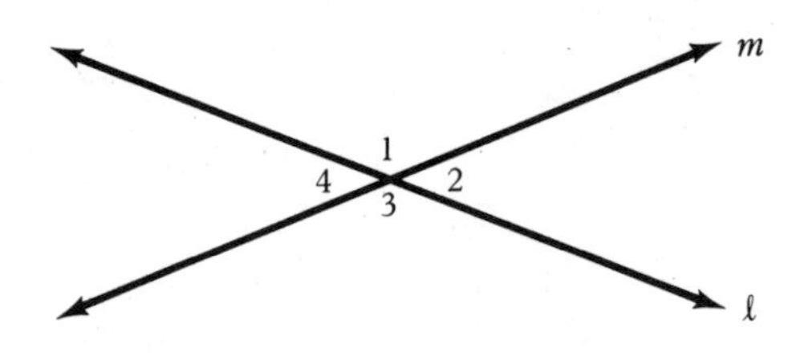

1. $\angle 1$ and $\angle 2$ are supplementary.
2. $\angle 3$ and $\angle 2$ are supplementary.
3. $\angle 1$ and $\angle 3$ are congruent.
4. $\angle 3$ and $\angle 4$ are supplementary.
5. $\angle 2$ and $\angle 4$ are congruent.

The situations above lead to the following theorem.

Theorem 4-9 **Vertical Angles Theorem.** If two lines intersect, the vertical angles are congruent.

PROOF

Step 1 This step is already completed by the statement of the theorem.

Step 2

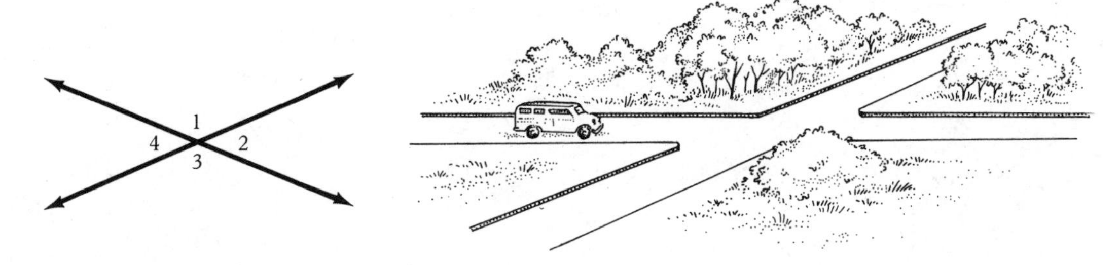

Step 3 **Given:** Two pairs of vertical angles,
$\angle 1$ and $\angle 3$
$\angle 2$ and $\angle 4$

Step 4 **Prove:** $\angle 1 \cong \angle 3$, and
$\angle 2 \cong \angle 4$

Step 5 I shall prove that $\angle 1 \cong \angle 3$ by using the fact that $\angle 1$ and $\angle 2$ form a linear pair, and that $\angle 2$ and $\angle 3$ form a linear pair. Then I shall use the Linear Pair Postulate and the Congruent Supplements Theorem.

The proof that $\angle 2 \cong \angle 4$ will be identical so I shall not repeat the proof a second time.

Step 6

Statements	Reasons
1. $\angle 1$ and $\angle 3$ are vertical angles	**1.** Given
2. $\angle 1$ and $\angle 2$ form a linear pair	**2.** Definition of linear pair
3. $\angle 1$ is supplementary to $\angle 2$	**3.** Linear Pair Postulate
4. $\angle 3$ and $\angle 2$ form a linear pair	**4.** Why?
5. $\angle 3$ is supplementary to $\angle 2$	**5.** Why?
6. $\angle 1 \cong \angle 3$	**6.** Congruent Supplements Theorem

The following theorem also relates to linear pairs of angles.

Theorem 4–10 If one angle of a linear pair is a right angle, then the other is also a right angle.

EXERCISES

A.

1. Name two pairs of right angles that are vertical angles.
2. Name a pair of acute angles that are vertical angles.
3. Name a pair of obtuse angles that are vertical angles.
4. Name six pairs of congruent angles.

(Exs. 1-4)

If $m\angle 2 = 35$, give the measures in exercises 5-8.

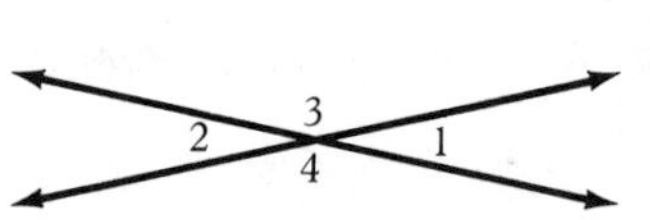

(Exs. 5-8)

5. $m\angle 3 = \underline{?}$
6. $m\angle 1 = \underline{?}$
7. $m\angle 4 = \underline{?}$
8. $m\angle 1 + m\angle 4 = \underline{?}$

Use the information given in exercises 9-11 to find the angle measures.

9. $m\angle RVQ = 4x$
   $m\angle SVT = 2x + 20$
   $m\angle RVQ = \underline{?}$
10. $m\angle QVT = 5x$
    $m\angle RVS = 8x - 45$
    $m\angle RVS = \underline{?}$
11. $m\angle RVQ = 2x + 30$
    $m\angle SVT = 3x + 20$
    $m\angle SVT = \underline{?}$

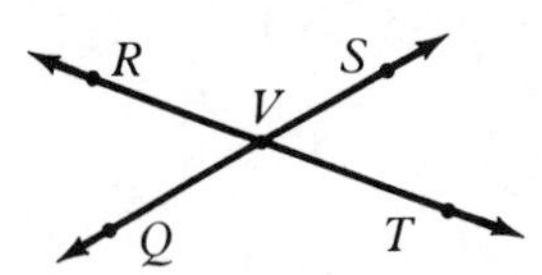

(Exs. 9-11)

B.

Write two-column proofs for these exercises. Often Theorem 4-9 can be used.

12. **Given:** $\overline{AB}$ and $\overline{CD}$ intersecting at O
    $\overline{AO} \cong \overline{OB}$
    $\angle A \cong \angle B$
    Prove: $\triangle AOC \cong \triangle BOD$

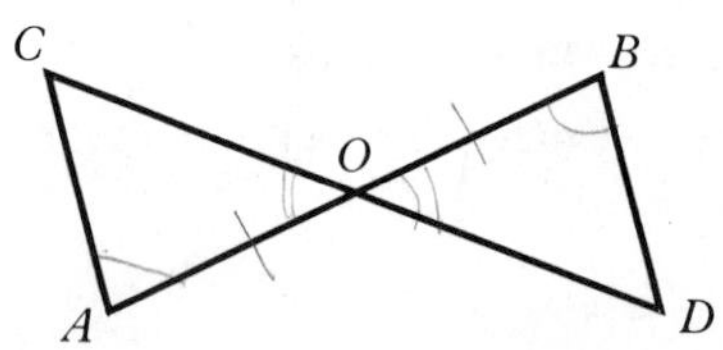

Activity

Mark two points A and B on your paper and lay down another sheet of paper as shown so that one side of the sheet is on A and the other side on B. Mark red point P_1. Do this again with the paper in another position and mark point P_2. Continue this until you have marked 20 different points. What is the locus of points P_1, P_2, P_3, P_4, P_5, P_6, etc.?

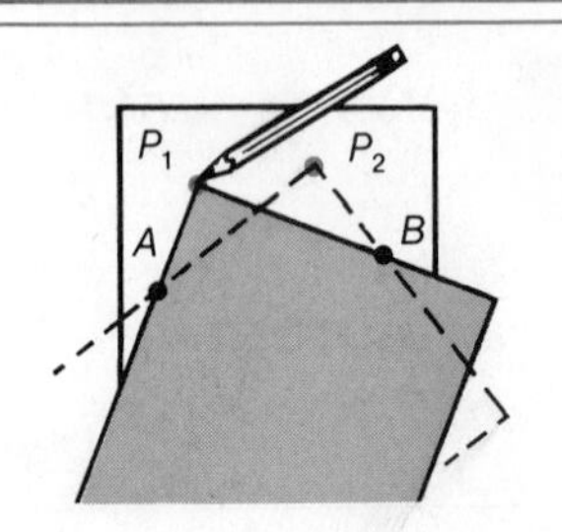

13. Given: $\overline{AB}$ and $\overline{CD}$ intersecting at O
$\overline{AB}$ bisects $\overline{CD}$.
$\angle C \cong \angle D$
Prove: $\triangle AOC \cong \triangle BOD$

14. Given: $\overline{AB}$ and $\overline{CD}$ intersect at their midpoints.
Prove: $\overline{AC} \cong \overline{BD}$

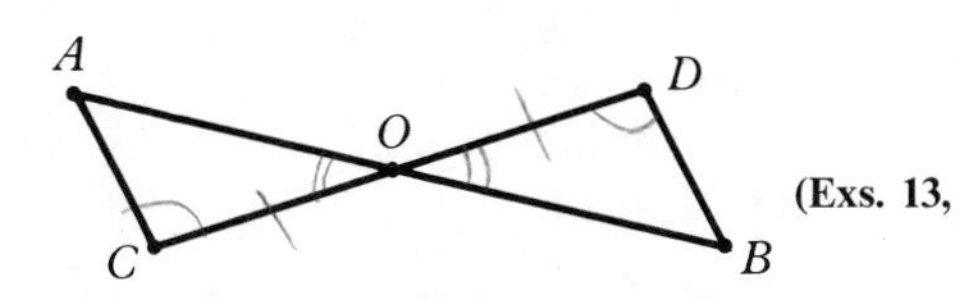

(Exs. 13, 14)

15. Given: $\overline{AE} \cong \overline{DE}$
$\overline{BE} \cong \overline{CE}$
Prove: $\overline{AB} \cong \overline{CD}$

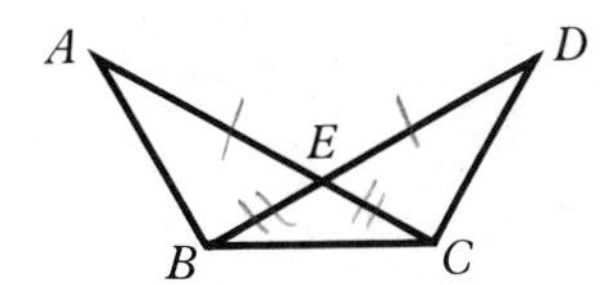

C.

16. Given: $\overrightarrow{BC}$ bisects $\angle ABD$.
$\angle 1 \cong \angle 2$
Prove: $\triangle ABC \cong \triangle DBC$

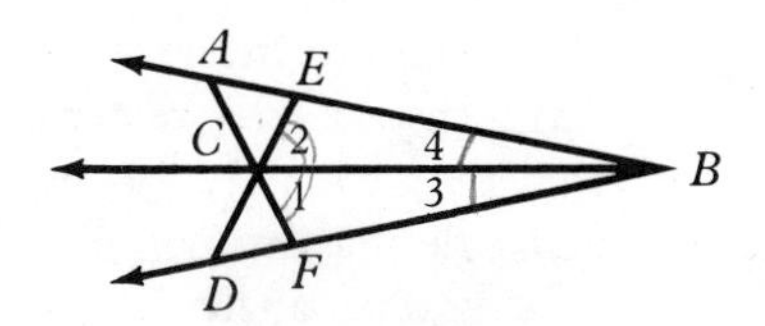

17. Given: $\overline{AE} \cong \overline{DE}$
$\overline{BE} \cong \overline{CE}$
Prove: $\triangle ABC \cong \triangle DCB$

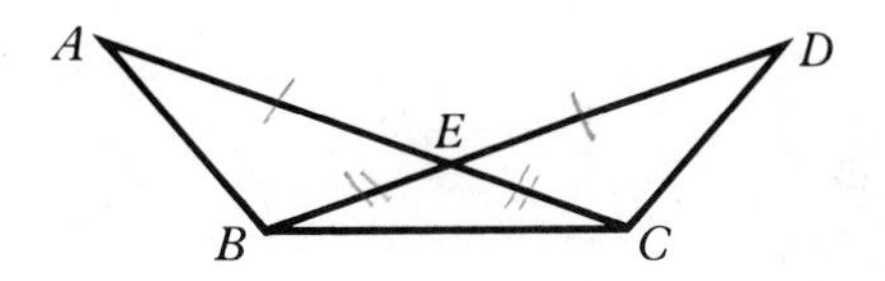

18. Prove: If two angles in a linear pair are congruent, then the angles are right angles.

19. Prove: If an angle is congruent to its supplement, then the angle is a right angle.

PROBLEM SOLVING

Suppose you have a board shaped as shown. You want to saw it into three pieces that can be rearranged to form a square. How can this be done, using two cuts? (*Hint:* Use the midpoint, M, of $\overline{BC}$.)

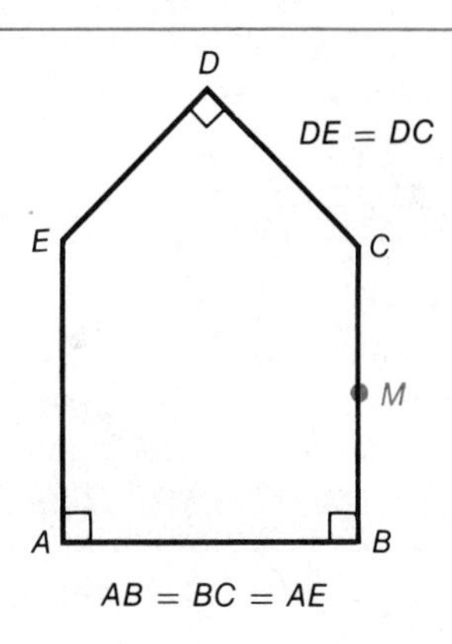

4–5 Proving Theorems—Using Exterior Angles

REVIEW: Some Inequality Properties of Real Numbers

Definition of Greater Than: $a > b$ means that $a = b + c$ and c is a positive number.

Transitive Property: If $a > b$ and $b > c$, then $a > c$.

Addition Property: If $a > b$, then $a + c > b + c$.

Multiplication Property: If $a > b$ and $c > 0$, $ac > bc$. If $a > b$ and $c < 0$, $ac < bc$.

Trichotomy Property: For real numbers a and b, one and only one of the following is true: $a = b$, $a > b$, or $a < b$.

The number properties listed above will be used to prove the theorem in this lesson. First, we need two definitions.

Exterior angle

Remote interior angles

Definition 4-5

An **exterior angle** of a triangle is an angle that forms a linear pair with one of the angles of the triangle.

Definition 4-6

The **remote interior angles** with respect to an exterior angle are the two angles of the triangle that are not adjacent to the exterior angle.

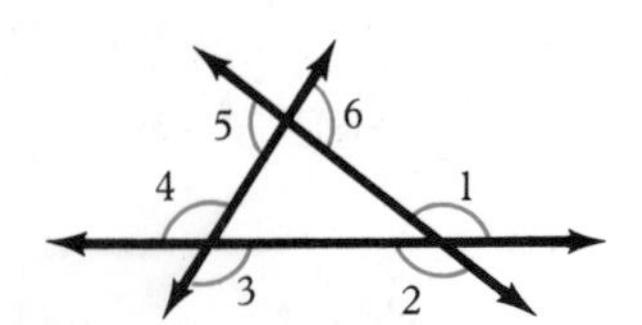

Note that each triangle has six exterior angles, as shown in this figure.

Trace exterior angle 1 and compare it with the remote interior angles in each triangle below.

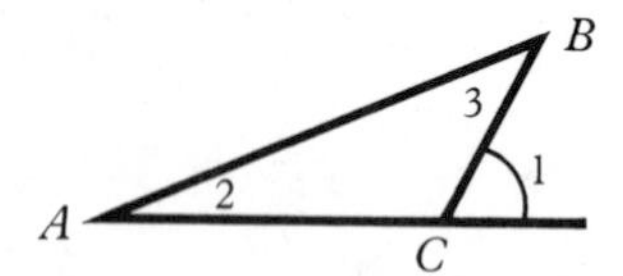

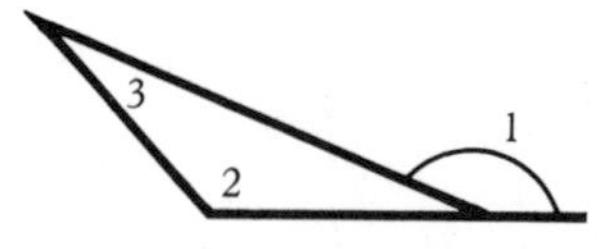

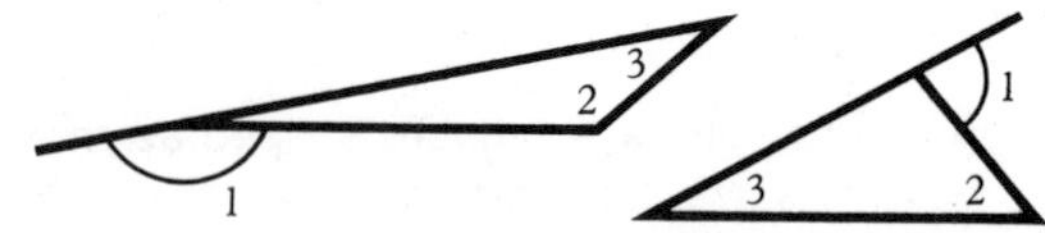

The comparisons lead to the following theorem:

Theorem 4–11 **The Exterior Angle Theorem.** The measure of an exterior angle of a triangle is greater than the measure of either remote interior angle.

PROOF

Given: $\triangle ABC$ with exterior angle, $\angle 1$
Prove: $m\angle 1 > m\angle 2$

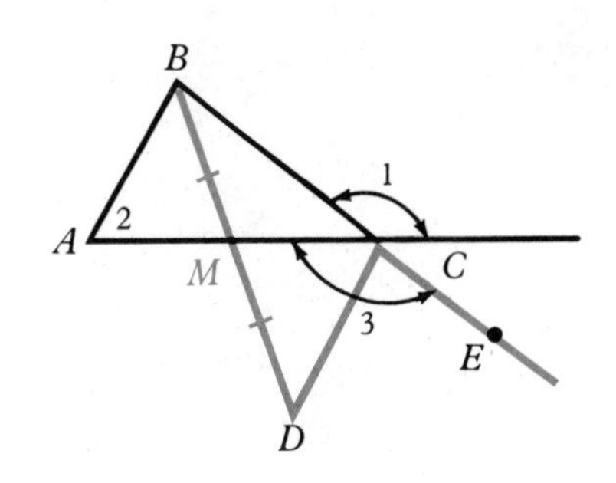

Plan: At this stage in your study of geometry, you would not be expected to plan a proof like this.

Statements	Reasons
1. $\angle 1$ is an exterior angle of $\triangle ABC$.	1. Given
2. Let M be the midpoint of $\overline{AC}$.	2. Choice of M
3. On $\overleftrightarrow{BM}$ choose point D such that $\overline{BM} \cong \overline{MD}$.	3. Point-Line Postulate, choice of D
4. $\overline{AM} \cong \overline{MC}$	4. Definition of midpoint
5. $\angle BMA \cong \angle DMC$	5. Why?
6. $\triangle AMB \cong \triangle CMD$	6. Why?
7. $\angle MCD \cong \angle 2$	7. CPCTC
8. $m\angle MCD = m\angle 2$	8. Definition of angle congruence
9. $m\angle MCD + m\angle DCE = m\angle 3$	9. Definition of between for rays
10. $m\angle 2 + m\angle DEC = m\angle 3$	10. Substitution
11. $m\angle 3 > m\angle 2$	11. Definition of greater than
12. $m\angle 1 = m\angle 3$	12. Why?
13. $m\angle 1 > m\angle 2$	13. Substitution

APPLICATION

Two observers, at points P_1 and P_2, watch a ship sail by. The angles their lines of sight make with the shore line ($\angle 1$, $\angle 2$) are constantly changing. $m\angle 1$ appears to be greater than $m\angle 2$ in both ship positions shown. Will $m\angle 1$ always be greater than $m\angle 2$ as the ship sails much further down the coast line?

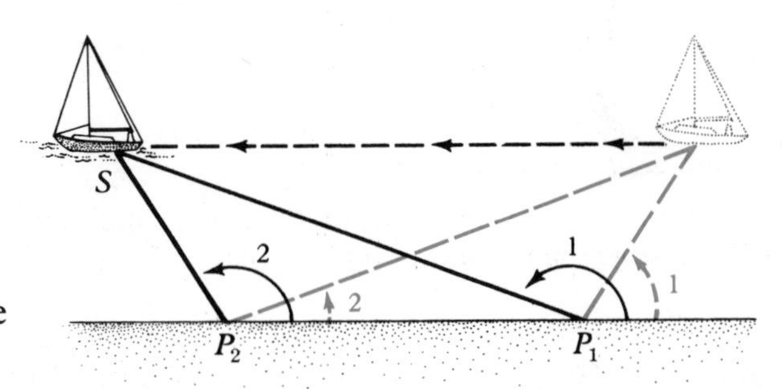

Answer. Because of the Exterior Angle Theorem, we know that $m\angle 1 > m\angle 2$, no matter what the location of the ship. Thus, the angle the observers' lines of sight make with the shore is always greater for the observer at point P_1.

EXERCISES

A.

1. Name the exterior angles. How many exterior angles does a triangle have in all?
2. Name the remote interior angles of $\angle DAC$.
3. Name the remote interior angles of $\angle HAB$.
4. $\angle ABC$ is a remote interior angle for which exterior angles?
5. Is $\angle DAH$ an exterior angle? Why?
6. What is the relationship of $\angle ICB$ to $\angle CBA$?
7. What is the relationship of $\angle ACB$ to $\angle FCI$?
8. What is the relationship of $\angle ABG$ to $\angle ABC$?

(Exs. 1-8)

B.

Explain why each statement is true in exercises 9–12.

9. $m\angle 1 > m\angle 2$
10. $m\angle 3 > m\angle 1$
11. $m\angle 3 > m\angle 4$
12. $m\angle 3 > m\angle 2$

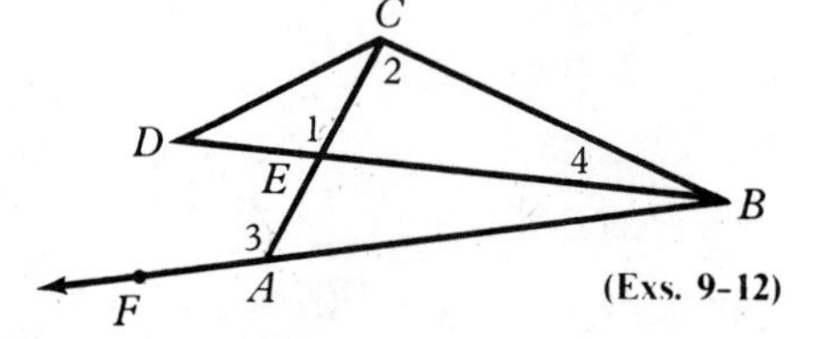

(Exs. 9-12)

13. Use the figure to prove that $m\angle ABD > m\angle EDF$.

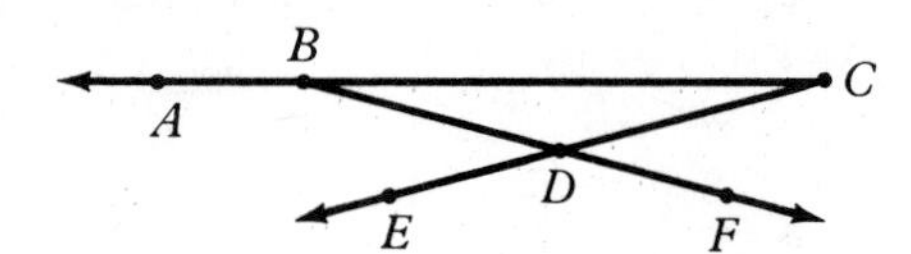

Activity

Trace and cut an equilateral triangle as shown and arrange the pieces to form a square.

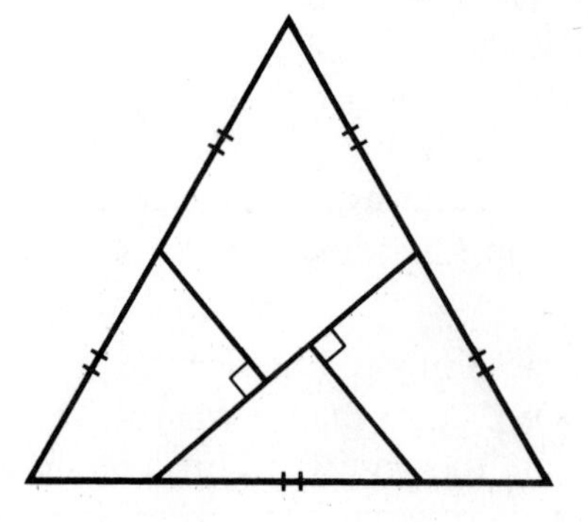

14. Use this figure to prove that $m\angle 1 > m\angle 6$.

15. Given: $\triangle ABC$ is a triangle with right angle $\angle B$.
Prove: $\angle RCB$ is an obtuse angle.

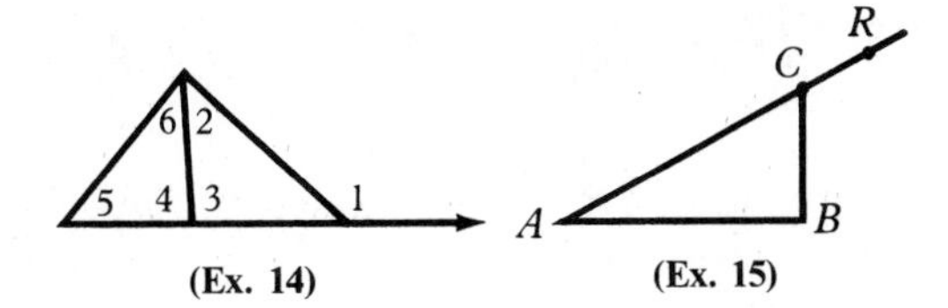

(Ex. 14) (Ex. 15)

C.

Use the Exterior Angle Theorem to prove the theorems in exercises 16–17.

16. A triangle with one right angle has two acute angles.

17. If a triangle has one obtuse angle, then the other two angles are acute.

18. On page 155, a proof is given that $m\angle 1 > m\angle 2$. Use a similar method and prove that $m\angle 1 > m\angle 3$. (*Hint:* Use the midpoint of $\overline{BC}$.)

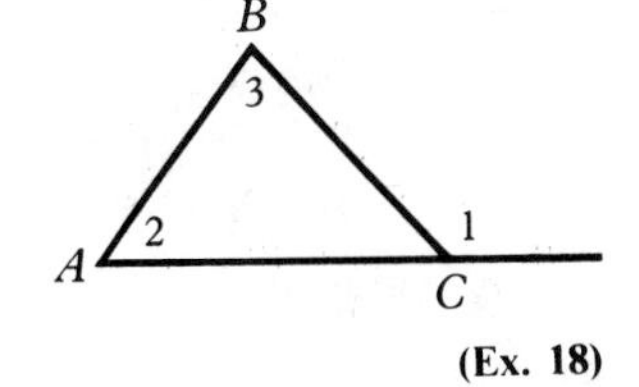

(Ex. 18)

19. Prove that a triangle cannot have both a right angle and an obtuse angle.

PROBLEM SOLVING

Auxiliary lines are sometimes introduced to help solve a problem. But we have to be sure that the lines that are introduced exist. Consider the following proof.

"Theorem": Every triangle is isosceles.

Given: $\triangle ABC$
Prove: $\triangle ABC$ is isosceles.

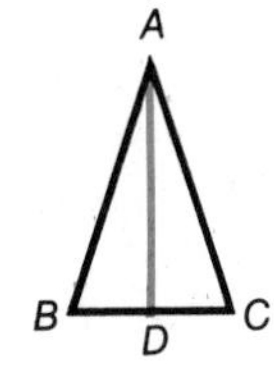

Statements	Reasons
1. Draw in the line through A and D, the midpoint of $\overline{BC}$, that is perpendicular to $\overline{BC}$.	**1.** Construction of $\overline{AD}$
2. $\overline{AD} \cong \overline{AD}$	**2.** Reflexive property of congruence
3. $\overline{BD} \cong \overline{DC}$	**3.** Def. of midpoint
4. $\angle ADB \cong \angle ADC$	**4.** Def. of perpendicular
5. $\triangle ADB \cong \triangle ADC$	**5.** SAS Postulate
6. $\overline{AB} \cong \overline{AC}$	**6.** Corresponding parts
7. $\triangle ABC$ is isosceles	**7.** Def. of isosceles

Explain what is wrong with the proof. Draw a counterexample to show that statement 1 describes a line that does not always exist.

4–6 Using Indirect Proof

The method of Direct Proof used so far involves starting with given conditions and deducing that a conclusion is true. Indirect Proof is illustrated by what might happen in this cartoon—if B.C. cooperates! Suppoose B.C. eats the berry but does not die. An indirect proof that the berry is not poison could be the following.

Suppose the berry is poison.
If B.C. eats it, he will die.
B.C. ate it, but didn't die.
Therefore, the berry is not poison!

This method of proof involves assuming the negation of what you want to prove. Using reasoning, we show that the assumption leads to a contradiction. Thus, the statement to be proved must be true.

B.C. by permission of Johnny Hart and Field Enterprises, Inc.

We summarize the steps for indirect proof below:

Steps for Proving a Theorem Using Indirect Proof

Step 1 Write the "GIVEN" and "PROVE" from the hypothesis and conclusion of the if-then statement.

Step 2 Assume the negation of the "PROVE" statement. (INDIRECT PROOF ASSUMPTION)

Step 3 Write the steps in the proof to show that the assumption leads to the contradiction of a known fact (theorem, definition, given information, etc.).

Step 4 Conclude that the assumption is false and that the "PROVE" statement is true.

We illustrate Indirect Proof by proving two theorems.

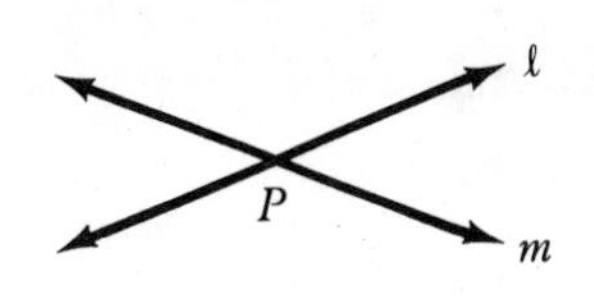

Theorem: If two lines intersect, the intersection is one point.

Given: Lines ℓ and m intersect at a point P.
Prove: P is the only point of intersection. } Step 1

Analysis: Step 2 of an indirect proof is to assume the negation of the "Prove" statement. The negation of "P is the only point of intersection" is "P is *not* the only point of intersection." This means that there is a second point of intersection. Then we show that having two such points leads to a contradiction of a postulate.

	Statements	Reasons
Step 2	1. Suppose P is not the only point of intersection of lines ℓ and m.	1. Indirect proof assumption
Step 3	2. Call the second point of intersection Q.	2. Restatement of 1
	3. ℓ contains both P and Q. m contains both P and Q.	3. Statements 1 and 2
	4. P and Q are contained in two lines (contradiction of Point-Line Postulate).	4. Restatement of 3
Step 4	5. Therefore, P is the only point of intersection of ℓ and m.	5. Logic of indirect proof

Theorem: If two lines are perpendicular to the same line, the two lines are parallel.

Given: $k \perp m$, $\ell \perp m$
Prove: $k \parallel \ell$ } Step 1

	Statements	Reasons
Step 2	1. Assume $k \nparallel \ell$ (k is not parallel to ℓ)	1. Indirect proof assumption
	2. k intersects ℓ at point C.	2. Restatement of 1
Step 3	3. $\triangle ABC$ is formed.	3. Definition of triangle
	4. $m\angle DAC > m\angle ABC$	4. Exterior Angle Theorem
	5. $k \perp m$, $\ell \perp m$	5. Given
	6. $\angle DAC$ and $\angle ABC$ are right angles.	6. Definition of perpendicular lines
	7. $m\angle DAC = m\angle ABC$ (contradiction of $m\angle DAC > m\angle ABC$)	7. All right angles have equal measures.
Step 4	8. Therefore, $k \parallel \ell$	8. Logic of indirect proof

EXERCISES

A.

For each "Prove" statement in exercises 1–10, write the indirect proof assumption you would use to begin the proof, together with the second statement that interprets the indirect proof assumption.

Example: **Prove:** $\ell \parallel m$
Indirect proof assumption: $\ell \nparallel m$
Second statement: Then ℓ intersects m.

1. **Prove:** $\ell \perp m$
2. **Prove:** $\angle A$ is supplementary to $\angle B$.
3. **Prove:** The adjacent sides are not parallel.
4. **Prove:** $\angle A$ is not a right angle.
5. **Prove:** $\overline{AB} \cong \overline{CD}$
6. **Prove:** $\angle A$ and $\angle B$ are not vertical angles.
7. **Prove:** $\angle A$ is an acute angle.
8. **Prove:** There is one and only one line through P and parallel to m.
9. **Prove:** $\triangle ABC$ is an isosceles triangle.
10. **Prove:** $\triangle ABC$ is not an equilateral triangle.

Which pairs of statements in exercises 11–16 would enable you to arrive at a contradiction in an indirect proof?

Examples: $\overline{AB}$ is longer than $\overline{CD}$, and $\overline{CD}$ is longer than $\overline{AB}$. } form a contradiction

$\triangle ABC$ is equilateral and $\triangle ABC$ is isosceles. } do not form a contradiction

11. Lines p and q are parallel and lines p and q do not intersect.
12. $\angle A \cong \angle B$ and $m\angle A > m\angle B$.
13. $\ell \perp m$ and $\ell \not\perp m$. (note: $\not\perp$ means "is not perpendicular to")
14. $\angle A$ and $\angle B$ form a linear pair. $m\angle A < 90$ and $m\angle B < 90$.
15. $\angle A$ is a right angle.
    $\angle A$ is an obtuse angle.
16. $\angle A$ and $\angle B$ are congruent.
    $\angle A$ and $\angle B$ are supplementary.

For exercises 17 and 18 select the statement that is contradictory to the given statement.

17. $\angle A$ and $\angle B$ are supplementary.

a. $m\angle A + m\angle B = 180$

b. $\angle A$ and $\angle B$ form a linear pair.

c. $\angle A$ and $\angle B$ are both acute angles.

d. $\angle A$ and $\angle B$ are vertical angles.

18. Lines p and q are not parallel.

a. Lines p and q have no points in common.

b. Lines p and q intersect.

c. Lines p and q are the same line.

d. Lines p and q lie in a plane and have no points in common.

Write a statement that contradicts the given statement in each of exercises 19–23.

19. $\angle A$ and $\angle B$ are complementary.

20. Lines p and q intersect.

21. $\triangle ABC \cong \triangle XYZ$

22. $ABCDE$ is a regular pentagon.

23. $m\angle A = 117$

For exercises 24–27, write the assumption that would be used in an indirect proof of the given theorem.

24. If two lines do not intersect, then they are not perpendicular.

25. If $AB \neq CD$, then $AB + EF \neq CD + EF$.

26. If a figure is a triangle, then the figure cannot contain two right angles.

27. If two angles form a linear pair, then they are supplementary.

B.

In exercises 28–30 an indirect proof is started. Give the missing reasons and continue the proof to reach a contradiction.

28. Given: In $\triangle ABC$, $\overline{AC} \ncong \overline{AB}$
D is the midpoint of $\overline{BC}$.
Prove: $\overline{AD}$ cannot be perpendicular to $\overline{BC}$.

Statements	Reasons
1. Suppose $\overline{AD} \perp \overline{BC}$.	**1.** Indirect proof assumption
2. $\angle ADC \cong \angle ADB$	**2.** ? All rt <'s are ≅
3. D is midpoint of $\overline{BC}$.	**3.** Given
4. $\overline{CD} \cong \overline{BD}$	**4.** ? Def of midpt
5. $\overline{AD} \cong \overline{AD}$	**5.** ? Reflex
6. $\triangle ADC \cong \triangle ADB$	**6.** SAS Postulate
7. $\overline{AC} \cong \overline{AB}$	**7.** CPCTC
8. ? $\overline{AC} \ncong \overline{AB}$	**8.** ? Given
9. ? ∴ $\overline{AD} \not\perp \overline{BC}$	**9.** ? Logic of Indirect proof

29. Given: $\overline{AD} \perp \overline{BC}$
$\overline{AB} \not\cong \overline{AC}$
Prove: $\overline{BD} \not\cong \overline{DC}$

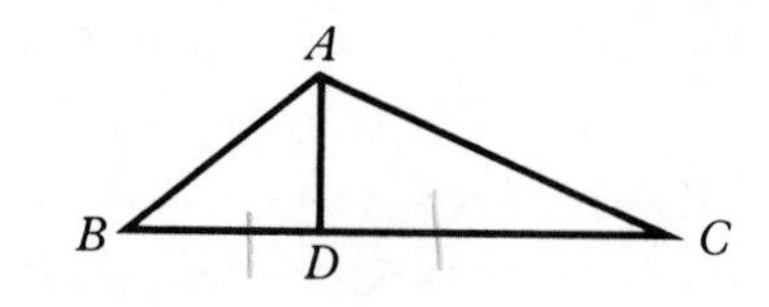

Statements	Reasons
1. Suppose $\overline{BD} \cong \overline{DC}$.	1. ? Indirect proof assump
2. $\overline{AD} \perp \overline{BC}$	2. ? Given
3. $\angle BDA \cong \angle ADC$	3. Definition of perpendicular
4. $\overline{AD} \cong \overline{AD}$	4. ? Reflex
5. $\triangle ADB \cong \triangle ADC$	5. ? SAS
6. ? AB ≅ AC	6. ? corr parts
7. ? AB ≇ AC	7. ? given
8. ? BD ≇ DC	8. ? logic of ind prf

Activity

Either the object pictured can exist in the real world or it cannot. Suppose it can . . . ?

Continue the above argument for each figure and see if you can reach a contradiction of real-world facts.

Look for other pictures of objects such as these which are contradictory.

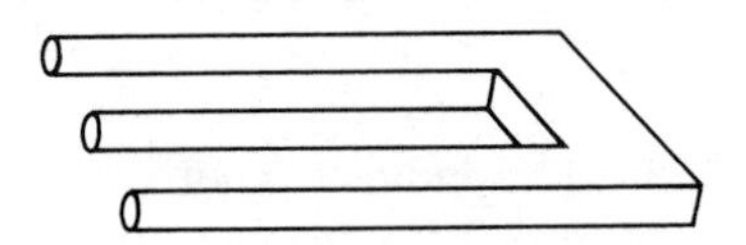

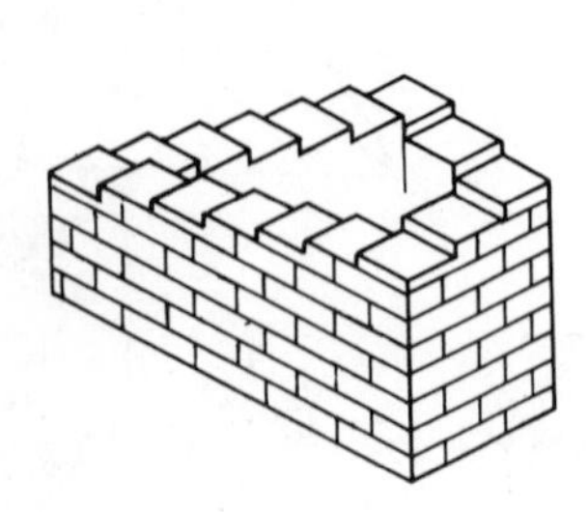

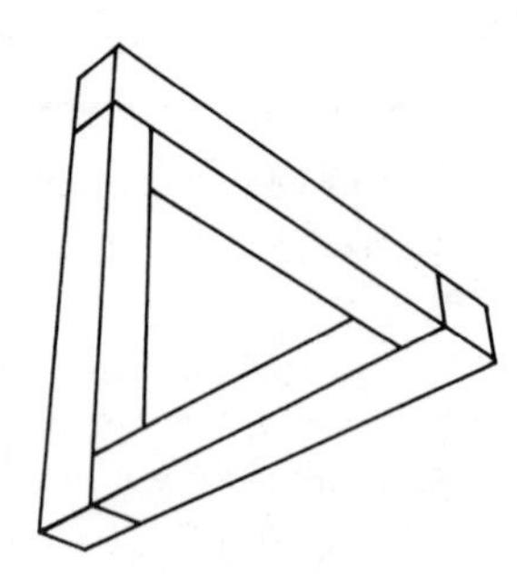

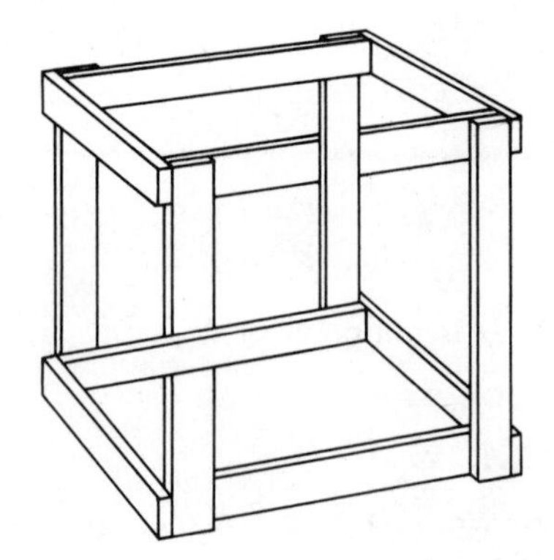

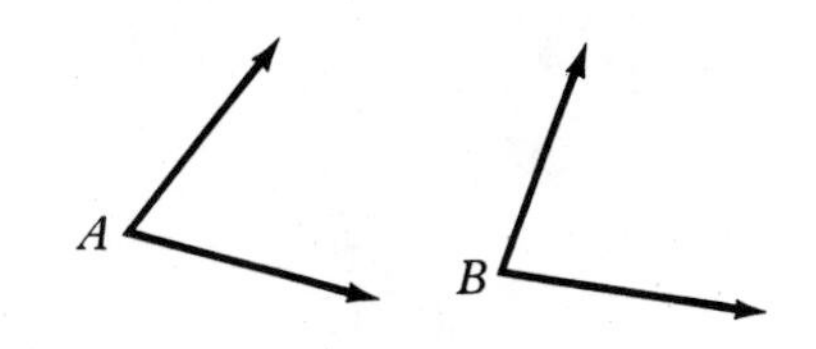

30. Given: $\angle A$ and $\angle B$ are acute.
Prove: $\angle A$ and $\angle B$ are not supplementary.

Statements	Reasons
1. Suppose $\angle A$ is supplementary to $\angle B$.	1. ?
2. $m\angle A + m\angle B = 180$	2. Definition of supplementary
3. $m\angle A < 90$, $m\angle B < 90$	3. Given, definition of acute angle
4. ?	4. Addition Property of Inequality
5. ?	5. ?

C.

31. How might a lawyer use indirect proof? Give an example.

Write a complete indirect proof for each theorem in exercises 32–35.

32. If $AB \neq CD$, then $AB + EF \neq CD + EF$.

33. If $\angle A$ is not congruent to $\angle B$, then $\angle A$ and $\angle B$ are not vertical angles.

34. Given:
$\angle 1$ and $\angle 4$ are not supplementary.
Prove:
$\angle 2$ and $\angle 3$ are not supplementary.

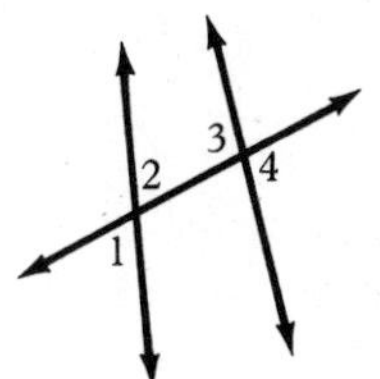

35. Given:
$\overline{AB} \cong \overline{PQ}$
$\overline{AC} \cong \overline{PR}$
$\angle A \ncong \angle P$
Prove: $\overline{BC} \ncong \overline{QR}$

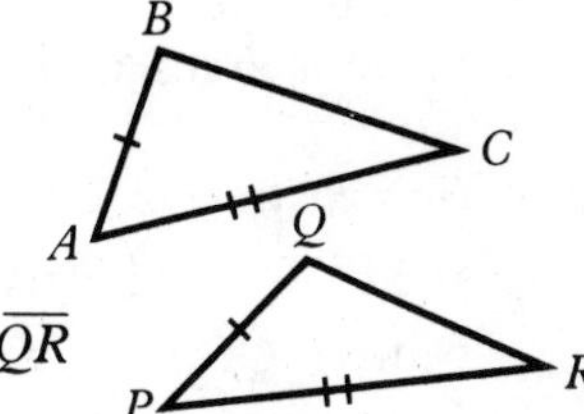

PROBLEM SOLVING

When an advertisement about a bargain radio for sale said "It's a steal," the store owner didn't realize how true it was. She was convinced that either Ann, Bob, Cal, or Dee had stolen the radio. Each person, in turn, made a statement, but only one of the four statements was true.

Ann said "I didn't take it."
Bob said "Ann is lying."
Cal said "Bob is lying."
Dee said "Bob took it."

Who told the truth? Who took the radio?

Important Ideas—Chapter 4

Terms

Complementary angles (p. 144)
Supplementary angles (p. 144)
Linear pair of angles (p. 144)
Vertical angles (p. 150)
Exterior angle of a triangle (p. 154)
Remote interior angle (p. 154)

Postulate

Linear Pair Postulate. If two angles form a linear pair, the angles are supplementary.

Theorems

4-1 The reflexive, symmetric, and transitive properties hold for angle and segment congruence.

4-2 In an isosceles triangle the segment from the vertex angle to the midpoint of the opposite side forms a pair of congruent triangles.

4-3 **Addition of Equal Angles.** If $m\angle APB = m\angle DQE$, $m\angle BPC = m\angle EQF$, $\overrightarrow{PB}$ is between $\overrightarrow{PA}$ and $\overrightarrow{PC}$, and $\overrightarrow{QE}$ is between $\overrightarrow{QD}$ and $\overrightarrow{QF}$, then $m\angle APC = m\angle DQF$.

4-4 **Subtraction of Equal Segments.** If $AC = DF$, $BC = EF$, B is between A and C, and E is between D and F, then $AB = DE$.

4-5 **Addition of Equal Segments.** If $AB = DE$, $BC = EF$, B is between A and C, and E is between D and F, then $AC = DF$.

4-6 **Subtraction of Equal Angles.** If $m\angle APC = m\angle DQF$, $m\angle BPC = m\angle EQF$, $\overrightarrow{PB}$ is between $\overrightarrow{PA}$ and $\overrightarrow{PC}$, and $\overrightarrow{QE}$ is between $\overrightarrow{QD}$ and $\overrightarrow{QF}$, then $m\angle APB = m\angle DQE$.

4-7 **Congruent Complements Theorem.** Two angles that are complementary to the same angle (or congruent angles) are congruent.

4-8 **Congruent Supplements Theorem.** Two angles that are supplementary to the same angle (or to congruent angles) are congruent.

4-9 **Vertical Angles Theorem.** If two lines intersect, the vertical angles are congruent.

4-10 If one angle of a linear pair is a right angle, then the other is also a right angle.

4-11 **Exterior Angle Theorem.** The measure of an exterior angle is greater than the measure of either remote interior angle.

Chapter 4—Review

1. Indicate whether the following statements are true or false.

a. If two angles are supplementary to congruent angles, then they are congruent.

b. The transitive property for congruence of segments states that $\overline{AB} \cong \overline{AB}$.

c. The sum of the measures of two complementary angles is 90°.

In exercises 2 and 3 a theorem is given in if-then form. Draw a picture and state the "Given" and "Prove" using the picture and its labeling.

2. If two angles of a triangle are congruent, then the triangle is isosceles.

3. If two lines are parallel to a third line then they are parallel.

4. Solve for x and find the measure of the angles.

a.

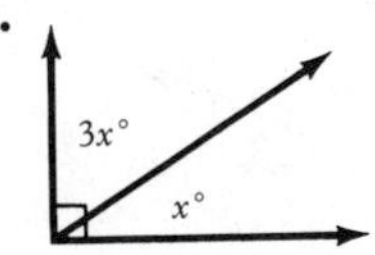

b.

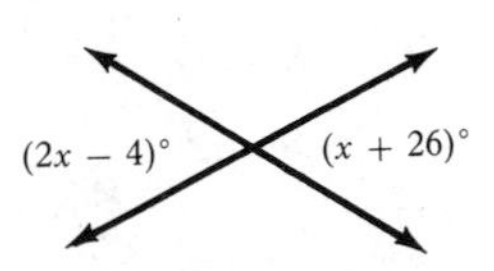

c.

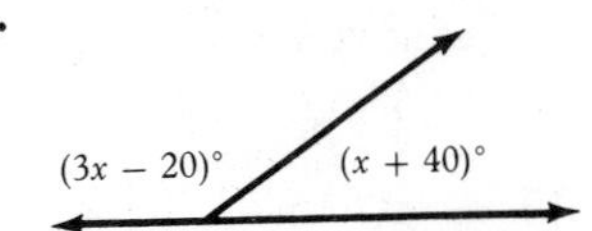

5. What is the measure of an angle that is congruent to its complement?

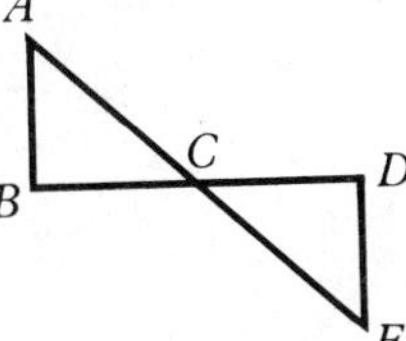

6. Given: $\overline{AB} \perp \overline{BD}$, $\overline{DE} \perp \overline{BD}$, $BC = CD$
Prove: $\triangle ABC \cong \triangle EDC$

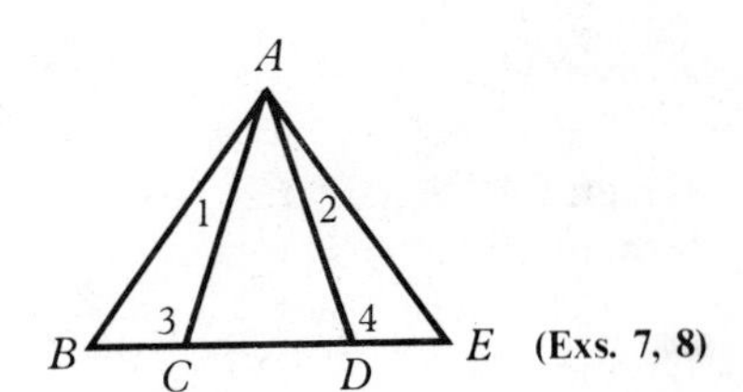

7. Given: $m\angle 1 = m\angle 2$
Prove: $m\angle BAD = m\angle CAE$

8. Given: $\overline{AB} \cong \overline{AE}$, $\angle E \cong \angle B$, and $\angle 1 \cong \angle 2$
Prove: $\angle ACD \cong \angle ADC$

9. For the following "Prove" statements, write the indirect proof assumption you would use to begin the proof.

a. $\overline{AB} \parallel \overline{CD}$

b. $\angle A$ and $\angle B$ are supplementary.

Chapter 4—Test

1. Indicate whether the following statements are true or false.
   a. The measure of an exterior angle of a triangle is greater than the measure of any angle of the triangle.
   b. If two angles are both supplementary and congruent, then each angle is a right angle.
   c. If two angles are supplementary then they form a linear pair.

In exercises 2 and 3 a theorem is given in if-then form. Draw a picture and state the "Given" and "Prove" using the picture and its labeling.

2. If a triangle is equilateral, then the measure of each angle is $60°$.
3. If a line segment joins the midpoints of two sides of a triangle, then the segment is parallel to the third side.
4. Solve for x and find the measures of the angles.

   a. $\angle A$ and $\angle B$ are complementary

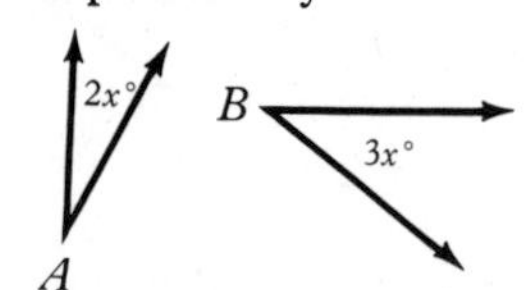

   b.

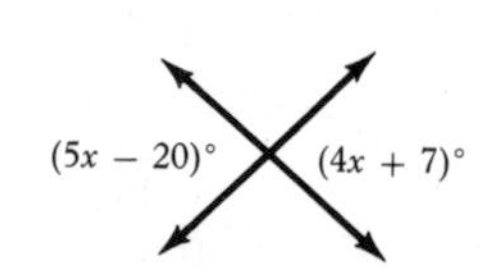

   c.

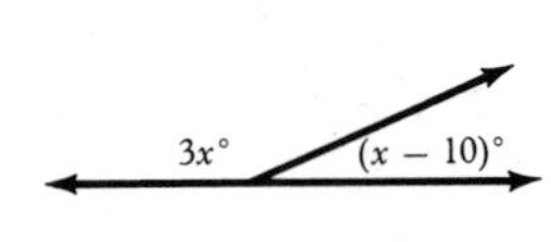

5. What is the measure of an angle whose measure is half the measure of its supplement?

6. **Given:** $m\angle 1 = m\angle 2$
   $m\angle 5 = m\angle 6$
   Prove: $AD = AB$

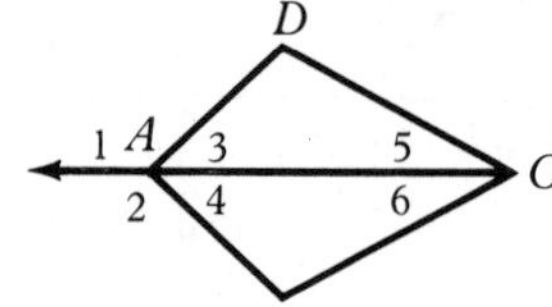
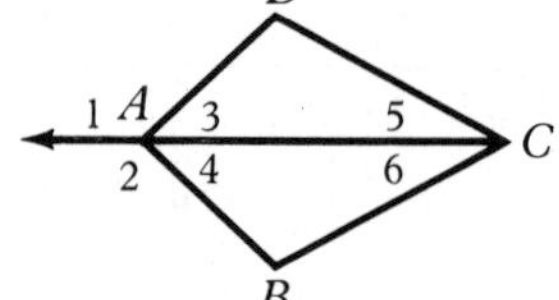

7. **Given:** $AB = CD$, $BD = CE$
   Prove: $AC = CE$

A B C D E

8. **Given:** $\angle 1 \cong \angle 2$, $\overline{DA} \perp \overline{AC}$, $\overline{EB} \perp \overline{AC}$ and $\overline{FC} \perp \overline{AC}$, B is midpoint of $\overline{AC}$.
   Prove: $\overline{AD} \cong \overline{CF}$

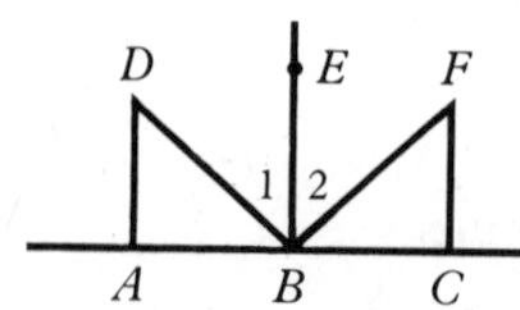

9. For the following "Prove" statements, write the indirect proof assumption you would use to begin the proof.
   a. $\overline{AB} \cong \overline{CD}$
   b. $\angle DEF$ is not a right angle

Problem Solving Techniques

Make a Table-I

A useful technique in solving problems is to make a table and see if a pattern can be observed. Study the example below.

How many squares can you find?

Example

How many squares are on an 8×8 checkerboard?

Consider the table on the right. The number of 1×1, 2×2, 3×3, and 4×4 squares are given. Can you observe a pattern and solve the problem?

Solution. The number of 1×1 squares is 8^2 squares. The number of 2×2 squares is 7^2. The pattern appears to be decreasing perfect squares. So we fill in the table with 16, 9, 4 and 1. To get the total we add and find that it is 204 squares.

Size of square	Number of squares
1×1	64
2×2	49
3×3	36
4×4	25
5×5	?
6×6	?
7×7	?
8×8	?

PROBLEMS

For each problem, make a table, observe a pattern, and solve the problem.

1. How many cubes are in an $8 \times 8 \times 8$ cube? (*Hint:* Make a table similar to the one above. One column lists the size of the cubes: $1 \times 1 \times 1$, $2 \times 2 \times 2$, $3 \times 3 \times 3$, etc. The second column gives the number of each sized cubes.)
2. How many diagonals does a ten-sided polygon have? (*Hint:* Make a table like the one on the right.)

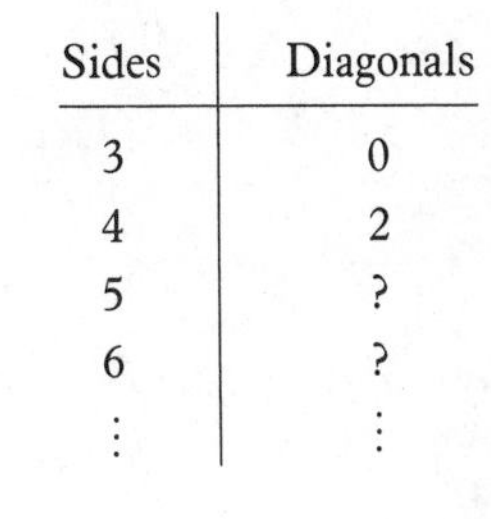

Sides	Diagonals
3	0
4	2
5	?
6	?
⋮	⋮

3. A cevian is a line segment which joins a vertex of a triangle and a point on the opposite side. How many triangles are formed if 8 cevians are drawn from one vertex of a triangle?

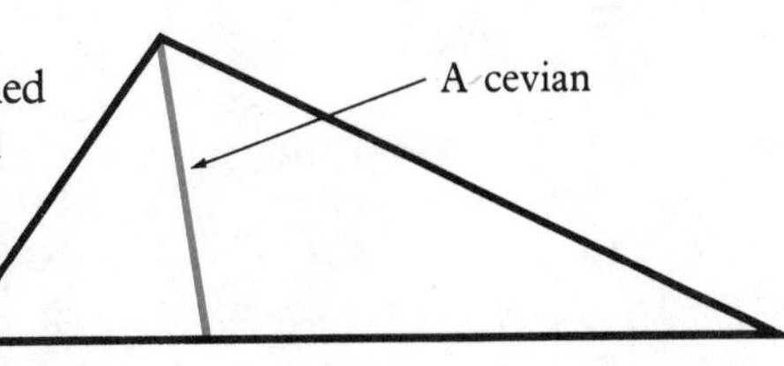

(Note that one cevian gives 3 triangles.)

CHAPTER 5

Parallel Lines and Planes

5–1 Basic Definitions

College students built this bi-plane and named it Chrysalis. It is pedal driven, much like a bicycle. During the summer of 1979 the plane made 320 flights.

This bi-plane uses several concepts that will be studied in this lesson, such as parallel lines, lines parallel to a plane, parallel planes, and nonparallel lines that do not intersect.

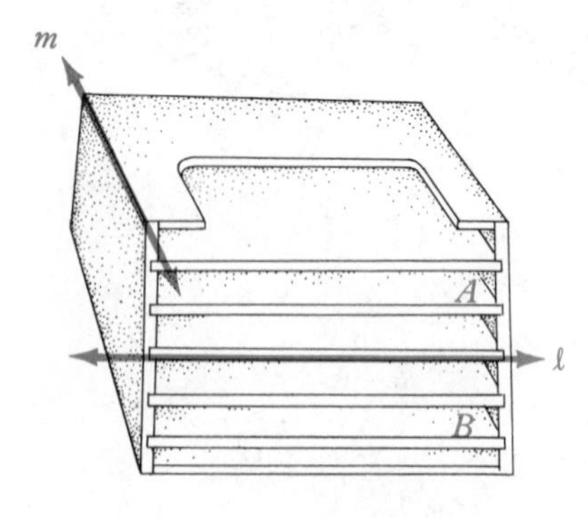

Lines ℓ and m do not lie in the same plane and they do not intersect. We call them *skew lines*.

Line ℓ is parallel to plane A.

Definition 5-1

Skew lines are two nonintersecting lines that do not lie in the same plane.

Definition 5-2

A line and a plane are parallel if they have no points in common.

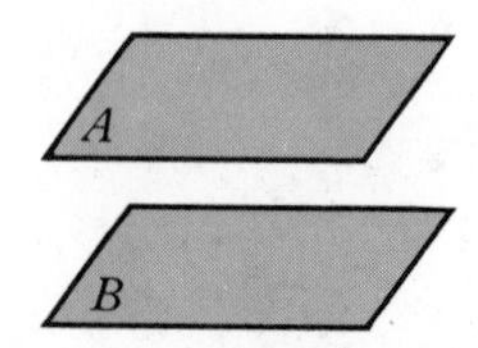

Planes A and B have no points in common. They are *parallel planes*.

Definition 5-3

Parallel planes are planes that have no points in common.

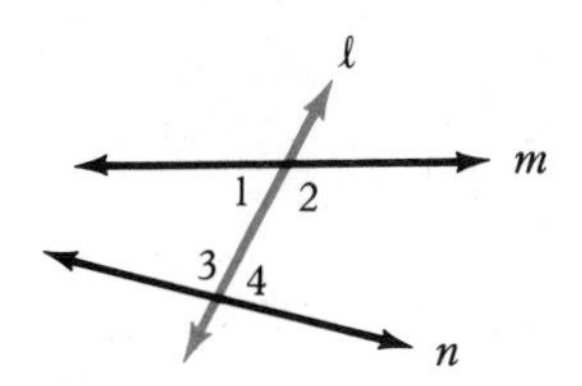

Interior angles

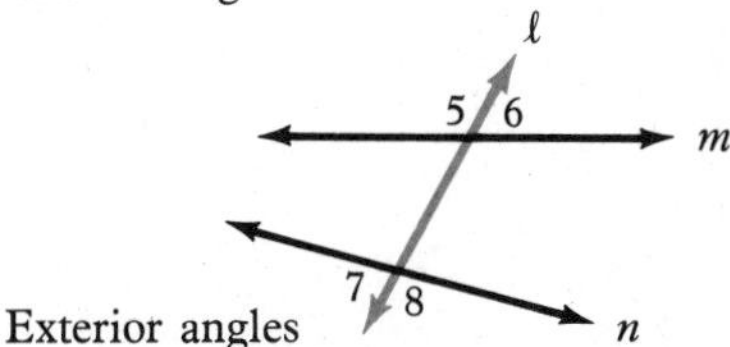

Exterior angles

Line ℓ intersects lines m and n in two different points to form *interior angles* and *exterior angles*. ℓ is called a *transversal.*

Definition 5-4

A **transversal** is a line that intersects two coplanar lines in two different points.

Two lines cut by a transversal form angles that are important in our study of parallel lines.

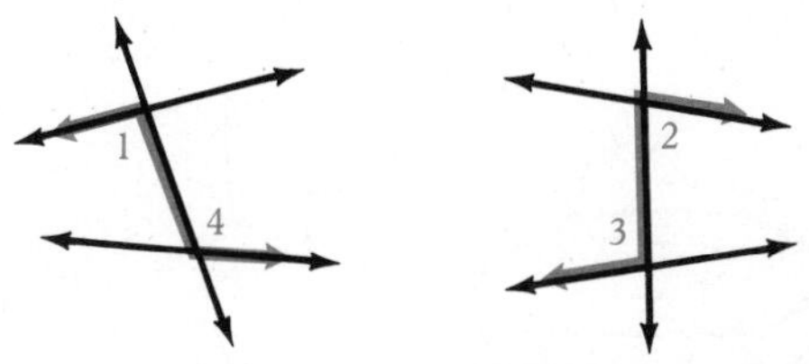

Alternate interior angles are two interior angles with different vertices on opposite sides of the transversal.

$\angle 1$ and $\angle 4$ are called *alternate interior angles.*

$\angle 2$ and $\angle 3$ are called *alternate interior angles.*

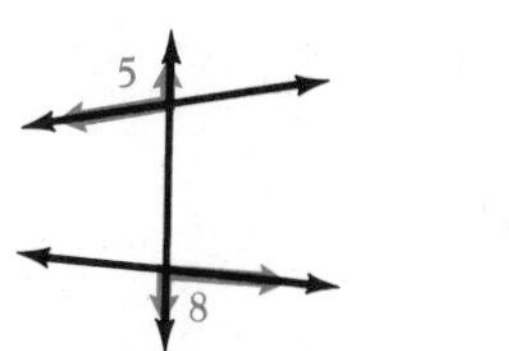

Alternate exterior angles are two exterior angles with different vertices on opposite sides of the transversal.

$\angle 5$ and $\angle 8$ are called *alternate exterior angles.*

$\angle 6$ and $\angle 7$ are called *alternate exterior angles.*

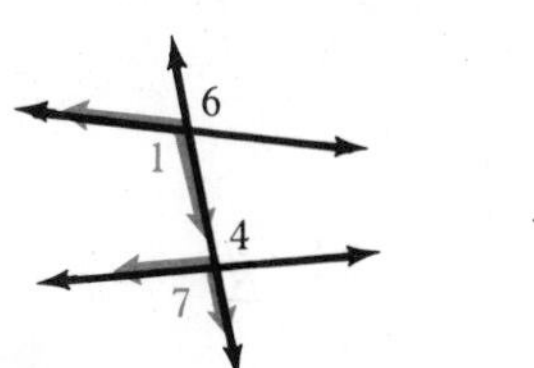

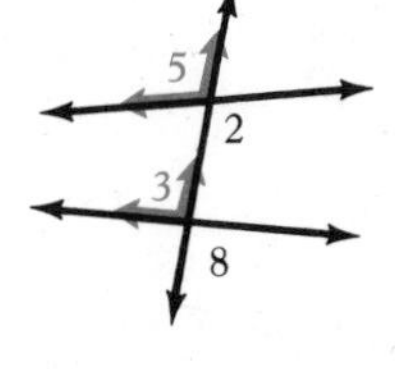

Corresponding angles are on the same side of the transversal. One of the angles is an exterior angle, one is an interior angle.

There are four pairs of *corresponding angles:* $\angle 1$ and $\angle 7$; $\angle 6$ and $\angle 4$; $\angle 5$ and $\angle 3$; $\angle 2$ and $\angle 8$.

EXERCISES

A.

Exercises 1–3 refer to the figure of a cube shown. A model of a cube or a shoe box may help you visualize the cube.

D C A B H G E F (Exs. 1-3)

1. Name four lines that are skew with $\overleftrightarrow{AB}$. EH, FG, CG, DH
2. Name six lines that are parallel to plane $ABCD$. EF, FG, GH, HE, EG, HF
3. Name three pairs of parallel planes.
4. Name two pairs of alternate interior angles. 3/6 4/5
5. Name two pairs of alternate exterior angles. 1/8 2/7
6. Name the angle that corresponds with $\angle 1$. 5

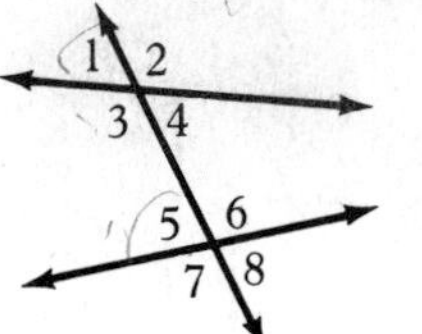

(Exs. 4-6)

B.

7. This figure shows a hexagonal-shaped nut. Name three pairs of parallel planes.
8. Several lines containing edges of this nut are skew with $\overleftrightarrow{AB}$. How many?
   3 GL, LK, PJ

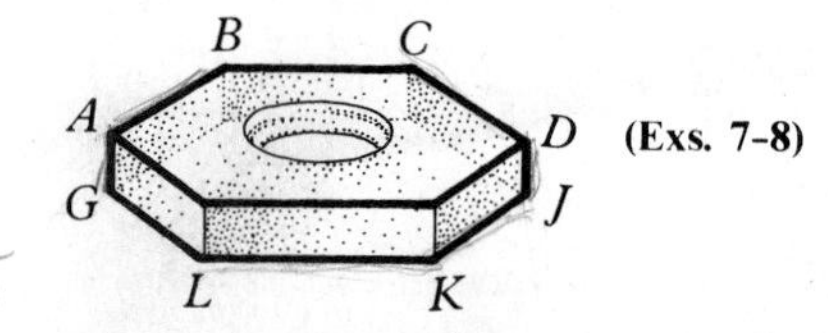

(Exs. 7-8)

Activity

How many points of intersection are formed by a given number of lines? It depends upon their positions relative to one another. *Example:* Three lines can form:

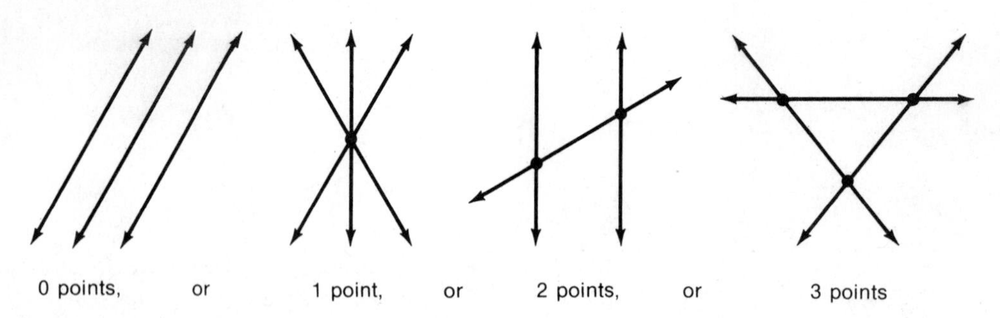

Experiment! See if four lines can be arranged to form one point of intersection, two points, three points, . . . , more than six points. What about five lines?

9. A carpenter builds a stairway by cutting triangles like $\triangle ABC$ and $\triangle CDE$ from a piece of lumber. $\angle DCE$ and $\angle FEG$ are corresponding angles relative to what pair of parallel lines and what transversal?

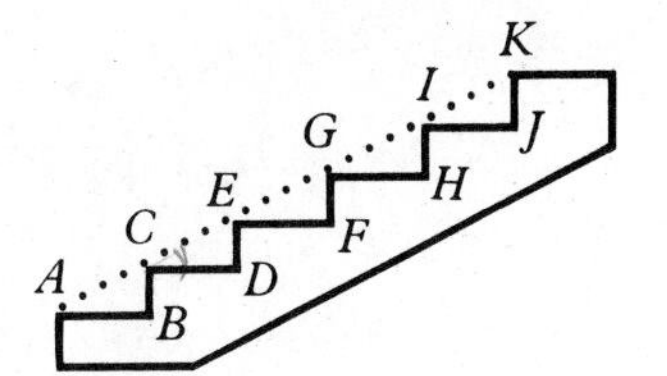

10. In a periscope a pair of mirrors are mounted parallel to each other as shown. The path of light becomes a transversal. Which pair of angles is an alternate interior pair? $\angle 1$ and $\angle 3$, $\angle 1$ and $\angle 4$, $\angle 2$ and $\angle 3$, or $\angle 2$ and $\angle 4$?

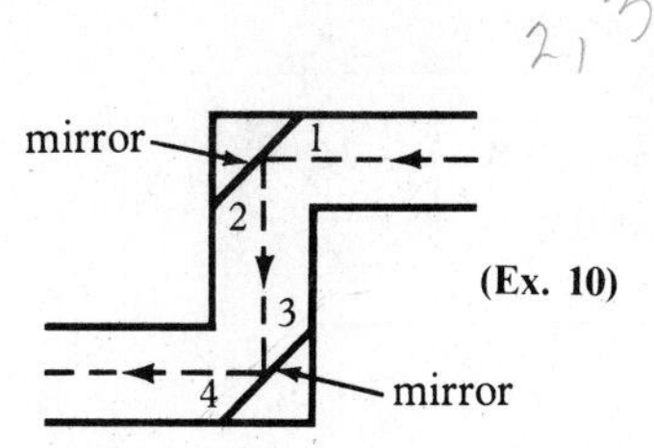

(Ex. 10)

11. Name two pairs of alternate interior angles both of which include $\angle 14$.

12. Name three pairs of alternate exterior angles all of which include $\angle 21$.

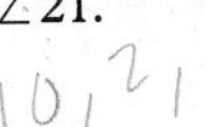

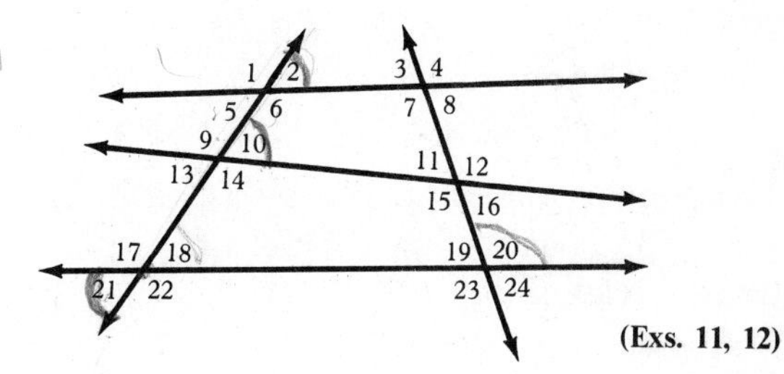

(Exs. 11, 12)

PROBLEM SOLVING

Make a grid of parallel lines like the one on the right.

1. Place five red markers on five intersections so that no two are on the same line.
2. Then place five blue markers on five intersections so that no two markers are on the same line.

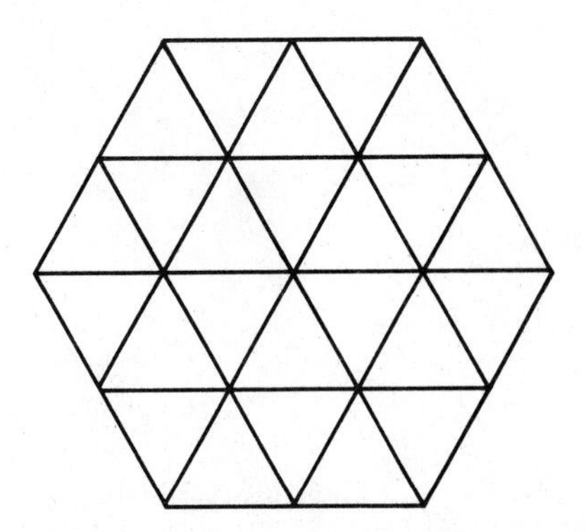

5–2 Theorems About Parallel Lines

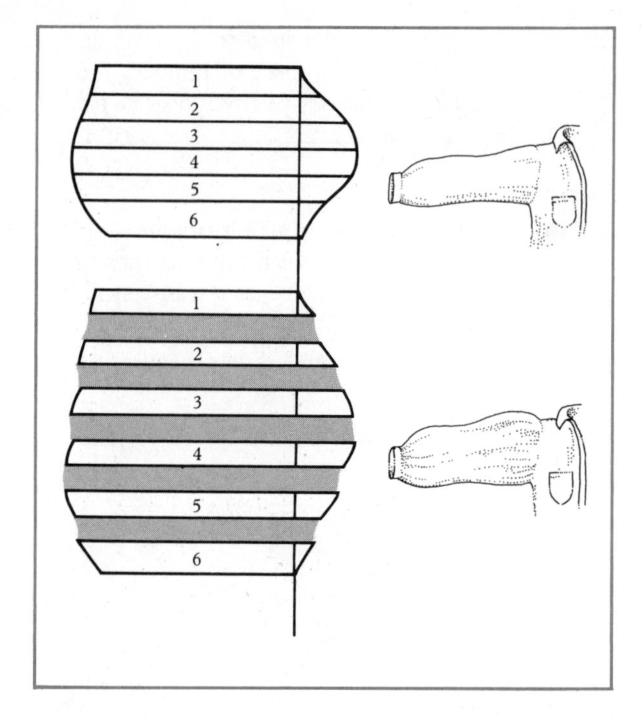

Parallel lines are used every day in a variety of ways. Steel workers install steel beams parallel to one another. Surveyors often determine property lines that are parallel to one another. Clothing designers also use parallel lines. Shown at the right is a basic pattern for a blouse sleeve. To make a pattern for a sleeve that has more fullness, the designer constructs parallel lines on the pattern. Then the strips formed by these parallel lines are cut out and spread apart to form the new pattern.

The pairs of angles formed by a pair of lines and a transversal are important in constructing parallel lines. These three figures suggest an important relationship.

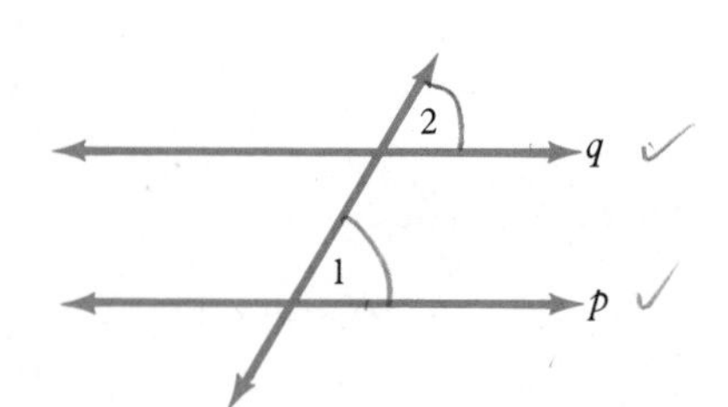

Given: $\angle 1 \cong \angle 2$
Observe that $p \parallel q$.

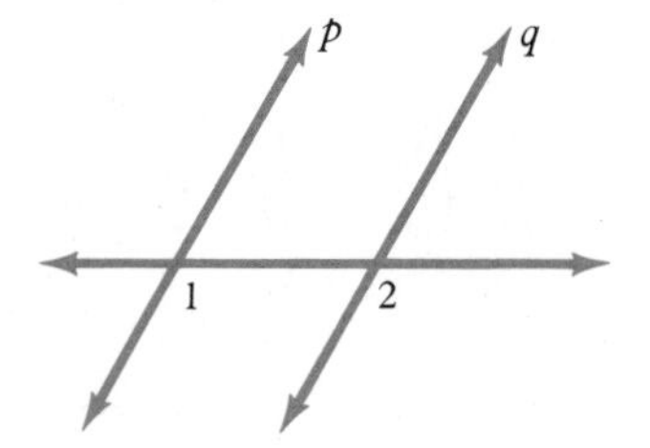

Given: $\angle 1 \cong \angle 2$
Observe that $p \parallel q$.

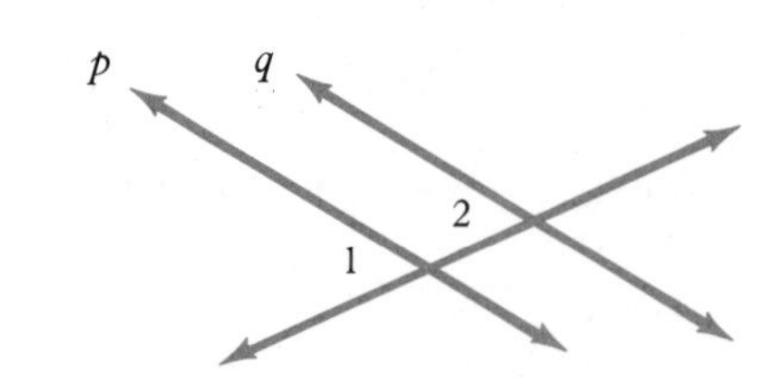

Given: $\angle 1 \cong \angle 2$
Observe that $p \parallel q$.

Theorem 5–1 If two lines are cut by a transversal and a pair of corresponding angles are congruent, then the lines are parallel.

PROOF

Given: Lines p, q, and r with $\angle 1 \cong \angle 2$
Prove: $p \parallel q$

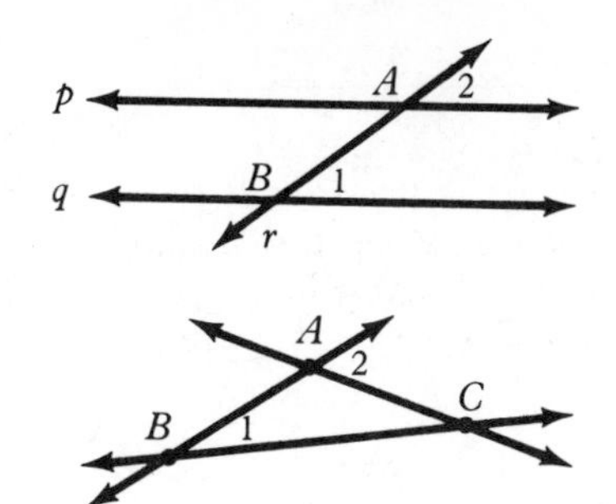

Plan: Assume that $p \nparallel q$. (note: $\nparallel$ means "is not parallel to") Then consider the triangle that would be formed, and find a contradiction.

Statements	Reasons
1. Suppose $p \nparallel q$.	1. Indirect proof assumption
2. Then p and q intersect at a point, say C, and $\triangle ABC$ is formed.	2. Restatement of 1
3. $\angle 2$ is an exterior angle of $\triangle ABC$.	3. Definition of exterior angle
4. $\angle 1$ is a remote interior angle of $\angle 2$.	4. Definition of remote interior angle
5. $m\angle 2 > m\angle 1$	5. Exterior Angle Theorem
6. $m\angle 1 = m\angle 2$ (contradiction to $m\angle 2 > m\angle 1$)	6. Given
7. Therefore, $p \parallel q$	7. Logic of indirect proof

There are three other related theorems. Match these figures with the theorems.

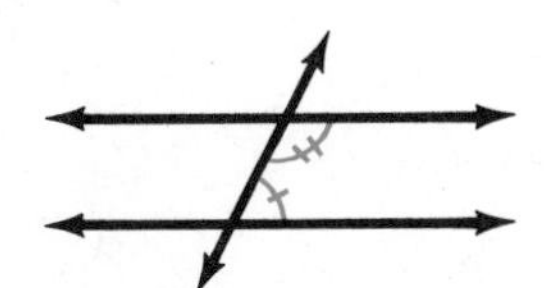
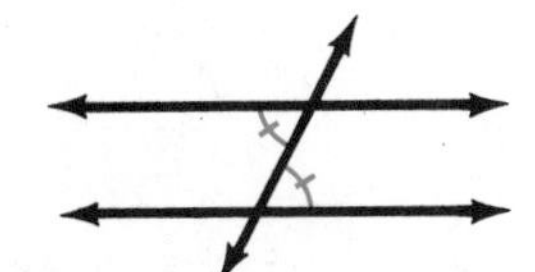

Theorem 5–2 If two lines are cut by a transversal and a pair of alternate interior angles are congruent, then the lines are parallel.

Theorem 5–3 If two lines are cut by a transversal and a pair of alternate exterior angles are congruent, then the lines are parallel.

Theorem 5–4 If two lines are cut by a transversal and a pair of interior angles on the same side of the transversal are supplementary, then the lines are parallel.

EXERCISES

A.

1. In each case below, which lines could you conclude are parallel? Which theorem justifies your answer?

a. $\angle 1 \cong \angle 9$

b. $\angle 3 \cong \angle 6$

c. $m\angle 8 + m\angle 10 = 180$

d. $\angle 4 \cong \angle 9$

e. $\angle 8 \cong \angle 12$

f. $\angle 1 \cong \angle 8$

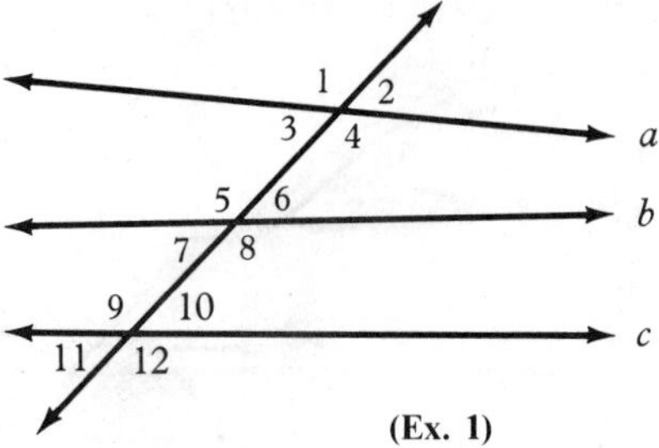

(Ex. 1)

2. List all the contradictory information in the figure at the right.

(Ex. 2)

3. Name four ways of proving that two lines are parallel.

4. Study the photo on page 170. Point out some examples of parallel segments and a transversal.

5. What angles could you prove congruent in order to conclude that $\overleftrightarrow{AB} \parallel \overleftrightarrow{DC}$ in the figure?

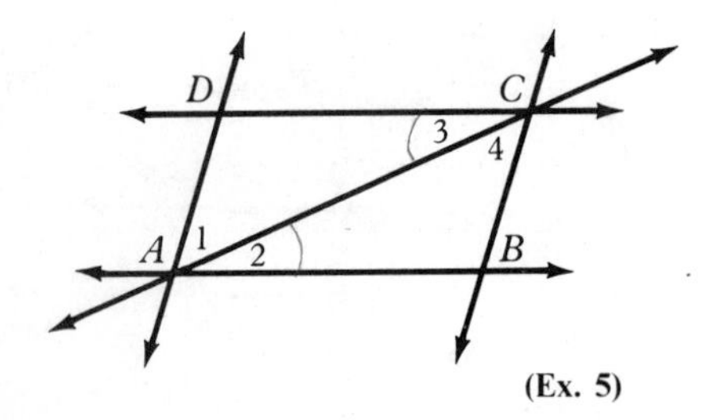

(Ex. 5)

6. Which pairs of angles could you prove congruent to show that $\overleftrightarrow{CD} \parallel \overleftrightarrow{AB}$ in the figure? 3,7 / 1,8 / 6,8 / 7,4

7. Which pairs of angles could you prove supplementary to conclude that $\overleftrightarrow{CD} \parallel \overleftrightarrow{AB}$ in the figure?

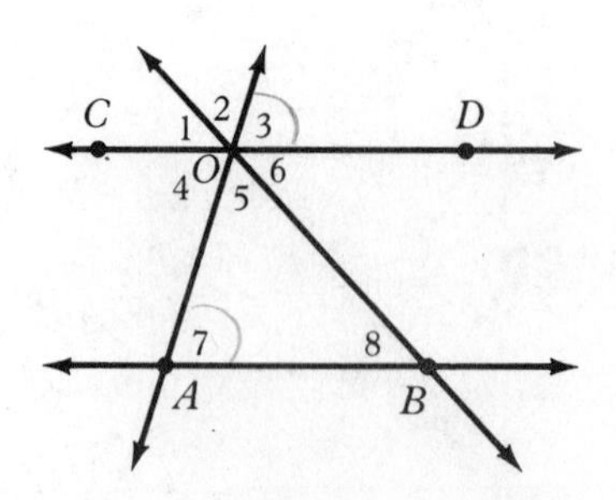

(Exs. 6, 7)

B.

8. Complete the following two-column proof of Theorem 5–2.
Given: $\angle 1 \cong \angle 2$
Prove: $p \parallel q$

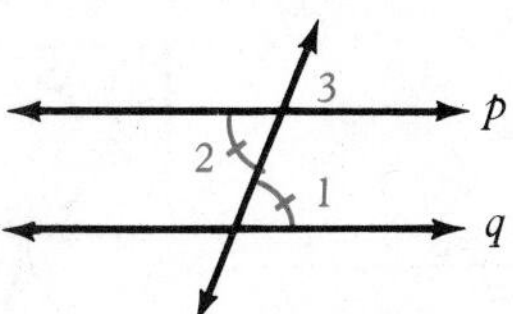

Statements	Reasons
1. $\angle 1 \cong \angle 2$	1. ? Given
2. $\angle 2 \cong \angle 3$	2. ? vert ∠s are ≅
3. $\angle 1 \cong \angle 3$	3. Transitive Property of Congruence
4. $p \parallel q$	4. ? If corr ∠s are ≅, then ∥ lines

For exercises 9–12, write a complete two-column proof.

9. Given: $\overline{AB} \cong \overline{DC}$
$\overline{AD} \cong \overline{BC}$
Prove: $\overline{AB} \parallel \overline{DC}$
(*Hint:* First prove $\triangle ABC \cong \triangle CDA$.)

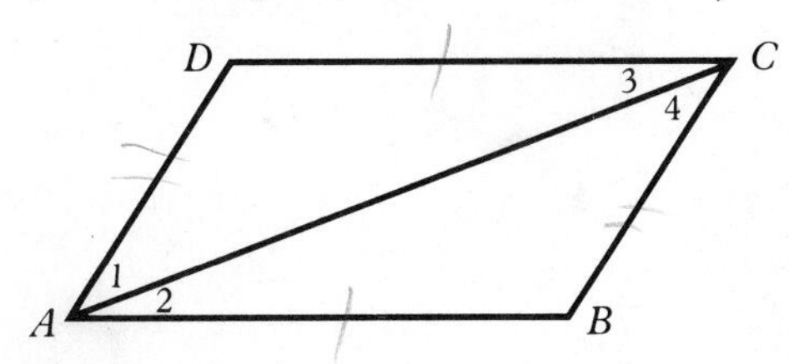

10. Given: $\overline{DO} \cong \overline{OB}$
$\overline{AO} \cong \overline{OC}$
Prove: $\overline{AB} \parallel \overline{DC}$

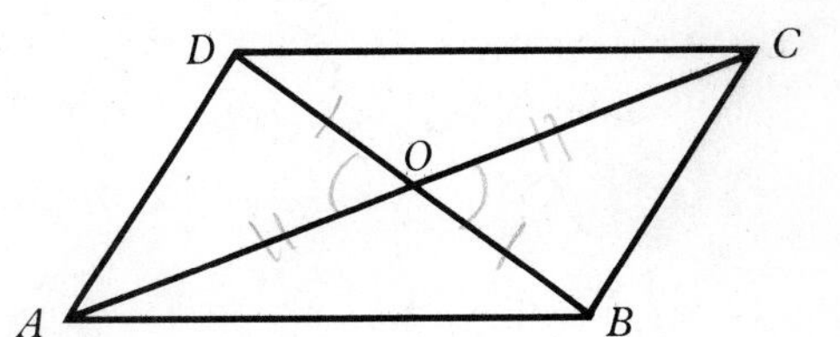

11. Given: $\overline{AB} \cong \overline{DE}$
$\overline{BC} \cong \overline{EF}$
$\overline{AF} \cong \overline{CD}$
Prove: $\overline{BC} \parallel \overline{FE}$

12. Given: $\overline{BC} \cong \overline{EF}$
$\angle BCA \cong \angle EFD$
$\overline{AF} \cong \overline{CD}$
Prove: $\overline{BA} \parallel \overline{DE}$

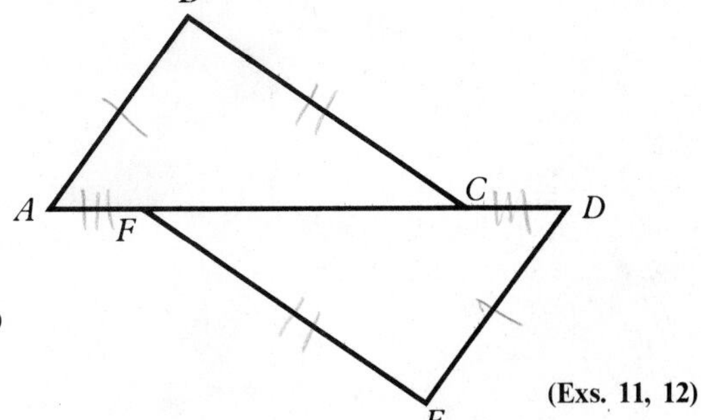

(Exs. 11, 12)

13. Prove that if two lines in a plane are perpendicular to a line, then they are parallel.

14. Prove Theorem 5-3.

15. Prove Theorem 5-4.

C.

16. Given: $\overline{AB} \perp \overline{BC}$
$\overline{DC} \perp \overline{BC}$
$\angle 1 \cong \angle 4$
Prove: $\overleftrightarrow{BF} \parallel \overleftrightarrow{GC}$

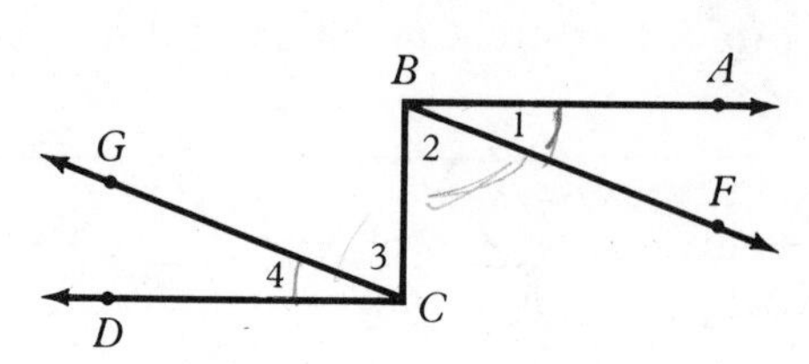

(Exs. 16-18)

17. Given: $\angle ABC \cong \angle BCD$
$\overrightarrow{BF}$ bisects $\angle ABC$.
$\overrightarrow{CG}$ bisects $\angle BCD$.
Prove: $\overleftrightarrow{BF} \parallel \overleftrightarrow{CG}$

18. Given: $\angle 2 \cong \angle 3$
$\angle 1 \cong \angle 4$
Prove: $\overleftrightarrow{AB} \parallel \overleftrightarrow{CD}$

19. Given: $m\angle 2 + m\angle 3 + m\angle 5 = 180$
$\angle 4 \cong \angle 5$
Prove: $\overline{AB} \parallel \overline{CD}$

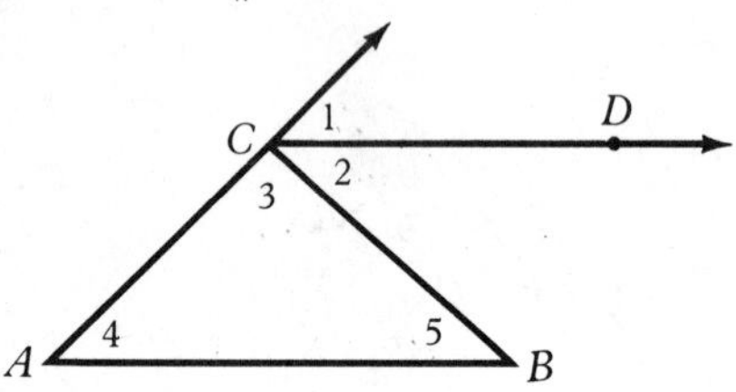

20. A draftsman uses a T-square to draw a pair of parallel lines across a page. Why can you be sure that these lines are parallel?

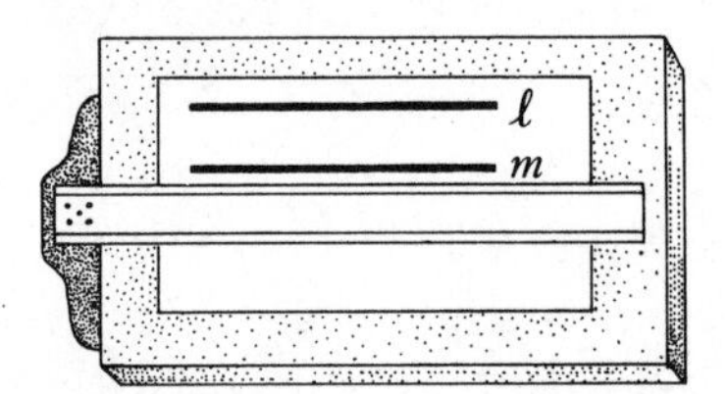

Activity

Draw a line ℓ and a point *P* not on that line.

Using only a compass and a straight edge construct a line through *P* that is parallel to ℓ. (Hint: Begin by drawing a line through *P* that intersects line ℓ.

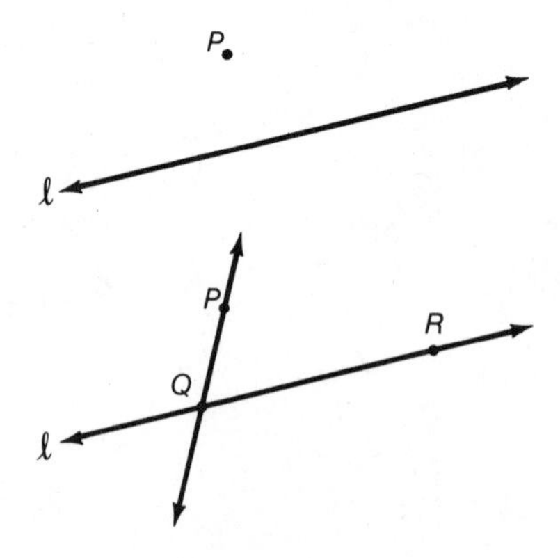

21. Given: $\overleftrightarrow{PM}$ is the perpendicular bisector of $\overline{AB}$.
$\angle A \cong \angle B$
$\overline{AD} \cong \overline{BC}$
Prove: $\overline{AB} \parallel \overline{CD}$
(*Hint:* Draw some auxiliary lines. An auxiliary line is a line that the solver adds to a figure in order to help prove a theorem or solve a problem.)

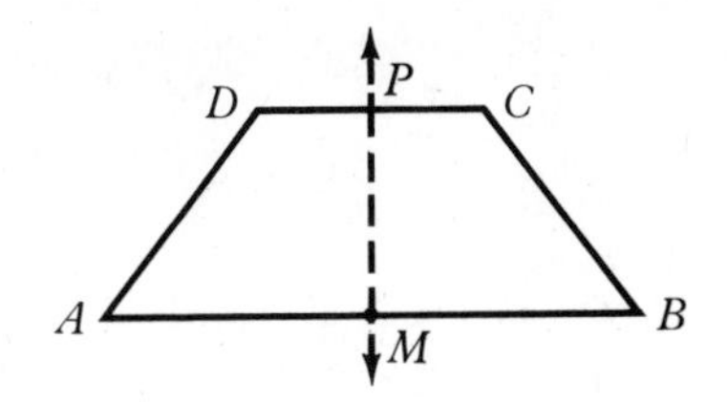

22. Given: $\angle BCD \cong \angle D$
$m\angle B + m\angle D = 180$
Prove: $\overleftrightarrow{AB} \parallel \overleftrightarrow{DC}$

23. A plumb line (a weight hanging by a string) is used to strike a chalk line on a wall. If the first sheet of wallpaper is hung along the chalk line, why should this ensure that the edge of the wallpaper is parallel to the doors, windows, and corners of the room?

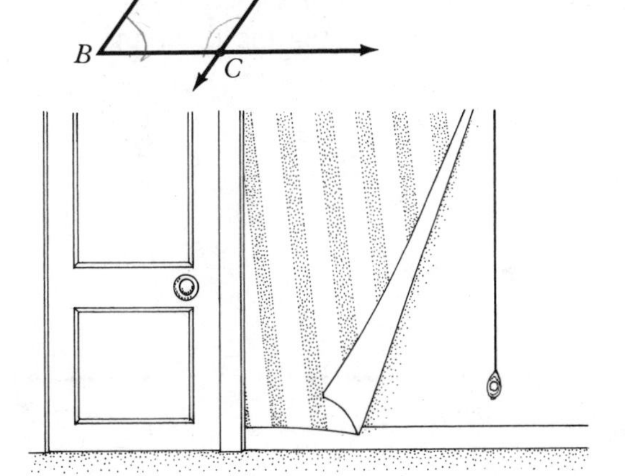

PROBLEM SOLVING

Some polygonal regions can be cut into pieces that can be arranged to form a new polygonal region. Copies of the pieces completely cover the strip between a pair of parallel lines.

Example:

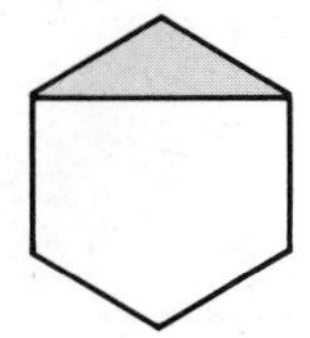

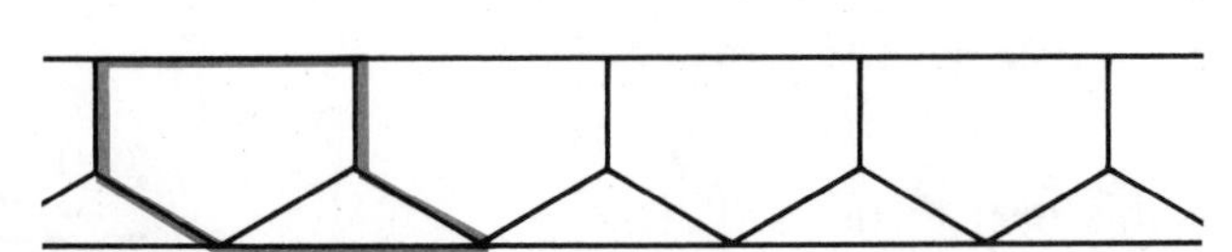

Show that the polygonal regions with the indicated cuts can be arranged to cover such a parallel strip.

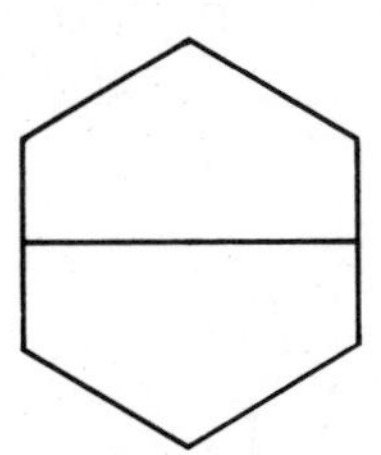

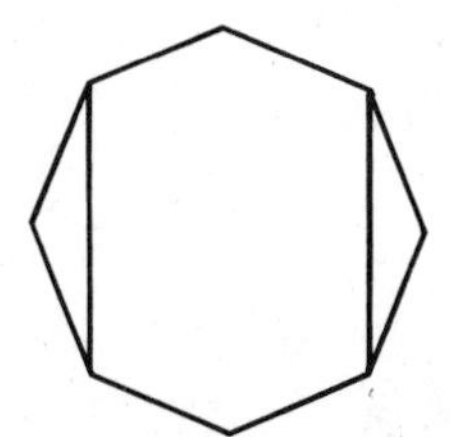

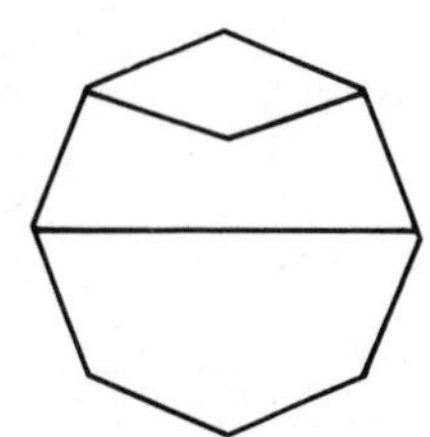

5–3 The Parallel Line Postulate

In the last activity you constructed a pair of parallel lines.

There are actually three related methods that could be summarized by these three figures. The correctness of these constructions can be established by using the theorems from the last section.

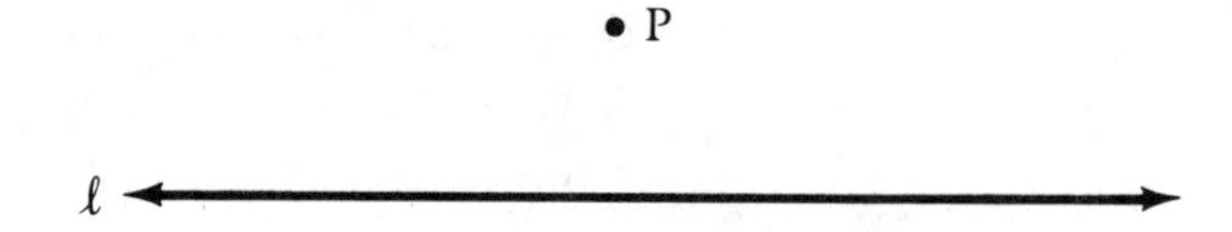

REVIEW: Construct a line through P that is parallel to ℓ.

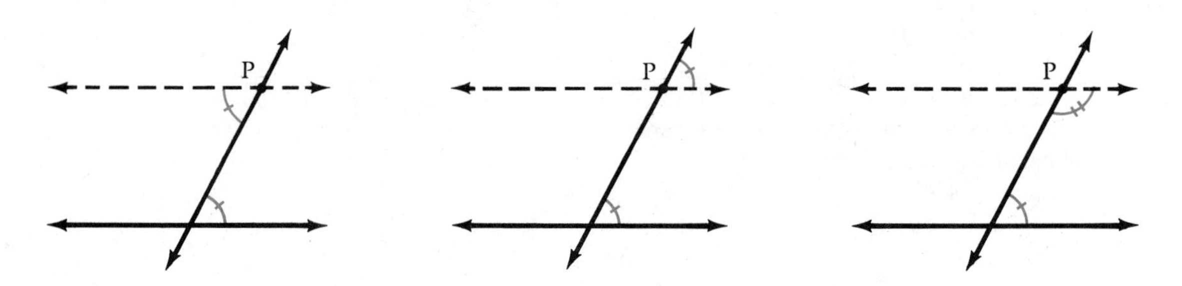

It seems natural to assume, as we do in the Parallel Postulate, that there is only one line through P that is parallel to ℓ. But why is it true? That question is historically significant (see the next page).

Parallel Postulate

Given a line ℓ and a point P not on ℓ, there exists only one line through P parallel to ℓ.

The proof of this next theorem illustrates the use of the Parallel Postulate.

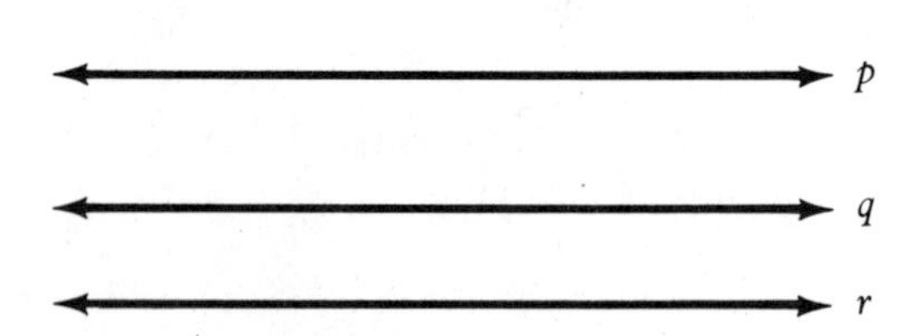

Theorem 5–5 Given lines p, q, and r, if $p \parallel q$ and $q \parallel r$, then $p \parallel r$.

PROOF

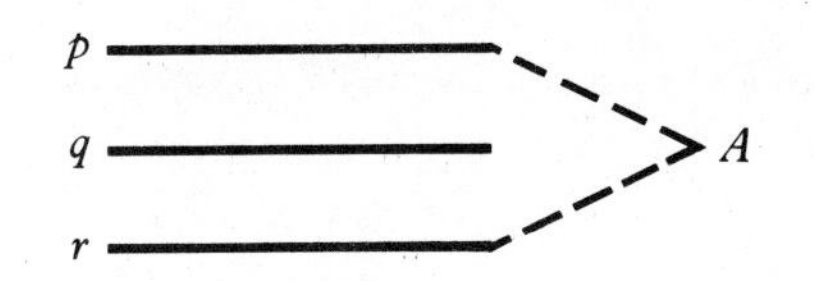

Given: Lines p, q, and r are three distinct lines, $p \parallel q$, $q \parallel r$
Prove: $p \parallel r$

Statements	Reasons
1. Suppose $p \nparallel r$	**1.** Indirect proof assumption
2. There is a point common to p and r. Call it A.	**2.** Restatement of 1
3. $p \parallel q$	**3.** Given
4. $r \parallel q$	**4.** Given
5. Lines p and r are two distinct lines through A parallel to q. (Contradiction of the Parallel Postulate which asserts that there is only one line through A parallel to q.)	**5.** Statements 3 and 4
6. Therefore $p \parallel r$	**6.** Logic of indirect proof

Karl Friedrich Gauss

HISTORICAL SIGNIFICANCE OF THE PARALLEL POSTULATE

For many centuries mathematicians attempted to prove that the Parallel Postulate was a theorem. Repeatedly these attempts failed. In the early nineteenth century three mathematicians, Karl Friedrich Gauss (1777–1855), Janos Bolyai (1802–1860), and Nicolai Ivanovitch Lobachevsky (1793–1856), working independently of one another, tried to eliminate the Parallel Postulate from the Euclidean Postulate System and prove it as a theorem. They used an indirect method. But rather than arriving at a contradiction, they found that this assumption led to an entirely new set of theorems—a totally new geometry. This important mathematical discovery led to what is called non-Euclidean geometry.

EXERCISES

A.

1. State the Parallel Postulate in your own words.
2. Which two words in the Parallel Postulate are the most important?
3. Which of these statements are true and which are false?
   - **a.** There is a line through A that is parallel to ℓ.
   - **b.** We could prove that there is a line through A parallel to ℓ even without using the Parallel Postulate.
   - **c.** The Parallel Postulate says that there is only one line through A parallel to ℓ.
   - **d.** If p is a line through A perpendicular to ℓ and q is a line through A perpendicular to p, then $q \parallel \ell$.

In exercises 4 and 5 determine whether the lines p and q can be proved parallel.

4.

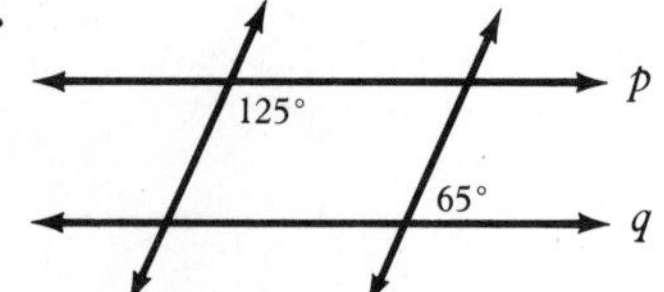

5.

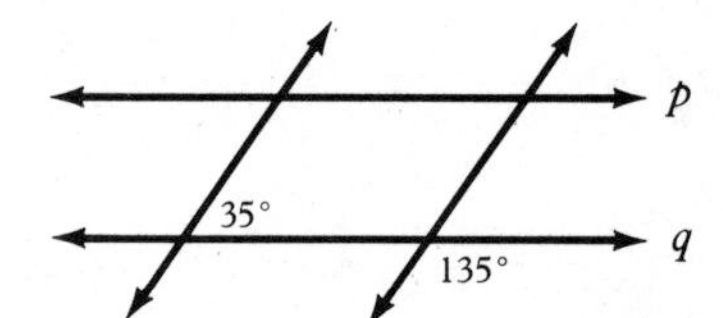

Activity

1. Draw with a straightedge any quadrilateral $WXYZ$.
2. Construct equilateral triangles on each side of the quadrilateral alternately inside and outside the quadrilateral and label the new vertices A, B, C, D.
3. What is true about $\overleftrightarrow{AD}$ and $\overleftrightarrow{BC}$? About $\overleftrightarrow{AB}$ and $\overleftrightarrow{CD}$?
4. State a generalization.

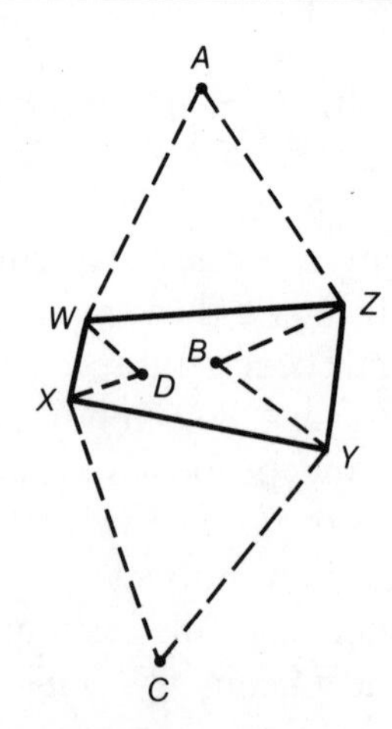

B.

6. Given: $\angle 1 \cong \angle 2$
$\angle 3 \cong \angle 4$
Prove: $p \parallel r$

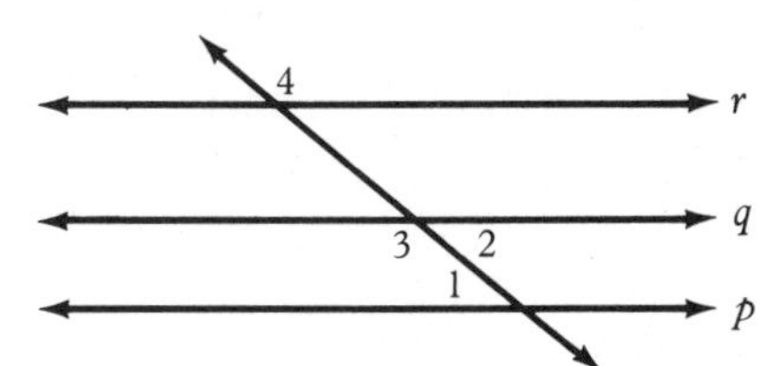

7. Given: $m\angle 1 + m\angle 2 = 180$
$m\angle 3 + m\angle 4 = 180$
Prove: $p \parallel r$

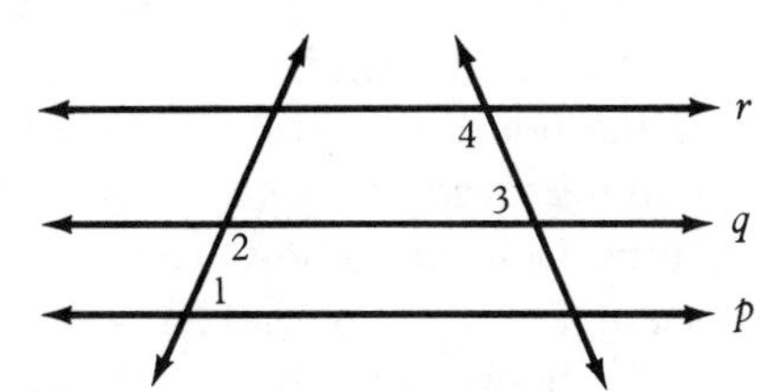

8. Given line ℓ and P, construct the perpendicular from P to ℓ. Call it m. Construct the line $\perp$ to m through P. Call this line r. What is the relationship between r and ℓ? Why?

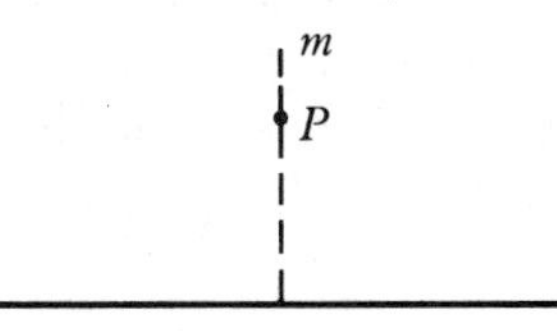

9. Show that the Activity on p. 178 results in a pair of parallel lines.

C.

For these exercises you may assume that Theorem 5-5 is true for lines in space in addition to lines in a plane.

10. If $\overline{AB}$, $\overline{CD}$, and $\overline{EF}$ are the edges of a cube as shown, show that $\overleftrightarrow{AB} \parallel \overleftrightarrow{EF}$.

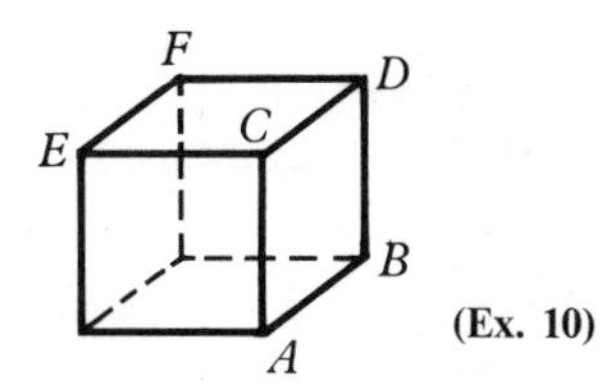

(Ex. 10)

11. If $\overline{AB}$, $\overline{CD}$, and $\overline{EF}$ are edges of three pages of a book (assume rectangular pages), prove that $\overleftrightarrow{AB}$, $\overleftrightarrow{CD}$, and $\overleftrightarrow{EF}$ are parallel to each other.

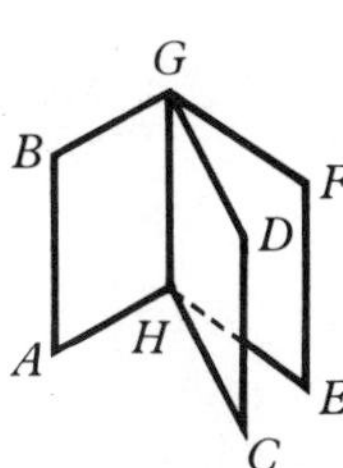

PROBLEM SOLVING

This photograph shows a flat-bed scissors truck raised to its maximum height. The support pieces labeled $\overline{AB}$ and $\overline{CD}$ bisect each other.

Explain why these conditions mean that the bed of the truck is parallel to the truck frame.

5–4 More Theorems About Parallel Lines

Many "do-it-yourselfers" purchase a pre-assembled fold-down ladder to install in the ceiling of the house or garage. These ladders are all manufactured the same length. The installer must determine how to cut the bottom section so that the ladder will sit firmly on the floor. Both the length and the angle must be considered. The fact that the ceiling and floor are parallel is important to the solution of this problem.

In these figures how are $\angle 1$ and $\angle 2$ related?

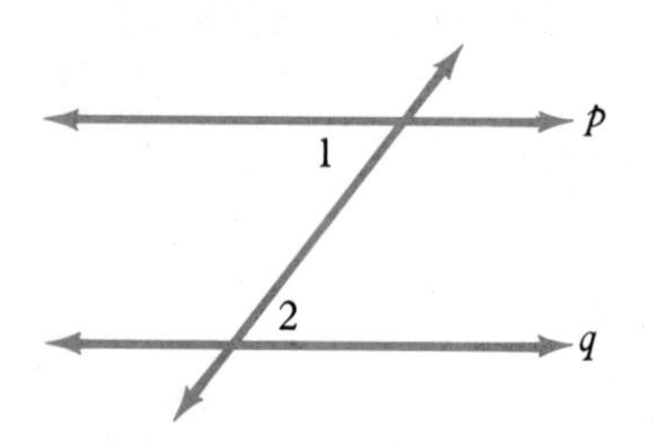

Given: $p \parallel q$
Observe that $\angle 1 \cong \angle 2$.

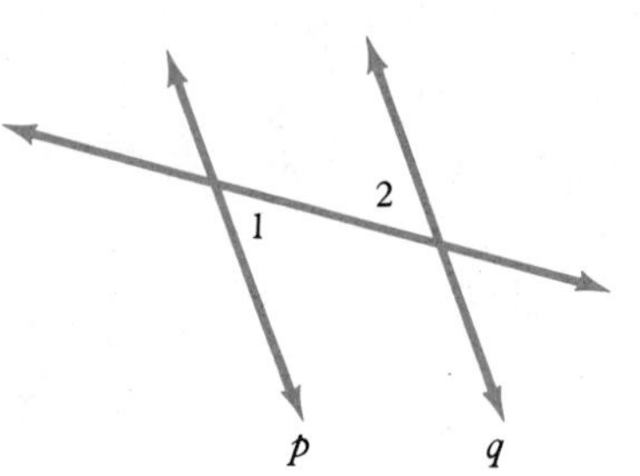

Given: $p \parallel q$
Observe that $\angle 1 \cong \angle 2$.

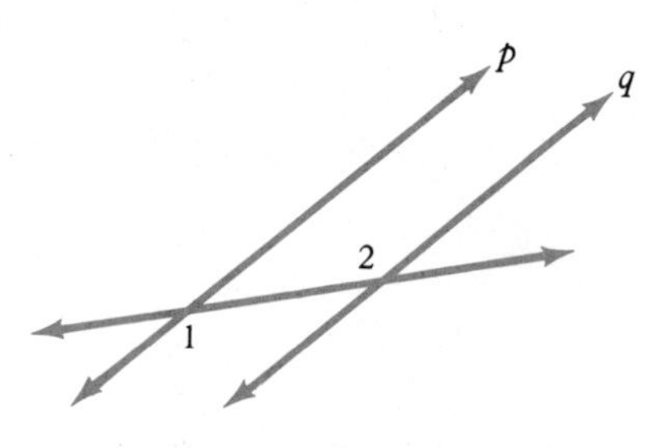

Given: $p \parallel q$
Observe that $\angle 1 \cong \angle 2$.

These figures suggest the following theorem.

Theorem 5–6 If two parallel lines are cut by a transversal, then alternate interior angles are congruent.

PROOF

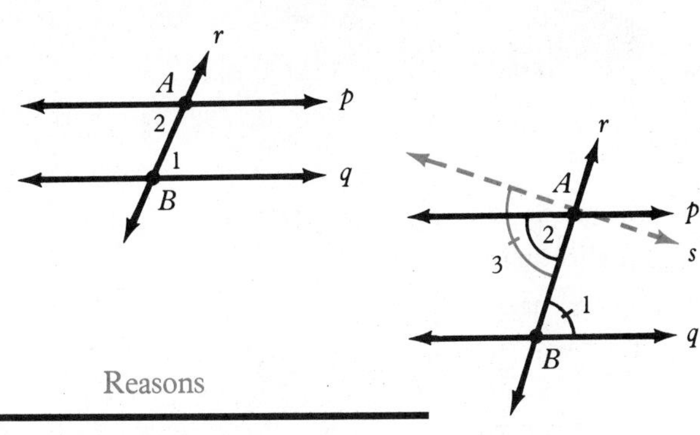

Given: Lines $p \parallel q$ with transversal r. $\angle 1$ and $\angle 2$ are alternate interior angles.
Prove: $\angle 1 \cong \angle 2$
Plan: Assume that $\angle 1$ is not congruent to $\angle 2$, and find a contradiction.

Statements	Reasons
1. $\angle 1$ is not congruent to $\angle 2$.	1. Indirect proof assumption
2. Construct a line through A so that $\angle 1 \cong \angle 3$, and $\angle 1$ and $\angle 3$ are alternate interior angles.	2. Construction
3. $q \parallel s$, A is on s.	3. If alternate interior angles are congruent, then the lines are parallel.
4. $p \parallel q$, A is on p.	4. Given
5. There are two lines through A parallel to q. (Contradiction of the Parallel Postulate)	5. Statements 3 and 4
6. $\angle 1 \cong \angle 2$	6. Logic of indirect proof

APPLICATION

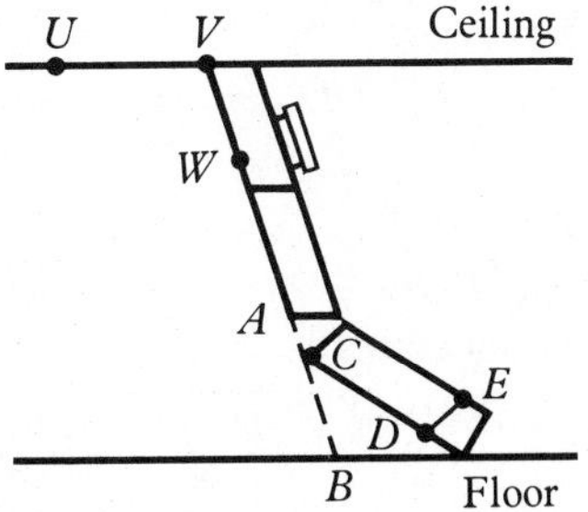

Theorem 5-6 can be used to solve the problem raised at the beginning of the lesson. How should the bottom sections be cut? Follow this procedure.

1. Measure AB and locate point D so that $AB = CD$.
2. Measure $\angle UVW$ and locate point E so that $m\angle UVW = m\angle CDE$.

There are several additional theorems stated here.

Theorem 5-7 If two parallel lines are cut by a transversal, then alternate exterior angles are congruent.

Theorem 5-8 If two parallel lines are cut by a transversal, then corresponding angles are congruent.

Theorem 5-9 If two parallel lines are cut by a transversal, then the interior angles on the same side of the transversal are supplementary.

EXERCISES

A.

In the figure for exercises 1–7 lines p and q are parallel and $m\angle 3 = 55$.

(Exs. 1-7)

1. $m\angle 1 = \underline{\ ?\ }$

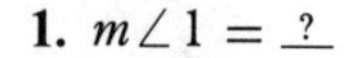

2. $m\angle 2 = \underline{\ ?\ }$
3. $m\angle 4 = \underline{\ ?\ }$
4. $m\angle 5 = \underline{\ ?\ }$
5. $m\angle 6 = \underline{\ ?\ }$
6. $m\angle 7 = \underline{\ ?\ }$
7. $m\angle 8 = \underline{\ ?\ }$

In the figure for exercises 8–12, lines p and q are parallel, $m\angle 1 = 125$ and $m\angle 4 = 143$.

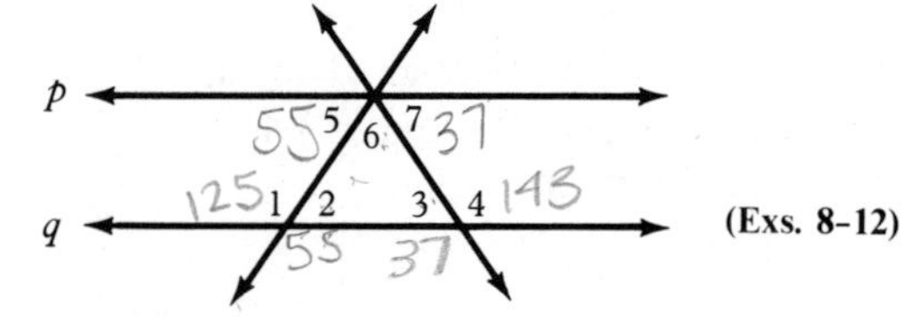

(Exs. 8-12)

8. $m\angle 2 = \underline{\ ?\ }$
9. $m\angle 3 = \underline{\ ?\ }$
10. $m\angle 5 = \underline{\ ?\ }$
11. $m\angle 7 = \underline{\ ?\ }$
12. $m\angle 6 = \underline{\ ?\ }$

In the figure for exercises 13–22, $\overleftrightarrow{AB} \parallel \overleftrightarrow{CD}$ and $\overleftrightarrow{AD} \parallel \overleftrightarrow{BC}$. Also $m\angle ADC = 110$ and $m\angle ACD = 28$.

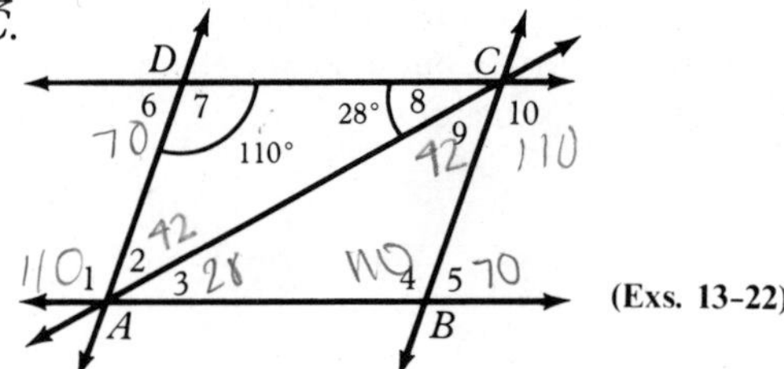

(Exs. 13-22)

13. $m\angle 1 = \underline{\ ?\ }$
14. $m\angle 10 = \underline{\ ?\ }$
15. $m\angle 3 = \underline{\ ?\ }$
16. $m\angle 4 = \underline{\ ?\ }$
17. $m\angle 5 = \underline{\ ?\ }$
18. $m\angle 6 = \underline{\ ?\ }$
19. $m\angle BCD = \underline{\ ?\ }$
20. $m\angle 9 = \underline{\ ?\ }$
21. $m\angle 2 = \underline{\ ?\ }$
22. $m\angle BAD = \underline{\ ?\ }$

23. Assume that $m\angle BCD = 70$ in the figure. What must the measures of $\angle ABC$, $\angle CDA$, and $\angle DAB$ be if $\overleftrightarrow{AB} \parallel \overleftrightarrow{CD}$ and $\overleftrightarrow{AD} \parallel \overleftrightarrow{BC}$.

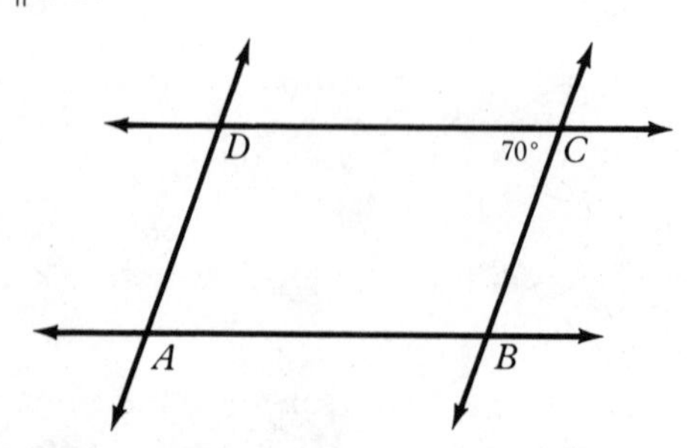

B.

For exercises 24 and 25, assume that lines p and q are parallel.

24. If $m\angle 1 = 2x + 3$ and $m\angle 4 = 7x - 12$, find $m\angle 1$ and $m\angle 2$.

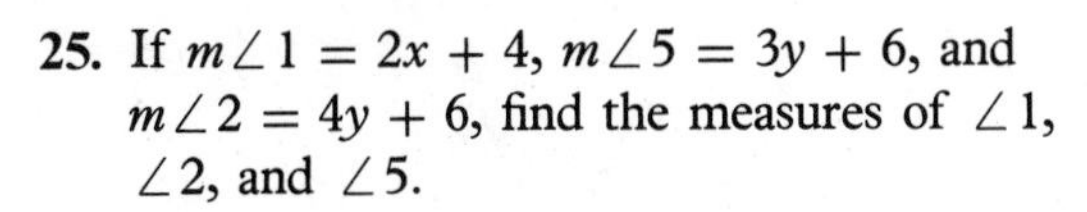

25. If $m\angle 1 = 2x + 4$, $m\angle 5 = 3y + 6$, and $m\angle 2 = 4y + 6$, find the measures of $\angle 1$, $\angle 2$, and $\angle 5$.

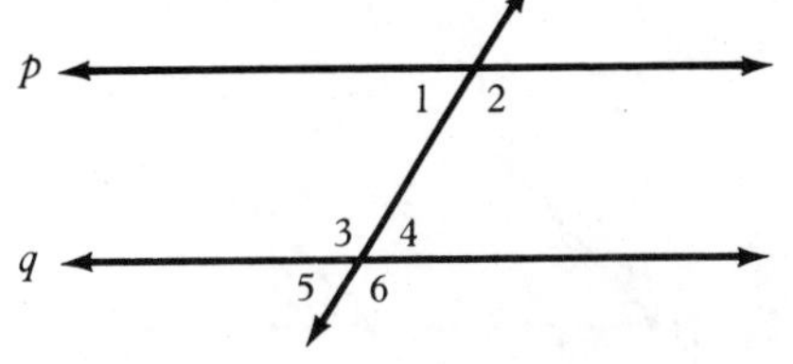

(Exs. 24, 25)

26. Prove Theorem 5–8.

27. Prove Theorem 5–9.

28. Prove Theorem 5–7.

29. Given: $s \parallel t$
$r \perp s$
Prove: $r \perp t$

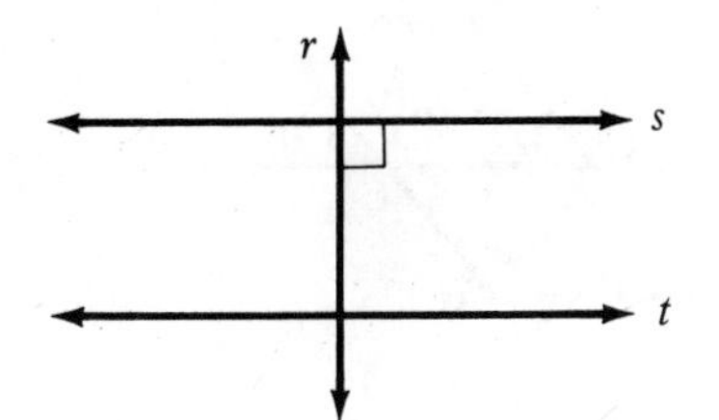

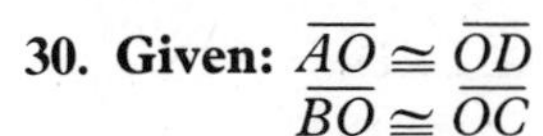

30. Given: $\overline{AO} \cong \overline{OD}$
$\overline{BO} \cong \overline{OC}$
Prove: $\overleftrightarrow{AB} \parallel \overleftrightarrow{CD}$

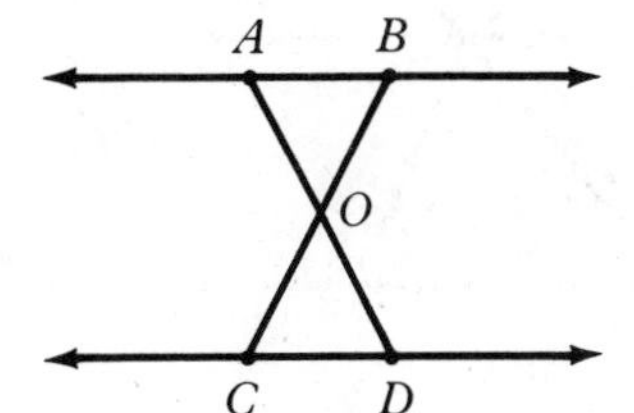

31. Given: $p \parallel q$
$s \parallel t$
Prove: $\angle 1 \cong \angle 7$
$\angle 2 \cong \angle 9$

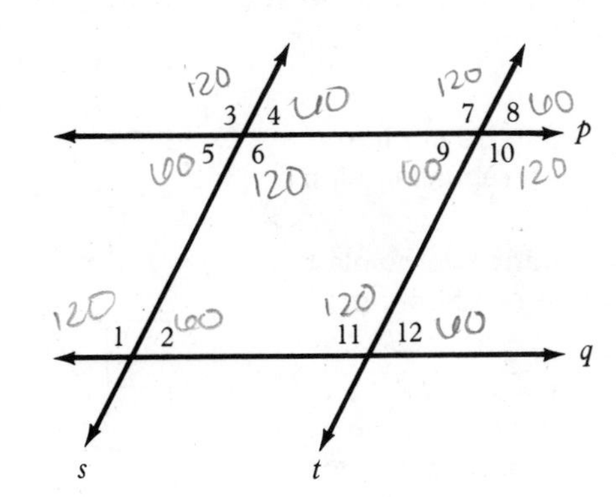

(Exs. 31–33)

32. Given: $p \parallel q$
$\angle 3 \cong \angle 11$
Prove: $s \parallel t$

33. Given: $s \parallel t$
$\angle 9$ and $\angle 1$ are supplementary
Prove: $p \parallel q$

C.

34. Given: $\overline{AB} \parallel \overline{CD}$
$\overline{BC} \parallel \overline{DE}$
Prove: $\angle B \cong \angle D$

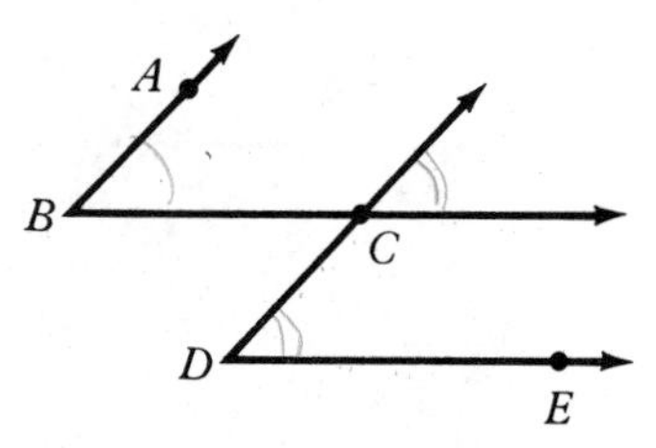

35. Given: $\angle A \cong \angle D$
$\overline{AB} \parallel \overline{DE}$
$\overline{AB} \cong \overline{DE}$
Prove: $\overline{BC} \cong \overline{EF}$

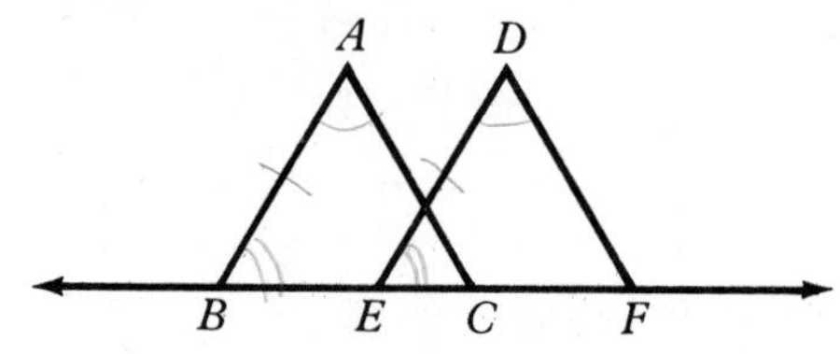

36. Given: $\overleftrightarrow{AB} \parallel \overleftrightarrow{DE}$
$\overrightarrow{AC}$ bisects $\angle BAD$.
$\overrightarrow{DF}$ bisects $\angle ADE$.
Prove: $\overleftrightarrow{AC} \parallel \overleftrightarrow{FD}$

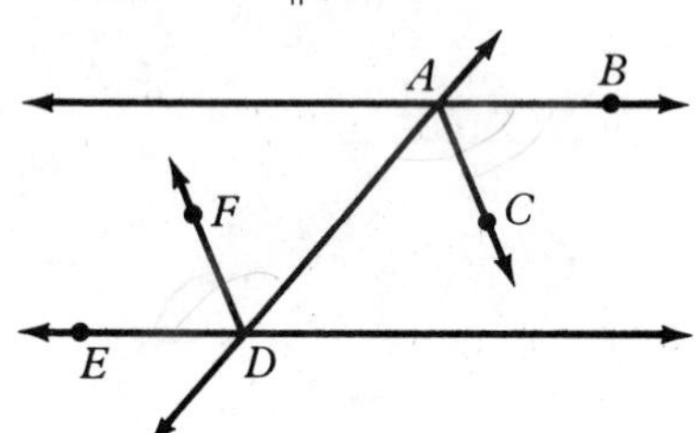

37. Given: $\overleftrightarrow{AB} \parallel \overleftrightarrow{CD}$
$\overleftrightarrow{BC} \parallel \overleftrightarrow{DE}$
Prove: $m\angle 1 + m\angle 4 = 180$

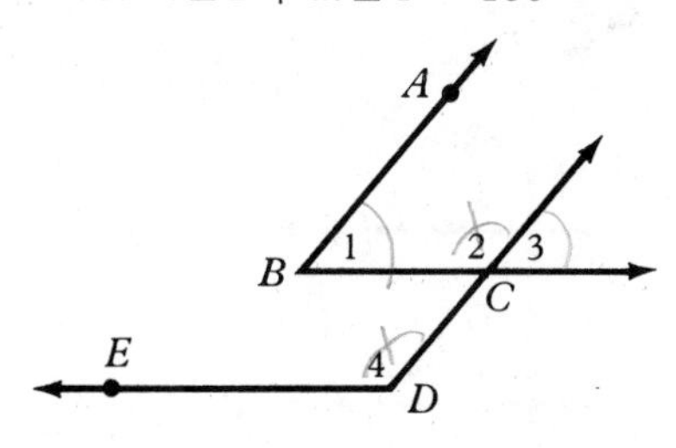

Activity

1. Begin with a polygon that can be cut into pieces and rearranged into a repeating strip pattern (as on page 179).
2. Label points A and B to be any two points that correspond to each other in neighboring pieces of the strip.
3. Draw a pair of parallel lines $\overleftrightarrow{AD}$ and $\overleftrightarrow{BC}$ as shown. Draw $\overline{AE} \perp \overline{BC}$. The pieces 1–5 so obtained can be arranged to form either the original polygon or a rectangle.
4. Repeat this three-step procedure for the polygons in the Problem Solving box on page 179. In each case arrange the pieces you produce to form a rectangle.

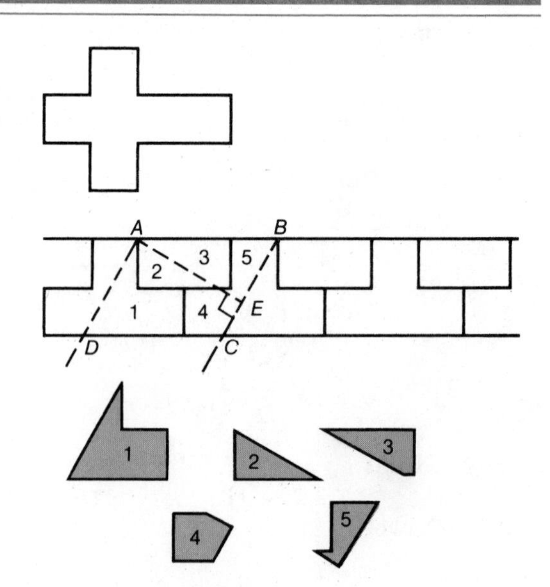

38. Given: $\overline{AD} \cong \overline{EC}$
$\overline{BC} \cong \overline{FD}$
$\overline{BC} \parallel \overline{FD}$
Prove: $\overline{AB} \parallel \overline{EF}$

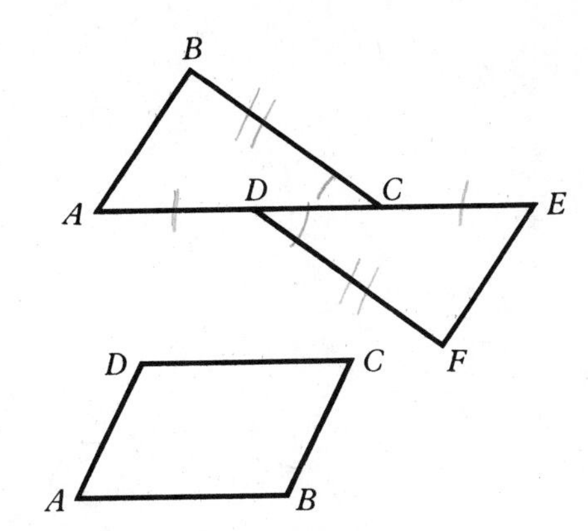

39. If $\overline{AB} \parallel \overline{CD}$ and $\overline{AD} \parallel \overline{BC}$, prove that $\angle B \cong \angle D$.

40. Prove: If two opposite sides of a quadrilateral are parallel and congruent, then the other two opposite sides are parallel and congruent.

41. An interior decorator is pasting strips of wallpaper on a wall to make a bold stripe pattern.
When cutting the paper, how does the decorator know that $\angle A$ and $\angle B$ should be congruent?

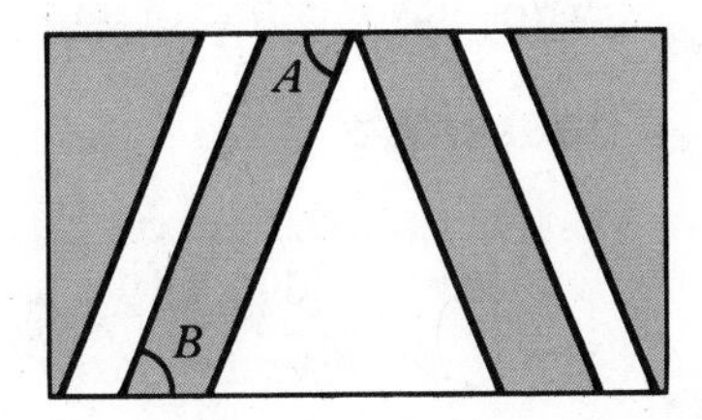

PROBLEM SOLVING

Light rays are bent as they pass through glass. Assume that a ray is bent the same amount entering a piece of glass as exiting the glass. Explain two things.

1. Why does a ray exit in a direction parallel to the direction it entered? That is, why is $\overleftrightarrow{AB}$ parallel to $\overleftrightarrow{CD}$?
2. Why do entering parallel rays exit as parallel rays? That is, why does $\overline{AB} \parallel \overline{WX}$ imply $\overline{CD} \parallel \overline{YZ}$?

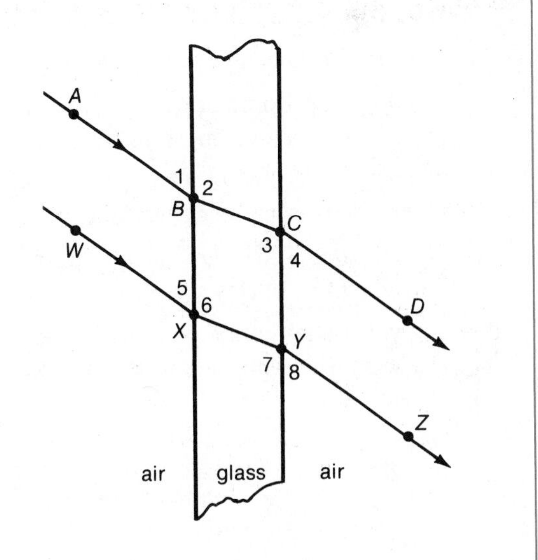

Important Ideas—Chapter 5

Terms

Skew lines (p. 170)
Parallel line and plane (p. 170)
Parallel planes (p. 170)
Transversal (p. 171)
Alternate interior angles (p. 171)
Alternate exterior angles (p. 171)
Corresponding angles (p. 171)

Postulate

Parallel Postulate: Given a line ℓ and a point P not on ℓ, there exists only one line through P parallel to ℓ.

Theorems

5-1 If two lines are cut by a transversal and a pair of corresponding angles are congruent, then the lines are parallel.

5-2 If two lines are cut by a transversal and a pair of alternate interior angles are congruent, then the lines are parallel.

5-3 If two lines are cut by a transversal and a pair of alternate exterior angles are congruent, then the lines are parallel.

5-4 If two lines are cut by a transversal and a pair of interior angles on the same side of the transversal are supplementary, then the lines are parallel.

5-5 Given lines p, q, and r, if $p \parallel q$ and $q \parallel r$ then $p \parallel r$.

5-6 If two parallel lines are cut by a transversal, then alternate interior angles are congruent.

5-7 If two parallel lines are cut by a transversal, then alternate exterior angles are congruent.

5-8 If two parallel lines are cut by a transversal, then corresponding angles are congruent.

5-9 If two parallel lines are cut by a transversal, then the interior angles on the same side of the transversal are supplementary.

Chapter 5—Review

1. **a.** Name pairs of alternate interior angles.
   b. Name pairs of alternate exterior angles.
   c. Name pairs of corresponding angles.

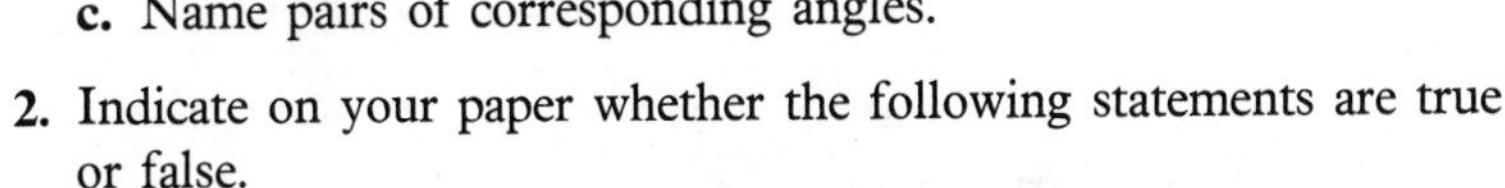

2. Indicate on your paper whether the following statements are true or false.
   a. If two lines are parallel and are cut by a transversal, then the corresponding angles are congruent.
   b. If two lines are cut by a transversal to form alternate interior angles, then the lines are parallel.
   c. If two lines are parallel to a third line, then the two lines are parallel.

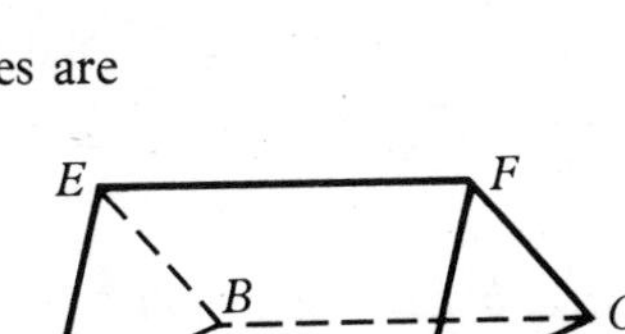

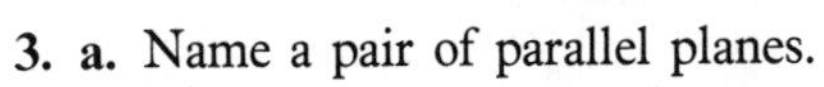

3. **a.** Name a pair of parallel planes.
   b. Name a pair of skew lines.

4. If $m\angle 6 = 120$ and $m\angle 12 = 60$, can you prove $a \parallel b$?

5. If $m\angle 13 = 55$, $a \parallel b$, and $c \parallel d$, find $m\angle 4$.

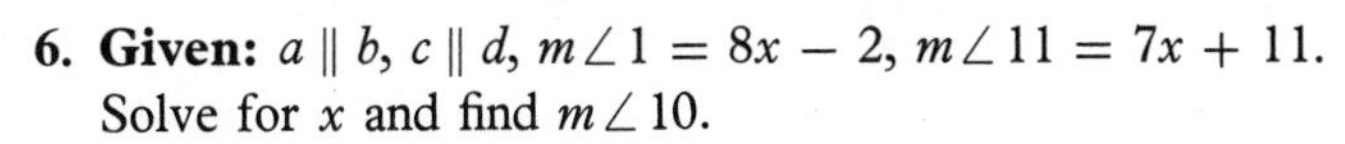

6. **Given:** $a \parallel b$, $c \parallel d$, $m\angle 1 = 8x - 2$, $m\angle 11 = 7x + 11$. Solve for x and find $m\angle 10$.

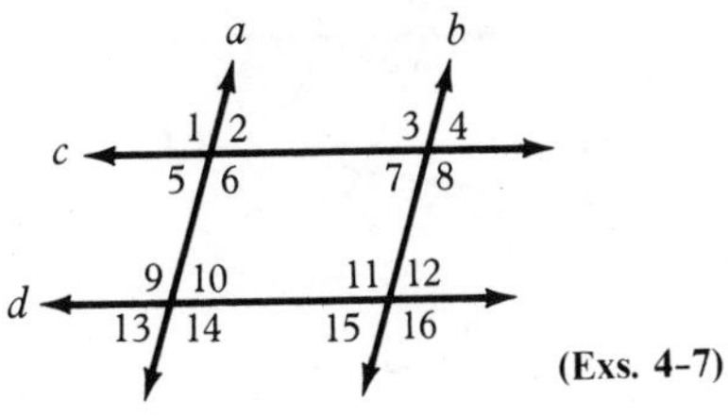

(Exs. 4-7)

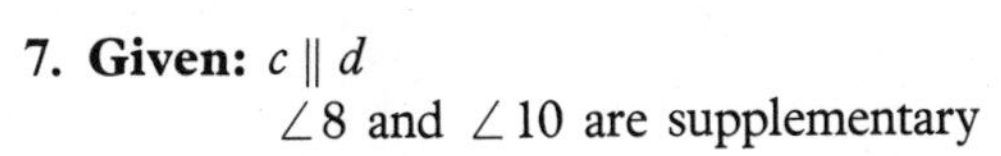

7. **Given:** $c \parallel d$
   $\angle 8$ and $\angle 10$ are supplementary
   Prove: $a \parallel b$

8. **Given:** $\angle ECD \cong \angle EAB$
   Prove: $\angle FDC \cong \angle FBA$

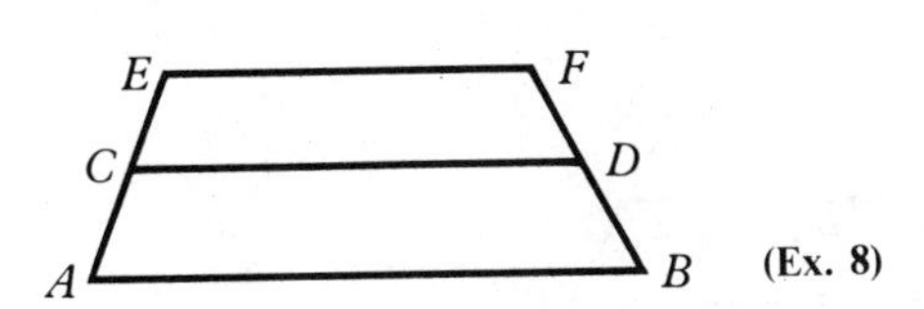

(Ex. 8)

Chapter 5—Test

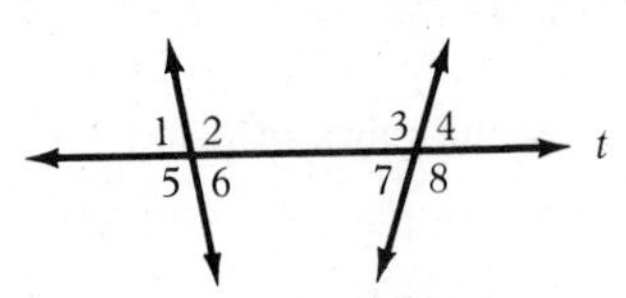

1. **a.** Name a pair of alternate interior angles that includes $\angle 2$.
   b. Name a pair of corresponding angles that includes $\angle 2$.

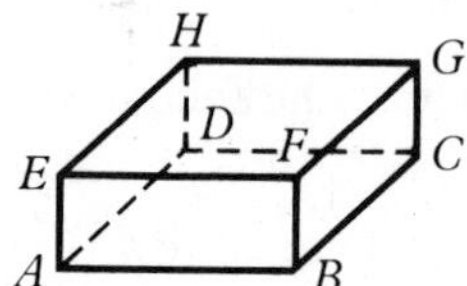

2. **a.** Name a pair of parallel planes.
   b. Name a pair of skew lines.

3. If $a \parallel b$, $m\angle 10 = 70$, and $m\angle 7 = 70$, is $c \parallel d$?

4. If $m\angle 6 = 115$, $m\angle 7 = 65$ and $m\angle 15 = 65$, find $m\angle 13$.

5. **Given:** $a \parallel b$, $c \parallel d$, $m\angle 11 = 7x$ and $m\angle 8 = 5x + 32$.
   Solve for x and find $m\angle 6$.

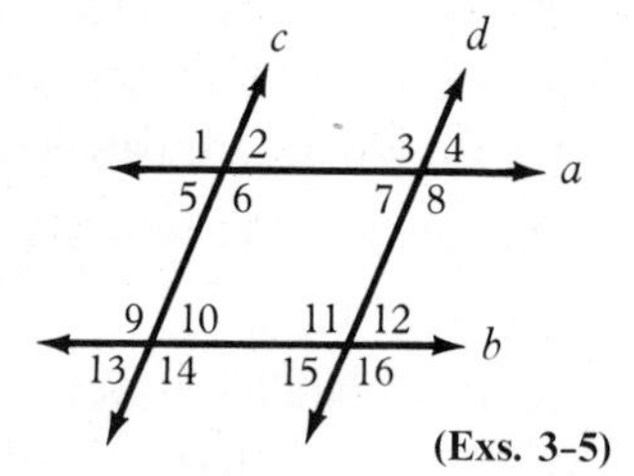

(Exs. 3-5)

6. If a intersects b, can $m\angle 1 = m\angle 2$? Explain.

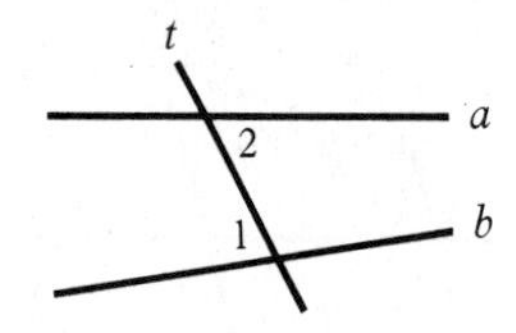

7. **Given:** $\angle 1 \cong \angle 2$
   $\angle 2$ and $\angle 3$ are supplementary
   Prove: $\overline{AB} \parallel \overline{ED}$

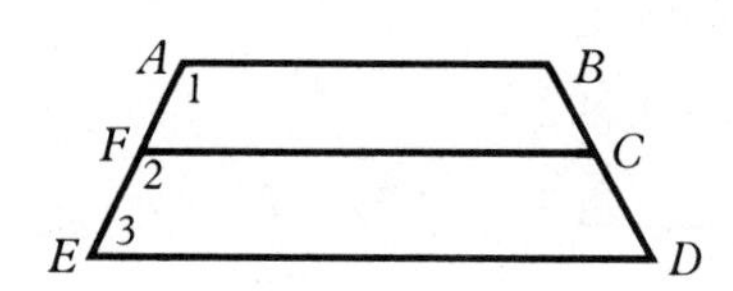

8. **Given:** $c \parallel d$, $\angle 8 \cong \angle 14$
   Prove: $a \parallel b$

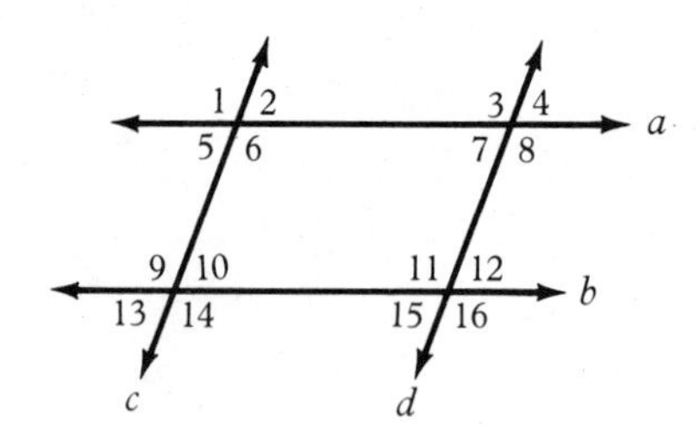

Algebra Review

Solve each equation for x.

1. $3x + 5 = 21 - x$
2. $10 - 6x = 4 + 2(1 - x)$
3. $5 - x = -3x$
4. $5 + 2(x - 4) = 19$
5. $\frac{1}{2}(2x - 6) = 2x + 5$
6. $\frac{2}{3}x + \frac{3}{4} = 1$
7. $4(x - 2) = 4 - (x + 2)$
8. $\frac{1}{2}x + 2(x - 4) = 17$
9. $2(x + 4) = 3(4 - x)$

Solve each inequality for x.

10. $-x > 9$
11. $x + 2 < 7$
12. $2x + 6 > 17$
13. $3(x - 2) < 8$
14. $15 - 2x < x$
15. $\frac{2x}{3} > 24$
16. $3x + 7 > 2x - 4$
17. $2|x| < 10$
18. $|x + 2| > 14$

Evaluate. Express fractions in lowest terms.

19. $\sqrt{8}$
20. $\sqrt{640}$
21. $\sqrt{27} + \sqrt{3}$
22. $8(8 - 6\sqrt{16})$
23. $\sqrt{75} - \sqrt{12}$
24. $\sqrt{108} + 3\sqrt{3}$
25. $\frac{7\sqrt{196}}{14\sqrt{64}}$
26. $\sqrt{\frac{4}{9}}$
27. $\sqrt{18} - \frac{\sqrt{8}}{8}$

Solve each system of equations for x and y.

28. $x = 2$
    $x + y = 5$
29. $2x + y = 14$
    $3x + y = 4$
30. $x = 2y + 1$
    $y = 2x - 20$
31. $x - y = 2$
    $x + y = 6$
32. $3x + 4y = 14$
    $x - 3y = -17$
33. $x + y = 10$
    $x - y = 18$
34. $3x + 4y = 18$
    $6x - 4y = 0$
35. $y = 2x$
    $x + 3y = 49$
36. $2x + y = 6$
    $-3x + 2y = 8\frac{1}{2}$

Solve.

37. A rectangle has a width three times its length. Find the length and width of the rectangle if its perimeter is 24.
38. A linear pair of angles have measures of $x + 20$ and $x + 30$. Find the measure of each angle.

Mineralogy: Symmetry

Minerals, as a rule, have regular arrangements of atoms that have some geometrical symmetry. While crystals do not always exhibit perfect symmetry, some have shapes that are close to the five regular polyhedra pictured below. Such crystals have axes of rotational symmetry and planes of reflectional symmetry.

Fluorite

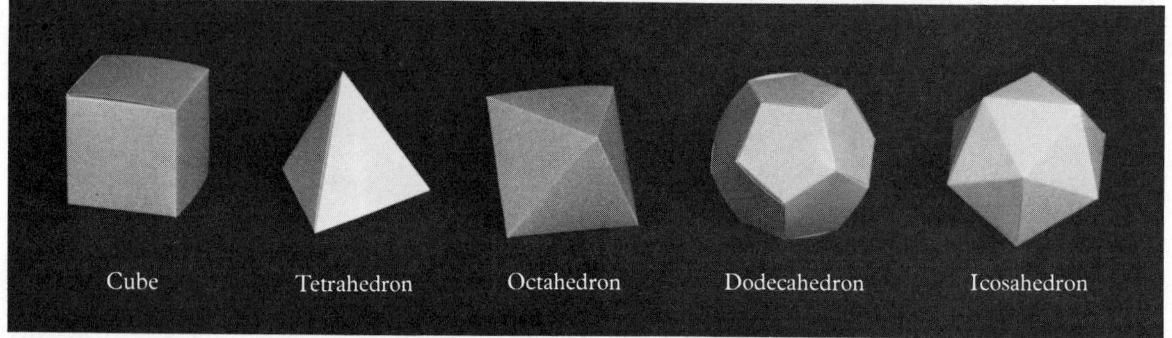

1 Find axes of rotational symmetry for a solid figure.

You can fold a pattern as shown here and make a model for a cube. Cut small slots and push a straw through the cube as shown in the picture. If the cube is rotated 90° four times around the straw axis, it returns to the starting position. Since this is true, we say the straw represents an *axis of rotational symmetry of order 4.*

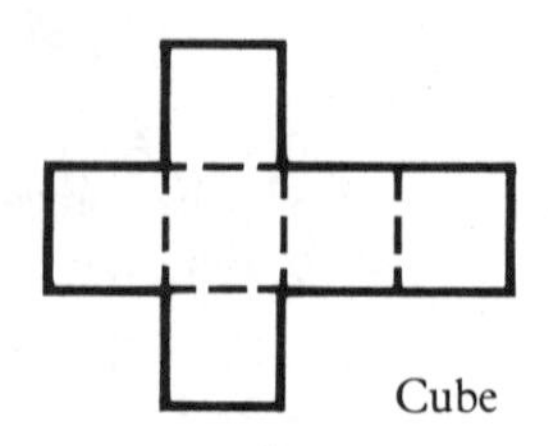

Cube

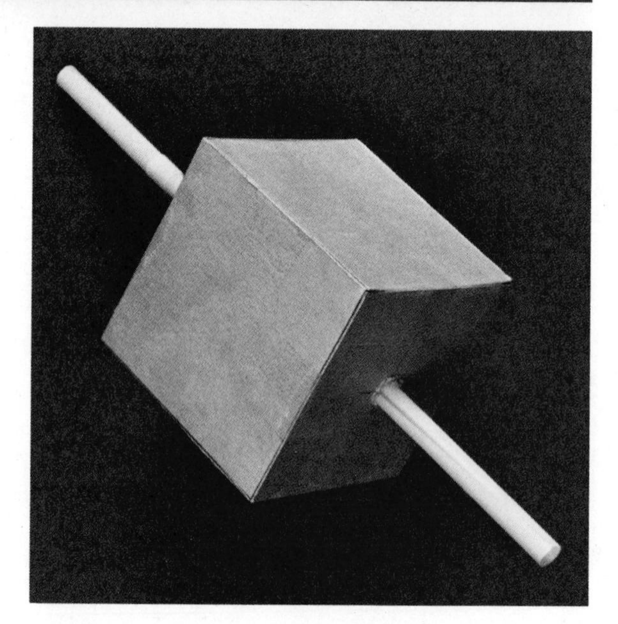

The three types of axes of symmetry for a cube are shown here.

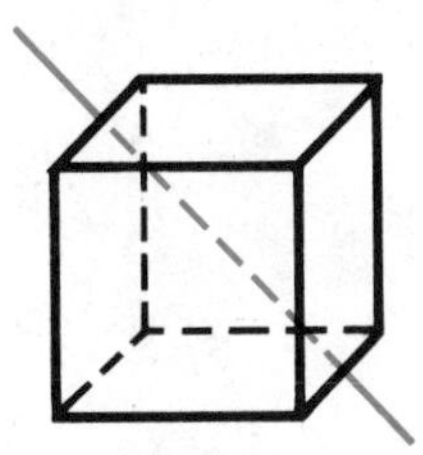

Order 2
A line through the midpoints of opposite edges

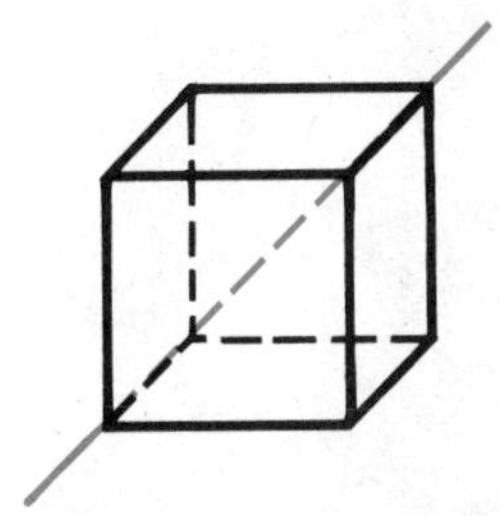

Order 3
A line through a pair of opposite vertices

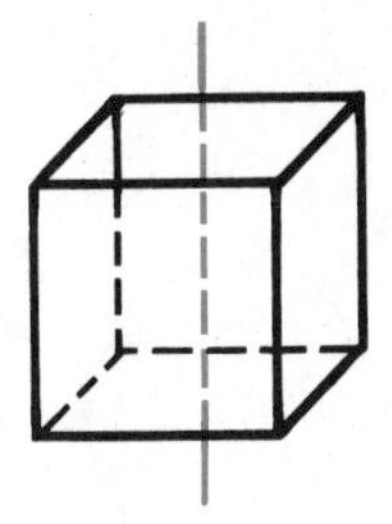

Order 4
A line through the centers of opposite faces

a. How many different axes of symmetry of order 2 are there for a given cube?

b. How many different axes of symmetry of order 3 are there for a given cube?

c. How many different axes of symmetry of order 4 are there for a given cube?

2 Find planes of reflectional symmetry for a solid figure.

You can construct a model of a cube using 12 congruent drinking straws fastened with pipe cleaners as shown in the picture. Cut "planes" from file cards or posterboard and use them to help you visualize planes of symmetry as shown.

a. A plane passing through opposite edges of a cube as shown here is a plane of symmetry for the cube. How many planes of symmetry of this type are there for a given cube?

b. A plane midway between a pair of opposite faces of a cube is a plane of symmetry for the cube. How many planes of symmetry of this type are there for a given cube?

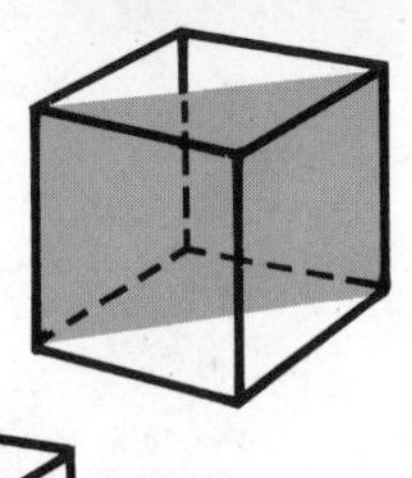

CHAPTER 6

Triangles

6–1 Classifying Triangles

The boat pictured here has sails that illustrate different shapes of triangles.

We can classify triangles according to the lengths of the sides or by the measure of the angles.

REVIEW: An **equilateral triangle** is a triangle with three congruent sides.

REVIEW: An **isosceles triangle** is a triangle with at least two congruent sides.

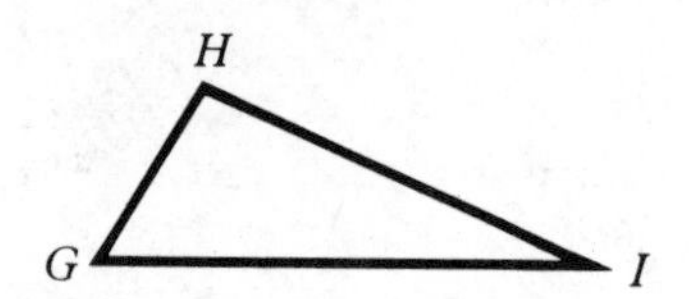

No sides are equal in length. $\triangle GHI$ is a *scalene triangle.*

Definition 6–1

A **scalene triangle** is a triangle with no congruent sides.

Triangles are also classified in terms of the measure of their angles.

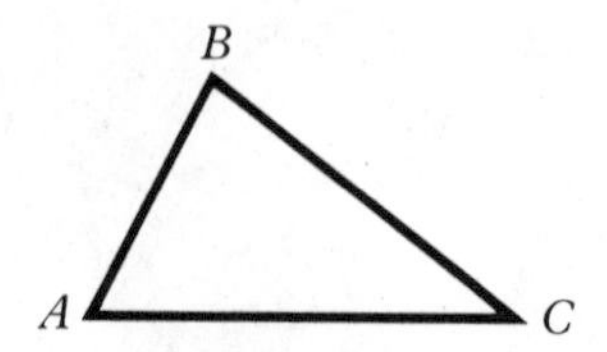

All angles are acute. $\triangle ABC$ is an *acute triangle.*

Definition 6–2

An **acute triangle** is a triangle with three acute angles.

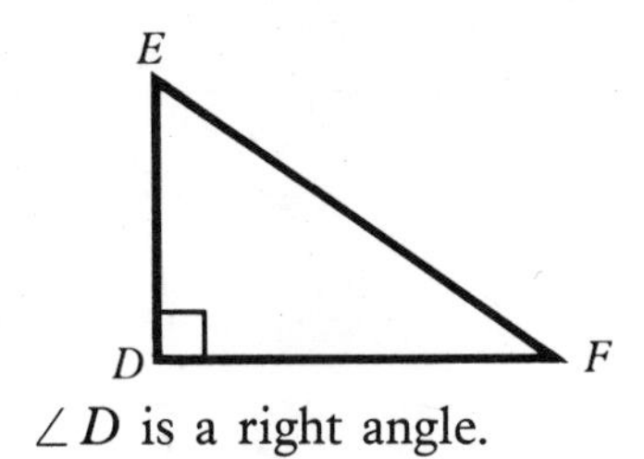

$\angle D$ is a right angle.

$\triangle DEF$ is a *right triangle*.
Side $\overline{EF}$ is the *hypotenuse*.
$\overline{DE}$ and $\overline{DF}$ are the *legs*.

Definition 6–3

A **right triangle** is a triangle with a right angle.

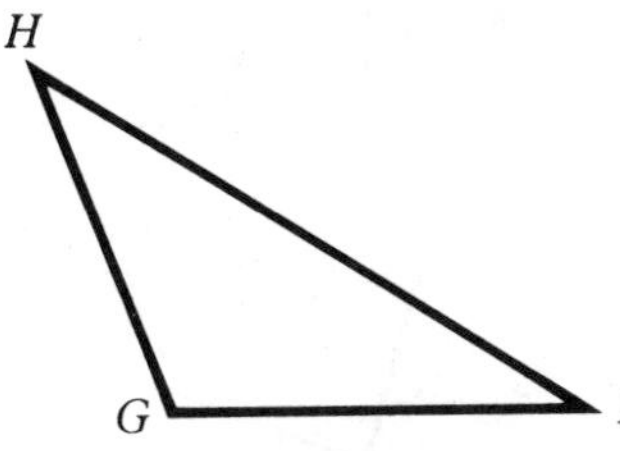

$\angle G$ is an obtuse angle.

$\triangle GHI$ is an *obtuse triangle*.

Definition 6–4

An **obtuse triangle** is a triangle with an obtuse angle.

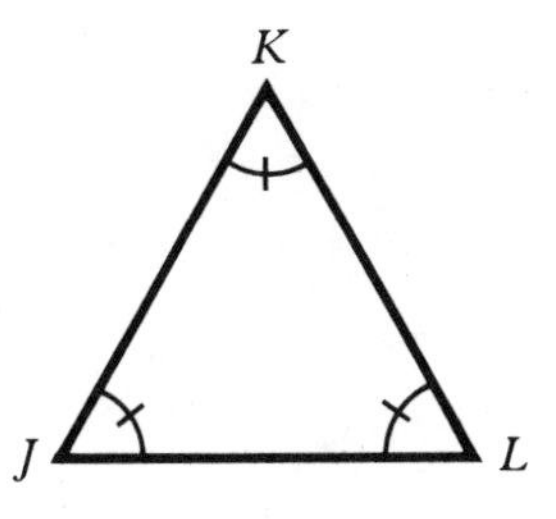

$\triangle JKL$ is an *equiangular triangle*.

Definition 6–5

An **equiangular triangle** is a triangle with three congruent angles.

For any triangle there are three segments called *altitudes*.

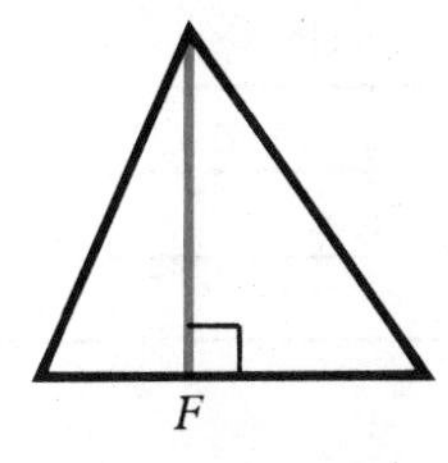

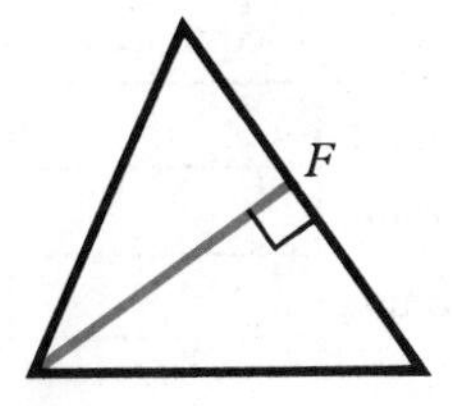

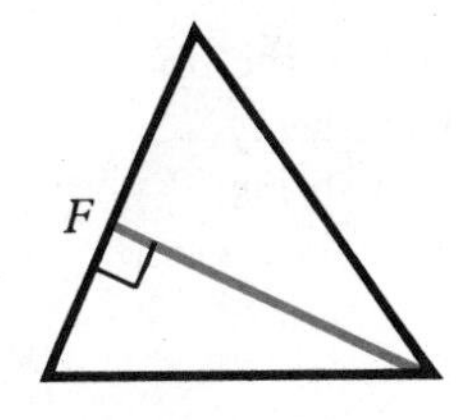

Definition 6–6

An **altitude** of a triangle is a segment from a vertex to a point F on the opposite side (perhaps extended) that is perpendicular to that opposite side.

Notice that in a right triangle two of the altitudes coincide with sides of the triangle. In an obtuse triangle two altitudes have feet on the extensions of the sides.

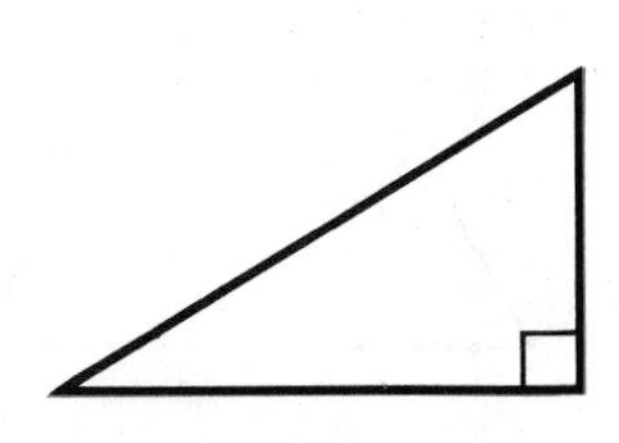

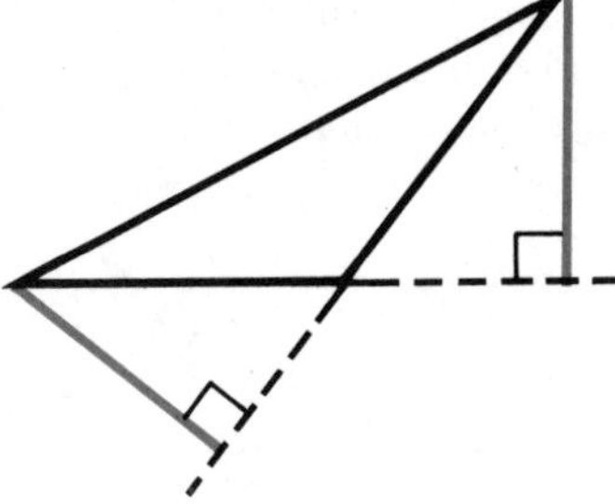

EXERCISES

A.

1. Classify each of these triangles as scalene, isosceles, or equilateral.

a.  **b.**  **c.**  **d.** 

2. Classify each of these triangles as acute, obtuse, or right.

a. 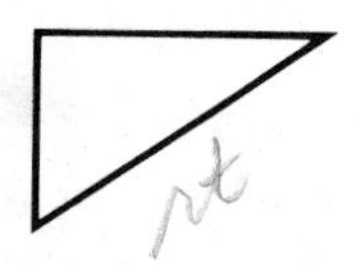 **b.**  **c.** 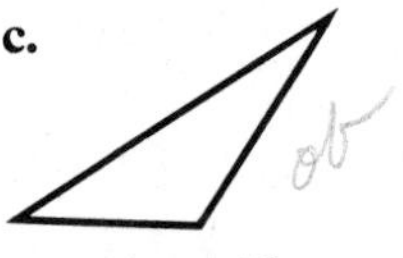 **d.** 

3. Name these parts of right triangle *MNP*.

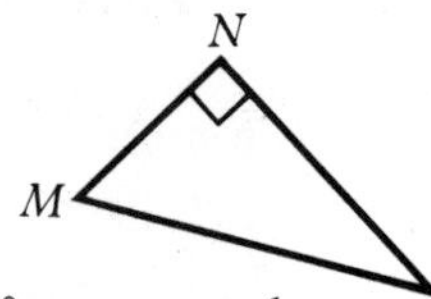

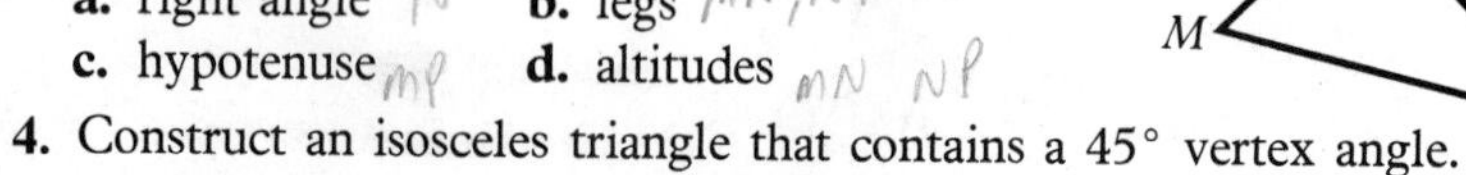

a. right angle **b.** legs
c. hypotenuse **d.** altitudes

4. Construct an isosceles triangle that contains a 45° vertex angle.

5. Construct a right, scalene triangle.

6. Construct an obtuse triangle that contains a 30° angle.

7. Construct an equilateral triangle. Construct an altitude.

8. Construct an obtuse triangle. Construct all three altitudes.

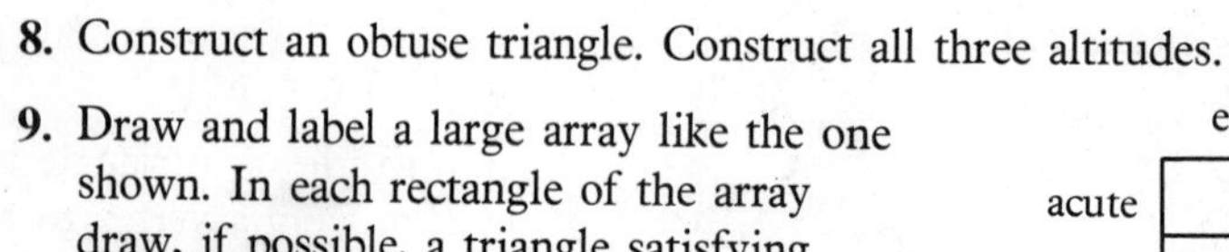

9. Draw and label a large array like the one shown. In each rectangle of the array draw, if possible, a triangle satisfying both conditions.

	equilateral	isosceles	scalene
acute			
right			
obtuse			

Activity

Trace three copies of the smaller star. Cut along the dotted lines and fit the pieces together to form this larger star.

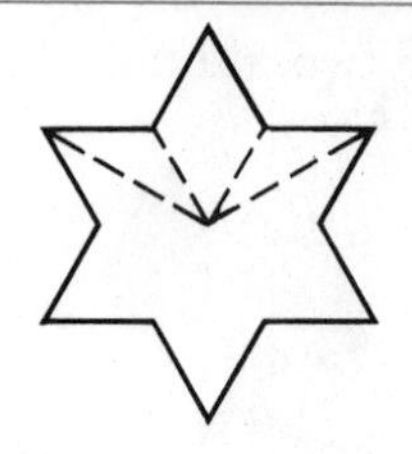

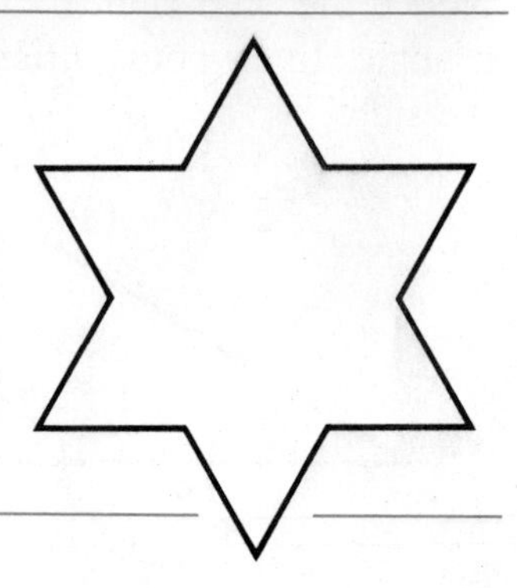

B.

10. Identify each triangle as acute, right, or obtuse.

a. $\triangle ABD$
b. $\triangle ABC$
c. $\triangle ADE$
d. $\triangle BDC$
e. $\triangle ACE$
f. $\triangle DCE$

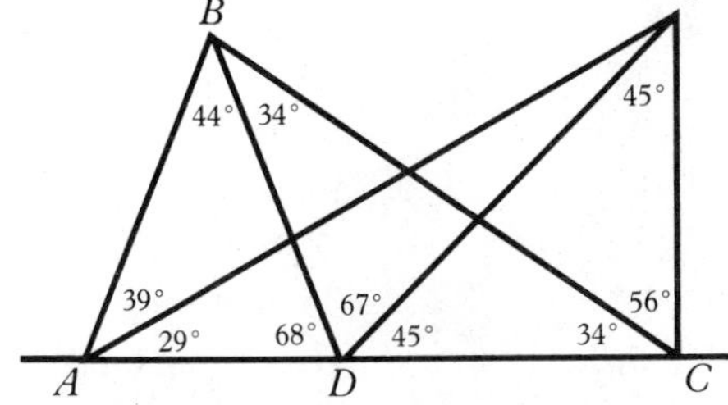

11. In the figure on the right, identify each altitude shown and its respective triangle.

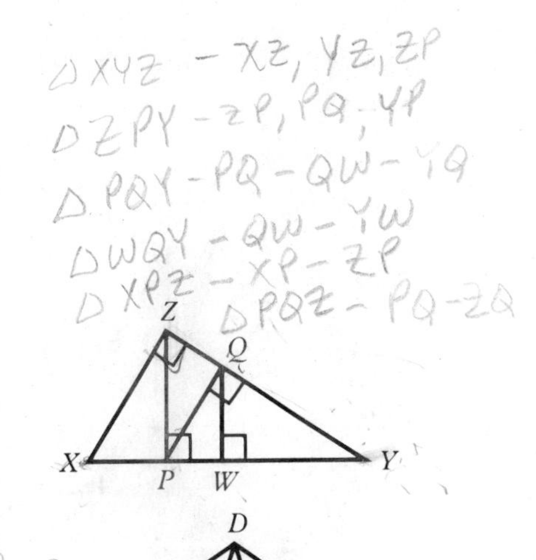

Exercises 12–14 refer to pentagon *ABCDH.*

12. Name two isosceles triangles with $\overline{AB}$ the unequal side.

13. Name two isosceles triangles that have $\overline{AB}$ as one of the equal sides.

14. Name an isosceles triangle with $\overline{FG}$ as one side.

15. Name all equilateral and all scalene triangles in the figure below.

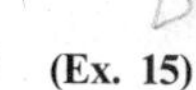

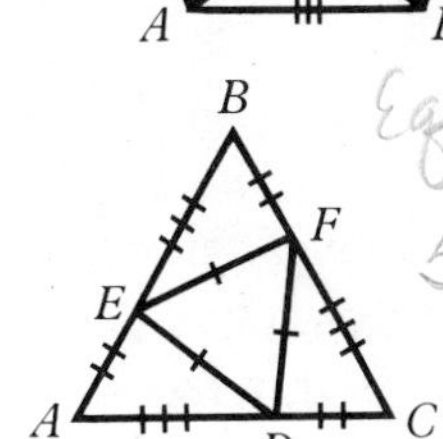

(Ex. 15)

C.

16. Why is an equilateral triangle also an isosceles triangle? Refer to the definition of "isosceles triangle" and explain.

17. Given: Isosceles triangle *ABC* with vertex angle *B*
$\overline{AE}$ is altitude from *A* to $\overline{BC}$
$\overline{CD}$ is altitude from *C* to $\overline{AB}$
$\overline{AD} \cong \overline{CE}$
Prove: $\angle BAE \cong \angle BCD$

18. Four equilateral triangles can be placed to form a larger equilateral triangle. How can four obtuse triangles be placed to form a larger obtuse triangle that is the same shape as the original triangle?

There are 27 different equilateral triangles in this figure. How many of them can you name?

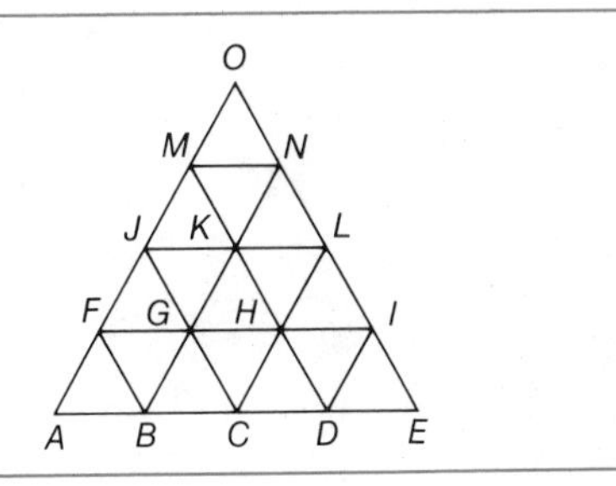

6–2 Isosceles Triangles

Thousands of geodesic domes have been constructed throughout the world. One of the largest was built in 1958. It is a car repair facility in Baton Rouge, Louisiana. This dome structure is 117 meters in diameter and 35 meters in height. A dome structure was also constructed for Montreal Expo in 1967. The photograph shows it under construction.

A dome structure is constructed by fitting together many triangles. Many of these triangles have sides equal in length, which means that they are either isosceles or equilateral (See Geometry in Our World, page 126).

We shall study some of the important properties of these two types of triangles in this lesson.

$\overline{AB} \cong \overline{AC}$

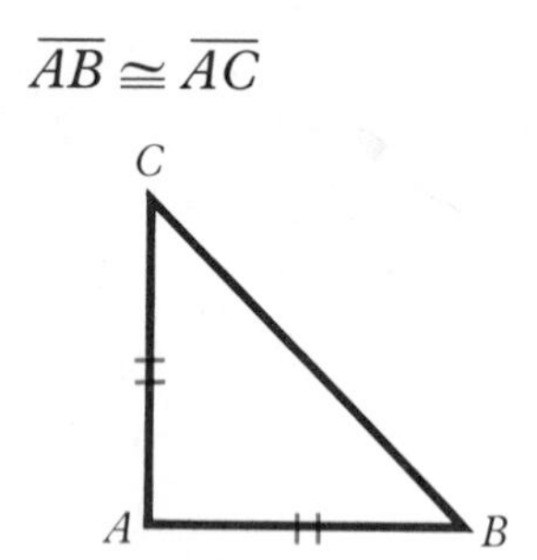

Observe that $m\angle B = m\angle C$.

$\overline{AC} \cong \overline{BC}$

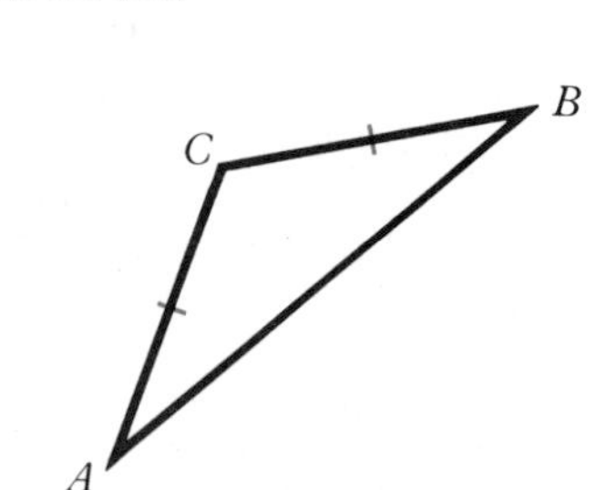

Observe that $m\angle A = m\angle B$.

$\overline{AB} \cong \overline{BC}$

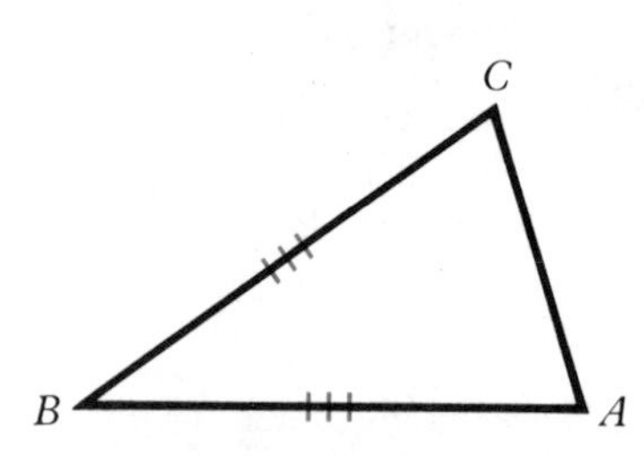

Observe that $m\angle A = m\angle C$.

Theorem 6–1 If a triangle is isosceles, then its base angles are congruent.

PROOF

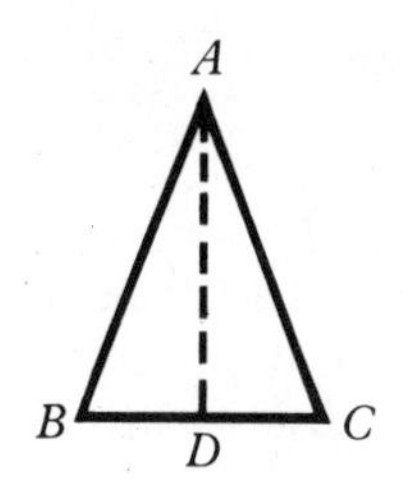

Given: Let $\triangle ABC$ be isosceles with $\overline{AB} \cong \overline{AC}$.
Prove: $\angle B \cong \angle C$.

Plan: Let D be the midpoint of $\overline{BC}$. Draw $\overline{AD}$ and prove that $\triangle ABD \cong \triangle ACD$.

Statements	Reasons
1. $\triangle ABC$ is isosceles with $\overline{AB} \cong \overline{AC}$	**1.** Given
2. D is the midpoint of $\overline{BC}$.	**2.** Every line segment has one and only one midpoint.
3. $\triangle ABD \cong \triangle ACD$	**3.** A segment from the vertex angle to the midpoint of the opposite side forms a pair of congruent triangles (Theorem 4–2).
4. $\angle B \cong \angle C$	**4.** CPCTC

APPLICATION

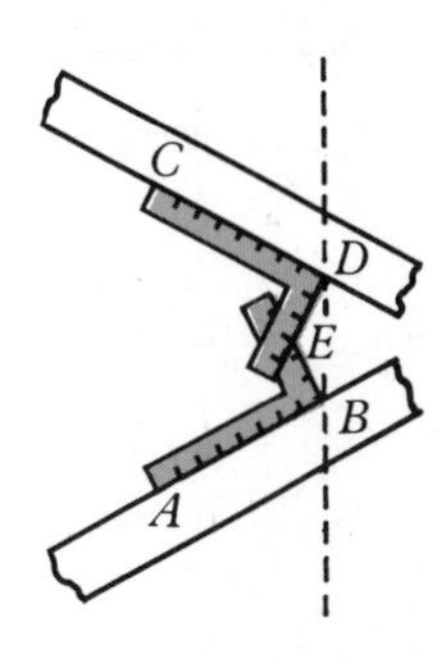

Two converging timbers are to be cut along a line so that a board can be nailed to the two timbers along this line.

Two carpenter's squares are positioned so that $BE = DE$. The points B and D determine the line so that $\triangle ABD \cong \triangle CDB$. Why? The carpenter's squares are positioned so that $\triangle BDE$ is an isosceles triangle. Therefore $\angle EBD \cong \angle EDB$, and we can conclude $m\angle ABD = 90 + m\angle EBD = m\angle EDB + 90 = m\angle CDB$.

Following are two more theorems. Theorem 6–2 is a special case of Theorem 6–1.

Theorem 6–2 If a triangle is equilateral, then it is equiangular.

Theorem 6–3 If two angles of a triangle are congruent, then the sides opposite these angles are congruent.

EXERCISES

A.

In exercises 1–3 segments labeled with identical "hatch marks" are assumed to be congruent. Name all pairs of angles that are congruent by using Theorem 6–1.

1.

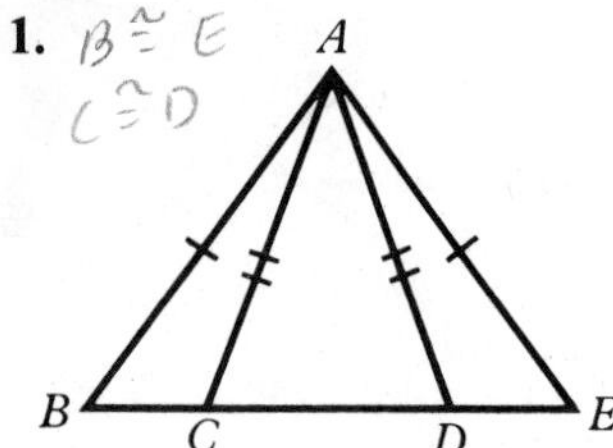

2.

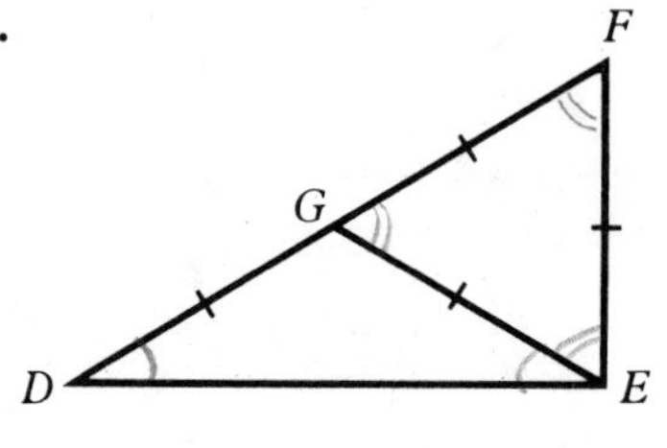

3.

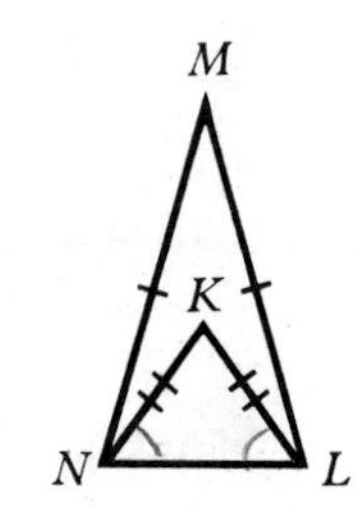

In exercises 4–6 angles labeled with identical "hatch marks" are assumed to be congruent. Name the isosceles triangles.

4.

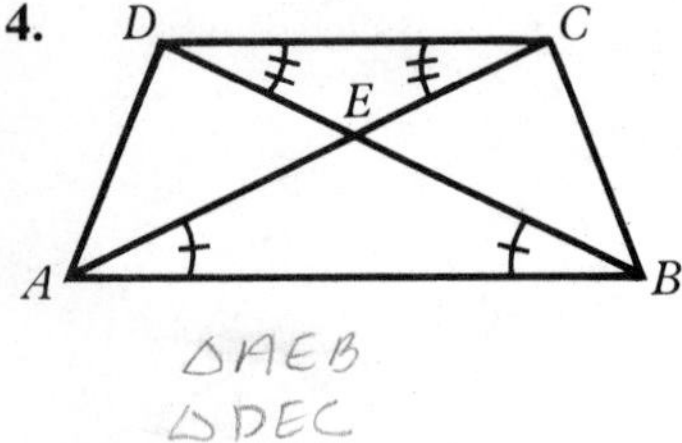

5.

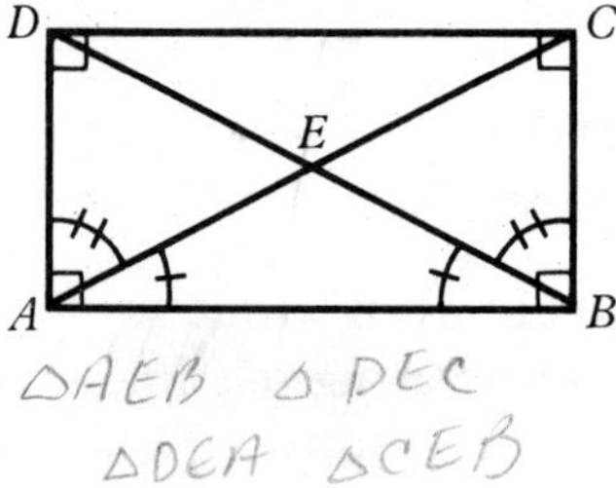

6.

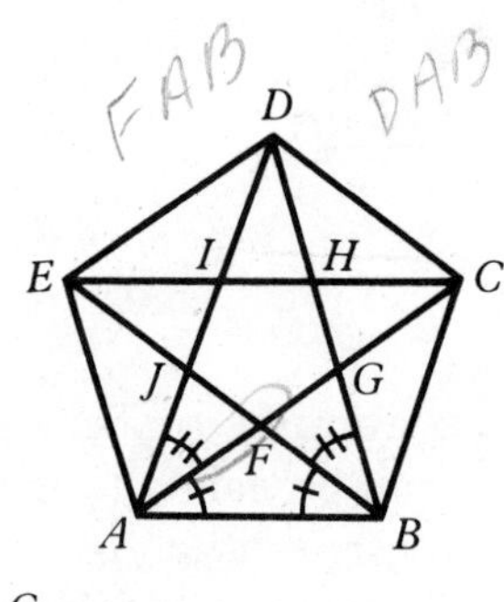

7. $m\angle ABC =$?

8. $CE =$?

9. $m\angle ACD =$?

10. $BC =$?

11. $AB =$?

12. $m\angle ADB =$?

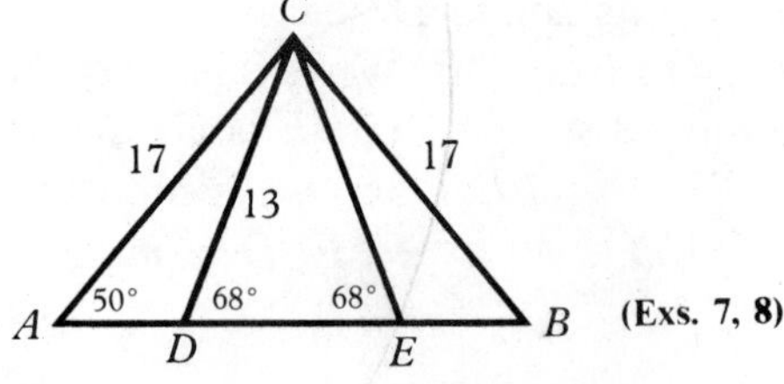

(Exs. 7, 8)

B.

13. $\triangle ABC$ is isosceles with $\overline{AB} \cong \overline{BC}$. If $AB = 4x$ and $BC = 6x - 15$, find AB and BC.

14. In $\triangle DEF$, $\overline{DE} \cong \overline{EF}$. If $DE = 4x + 15$, $EF = 2x + 45$, and $DF = 3x + 15$, find the lengths of the sides of the triangle.

15. In $\triangle XYZ$, $\overline{XY} \cong \overline{YZ}$. If $m\angle X = 4x + 60$, $m\angle Y = 2x + 30$, and $m\angle Z = 14x + 30$, find $m\angle X$, $m\angle Y$, and $m\angle Z$.

16. In $\triangle ABC$, $\angle A \cong \angle C$. If $AB = 4x + 25$, $BC = 2x + 45$, and $AC = 3x - 15$, find the lengths of the three sides.

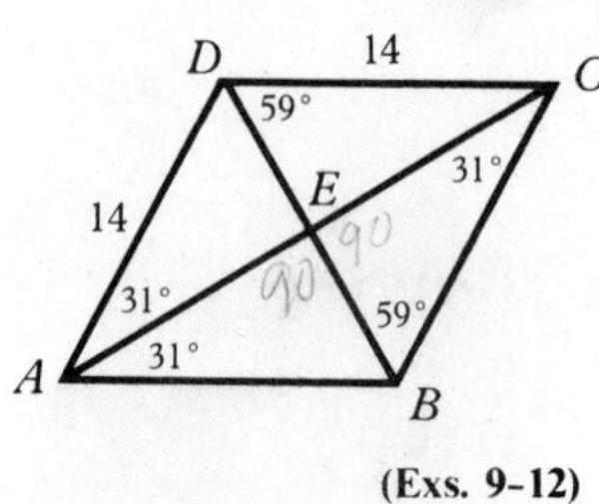

(Exs. 9-12)

For exercises 17–24, write two-column proofs.

17. Given: $\overline{AB} \cong \overline{AC}$
$\overline{DB} \cong \overline{DC}$
Prove: $\angle 1 \cong \angle 2$

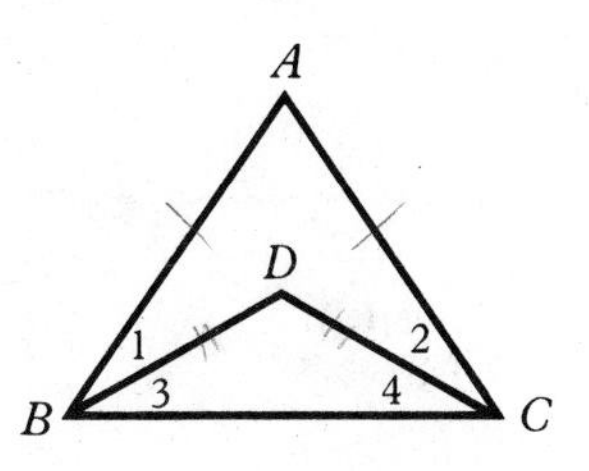

18. Given: $ABCD$ is a quadrilateral with $\overline{AB} \cong \overline{BC}$ and $\overline{DA} \cong \overline{DC}$.
Prove: $\angle BAD \cong \angle BCD$
(*Hint:* Add an auxiliary line.)

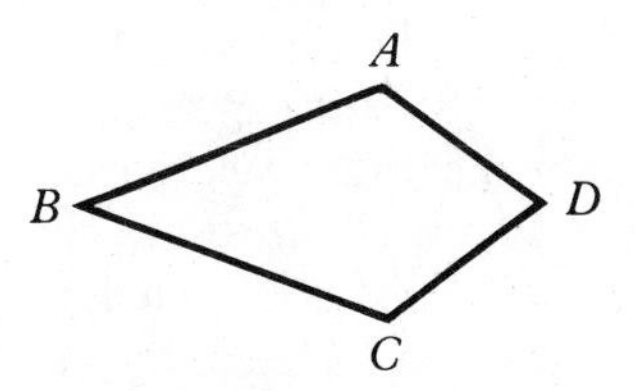

19. Given: $\overline{AC} \cong \overline{AD}$, $\overline{BC} \cong \overline{ED}$
Prove: $\triangle ABE$ is isosceles.

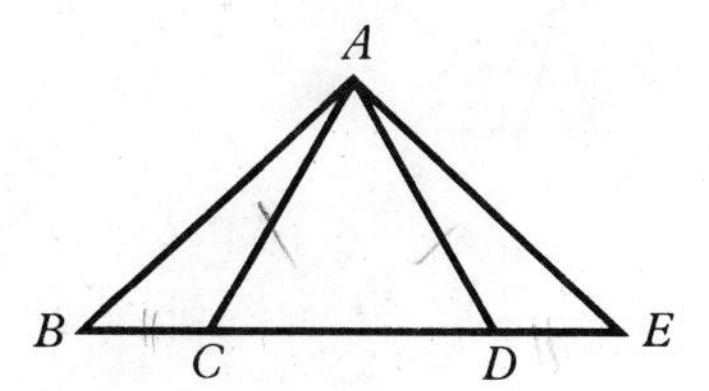

20. Given: $\overline{AC} \cong \overline{AD}$, $\angle 1 \cong \angle 2$
Prove: $\triangle ABD \cong \triangle AEC$

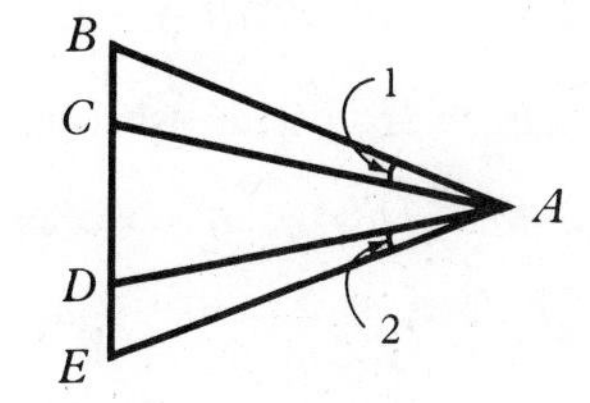

21. Given: $\overline{AB} \cong \overline{AC}$
$\overline{BE}$ bisects $\angle B$.
$\overline{CD}$ bisects $\angle C$.
Prove: $\overline{CD} \cong \overline{BE}$

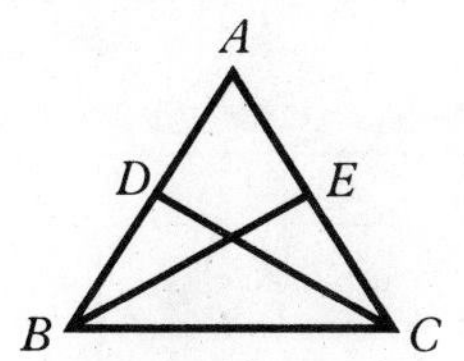

22. Given: $\overline{AB} \cong \overline{AC}$
$\overline{BE}$ bisects $\angle B$.
$\overline{CD}$ bisects $\angle C$.
Prove: $\overline{AD} \cong \overline{AE}$

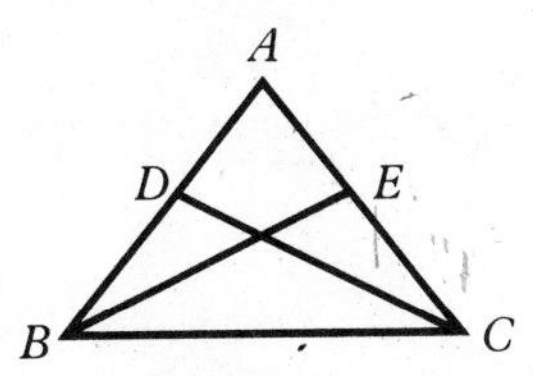

23. Given: $\overline{AB} \cong \overline{AC}$
$\angle 1 \cong \angle 2$
Prove: $\triangle BCD$ is isosceles.

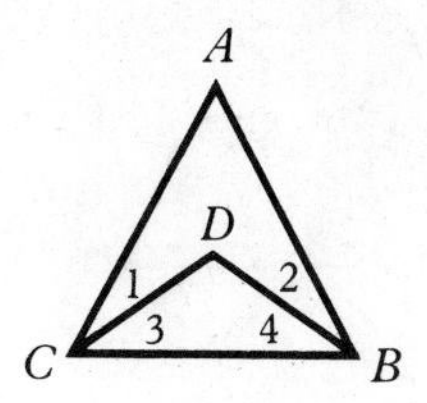

24. Given: $\angle ABC \cong \angle ADC$
$\angle 1 \cong \angle 2$
Prove: $\overline{AB} \cong \overline{AD}$ and $\overline{BC} \cong \overline{DC}$

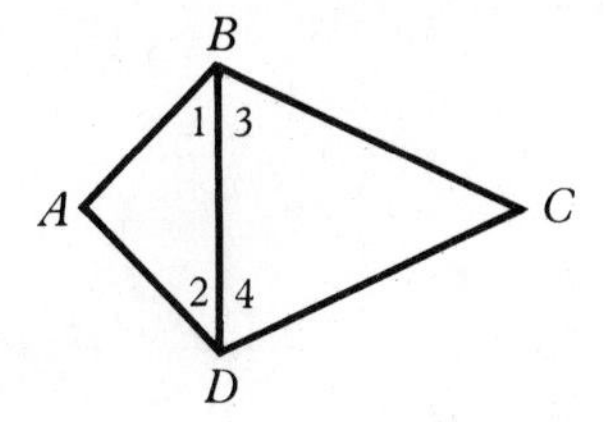

25. **Given:** $\angle ABC$ and $\angle D$ are supplementary.
Prove: $\triangle ABD$ is isosceles.

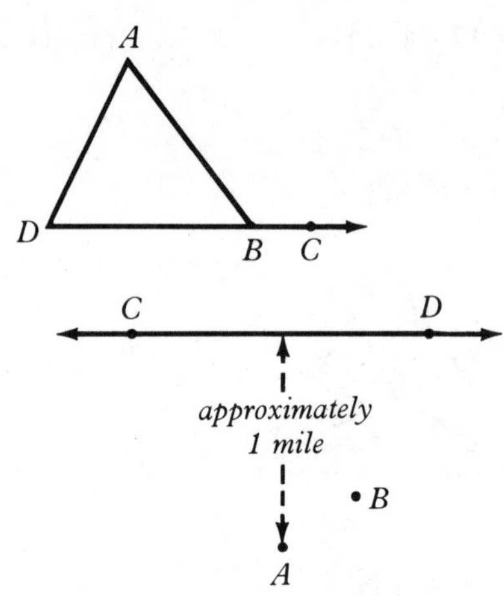

26. A survey team has been asked to locate a point on property line CD that is equal in distance from two previously located survey pins A and B. Because of the magnitude of the distances, direct measurement with a tape measure is not feasible. Points A and B are close together. Transits are located at each point. How can the team locate the desired point?

C.

In exercises 27–28, $ABCDE$ is a regular pentagon.

27. Prove that $\triangle ABG$ is an isosceles triangle.

28. Prove that $\triangle AFG$ is an isosceles triangle.

29. Prove Theorem 6–2.

30. Prove Theorem 6–3.

31. Prove that the bisector of the vertex angle of an isosceles triangle is the perpendicular bisector of the opposite side.

32. Prove that if $\triangle ABC \cong \triangle DEF$ and $\triangle DEF \cong \triangle GHI$, then $\triangle ABC \cong \triangle GHI$. (Transitive property of congruent triangles.)

A E B F G D C

(Exs. 27, 28)

Activity

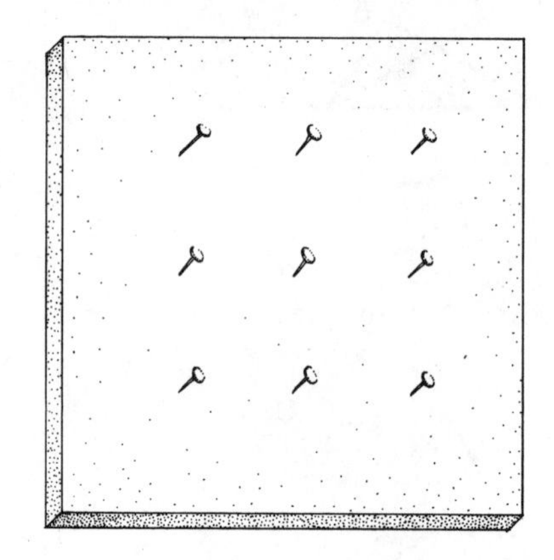

On a geoboard with 3 nails on a side or on 3-by-3 dot paper show:

1. Segments of five different lengths.
2. Angles of ten different sizes.
3. Triangles of seven different sizes and shapes.

33. Prove that the bisectors of the base angles of an isosceles triangle are congruent.

34. Prove that the line segments joining the midpoint of the base of an isosceles triangle to the midpoints of the legs are congruent.

35. In triangle ABC, $\overline{AB} \cong \overline{AC}$. X is the midpoint of $\overline{AB}$ and Y is the midpoint of $\overline{AC}$. $\overleftrightarrow{XW}$ is drawn perpendicular to $\overline{AB}$; $\overleftrightarrow{YZ}$ is drawn perpendicular to $\overleftrightarrow{AC}$; W and Z are points on $\overleftrightarrow{BC}$. Prove that $\overline{XW} \cong \overline{YZ}$.

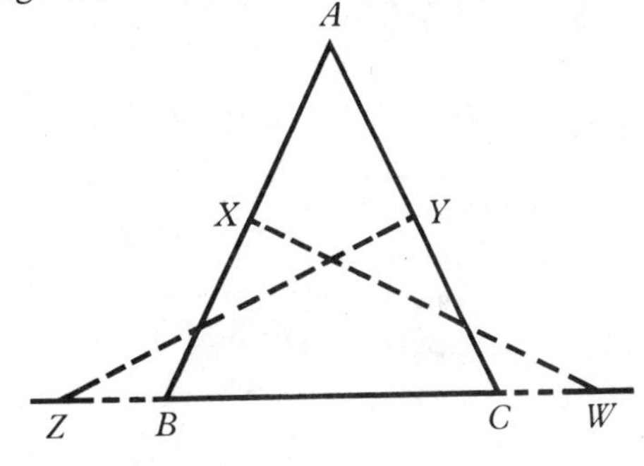

(Ex. 35)

36. Prove that an equiangular triangle is equilateral.

37. Suppose that $\triangle ABC$ is an isosceles triangle with $\overline{AC} \cong \overline{BC}$, and that $\overline{AD}$ and $\overline{BE}$ intersect at P so that $\angle PAB \cong \angle PBA$. Prove that $\triangle PDE$ is an isosceles triangle.

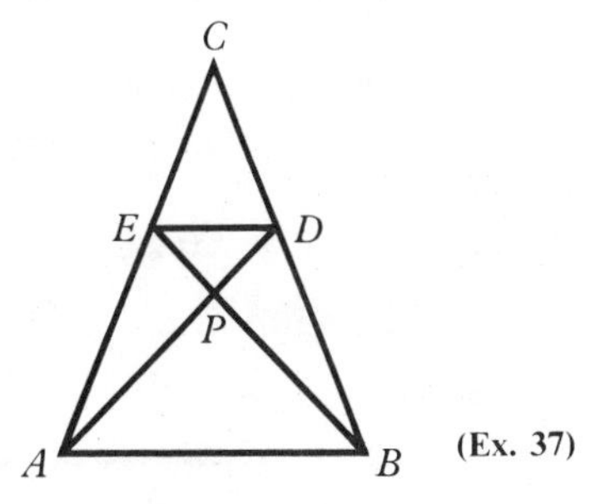

(Ex. 37)

PROBLEM SOLVING

How many equilateral triangles are there?

How many kites are there? (A kite is a quadrilateral with exactly two pairs of congruent adjacent sides.)

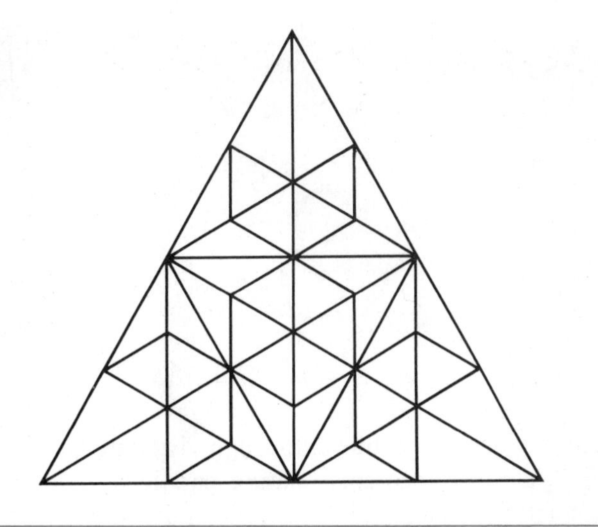

6–3 Measures of the Angles of a Triangle

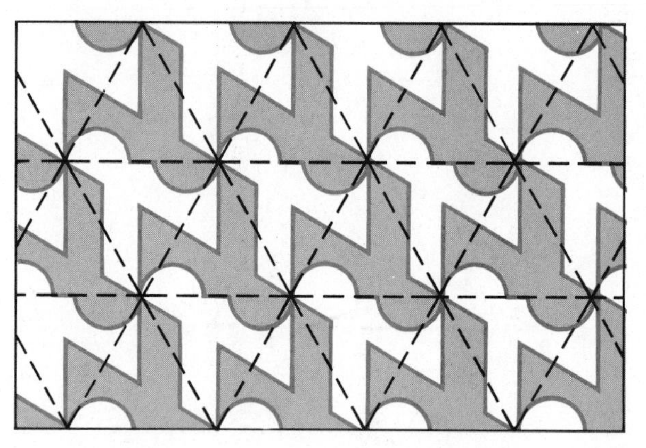

Geometric patterns and designs are interesting and important to an interior decorator. (See Geometry In Our World, p. 40.) Many such patterns, when carefully analyzed, are built around a triangular shape that is repeated.

The theorem in this section describes a property of triangles that gives them a "patternmaking" quality.

In Chapter 2 we saw that if the corners of a triangle are cut off and fitted together, the sum of the angles appears to be 180°.

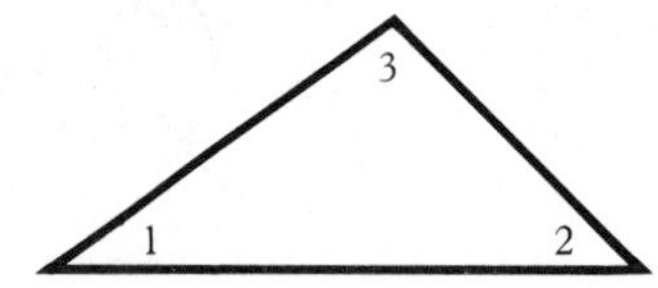

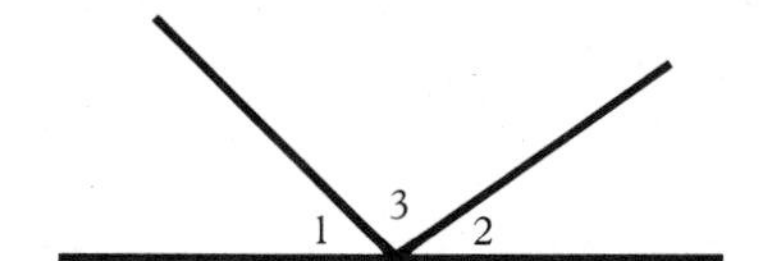

We now state this as a theorem.

Theorem 6–4 The sum of the measures of the angles of a triangle is 180°.

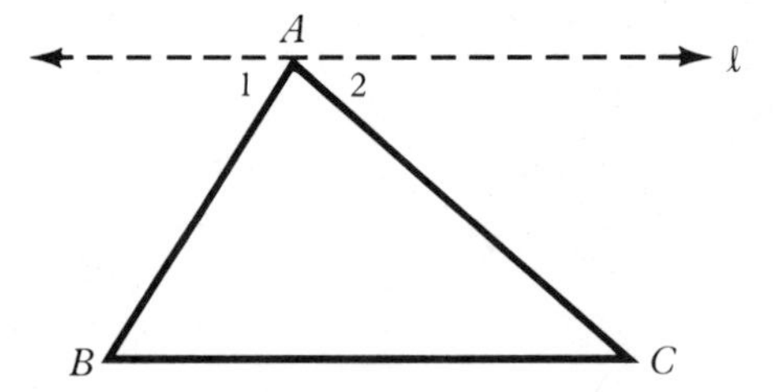

PROOF

Given: A triangle ABC
Prove: $m\angle A + m\angle B + m\angle C = 180$

Plan: Construct a line ℓ through A parallel to $\overline{BC}$, and use theorems relating parallel lines and a transversal. (Line ℓ is an auxiliary line.)

Statements	Reasons
1. Let ℓ be a line through A parallel to $\overline{BC}$.	**1.** Construction
2. $\angle 1 \cong \angle B$, $\angle 2 \cong \angle C$	**2.** If two lines are parallel, then the alternate interior angles are congruent.
3. $m\angle 1 + m\angle A + m\angle 2 = 180$	**3.** Definition of between for rays and Linear Pair Postulate
4. $m\angle B + m\angle A + m\angle C = 180$	**4.** Substitution

APPLICATION

Since the sum of the measures of the angles of a triangle is 180° (in the figure $a + b + c = 180$) congruent copies of a triangle can be arranged around a point as shown in the figure and extended to cover the plane. These triangular patterns form the basis for more intricate patterns as shown at the beginning of the lesson.

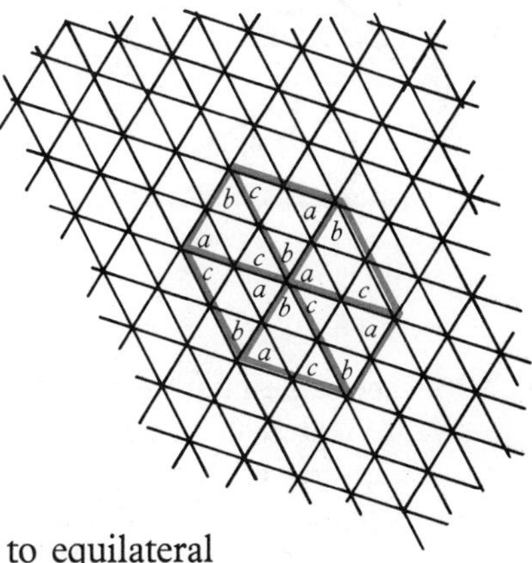

The next theorem can be proved by applying Theorem 6–4 to equilateral triangles.

Theorem 6–5 The angles of an equilateral triangle each have a measure of 60°.

The theorem stated below is useful when solving certain geometric problems. It is stated and illustrated here and will be proved as an exercise.

$x = a + b$, where x is the measure of the exterior angle and a and b are measures of remote interior angles.

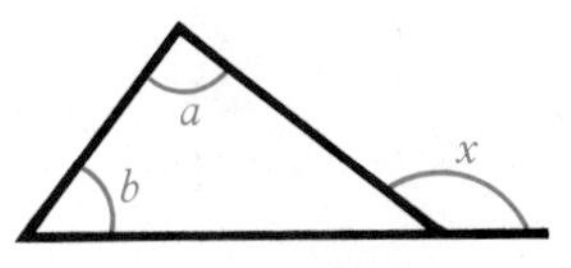

Theorem 6–6 The measure of an exterior angle of a triangle is equal to the sum of the measures of its two remote interior angles.

EXERCISES

A.

Find the measures of the indicated angles in exercises 1–9. Hatch marks indicate congruent segments.

1.

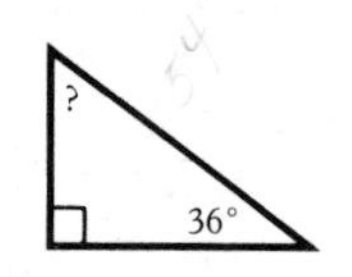

2.

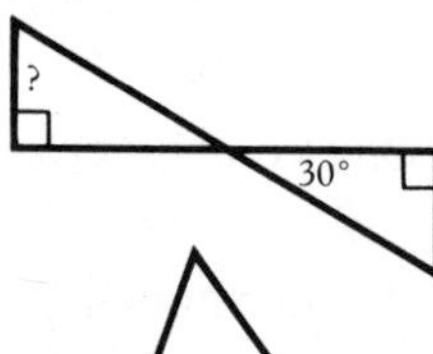

3.

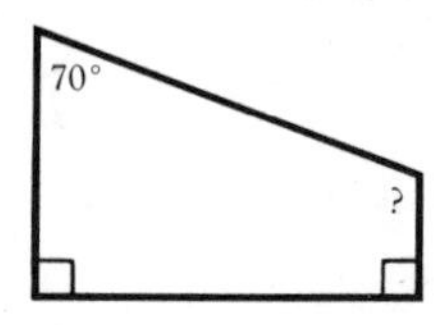

4.

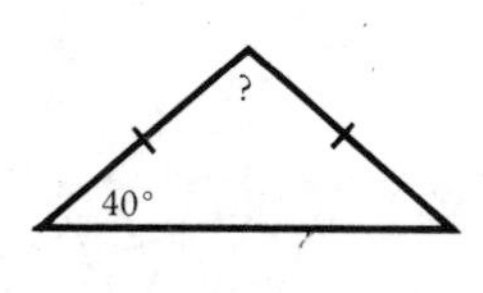

5.

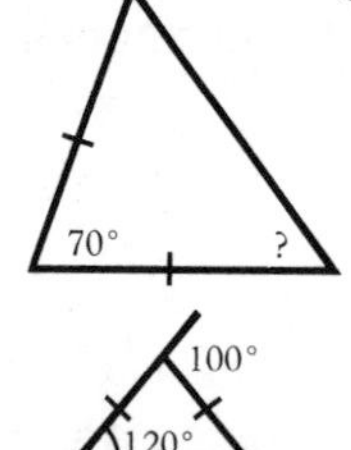

6.

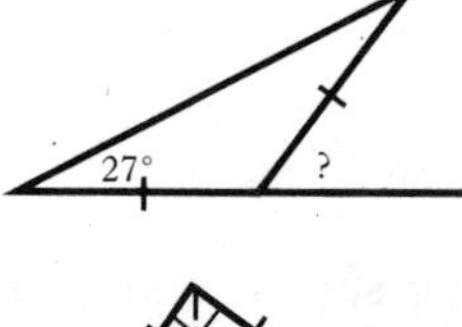

7.

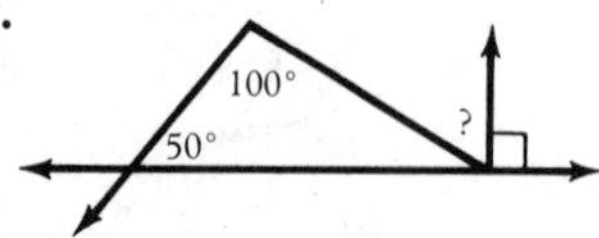

8.

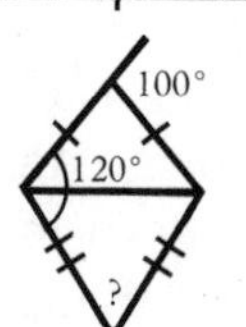

9.

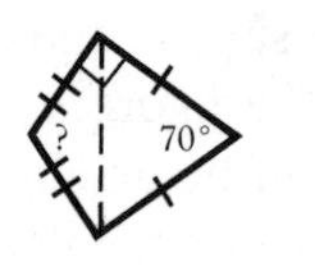

B.

10. The angle measures of the base angles of an isosceles triangle are represented by x and the vertex angle by $2x + 30$. Find the measures of each angle.

11. The measures of the angles of a triangle are represented by $2x + 15$, $x + 20$, and $3x + 25$. Find the measures of the angles.

12. Prove that the angles of an equilateral triangle each have a measure of 60°.

13. Prove that the base angles of an isosceles right triangle each have a measure of 45°.

14. A machinist must make a steel plate with holes drilled as shown. The machinist must first calculate the measures of $\angle 3$ and $\angle 4$. Find $m\angle 3$ and $m\angle 4$.

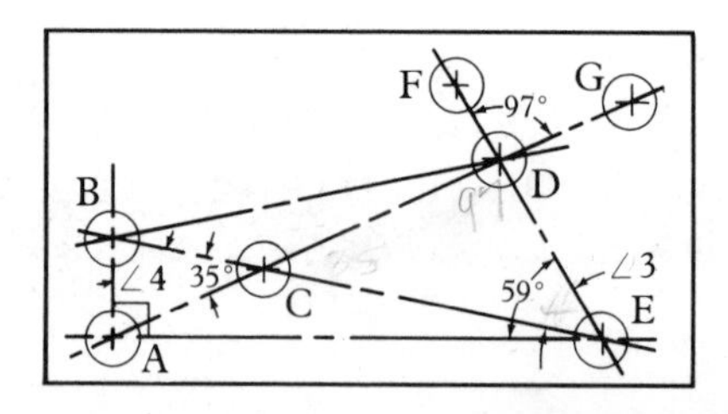

Activity

Trace and cut out the three small hexagons and cut along all the dotted lines. Use the 13 pieces to form a large regular hexagon.

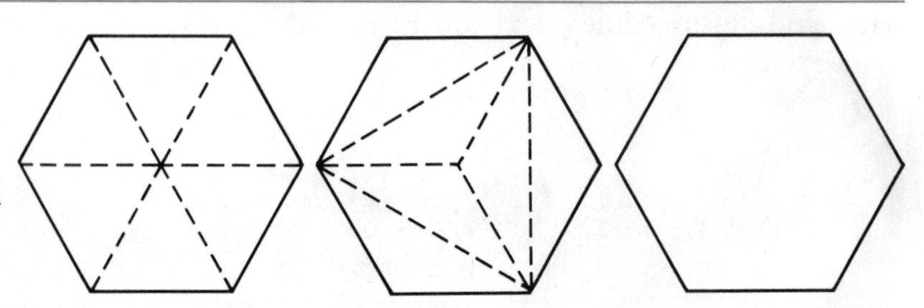

15. Prove that the base angles of an isosceles triangle are acute.

16. In $\triangle ABC$ and $\triangle DEF$, $\angle A \cong \angle D$ and $\angle B \cong \angle E$. Prove that $\angle C \cong \angle F$.

17. Prove that the acute angles of a right triangle are complementary.

C.

18. Given: $\overleftrightarrow{AB} \parallel \overleftrightarrow{DE}$
Prove: $m\angle B + m\angle C + m\angle D = 180$

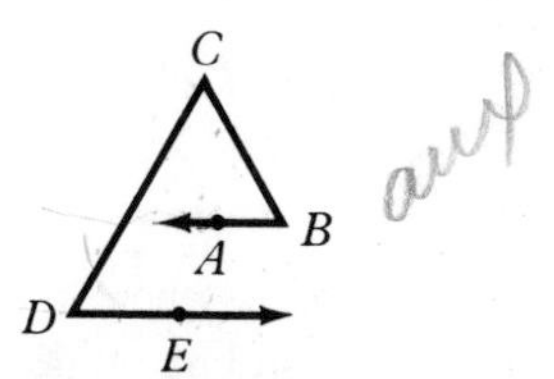

19. Given: $\overrightarrow{CE}$ bisects $\angle BCD$.
$\overline{AC} \cong \overline{BC}$
Prove: $\overleftrightarrow{CE} \parallel \overleftrightarrow{AB}$

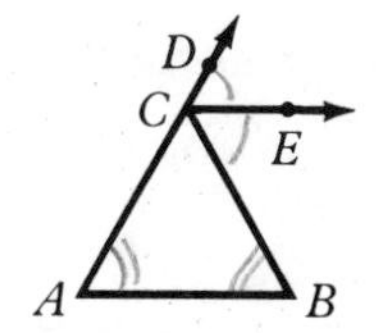

20. Given: $\overline{DE} \perp \overline{AE}$
$\overline{DB} \perp \overline{AB}$
Prove: $m\angle CAB = m\angle CDE$

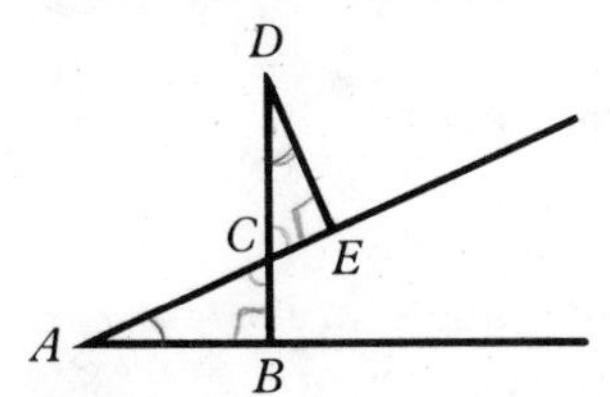

21. Given: $\overleftrightarrow{AB}$, $\overleftrightarrow{BC}$, $\overleftrightarrow{CD}$, and $\overleftrightarrow{AD}$ as shown
Prove: $m\angle 1 + m\angle 2 = m\angle C + m\angle B$

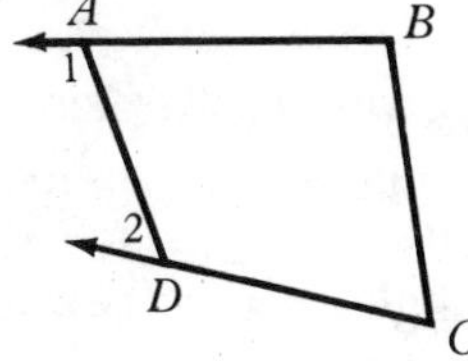

22. Prove that the sum of the angles of a quadrilateral is 360°.

23. Prove Theorem 6–6.

PROBLEM SOLVING

Trace each figure and finish drawing the dotted lines to divide each figure into four identical parts, each the same shape as the original figure.

A

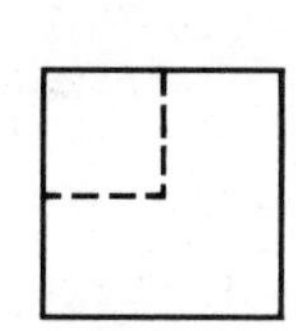

B

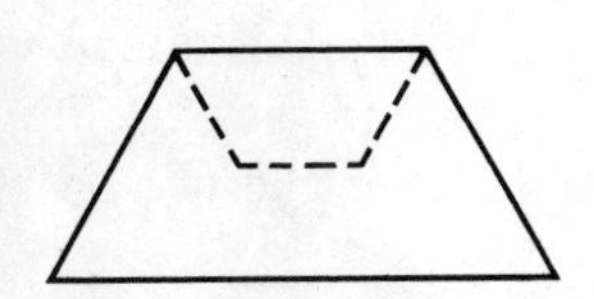

C

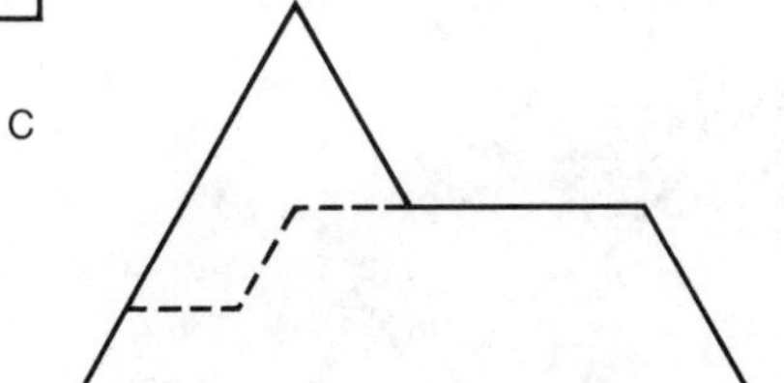

D

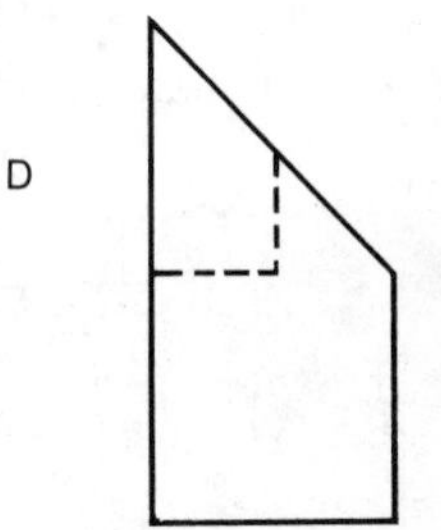

6–4 The AAS Congruence Theorem

On cannibal island
there lay some trees,
An oak, a maple, and an elm chinese.
As ye strike a path
from elm to oak
You'll find the treasure
of which I've spoke.
Just find the spot
and bet your socks
On a triangle congruent to
my triangle of rocks.

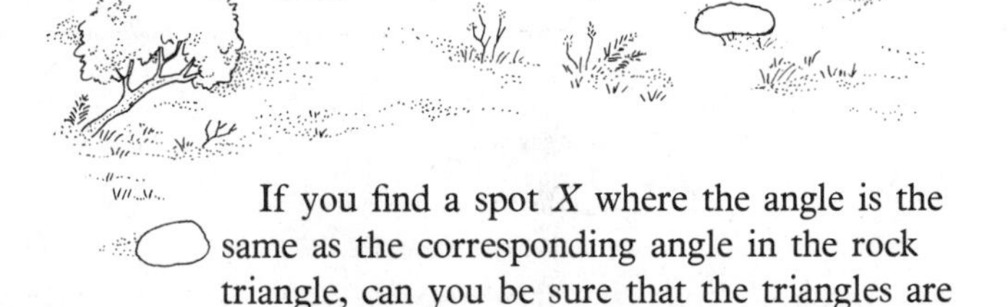

If you find a spot X where the angle is the same as the corresponding angle in the rock triangle, can you be sure that the triangles are congruent?

A pirate who was a frustrated geometer laid out three large rocks, and wrote the poem shown above.

In the triangles below, two angles and a side opposite one angle are congruent. Use tracing paper to convince yourself that the triangles are congruent.

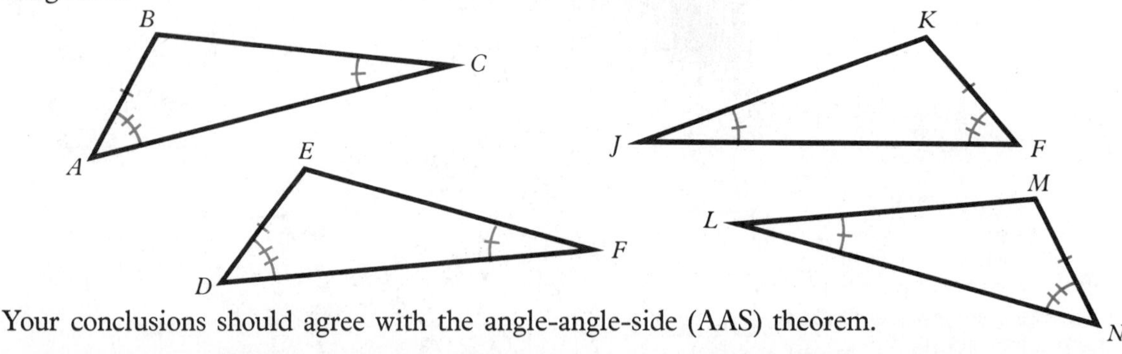

Your conclusions should agree with the angle-angle-side (AAS) theorem.

Theorem 6–7 **AAS Theorem.** If two angles and a side opposite one angle in a triangle are congruent to two angles and the corresponding side of a second triangle, then the two triangles are congruent.

PROOF

Given: $\triangle ABC$ and $\triangle DEF$ with
$\angle A \cong \angle D$
$\angle B \cong \angle E$
$\overline{BC} \cong \overline{EF}$

Prove: $\triangle ABC \cong \triangle DEF$

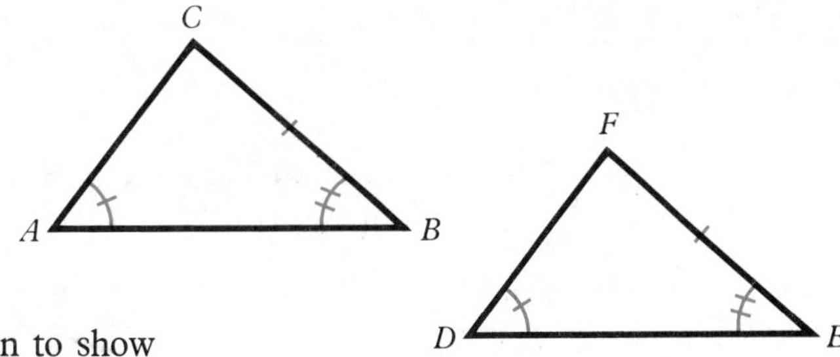

Plan: We shall use the given information to show that $\angle C \cong \angle F$ and then use the ASA postulate.

Statements	Reasons
1. $\angle A \cong \angle D$, $\angle B \cong \angle E$	1. Given
2. $m\angle A + m\angle B + m\angle C = 180$; $m\angle D + m\angle E + m\angle F = 180$	2. The sum of the measures of the three angles of a triangle is $180°$.
3. $m\angle A + m\angle B + m\angle C = m\angle D + m\angle E + m\angle F$	3. Substitution
4. $m\angle C = m\angle F$	4. Subtraction of equals property
5. $\angle C \cong \angle F$	5. Definition of congruent angles
6. $\overline{BC} \cong \overline{EF}$	6. Why?
7. $\triangle ABC = \triangle DEF$	7. Why?

APPLICATION

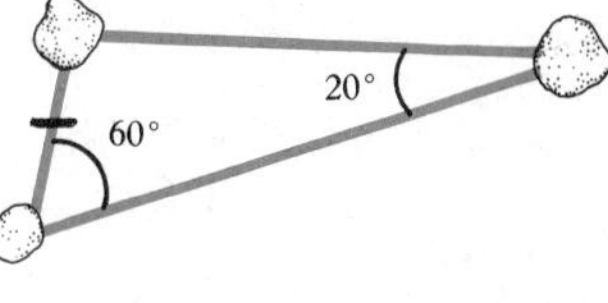

Theorem 6–7 provides an answer to the puzzle problem on page 212. Since two angles and a side opposite one of the angles of the "tree triangle" are congruent to two angles and the side opposite one of the angles of the "rock triangle," the two triangles are congruent and X marks the spot of the treasure!

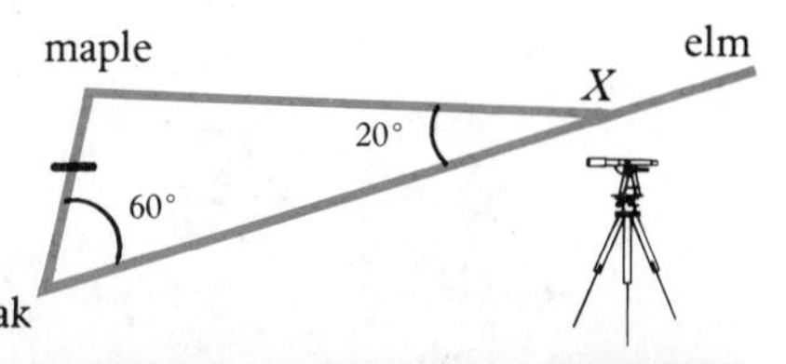

When Theorem 6–7 is applied to a right triangle we obtain the hypotenuse-angle (HA) theorem stated below.

Theorem 6–8 **HA Theorem.** If the hypotenuse and an acute angle of one right triangle are congruent to a hypotenuse and an acute angle of another right triangle, then the triangles are congruent.

EXERCISES

A.

For exercises 1–6 indicate whether the given pair of triangles is congruent by AAS, HA, SAS, ASA, or none of these.

1.

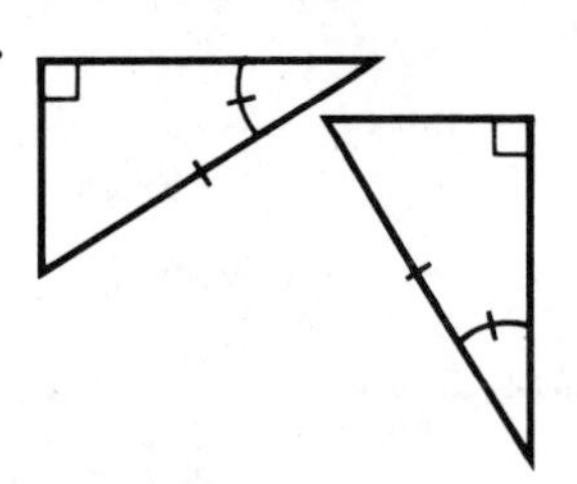

2.

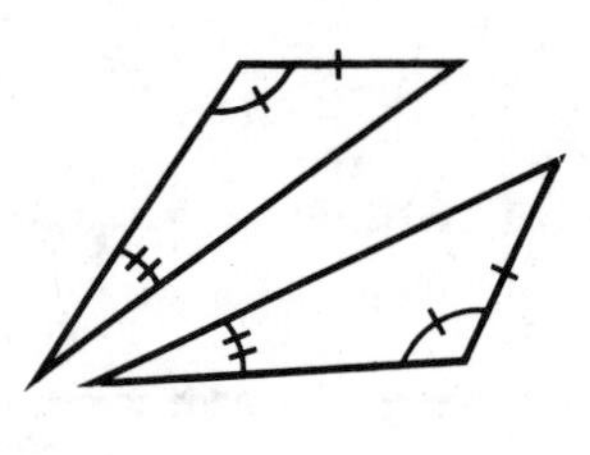

3.

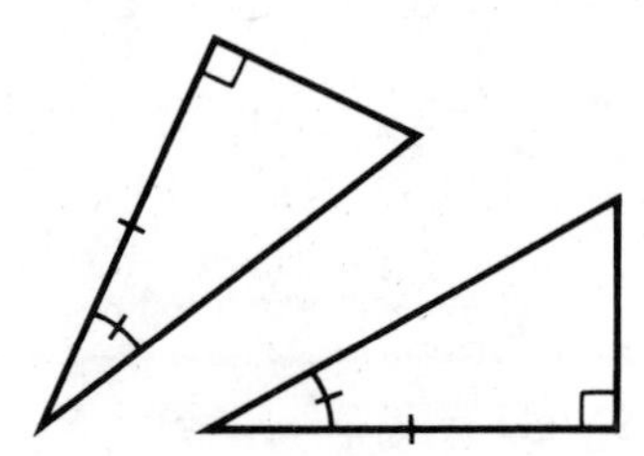

4.

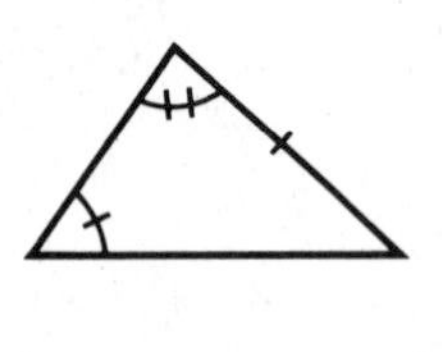

5.

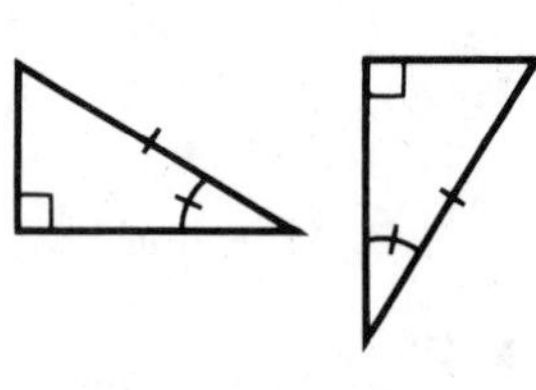

6.

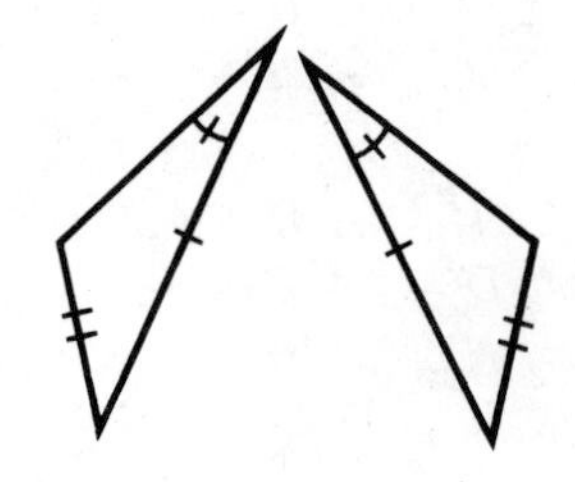

B.

Using the information given in exercises 7–8, prove that $\triangle ACD \cong \triangle BCD$.

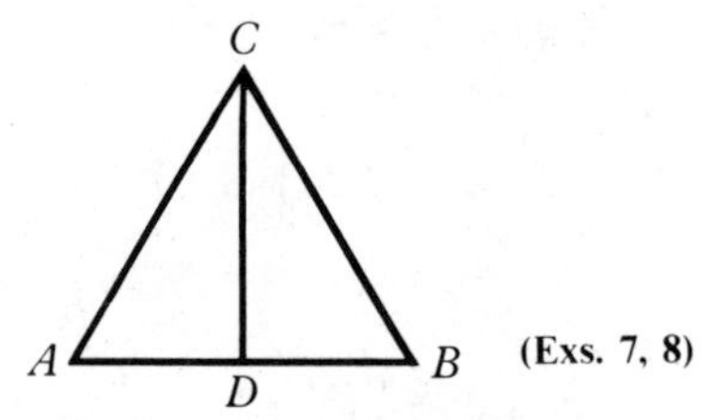

(Exs. 7, 8)

7. Given: $\overline{CD} \perp \overline{AB}$
$\angle A \cong \angle B$

8. Given: $\overline{CD}$ bisects $\angle C$.
$\angle A \cong \angle B$

9. Given: $\angle 1 \cong \angle 2$
$\angle C \cong \angle D$
Prove: $\triangle ABC \cong \triangle BAD$

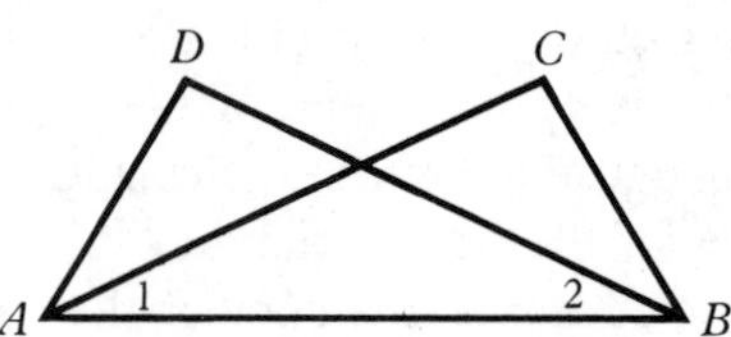

Activity

Cut straws of the following lengths:
- two 10 cm long
- two 17.3 cm long
- one 20 cm long
- one 30 cm long

How many different shaped triangles can be made using these six straws?

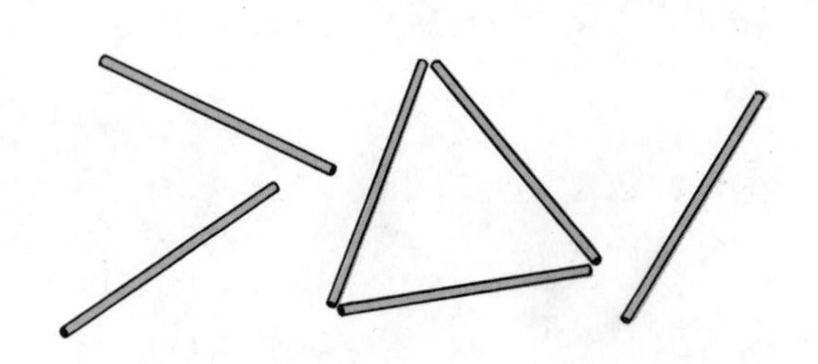

10. Given: $\triangle ABC$ is isosceles with vertex angle C.
$\angle D \cong \angle E$
Prove: $\triangle ABE \cong \triangle BAD$

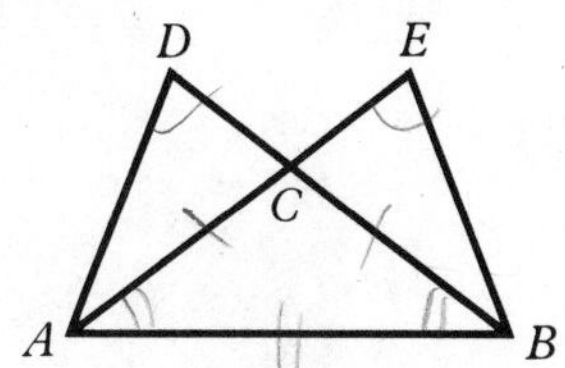

11. Given: $\overline{BE} \cong \overline{CF}$
$\angle A \cong \angle D$
$\angle ACB \cong \angle DEF$
Prove: $\triangle ABC \cong \triangle DFE$

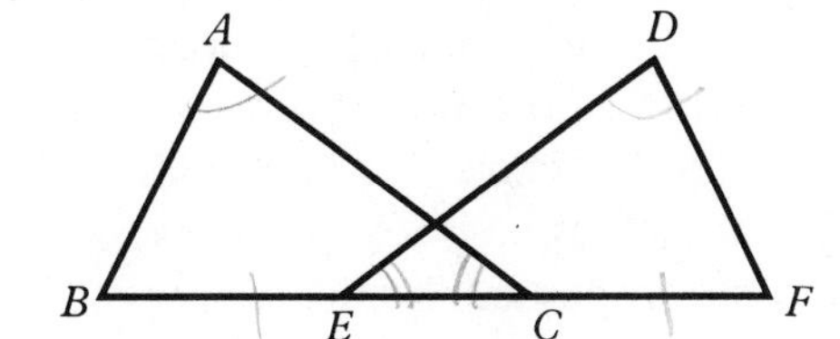

12. Write a two-column proof for Theorem 6–7.

13. Write a two-column proof for Theorem 6–8.

C.

14. Given: $\angle A \cong \angle B$
$\angle ADC \cong \angle BEC$
Prove: $\triangle AEC \cong \triangle BDC$

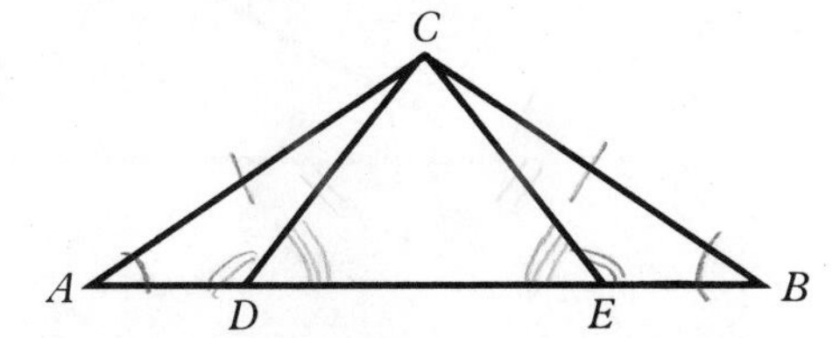

15. Given: $ABCDE$ is a regular pentagon.
Prove: $\triangle AFE \cong \triangle BFC$

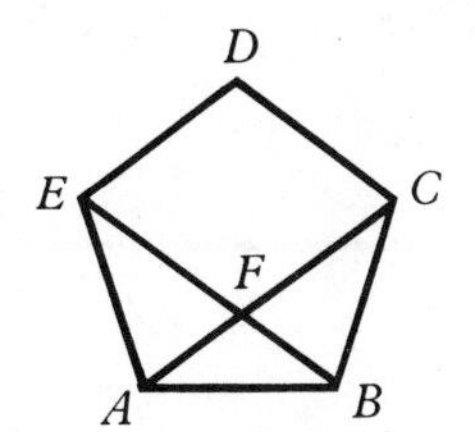

16. Prove that the segments from a point on an angle bisector perpendicular to the sides of the angle are congruent.

17. Prove that if perpendiculars are drawn from any point on the base of an isosceles triangle to the congruent sides, the angles formed on the base of the triangle are congruent.

PROBLEM SOLVING

If the triangles and hexagons in this pattern were colored so that any two polygons with a common vertex had different colors, what is the smallest number of colors required to accomplish this coloring?

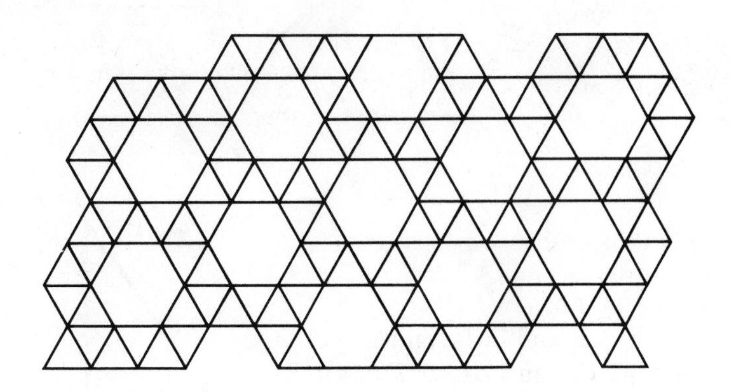

6–5 The HL Congruence Theorem

Suppose you want to install an outdoor basketball backstop to a wall. How can you be sure that the backstop will be parallel to the wall? The braces connecting the backstop to the wall are important in the answer.

Consider the following pairs of triangles.

$\overline{AC} \cong \overline{DF}$
$\overline{BC} \cong \overline{EF}$

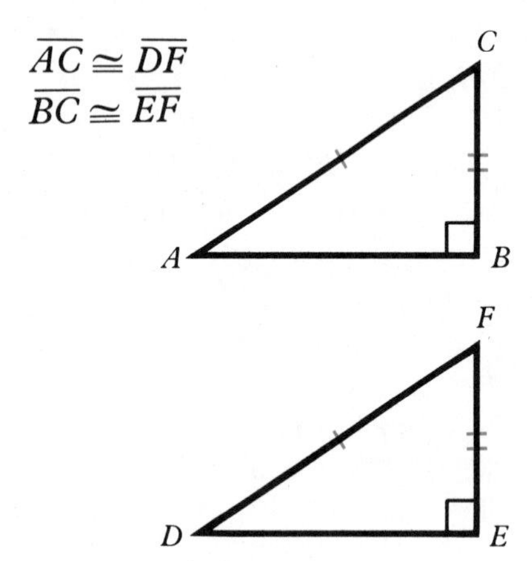

Use tracing paper to conclude:
$\triangle ABC \cong \triangle DEF$

$\overline{GI} \cong \overline{JL}$
$\overline{GH} \cong \overline{JK}$

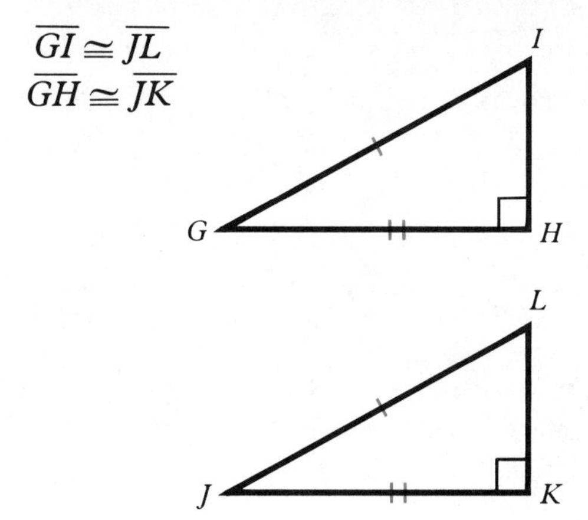

$\triangle GHI \cong \triangle JKL$

Theorem 6–9 **HL Theorem.** If the hypotenuse and a leg of one right triangle are congruent to the hypotenuse and a leg of a second right triangle, then the triangles are congruent.

PROOF

Given: $\triangle ABC$ and $\triangle DEF$ with $\angle B$ and $\angle E$ right angles. $\overline{BC} \cong \overline{EF}$, and $\overline{AC} \cong \overline{DF}$.
Prove: $\triangle ABC \cong \triangle DEF$

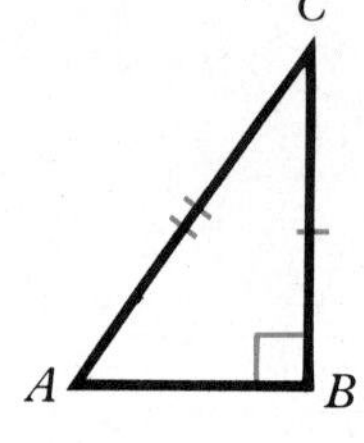

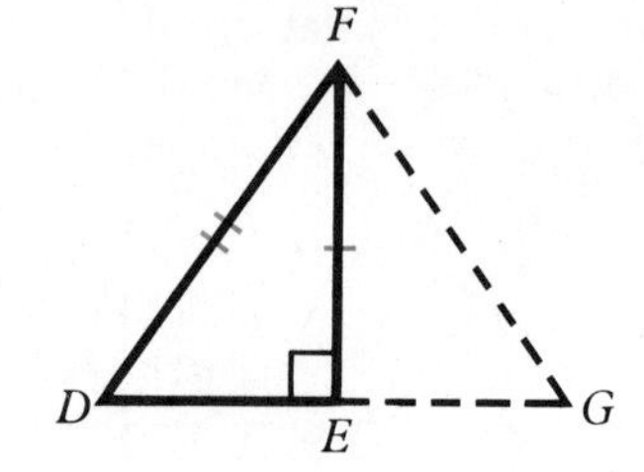

Statements	Reasons
1. Draw $\overrightarrow{DE}$	1. Construction
2. Choose G on $\overrightarrow{DE}$ so that $\overline{EG} \cong \overline{AB}$	2. Choice of G
3. $\angle ABC$ and $\angle DEF$ are right angles	3. Given
4. $\angle GEF$ is a right angle	4. If one angle of a linear pair is a right angle, then the other is a right angle.
5. $m\angle ABC = m\angle DEF = m\angle GEF = 90$	5. Definition of right angle
6. $\angle ABC \cong \angle DEF \cong \angle GEF$	6. Definition of congruent angles
7. $\overline{BC} \cong \overline{EF}$	7. Given
8. $\triangle ABC \cong \triangle GEF$	8. Why?
9. $\overline{AC} \cong \overline{GF}$	9. CPCTC
10. $\overline{AC} \cong \overline{DF}$	10. Given
11. $\overline{GF} \cong \overline{DF}$	11. Transitive property of segment congruence
12. $\angle FDE \cong \angle FGE$	12. If a triangle is isosceles, then its base angles are congruent
13. $\overline{EF} \cong \overline{EF}$	13. Why?
14. $\triangle DEF \cong \triangle GEF$	14. AAS Theorem
15. $\triangle ABC \cong \triangle DEF$	15. Transitive property of congruent triangles (See p. 206, Ex. 32)

APPLICATION

Consider the question asked at the beginning of the lesson. The backstop should be mounted so that $\overline{AC} \perp \overline{AB}$ and $AB = CD$. In order for the backboard to be parallel to the wall, $\overline{AC}$ and $\overline{ED}$ must be equal in length. If $\overline{AD} \cong \overline{BC}$, then $\triangle ABC \cong \triangle EAD$ by Theorem 6-9 (HL) and $\overline{AC} \cong \overline{ED}$. Notice that in order to have the congruent triangles, we had to have braces $\overline{AD}$ and $\overline{BC}$ be the same length.

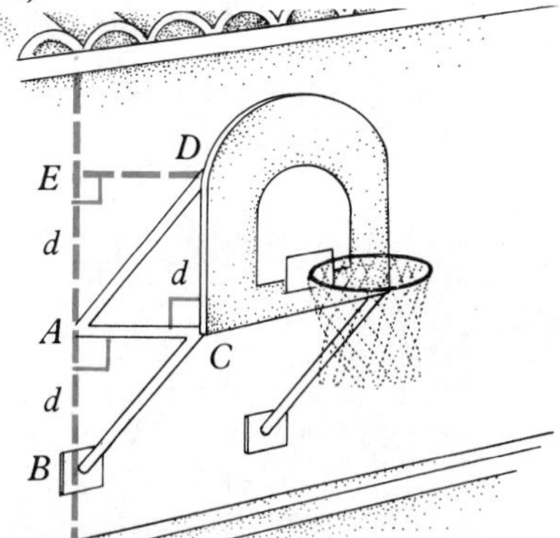

Theorem 6-9 is used in the proof of this next important theorem.

Theorem 6-10 If a point P is equidistant from a pair of points A and B, then P lies on the perpendicular bisector of $\overline{AB}$. Conversely, a point on the perpendicular bisector of $\overline{AB}$ is equidistant from A and B.

EXERCISES

A.

In exercises 1–4 decide whether the given information determines congruence by HL, HA, AAS, ASA, or none of these.

1. **Given:** $\overline{AB} \cong \overline{DE}$, $\overline{AC} \cong \overline{DF}$
2. **Given:** $\angle A \cong \angle D$, $\overline{BC} \cong \overline{EF}$.
3. **Given:** $\angle B \cong \angle E$, $\overline{AB} \cong \overline{DE}$
4. **Given:** $\overline{AC} \cong \overline{DF}$, $\angle A \cong \angle D$

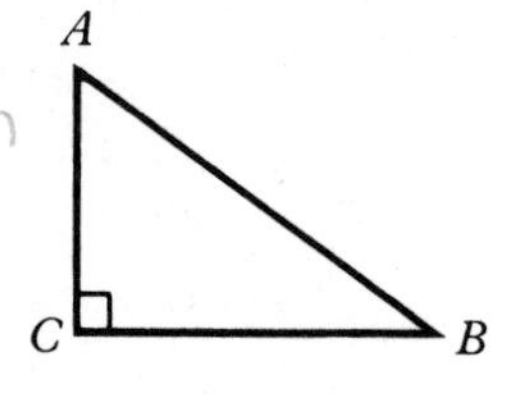

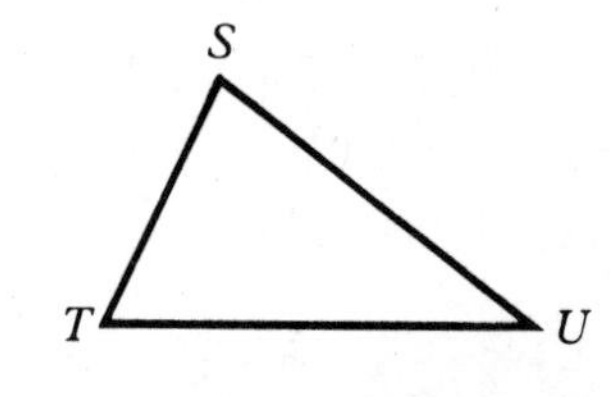

(Exs. 1-4)

In exercises 5–9 decide whether the given conditions insure that the triangles are congruent. If they are not, provide a counterexample.

5. **Given:** $\overline{PQ} \cong \overline{ST}$, $\angle P \cong \angle S$, $\angle Q \cong \angle T$
6. **Given:** $\overline{PQ} \cong \overline{TU}$, $\overline{QR} \cong \overline{SU}$, $\angle Q \cong \angle U$
7. **Given:** $\angle P \cong \angle S$, $\angle Q \cong \angle T$, $\angle R \cong \angle U$
8. **Given:** $\angle Q \cong \angle T$, $\overline{PQ} \cong \overline{ST}$, $\overline{PR} \cong \overline{SU}$
9. **Given:** $\overline{PQ} \cong \overline{SU}$, $\overline{QR} \cong \overline{ST}$, $\overline{PR} \cong \overline{TU}$

(Exs. 5-9)

B.

For exercises 10–11 assume that $\overline{AB} \cong \overline{DE}$ and $\overline{AC} \cong \overline{DF}$.

10. If $BC = 2x - 3$ and $EF = x + 5$, find the lengths BC and EF.
11. If $m\angle A = 4x - 5$ and $m\angle D = 2x + 25$, find $m\angle B$ and $m\angle E$.

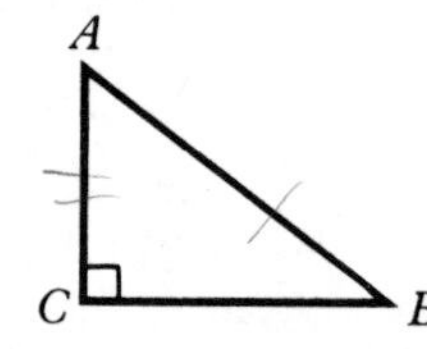

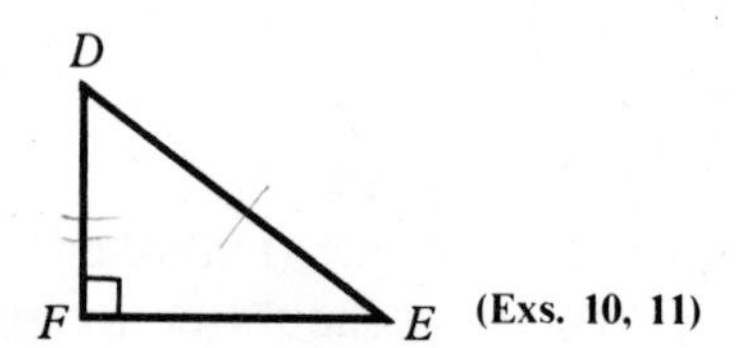

(Exs. 10, 11)

Activity

Trace and cut out all 13 pieces of these two smaller regular 12-gons and arrange them to form a large regular 12-gon.

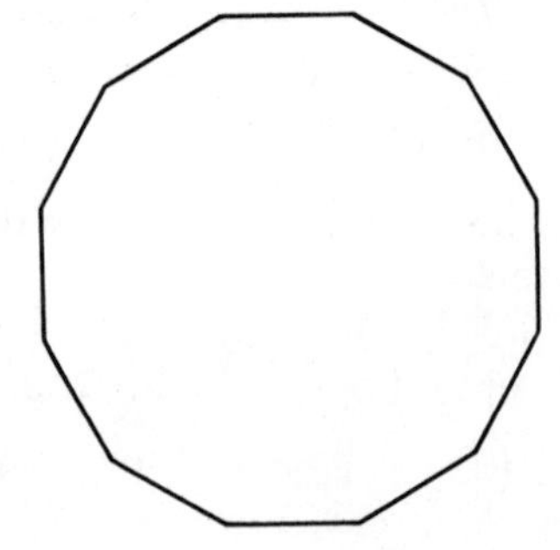
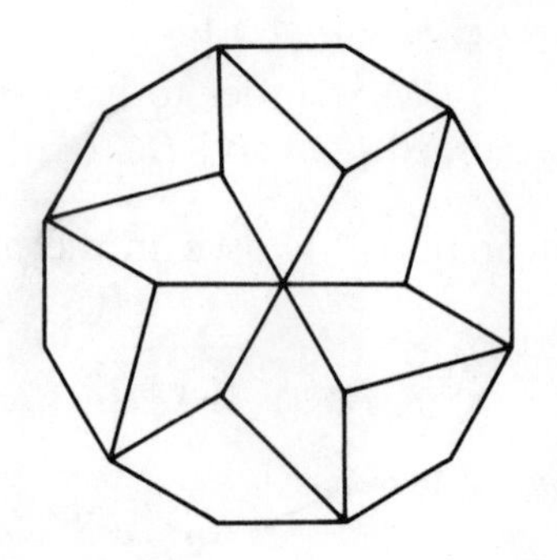

12. Given: $\overline{BD} \cong \overline{CE}$
$\overline{BD}$ and $\overline{CE}$ are altitudes.
Prove: $\triangle ABC$ is isosceles.

13. Given: $\overline{BD}$ and $\overline{CE}$ are altitudes.
$\angle ABC \cong \angle ACB$
Prove: $\triangle BFC$ is isosceles.

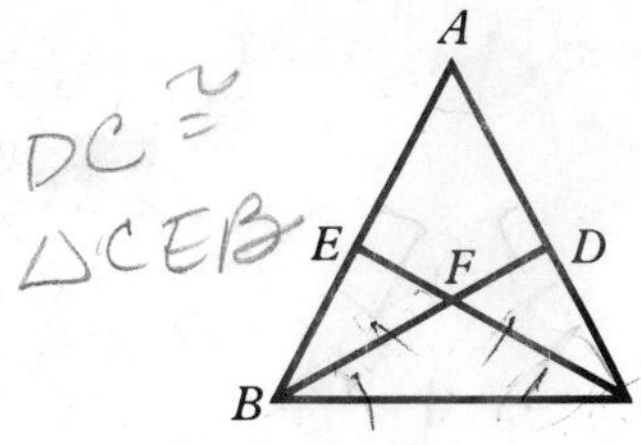

(Exs. 12, 13)

C.

For exercises 14–16, $\overline{BE} \cong \overline{CD}$ and $\overline{BD}$ and $\overline{CE}$ are altitudes.

14. Prove that $\triangle EFB \cong \triangle DFC$.

15. Prove that $\triangle AED$ is isosceles.

16. Prove that $\overleftrightarrow{ED} \parallel \overleftrightarrow{BC}$.

17. Prove Theorem 6–10.

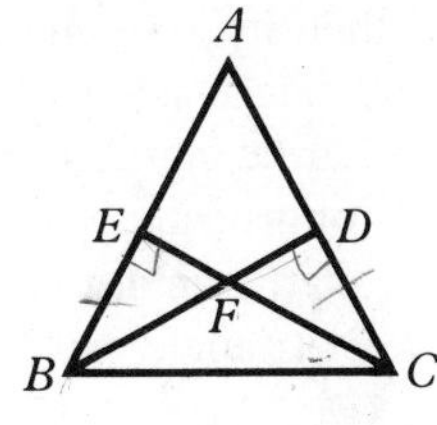

(Exs. 14–16)

18. A milling cutter with seven teeth is made by cutting seven right triangles out of a 7-sided regular polygon. If $\overline{AB}$ is cut the same length for each tooth, why are the sharp points of the cutter all the same size angle?

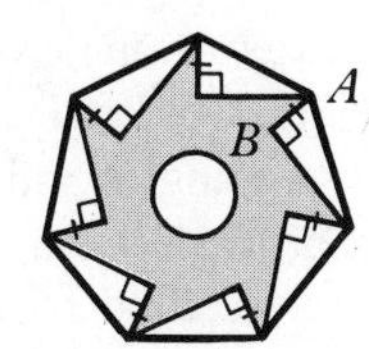

PROBLEM SOLVING

Pictured at the right is a square based pyramid.

1. Which of these networks can be folded into the shaped pyramid?

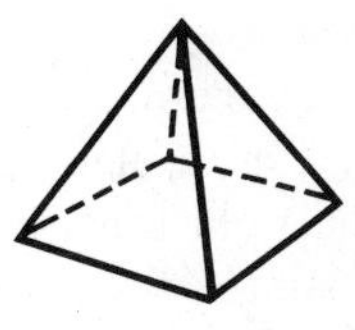

A

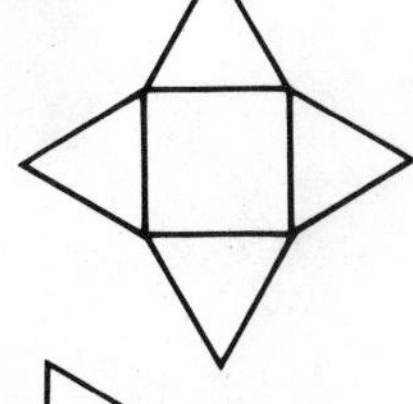

B

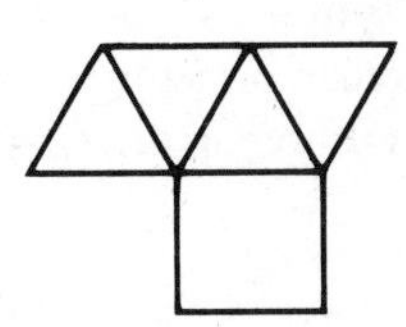

C

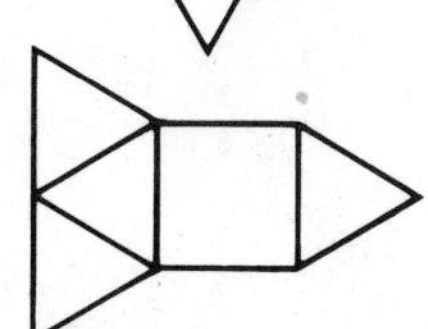

D

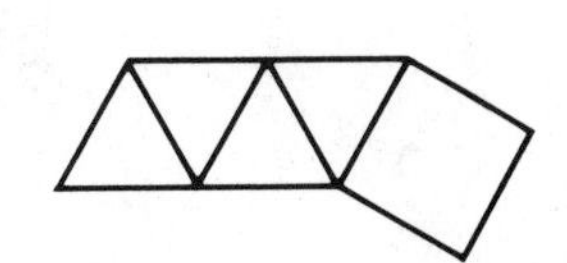

2. Make larger networks like each of the above. Check your guess by trying to make a model of each.

Important Ideas—Chapter 6

Terms

Scalene triangle (p. 198)
Acute triangle (p. 198)
Right triangle (p. 199)
Hypotenuse (p. 199)
Obtuse triangle (p. 199)
Equiangular triangle (p. 199)
Altitude (p. 199)

Theorems

6-1 If a triangle is isosceles, then its base angles are congruent.

6-2 If a triangle is equilateral, then it is equiangular.

6-3 If two angles of a triangle are congruent, then the sides opposite these angles are congruent.

6-4 The sum of the measures of the angles of a triangle is $180°$.

6-5 The angles of an equilateral triangle each have a measure of $60°$.

6-6 The measure of an exterior angle of a triangle is equal to the sum of measures of its two remote interior angles.

6-7 **AAS Theorem.** If two angles and a side opposite one angle in a triangle are congruent to two angles and the corresponding side of a second triangle, then the two triangles are congruent.

6-8 **HA Theorem.** If the hypotenuse and an acute angle of one right triangle are congruent to a hypotenuse and an acute angle of another right triangle, then the triangles are congruent.

6-9 **HL Theorem.** If the hypotenuse and a leg of one right triangle are congruent to the hypotenuse and a leg of a second right triangle, then the triangles are congruent.

6-10 If a point P is equidistant from a pair of points A and B, then P lies on the perpendicular bisector of $\overline{AB}$. Conversely, a point on the perpendicular bisector of $\overline{AB}$ is equidistant from A and B.

Chapter 6—Review

1. Indicate whether the following statements are true or false.
   - **a.** A scalene triangle can never be an acute triangle.
   - **b.** An isosceles triangle can also be a right triangle.
   - **c.** A right triangle has exactly one altitude.
   - **d.** If two angles of a triangle have measures of 60° and 90°, then the triangle is isosceles.

2. If $m\angle ACD = 120$ and $m\angle ABC = 50$, find $m\angle BAC$.

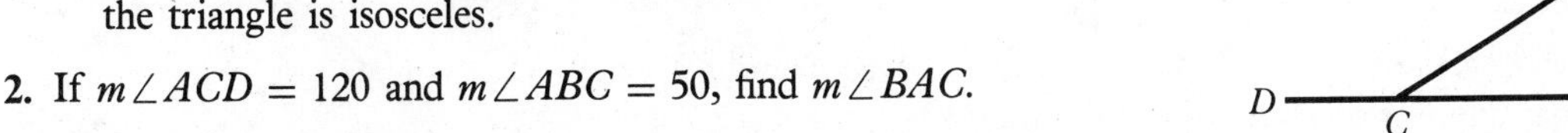

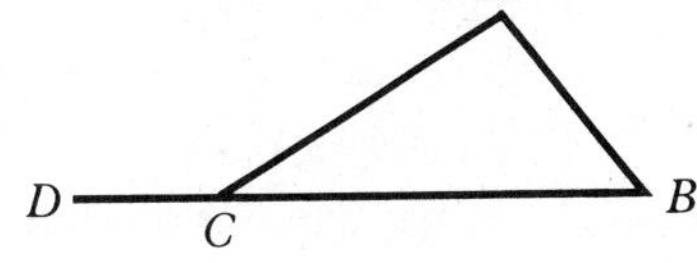

3. The measures of the two base angles of an isosceles triangle are represented by $x + 20$ and $3x - 40$. Find the measure of the vertex angle.

4. **Given:** $\overline{AC} \cong \overline{BC}$, $\overline{AD} \cong \overline{BD}$
   Prove: $\angle CAD \cong \angle CBD$

5. **Given:** $\angle C \cong \angle D$
   $\angle 1 \cong \angle 2$
   Prove: $\overline{AD} \cong \overline{BC}$

6. **Given:** $m\angle B = m\angle C = 90$
   $\angle 1 \cong \angle 2$
   Prove: $\overline{BD} \cong \overline{CD}$

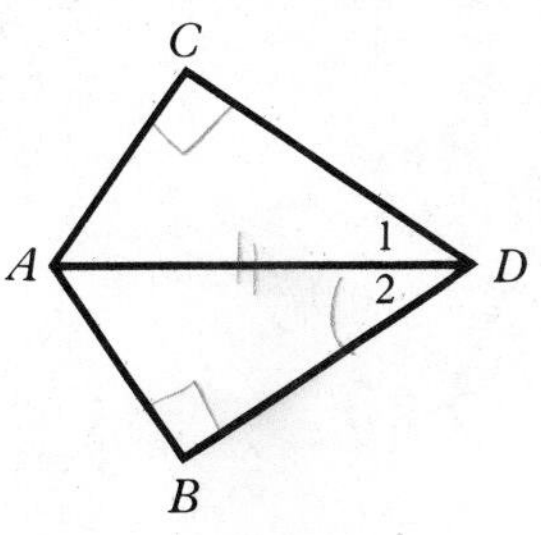

7. **Given:** $\overline{CX}$ is an altitude to $\overline{AB}$.
   $\overline{AY}$ is an altitude to $\overline{CB}$.
   $\overline{CX} \cong \overline{AY}$
   Prove: $\triangle ABC$ is isosceles

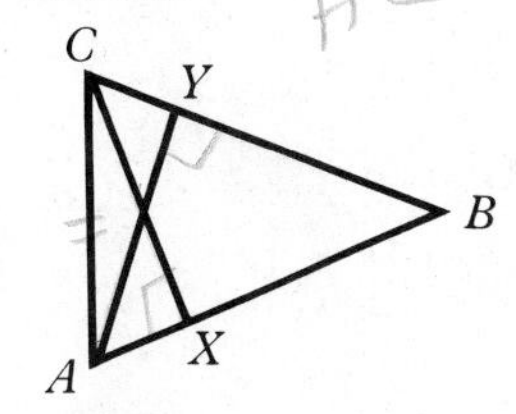

8. **a.** $m\angle DFE = m\angle 5 + m\angle 1$
   $= m\angle 2 + m\angle 4$. Why?
   b. If $m\angle 4 = 80$ and $m\angle 3$
   $= 35$, find $m\angle 5$.

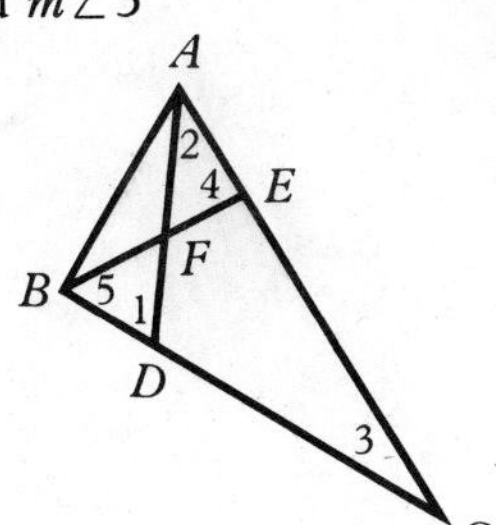

9. **Given:** $\triangle KMN$ is isosceles.
   $\angle 1 \cong \angle 2$
   Prove: $\triangle KHG$ is isosceles.

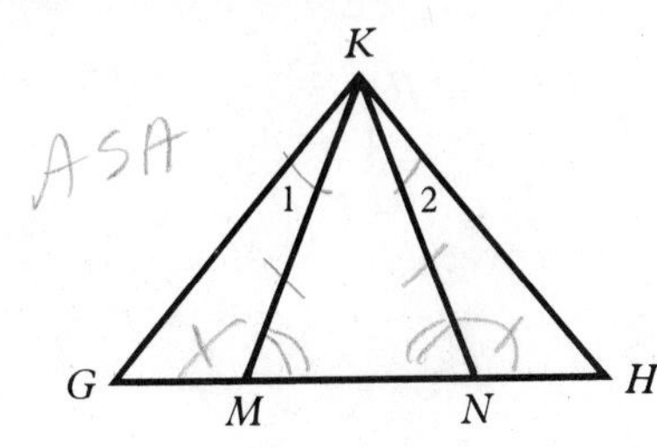

Chapter 6—Test

1. Indicate whether the following statements are true or false.

   a. An equilateral triangle is equiangular.

   b. An obtuse triangle can have a right angle.

   c. If an acute angle of one right triangle is congruent to an acute angle of another right triangle, then the two triangles are congruent.

   d. If two angles of a triangle have measures of 100° and 40°, then the triangle is isosceles.

2. If $\overline{AB} \cong \overline{BC}$ and $m\angle BAD = 116$, find $\angle B$.

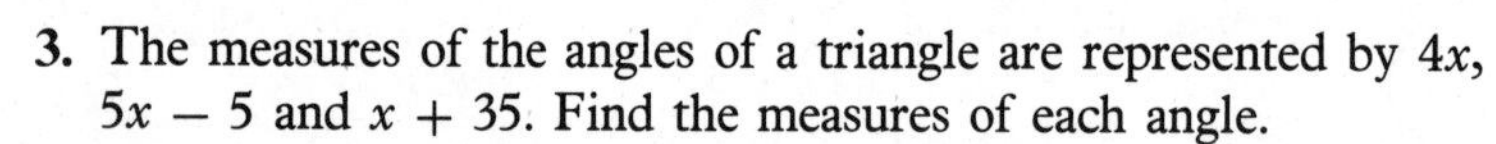

3. The measures of the angles of a triangle are represented by $4x$, $5x - 5$ and $x + 35$. Find the measures of each angle.

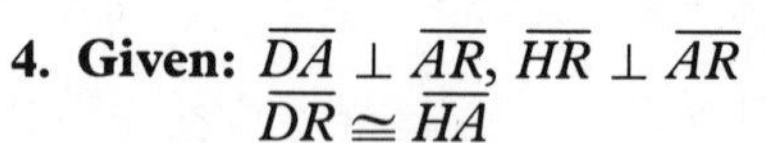

4. **Given:** $\overline{DA} \perp \overline{AR}$, $\overline{HR} \perp \overline{AR}$
   $\overline{DR} \cong \overline{HA}$
   Prove: $\overline{DA} \cong \overline{HR}$

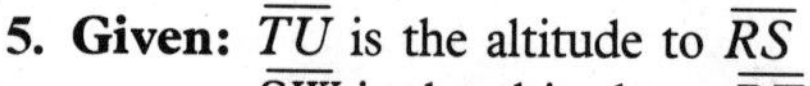

5. **Given:** $\overline{TU}$ is the altitude to $\overline{RS}$
   $\overline{SW}$ is the altitude to $\overline{RT}$
   $\angle 1 \cong \angle 2$
   Prove: $\triangle RST$ is isosceles

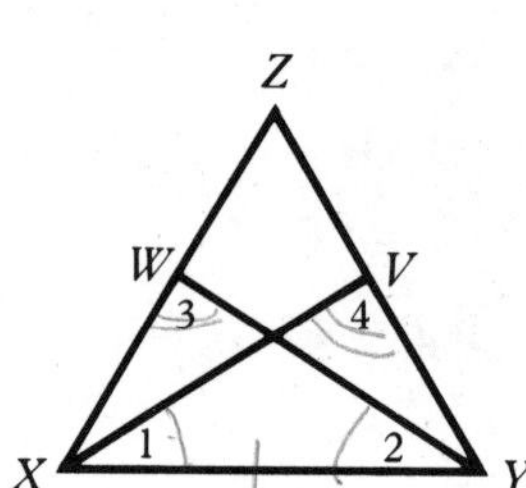

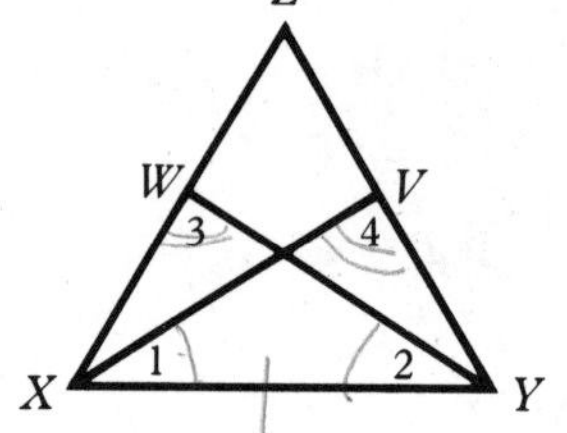

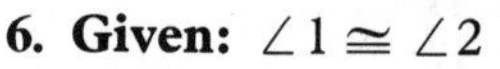

6. **Given:** $\angle 1 \cong \angle 2$
   $\angle 3 \cong \angle 4$
   Prove: $\overline{XV} \cong \overline{YW}$

7. Prove that the altitude to the base of an isosceles triangle is also the angle bisector of the vertex angle.

8. a. If $m\angle 2 = 20$ and $m\angle 3 = 35$, find $m\angle 1$.
   b. If $m\angle BEC = 100$ and $m\angle BAE = 65$, find $m\angle ABE$.

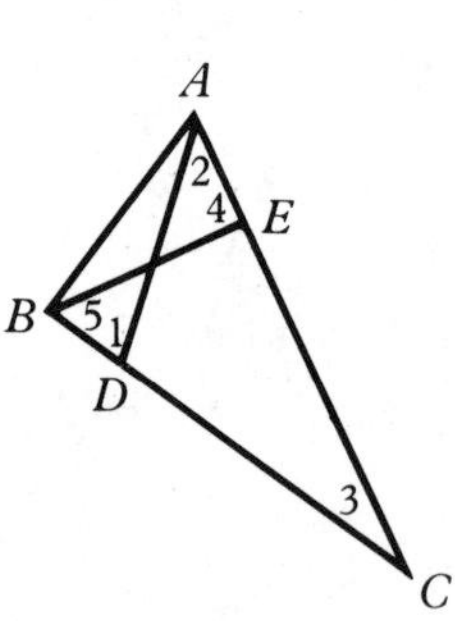

9. **Given:** $\overline{JH} \parallel \overline{FG}$
   $\angle 1 \cong \angle 3$
   $\overline{JH} \cong \overline{JF}$
   Prove: $\triangle JGH$ is isosceles.

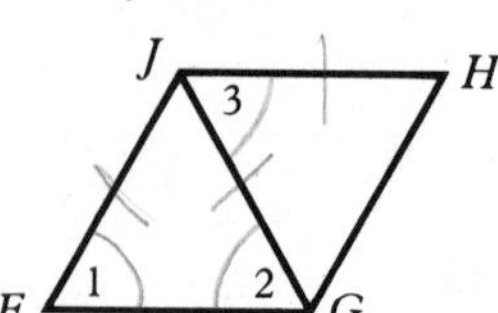

Problem Solving Techniques

Make a Table-II

In a previous section on problem solving techniques we suggested making a table to help solve problems. Here are some more problems in which making a table can be useful.

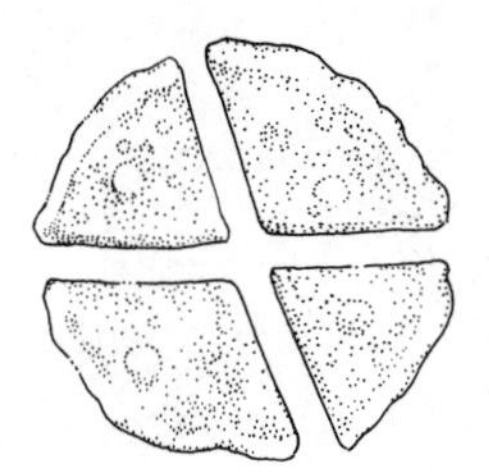

2 cuts, 4 pieces
8 cuts, how many pieces?

PROBLEMS

For each problem, make a table, observe a pattern, and solve the problem.

1. What is the maximum number of pieces of pizza that can be obtained if the pizza is cut 8 times? (*Hint:* Construct a table. One column should be the number of cuts and the second column should be the maximum number of pieces.)

2. A region of the plane that is bounded on all sides by a line is called a *bounded region.* How many bounded regions are formed if 9 lines are drawn?

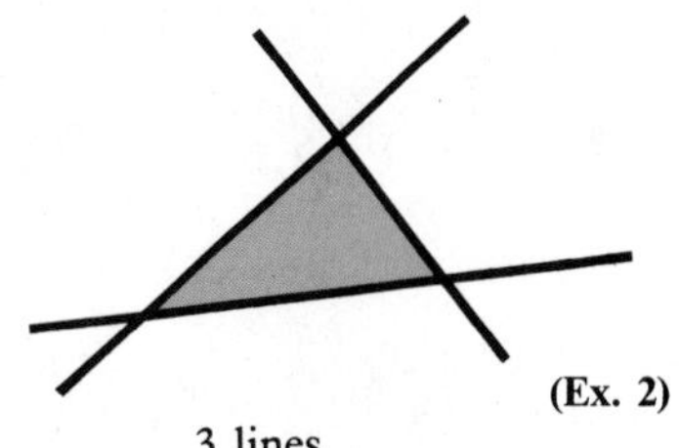

(Ex. 2)
3 lines
1 bounded region

3. A triangular number (T) is one that can be represented geometrically as shown. T_1, T_2, T_3, and T_4 are illustrated on the right. Can you find T_5 and T_6? Can you predict what the tenth triangular number (T_{10}) is?

	configuration	number
T_1	•	1
T_2	(3 dots)	3
T_3	(6 dots)	6
T_4	(10 dots)	10
T_5	?	?
T_6	?	?

4. A pentagonal number (P) is another number that can be represented geometrically as shown. Can you find P_5 and P_6? Can you predict what the tenth pentagonal number (P_{10}) will be?

	configuration	number
P_1	•	1
P_2	(pentagon)	5
P_3	(nested pentagons)	12
P_4	(nested pentagons)	22
P_5	?	?
P_6	?	?

5. A heptagonal number (H) is represented geometrically by drawing heptagons (seven sides) in a manner similar to problems 3 and 4. Find H_3 and H_4. Can you predict what the tenth heptagonal number (H_{10}) will be?

CHAPTER 7

More on Triangles

7–1 The Pythagorean Theorem

One of the best known and most useful theorems in plane geometry is the Pythagorean Theorem, named after the Greek mathematician Pythagoras.

The theorem says that the area of the square built upon the hypotenuse of a right triangle is equal to the sum of the areas of the squares built upon the legs of the triangle.

REVIEW: The definitions of right triangle, hypotenuse, and legs of a right triangle, page 199.

In Examples 1–3, find a way of counting the tiny unit squares to show that the area of squares A and B equals the area of the square C on the hypotenuse.

Example 1

Example 2

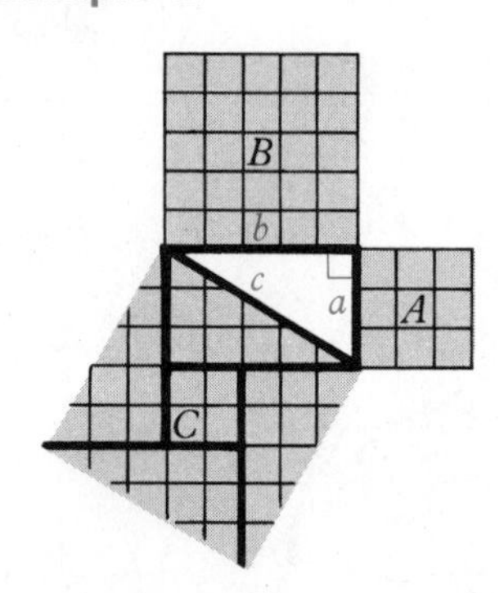

Example 3

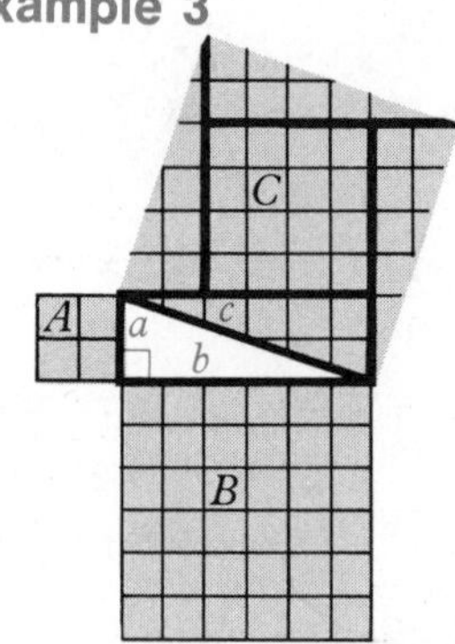

Theorem 7–1 **Pythagorean Theorem.** If $\triangle ABC$ is a right triangle, then the square of the length of the hypotenuse equals the sum of the squares of the lengths of the legs.

PROOF

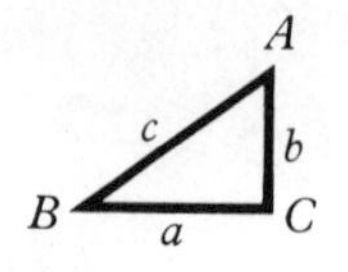

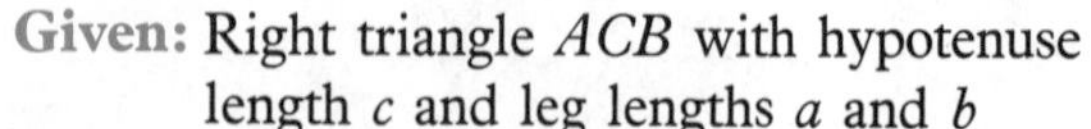

Given: Right triangle ACB with hypotenuse length c and leg lengths a and b

Prove: $c^2 = a^2 + b^2$

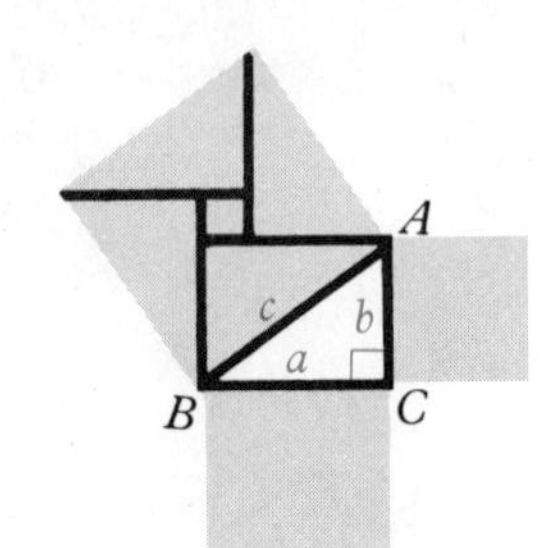

Analysis: Build squares upon $\triangle ABC$ like those shown in Examples 1–3. The square upon a has area a^2. The square upon side b has area b^2. The square upon c has area c^2.

The square upon side c consists of four triangles congruent to $\triangle ABC$ and a square. The figure shows that the length of the side of the small square is $a - b$. We can find the area of the large square by adding the areas of the four triangles to the area of the small square. The area of the triangles is $\frac{1}{2}ab$. The area of the square is $(a - b)^2$. So

$$c^2 = 4(\tfrac{1}{2}ab) + (a - b)^2$$
$$= 2ab + (a^2 - 2ab + b^2) = a^2 + b^2.$$

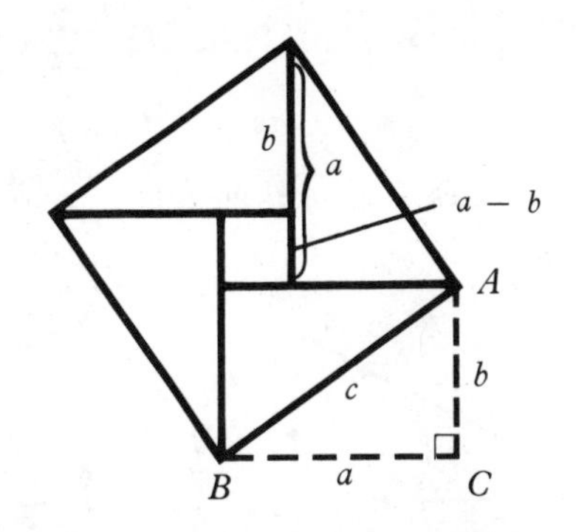

APPLICATION

An advertisement for a television set states that the screen is 25 inches. The screen is approximately 19.5 inches wide and 15.5 inches high. Why is it legitimate to advertise a 25-inch screen?

Answer. The manufacturer is actually stating the length of the diagonal of the screen.

$$AB^2 + BC^2 = AC^2$$
$$19.5^2 + 15.5^2 = 620.5$$
$$AC \doteq 24.9$$

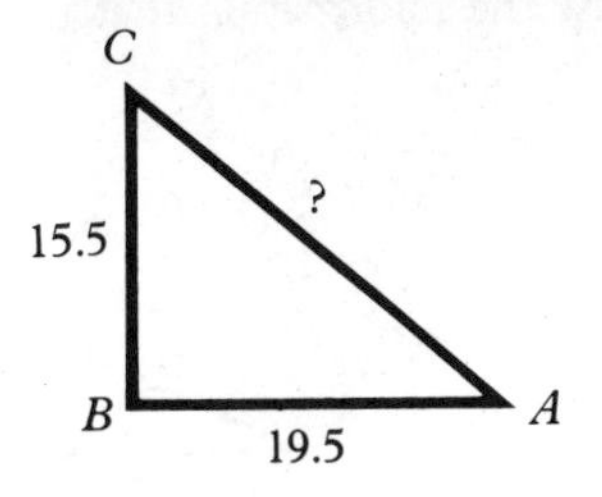

So the diagonal of the screen is almost 25 inches.

The next theorem is the converse of the Pythagorean Theorem.

Theorem 7-2 If $\triangle ABC$ has side lengths a, b, and c and $c^2 = a^2 + b^2$, then $\triangle ABC$ is a right triangle.

Example

$\triangle ABC$ is a right triangle because

$$(\sqrt{7})^2 + 1^2 = (2\sqrt{2})^2. \qquad (7 + 1 = 8)$$

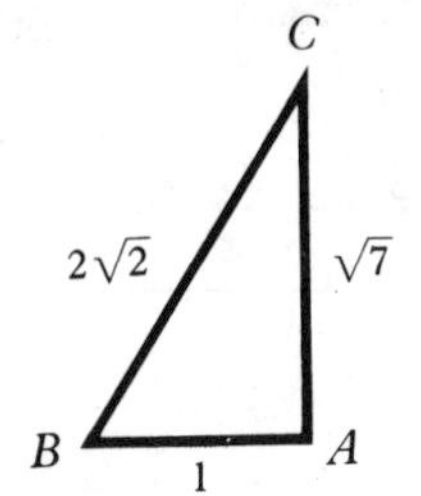

EXERCISES

A.

For exercises 1–6 state whether or not the given equation is correct.

1.

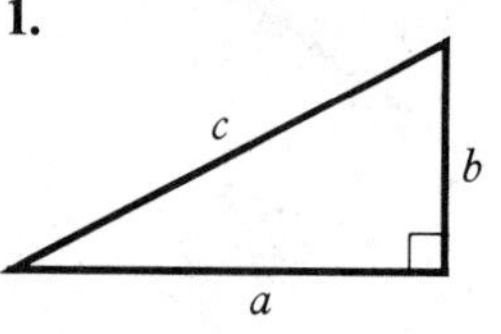

$c^2 = a^2 + b^2$

2.

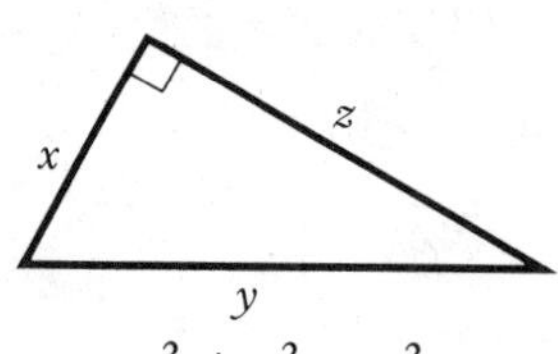

$x^2 + y^2 = z^2$

3.

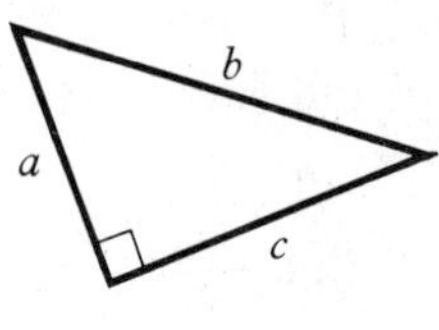

$c^2 = a^2 + b^2$

4.

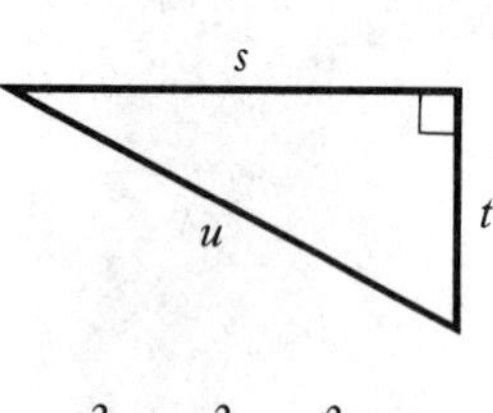

$s^2 = u^2 - t^2$

5.

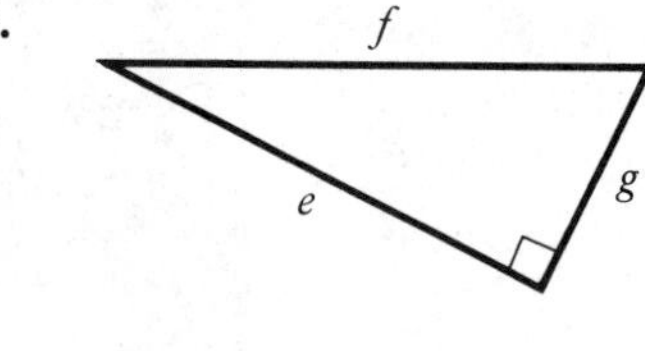

$f = \sqrt{e^2 + g^2}$

6.

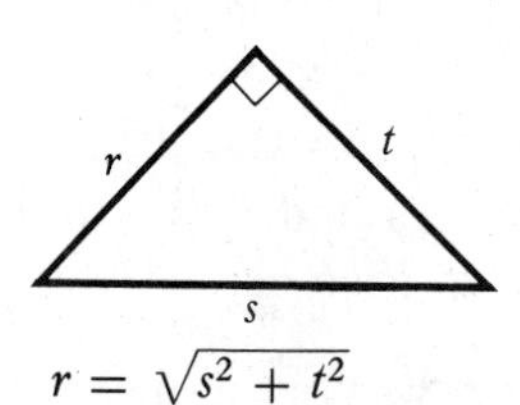

$r = \sqrt{s^2 + t^2}$

For exercises 7–12 use the information that is marked on the figure to find the value of x.

7.

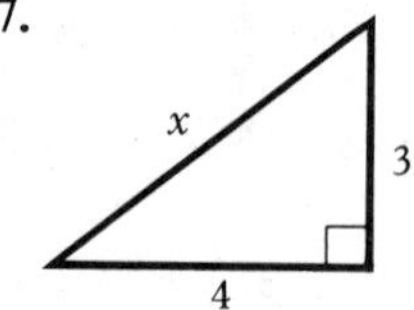

8.

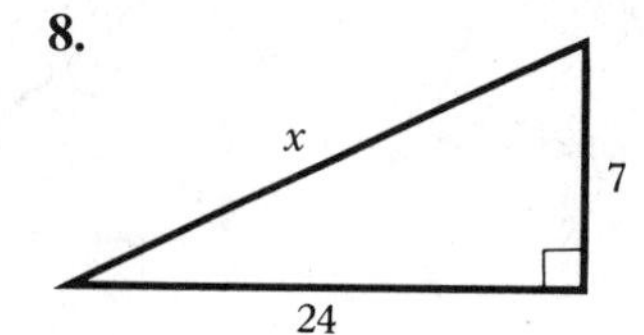

9.

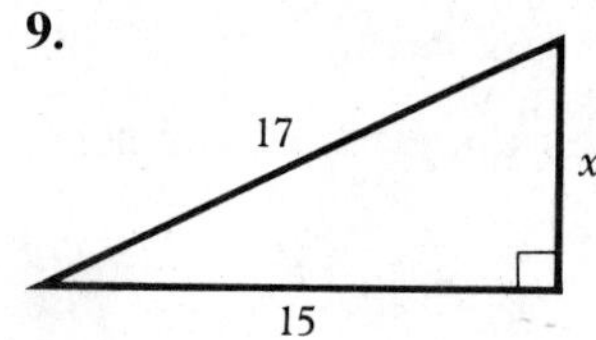

10.

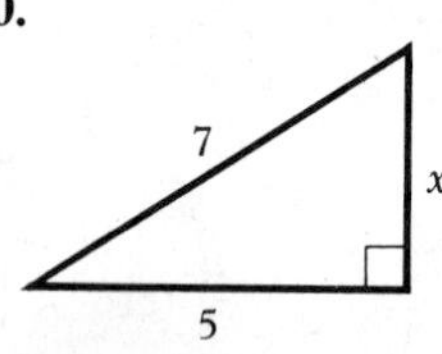

11.

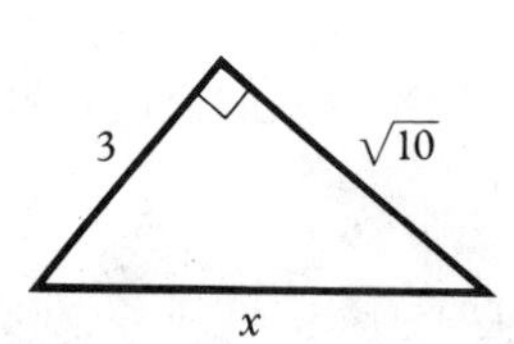

12.

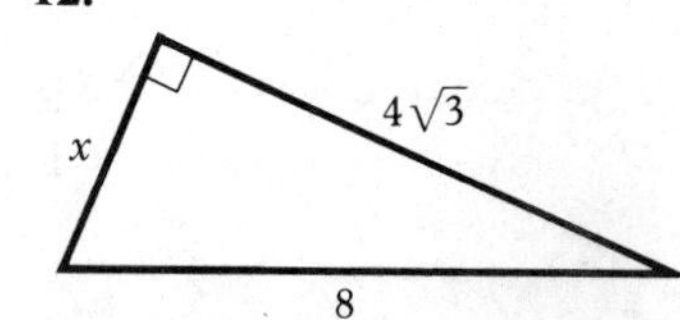

For exercises 13–18, use right triangle ABC.

13. If $AB = 6$, and $AC = 8$ then $BC = \underline{?}$

14. If $BC = 15$, and $AB = 9$ then $AC = \underline{?}$

15. If $AC = 2$ and $AB = 2$ then $BC = \underline{?}$

16. If $BC = \sqrt{15}$ and $AB = \sqrt{10}$ then $AC = \underline{?}$

17. If $AC = \sqrt{2}$ and $AB = \sqrt{3}$ then $BC = \underline{?}$

18. If $AB = 2\sqrt{3}$ and $BC = 6$ then $AC = \underline{?}$

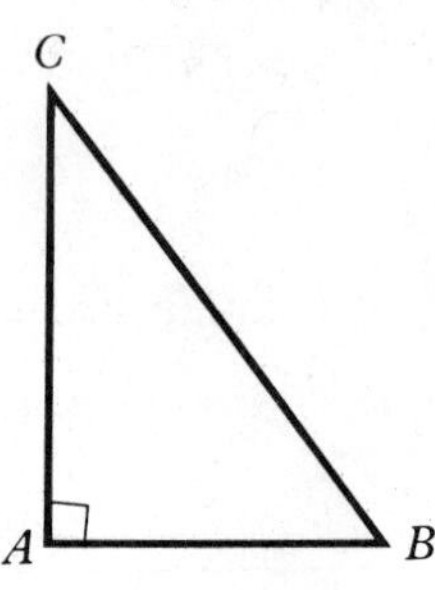

B.

For exercises 19–24, decide whether or not the given numbers can be the lengths of sides for a right triangle.

19. 10, 24, 26
20. 20, 21, 29
21. 8, 15, 17
22. 7, 25, $\sqrt{674}$
23. 5, 13, $\sqrt{195}$
24. 5, 12, 13

25. Find the length of the diagonal of a rectangle whose sides have lengths 10 and 18.

26. A door is 6 feet 6 inches tall and 36 inches wide. What is the widest sheet of plywood that can be carried through the door?

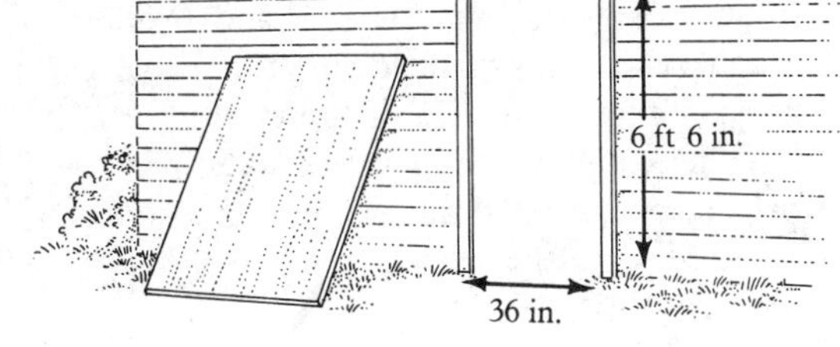

(Ex. 26)

27. A 6-foot ladder is placed against a wall with its base 2 feet from the wall. How high above the ground is the top of the ladder?

C.

28. Find the lengths of $\overline{AB}$, $\overline{AC}$, $\overline{AD}$, and $\overline{AE}$.

29. Construct with straightedge and compass segments with lengths $\sqrt{6}$ and $\sqrt{7}$.

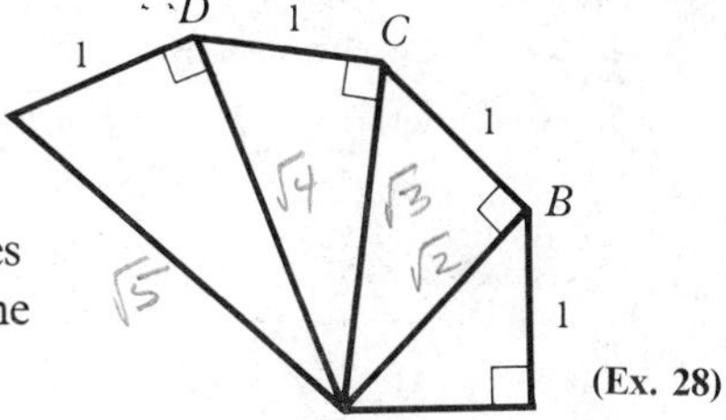

(Ex. 28)

30. A person travels 8 miles due north, 3 miles due west, 7 miles due north, 11 miles due east. How far is that person from the starting point?

31. Use the squares with side length $a + b$ to show the Pythagorean Theorem is true.

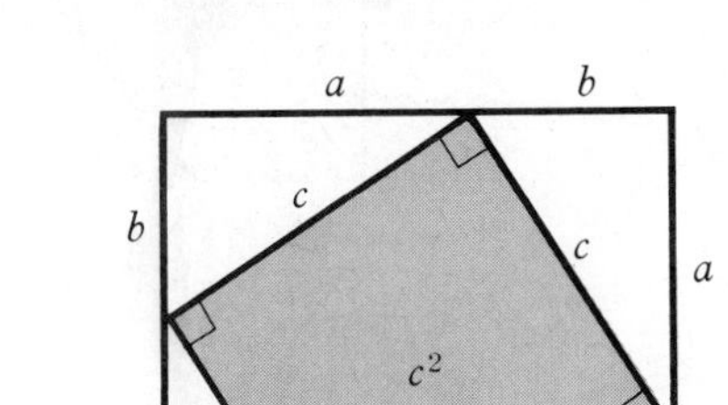

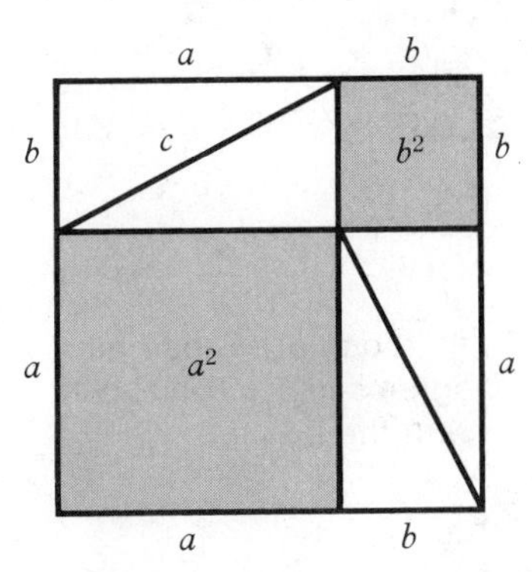

32. A 36-foot extension ladder must keep a 4-foot overlap when it is fully extended. If the base of the ladder is 10 feet from the building, how high up the building will the ladder reach?

33. (Use a calculator.)
If a row of shingles is 6 inches wide, how many rows of shingles are needed on each side of this roof.

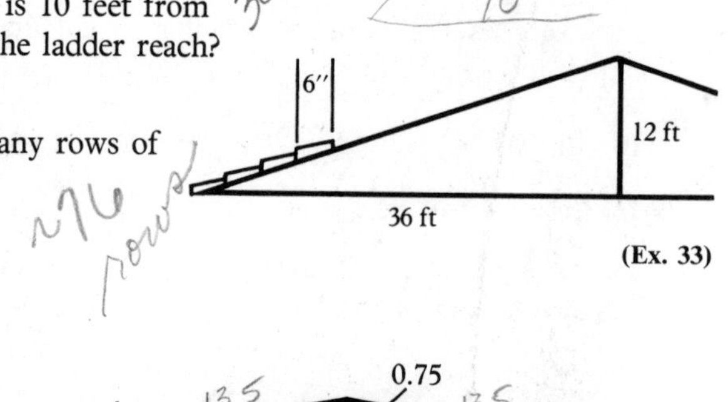

(Ex. 33)

34. (Use a calculator.)
Surveying engineers want to measure the distance between two points A and B on rough land. They want to find the actual horizontal distance AB. If the earth is 0.75 meters higher midway between the two stakes, and if the measuring tape reads 27.0 meters, what is the actual distance AB?

A
0.75
B

(Ex. 34)

Activity

In a room 8 feet wide, 8 feet high, and 15 feet long, a fly crawls from the middle of the front wall, 1 foot above the floor, to the middle of the back wall, 1 foot below the ceiling.

1. Guess which one of the four paths below is the shortest one.

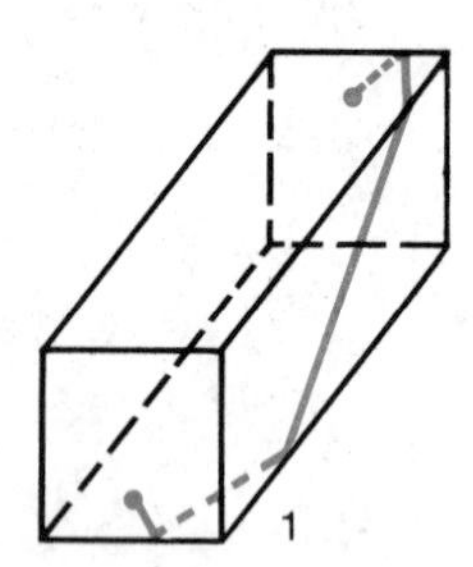

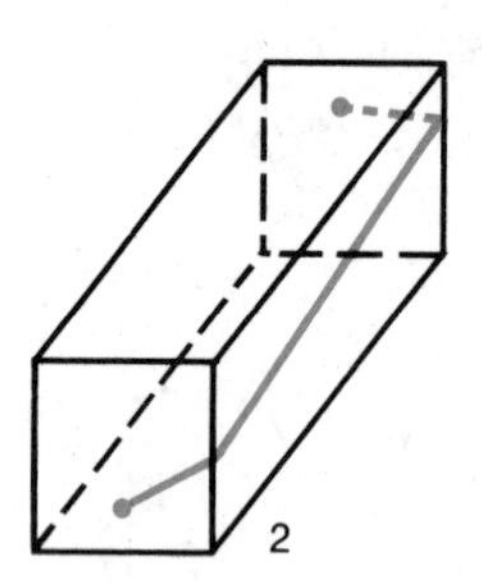

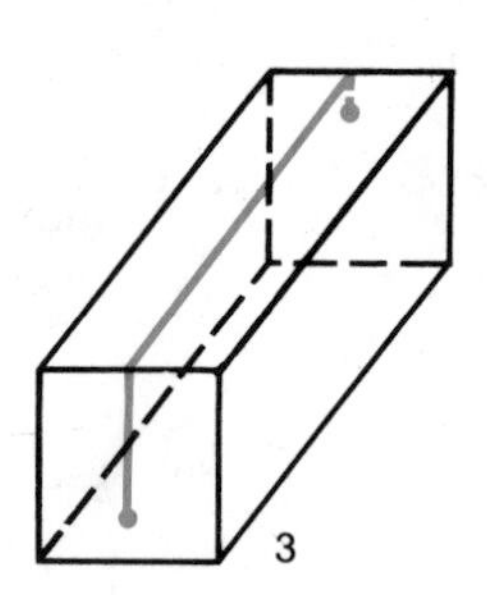

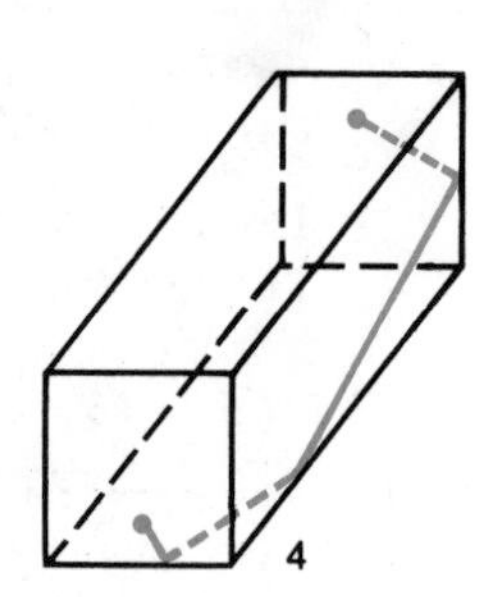

2. Make a box representing this room, draw the paths, and measure their lengths. (Any one of the diagrams in the PROBLEM SOLVING on the next page can be used to construct the box.)

35. A stairway will be built out of a piece of lumber called a *stringer*. (Refer to page 173, exercise 9.) The stringer runs from *A* to *B*. It covers a horizontal distance of 14 feet and a height of 9 feet 6 inches. What length piece of lumber must be bought for the stringer? (*Hint:* Lumber is sold in even foot lengths.)

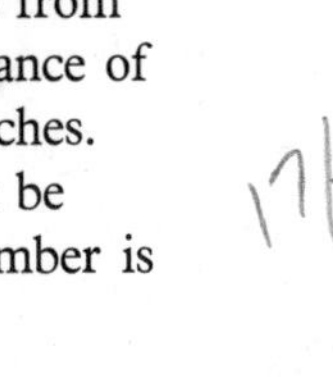

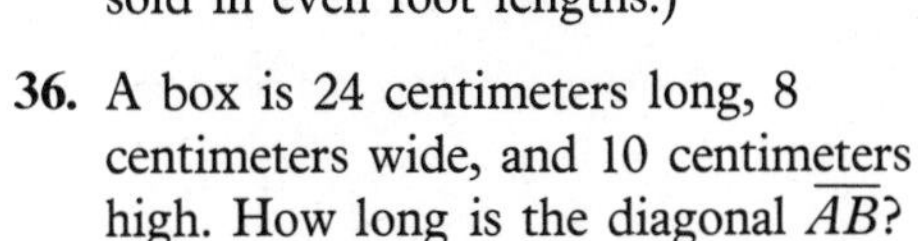

36. A box is 24 centimeters long, 8 centimeters wide, and 10 centimeters high. How long is the diagonal $\overline{AB}$?

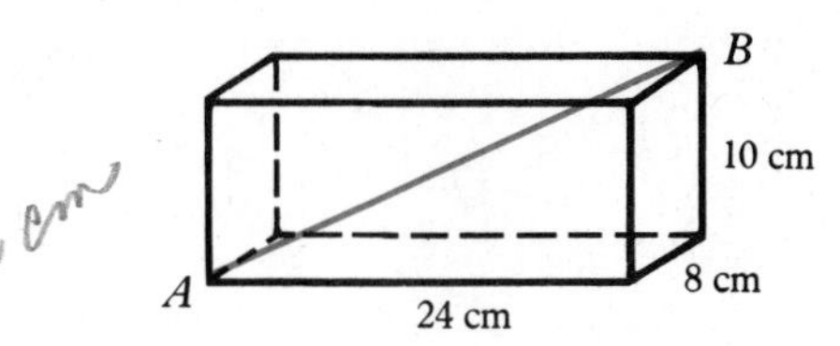

PROBLEM SOLVING

1. Imagine that the box from the Activity on page 230 has been cut apart. Match each of the four paths of the fly shown on page 230 with one of the "flattened out" diagrams below.

a

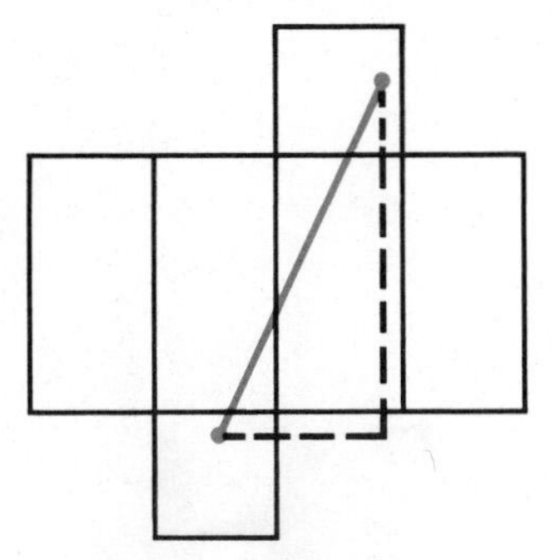

b

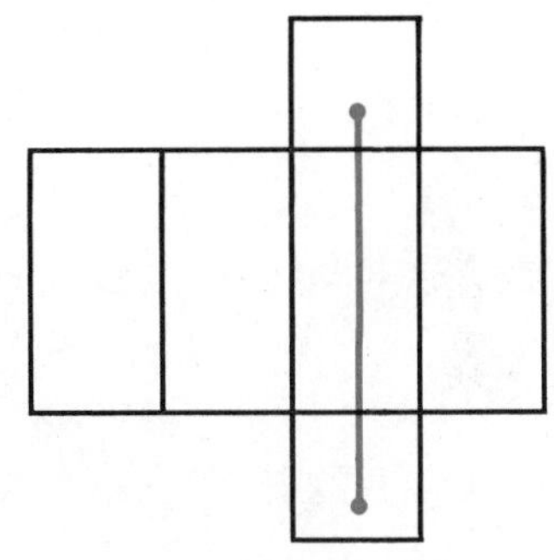

c

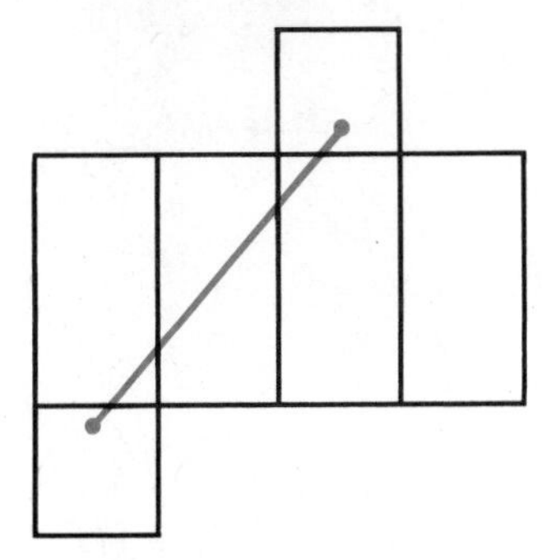

d

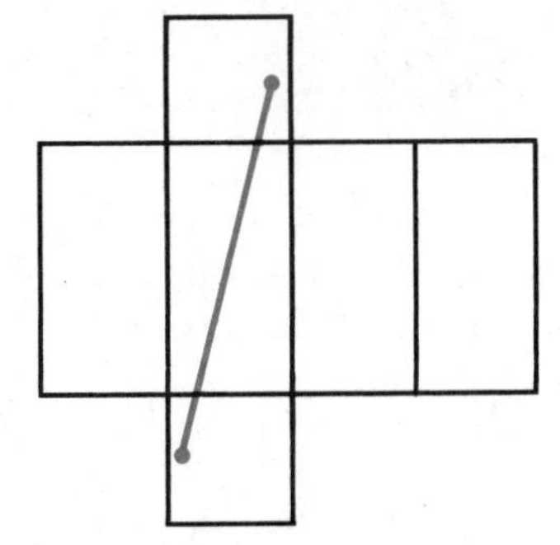

2. Complete a right triangle and calculate the length of each path.

7–2 Special Triangles

The figures and table on the right show the dimensions and specifications for two different kinds of machine nuts.

The dimension labeled F tells the size wrench needed for the nut. How can dimensions G be calculated? Knowledge of 45°-45°-90° and 30°-60°-90° triangles will help in this calculation.

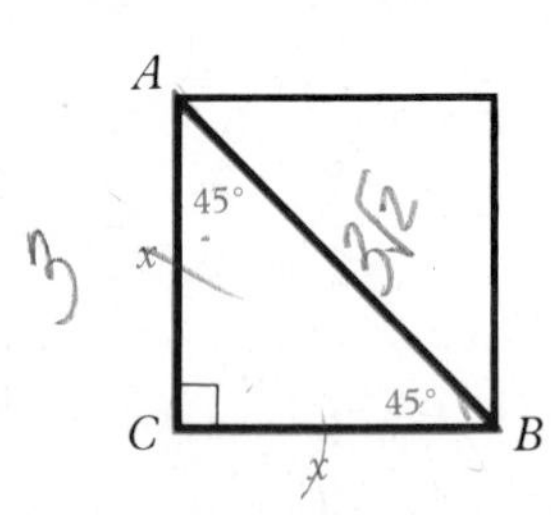

A 45°-45°-90° triangle is formed by 2 sides of a square and a diagonal.

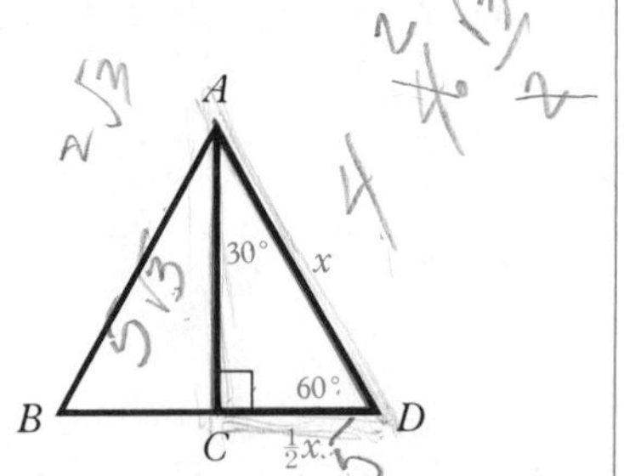

A 30°-60°-90° triangle is formed by an altitude in an equilateral triangle.

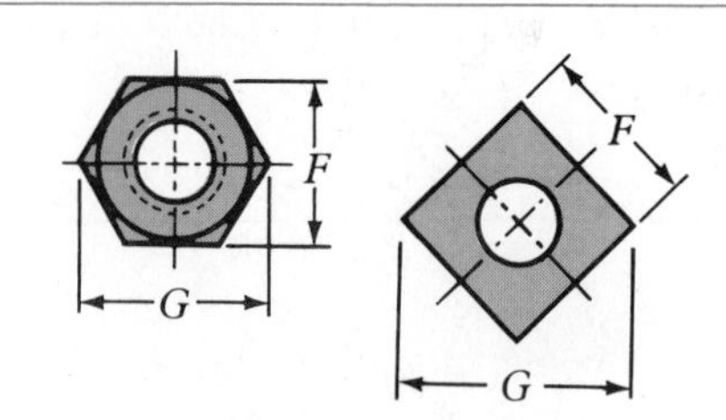

Square and Hexagon Machine Nuts

Nominal Size	F Width Across Flats	G Width Across Corners Square	G Width Across Corners Hex.
	Basic	Max.	Max.
0	5/32	0.221	0.180
1	5/32	0.221	0.180
2	3/16	0.265	0.217
3	3/16	0.265	0.217
4	1/4	0.354	0.289

Theorem 7–3 The length of the hypotenuse of a 45°-45°-90° triangle is $\sqrt{2}$ times the length of a leg.

Theorem 7–4 The length of the longer leg of a 30°-60°-90° triangle is $\frac{\sqrt{3}}{2}$ times the length of the hypotenuse or $\sqrt{3}$ times the length of the shorter side.

The proof of Theorem 7–3 is left as an exercise. We suggest a proof of Theorem 7–4 by applying the Pythagorean Theorem to $\triangle ACD$ above:

$$x^2 = (AC)^2 + \left(\frac{1}{2}x\right)^2$$

$$(AC)^2 = x^2 - \frac{x^2}{4} = x^2\left(1 - \frac{1}{4}\right)$$

$$AC = \sqrt{\frac{3}{4}}x = (\sqrt{3})\left(\frac{x}{2}\right) = \frac{\sqrt{3}}{2}(x)$$

These two theorems can be used to find unknown lengths in special triangles.

Example 1

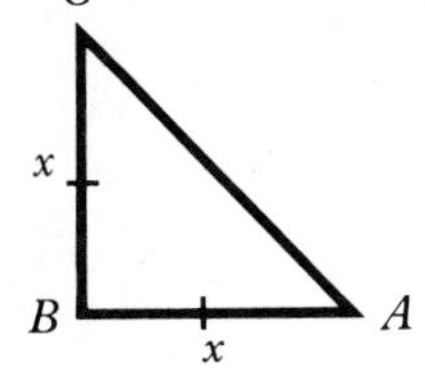

1. $\angle A$ and $\angle C$ must be 45° angles.
2. By Theorem 7-3, $x\sqrt{2} = 12$

   so $x = \dfrac{12}{\sqrt{2}} \cdot \dfrac{\sqrt{2}}{\sqrt{2}} = \dfrac{12\sqrt{2}}{2} = 6\sqrt{2}$

Example 2

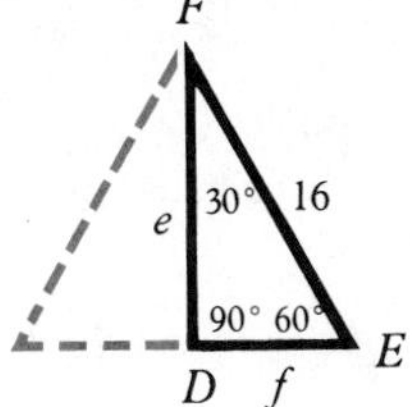

1. $\overline{ED}$ is an altitude of an equilateral triangle so

   $f = \dfrac{16}{2} = 8.$

2. By Theorem 7-4, $e = \sqrt{3} \cdot f$
   or $e = 8\sqrt{3}.$

APPLICATION 1

How far is it from home plate to second base on a baseball diamond? Recall that the distance from home plate to first base is 90 feet. Since $\triangle HFS$ is a 45°-45°-90° triangle, Theorem 7-3 says that

$$HS = \sqrt{2}(90) \doteq 127.28 \text{ feet.}$$

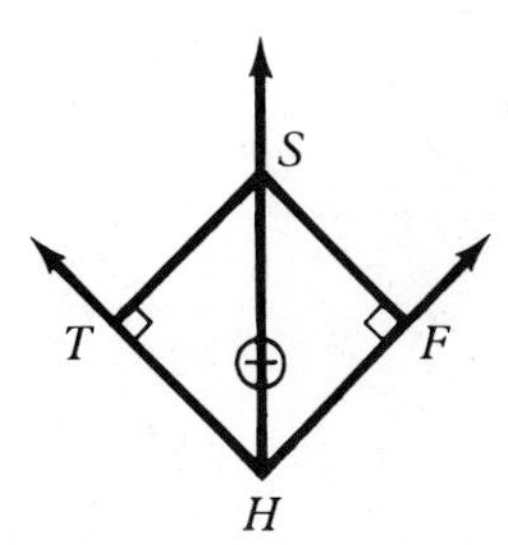

NOTE: $\sqrt{2}$ and $\sqrt{3}$ can only be approximated with a decimal number.

APPLICATION 2

The machine nuts used in the specification at the beginning of this lesson are square and regular hexagon in shape. Therefore $\triangle ABC$ is a 45°-45°-90° triangle and $\triangle DEF$ is a 30°-60°-90° triangle.

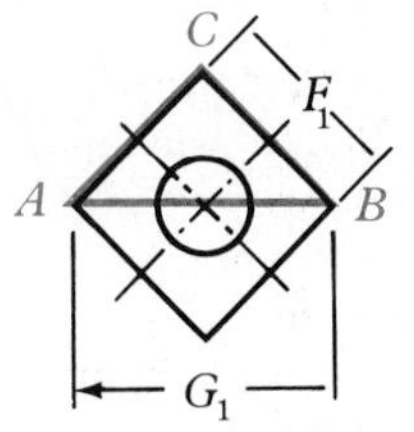

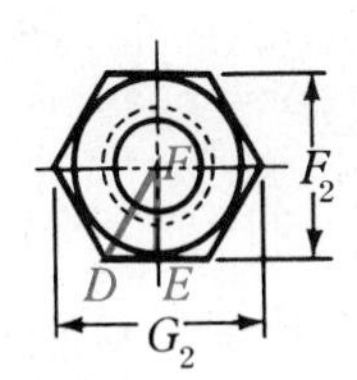

From Theorem 7-3, $G_1 = \sqrt{2}F_1$.

From Theorem 7-4, $FE = \sqrt{3}\,DE$

$$F_2 = 2FE = 2\sqrt{3}\,DE$$

$$DE = \frac{F_2}{2\sqrt{3}}$$

$$G_2 = 4\,DE = \frac{2}{\sqrt{3}}F_2.$$

For size 4 hexagonal machine nuts with $F_2 = \frac{1}{4}$, $G_2 = 4\,DE = \dfrac{2}{\sqrt{3}} \cdot \dfrac{1}{4} \doteq 0.289.$
Notice that this is the value given in the table.

EXERCISES

A.

For exercises 1-4 use Theorem 7-3 to find the lengths of the indicated sides.

1.

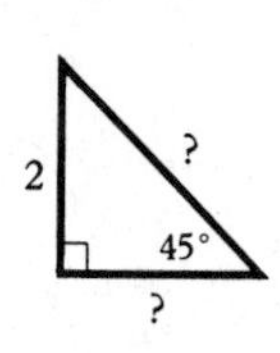

2.

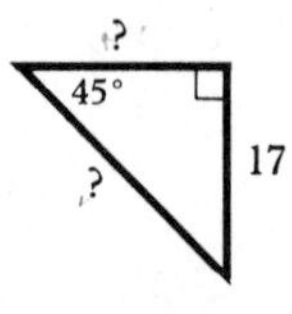

3.

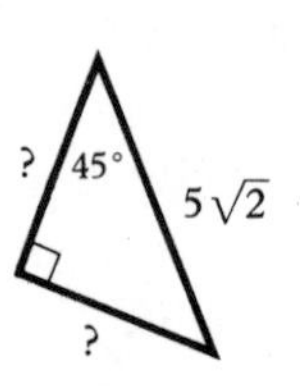

4.

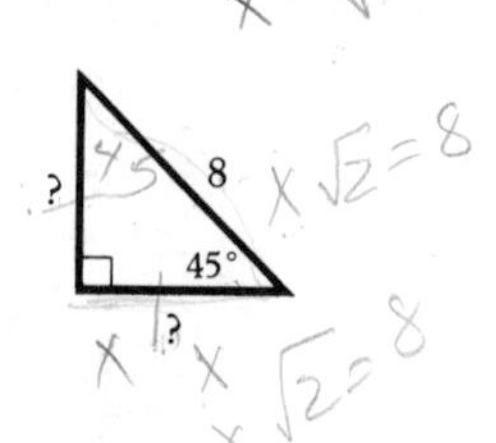

For exercises 5-12 use Theorem 7-4 to find the lengths of the sides of the triangle.

5.

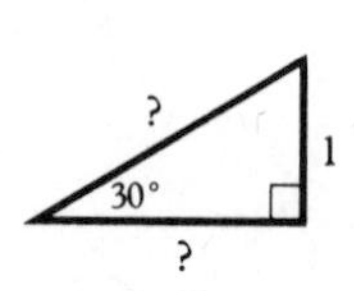

6.

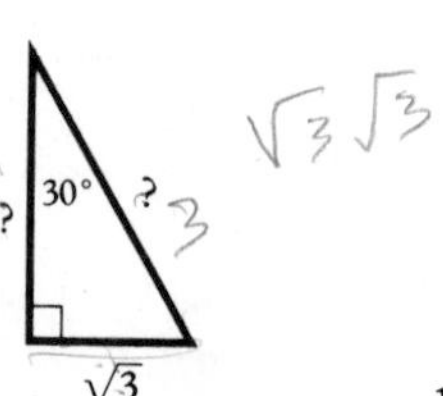

7.

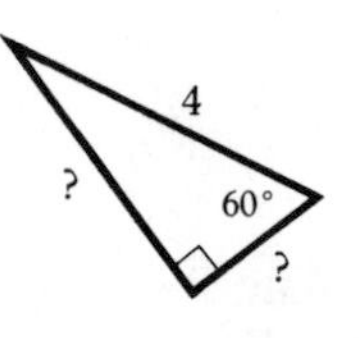

8.

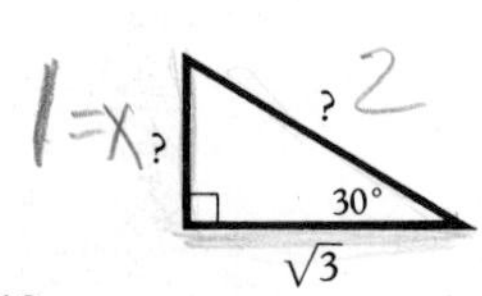

9.

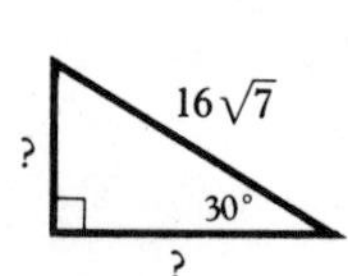

10.

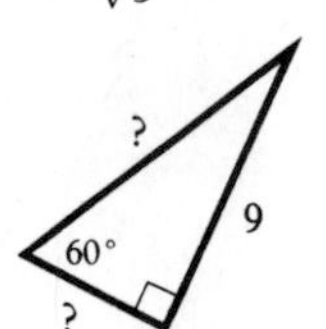

11.

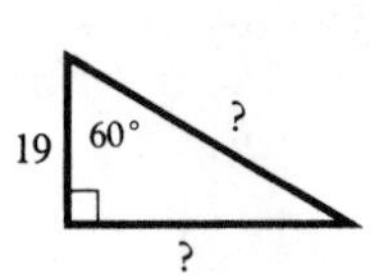

12.

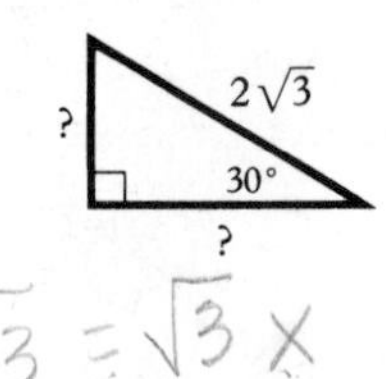

Activity

Use commercially-produced materials or cut from posterboard as many equilateral triangle patterns as you need and put them together with rubber bands as shown in the photograph.

There are eight convex solid figures that can be made using only equilateral triangle pieces of one size. How many of these can you make?

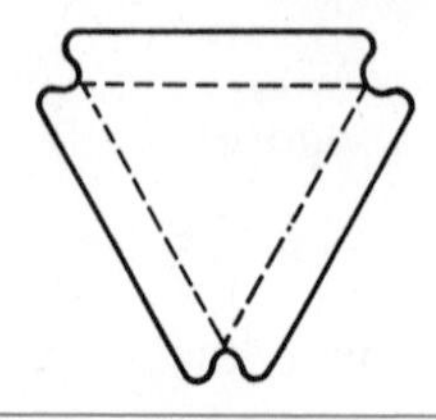

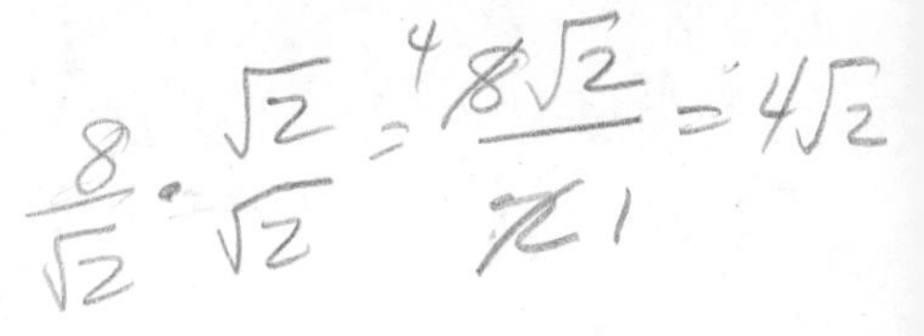

B.

13. In a right triangle one acute angle has a measure that is twice the measure of the other acute angle. If the length of the longer leg is 5, what is the length of the hypotenuse?

14. A window has a clear opening 41 inches wide and 26 inches high. Will a ping-pong table top 48 inches wide fit through the window?

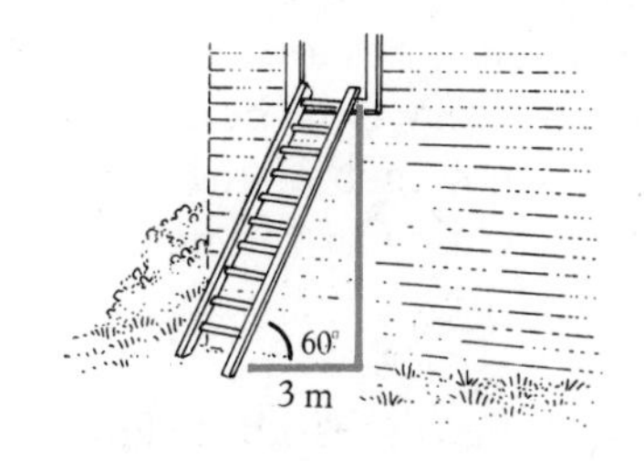

15. A ladder leaning against a wall makes a 60° angle with the ground. If the base of the ladder is 3 meters from the building, how high above the ground is the top of the ladder?

16. Prove Theorem 7-3.

C.

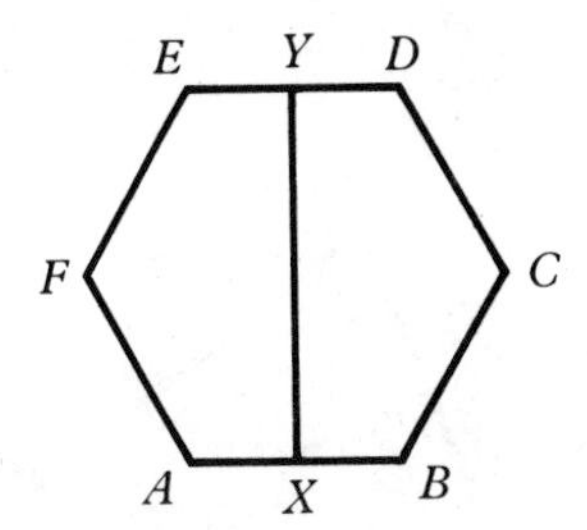

17. Prove that the altitude of an equilateral triangle with side of length s is $s\frac{\sqrt{3}}{2}$.

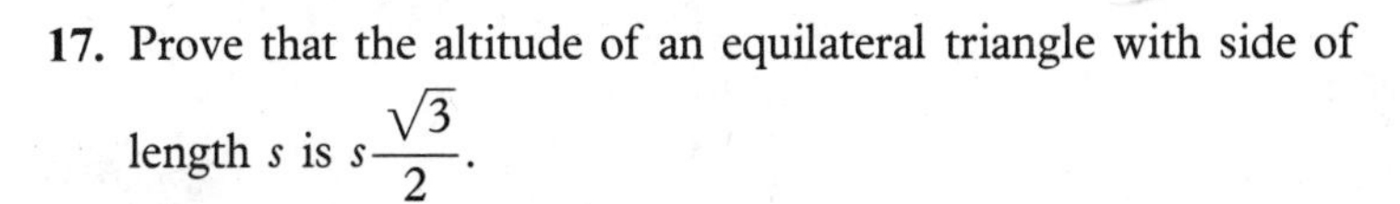

18. If the length of the side of a regular hexagon $ABCDEF$ is s, what is the length of $\overline{XY}$ if X and Y are midpoints of opposite sides?

19. If an equilateral triangle has side length s, find the radius of the circle that contains the three vertices.

20. An architect is calculating the dimensions for a regular hexagon shaped window. If the height of the opening is 120 cm, find the width AB. ($m\angle ADF = 120$)

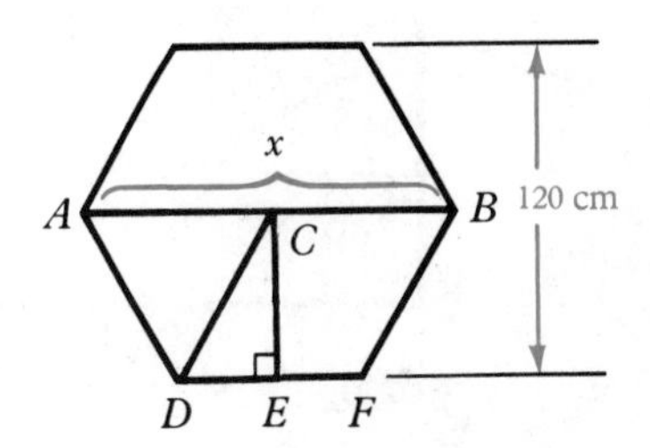

PROBLEM SOLVING

Consider a square-based pyramid whose edges all have length 2. Suppose points B and C are the midpoints of the indicated edges.

1. Find the lengths of $\overline{AB}$ and $\overline{AC}$.
2. Find the length of the altitude $\overline{AD}$ of the pyramid.
3. Is $\triangle ABC$ an equilateral triangle?

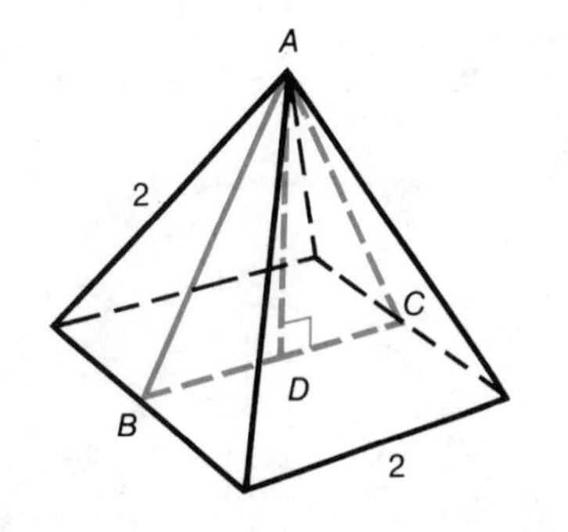

7–3 Triangle Concurrency Theorems

A manufacturer produces a product that is sold primarily in three major cities. A new factory is to be located an equal distance from each of the three cities. How can the location of the new factory be found?

The discussion below answers this question.

Construct the perpendicular bisectors of the sides of a triangle.

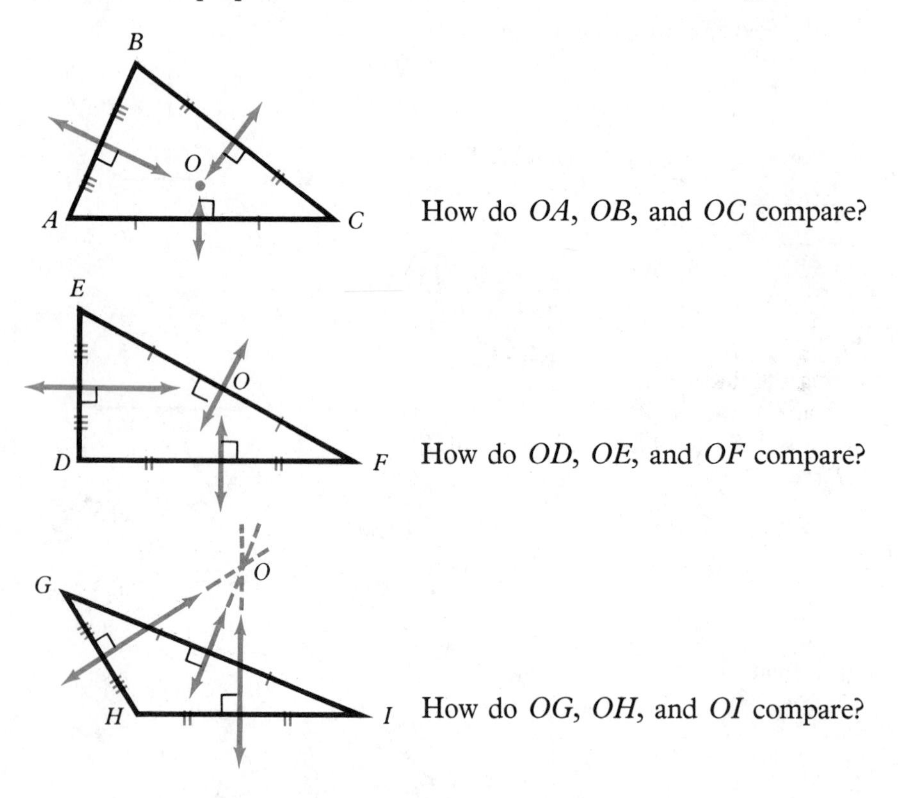

How do OA, OB, and OC compare?

How do OD, OE, and OF compare?

How do OG, OH, and OI compare?

Theorem 7–5 The perpendicular bisectors of the sides of a triangle intersect in a point O that is equidistant from the three vertices of the triangle.

PROOF

Given: $\triangle ABC$ with perpendicular bisectors ℓ, ℓ', and ℓ''.
Prove: ℓ, ℓ', and ℓ'' are concurrent in a point O and that $OA = OB = OC$.

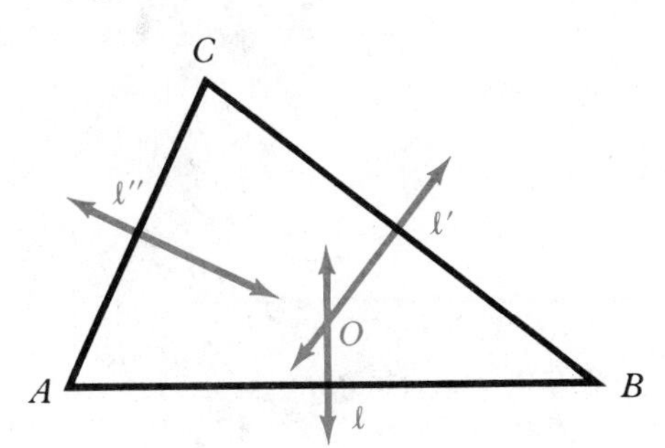

Statements	Reasons
1. ℓ is the perpendicular bisector of $\overline{AB}$	**1.** Given
2. ℓ' is the perpendicular bisector of $\overline{BC}$	**2.** Given
3. ℓ and ℓ' intersect in a point O	**3.** If $\overline{AB} \nparallel \overline{BC}$ then $\ell \nparallel \ell'$.
4. $OA = OB$	**4.** A point on a perpendicular bisector is equidistant from the endpoints.
5. $OB = OC$	**5.** Why?
6. $OA = OC$	**6.** Transitive property of equality
7. O is on the perpendicular bisector of $\overline{AC}$.	**7.** A point equidistant from two points is on the perpendicular bisector of the segment determined by those points.
8. O lies on ℓ, ℓ', ℓ'' and $OA = OB = OC$.	**8.** Statements 4–8

APPLICATION

At the beginning of the lesson we asked how a point can be located equidistant from three cities. Theorem 7-5 answers the question.

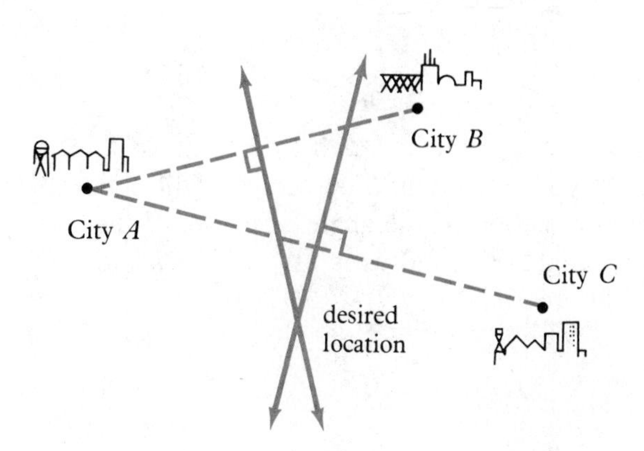

The perpendicular bisectors determine a point that is equidistant from the *vertices* of the triangle. We can also locate a point that is equidistant from the *sides* of the triangle.

In $\triangle ABC$ the three angle bisectors have been constructed.

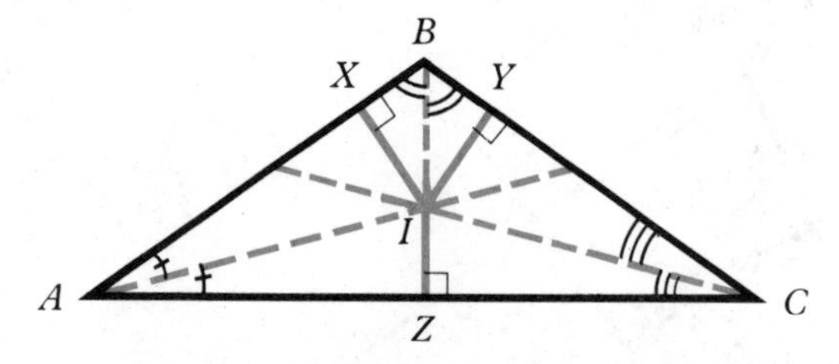

How do IX, IY, and IZ compare?

Theorem 7–6 The angle bisectors of the angles of a triangle are concurrent in a point I that is equidistant from the three sides of the triangle.

The points determined by the perpendicular bisectors (Theorem 7–5) and the angle bisectors (Theorem 7–6) are the centers of circles that have a special relationship with the triangle.

Circle O contains the three vertices of $\triangle ABC$. The center is the point of intersection of the perpendicular bisectors. The radius is OA. Circle O is called the *circumscribed circle.*

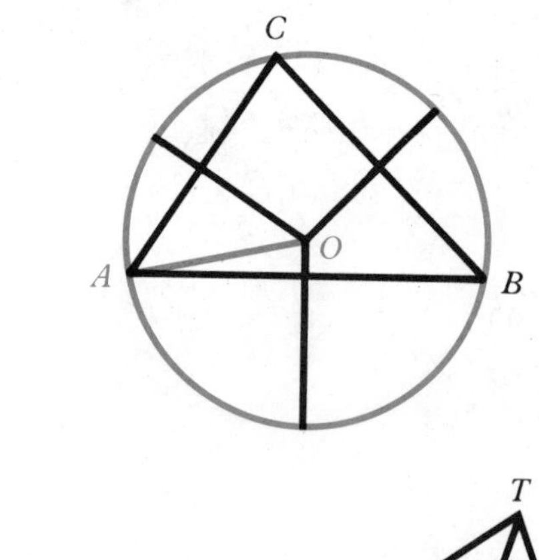

Circle I touches each side of $\triangle RST$ in exactly one point. The center is the point of intersection of the angle bisectors of the triangle. The radius is IW. Circle I is called the *inscribed circle.*

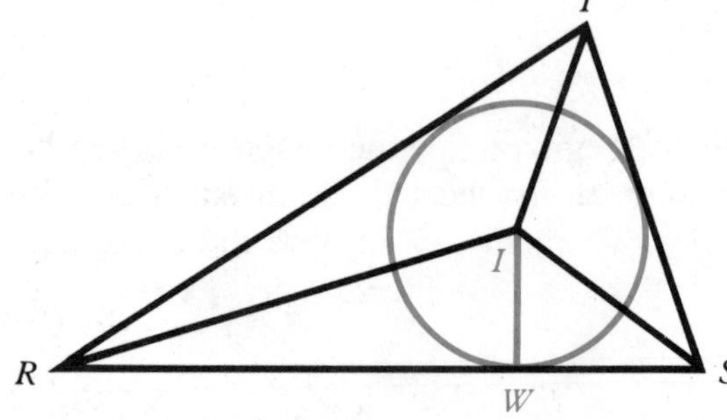

If you were to construct a triangle and its three altitudes, you would see that the lines containing the altitudes are concurrent.

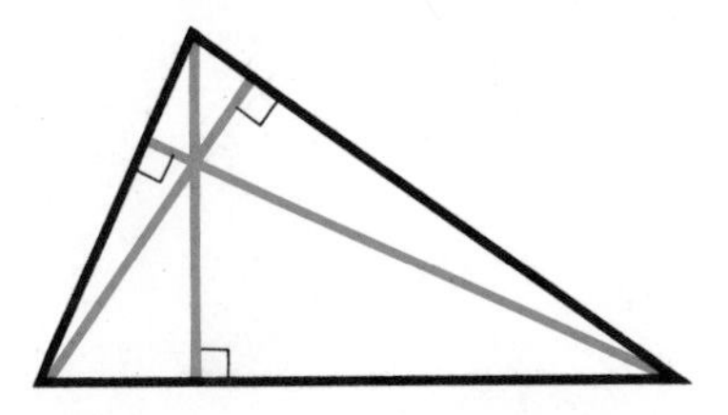

Theorem 7-7 The lines that contain the altitudes of a triangle intersect in a point.

For any triangle there are three segments called *medians*.

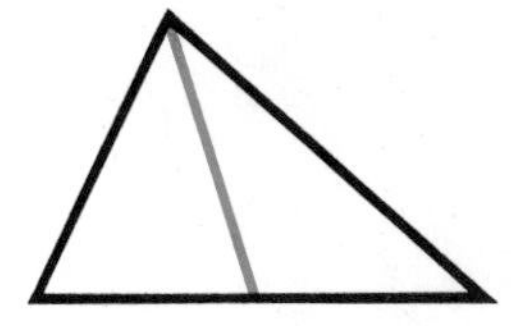

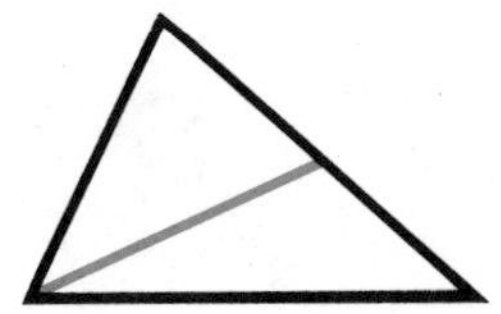

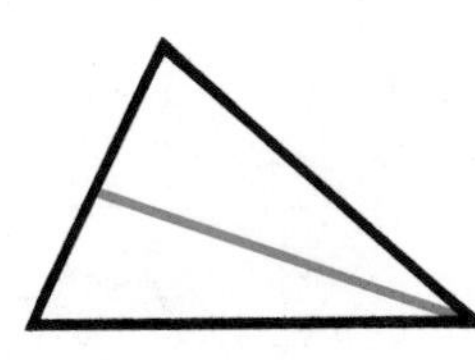

Definition 7-1

A **median** of a triangle is a segment joining a vertex to the midpoint of the opposite side.

If you were to construct the three medians of a triangle, you would see that the three medians are also concurrent.

There is another interesting relationship.

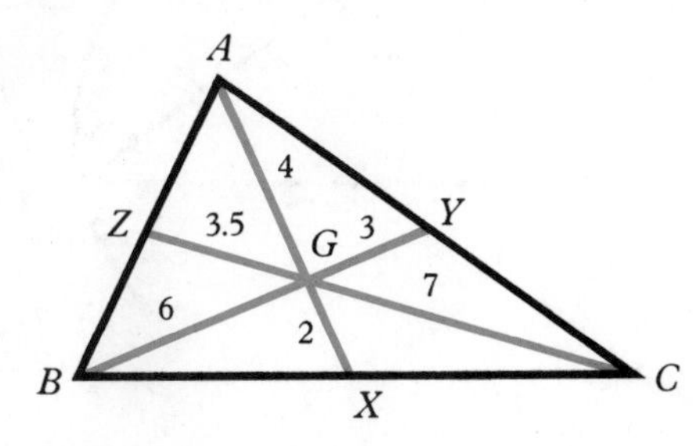

How do AG and AX compare?
How do BG and BY compare?
How do CG and CZ compare?

The following theorem is stated without proof.

Theorem 7-8 The medians of a triangle intersect in a point that is two thirds of the way from each vertex to the opposite side.

EXERCISES

A.

1. For $\triangle ABC$ name an altitude, an angle bisector, and a median.

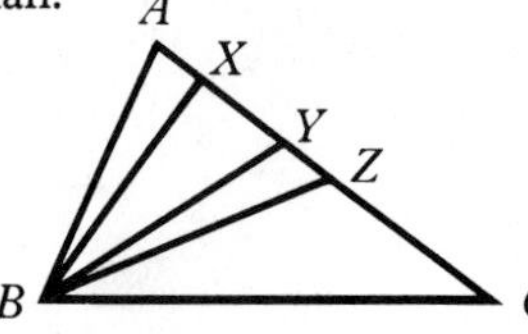

2. For $\triangle ABC$ the lines p and q are perpendicular bisectors of sides. If $OA = 5$, find OB and OC.

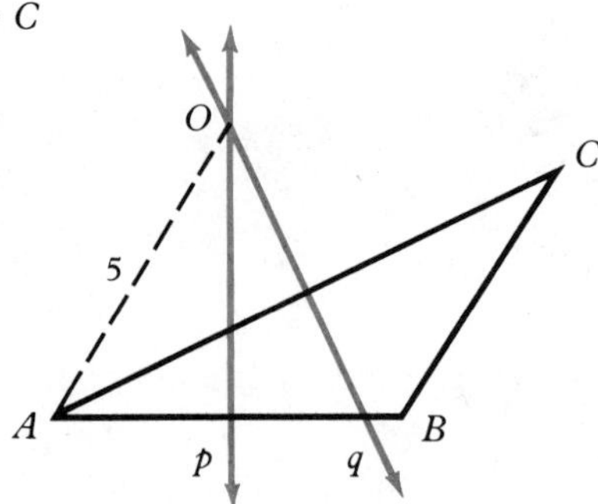

In $\triangle ABC$ $\overline{AX}$, $\overline{BY}$, and $\overline{CZ}$ are medians.

3. If $AZ = 3$, what is ZB?
4. If $CG = 4$, what is GZ?
5. If $AB = BY$, what is BG?

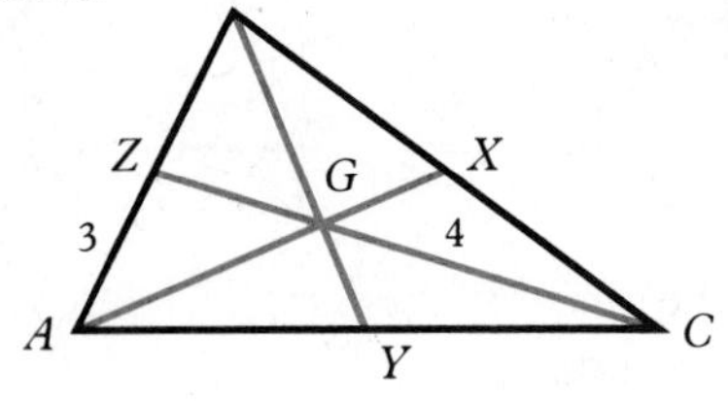

6. Trace $\triangle ABC$ and the circle that passes through the points A, B, and C. Use a compass and straight edge to find the center of the circle. (*Hint:* Use Theorem 7–5.)

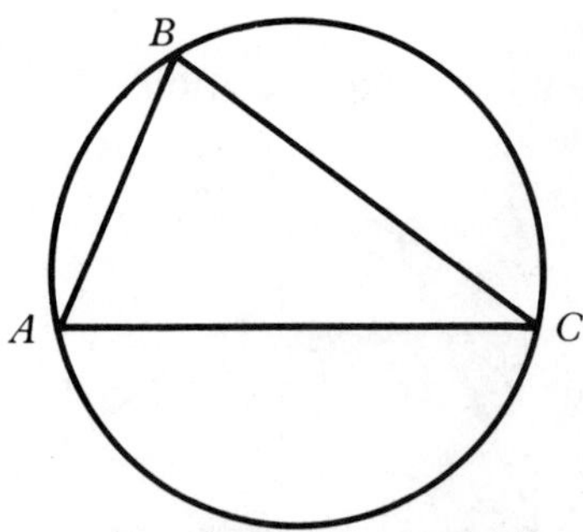

Exercises 7–12 ask for a construction to be completed. Use a straight edge and compass or Mira for these constructions. Each exercise should fill nearly a full sheet of paper.

7. Illustrate Theorem 7–5 by constructing a triangle and all three perpendicular bisectors.

8. Illustrate Theorem 7–6 by constructing a triangle and all three angle bisectors.

9. Illustrate Theorem 7–7 by constructing a triangle and all three altitudes.

10. Illustrate Theorem 7–8 by constructing a triangle and all three medians.

11. Draw a triangle and construct the circumscribed circle. (*Hint:* Theorem 7–5 tells how to find the center of this circle.)

12. Construct $\triangle ABC$ with sides 14 cm, 17 cm, and 20 cm. Very accurately construct the intersections of the medians, altitudes, and perpendicular bisectors of the sides. (Your construction should verify that these three points lie on a line.)

Discover the answers to exercises 13–16 by experimenting with sketches. Fill in the blank with the word "always," "sometimes," or "never."

13. The altitudes of a triangle _?_ intersect inside the triangle.

14. The medians of a triangle _?_ intersect outside the triangle.

15. The perpendicular bisectors of the sides of a triangle _?_ intersect inside the triangle.

16. The angle bisectors of a triangle _?_ intersect inside the triangle.

17. The center of the circumscribed circle _?_ lies inside the triangle.

18. The center of the inscribed circle _?_ lies inside the triangle.

In exercises 19 and 20 fill in the first blank with one of the words "acute," "right," or "obtuse," and fill in the second blank with one of the words "inside," "on," or "outside."

19. The point of intersection of the lines containing the altitudes of a _?_ triangle is _?_ the triangle.

20. The point of intersection of the perpendicular bisectors of the sides of a _?_ triangle is _?_ the triangle.

B.

21. Draw a triangle and construct the inscribed circle.

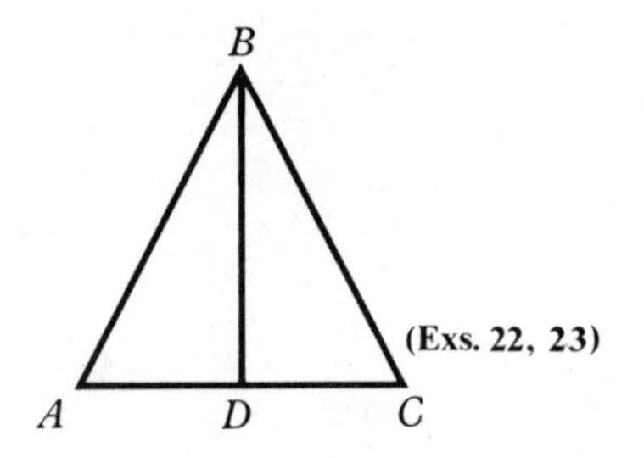

(Exs. 22, 23)

22. Prove that the median from the vertex angle of an isosceles triangle is also an altitude.

23. Prove that the median from the vertex angle of an isosceles triangle is also the angle bisector.

24. Prove that an altitude of an equilateral triangle is also a median of the triangle.

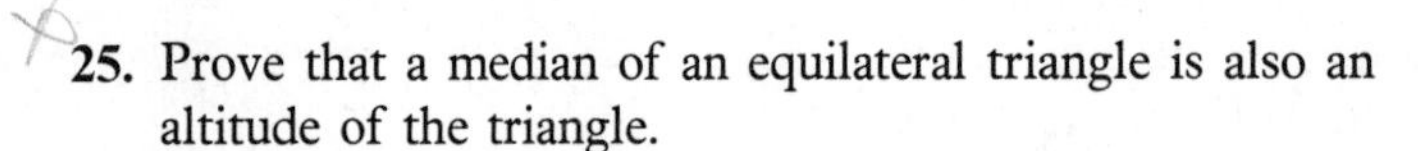

25. Prove that a median of an equilateral triangle is also an altitude of the triangle.

26. Prove that the medians from the base angles of an isosceles triangle are congruent.

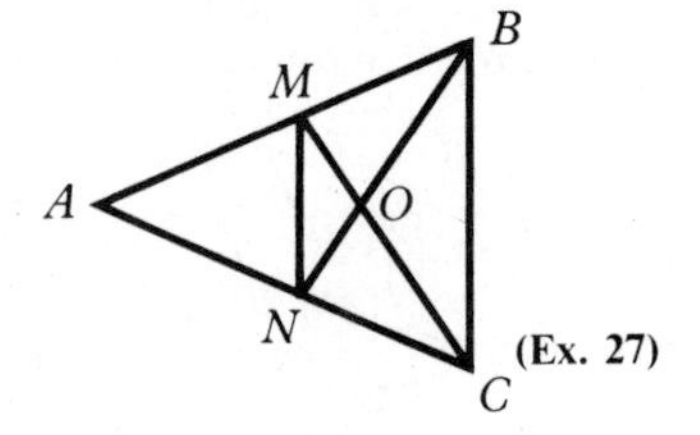

(Ex. 27)

27. In $\triangle ABC$, $AB = AC$, and $\overline{BN}$ and $\overline{CM}$ are angle bisectors. Prove that $\triangle MON$ is an isosceles triangle.

Activity

Centroid means center of mass. If a triangle could be "balanced," its "balance point" would be its centroid.

Experiment: Cut out a large triangular shape from a piece of cardboard or a thin piece of wood. (Your triangle should be scalene.)

Find the centroid of the figure.

Can you balance the object from that point? Can you spin the object?

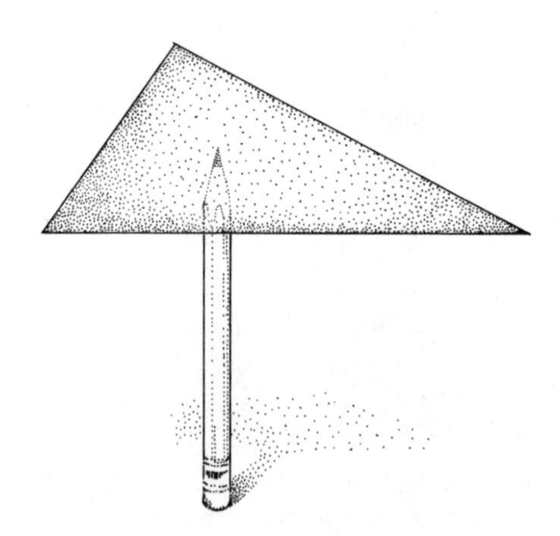

C.

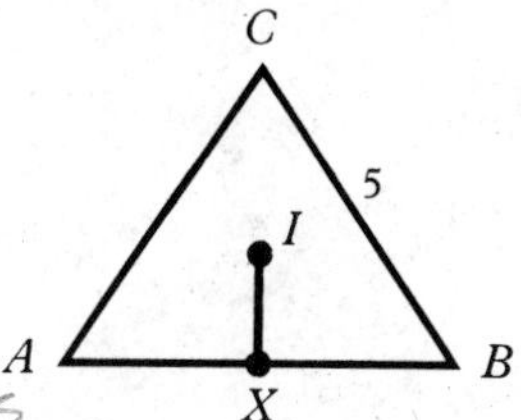

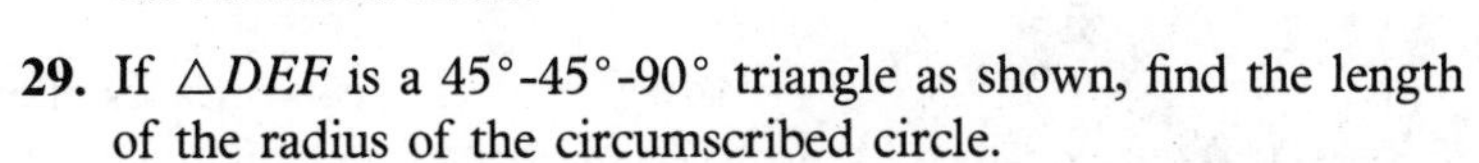

28. If $\triangle ABC$ is equilateral, find the length IX of the radius of the inscribed circle.

29. If $\triangle DEF$ is a 45°-45°-90° triangle as shown, find the length of the radius of the circumscribed circle.

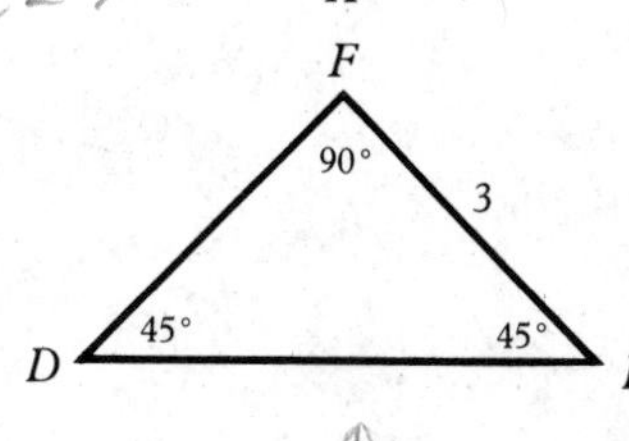

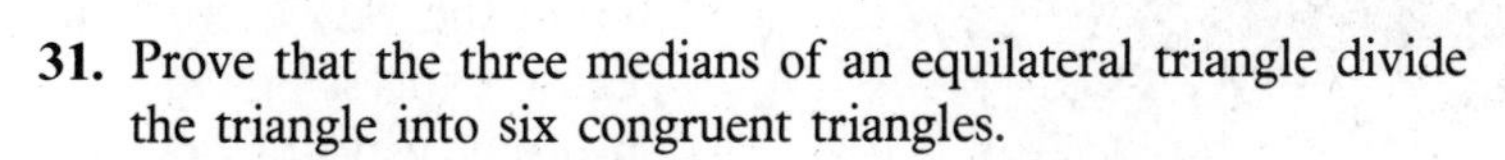

30. Prove that the point of intersection of the angle bisectors of an isosceles triangle is on the altitude from the vertex angle.

31. Prove that the three medians of an equilateral triangle divide the triangle into six congruent triangles.

32. Prove that in an equilateral triangle the perpendicular bisectors of the sides, the angle bisectors, the altitudes, and the medians all intersect in the same point.

33. Prove that the altitudes from the base angles of an isosceles triangle are congruent.

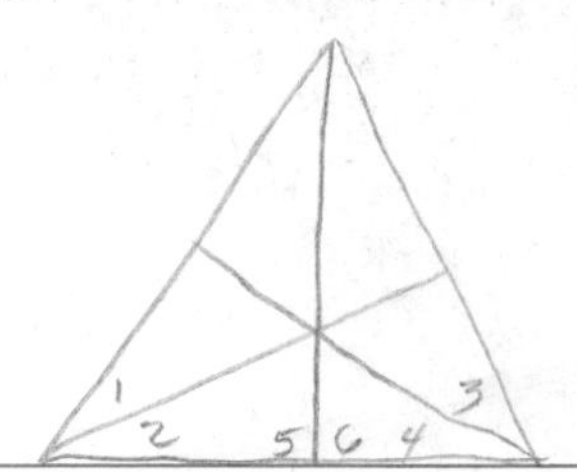

PROBLEM SOLVING

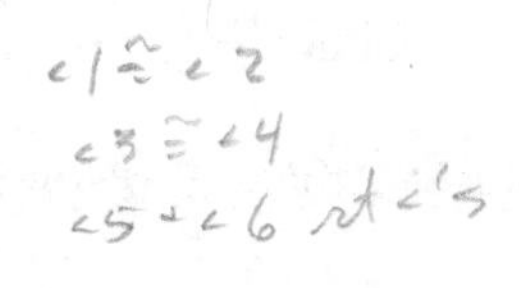

CDEF is a strip of paper 5 cm wide and $\overline{AB}$ is a crease parallel to $\overline{CF}$.

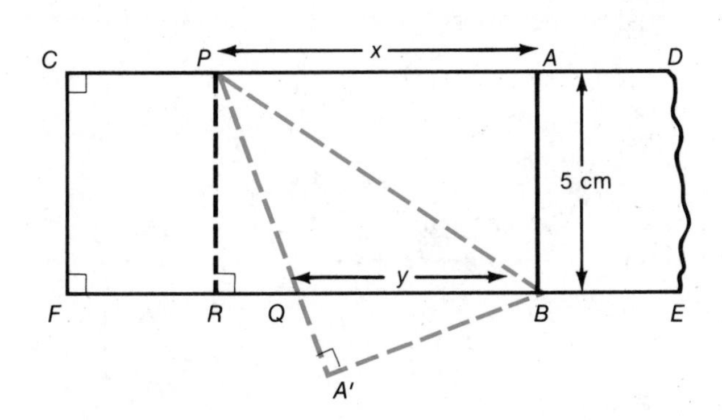

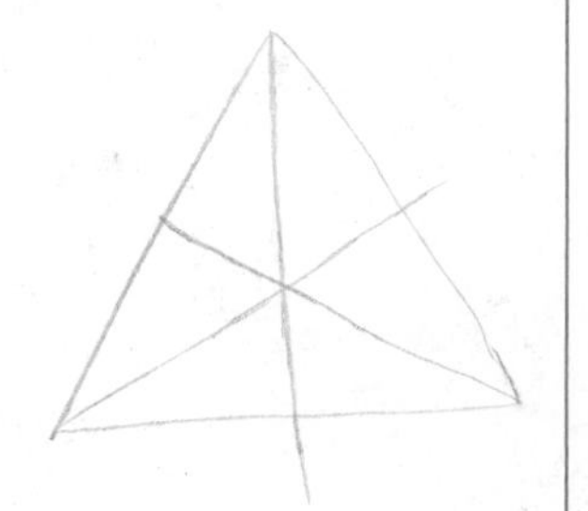

Let P be any point on $\overline{CA}$ and fold along $\overline{PB}$ locating point Q.

Let $PA = x$ and $QB = y$.

1. Show that $PQ = QB = y$.

2. Show that x and y are related by $y = \dfrac{x^2 + 25}{2x}$.

(*Hint:* Show that $\triangle PQR \cong \triangle BQA'$ and use the Pythagorean Theorem.)

7–4 Triangle Inequality

We often hear phrases like "The shortest distance between two points is a straight path," or "It is 100 m the way a crow flies." These expressions are informal ways of describing an important relationship that we shall state as a postulate.

The following three examples suggest the postulate.

Measure the sides.

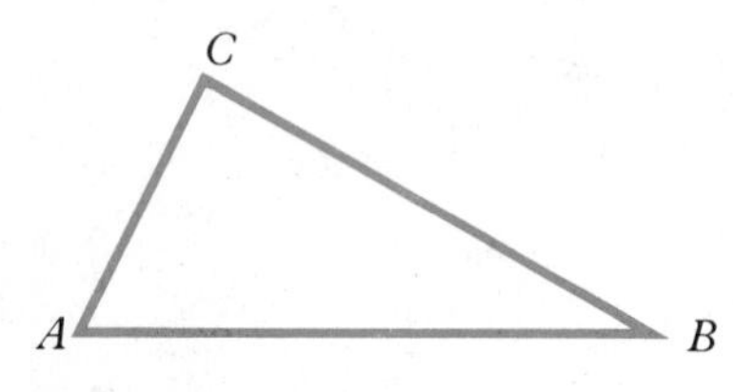

Observe that
$AB < AC + CB$.

Measure the sides.

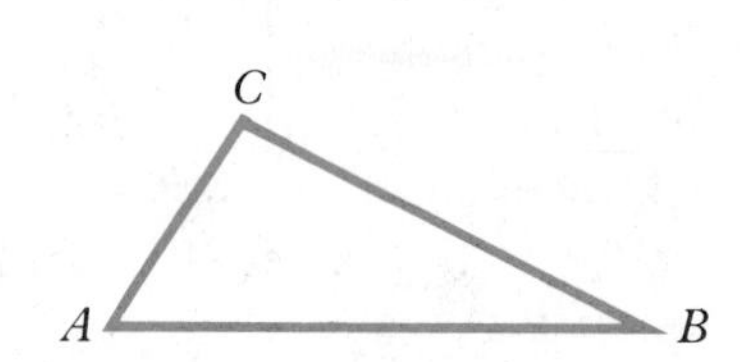

Observe that
$AC < AB + CB$.

Measure the sides.

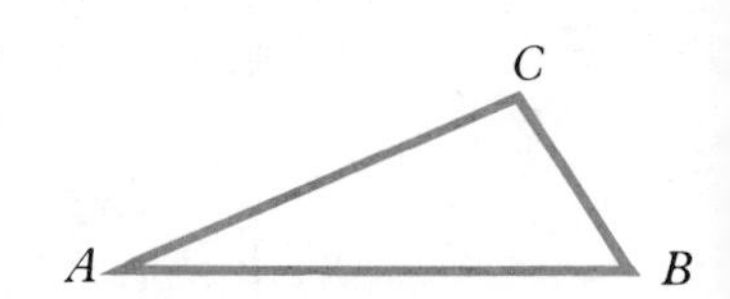

Observe that
$CB < AB + AC$

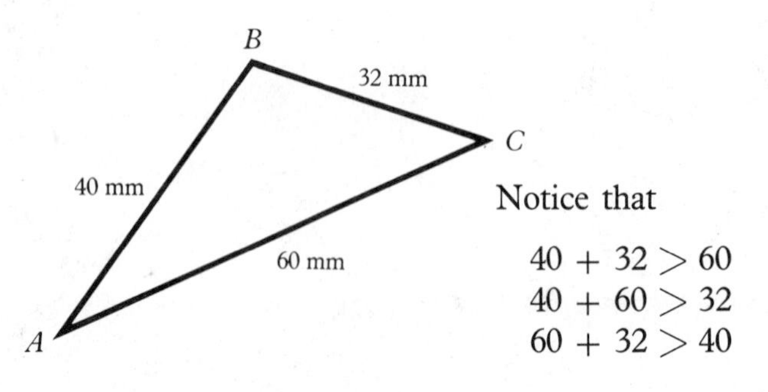

Notice that

$40 + 32 > 60$
$40 + 60 > 32$
$60 + 32 > 40$

Triangle Inequality Postulate

The sum of the lengths of two sides of a triangle is greater than the length of the third side.

APPLICATION 1

A railroad company is to build an engine house to service four cities located at the vertices $ABCD$ of a quadrilateral as shown here. Where should the engine house H be located so that the length, and hence the construction costs, of the roadbed $AH + BH + CH + DH$ is a minimum?

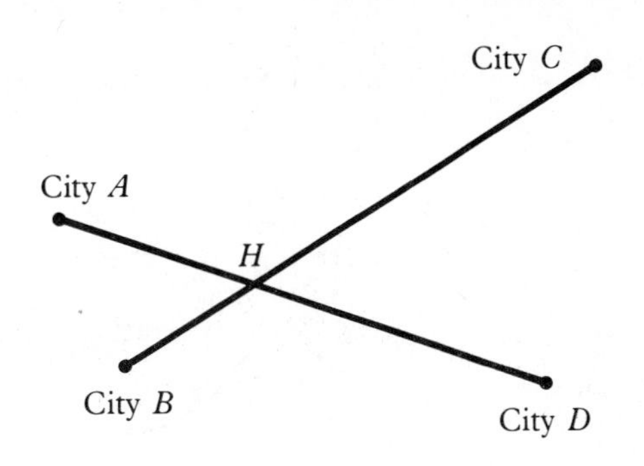

Answer. At the point of intersection of the diagonals of $ABDC$.

Suppose H' is some other location. Then by the Triangle Inequality Postulate

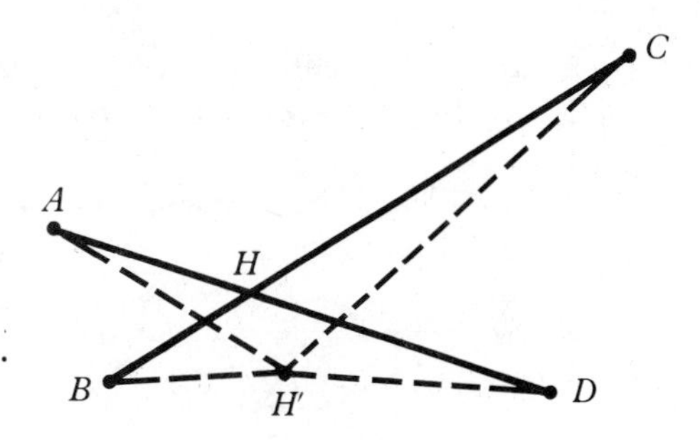

1. $BH + CH < BH' + CH'$ in $\triangle BCH'$,
2. $AH + DH < AH' + DH'$ in $\triangle ADH'$.

Therefore,
$AH + BH + CH + DH < AH' + BH' + CH' + DH'$.

APPLICATION 2

If cities are located at points A, B, C, and D as shown in the figure, what is the minimum length track from a centrally located point H to each of the cities?

Answer. From Application 1 we see that the minimum length track is the sum of the lengths of the diagonals $\overline{AC}$ and $\overline{BD}$. To find the length of these diagonals, first we must find BE and CE. Since the length of the shorter leg of a 30°-60°-90° triangle is half the length of the hypotenuse, then $BE = 23$ km. The longer leg, CE, has a length of $23\sqrt{3}$ km or approximately 39.84 km.

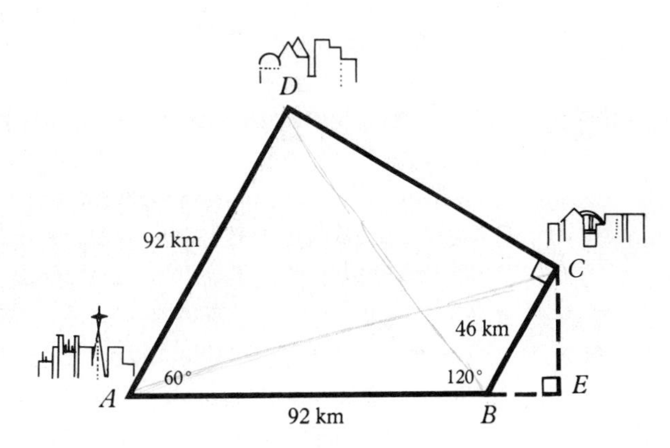

Applying the Pythagorean Theorem to $\triangle AEC$,

$$AC = \sqrt{AE^2 + CE^2}$$
$$= \sqrt{13{,}225 + 1587} \doteq 121.7 \text{ km}.$$
$$BD = 92 \text{ km}.$$

Therefore, the minimum length is approximately 121.7 km + 92 km = 213.7 km.

EXERCISES

A.

In exercises 1–7 decide whether or not the given set of numbers could be the lengths of the sides of a triangle.

1. $\{4, 5, 7\}$ **2.** $\{4, 5, 17\}$ **3.** $\{6, 13, 7\}$ **4.** $\{9, 13, 17\}$

5. $\{7, 7, 13\}$ **6.** $\{j, k, j + k\}$ **7.** $\{a, 3a, 3a\}$

B.

8. If two sides of a triangle have lengths 2 and 5, then the length of the third side is greater than _?_, and less than _?_.

9. If the lengths of two sides of a triangle are 7 and 9, what are the possible lengths of the third side?

10. Prove that for any quadrilateral $ABCD$, $AB + BC + CD > AD$.

(Ex. 10)

Activity

Construct a triangle with sides of length 8 cm, 11 cm, and 15 cm, and construct the following points.

a. The midpoint of the three sides

b. The feet of the three altitudes

c. The intersection of the three altitudes. Label this point H.

d. The midpoints of the segments joining H with the vertices of the triangle

How do the nine points constructed in parts a, b, and d appear to be related?

11. Prove that the shortest path between two points A and B is the segment joining them.

C.

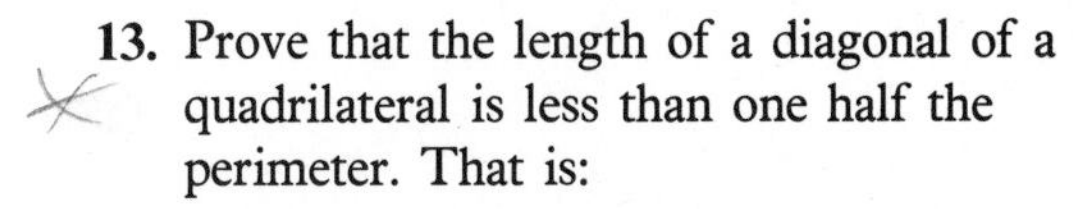

12. Prove that the sum of the lengths of the sides of a quadrilateral is greater than the sum of the lengths of the diagonals.

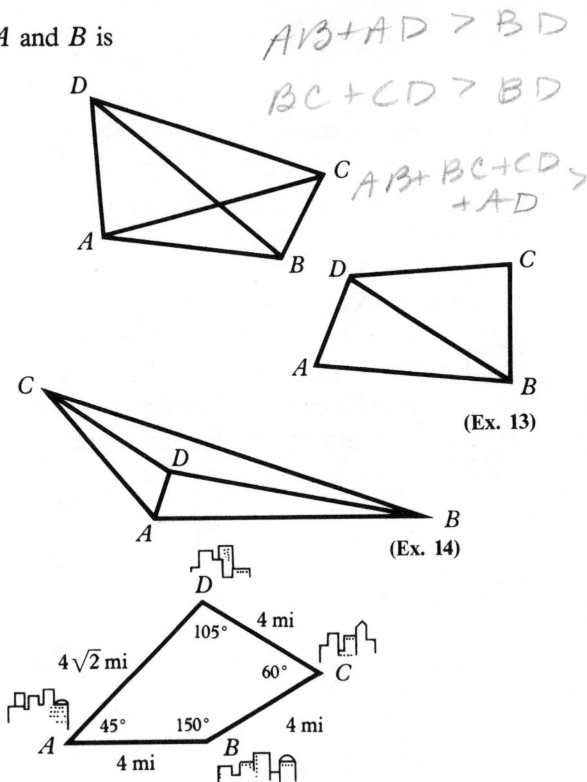

(Ex. 13)

(Ex. 14)

13. Prove that the length of a diagonal of a quadrilateral is less than one half the perimeter. That is:

$$BD < \frac{AB + BC + CD + AD}{2}.$$

14. Prove that if D is a point in the interior of $\triangle ABC$, then

$$\tfrac{1}{2}(AB + BC + AC) < AD + BD + CD.$$

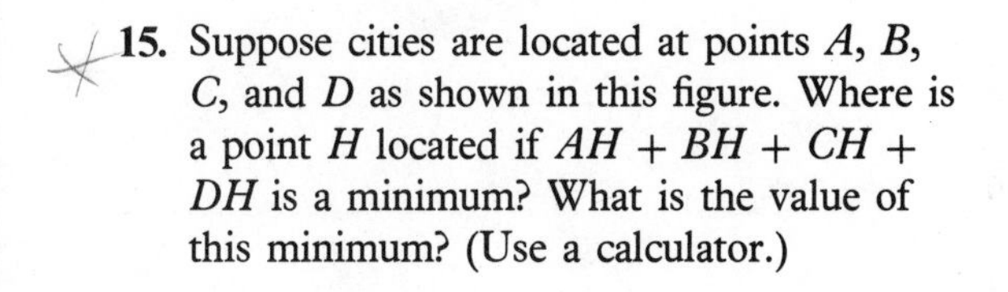

15. Suppose cities are located at points A, B, C, and D as shown in this figure. Where is a point H located if $AH + BH + CH + DH$ is a minimum? What is the value of this minimum? (Use a calculator.)

PROBLEM SOLVING

This sketch shows a front and side view of a picture that is supported against the wall along its bottom $\overline{CD}$, and slants away from the wall at the top. It is supported at the top with a wire AOB, O being a nail on the wall.

Find the length of the wire AOB.

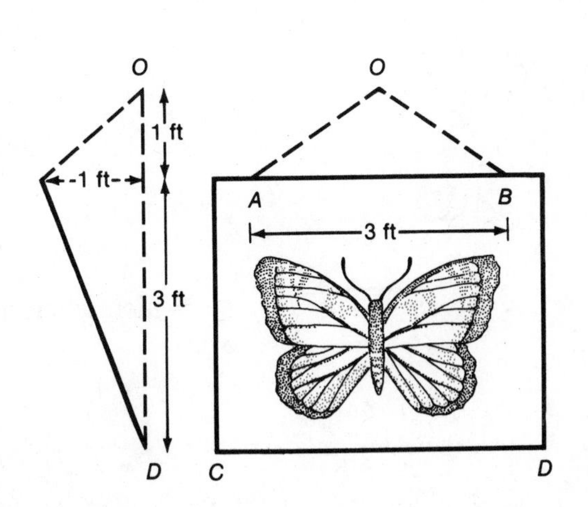

7–5 Inequalities in a Triangle

Imagine a physical setting involving rather large distances that cannot be measured directly. Sometimes the actual distance does not need to be known but only a comparison between two distances. For example, a ship may want to compare its distance from a point on shore to its distance from an island, in order to make sure it is staying outside an imaginary line halfway between the shore and the island. The theorem in this lesson will provide one method for doing this.

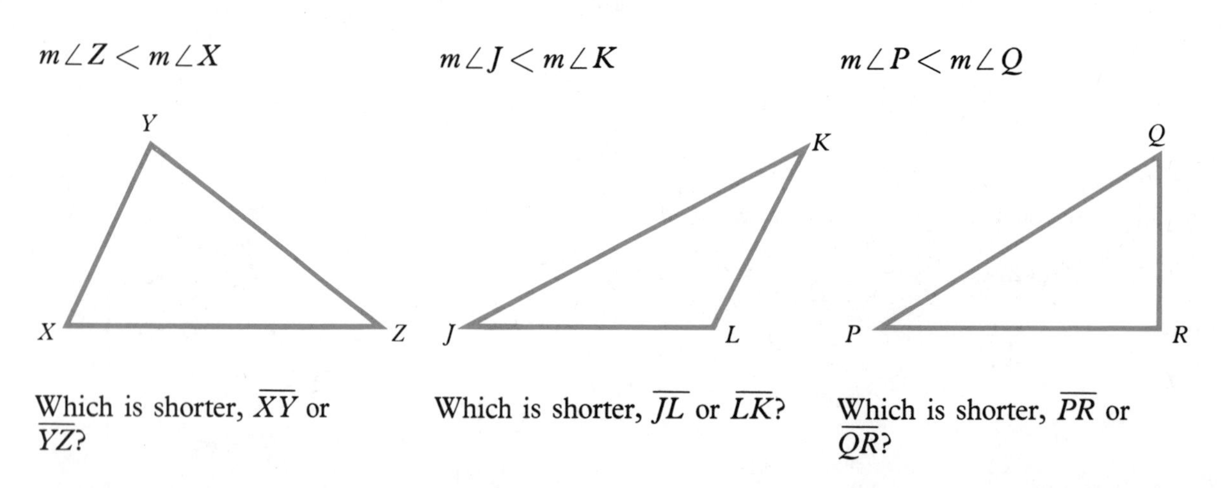

$m\angle Z < m\angle X$ — Which is shorter, $\overline{XY}$ or $\overline{YZ}$?

$m\angle J < m\angle K$ — Which is shorter, $\overline{JL}$ or $\overline{LK}$?

$m\angle P < m\angle Q$ — Which is shorter, $\overline{PR}$ or $\overline{QR}$?

Theorem 7–9 If the measures of two angles of a triangle are unequal, then the length of the side opposite the smaller angle is less than the length of the side opposite the larger angle.

PROOF

Given: $\triangle ABC$ with $m\angle B < m\angle A$
Prove: $AC < BC$

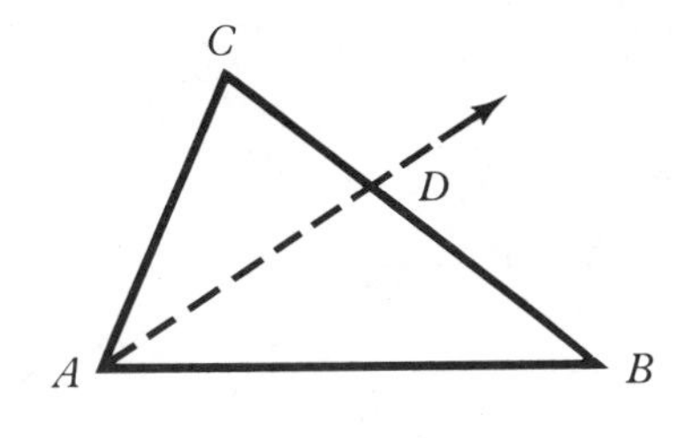

Statements	Reasons
1. $m\angle B < m\angle A$	**1.** Given
2. There exists a point D on $\overrightarrow{BC}$ so that $m\angle BAD = m\angle B$.	**2.** Protractor Postulate
3. $\overline{AD} \cong \overline{BD}$	**3.** If two angles of a triangle are congruent, then the sides opposite them are congruent.
4. $AD = BD$	**4.** Why?
5. $AC < AD + DC$	**5.** Why?
6. $AD + DC = BD + DC$	**6.** Addition of equals property
7. $BD + DC = BC$	**7.** Definition of between for points
8. $AC < BC$	**8.** Substitution Principle

APPLICATION

How can a ship determine that its position is outside an imaginary boundary line that is halfway between the shore and an island?

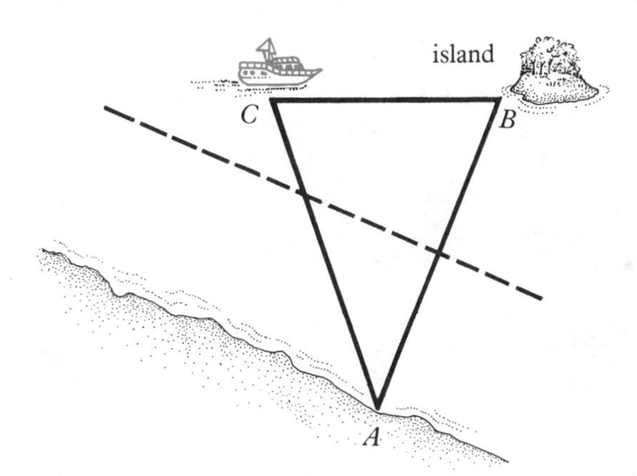

Answer. Persons located at both points A and B determine, by using radio, radar, or laser beams, that $m\angle A < m\angle B$. When this information is radioed to the ship, the ship's captain concludes from Theorem 7-9 that $CB < CA$.

The converse of Theorem 7-9 is stated here without proof.

Theorem 7–10 If the lengths of two sides of a triangle are unequal, then the measure of the angle opposite the shorter side is less than the measure of the angle opposite the longer side.

EXERCISES

A.

In exercises 1–4 name the shortest side and the longest side of the given triangle.

1. B, A 65°, C 40°

2. E, D (right angle), F 30°

3.

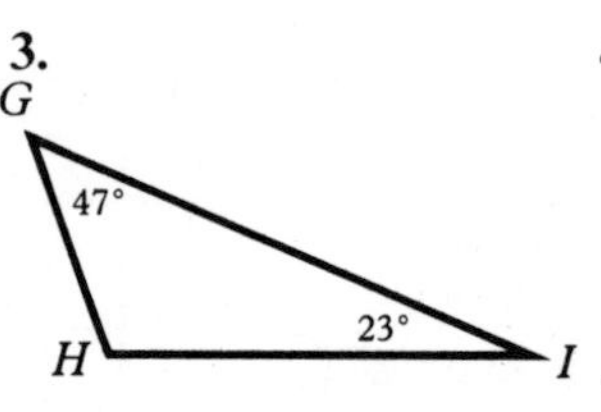

4.

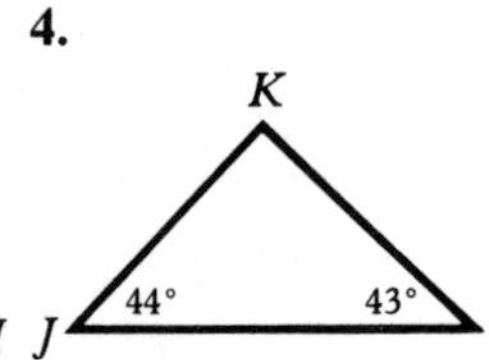

In exercises 5–8 list the sides from shortest to longest for a triangle $\triangle ABC$ if:

5. $m\angle A = 46$, $m\angle B = 30$

6. $m\angle C = 101$, $m\angle B = 70$.

7. $m\angle A = 59$, $m\angle C = 61$.

8. $m\angle B = 48$, $m\angle A = 47$.

In exercises 9–10 list the angles from the one with smallest measure to one with largest measure for $\triangle ABC$ if:

9. $AB = 17$, $BC = 21$, $AC = 18$.

10. $AB = 15$, $AC = 16$, $BC = 17$

B.

11. List the sides of the quadrilateral from shortest side to longest side.

12. List all the segments in this figure from the one with shortest length to the one with the longest length. (Assume that all the indicated angle measures are correct.)

Activity

Use a 3-by-3 square array of dots. There are eight triangles different in size and shape that can be drawn.

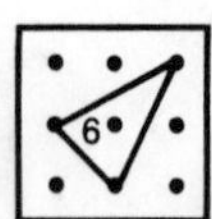

There are over 30 different triangles that can be drawn on a 4 by 4 square array of dots. Draw as many of these triangles as you can.

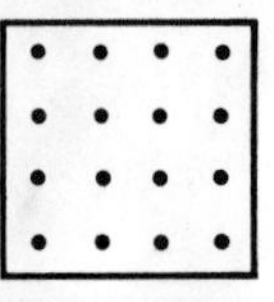

Suggestion: Be systematic. Do not start by drawing at random. (If dot paper is not available, graph paper can be used.)

13. **Given:** $m\angle DBC = m\angle BCD = 45$

    Prove: $CD < AB$

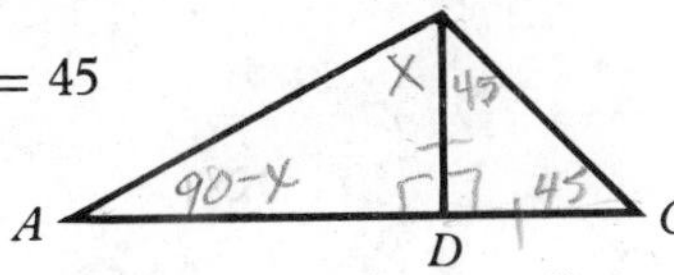

14. Prove that the perpendicular segment from a point to a line is the shortest segment from the point to the line.

C.

15. Prove that the median from vertex Y of scalene triangle XYZ is longer than the altitude from vertex Y.

16. Prove that the sum of the lengths of the three altitudes of $\triangle ABC$ is less than the sum of the lengths of the sides of the triangle.

17. The three main work centers in the kitchen are the refrigerator, sink, and stove. You can picture them as the points of a triangle. One rule of thumb is: The three sides of the "kitchen triangle" should add up to more than 12 feet and less than 22 feet. Also, the shortest side of the triangle should be between the sink and the stove.

    Below is a chart of possible "kitchen triangles." First decide whether each triangle is possible. Then state whether each triangle follows the rule of thumb.

	Stove-Sink	Stove-Refrigerator	Refrigerator-Sink
a.	5 feet	4 feet	8 feet
b.	10 feet	11 feet	11 feet
c.	6 feet	8 feet	7 feet
d.	3 feet	7 feet	4 feet
e.	3 feet	8 feet	4 feet

PROBLEM SOLVING

Suppose that *ABCD* is a flexible wire. *A* is a fixed point and *C* is a fixed pulley. *B* is a weight that slides freely along the wire so that *AB* and *CB* are always equally inclined to the vertical. Find how far *B* rises if *D* is pulled down 2 meters.

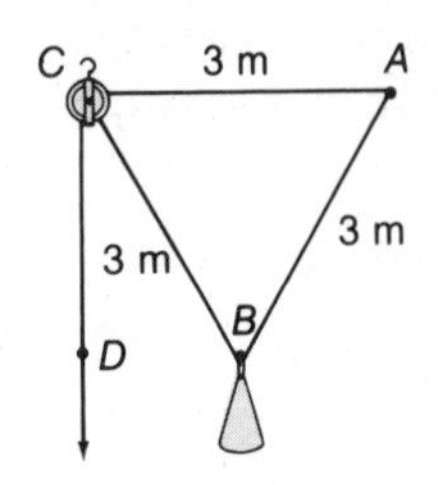

Important Ideas—Chapter 7

Terms

Median (p. 239)

Postulates

Triangle Inequality Postulate. The sum of the lengths of two sides of a triangle is greater than the length of the third side.

Theorems

7-1 **Pythagorean Theorem.** If $\triangle ABC$ is a right triangle, then the square of the length of the hypotenuse equals the sum of the squares of the lengths of the legs.

7-2 If $\triangle ABC$ has side lengths a, b, and c, and $c^2 = a^2 + b^2$, then $\triangle ABC$ is a right triangle.

7-3 The length of the hypotenuse of a 45°-45°-90° triangle is $\sqrt{2}$ times the length of a leg.

7-4 The length of the longer leg of a 30°-60°-90° triangle is $\frac{\sqrt{3}}{2}$ times the length of the hypotenuse or $\sqrt{3}$ times the length of the shorter side.

7-5 The perpendicular bisectors of the sides of a triangle intersect in a point O that is equidistant from the three vertices of the triangle.

7-6 The angle bisectors of the angles of a triangle are concurrent in a point I that is equidistant from the three sides of the triangle.

7-7 The lines that contain the altitudes of a triangle intersect in a point.

7-8 The medians of a triangle intersect in a point that is two thirds of the way from each vertex to the opposite side.

7-9 If the measures of two angles of a triangle are unequal, then the length of the side opposite the smaller angle is less than the length of the side opposite the larger angle.

7-10 If the lengths of two sides of a triangle are unequal, then the measure of the angle opposite the shorter side is less than the measure of the angle opposite the longer side.

Chapter 7—Review

1. Indicate whether the following problems are true or false.
   a. A triangle can have side lengths of 2 cm, 3 cm, and 5 cm.
   b. In $\triangle ABC$, $m\angle A = 120$, $m\angle B = 20$, and $m\angle C = 40$. The longest side is $\overline{BC}$.
   c. A rectangle with dimensions 10 cm by 24 cm has a 26 cm diagonal.
   d. If the longer leg of a 30°-60°-90° triangle has a length of $3\sqrt{3}$, then the hypotenuse has length of 6.

2. What is the longest side of the figure given the indicated angle measures? (Figure is not drawn to scale.)

(Ex. 2)

3. Find the length of a leg of an isosceles right triangle if the length of the hypotenuse is 4 cm.

4. If $\overline{AB} \cong \overline{BC} \cong \overline{CD} \cong \overline{AD}$, and $\overline{AC} \perp \overline{BD}$ with $BD = AB = 2$, find AC.

(Ex. 4)

5. Prove that the median $\overline{SQ}$ of isosceles triangle RST is also the perpendicular bisector of the base.

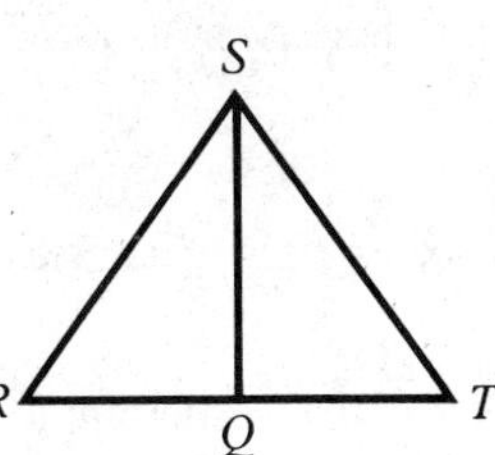

(Ex. 5)

6. Locate the point that is equal distance from points M, N, and O.

N

M

O

(Ex. 6)

7. If a 20 foot ladder is placed so that the foot of the ladder is 12 feet from a wall, how high above the ground will the ladder reach?

8. E and D are midpoints of $\overline{AC}$ and $\overline{AB}$. If $EP = 4$, find EB.

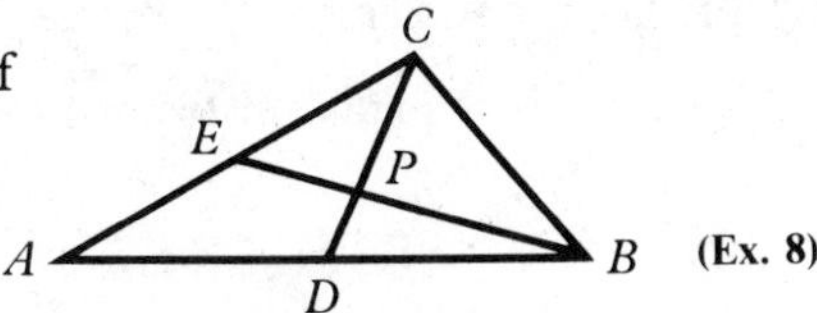

(Ex. 8)

9. **Given:** $\overline{YZ}$ is the longest side of quadrilateral $XYZW$. $\overline{XW}$ is the shortest side.
   Prove: $m\angle X > m\angle Z$

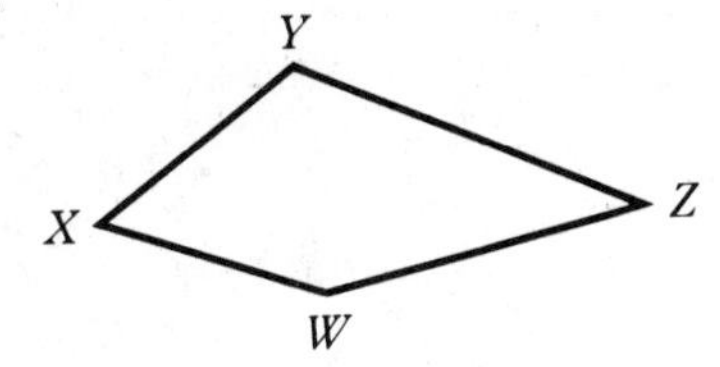

Chapter 7—Test

1. Indicate whether the following are true or false.
   a. A triangle can have side lengths of 6, 6, and 13.
   b. If a triangle has side lengths of 16, 30, and 44, then the triangle is a right triangle.
   c. If the vertex angle of an isosceles triangle is 30°, then the base of the triangle is the shortest side.
   d. If the longer leg of a 30°-60°-90° triangle has length 2, then the length of the hypotenuse is $\frac{2\sqrt{3}}{3}$.

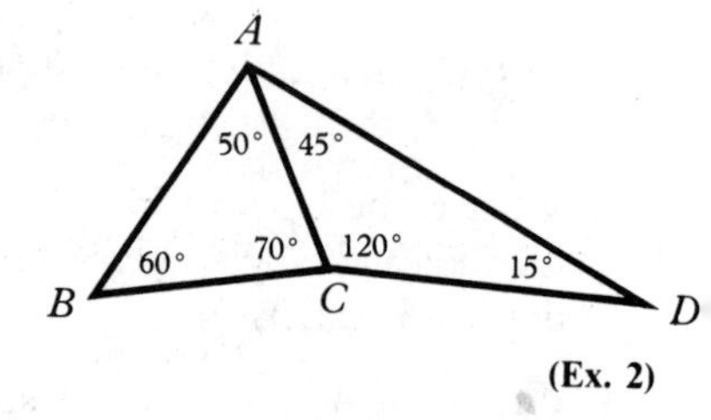

(Ex. 2)

2. What is the shortest side of the figure, given the indicated angle measures? (Figure is not drawn to scale.)

3. In the given figure, $\overline{CD}$ is perpendicular to $\overline{AB}$. If $AC = 4$, find AD and CD.

C, 4, 4, 60°, A, D, B (Ex. 3)

4. $\triangle ABC$ and $\triangle BCD$ are isosceles right triangles. If $AC = 2$, find BD.

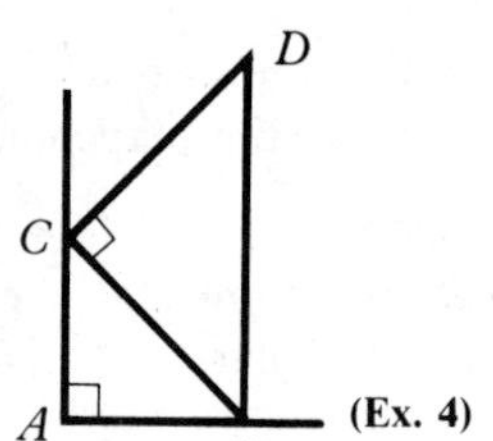

(Ex. 4)

5. Prove that the angle bisector of the vertex angle of an isosceles triangle is also a median.

6. $\overline{SW}$ and $\overline{RV}$ are medians of $\triangle RST$. $SL = 4$, $SW = 6$, and $RV = 9$. Find RL.

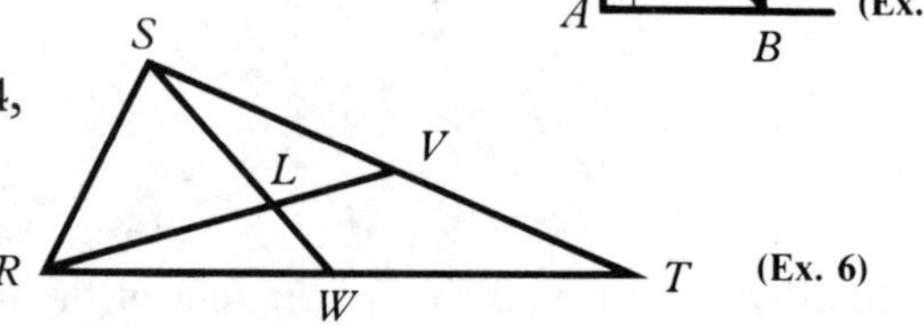

(Ex. 6)

7. If a brace for a wall is placed 80 cm from the wall and it touches the wall 150 cm from the floor, how long is the brace?

8. In $\triangle ABC$ locate the point that is equidistant from sides $\overline{AB}$, $\overline{BC}$, and $\overline{AC}$.

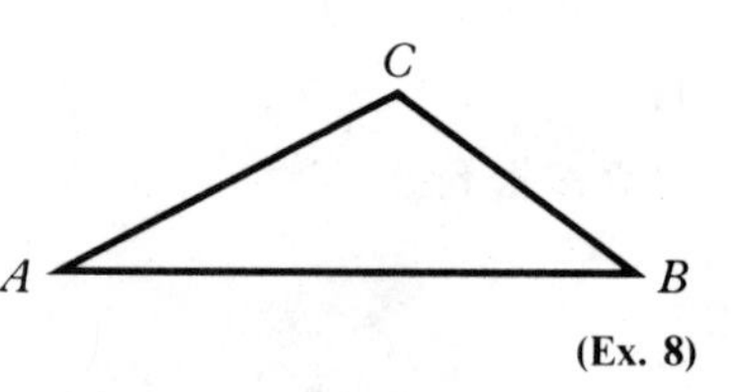

(Ex. 8)

9. **Given:** $DE = EF$, $DG = FG$
   $DE < DG$
   Prove: $m\angle G < m\angle E$

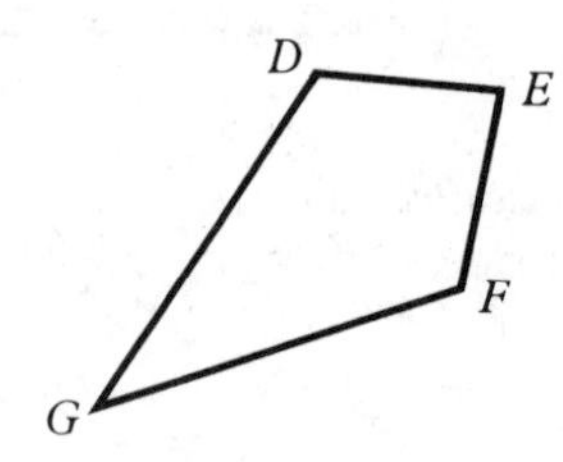

Cumulative Review—Chapters 4–7

1. Use the figure of a cube to identify the following:

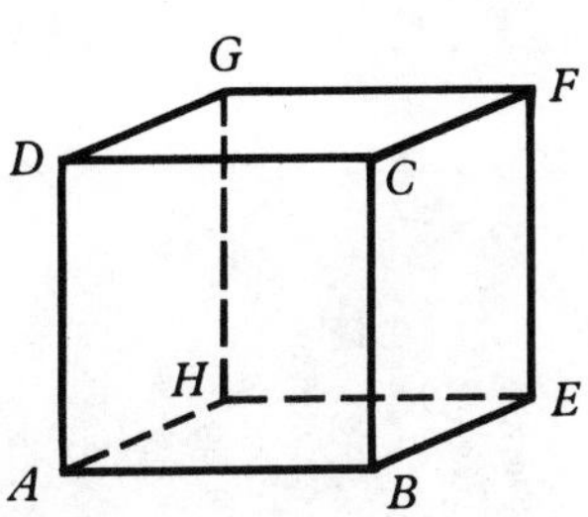

a. a line parallel to plane *ABEH*

b. a line skew to $\overleftrightarrow{DC}$

c. a plane perpendicular to $\overleftrightarrow{CB}$

d. a line parallel to $\overleftrightarrow{GC}$

e. a plane parallel to plane *CFEB*.

2. Assume line a is parallel to line b and line c is parallel to line d.

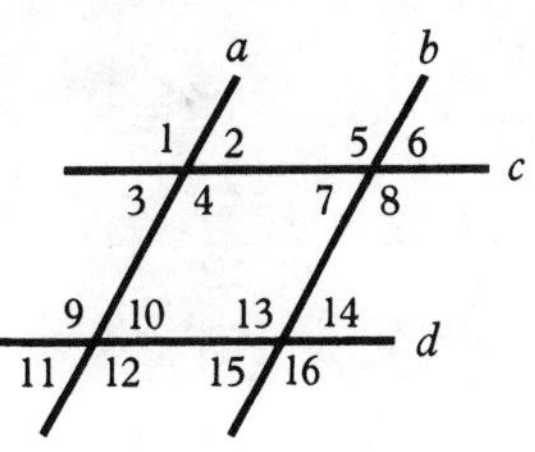

a. If $m\angle 1 = 105$, find $m\angle 14$.

b. If $m\angle 5 = 2x - 10$ and $m\angle 10 = x + 5$, find $m\angle 5$ and $m\angle 10$.

c. If $m\angle 12$ is 10 more than twice the measure of $\angle 11$, find $m\angle 12$ and $m\angle 11$.

3. Given: $\angle 1 \cong \angle 2$, $\angle 3 \cong \angle 4$
Prove: $\triangle ABC \cong \triangle AED$

4. Given: $\overline{DE} \cong \overline{BC}$, $\overline{AD} \cong \overline{AC}$
Prove: $\triangle BDA \cong \triangle ECA$

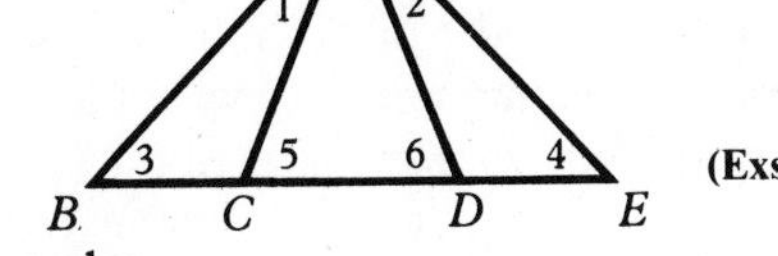

(Exs. 3, 4)

5. If $\angle ACB$ is the vertex angle of isosceles triangle ABC and $m\angle 2 = 70$, find $m\angle 5$.

6. If $\overline{AD} \parallel \overline{BC}$, $m\angle 3 = 45$, $m\angle 1 = 65$, find $m\angle 2$.

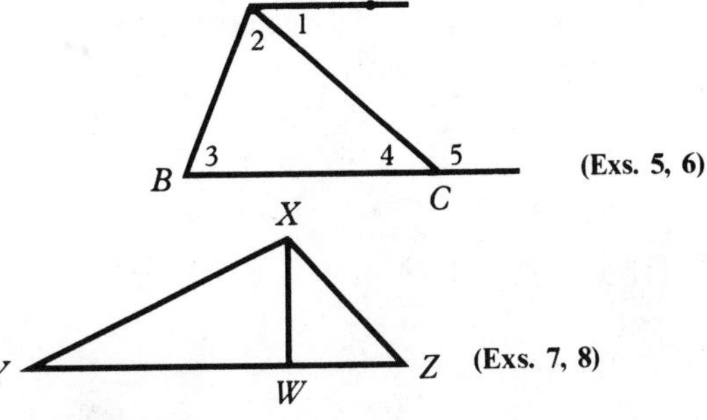

(Exs. 5, 6)

7. If $\overline{XW}$ is perpendicular to $\overline{YZ}$, $m\angle Y = 30$, $m\angle Z = 45$, and $XW = 3$, find the lengths of $\overline{XY}$, $\overline{YW}$, and $\overline{XZ}$.

8. If $\overline{XZ}$ is an altitude to $\overline{XY}$, $XY = 12$, and $XZ = 5$, find YZ.

(Exs. 7, 8)

9. If two shorter sides of a triangle have lengths of 5 cm and 3 cm, is it possible for the longest side to have a length of 7 cm? Why?

10. Given: Quadrilateral *ABCD*

Find: a. $m\angle ADB$

b. $m\angle BDC$

c. $m\angle ADC$

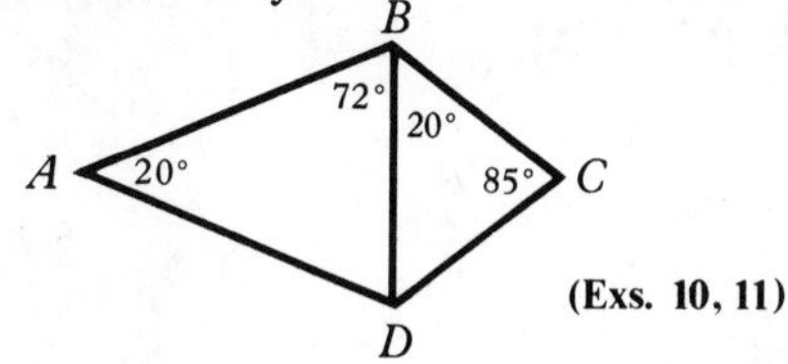

(Exs. 10, 11)

11. List the sides of quadrilateral *ABCD* from shortest side to longest side.

Computer Graphics: Computer Aided Design

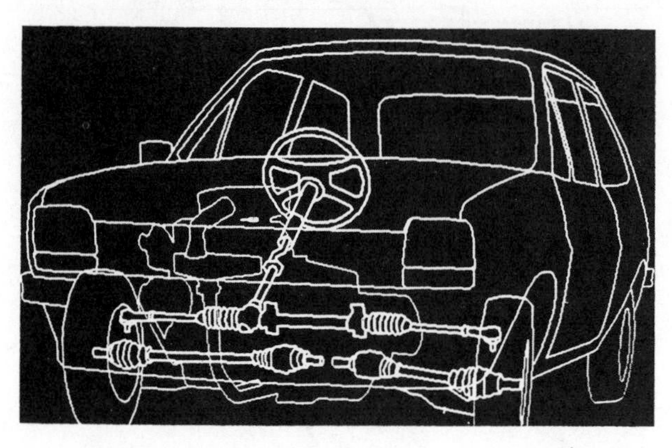

Computer graphics has revolutionized the job of an industrial designer. The designer must be able to imagine and analyze complex shapes composed of geometric figures. With computer-aided-design (CAD) the designer uses the computer to draw the designs.

The photograph shows an automobile design generated by a computer. The computer can display this design in an unlimited number of positions. The view from the top, bottom, side, front, or back can be displayed on the screen.

The photographs below show designers at computer terminals. The designer on the right is using an electronic pen to alter the dimensions of a section template. By touching the screen with the pen, he is communicating with the computer.

The designer on the left is working with a cross-section of a 3-dimensional model. The table in front of him is used to give the computer commands. By placing the electronic pen on different squares, he can add or delete portions of the drawing. He can ask for an enlargement of part of the drawing. The computer library includes drawings for standard parts, such as bearings and gears. These parts can be added to the design.

Computer graphics has recently been more available to students through the use of microcomputers. On one popular microcomputer model the screen is divided into 280 (invisible) rows and 160 (invisible) columns. For example, the small space that lies in the fortieth row and twentieth column is the point named (40, 20). By lighting a large set of points, lines appear on the screen. For example, the following program displays a rectangle on the screen whose corners are the points (40, 20), (220, 20), (220, 120), and (40, 120).

The program, or list of instructions to the computer, is shown below. Line 10 tells the computer to prepare to receive instructions about graphics (HGR). In line 20, HPLOT is an instruction to draw a line on the screen from the point at (40, 20) to the point at (220, 20). Check the other instructions to see how the rectangle was drawn.

```
10  HGR
20  HPLOT 40, 20 TO 220, 20
30  HPLOT 40, 20 TO 40, 120
40  HPLOT 40, 120 TO 220, 120
50  HPLOT 220, 20 TO 220, 120
60  END
```

1. Write the HPLOT commands that will form a square on the computer screen.
2. Write four HPLOT commands that will form a rectangle twice as high as wide.
3. Create a figure that consists of line segments. Then write HPLOT commands that will put your figure on the TV screen.

CHAPTER 8

Quadrilaterals and Polygons

8–1 Quadrilaterals

REVIEW: A **quadrilateral** is the union of four segments determined by four points, no three of which are collinear. The segments intersect only at the endpoints.

Our world is full of examples of four-sided figures of all shapes and sizes. We can classify them in terms of sides, angles, and relationships between sides and angles.

In this chapter we shall study these classifications and learn some properties of quadrilaterals.

The figures below illustrate some important terms for quadrilaterals.

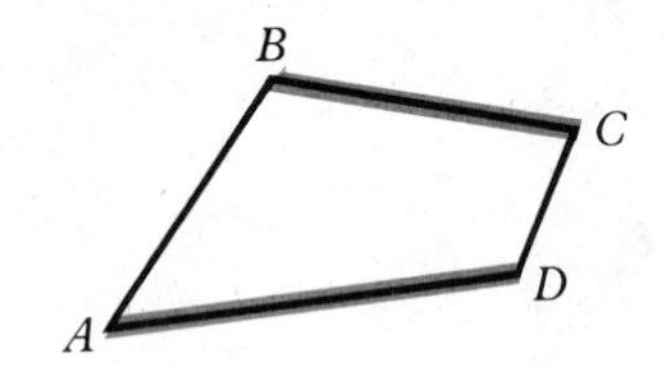

Sides $\overline{BC}$ and $\overline{AD}$ have no vertex in common. They are a pair of *opposite sides.* Sides $\overline{AB}$ and $\overline{DC}$ are also opposite sides.

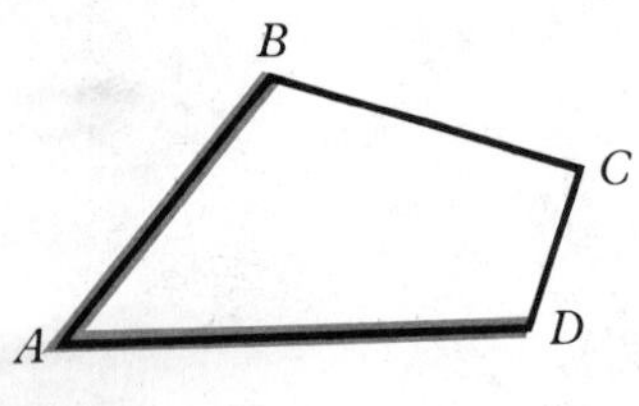

Sides $\overline{AB}$ and $\overline{AD}$ have a vertex in common. They are a pair of *adjacent sides.* Other pairs of adjacent sides are $\overline{AB}$ and $\overline{BC}$, $\overline{BC}$ and $\overline{CD}$, and $\overline{AD}$ and $\overline{DC}$.

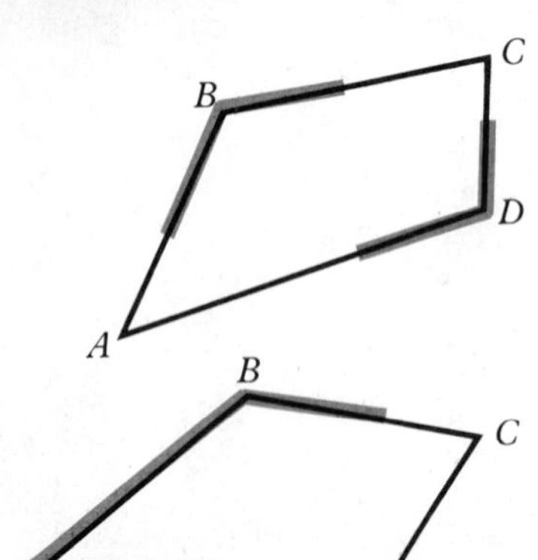

Angles B and D have no side in common. They are a pair of *opposite angles.* Angles A and C are also opposite angles.

Angles A and B have side $\overline{AB}$ in common. They are a pair of *adjacent angles.* Other pairs of adjacent angles are $\angle B$ and $\angle C$, $\angle C$ and $\angle D$, and $\angle D$ and $\angle A$.

We now describe the basic types of quadrilaterals.

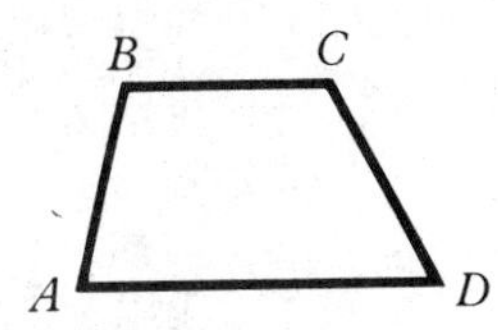

One pair of opposite sides are parallel.

ABCD is a *trapezoid.* $\overline{BC}$ and $\overline{AD}$ are *bases* of the trapezoid.

Definition 8–1

A **trapezoid** is a quadrilateral with exactly one pair of parallel sides.

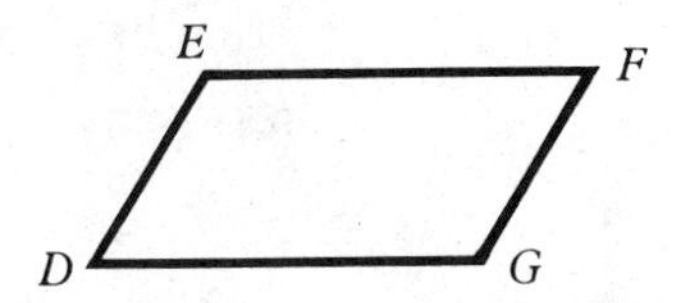

Both pairs of opposite sides are parallel.

EDGF is a *parallelogram.*

Definition 8–2

A **parallelogram** is a quadrilateral with both pairs of opposite sides parallel.

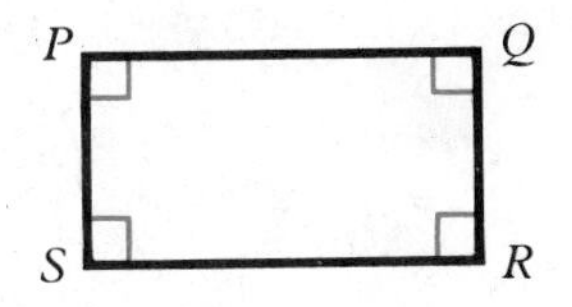

All four angles are right angles.

PQRS is a *rectangle* (and also a parallelogram).

Definition 8–3

A **rectangle** is a parallelogram with four right angles.

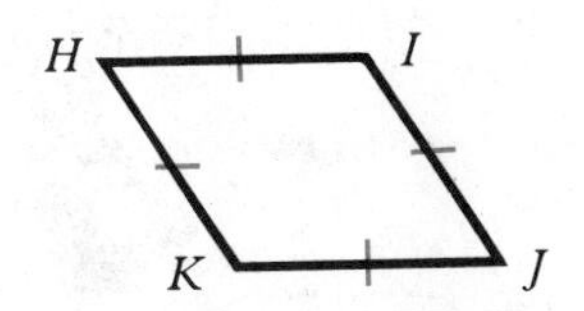

All four sides are congruent.

HIJK is a *rhombus* (and also a parallelogram).

Definition 8–4

A **rhombus** is a parallelogram with four congruent sides.

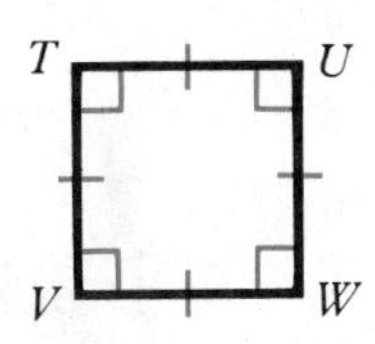

All four angles are right angles. All four sides are congruent.

TUWV is a *square* (and also a rectangle, a rhombus, and a parallelogram).

Definition 8–5

A **square** is a rectangle with four congruent sides.

EXERCISES

A.

For exercises 1-4 refer to quadrilateral $ABCD$.

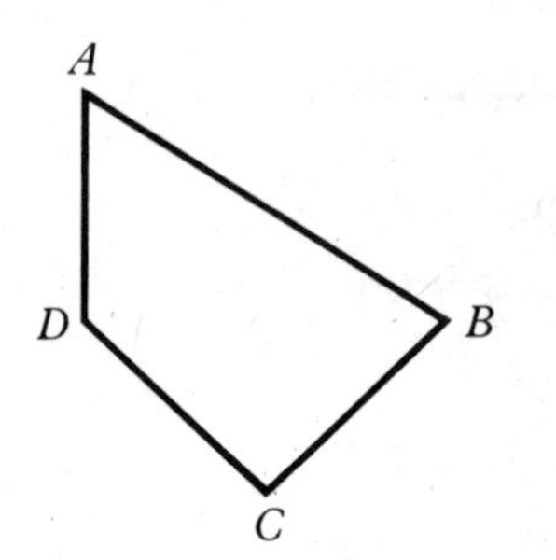

(Exs. 1-4)

1. Name the side opposite $\overline{AB}$.
2. Name the angles adjacent to $\angle C$.
3. Name the sides adjacent to $\overline{BC}$.
4. Name the angle opposite $\angle D$.

Answer true or false for exercises 5-12.

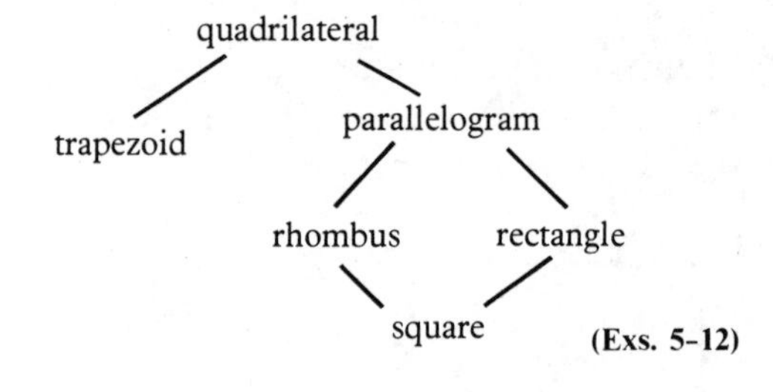

(Exs. 5-12)

5. A square is a rectangle.
6. A rectangle is a parallelogram.
7. A parallelogram is a rhombus.
8. A trapezoid is a parallelogram.
9. Some parallelograms are rectangles.
10. A rhombus is a square.
11. Some rhombuses are rectangles.
12. A parallelogram is a trapezoid.

B.

13. Construct a parallelogram with a 30° angle.
14. Construct a rhombus with a 60° angle.
15. Construct a trapezoid with two right angles.
16. Construct a rectangle with its width one half its length.

Activity

1. Trace this regular 12-gon and the parallelogram with sides $\overline{AL}$ and $\overline{LK}$.
2. Draw a parallelogram with sides $\overline{KJ}$ and $\overline{KX}$. Draw another with sides $\overline{AX}$ and $\overline{AB}$.
3. Guess how many parallelograms result if this process continues until the 12-gon has been divided into parallelograms.
4. Complete your construction to check your guess.

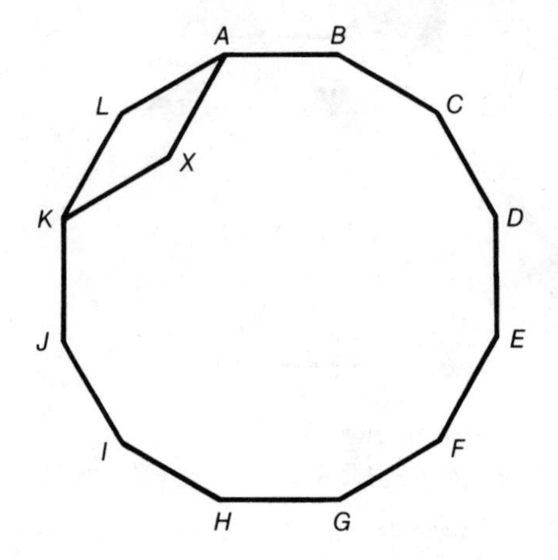

17. Construct a trapezoid with a pair of 45° base angles.

Draw and name the quadrilateral described in each of exercises 18–20.

18. The quadrilateral has two pairs of parallel sides, no right angles, and no pair of adjacent sides congruent.

19. The quadrilateral has at least one pair of congruent adjacent sides, at least one pair of congruent opposite sides, and no right angles.

20. The quadrilateral has at least one pair of parallel sides, no congruent adjacent sides, and exactly one pair of congruent opposite sides.

C.

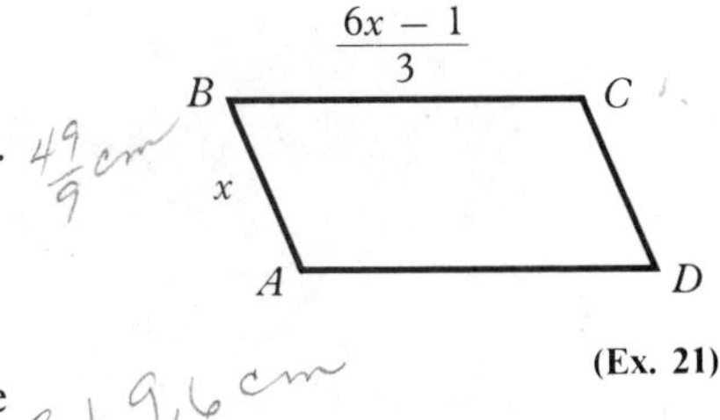

(Ex. 21)

21. The perimeter (distance around) the parallelogram is 32 cm. What is the length of each side (to the nearest millimeter)?

22. The longer base of a trapezoid is the square of the shorter base. The nonparallel sides are congruent. The nonparallel side is 3 more than the shorter base. If the perimeter of the trapezoid is 24 cm, what are the lengths of the sides?

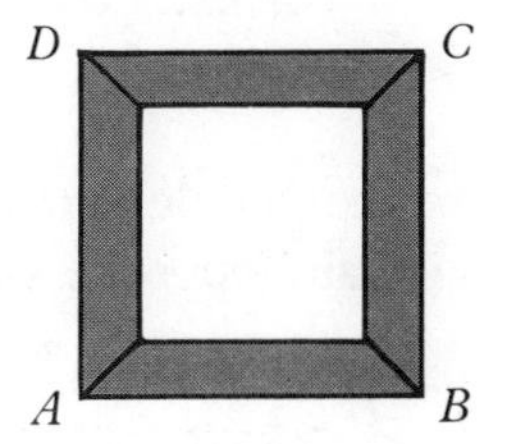

23. Suppose you try to make a square picture frame. You cut four pieces of wood and glue them together so that $AB = BC = CD = AD$. Which of the following statements are known to be true using definitions only?

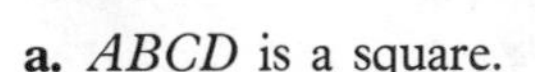

a. *ABCD* is a square. **b.** *ABCD* is a rectangle.
c. *ABCD* is a rhombus. **d.** *ABCD* is a parallelogram.

PROBLEM SOLVING

Shown below is a quadrilateral formed by an array of five lines.

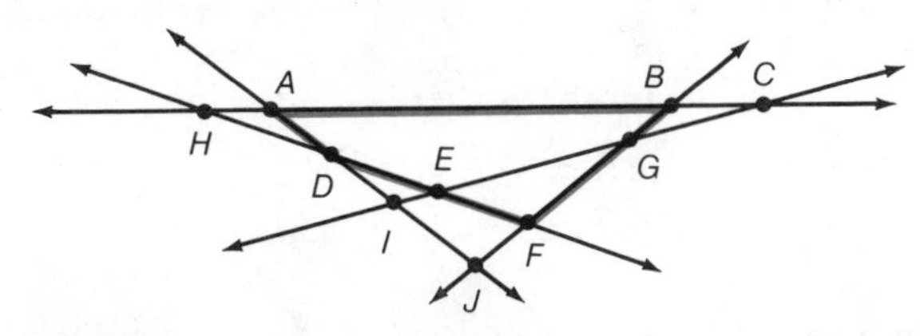

These three quadrilaterals can also be found. Name them.

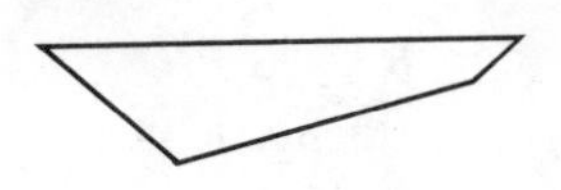  

There are at least six more quadrilaterals in the array. Trace and name them.

8–2 Parallelograms

The parallelograms shown in the design have special side and angle relationships.

In the parallelograms below the measures of some pairs of opposite angles and opposite sides are given.

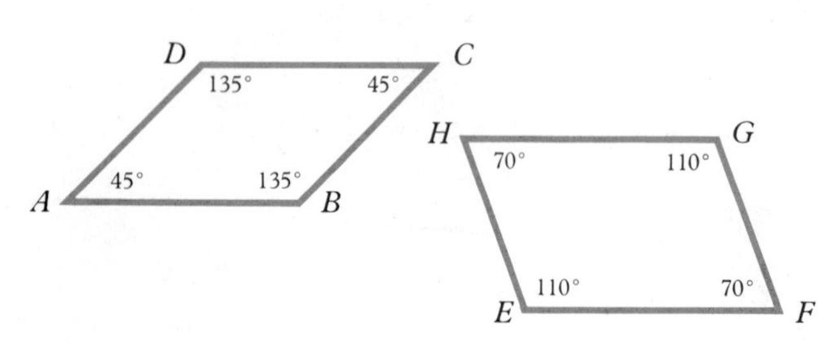

Observe that

$\angle A \cong \angle C$, $\angle B \cong \angle D$,
$\angle E \cong \angle G$, $\angle F \cong \angle H$.

Observe that

$\overline{AB} \cong \overline{CD}$, $\overline{AD} \cong \overline{BC}$
$\overline{EF} \cong \overline{GH}$, $\overline{EH} \cong \overline{FG}$.

These observations suggest two basic properties of parallelograms.

Theorem 8–1 The opposite angles of a parallelogram are congruent.

Theorem 8–2 The opposite sides of a parallelogram are congruent.

PROOF

Given: $ABCD$ is a parallelogram.
Prove: $\angle A \cong \angle C$, $\angle B \cong \angle D$
$\overline{AB} \cong \overline{CD}$, $\overline{AD} \cong \overline{BC}$

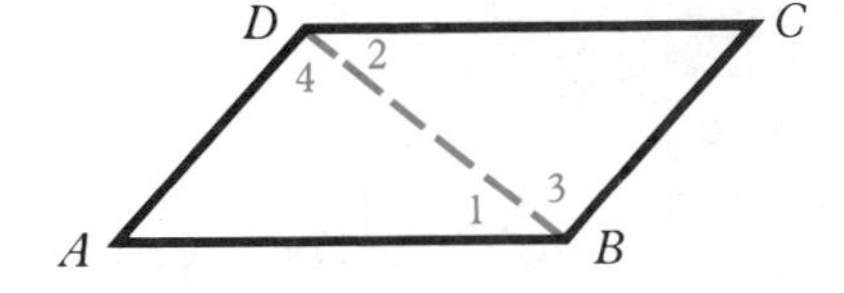

Plan: Draw diagonal $\overline{BD}$ and prove $\triangle ABD \cong \triangle CDB$.

Statements	Reasons
1. $ABCD$ is a parallelogram.	**1.** Given
2. $\overline{AB} \parallel \overline{CD}$	**2.** Definition of parallelogram
3. $\overline{BC} \parallel \overline{AD}$	**3.** Why?
4. $\angle 1 \cong \angle 2$	**4.** If two parallel lines are cut by a transversal, then alternate interior angles are congruent.
5. $\angle 3 \cong \angle 4$	**5.** Why?
6. $\overline{BD} = \overline{BD}$	**6.** Why?
7. $\triangle ABD \cong \triangle CDB$	**7.** Why?
8. $\overline{AB} \cong \overline{CD}$	**8.** CPCTC
9. $\angle A \cong \angle C$	**9.** CPCTC

By repeating this proof using the diagonal $\overline{AC}$ we can prove that $\overline{AD} \cong \overline{BC}$ and $\angle B \cong \angle D$.

APPLICATION

Any production process must include a check on the quality of the item produced. In the production of pattern blocks the check might involve measuring opposite angles of the quadrilateral. The contrapositive of Theorem 8–1 says that if opposite angles are not congruent, then the block cannot be a parallelogram and should be discarded.

Another important theorem that will be proved as an exercise is stated next.

> **Theorem 8–3** Each pair of adjacent angles of a parallelogram are supplementary angles.

EXERCISES

A.

In exercises 1–3, assume $ABCD$ is a parallelogram.

1. Name two pairs of congruent segments.
2. Name two pairs of congruent angles.
3. Name four pairs of supplementary angles.

(Exs. 1-3)

In exercises 4–11, assume $ABCD$ is a parallelogram.

4. $m\angle C = \underline{?}$
5. $m\angle ABC = \underline{?}$
6. $m\angle ABD = \underline{?}$
7. $m\angle ADB = \underline{?}$
8. $m\angle DBC = \underline{?}$
9. $m\angle ADC = \underline{?}$
10. $AD = \underline{?}$
11. $CD = \underline{?}$

(Exs. 4-11)

In exercises 12–15, assume $ABCD$ is a parallelogram.

12. $m\angle ABC = \underline{?}$
13. $m\angle DOC = \underline{?}$
14. $m\angle ADC = \underline{?}$
15. $m\angle BOC = \underline{?}$
16. Write Theorem 8–1 in if-then form, and then state its contrapositive.
17. Write Theorem 8–2 in if-then form, and then state its contrapositive.

(Exs. 12-15)

Use the contrapositives in exercises 16 and 17 to determine which of the figures in exercises 18–23 *cannot* be parallelograms.

18.

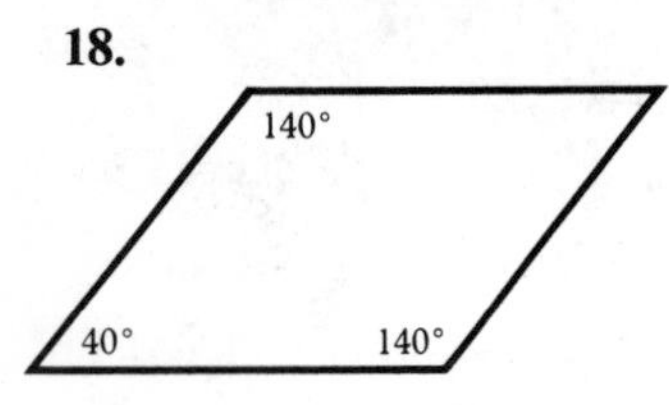

19.

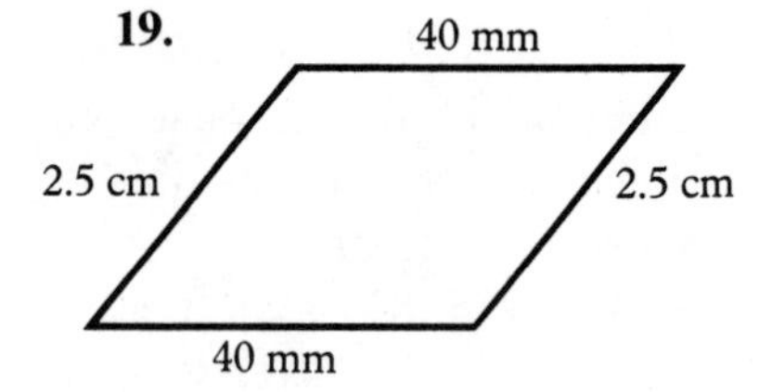

20.

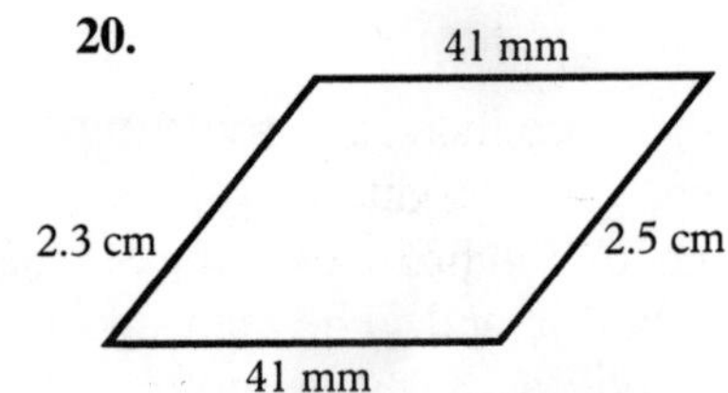

21.

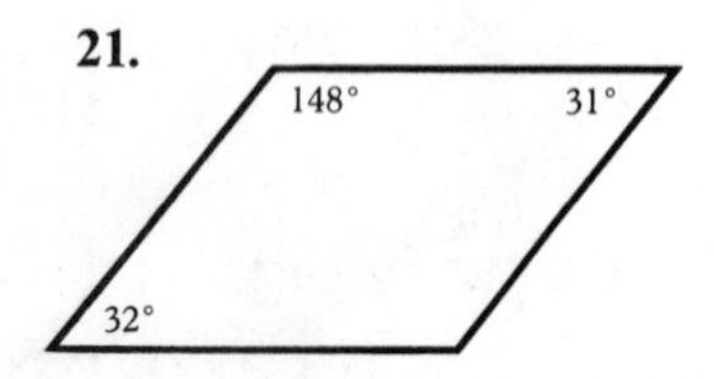

22.

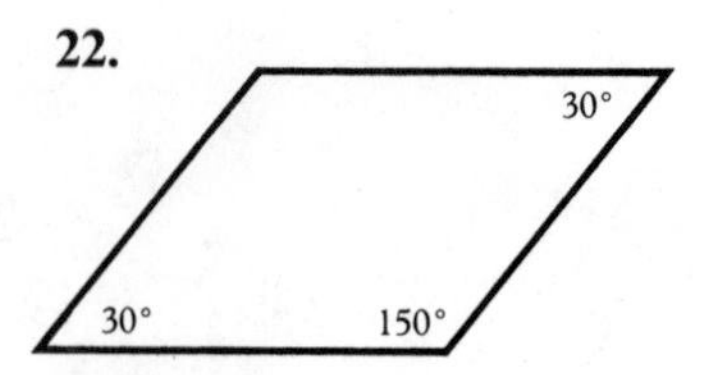

23.

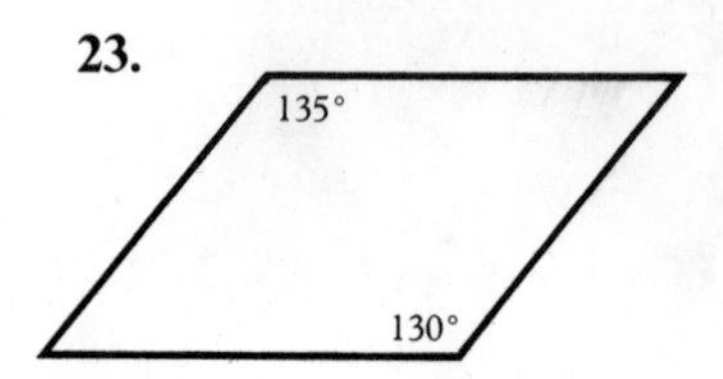

For exercises 24–26, find the measures of all angles of the parallelogram.

24.

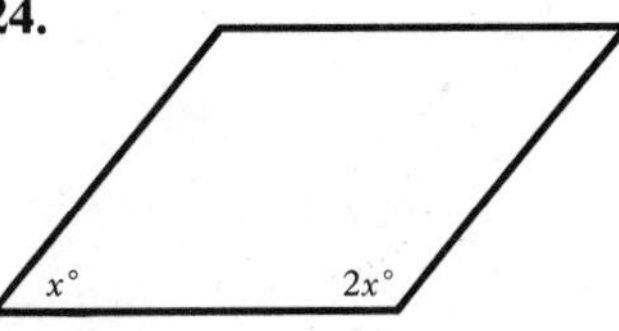

25.

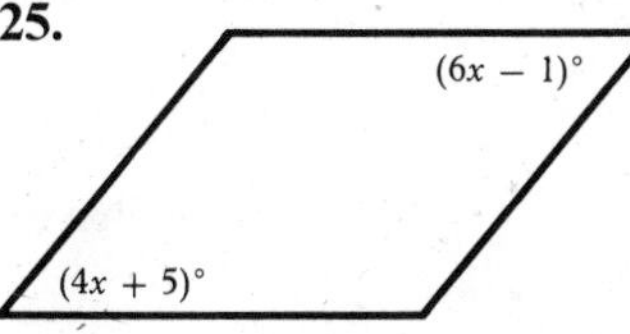

26.

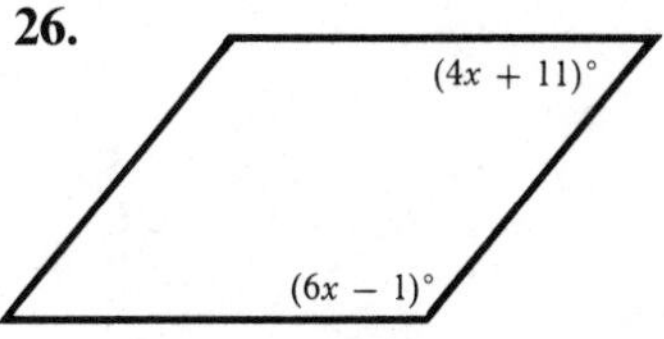

27. *ABCD* is a parallelogram. If $AB = x + 5$ and $CD = 2x - 7$, find the length of $\overline{AB}$.

28. *ABCD* is a parallelogram. If $AB = 2x$, $CD = 3y + 4$, $BC = x + 7$, and $AD = 2y$, find the lengths of the sides of the parallelogram.

D C A B

(Exs. 27, 28)

29. Part of the structural support system for a bridge is shown. $\overline{AB} \parallel \overline{CD}$, $\overline{DF} \parallel \overline{CB}$, and $\overline{AD} \parallel \overline{EC}$. Find $m\angle CGF$.

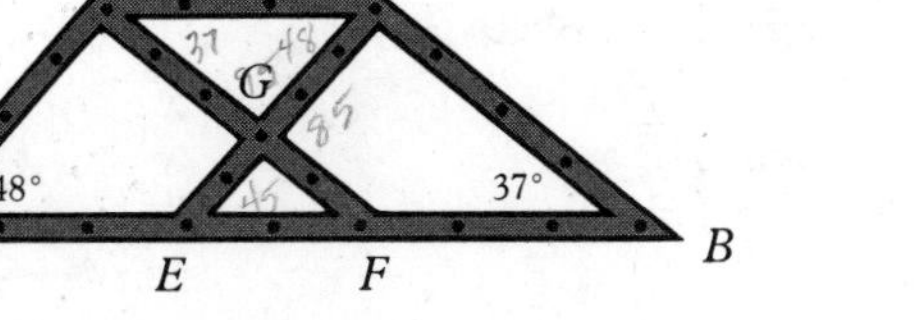

30. Given: *ABCD* is a parallelogram.
AECF is a parallelogram.
Prove: $\triangle CDF \cong \triangle ABE$

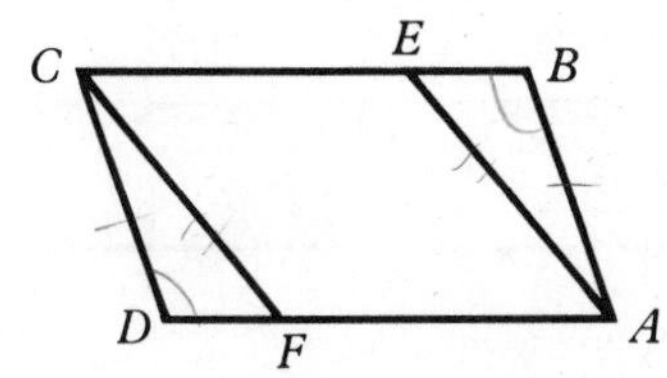

31. Given: *ABCD* is a parallelogram.
$\overline{FG}$ bisects $\overline{DB}$.
Prove: $\overline{DB}$ bisects $\overline{FG}$.

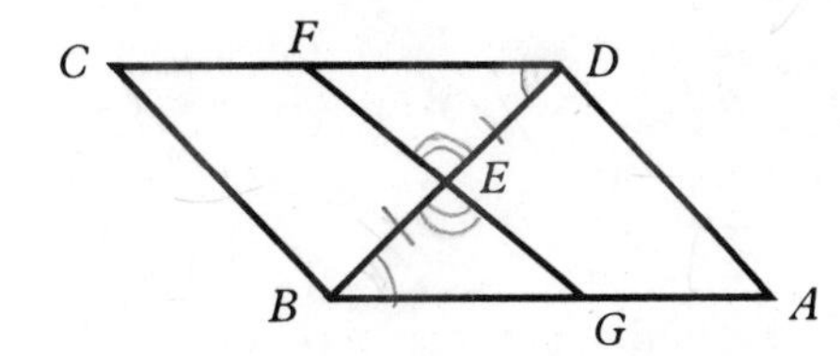

32. Given: *ABCD* is a parallelogram.
A, F, E, and *C* are collinear.
$\overline{AF} \cong \overline{CE}$
Prove: $\overline{DE} \parallel \overline{BF}$

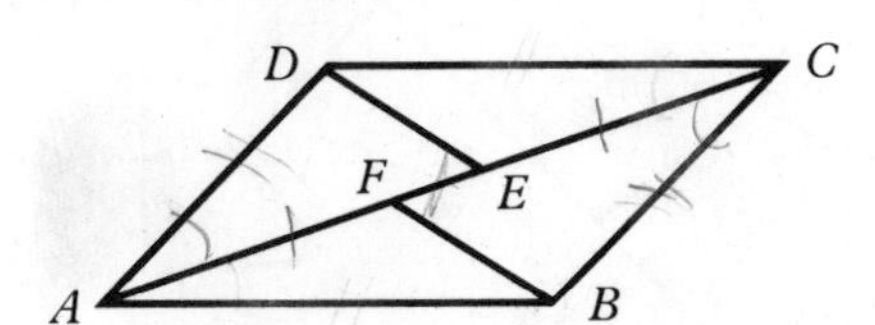

33. Given: *ABCD* is a parallelogram.
$\overline{AE} \cong \overline{CF}$
Prove: $\overline{CE} \cong \overline{AF}$

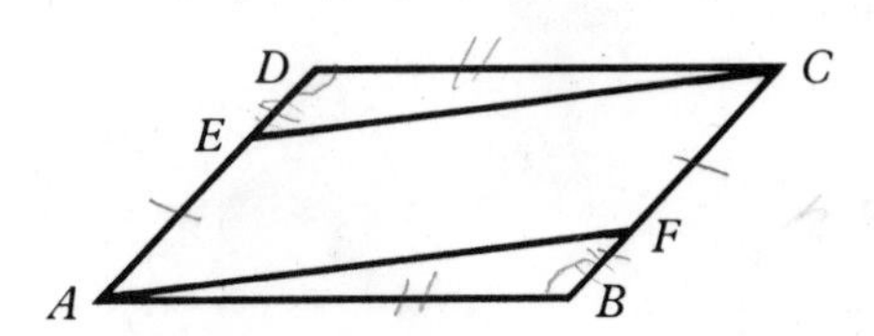

34. Prove that the diagonals of a parallelogram bisect each other.

C.

35. Prove that a parallelogram with one right angle is a rectangle.

36. Given: $ABCD$ is a parallelogram.
$\overrightarrow{AE}$ bisects $\angle A$.
$\overrightarrow{DE}$ bisects $\angle D$.
Prove: $\overline{AE} \perp \overline{DE}$

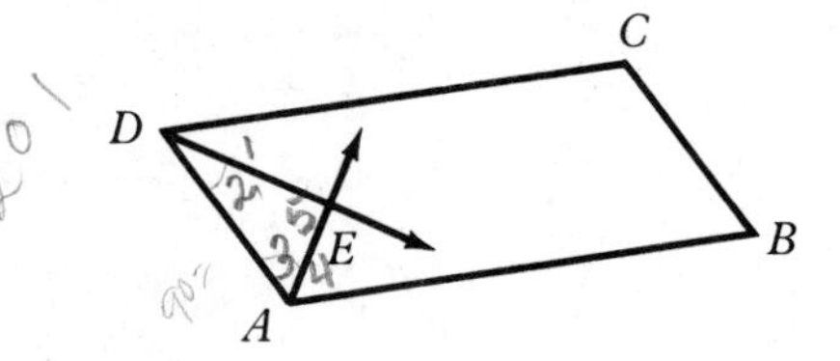

37. Given: $ABCD$ is a parallelogram.
$\overline{DE} \perp \overline{AB}$
$\overline{CF} \perp \overleftrightarrow{AB}$
Prove: $\triangle ADE \cong \triangle BCF$ and $CDEF$ is a rectangle.

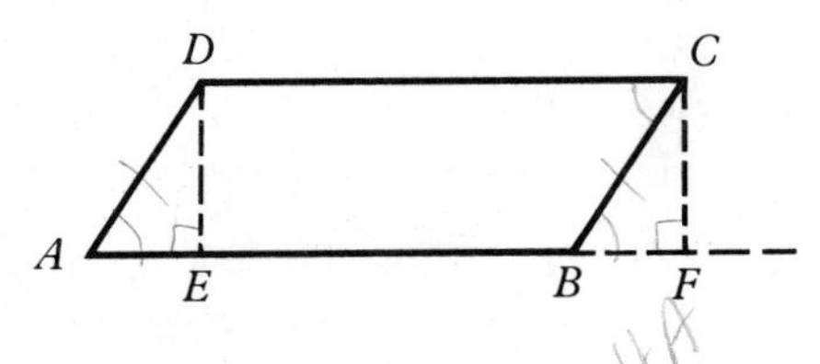

38. Given: $ABCD$ is a parallelogram.
$\overline{AE}$ bisects $\angle A$.
$\overline{CF}$ bisects $\angle C$.
Prove: $\overline{AE} \cong \overline{CF}$

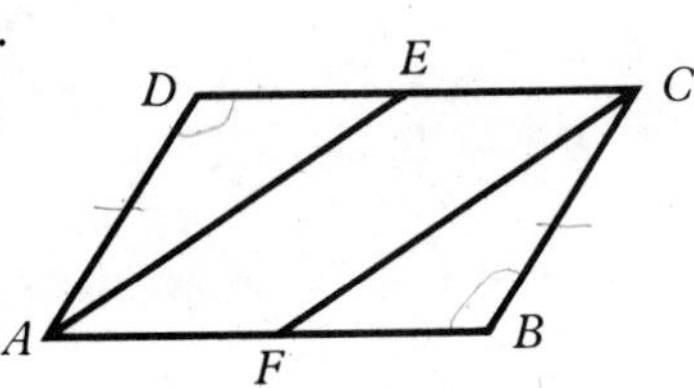

39. Prove Theorem 8–3.

Activity

Trace this tangram puzzle and cut out the pieces.

Use the five small pieces to form a square. Can you place the two large pieces around the square to form:

1. a triangle? **2.** a parallelogram?

3. a trapezoid? **4.** a rectangle?

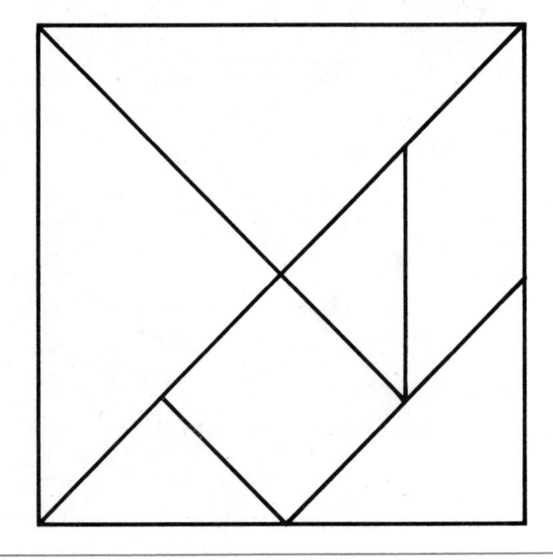

In the figure a regular 12-gon has been divided into parallelograms. Use the definition of regular polygon and the theorems from this section to answer exercises 40–48. Also accept as given for exercises 40–48 that $m\angle ALK = 150$.

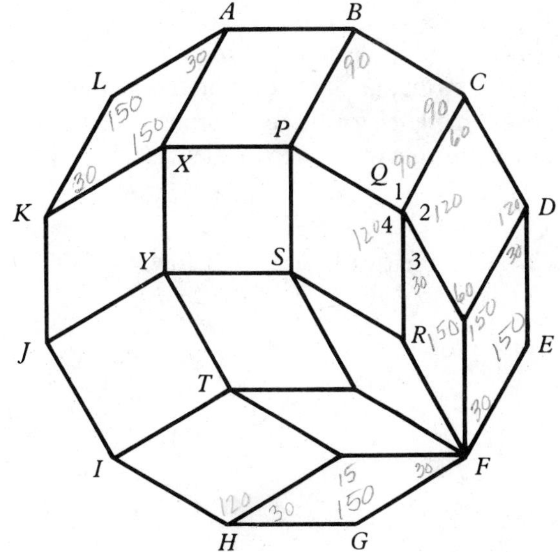

40. $m\angle BPX = \underline{?}$

41. $m\angle 1 = \underline{?}$

42. $m\angle 2 = \underline{?}$

43. $m\angle 3 = \underline{?}$

44. $m\angle 4 = \underline{?}$

45. Prove that $\overline{AB} \cong \overline{XY}$.

46. Prove that three of the polygons in the figure are squares.

47. Prove that $PQRS$ is a rhombus.

48. Select any parallelogram in the figure. Prove that it is a rhombus.

PROBLEM SOLVING

Fact: When two parallel planes in space are cut by a third plane, the intersecting lines are parallel lines. This fact can be used to solve the following problems.

The region common to a cube solid and a plane is called a *cross section* of a cube solid.

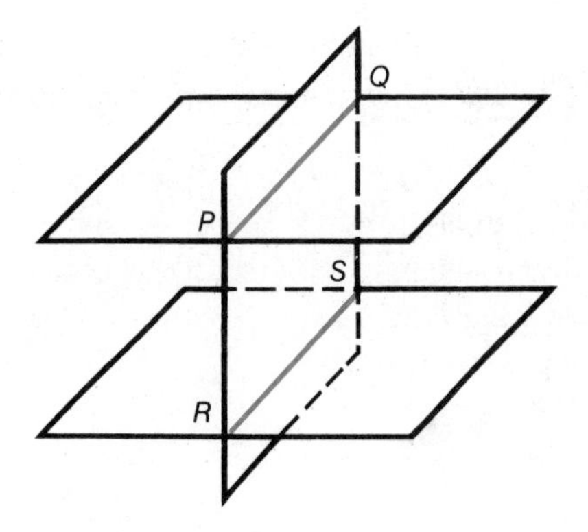

1. Why does *each* quadrilateral cross section of a cube solid have at least one pair of parallel edges?

2. Why does *each* pentagonal cross section of a cube solid have two pairs of parallel edges?

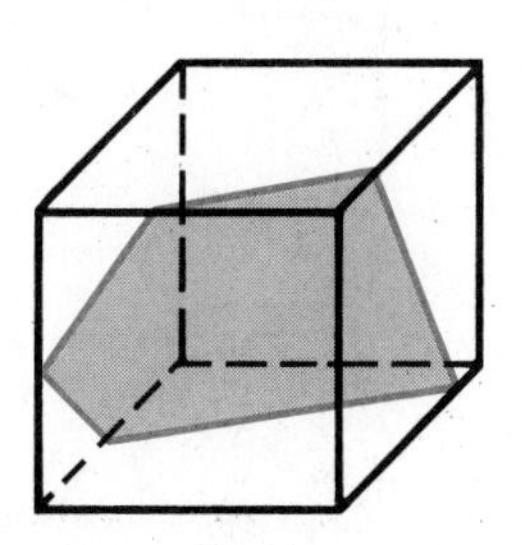

8–3 Quadrilaterals That Are Parallelograms

When two children are swinging on a two-person swing, are the seats of the swing always parallel to the top frame? The theorem in this lesson will give the answer.

Consider the quadrilaterals below.

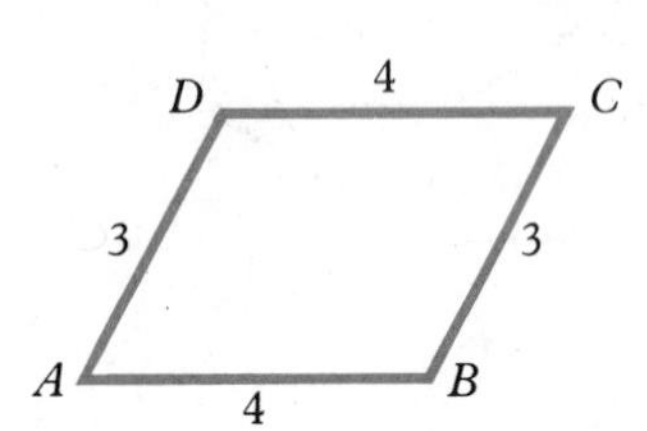

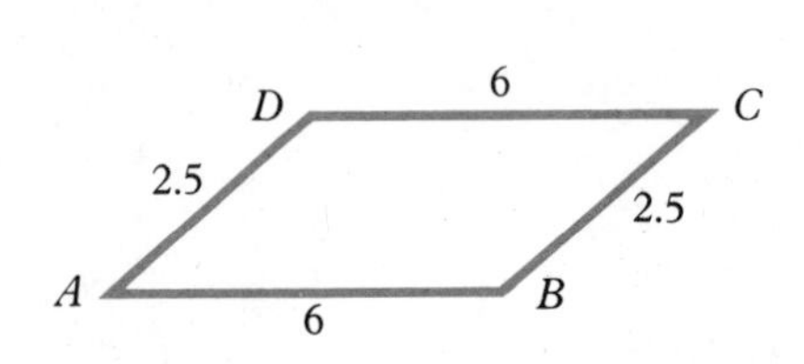

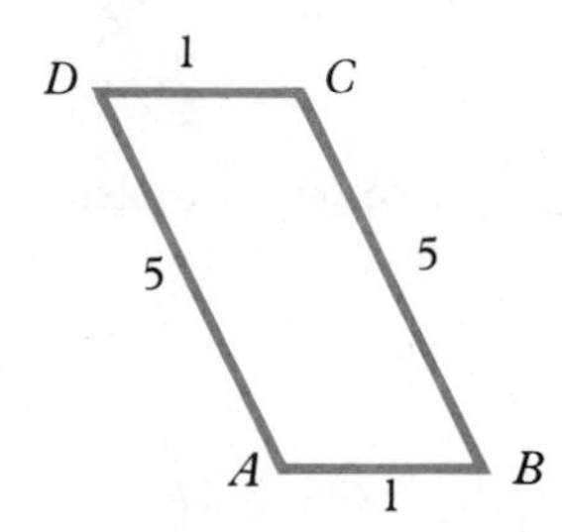

In each case, is $ABCD$ a parallelogram?

Theorem 8–4 If opposite sides of a quadrilateral are congruent, then the quadrilateral is a parallelogram.

PROOF

Given: Quadrilateral $ABCD$ with $\overline{AD} \cong \overline{BC}$ and $\overline{AB} \cong \overline{CD}$

Prove: $ABCD$ is a parallelogram.

Plan: Draw auxiliary segment $\overline{AC}$ and prove $\triangle ABC \cong \triangle CDA$.

Statements	Reasons
1. $\overline{AB} \cong \overline{CD}$	**1.** Given
2. $\overline{BC} \cong \overline{DA}$	**2.** Given
3. $\overline{AC} \cong \overline{AC}$	**3.** Reflexive Property
4. $\triangle ABC \cong \triangle CDA$	**4.** SSS Postulate
5. $\angle 1 \cong \angle 2$	**5.** Why?
6. $\overline{AB} \parallel \overline{CD}$	**6.** Why?
7. $\angle 3 \cong \angle 4$	**7.** CPCTC
8. $\overline{AD} \parallel \overline{BC}$	**8.** Why?
9. *ABCD* is a parallogram.	**9.** Definition of parallelogram

APPLICATION

The answer to the question posed at the beginning of the lesson is yes. The seats are always parallel to the top frame segment *AB*. There are four metal poles bolted together at points *A*, *B*, *C*, and *D* so that $\overline{AB}$ and $\overline{CD}$, and $\overline{AD}$ and $\overline{BC}$ are the same length. Theorem 8-4 tells us that as the swing moves, *ABCD* is always a parallelogram and $\overline{CD}$ is parallel to $\overline{AB}$.

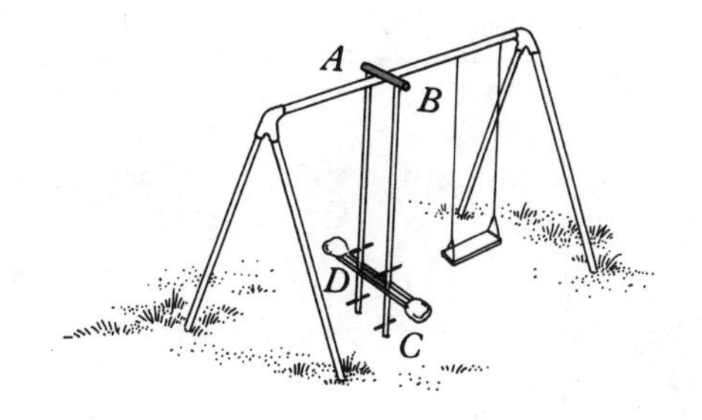

The next two theorems give other methods for proving that a quadrilateral is a parallelogram.

Theorem 8–5 If a quadrilateral has one pair of opposite sides parallel and congruent, then it is a parallelogram.

Theorem 8–6 If the opposite angles of a quadrilateral are congruent, then the quadrilateral is a parallelogram.

EXERCISES

A.

Use the theorems of this section to decide whether each quadrilateral is a parallelogram. Base your decision on the given measurements rather than the shape of the drawings.

1.

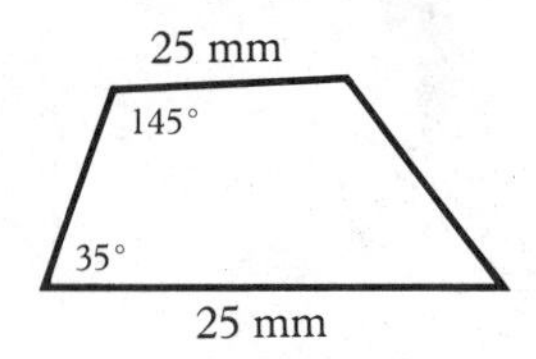

2.

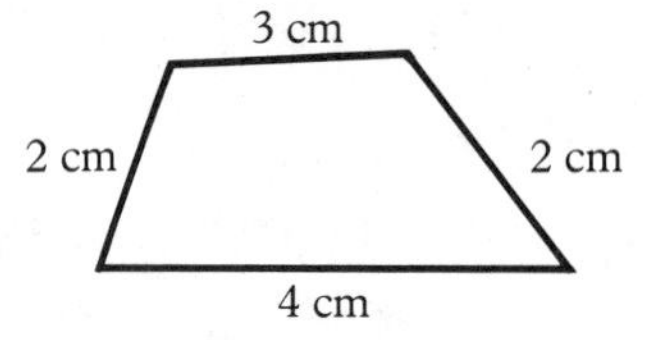

3.

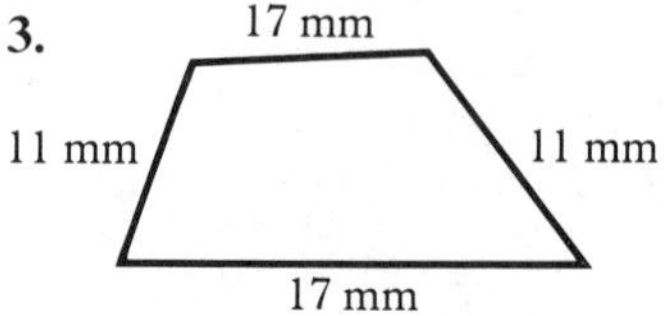

4.

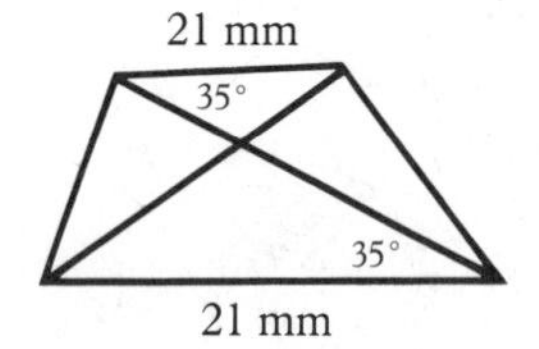

5.

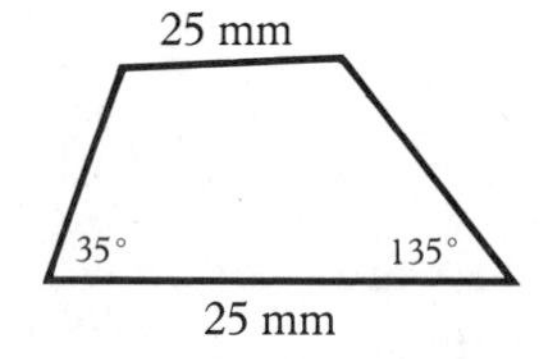

6.

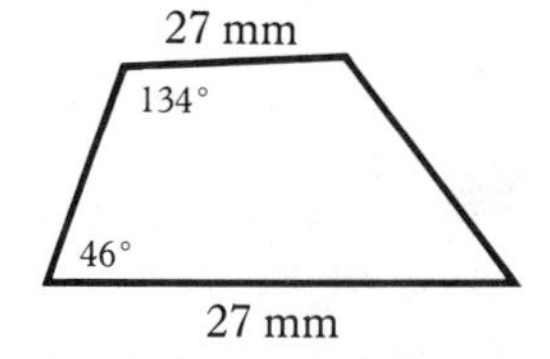

In exercises 7–9, find the value of x that makes the quadrilateral a parallelogram.

7.

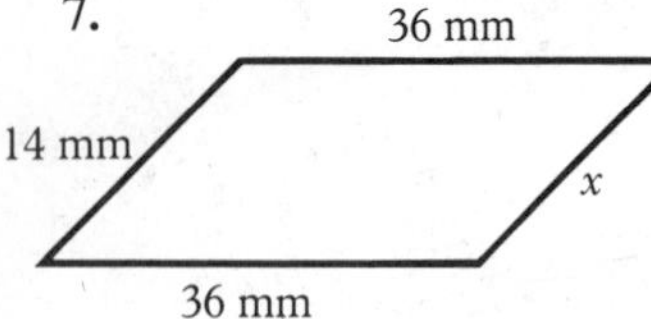

8.

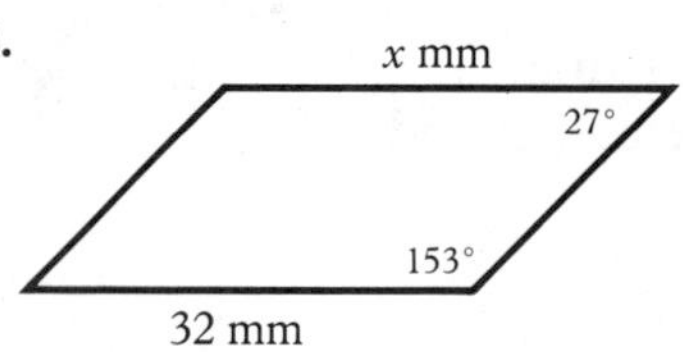

9.

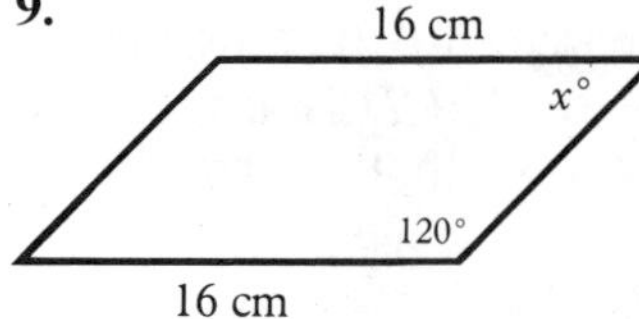

B.

In exercises 10–12, find values of x and y that make $ABCD$ a parallelogram.

10. $AB = 2x + 4$, $CD = 4x - 20$, $AD = 2y$, $BC = y + 5$

11. $m\angle A = 2x - 60$, $m\angle D = x - 5$, $AB = 4y + 6$, $CD = 6y - 10$

12. $AB = 6x + 30$, $BC = 2x - 5$, $CD = 2y - 10$, $AD = y - 35$

(Exs. 10–12)

13. A parking lot is to be marked for slant parking. A string is stretched from A to B with marks made every 9 feet at X_1, $X_2, \ldots, X_6$. A second string is stretched parallel to $\overline{AB}$ from C to D with marks located every 9 feet at Y_1, $Y_2, \ldots, Y_6$. Why are all painted lines parallel?

14. Complete the proof of Theorem 8-5.

15. Given: *ABCD* is a parallelogram.
BCEF is a parallelogram.
Prove: *ADEF* is a parallelogram.

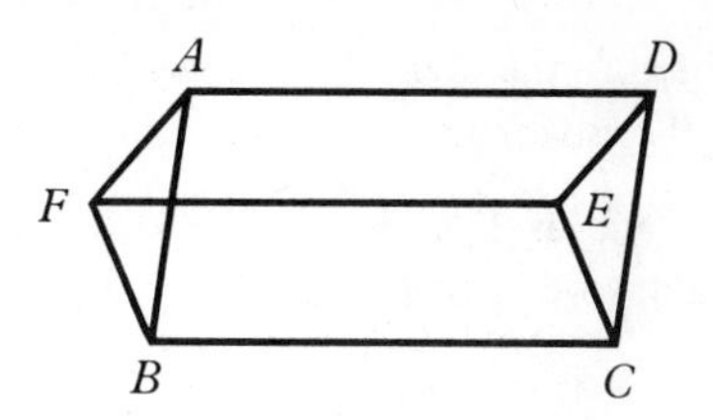

16. Given: *ABCD* is a parallelogram.
E is the midpoint of $\overline{AD}$.
F is the midpoint of $\overline{BC}$.
Prove: *AFCE* is a parallelogram.

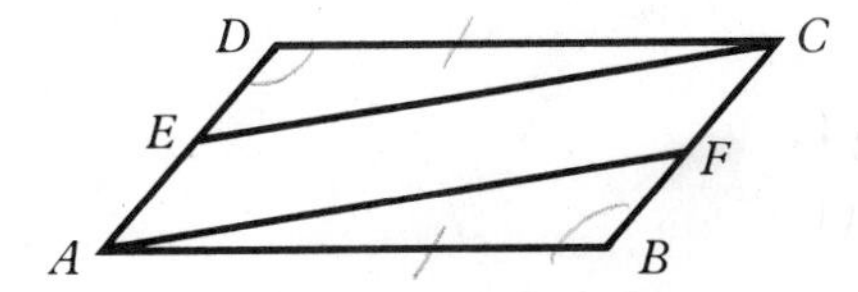

17. Given: *ABCD* is a parallelogram.
E, F, G, and *H* are midpoints of sides as shown.
Prove: *EFGH* is a parallelogram.

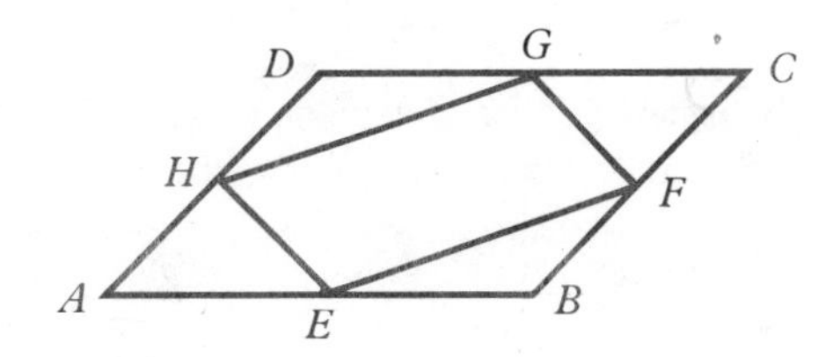

18. Given: *ABCD* is a parallelogram and $AE = CF$.
Prove: *BFDE* is a parallelogram.

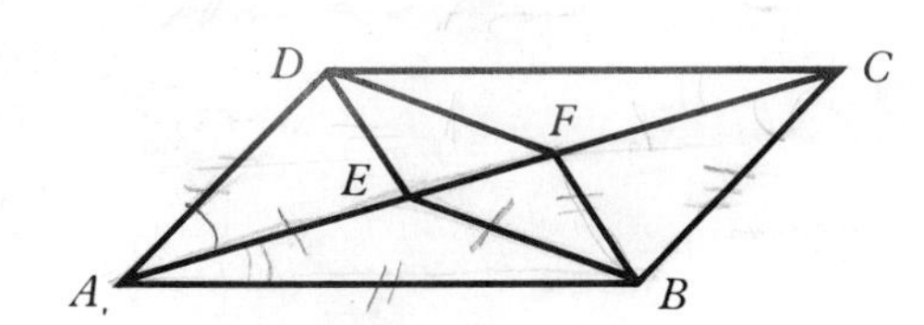

19. Given: *ABCD* is a parallelogram.
E is the midpoint of $\overline{AB}$.
F is the midpoint of $\overline{CD}$.
Prove: *AEFD* is a parallelogram.

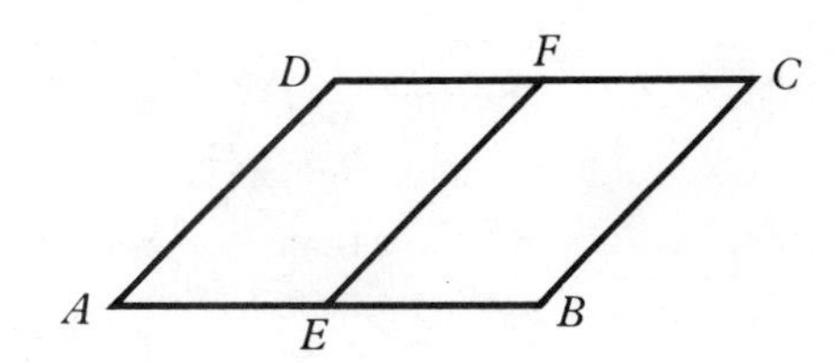

C.

20. a. Given: *ABCDEF* is a regular hexagon.
$m\angle AFE = 120$, $\overline{OA}$, $\overline{OC}$, and $\overline{OE}$ bisect $\angle A$, $\angle C$, and $\angle E$ respectively.
Prove: *ABCO* is a rhombus.

b. Are *CDEO* and *EFAO* also rhombuses?

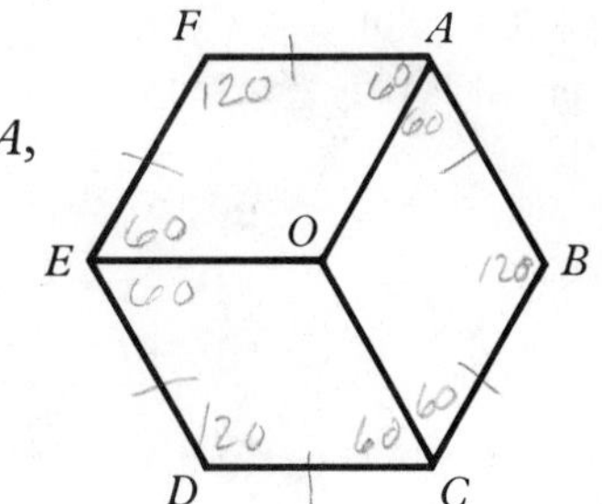

21. Prove that if the diagonals of a quadrilateral bisect each other, then the quadrilateral is a parallelogram.

22. Prove that if angles B and D in quadrilateral $ABCD$ are both supplementary to angle A, then $ABCD$ is a parallelogram.

23. **Given:** $ABCD$ is a parallelogram.
E, F, G, and H are midpoints of sides.
Prove: The figure $AEIH$ is a parallelogram.

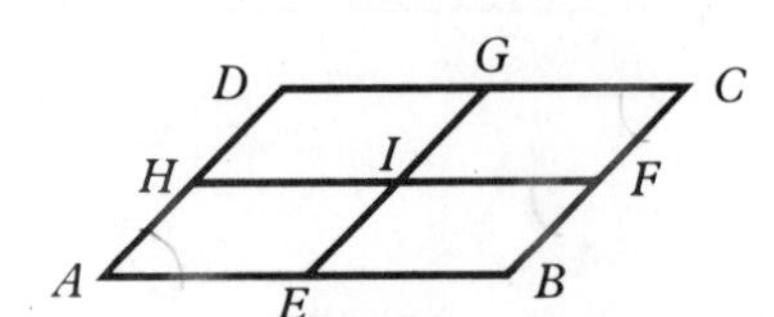

24. **Given:** $ABCD$ is a parallelogram.
E, F, G, and H are midpoints of sides as shown.
Prove: The figure $WXYZ$ is a parallelogram.

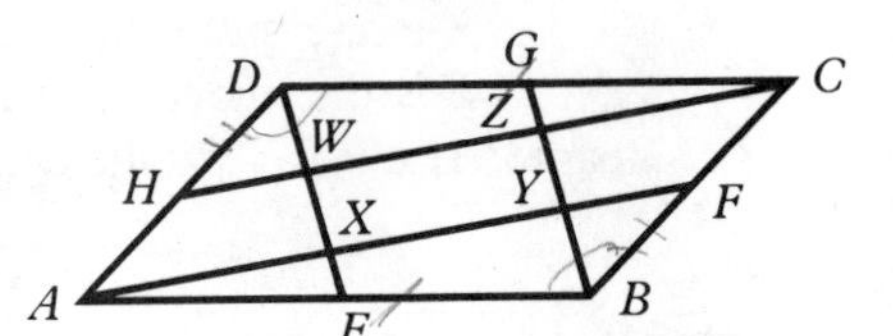

25. **Given:** $ABCDE$ is a regular pentagon.
Prove: The figure $ABCF$ is a rhombus.

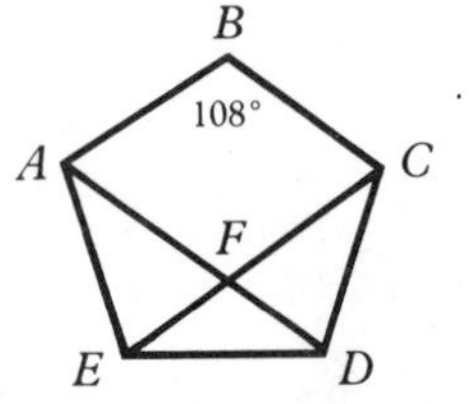

Activity

Draw a large circle with center O and follow the directions below to construct a regular pentagon.

1. Label any point on the circle V_1 and construct $\overline{OB}$ perpendicular to $\overline{OV_1}$.
2. Join V_1 to C, the midpoint of $\overline{OB}$.
3. Bisect angle OCV_1 to obtain the point N on $\overline{OV_1}$.
4. Construct the perpendicular to $\overline{OV_1}$ at N and obtain the point V_2.

The segment $\overline{V_1V_2}$ is one side of a regular pentagon.

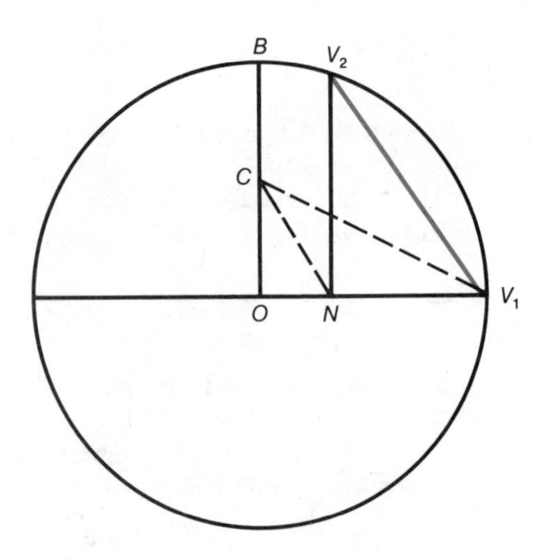

26. Prove that if the diagonals of a parallelogram are congruent, then the figure is a rectangle.

27. Given: $ABCD$ is a square.
$BE = BC$, $\overline{EF} \perp \overline{BD}$
Prove: $DE = EF = FC$

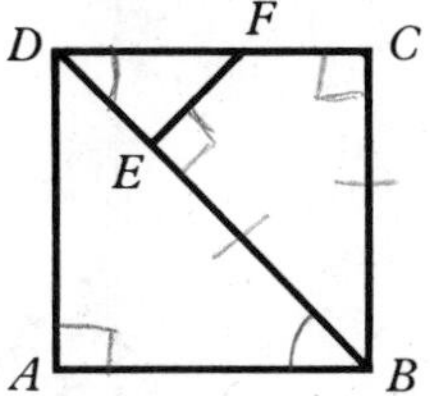

28. Given: $EFGH$ is a parallelogram.
$\overline{HD} \cong \overline{FB}$, $\overline{AE} \cong \overline{CG}$
Prove: $ABCD$ is a parallelogram.

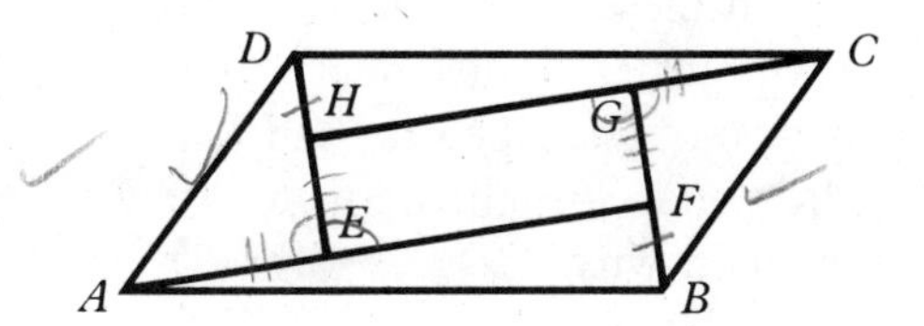

29. A carpenter wants to construct parallel lines on a board. This can be done by using a carpenter square twice. Each time the tool is placed at the same angle with the board and equal units are marked off. Explain why this method assures that $\overline{AB}$ will be parallel to $\overline{CD}$.

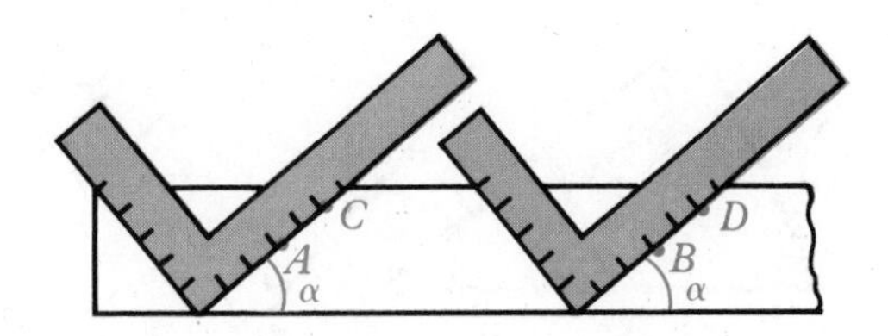

PROBLEM SOLVING

When a plane intersects a cube, the region common to the plane and the cube solid is called a *cross section* of the cube solid.

1. How many of these quadrilaterals and their interiors occur as a cross section of a cube?

a. square **b.** non-square rectangle

c. rhombus **d.** non-rhombic parallelogram

e. trapezoid **f.** kite

2. For each type of cross section that exists trace the cube at the right and sketch the cross section.

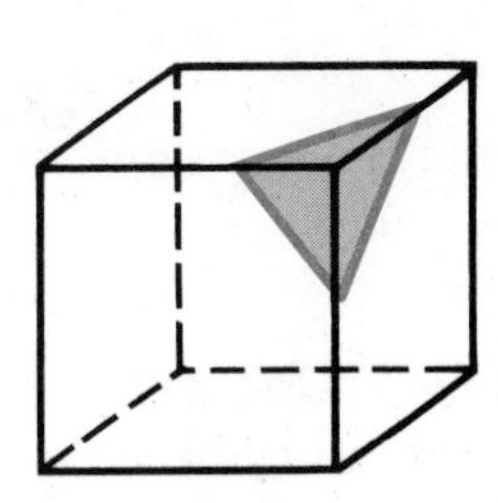

8–4 The Midsegment Theorem

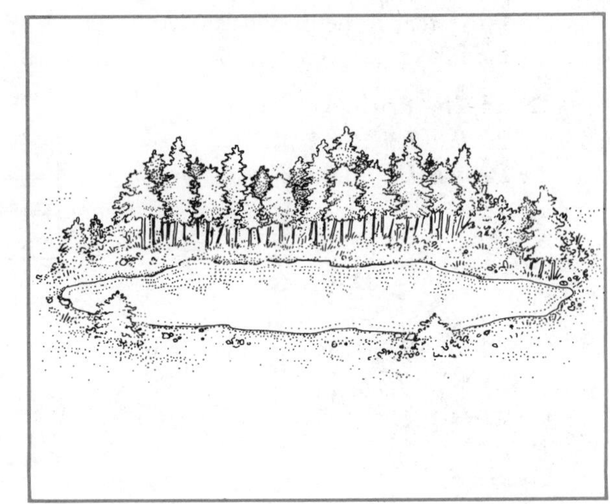

A surveying team needs to find the distance across a large pond. The team chooses any point. From that point they measure to each side of the pond. They locate the two points that are halfway between the edge of the pond and their chosen point. The distance between these two midpoints will be one-half the distance across the pond. The theorem in this lesson helps to explain why.

In the triangles below, D and E are midpoints. The segments and angles have the measures shown.

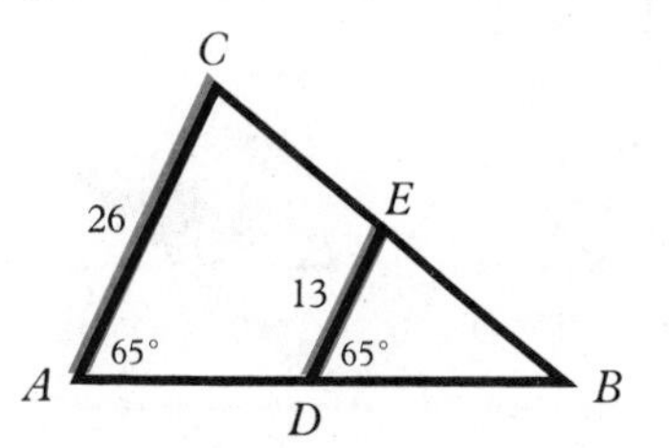

Observe: $DE = \frac{1}{2}AC$.
Since $\angle EDB \cong \angle CAB$, $\overline{DE} \parallel \overline{AC}$.

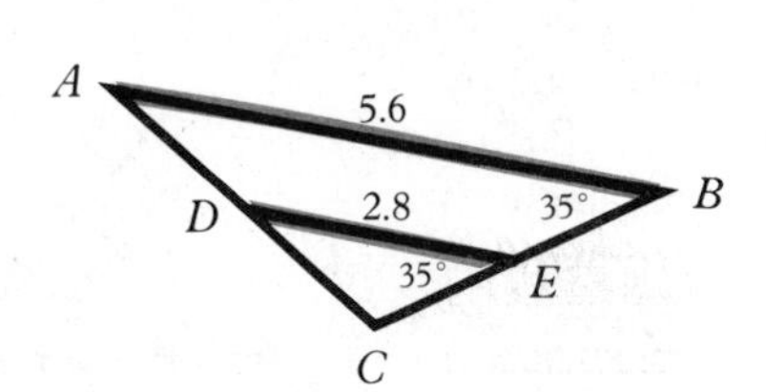

Observe: $DE = \frac{1}{2}AB$.
Since $\angle CED \cong \angle CBA$, $\overline{DE} \parallel \overline{AB}$.

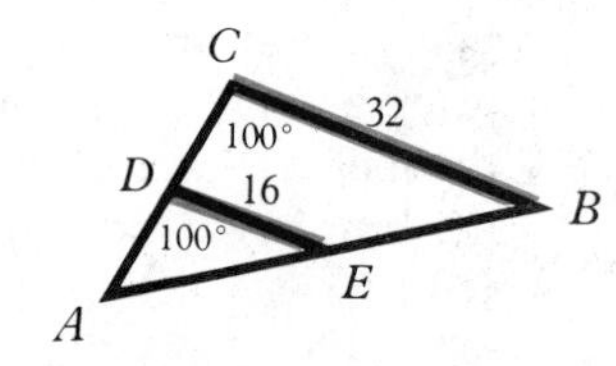

Observe: $DE = \frac{1}{2}CB$.
Since $\angle ADE \cong \angle ACB$, $\overline{DE} \parallel \overline{CB}$.

Theorem 8–7 **Midsegment Theorem.** A segment joining the midpoints of two sides of a triangle is parallel to the third side and half its length.

PROOF

Given: Any $\triangle ABC$ with
X the midpoint of $\overline{AB}$,
Y the midpoint of $\overline{AC}$.

Prove: $\overline{XY} \parallel \overline{BC}$ and
$XY = \frac{1}{2}BC$

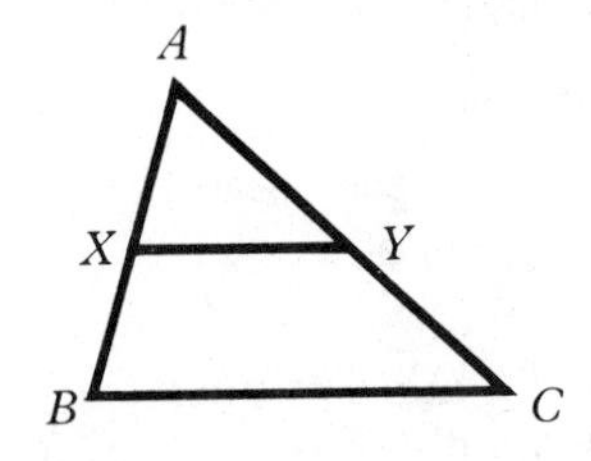

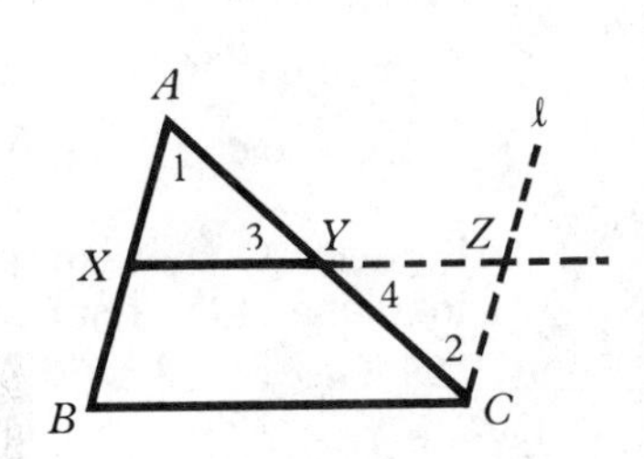

Plan: Draw a line ℓ through C and parallel to $\overline{AB}$. Then extend $\overline{XY}$ until it intersects ℓ at Z. Show that two congruent triangles are formed (Steps 3-6). Then show that $BCZX$ is a parallelogram (Steps 10–13).

Statements	Reasons
1. X is the midpoint of $\overline{AB}$. Y is the midpoint of $\overline{AC}$.	1. Given
2. Line ℓ is drawn through C and parallel to $\overline{AB}$, and $\overline{XY}$ is extended to form $\triangle CYZ$.	2. Construction
3. $AY = YC$	3. Definition of midpoint
4. $\angle 1 \cong \angle 2$	4. If two lines are parallel, then alternate interior angles are congruent.
5. $\angle 3 \cong \angle 4$	5. Why?
6. $\triangle AXY \cong \triangle CZY$	6. ASA Postulate
7. $XY = ZY$	7. CPCTC
8. Y is the midpoint of $\overline{XZ}$.	8. Definition of midpoint
9. $XY = \frac{1}{2}XZ$	9. Algebra
10. $CZ = AX$	10. Statement 6 and CPCTC
11. $AX = XB$	11. Definition of midpoint
12. $CZ = XB$; $\overline{CZ} \parallel \overline{AB}$	12. Transitive property; Statement 2
13. $BCZX$ is a parallogram.	13. If a quadrilateral has one pair of opposite sides parallel and congruent, then it is a parallelogram.
14. $\overleftrightarrow{XY} \parallel \overleftrightarrow{BC}$	14. Definition of parallelogram
15. $\overline{XZ} \cong \overline{BC}$	15. Opposite sides of a parallelogram are congruent.
16. $XY = \frac{1}{2}BC$	16. Substitution in Statements 9 and 15

Note that the conclusion of the theorem follows from statements 14 and 16.

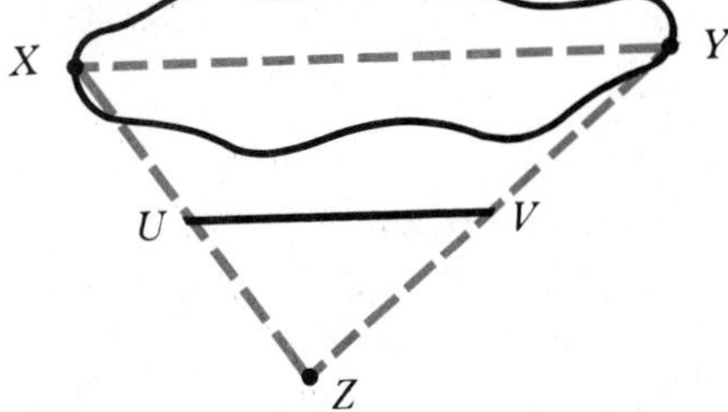

APPLICATION

The surveyor's method was a direct application of Theorem 8–7. Since U and V are the midpoints of $\overline{ZX}$ and $\overline{ZY}$, $UV = \frac{1}{2}XY$, or $XY = 2UV$.

The following theorem can be proved using Theorem 8–7. See exercise 33.

Theorem 8–8 The midpoints of the sides of a quadrilateral are the vertices of a parallelogram.

EXERCISES

A.

In this figure D and E are midpoints.

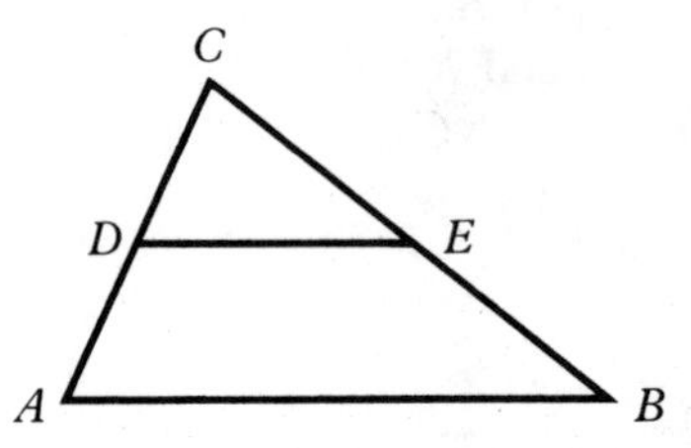

1. If $AB = 8$, then $DE = \underline{?}$
2. If $AC = 9$, then $AD = \underline{?}$
3. If $BE = 5$, then $BC = \underline{?}$
4. If $AB = 15$, then $DE = \underline{?}$
5. If $DE = 17$, then $AB = \underline{?}$

For exercises 6–14, state either the missing number(s) or state "cannot determine."

6.

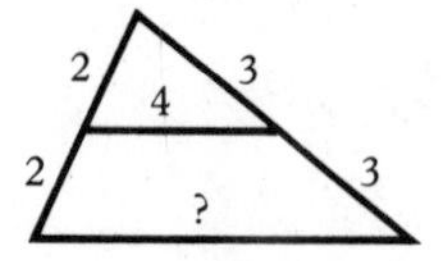

7.

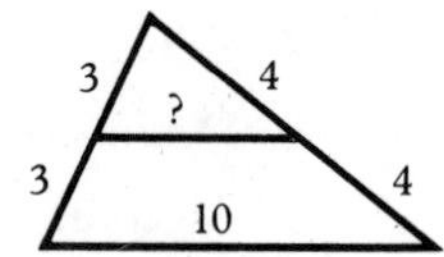

8.

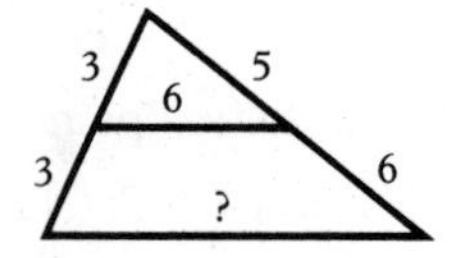

9.

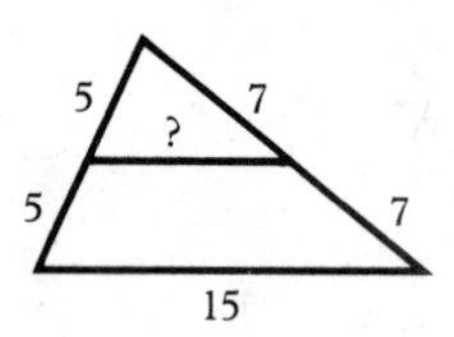

10.

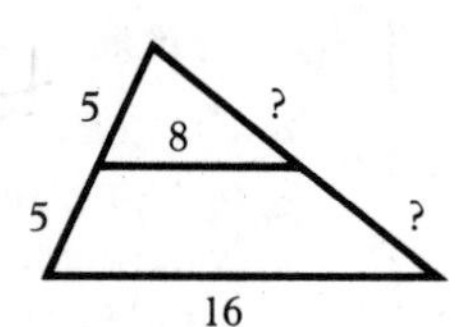

11.

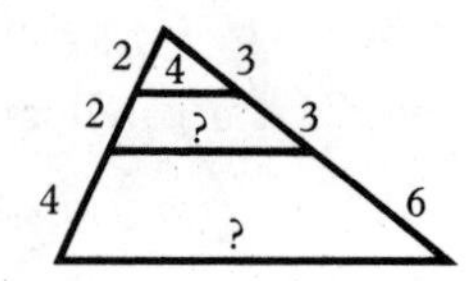

12.

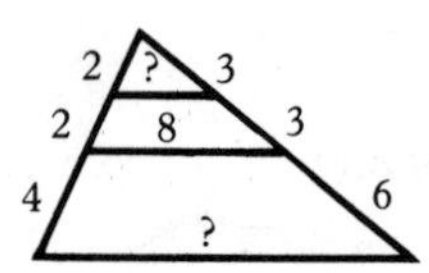

13.

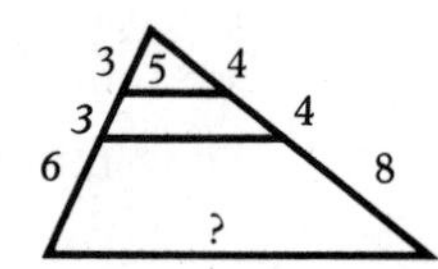

14.

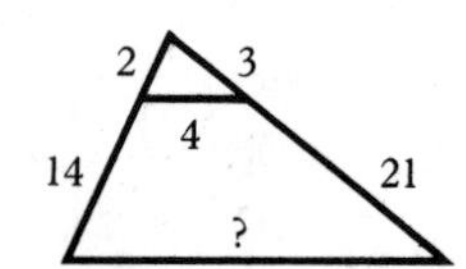

In exercises 15–17, exactly one of the numbers a, b, or c can be determined. Find it.

15.

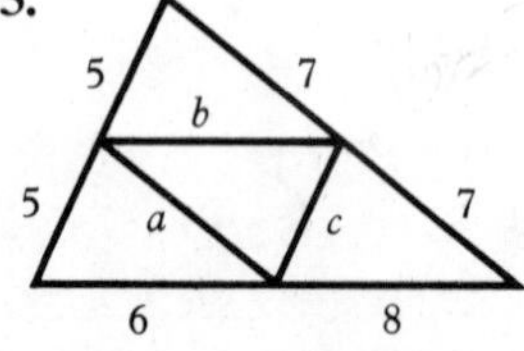

16.

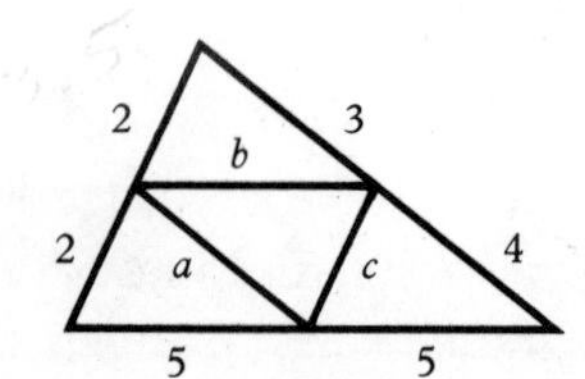

17.

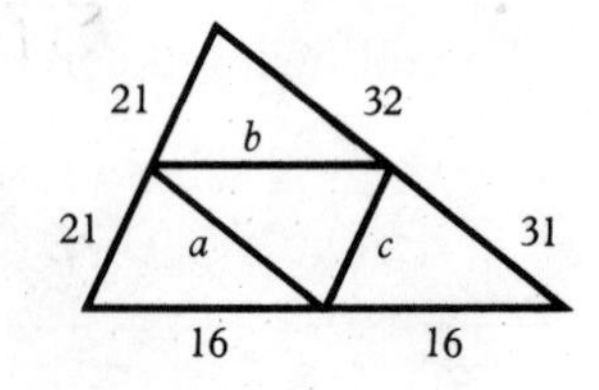

B.

In the triangle on the right M and N are midpoints.

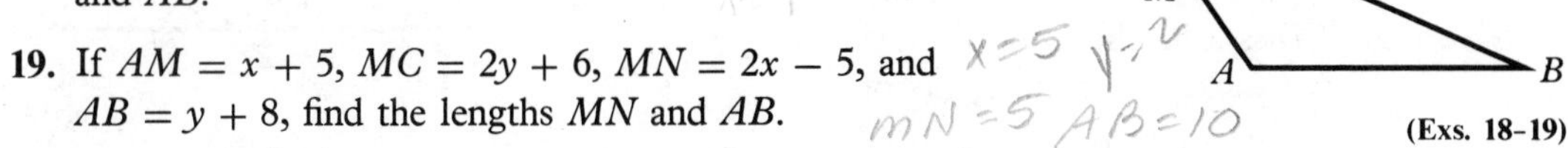

18. If $MN = x + 8$ and $AB = 4x + 14$, find the lengths MN and AB.

19. If $AM = x + 5$, $MC = 2y + 6$, $MN = 2x - 5$, and $AB = y + 8$, find the lengths MN and AB.

(Exs. 18–19)

For exercises 20–22, use Theorem 8-8 to decide whether or not $ABCD$ is a parallelogram.

20.

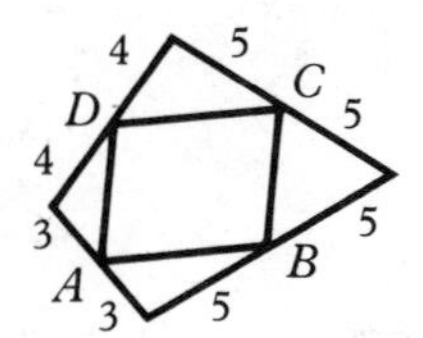

21.

22.

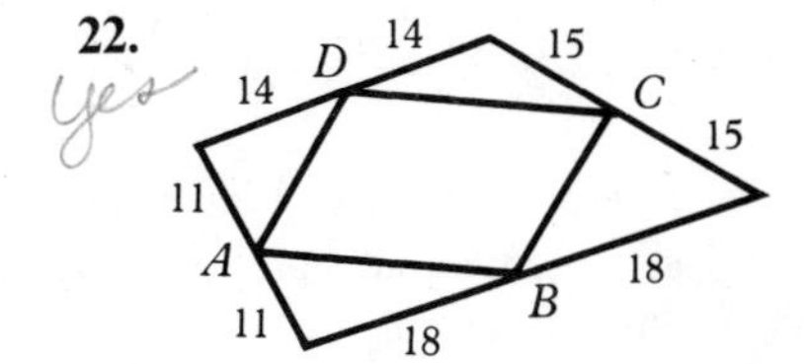

For exercises 23–26 write complete two-column proofs.

23. Given: F is the midpoint of $\overline{AC}$.
D is the midpoint of $\overline{BC}$.
E is the midpoint of $\overline{AB}$.
Prove: $AEDF$ is a parallelogram.

24. Given: $\triangle ABC$ is isosceles with $AB = AC$.
D is the midpoint of $\overline{AB}$.
E is the midpoint of $\overline{CB}$.
Prove: $\triangle BDE$ is isosceles.

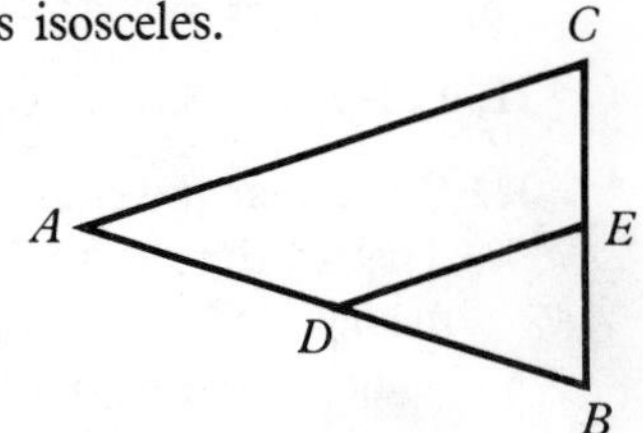

25. Given: $ABCDEF$ is a hexagon with $\overline{AB} \parallel \overline{DE}$ and $AB = DE$.
W, X, Y, and Z are midpoints of sides as shown.
Prove: $WXYZ$ is a parallelogram.

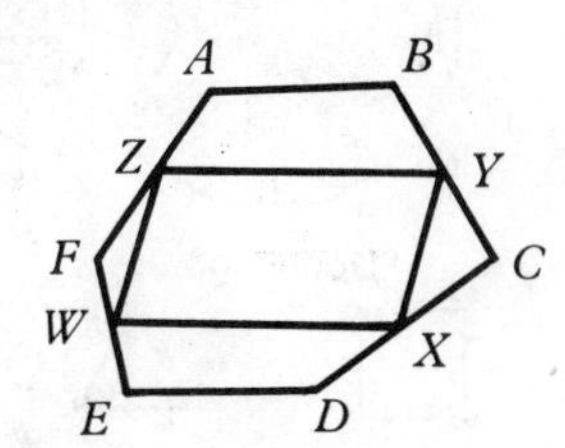

(*Hint:* Use auxiliary segments $\overline{AE}$ and $\overline{BD}$.)

26. Given: $\triangle ABC$ is equilateral.
D, E, and F are midpoints of sides as shown.
Prove: $\triangle DEF$ is equilateral.

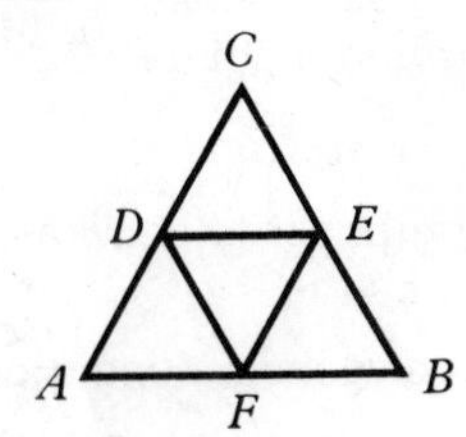

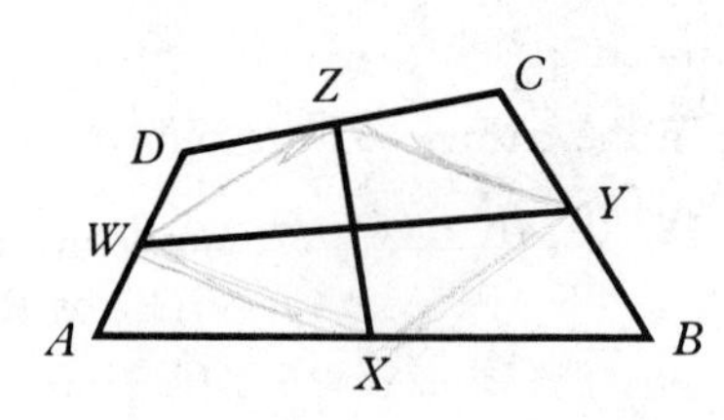

27. Given: W, X, Y, and Z are midpoints of the sides of quadrilateral $ABCD$.

Prove: $\overline{WY}$ and $\overline{XZ}$ bisect each other.

(*Hint:* Use auxiliary lines.)

28. Given: $ABCD$ is a parallelogram. E, F, G, and H are midpoints of $\overline{AO}$, $\overline{BO}$, $\overline{CO}$, and $\overline{DO}$, respectively.

Prove: $EFGH$ is a parallelogram.

C.

Exercises 29–32 all have the following given information. The statement in any one of these exercises may be used to complete any succeeding exercise.

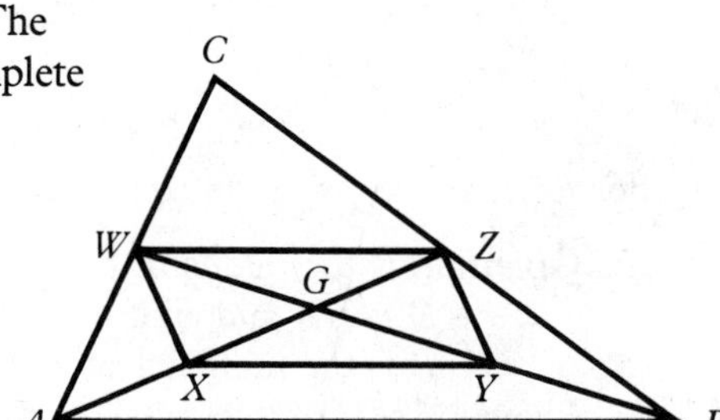

Given: $\overline{AZ}$ and $\overline{BW}$ are medians of $\triangle ABC$.
X is the midpoint of $\overline{AG}$.
Y is the midpoint of $\overline{BG}$.

29. Prove that $\overline{WZ} \parallel \overline{XY}$.

30. Prove that $WXYZ$ is a parallelogram.

31. Prove that $AX = XG = GZ$ and $BY = YG = GW$.

32. Prove that the centroid of a triangle trisects each median. That is, the centroid divides the median into one third of the median and two thirds of the median. (The centroid is the point of intersection of the medians.)

Activity

You can fit three of these polygons around a point P like this.

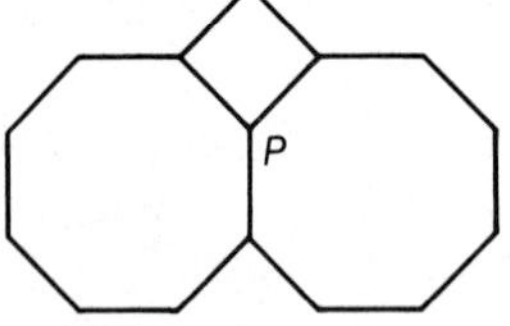

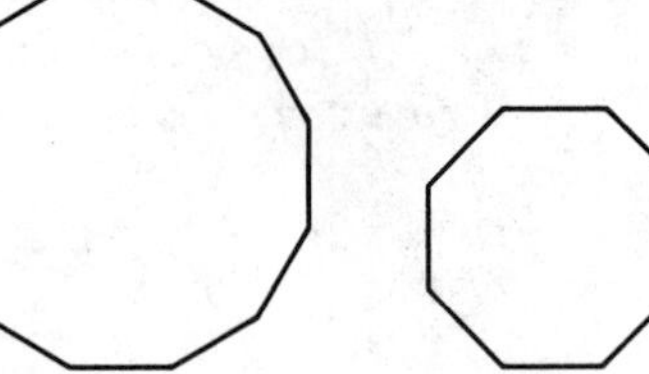

Dodecagon

Octagon

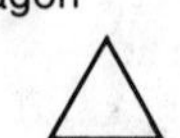

Square

Equilateral triangle

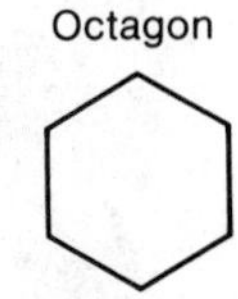

Hexagon

Use tracing paper to show as many different ways as you can to

1. fit three polygons around a point.
2. fit four polygons around a point.
3. fit five polygons around a point.

Can you draw a design by continuing to fit polygons together?

33. Complete the following proof of Theorem 8-8.

Given: $ABCD$ is any quadrilateral.
W, X, Y, and Z are midpoints of sides of $ABCD$ as shown.

Prove: $WXYZ$ is a parallelogram.

Plan: Add auxiliary segments $\overline{DB}$, $\overline{ZW}$, $\overline{YX}$, $\overline{ZY}$, and $\overline{WX}$. Apply Theorem 8-7 to $\triangle ABD$ and $\triangle BCD$.

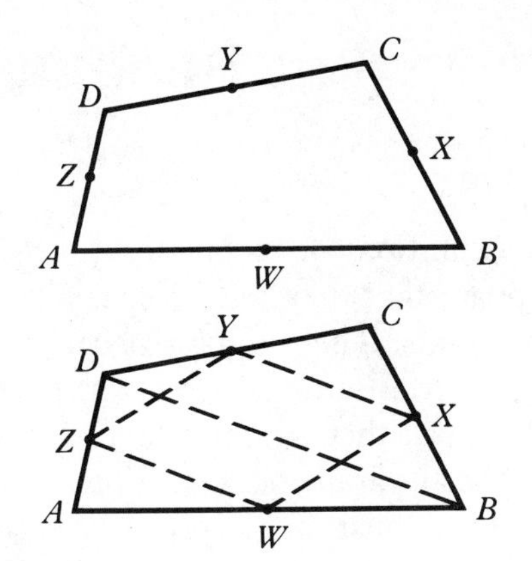

Exercises 34–36 have the following given information.

Given:

a. $ABCD$ is a parallelogram.

b. W, X, Y, and Z are the midpoints of the sides.

c. Each dashed line is a diagonal of a polygon.

34. Prove that $WOZD$ is a parallelogram. A similar proof will show that $AXOW$, $XBYO$, and $OYCZ$ are parallelograms. (*Hint:* First show that $AXZD$ and $WYCD$ are parallelograms.)

35. Prove that $A'B'C'D'$ is a parallelogram.

36. Prove that each side of $A'B'C'D'$ is parallel to and half as long as the corresponding side of $ABCD$.

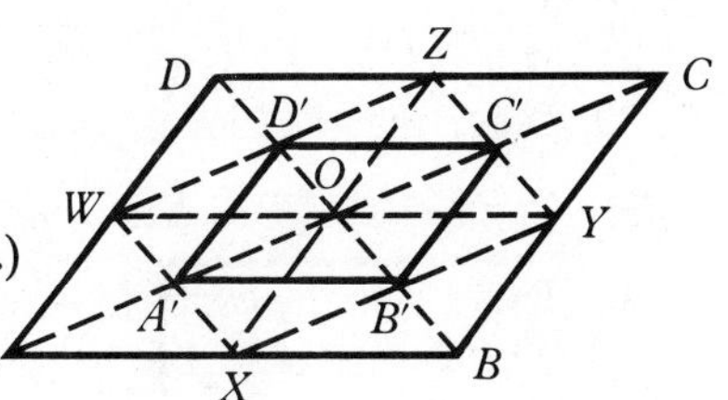

(Exs. 34–36)

PROBLEM SOLVING

Pictured here is a cube, all of whose edges have length 1. Suppose that points B and D are the midpoints of the edges shown.

1. Show that $ABCD$ is a rhombus.

2. Find the lengths of the sides.

3. Find the lengths of the diagonals $\overline{BD}$ and $\overline{AC}$.

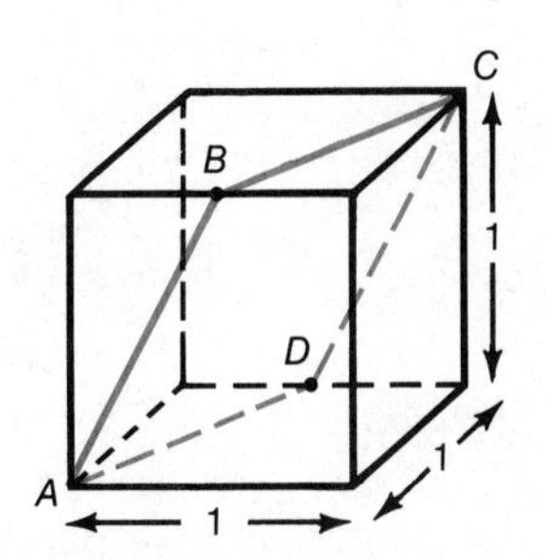

8–5 Rectangles, Rhombuses, and Squares

Recall from the definitions of rectangle, rhombus, and square that they are all special types of parallelograms. These figures occur in a variety of industrial settings. Frequently it is necessary to check that an object actually is one of these special parallelograms. For example, a contractor must make sure that the foundation wall of a building is an exact rectangle.

In this lesson we shall study how these three types of parallelograms are determined by their diagonals.

These parallelograms are also rectangles.

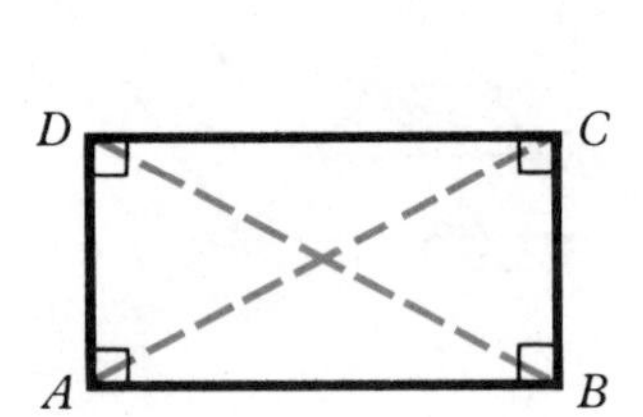

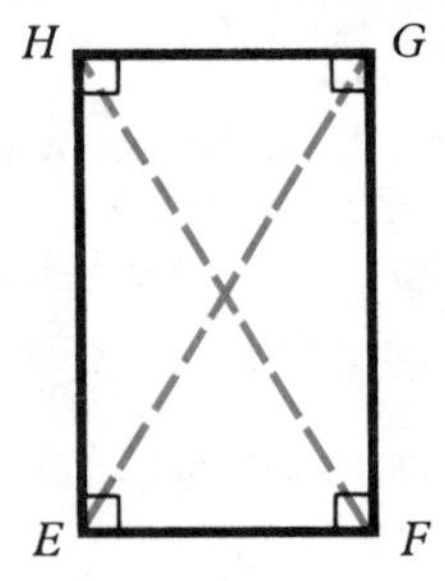

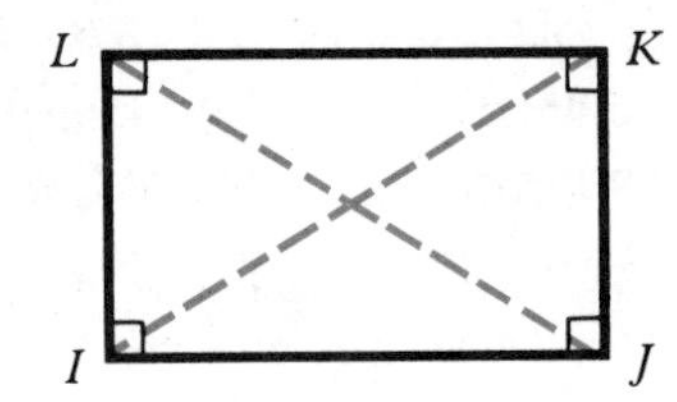

Observe: $\overline{AC} \cong \overline{BD}$. Observe: $\overline{EG} \cong \overline{FH}$. Observe: $\overline{IK} \cong \overline{JL}$.

These observations support this theorem.

Theorem 8–9 A parallelogram is a rectangle if and only if its diagonals are congruent.

We must prove two things.

I. If the diagonals of a parallelogram are congruent, then the parallelogram is a rectangle.

II. If a parallelogram is a rectangle, then the diagonals are congruent.

Outline for I.

Given: $ABCD$ is a parallelogram.
$\overline{AC} \cong \overline{BD}$
Prove: $ABCD$ is a rectangle.

Plan: Prove that $\triangle ABD \cong \triangle BAC$, and that $\angle A$ and $\angle B$ are congruent and supplementary. Similarly for $\angle C$ and $\angle D$.

Outline for II.

Given: $ABCD$ is a rectangle.
Prove: $\overline{AC} \cong \overline{BD}$.

Plan: Prove that $\triangle ABD \cong \triangle BAC$.

This proof will be completed as an exercise.

APPLICATION

The concrete footings for a house form a rectangular shape slightly larger than the rectangle of the house. On these footings the contractor must locate four points A, B, C, and D that are to become the actual corners of the house. These four points must be accurately located so that $ABCD$ is a perfect rectangle. After measuring to make $AB = CD$ and $AD = BC$, the next step is to measure the diagonals. If $AC = BD$, then $ABCD$ is a rectangle.

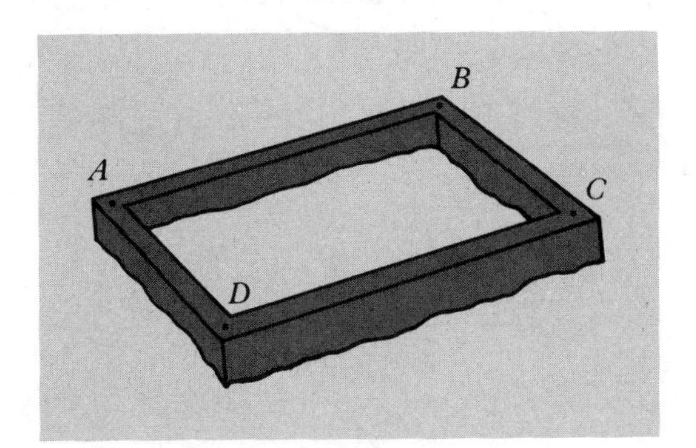

Is $ABCD$ an exact rectangle?

Proofs of these last two theorems will be found as exercises.

Theorem 8–10 A parallelogram is a rhombus if and only if its diagonals are perpendicular to each other.

Theorem 8–11 A parallelogram is a rhombus if and only if each diagonal bisects a pair of opposite angles.

EXERCISES

A.

1. In rectangle $ABCD$ name all pairs of congruent segments.

For exercises 2–4, assume that quadrilateral $ABCD$ has been distorted into the desired shape.

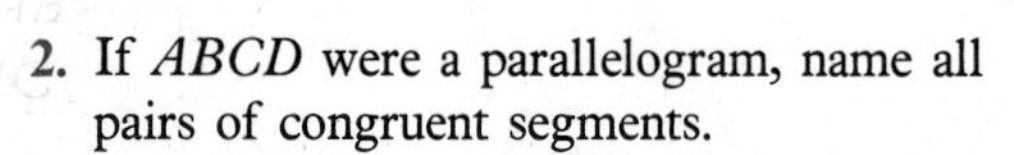

2. If $ABCD$ were a parallelogram, name all pairs of congruent segments.
3. If $ABCD$ were a rhombus, name all the angles that must be right angles.
4. If $ABCD$ were a rhombus, name all the angles that must be congruent to $\angle CAB$.

(Exs. 2–4)

Which of these parallelograms would be rectangles? (Assume that the given information is correct even though the figure may be distorted.)

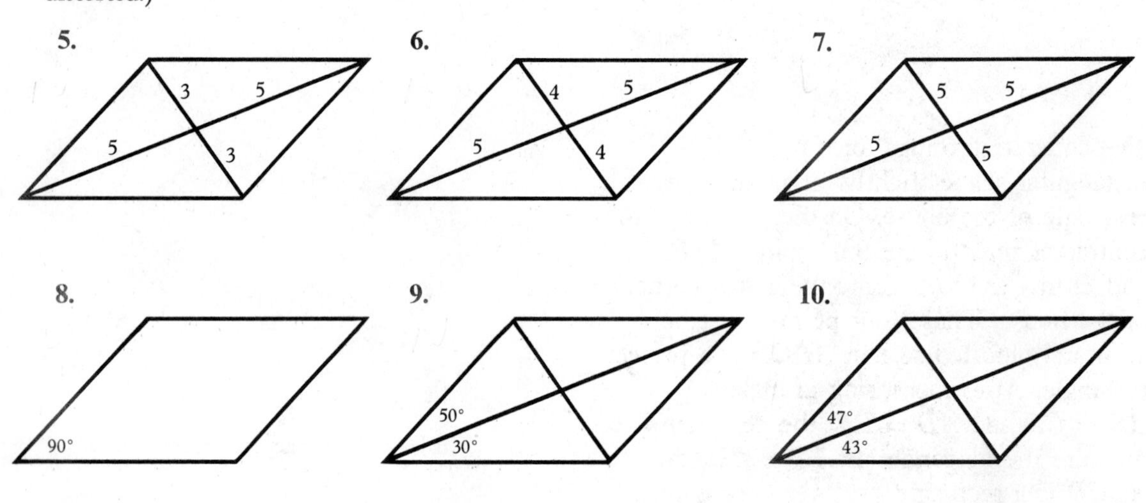

Which of these parallelograms would be rhombuses? (Assume that the given information is correct even though the figure may be distorted.)

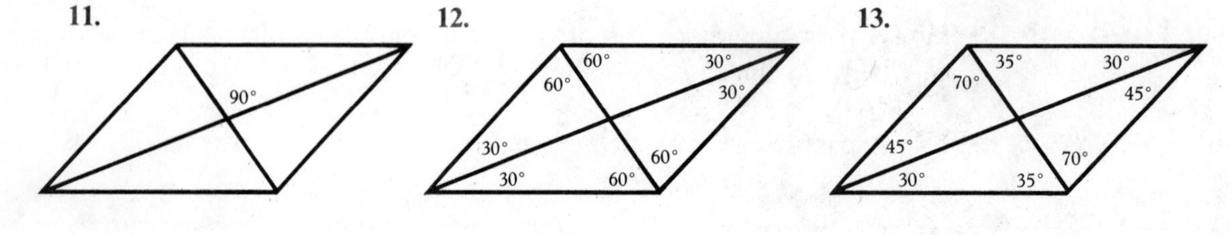

For exercises 14–20, decide whether the given statement is true or false.

14. Every rectangle is a parallelogram.

15. Every rhombus is a rectangle.

16. Every square is a rhombus.

17. Some rhombuses are squares.

18. Some rhombuses are rectangles that are not squares.

19. If the diagonals of a quadrilateral are congruent, then the figure is a rectangle.

20. The diagonals of a square are perpendicular.

B.

For exercises 21–25 draw, if possible, a parallelogram satisfying each of the following conditions. If it is not possible, write "not possible."

21. All angles congruent

22. Diagonals that bisect each other

23. All sides congruent with diagonals that are not perpendicular

24. No right angles with congruent diagonals

25. Congruent and perpendicular diagonals

26. $ABCD$ is a parallelogram.
$AB = 2x + 4$
$DC = 3x - 11$
$AD = x + 19$
Show that $ABCD$ is a rhombus.

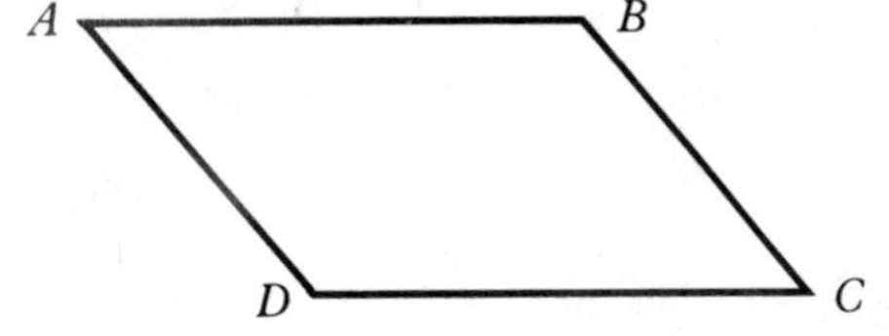

27. $ABCD$ is a rhombus.
$m\angle DEC = 4x + 10$
$m\angle DAB = 3x + 4$
Find $m\angle ABC$.

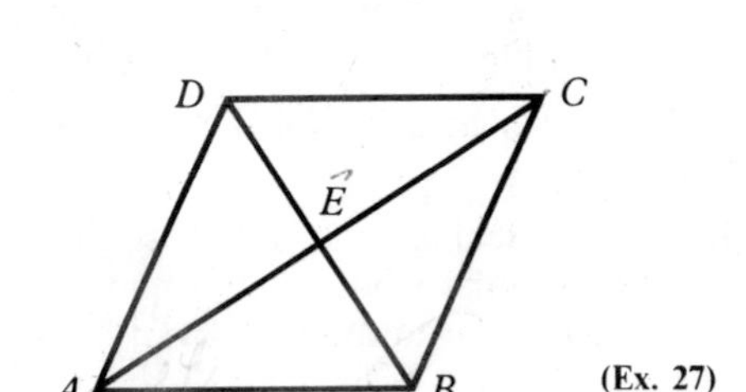

(Ex. 27)

28. $ABCD$ is a parallelogram.
$AB = 4x - 5$ $AC = 3x - 2$
$CD = 2x + 23$ $BD = 2x + 12$
Show that $ABCD$ is a rectangle.

29. Given: *ABCD* is a rectangle.
ACBE is a parallelogram.
Prove: $\triangle DBE$ is isosceles.

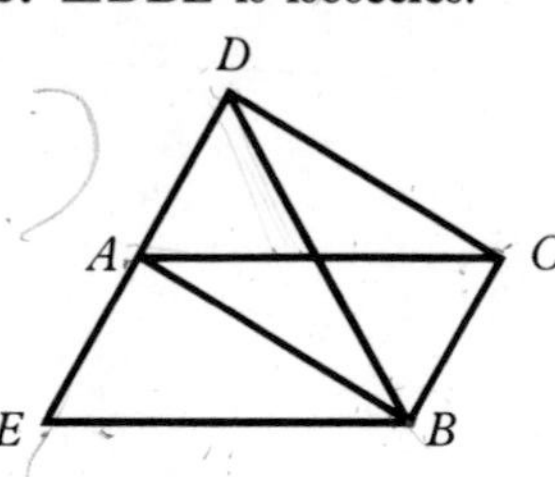

30. Given: *ABCD* is a rectangle.
Prove: $\triangle ABO$ is isosceles.

31. Given: *ABCD* is a square.
$AH = DG = CF = BE$
Prove: *EFGH* is a square.

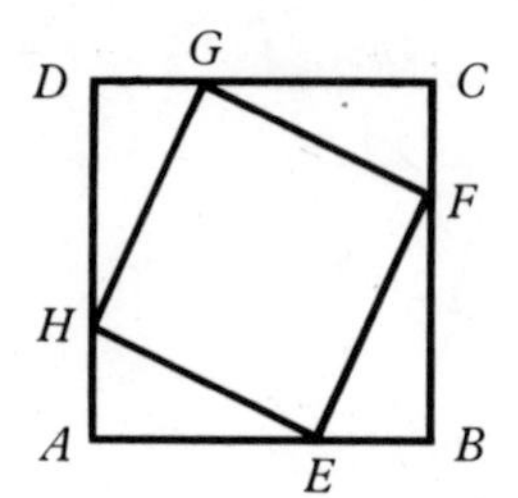

32. Given: *WXYZ* is a rhombus.
R is the midpoint of $\overline{WV}$.
T is the midpoint of $\overline{VY}$.
S is a point on $\overline{VZ}$.
Prove: $\triangle RST$ is isosceles.

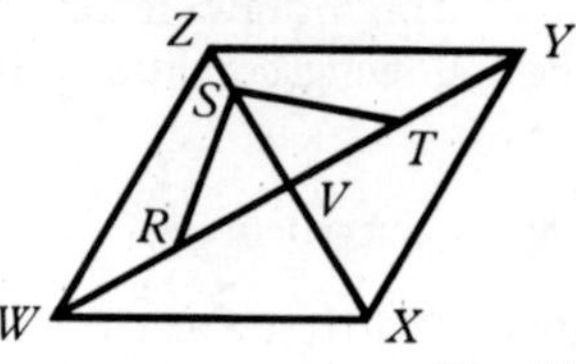

(Exs. 32, 33)

33. Given: *WXYZ* is a rhombus.
Prove: $\overline{WY}$ and $\overline{XZ}$ divide *WXYZ* into four congruent triangles.

34. Complete the proof of Theorem 8-9.

Activity

Suppose you need to draw a 7-column chart for a social studies report. Your space is 5 inches wide. Here is how you can draw the chart without doing any calculations.

1. Set a ruler as shown and mark the seven inch-points.
2. Draw vertical lines through each point parallel to the sides of the chart (or perpendicular to the bottom of the chart).

Experiment with drawing 9 columns in a 7-inch space, 4 columns in a 5-inch space.

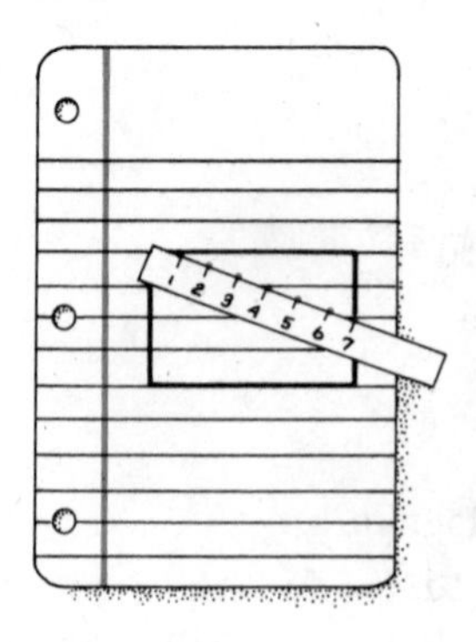

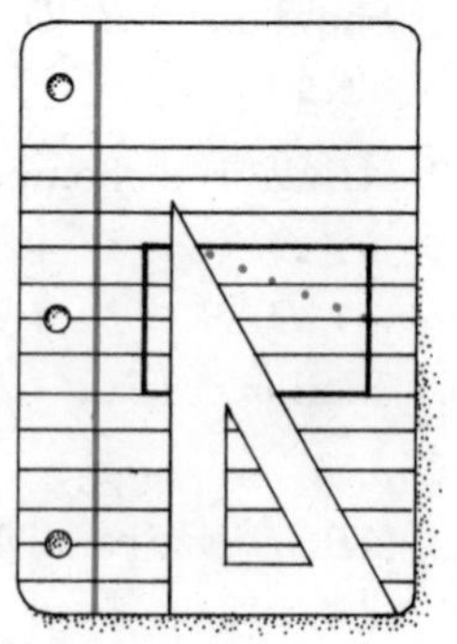

35. A building is to be $85' \times 40'$. Stakes are placed as shown and string is stretched. The outside corners of the building will be at the points where the strings cross.

a. After the string has been stretched the contractor measures $\overline{WY}$ and $\overline{XZ}$. Why?

b. If WY is 93 feet and XZ is 94 feet, which way should stakes E and F be moved to make $WXYZ$ a rectangle?

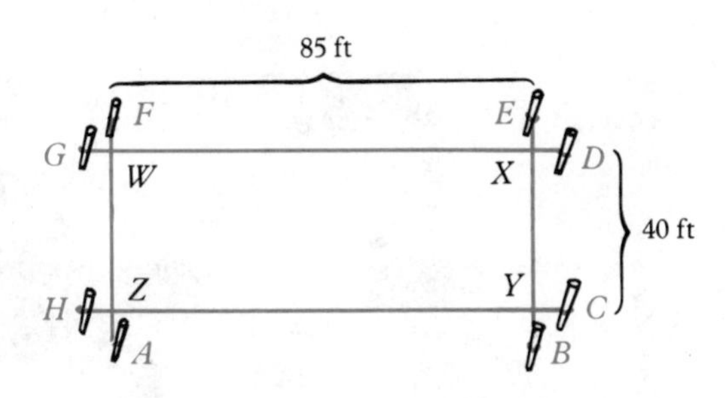

C.

36. **Given:** $WXYZ$ is a square.
$AW = BX = CY = DZ$
Prove: $ABCD$ is a square.

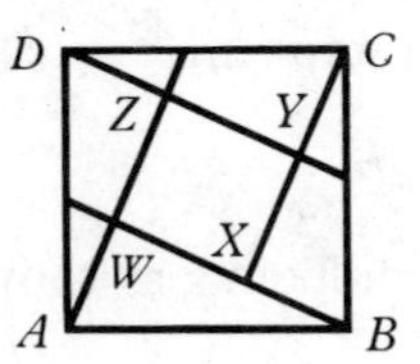

37. **Given:** $ABCD$ is a square.
$AH = DG = CF = BE$
Prove: $EG = HF$ and $\overline{EG} \perp \overline{HF}$

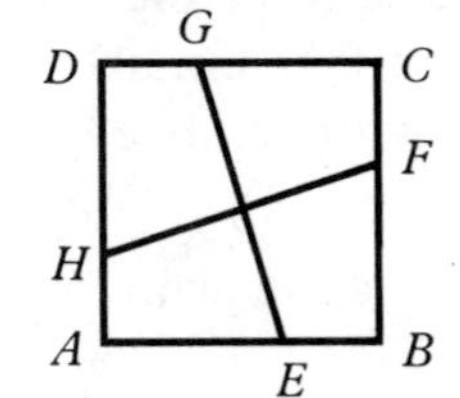

38. Prove Theorem 8–10.

39. Prove Theorem 8–11.

40. **Given:** $ABCD$ is a rhombus.
E, F, G, and H are midpoints.
Prove: $EFGH$ is a rectangle.

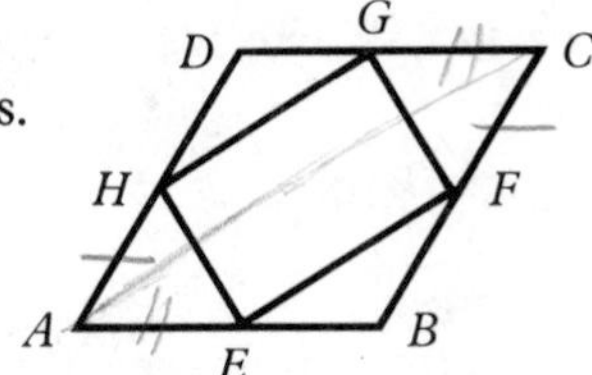

PROBLEM SOLVING

If the center O of a cube is joined to the vertices of a face, a square-based pyramid is formed. Suppose the length of an edge of the cube is 1.

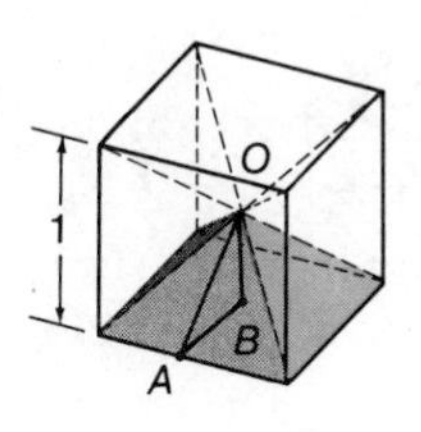

1. If B is the center of the square base, what is the length of $\overline{OB}$?

2. If A is the midpoint of an edge, what is the length of $\overline{OA}$?

If square-based pyramids like the one above are affixed on the faces of a cube, a solid is formed whose faces are rhombuses.

3. How many rhombic faces does this solid have?

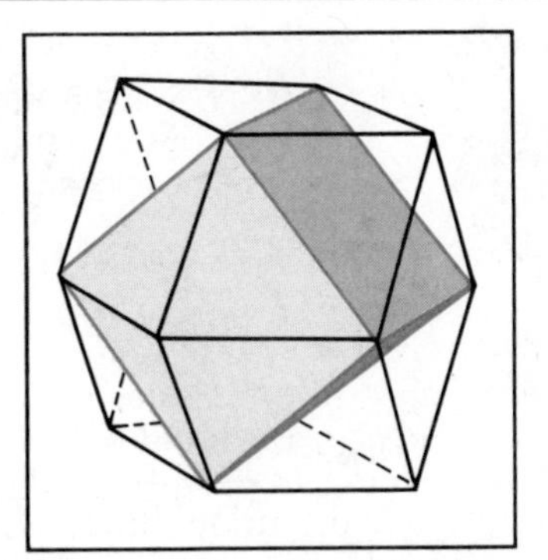

Cube with square-based pyramid affixed to each face.

8-6 Trapezoids

Recall that a trapezoid is a quadrilateral with exactly one pair of parallel sides. One example of a trapezoid would be the roof of a house. In this lesson we shall study a theorem about trapezoids that could be useful in estimating the construction costs of a project.

E and F are midpoints as shown.

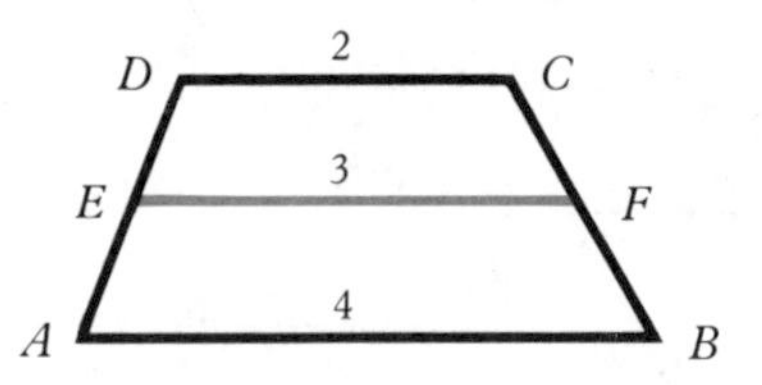

Observe that $EF = \frac{1}{2}(AB + CD)$ and $\overline{EF} \parallel \overline{AB} \parallel \overline{CD}$.

U and V are midpoints as shown.

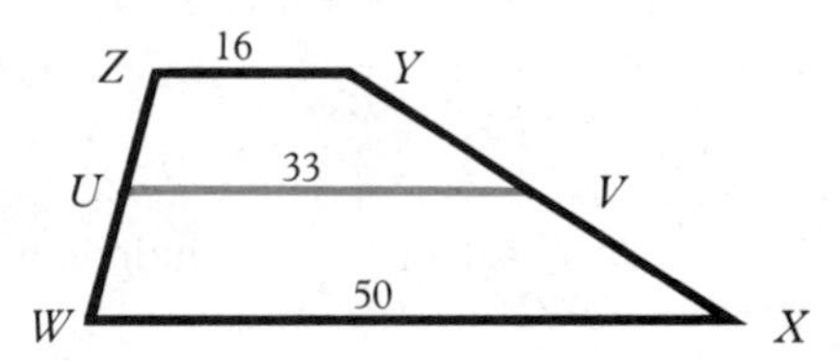

Observe that $UV = \frac{1}{2}(WX + YZ)$ and $\overline{UV} \parallel \overline{WX} \parallel \overline{YZ}$.

Theorem 8-12 The segment joining the midpoints of the two nonparallel sides of a trapezoid is parallel to the two bases and has a length equal to one half the sum of the lengths of the bases.

PROOF

Given: $ABCD$ is a trapezoid with $\overline{DC} \parallel \overline{AB}$.
E the midpoint of $\overline{AD}$ and
F the midpoint of $\overline{BC}$.

Prove: $\overline{EF} \parallel \overline{AB}$, $\overline{EF} \parallel \overline{DC}$,
and $EF = \frac{1}{2}(AB + CD)$

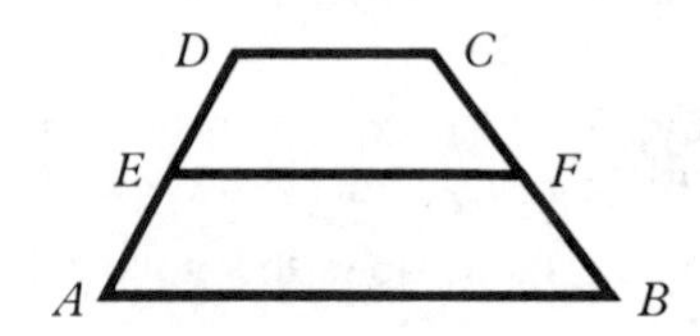

Plan: Extend $\overline{AB}$ and $\overline{DF}$ to meet at G. Then prove that F is the midpoint of $\overline{DG}$ and use the Midsegment Theorem.

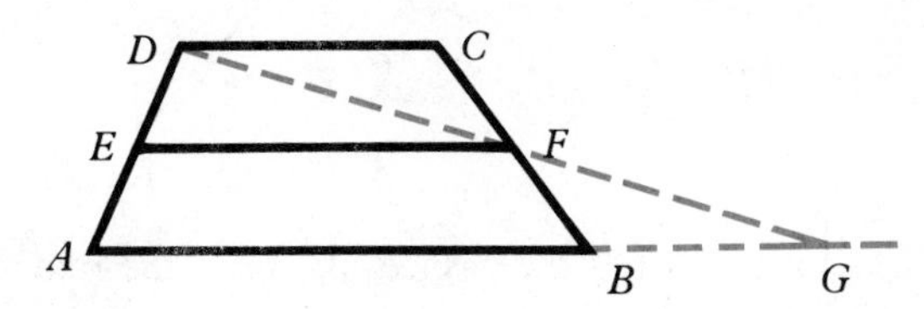

Statements	Reasons
1. Extend $\overline{AB}$.	1. Construction
2. Draw $\overrightarrow{DF}$ intersecting $\overrightarrow{AB}$ at G.	2. Construction
3. $\overline{DC} \parallel \overline{AB}$	3. Definition of trapezoid
4. $\angle BGF \cong \angle CDF$	4. Why?
5. $\overline{CF} \cong \overline{BF}$	5. Why?
6. $\angle BFG \cong \angle DFC$	6. Why?
7. $\triangle BFG \cong \triangle CFD$	7. Why?
8. $\overline{DF} \cong \overline{GF}$	8. Why?
9. F is the midpoint of $\overline{DG}$.	9. Why?
10. $\overline{EF} \parallel \overline{AB}$ and $\overline{EF} \parallel \overline{DC}$	10. Midsegment Theorem

It remains to show that $EF = \frac{1}{2}(AB + CD)$. This proof will be completed in an exercise.

APPLICATION

In estimating the construction costs of a roof the area of the trapezoid must be calculated. This area is equal to the area of the rectangle $ABCD$. By Theorem 8-12, $XY = \frac{1}{2}(RS + TU)$, and area $(ABCD) = h(XY) = \frac{1}{2}h(RS + TU)$.

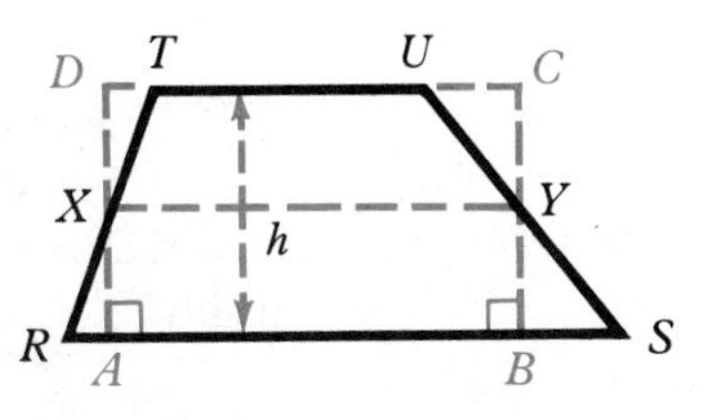

The following theorem states properties of a special kind of trapezoid.

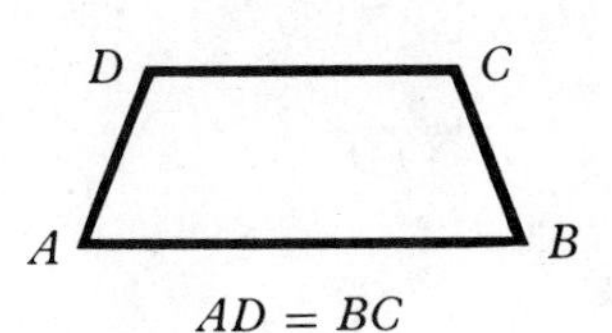

$AD = BC$

$\overline{AD}$ and $\overline{BC}$ are nonparallel sides. $\angle A$ and $\angle B$ together are called *base angles.* $\angle C$ and $\angle D$ together are another pair of base angles.

Definition 8-6

An **isosceles trapezoid** is a trapezoid with congruent nonparallel sides.

The proof of this theorem is left for the student in exercises 13 and 15.

Theorem 8-13 In an isosceles trapezoid base angles are congruent and the diagonals are congruent.

EXERCISES

A.

For exercises 1–9 the dashed line joins the midpoints of the two nonparallel sides of the trapezoid. Find the value of x.

1.

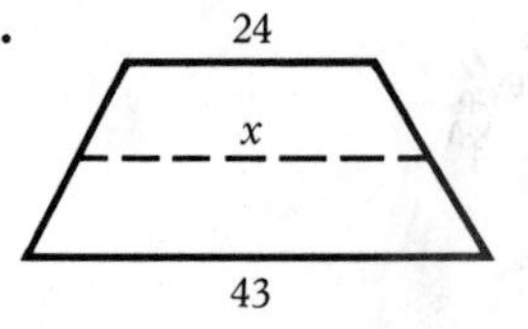

2.

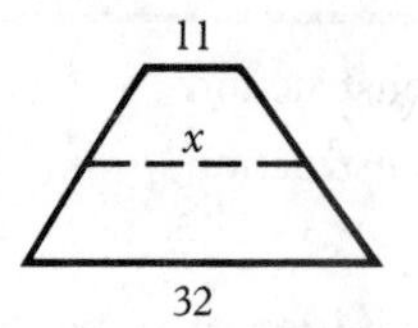

3.

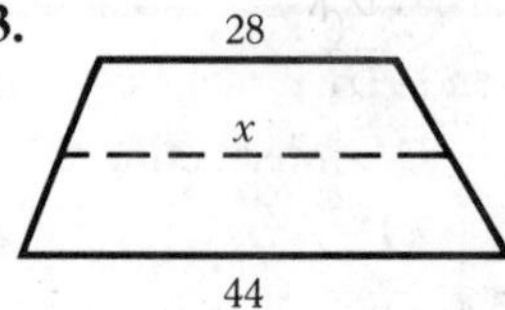

4.

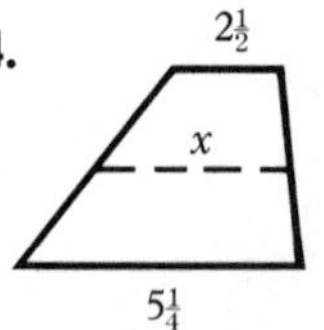

5.

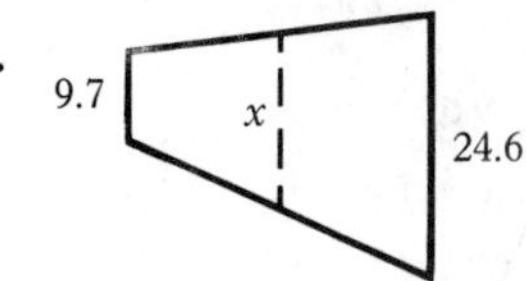

6.

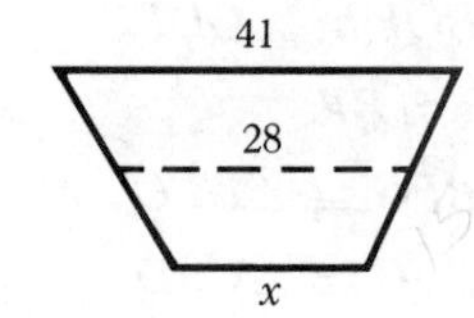

7.

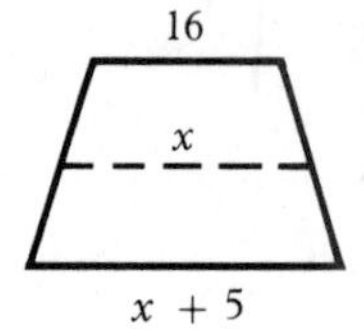

8.

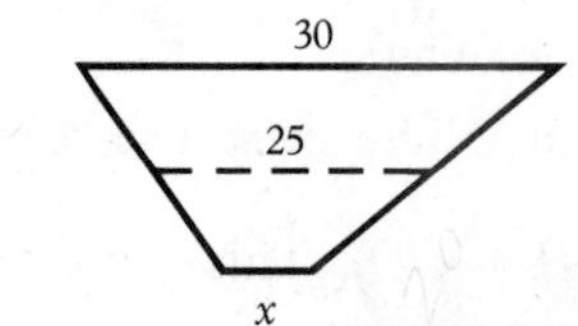

9.

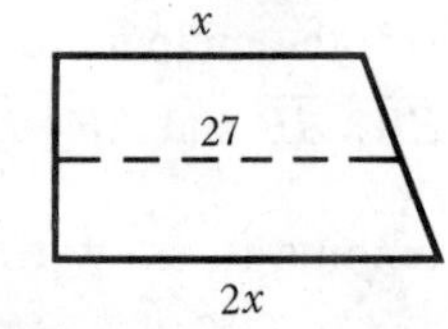

B.

10. A dam is constructed with a trapezoidal cross section 10 feet across the top and 38 feet across the base. What is the "average width" AB of the dam?

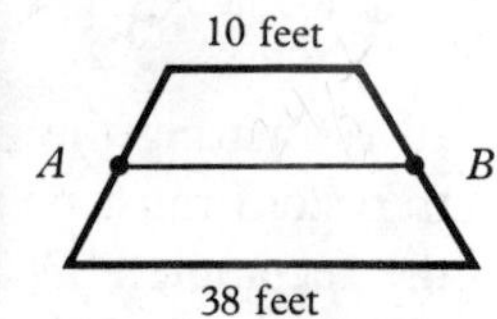

Activity

Shown here is a polygon formed by placing together along common edges four congruent copies of the given parallelogram.

Draw at least nine different shaped polygons using this method of placing together four copies of the given parallelogram.

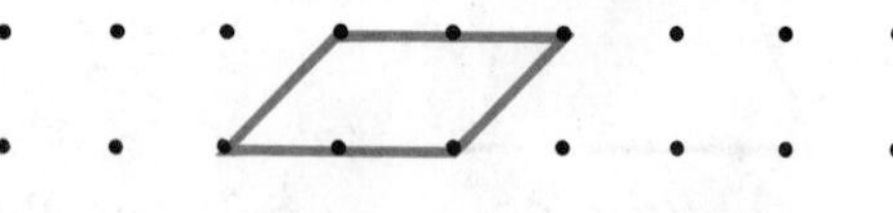

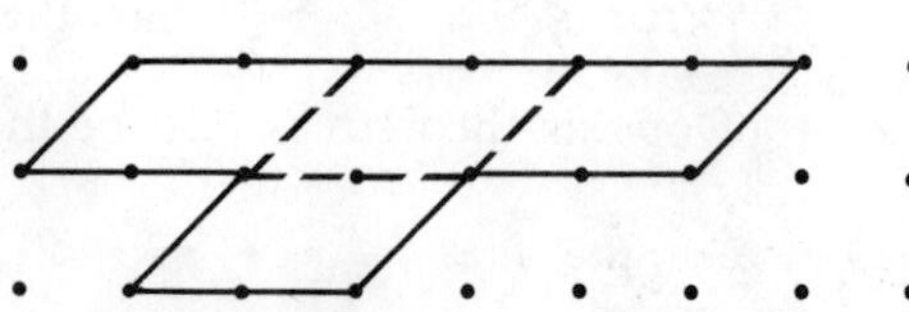

11. Given: $ABCD$ is a trapezoid with $\overline{AB} \parallel \overline{CD}$. P is on $\overline{CD}$ so that $\overline{AP}$ bisects $\angle A$.
Prove: $\triangle APD$ is isosceles.

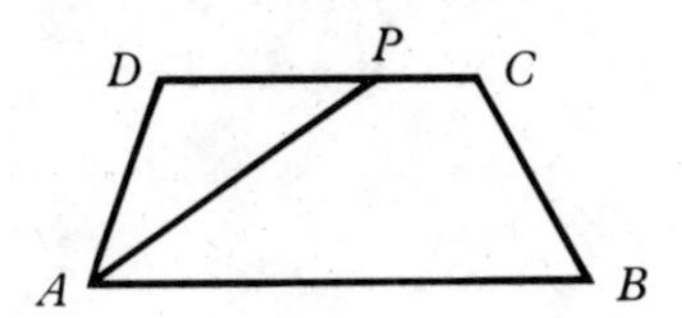

12. Given: $ABCD$ is a trapezoid with $\overline{AB} \parallel \overline{CD}$. $\overline{AD} \cong \overline{BC}$ $\overline{AC}$ and $\overline{BD}$ intersect at E.
Prove: $\triangle CDE$ is isosceles.

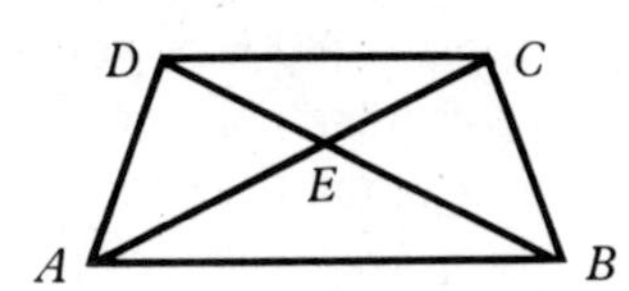

13. Given: $ABCD$ is an isosceles trapezoid with $\overline{AB} \parallel \overline{CD}$.
Prove: $\overline{AC} \cong \overline{BD}$

14. Given: $ABCD$ is a trapezoid with $\overline{AB} \parallel \overline{CD}$ and $\overline{AE} \cong \overline{BE}$.
Prove: $\overline{AD} \cong \overline{BC}$

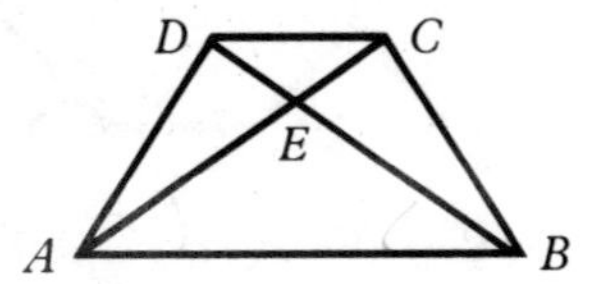

C.

15. Given: $ABCD$ is an isosceles trapezoid with $\overline{AB} \parallel \overline{CD}$.
Prove: $\angle A \cong \angle B$
(*Hint:* Construct a line through D parallel to $\overline{BC}$.)

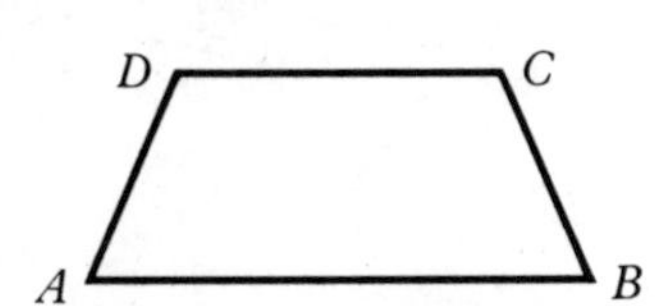

16. Given: $\triangle ABC$ is isosceles with $\overline{AB} \cong \overline{AC}$, $\angle AED \cong \angle B$.
Prove: $BCDE$ is a trapezoid with $\overline{BE} \cong \overline{CD}$.

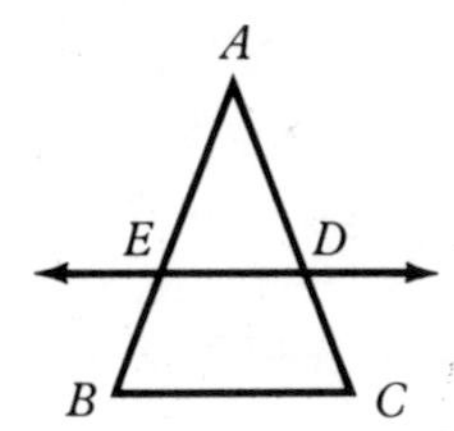

PROBLEM SOLVING

1. Trace a regular hexagon. Can you cut it to form
   a. 6 equilateral triangles?
   b. 2 isosceles trapezoids?
   c. 3 congruent rhombuses?

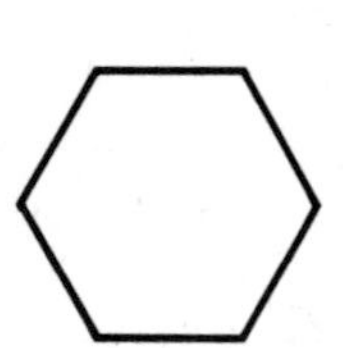

2. Trace two regular hexagons. Can you cut them to produce equilateral triangles?
3. Trace an equilateral triangle. Can you cut it to form 3 congruent 5-sided figures.

   (*Hint:* Use a figure Y at the center.)

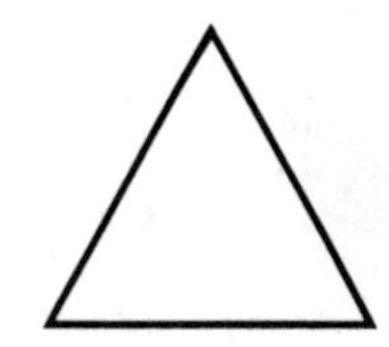

8–7 The Angles of a Polygon

The activity on page 280 asks you to look for combinations of regular polygons that fit together around a point P.

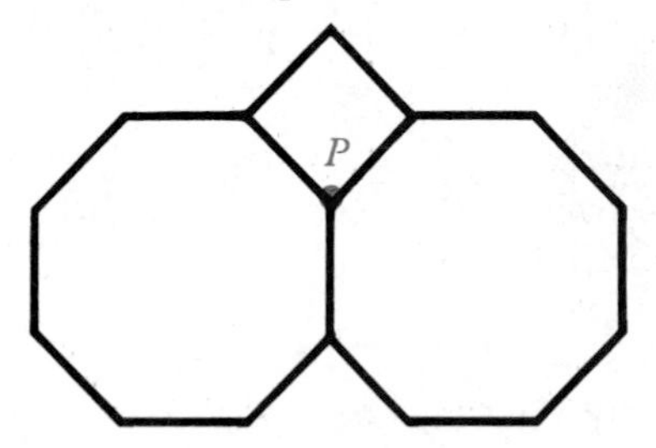

The measures of the vertex angles of polygons determine whether or not they really fit together.

We first ask what is the sum of the angle measures of a polygon? To answer this question, we draw diagonals from one vertex of the polygon to form triangles.

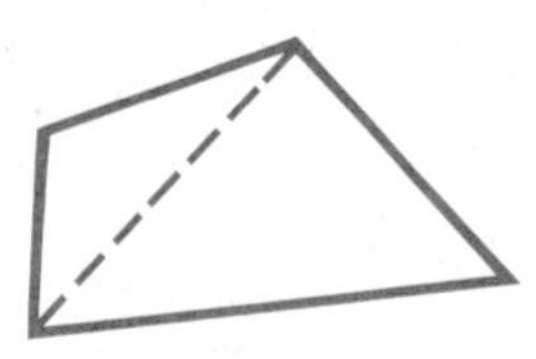

Quadrilateral

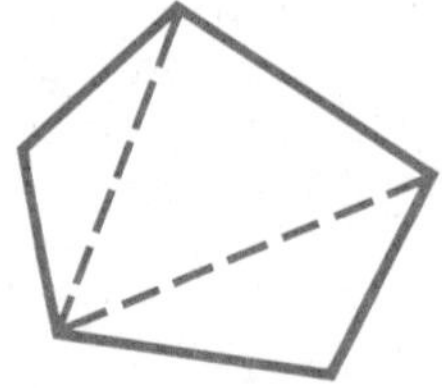

Pentagon

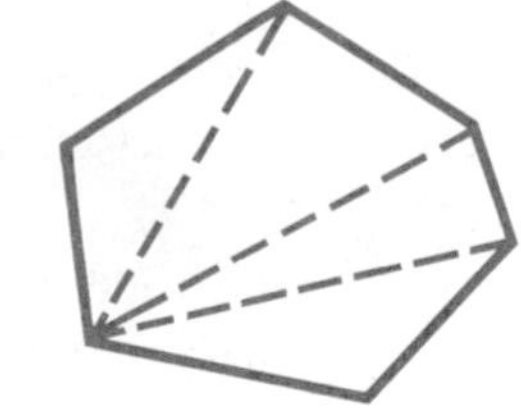

Hexagon

In each of these cases the sum of the measures of the angles of the polygon is the sum of the measures of the angles of the triangles. This observation leads to this table.

Polygon	Number of sides	Number of triangles	Sum of the measures of the angles
quadrilateral	4	2	$2(180°) = 360°$
pentagon	5	3	$3(180°) = 540°$
hexagon	6	4	$4(180°) = 720°$
⋮	⋮	⋮	⋮
n-gon	n	$n - 2$	$(n - 2)180°$

The inductive reasoning demonstrated by the preceding table suggests these two theorems.

Theorem 8–14 The sum of the measures of the angles of a convex polygon of n sides is $(n-2)180°$.

Theorem 8–15 The measure of an angle of a regular polygon of n sides is $\frac{(n-2)}{n}180°$.

APPLICATION

An artist working on a mosaic may ask which combinations of three or four of these regular polygons will fit together around a point as shown at the beginning of the lesson.

Step 1 Use Theorem 8–15 to find the measure of the angles of each of these regular polygons.

Step 2 Use trial and error to find combinations of the numbers found in Step 1 whose sum is 360°.

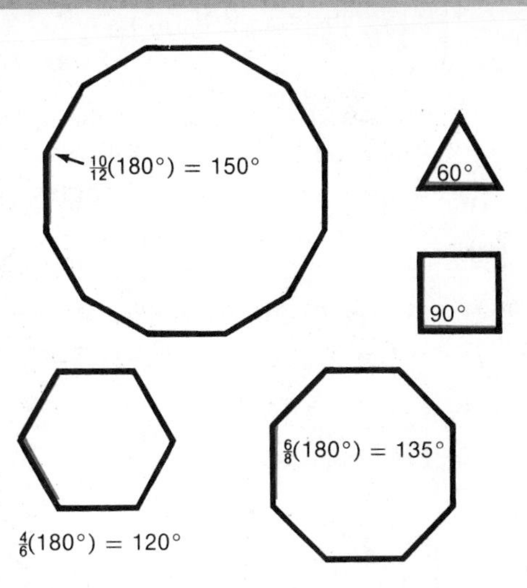

Consider the pentagon on the left. An exterior angle at each vertex is labeled. If we cut out these exterior angles and arrange them around a point, we see that their sum is 360°.

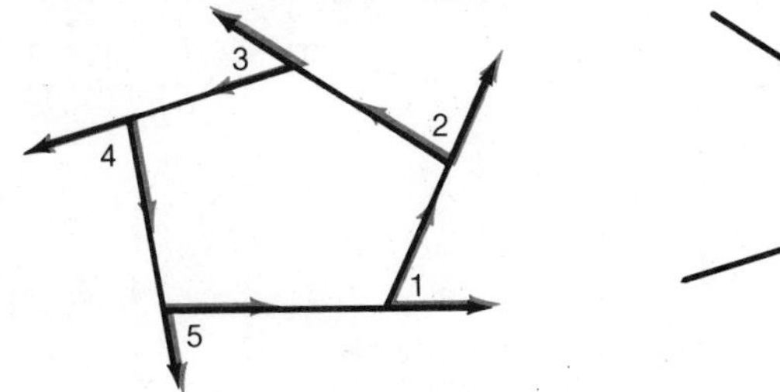

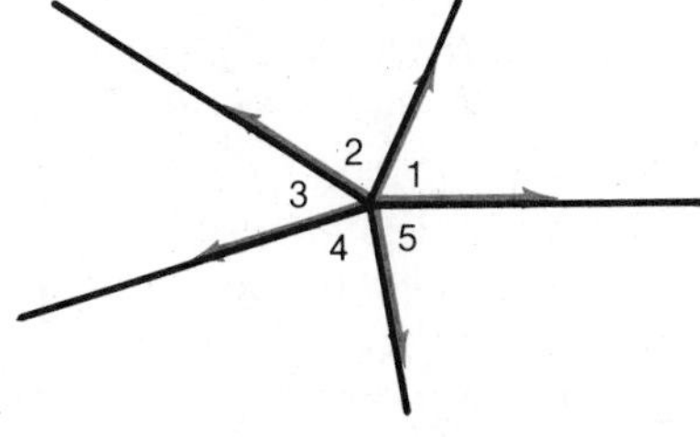

$m\angle 1 + m\angle 2 + m\angle 3 + m\angle 4 + m\angle 5 = 360$

Theorem 8–16 The sum of the measures of the exterior angles of a polygon, one at each vertex, is 360°.

EXERCISES

A.

In exercises 1–3 the number of sides of a convex polygon is given. The diagonals from one vertex of the polygon divides the polygon into how many triangles?

1. 10 **2.** 25 **3.** x

In exercises 4–9 the number of sides of a convex polygon is given. Find the sum of the measures of the angles of the polygon.

4. 6 **5.** 12 **6.** 24

7. 36 **8.** 100 **9.** p

In exercises 10–15 the sum of the measures of the interior angles is given. Find the number of sides of the polygon.

10. 7020° **11.** 1980° **12.** 6120°

13. 1800° **14.** 1260° **15.** 3420°

In exercises 16–21 the number of sides of a regular polygon is given. Find the measure of a vertex angle of the polygon.

16. 7 **17.** 9 **18.** 10

19. 15 **20.** 20 **21.** 100

Activity

1. Use a ruler and protractor to draw a regular 12-gon with each edge 3 cm long.

2. Use a ruler and protractor to draw a regular 15-gon with each edge 3 cm long.

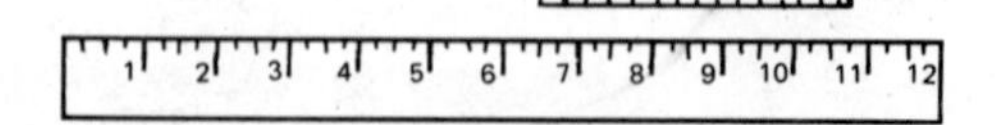

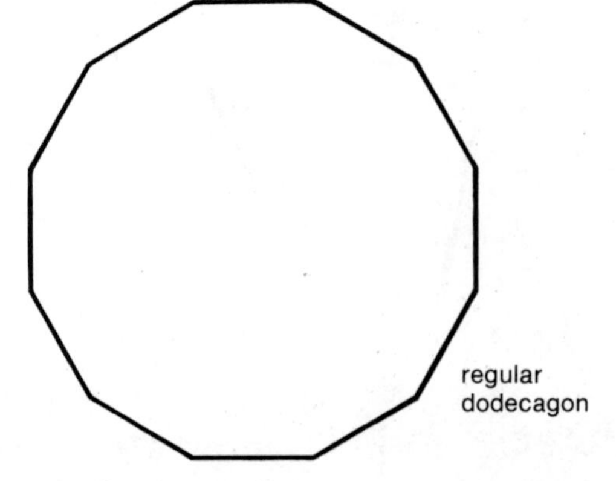

B.

22. The sum of the measures of seven angles of an octagon is 1000°. What is the measure of the eighth angle?

23. What is the measure of each exterior angle of a regular octagon? Of a regular 12-gon?

24. How many sides does a regular polygon have if each exterior angle has a measure of 15°? of 18°?

25. How many sides does a regular polygon have if each interior angle has a measure of 108°? of 144°?

26. Show that two regular pentagons and a regular 10-gon will fit together around a point. (See application.)

27. Show that an equilateral triangle, a regular 7-gon, and a regular 42-gon will fit together around a point.

C.

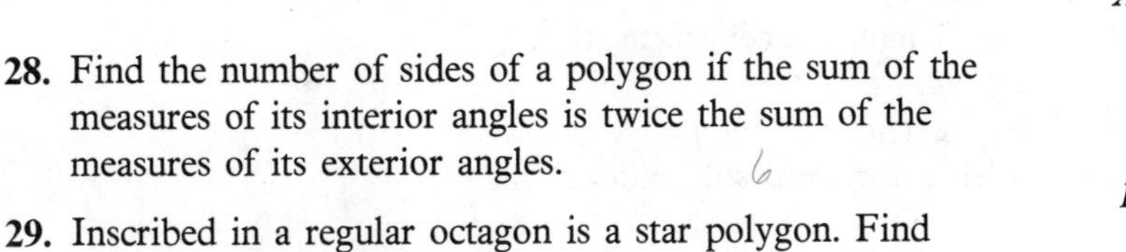

28. Find the number of sides of a polygon if the sum of the measures of its interior angles is twice the sum of the measures of its exterior angles.

29. Inscribed in a regular octagon is a star polygon. Find $m\angle ABC$. Prove that your answer is correct.

30. Prove that $\overline{AB} \parallel \overline{DE}$.

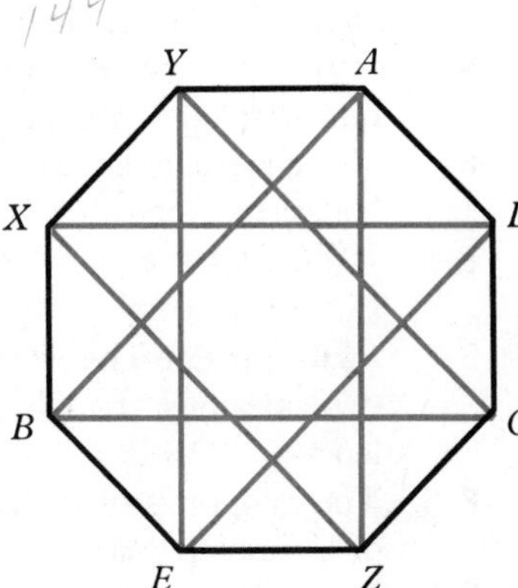

(Exs. 29–30)

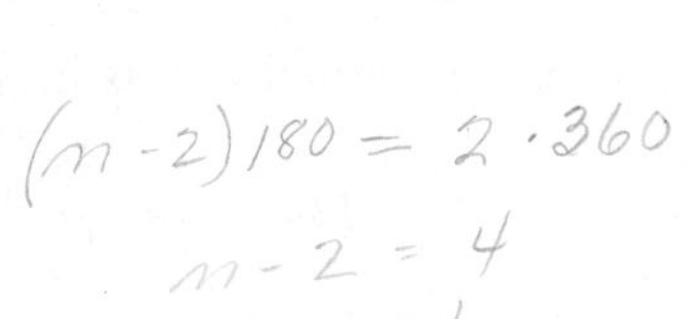

PROBLEM SOLVING

A steel plate is to be made with holes drilled as shown.

1. If $m\angle 1 = 37$, find $m\angle 2$.

2. If $m\angle 1 = 43$, find $m\angle 2$.

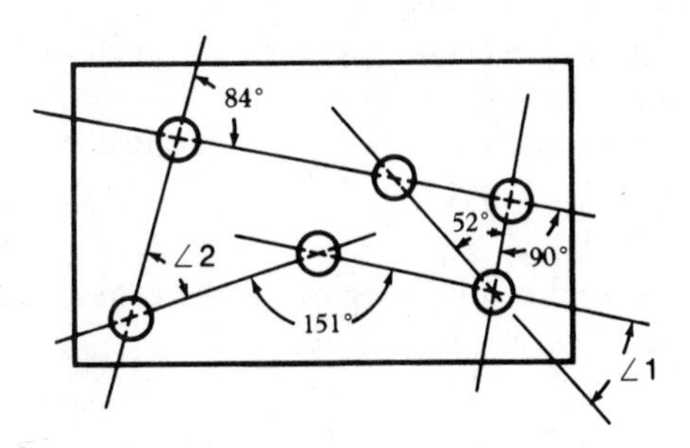

Important Ideas—Chapter 8

Terms

Trapezoid (p. 261)	Rhombus (p. 261)
Parallelogram (p. 261)	Square (p. 261)
Rectangle (p. 261)	Isosceles trapezoid (p. 289)

Theorems

8-1 The opposite angles of a parallelogram are congruent.

8-2 The opposite sides of a parallelogram are congruent.

8-3 Each pair of adjacent angles of a parallelogram are supplementary angles.

8-4 If the opposite sides of a quadrilateral are congruent, then the quadrilateral is a parallelogram.

8-5 If a quadrilateral has one pair of opposite sides parallel and congruent, then it is a parallelogram.

8-6 If the opposite angles of a quadrilateral are congruent, then the quadrilateral is a parallelogram.

8-7 **Midsegment Theorem.** A segment joining the midpoints of two sides of a triangle is parallel to the third side and half its length.

8-8 The midpoints of the sides of a quadrilateral are the vertices of a parallelogram.

8-9 A parallelogram is a rectangle if and only if its diagonals are congruent.

8-10 A parallelogram is a rhombus if and only if its diagonals are perpendicular to each other.

8-11 A parallelogram is a rhombus if and only if each diagonal bisects a pair of opposite angles.

8-12 The segment joining the midpoints of the two nonparallel sides of a trapezoid is parallel to the two bases and has a length equal to one half the sum of the lengths of the bases.

8-13 In an isosceles trapezoid base angles are congruent and the diagonals are congruent.

8-14 The sum of the measures of the angles of a convex polygon of n sides is $(n - 2)180°$.

8-15 The measure of an angle of a regular polygon of n sides is $\frac{(n - 2)}{n}180°$.

8-16 The sum of the measures of the exterior angles of a polygon, one at each vertex, is $360°$.

Chapter 8—Review

1. Indicate on your paper whether the following statements are true or false.
   - **a.** If the diagonals of a parallelogram are congruent, then the figure must be a rectangle.
   - **b.** If the diagonals of a parallelogram are perpendicular, then the figure must be a square.
   - **c.** If a figure is a square, then it must be a rhombus.
   - **d.** If the diagonals of a trapezoid are congruent, then the figure is a parallelogram.

2. Suppose $ABCD$ is a parallelogram, $m\angle B = 110$, and $m\angle 2 = 30$. Find $m\angle 4$.

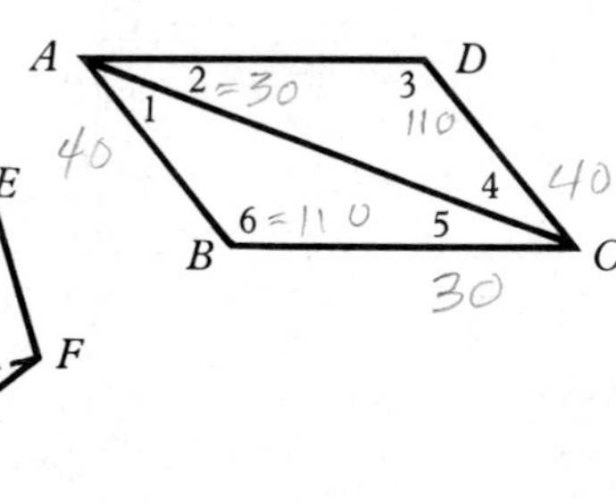

3. **Given:** Figure $ABCD$ is a parallelogram.
   $\overline{EF} \parallel \overline{DA}$, $\overline{EF} \cong \overline{DA}$
   Prove: Figure $BCEF$ is a parallelogram.

4. **Given:** Figure $BCDE$ is a rhombus.
   E is the midpoint of $\overline{AB}$, $m\angle 1 = 60$.
   Prove: Figure $ABCD$ is an isosceles trapezoid.

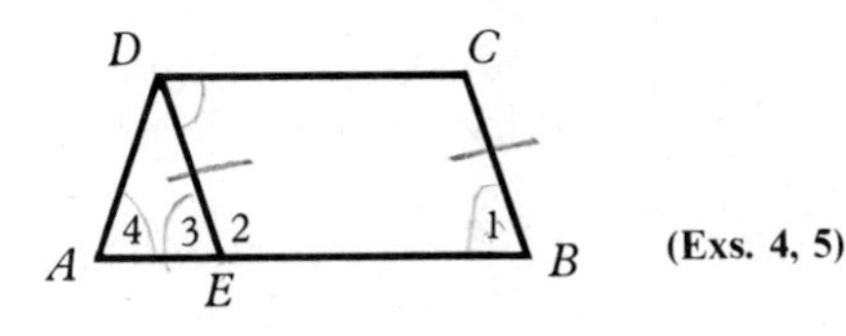

(Exs. 4, 5)

5. **Given:** $EBCD$ is a parallelogram,
   $m\angle 1 = m\angle 4$.
   Prove: $AD = DE$.

6. Suppose E, F, G, and H are midpoints. If $m\angle 1 = 30$ and $m\angle 2 = 50$, find $m\angle EFG$.

7. Suppose E, F, G, and H are midpoints. If $AC = 12$ and $BD = 8$, find $EF + FG + GH + EH$.

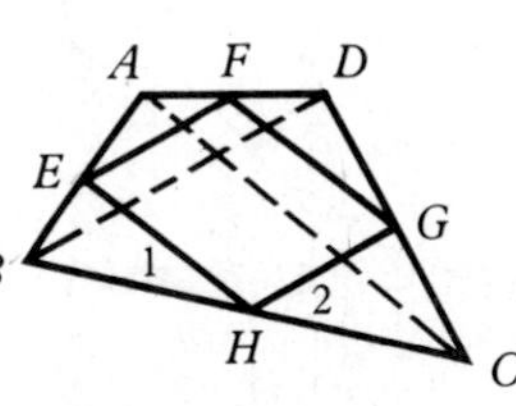

(Exs. 6, 7)

8. Find the measure of each angle of a regular 12-sided polygon.

9. If four angles of a pentagon have measures of 100°, 70°, 150°, and 120°, find the measure of the fifth angle.

10. Suppose $ABCD$ is a rectangle. If $AD = 5$ and $CD = 12$ find BX.

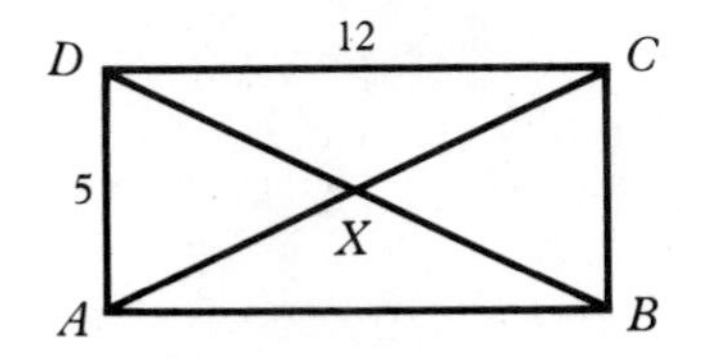

Chapter 8—Test

1. Indicate on your paper whether the following statements are true or false.

   a. If a quadrilateral has one pair of congruent sides, then it is a parallelogram.

   b. If a quadrilateral has congruent diagonals, then it must be a rectangle.

   c. The sum of the exterior angles of a regular pentagon is $360°$.

   d. If a parallelogram has one right angle, it is a rectangle.

2. $ABCD$ is a trapezoid. M and N are midpoints. $AD = 6$, and $MN = 10$. Find BC.

(Ex. 2)

3. Suppose D, E, and F are midpoints. If $AB = 4$, $AC = 5$, and $BC = 6$, find $DE + EF + DF$.

4. **Given:** $\triangle ABC$ is equilateral.
   D, E, and F are midpoints.
   Prove: $\triangle DEF$ is equilateral.

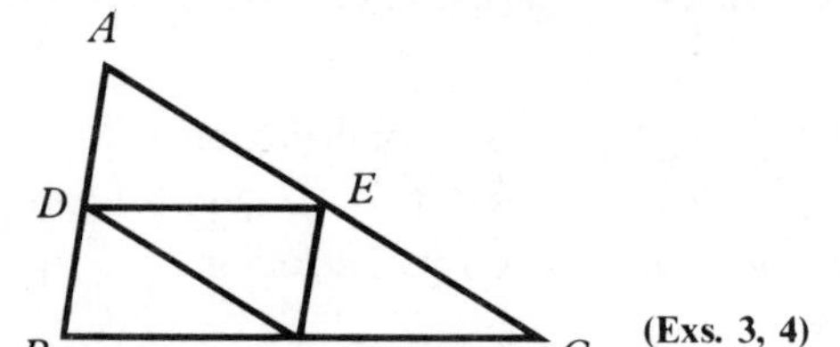

(Exs. 3, 4)

5. $PQRS$ is a parallelogram. If $m\angle P = 4x + 20$ and $m\angle Q = x + 10$, find $m\angle P$.

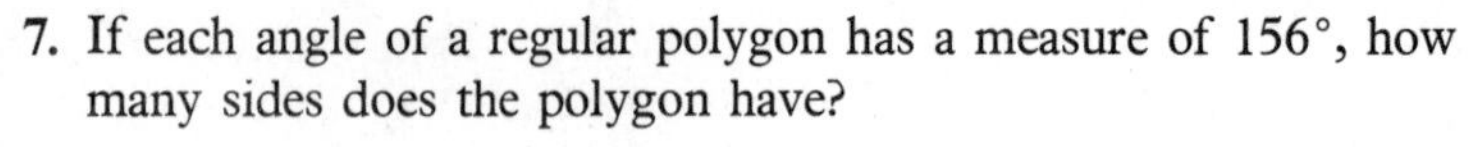

6. If $m\angle 1 + m\angle 2 + m\angle 3 + m\angle 4 + m\angle 5 = 290$, find $m\angle 6$.

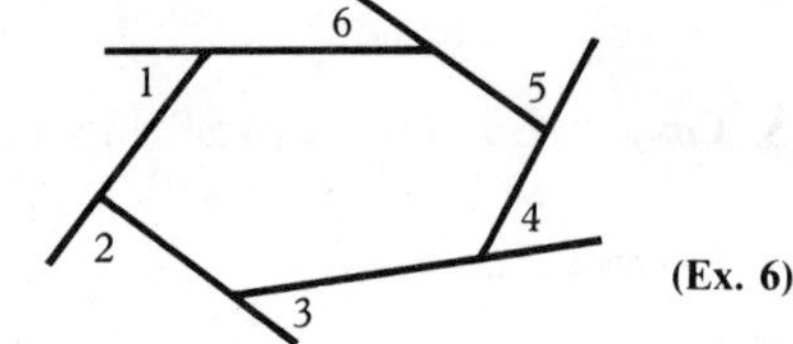

(Ex. 6)

7. If each angle of a regular polygon has a measure of $156°$, how many sides does the polygon have?

8. **Given:** $AD = DB$ and $AE = EC$
   $AF = FD$ and $AG = GE$
   Prove: $\overline{FG} \parallel \overline{BC}$

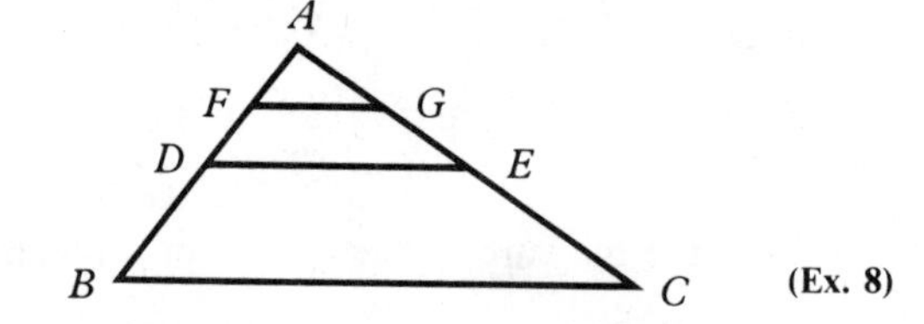

(Ex. 8)

9. The figures shown are two overlapping rectangles. Find the sum, $a + b + c + d$.

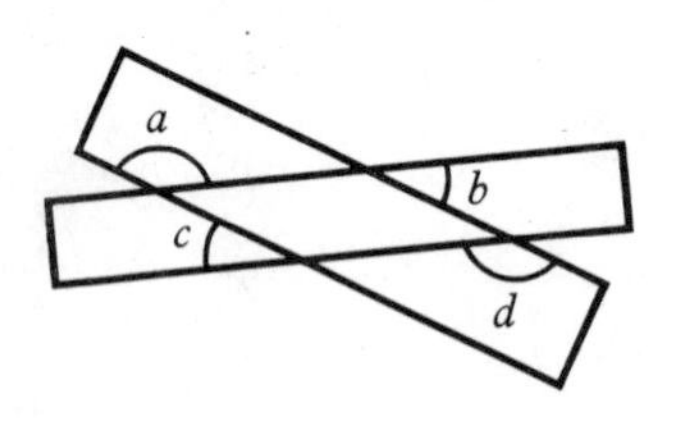

Algebra Review

Solve the following proportions for x.

1. $\frac{x}{2} = \frac{6}{3}$
2. $\frac{3}{4} = \frac{6}{x}$
3. $\frac{x}{x-2} = \frac{21}{15}$
4. $\frac{x-3}{6} = \frac{4-x}{-5}$
5. $\frac{5}{6} = \frac{5x}{x+60}$
6. $\frac{x}{3} = \frac{4}{x-1}$
7. $\frac{2x-3}{2} = \frac{5x}{6}$
8. $\frac{x-2}{x+5} = \frac{6}{20}$
9. $\frac{x+2}{5} = \frac{1}{x-2}$

Solve each system.

10. $2x - 4y = 30$
    $3x + 2y = -3$
11. $y = 3x - 5$
    $x = -2y - 10$
12. $2(x-2) + y = -18$
    $3x + 2(y-1) = -26$
13. $2x + 5y = 7$
    $x = -\frac{3}{2}$
14. $5x + 8y = 1$
    $2x - 7y = -20$
15. $2x + y + 3 = 0$
    $8x - \frac{y}{3} + 25 = 0$
16. $x + 2y - 4 = 0$
    $\frac{5}{2}x - 13y - 10 = 0$
17. $\frac{3}{2}p + \frac{4}{3}q = 2$
    $8q = 3p + 4$
18. $m - \frac{n-2}{3} = 0$
    $0.2m + 0.3n = 5$

Solve for x.

19. $\sqrt{x} - 9 = 0$
20. $\sqrt{x+4} = 5$
21. $\sqrt{x+2} + 4 = 7$
22. $\sqrt{x^2-9} = 4$
23. $\sqrt{2+x} = 0$
24. $\sqrt{x} + 4 = \sqrt{x} - 2$

Solve for x.

25. $(x+2)(x-5) = 0$
26. $(2x+5)(3x-1) = 0$
27. $x^2 - 10x + 25 = 0$
28. $(x-4)^2 = 9$
29. $x^2 - x - 12 = 0$
30. $4x^2 - 9 = 0$

Solve.

31. The measures of the angles of a triangle are in a ratio of 2:3:5. Find the measures of the angles.
32. The perimeter of a rectangle is 160. If the ratio of the width to the length is 7:9, find the dimensions of the rectangle.

Architecture: The Golden Rectangle

The *Golden Rectangle* was considered by the early Greeks to be one of the most beautifully proportioned geometric forms. It has been used by architects for centuries in planning temples, skyscrapers, and buildings of all kinds.

The Greeks built the Parthenon in Athens in the 5th century B.C. The rectangle that encloses the front face is a Golden Rectangle.

The *Golden Rectangle* is a rectangle such that if a unit square is cut off one end, the sides of the remaining smaller rectangle will be in the same ratio as those in the original rectangle. Since the ratios of pairs of corresponding sides of the large and small rectangle ($ABCD$ and $EBCF$) are equal, we can use this ratio

$$\frac{1 + a}{1} = \frac{1}{a}$$

and calculate the length of the longest side of a Golden Rectangle with width one. Find this length.

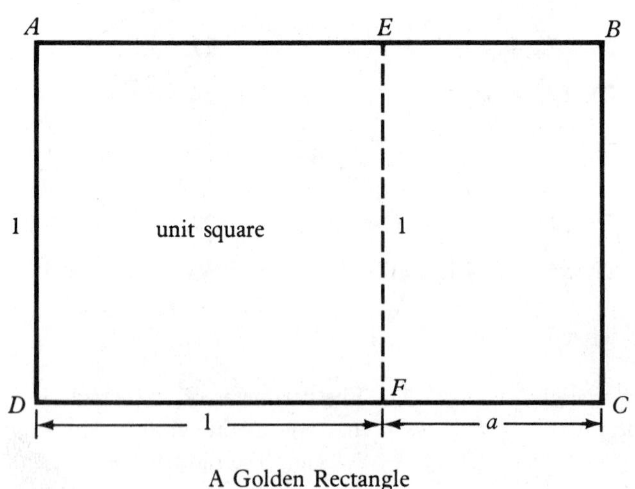

A Golden Rectangle

Constructing a Golden Rectangle

Using compass and straightedge, follow the steps below to construct a Golden Rectangle.

Step 1 Construct a unit square $ABCD$.

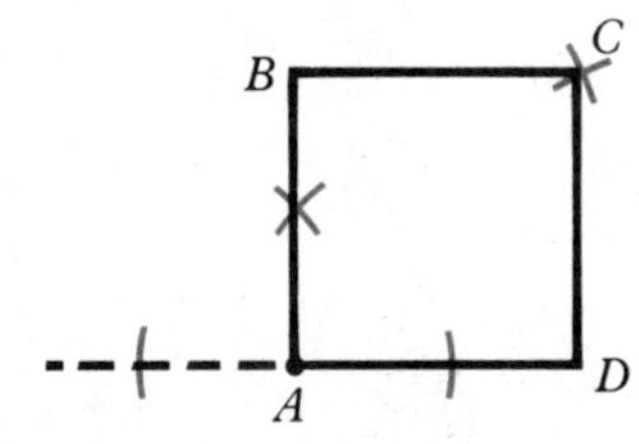

Step 2 Construct the midpoint of side $\overline{AD}$. Using M as center and radius MC, draw an arc which intersects $\overrightarrow{AD}$ at point E.

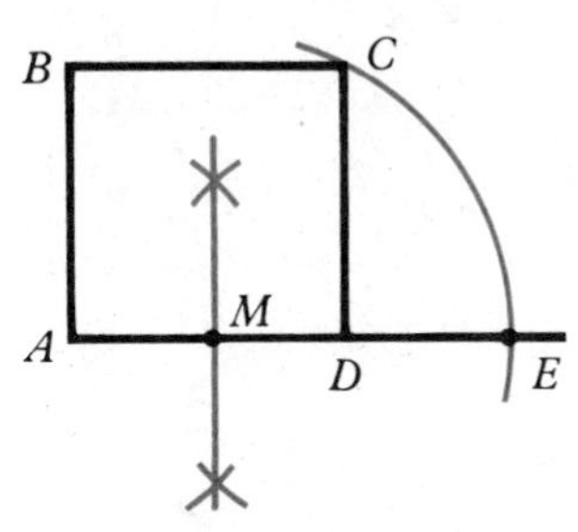

Step 3 Construct $\overline{EF} \perp \overline{AE}$ and complete the Golden Rectangle $ABFE$.

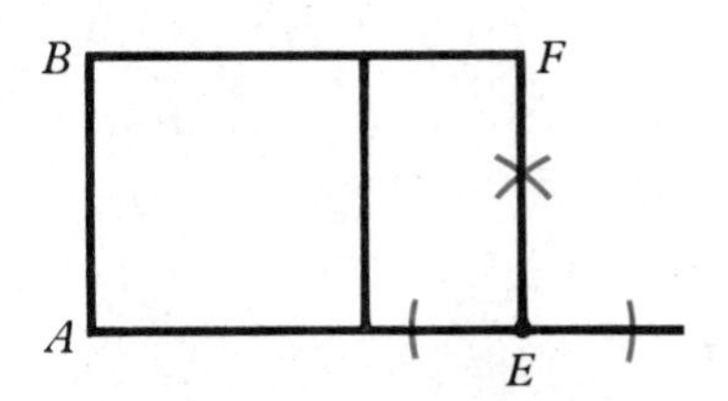

CHAPTER 9

Similarity

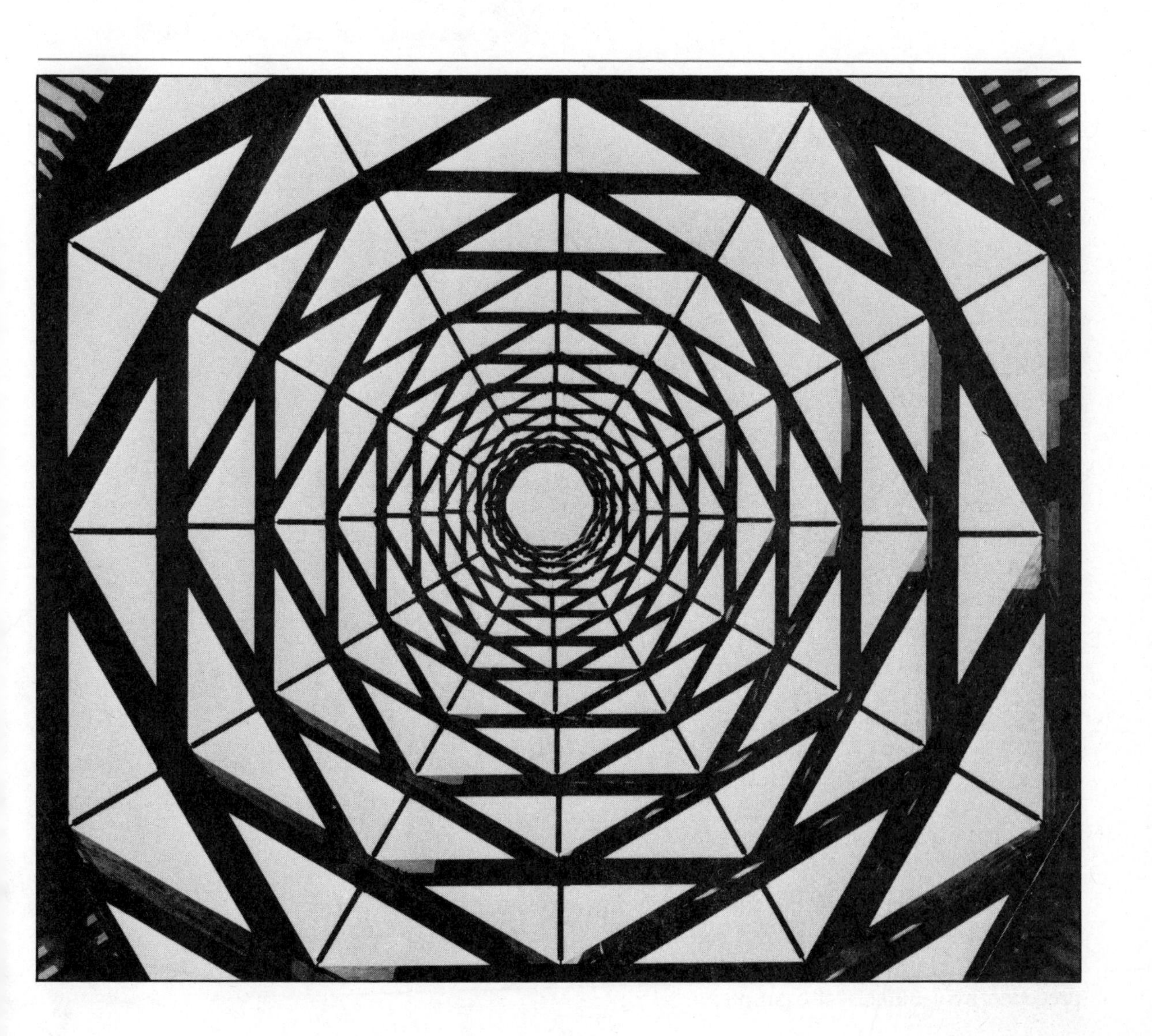

9–1 Proportions

In this chapter you will study polygons that have the same shape—but not necessarily the same size. There are many triangles in this photograph that have the same shape.

The idea of same shape is involved in an enlargement or a reduction. Consider the two photographs below.

5 cm

4 cm

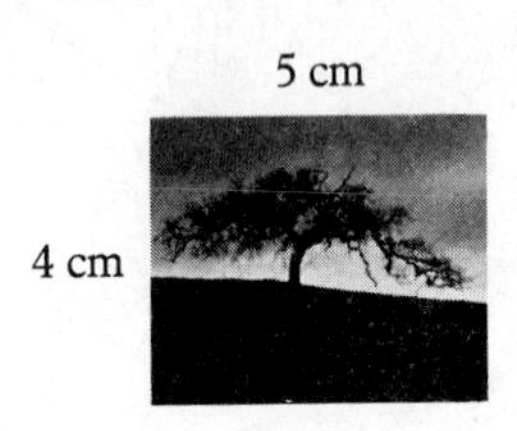

10 cm

8 cm

Both of these photographs are of the same subject, but one is larger than the other. Both pictures have the "same shape." If we compare the ratio of width to length of each picture, we see that the ratios are equal.

$$\frac{4\text{ cm}}{5\text{ cm}} = \frac{8\text{ cm}}{10\text{ cm}}$$

This equation is called a *proportion* because it is made up of two equal ratios, $\frac{4}{5}$ and $\frac{8}{10}$.

Definition 9–1

A **proportion** is an equality between two ratios. The ratios $\frac{a}{b}$ and $\frac{c}{d}$ are proportional if $\frac{a}{b} = \frac{c}{d}$. $b \neq 0$, $d \neq 0$.

(It is important to remember that a denominator cannot be equal to zero.)

In this lesson we shall review some of the algebraic properties of proportion. The proofs of these theorems will be omitted, but each will be preceded by a numerical example.

Example 1 In a proportion cross products are equal.

$$\frac{4}{8} = \frac{2}{4} \quad \text{or} \quad 4 \times 4 = 2 \times 8$$

Theorem 9–1 If $\frac{a}{b} = \frac{c}{d}$, then $a \times d = b \times c$.

Example 2 In a proportion, 1 can be added to both sides.

If $\frac{9}{3} = \frac{12}{4}$, then $\frac{9}{3} + \frac{3}{3} = \frac{12}{4} + \frac{4}{4}$ or $\frac{9+3}{3} = \frac{12+4}{4}$.

Theorem 9–2 If $\frac{a}{b} = \frac{c}{d}$, then $\frac{a+b}{b} = \frac{c+d}{d}$.

Example 3 In a proportion, 1 can be subtracted from both sides.

If $\frac{9}{3} = \frac{12}{4}$, then $\frac{9}{3} - \frac{3}{3} = \frac{12}{4} - \frac{4}{4}$ or $\frac{9-3}{3} = \frac{12-4}{4}$.

Theorem 9–3 If $\frac{a}{b} = \frac{c}{d}$, then $\frac{a-b}{b} = \frac{c-d}{d}$.

Example 4 If $\frac{9}{3} = \frac{12}{4}$, then $\frac{9}{12} = \frac{3}{4}$.

Theorem 9–4 If $\frac{a}{b} = \frac{c}{d}$, then $\frac{a}{c} = \frac{b}{d}$.

Example 5 If $9 \times 4 = 3 \times 12$, then $\frac{9}{3} = \frac{12}{4}$.

Theorem 9–5 If $a \times d = b \times c$, then $\frac{a}{b} = \frac{c}{d}$.

EXERCISES

A.

1. Given that $\frac{4}{5} = \frac{12}{15}$, which theorem is used to conclude each of the following:

   a. $\frac{4}{12} = \frac{5}{15}$ b. $\frac{9}{5} = \frac{27}{15}$ c. $\frac{-1}{5} = \frac{-3}{15}$.

2. Suppose $\frac{AD}{DB} = \frac{AE}{EC}$. Which theorem is used to conclude each of the following:

   a. $\frac{AD - DB}{DB} = \frac{AE - EC}{EC}$ b. $\frac{AD}{AE} = \frac{DB}{EC}$

   c. $\frac{AD + DB}{DB} = \frac{AE + EC}{EC}$.

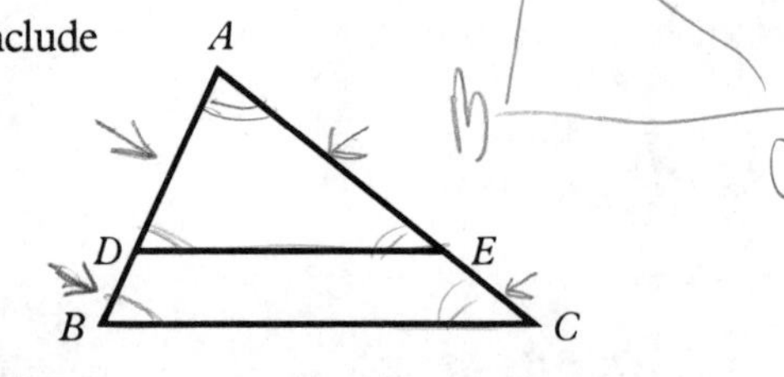

3. Use Theorem 9-5 and the following products to form proportions.

   a. $3 \times 4 = 2 \times 6$ b. $\sqrt{2} \times \sqrt{3} = 1 \times \sqrt{6}$

   c. $2 \cdot MN = 3 \cdot XY$ d. $AB \cdot CD = EF \cdot GH$

4. Use Theorem 9-1 to solve the following proportions for x.

   a. $\frac{4}{5} = \frac{x}{25}$ b. $\frac{6}{9} = \frac{18}{x}$ c. $\frac{x - 4}{x} = \frac{3}{4}$

B.

5. State the contrapositive of Theorem 9-1. Use this contrapositive to show that the following statements are not proportions.

   a. $\frac{12}{13} = \frac{13}{14}$ b. $\frac{23}{33} = \frac{31}{41}$ c. $\frac{\sqrt{2}}{\sqrt{3}} = \frac{\sqrt{2} + 1}{\sqrt{3} + 1}$

Activity

A 1-cm square grid has been superimposed on this cartoon. Draw an enlargement of this cartoon by using a 2-cm square grid.

6. The measures of two complementary angles are in a ratio of $\frac{2}{3}$. Find the measures of these angles.
7. If 2 calculators cost $28, how much should 5 calculators cost?
8. Two numbers are in a ratio of 2:3. What is the ratio of their squares?
9. The measures of two supplementary angles are in a ratio of $\frac{3}{5}$. Find the measures of the angles.
10. A 56 cm segment is divided into a ratio of 3 to 5. Find the length of the two segments.
11. A 5×7 photograph is enlarged by a factor of $\frac{5}{2}$. What size is the enlargement?
12. The area of two triangles are in a ratio of 4 to 9. The smaller triangle has an area of 50 cm^2. Find the area of the larger triangle.

13. Solve the proportion for x. $\dfrac{-3}{x} = \dfrac{x-8}{5}$

PROBLEM SOLVING

1. Use a ruler and the scale indicated below to find the actual distance across this church both east-west and north-south.
2. Write down the proportions used in answering Problem 1.
3. If the walls from *A*, north around the church to *F*, are poured concrete walls that cost $20/foot, estimate the total cost of pouring these walls.

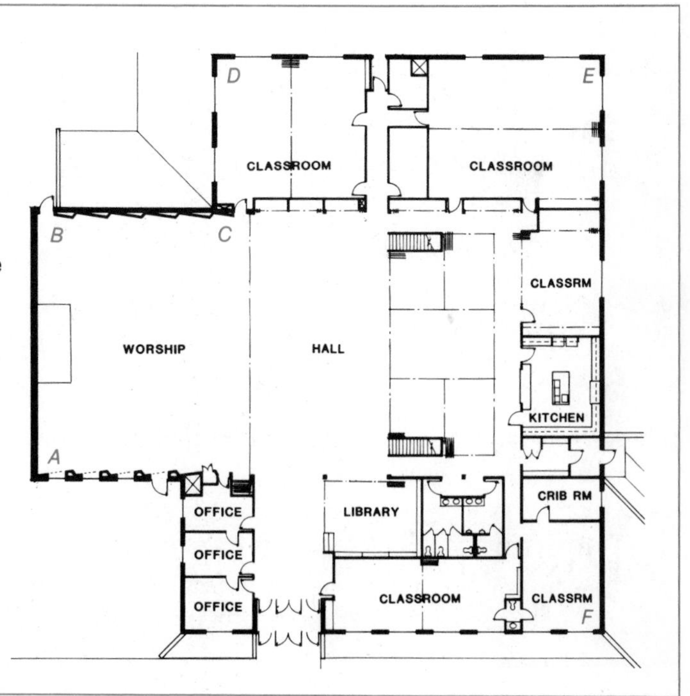

NORTH

FLOOR PLAN

0' 4' 8' 16' 32'

SCALE IN FEET

9–2 The Side-Splitting Theorem

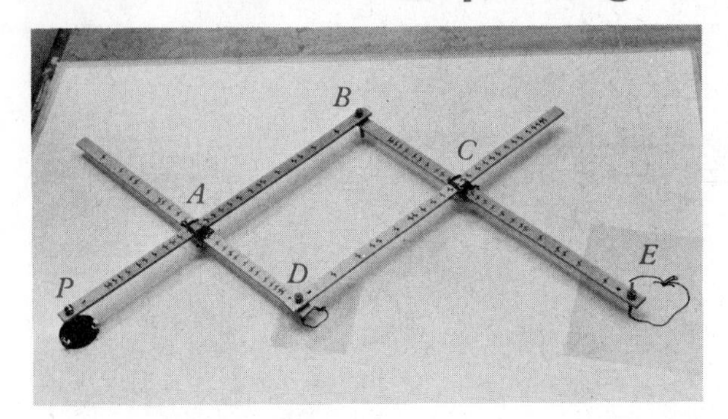

A mechanical linkage called a pantograph can be used by draftsmen and others to enlarge or reduce drawings, as shown here. The instrument lies flat and is fastened down at a pivot point P. As the stylus at point D traces a figure, the pencil at point E draws an enlarged figure. The pantograph is based upon the theorem in this lesson.

In the triangles below a segment has been drawn parallel to one side of the triangle.

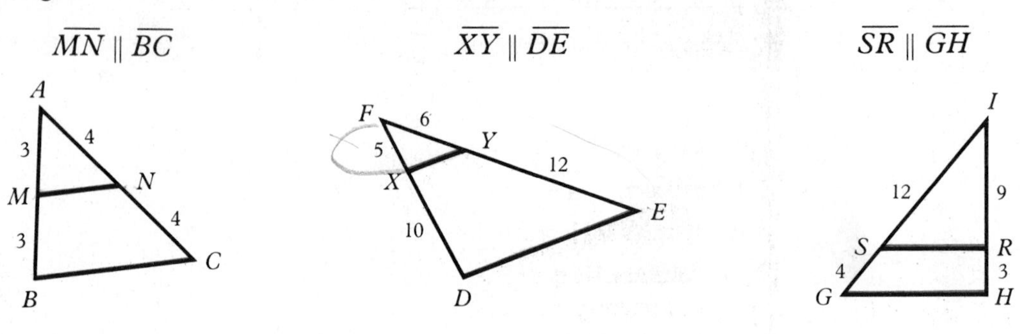

Observe that

$$\frac{AM}{MB} = 1, \frac{AN}{NC} = 1, \qquad \frac{FX}{XD} = \frac{1}{2}, \frac{FY}{YE} = \frac{1}{2}, \qquad \frac{IS}{SG} = \frac{3}{1}, \frac{IR}{RH} = \frac{3}{1},$$

or or or

$$\frac{AM}{MB} = \frac{AN}{NC}. \qquad \frac{FX}{XD} = \frac{FY}{YE}. \qquad \frac{IS}{SG} = \frac{IR}{RH}.$$

These observations are summarized by this theorem.

Theorem 9–6 **Side-Splitting Theorem.** If a line is parallel to one side of a triangle and intersects the other two sides, then it divides the two sides proportionally.

Example 1

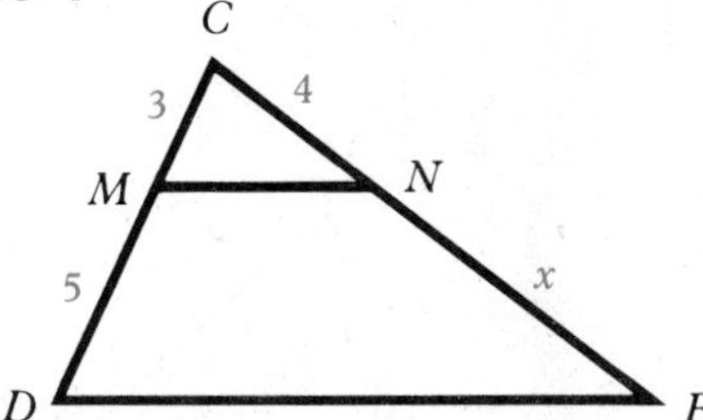

In this figure $\overline{MN} \parallel \overline{DE}$. Find NE.

By Theorem 9–6, $\frac{CM}{MD} = \frac{CN}{NE}$,

hence $\frac{3}{5} = \frac{4}{x}$,

$3x = 20$,

or $x = \frac{20}{3}$.

Example 2

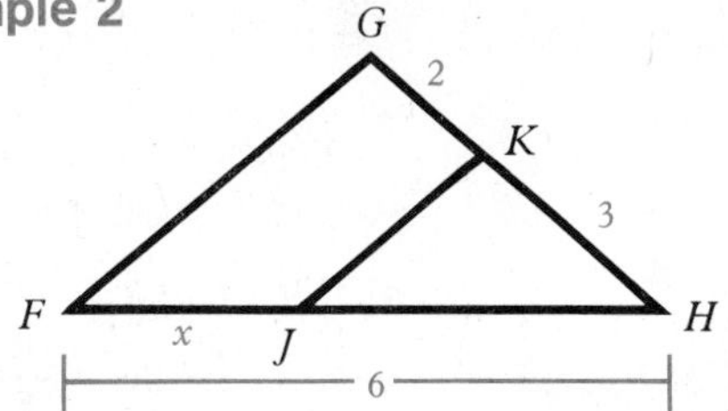

Find FJ in the figure shown if $\overline{GF} \parallel \overline{KJ}$.

By Theorem 9–6, $\frac{GK}{KH} = \frac{FJ}{JH}$,

$\frac{2}{3} = \frac{x}{6 - x}$,

$3x = 12 - 2x$,

$5x = 12$,

or $x = \frac{12}{5}$.

APPLICATION

1. A pantograph is constructed so that $AB = CD$, $AD = BC$, and P, D, and E are collinear. Therefore by Theorem 8–4 we can conclude that $ABCD$ is a parallelogram.
2. Since $ABCD$ is a parallelogram, $\overline{AD} \parallel \overline{BE}$ in $\triangle PBE$. Therefore, by Theorem 9–6, we can conclude that the ratio $\frac{PD}{DE}$ is always constant and equal to the ratio $\frac{PA}{AB}$. This fact helps explain why the pantograph works.

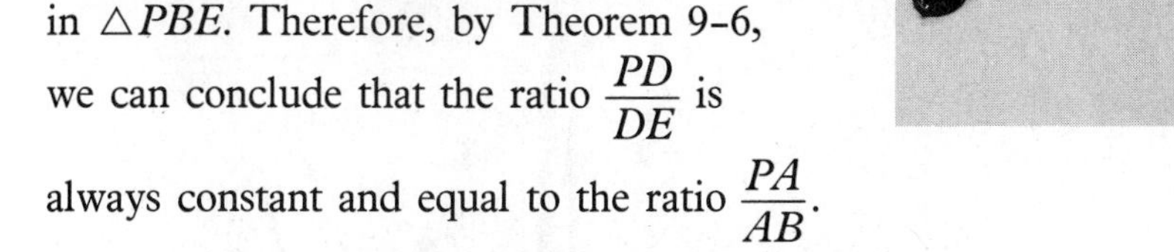

The converse of Theorem 9–6 is also true and is stated here.

Theorem 9–7 If a line intersects two sides of a triangle and divides them proportionally, then the line is parallel to the third side.

EXERCISES

A.

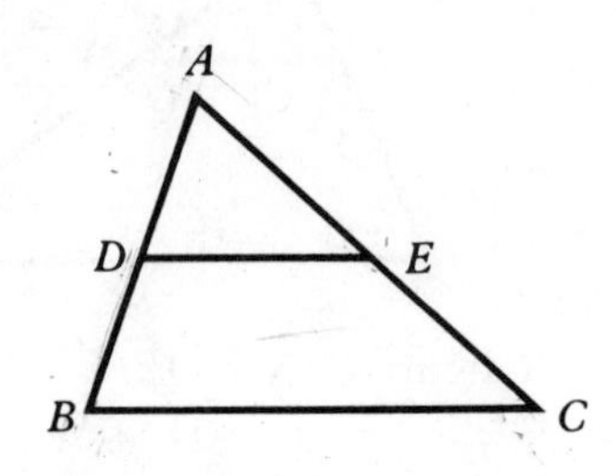

(Exs. 1, 2)

1. Assume $\overline{DE} \parallel \overline{BC}$. Indicate whether the following are true or false.

   a. $\frac{AD}{DB} = \frac{AE}{EC}$ b. $\frac{AB}{AD} = \frac{AC}{AE}$

   c. $\frac{AB}{DB} = \frac{AC}{EC}$ d. $\frac{AD}{AE} = \frac{EC}{BD}$

   e. $\frac{AD}{AE} = \frac{AB}{AC}$ f. $\frac{AD}{AB - AD} = \frac{AE}{AC - EC}$

2. Indicate whether the following are true or false.

   a. If $\frac{DB}{AD} = \frac{EC}{AE}$, then $\overline{DE} \parallel \overline{BC}$. b. If $\frac{DB}{AE} = \frac{EC}{AD}$, then $\overline{DE} \parallel \overline{BC}$.

   c. If $\frac{AB}{AD} = \frac{AC}{AE}$, then $\overline{DE} \parallel \overline{BC}$. d. If $\frac{AD}{AB} = \frac{EC}{AC}$, then $\overline{DE} \parallel \overline{BC}$.

   e. If $\frac{DB}{AB - DB} = \frac{EC}{AC - EC}$, then $\overline{DE} \parallel \overline{BC}$. f. If $\frac{AD + DB}{AD} = \frac{AE + EC}{AE}$, then $\overline{DE} \parallel \overline{BC}$.

In exercises 3–8, find the value of x. Assume the lines that appear parallel are parallel.

3. 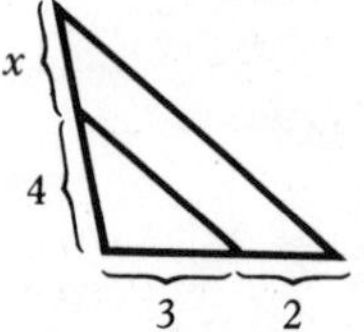

4. 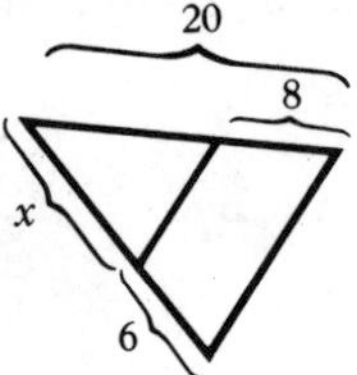

5. 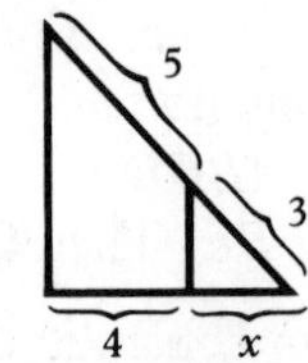

6. 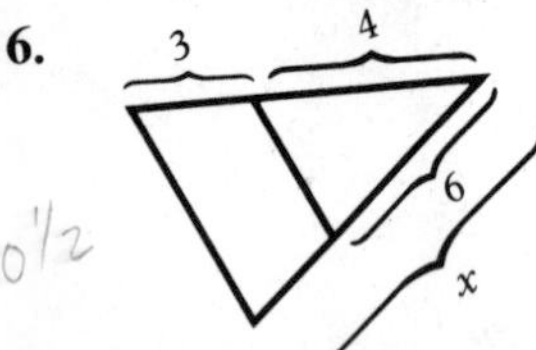

7. 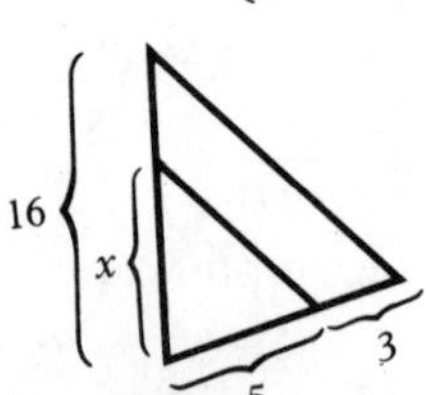

8. 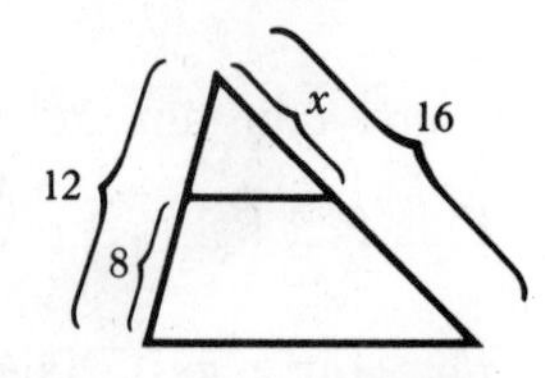

Activity

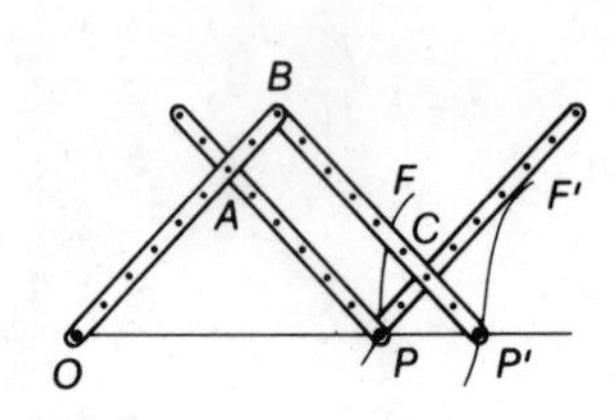

For this activity you will need strips of cardboard or wood about 30 cm long and some fasteners.

1. Make a pantograph by fastening strips together so that $AB = PC$ and $AP = BC$.
2. Use it to draw an enlargement of some figure.

B.

9. Given: $\overline{RS} \parallel \overline{ZX}$, $\overline{RX} \parallel \overline{TS}$

Prove: $\frac{TY}{RT} = \frac{RY}{RZ}$

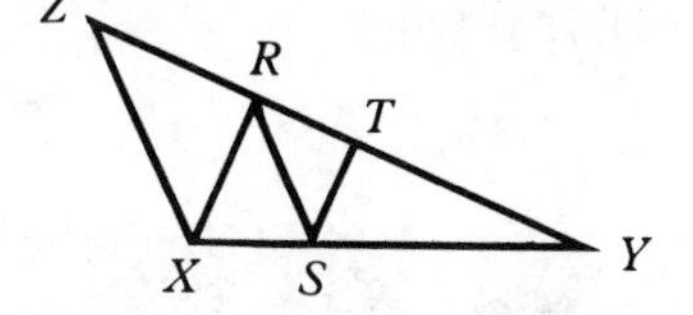

10. Given: $ABCD$ is a trapezoid.
$\overline{EF} \parallel \overline{AB}$, $\overline{EF} \parallel \overline{DC}$

Prove: $\frac{AE}{ED} = \frac{BF}{FC}$

(*Hint:* Draw $\overline{BD}$. Consider $\triangle ABD$ and $\triangle BCD$.)

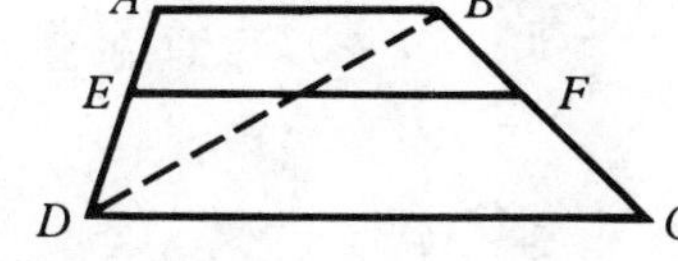

11. Given: $ABCD$ is a trapezoid.
$\overline{EF} \parallel \overline{AB}$, $\overline{EF} \parallel \overline{DC}$,
$\frac{AE}{ED} = \frac{1}{4}$, $BC = 30$

Find: BF and FC

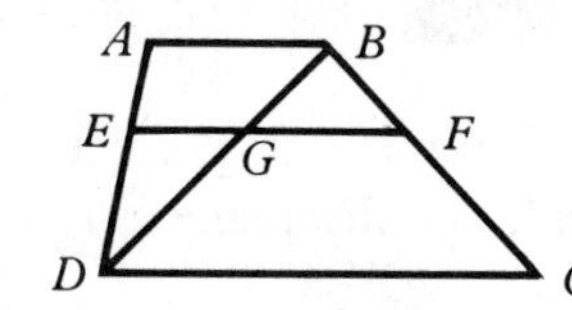

(Exs. 11, 12)

12. Given: $ABCD$ is a trapezoid.
$\overline{EF} \parallel \overline{AB}$, $\overline{EF} \parallel \overline{DC}$,
$\frac{BG}{GD} = \frac{3}{4}$, $AD = 8$, $BC = 12$

Find: AE, ED, BF, FC

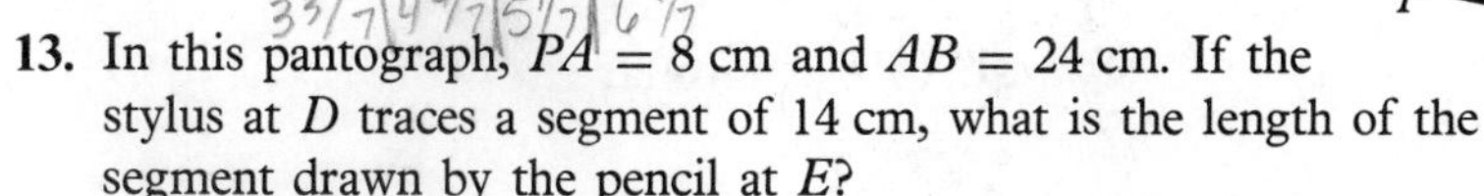

13. In this pantograph, $PA = 8$ cm and $AB = 24$ cm. If the stylus at D traces a segment of 14 cm, what is the length of the segment drawn by the pencil at E?

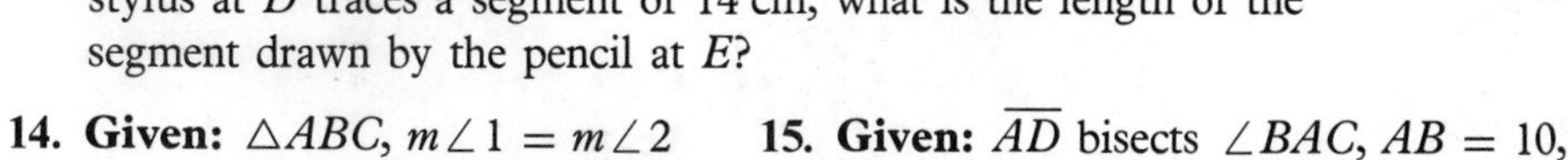

14. Given: $\triangle ABC$, $m\angle 1 = m\angle 2$

Prove: $\frac{BD}{DC} = \frac{AB}{AC}$

(*Hint:* Construct $\overline{FB} \parallel \overline{AD}$.)

15. Given: $\overline{AD}$ bisects $\angle BAC$, $AB = 10$, $AC = 15$, $BC = 18$

Find: BD and DC

(*Hint:* See exercise 14.)

F
A
1
2
B
D
C

(Exs. 14, 15)

16. Given: $\triangle ABC$, $m\angle 1 = m\angle 2$

Prove: $\frac{BD}{DC} = \frac{AB}{AC}$

(*Hint:* Use the Side-Splitting Theorem and an auxiliary line.)

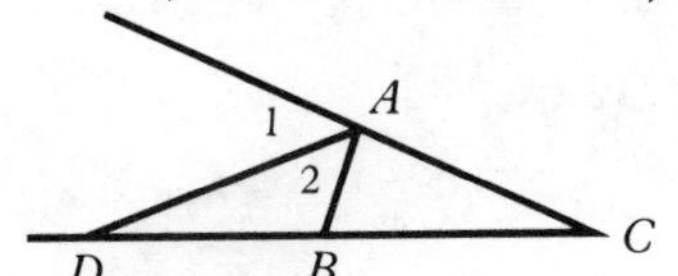

PROBLEM SOLVING

In this pentagon-based pyramid:

$\overline{WX} \parallel \overline{BC}$, $\overline{XY} \parallel \overline{CD}$, $\overline{YZ} \parallel \overline{DE}$, and $AW = 2$, $WB = 3$, $AE = 6$

Find AZ and ZE.

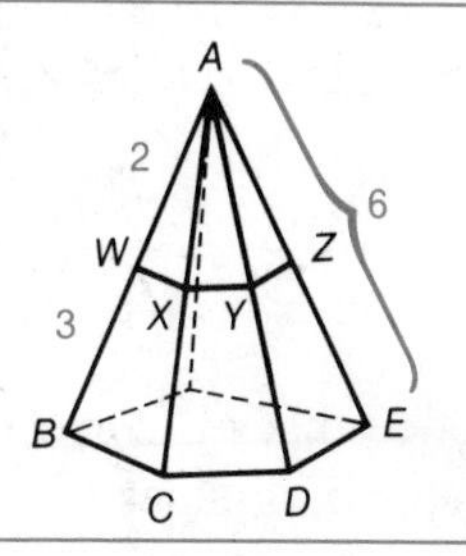

9–3 Similar Polygons

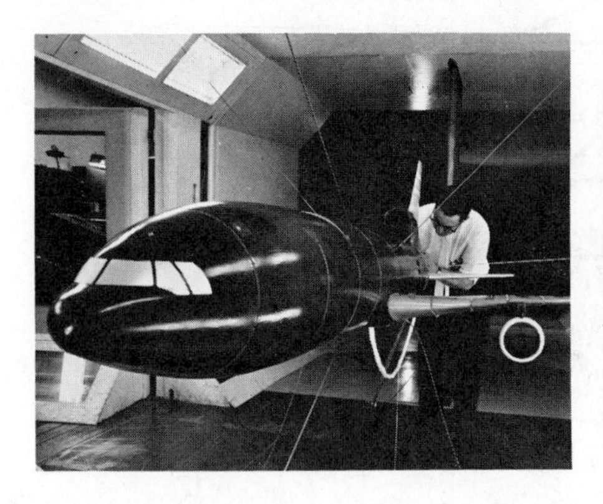

Industrial designers often build models of projects that will eventually be constructed full size. The model of the plane has the same shape as the actual aircraft.

In this lesson we shall focus our attention on polygons, and we shall describe what is meant by *identical in shape,* or *similar.* Consider these figures.

$ABCDE$ is similar to $A'B'C'D'E'$.

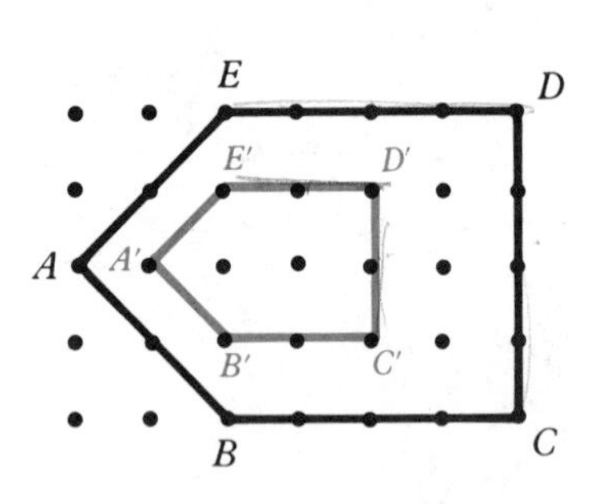

$\angle A \cong \angle A'$, $\angle B \cong \angle B'$, $\angle C \cong \angle C'$
$\angle D \cong \angle D'$, $\angle E \cong \angle E'$

$$\frac{AB}{A'B'} = \frac{BC}{B'C'} = \frac{CD}{C'D'} = \frac{DE}{D'E'} = \frac{AE}{A'E'} = 2$$

$WXYZ$ is similar to $W'X'Y'Z'$.

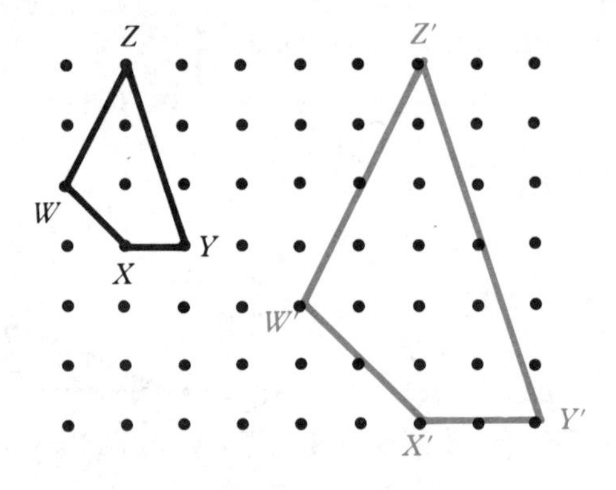

$\angle W \cong \angle W'$, $\angle X \cong \angle X'$,
$\angle Y \cong \angle Y'$, $\angle Z \cong \angle Z'$

$$\frac{WX}{W'X'} = \frac{XY}{X'Y'} = \frac{YZ}{Y'Z'} = \frac{WZ}{W'Z'} = \frac{1}{2}$$

Notice that all corresponding angles are congruent and that the ratios of corresponding sides are equal.

The symbol "$\sim$" means "is similar to."
$ABCD \sim A'B'C'D'$ means that $ABCD$ is similar to $A'B'C'D'$.

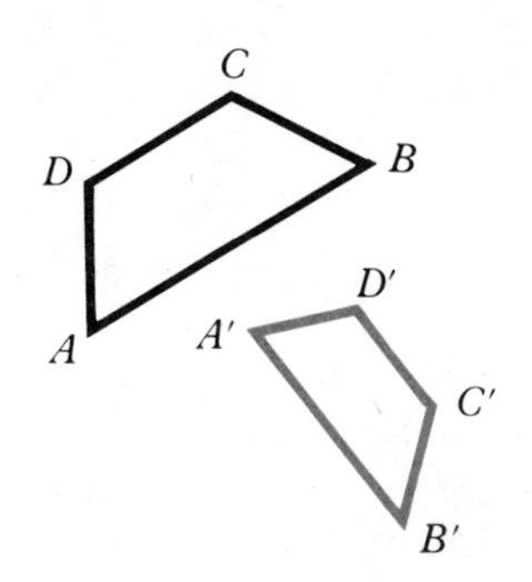

Definition 9–2

Two polygons are **similar** if there is a correspondence between vertices such that corresponding angles are congruent and corresponding sides are proportional.

Example 1 If we are given that $ABCD \sim A'B'C'D'$, then we can conclude:

1. $\angle A \cong \angle A'$, $\angle B \cong \angle B'$, $\angle C \cong \angle C'$, $\angle D \cong \angle D'$.
2. $\dfrac{AB}{A'B'} = \dfrac{BC}{B'C'} = \dfrac{CD}{C'D'} = \dfrac{AD}{A'D'}$.

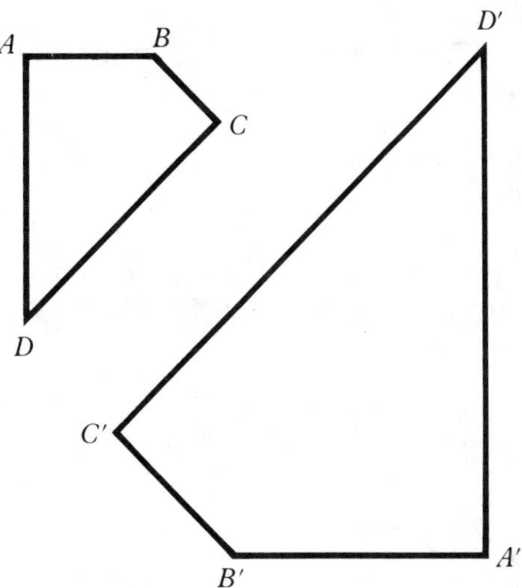

Example 2 If we are given that

1. $\angle A \cong \angle A'$, $\angle B \cong \angle B'$, $\angle C \cong \angle C'$, $\angle D \cong \angle D'$ and
2. $\dfrac{AB}{A'B'} = \dfrac{BC}{B'C'} = \dfrac{CD}{C'D'} = \dfrac{AD}{A'D'}$,

then we can conclude that $ABCD \sim A'B'C'D'$.

APPLICATION

If you have a scaled map, then a figure on the map is similar to the figure it represents. Given a scaled map of locations A, B, and C, then $\triangle ABC \sim \triangle A'B'C'$.

If $A'C' = 36$ mm, $A'B' = 24$ mm, and $AB = 32$ m, find AC.

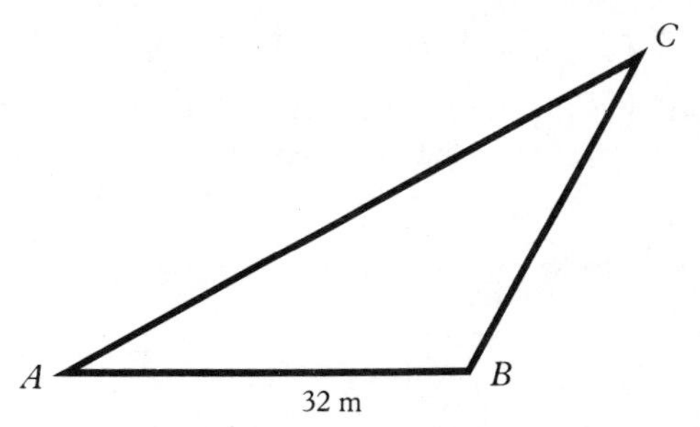

Solution: $\dfrac{AB}{A'B'} = \dfrac{AC}{A'C'}$ or $\dfrac{32\text{ m}}{24\text{ mm}} = \dfrac{AC}{36\text{ mm}}$.

Therefore $AC = \dfrac{32\text{ m} \times 36\text{ mm}}{24\text{ mm}} = 48$ m.

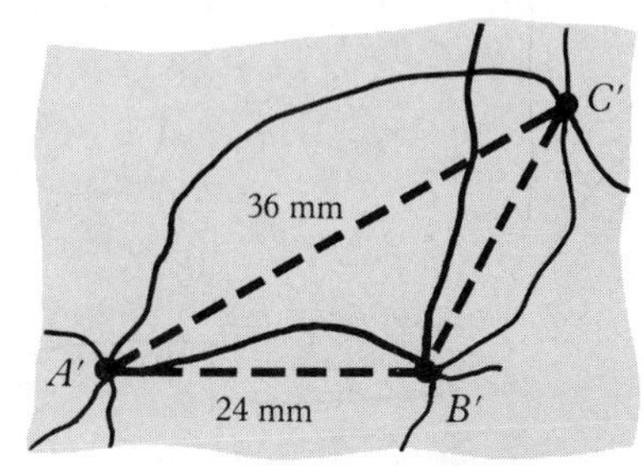

EXERCISES

A.

For exercises 1–4, decide whether or not the given pair of polygons are similar.

1.

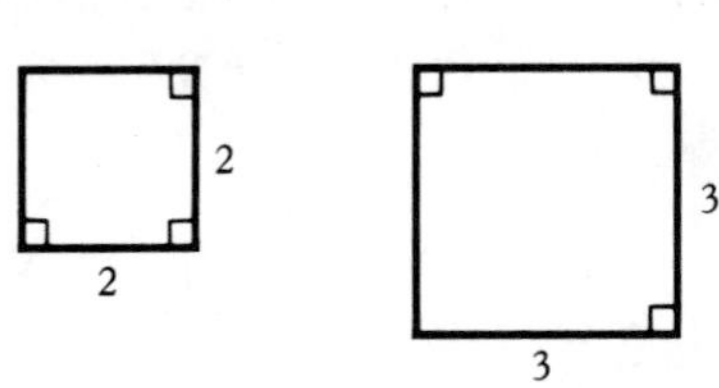

2.

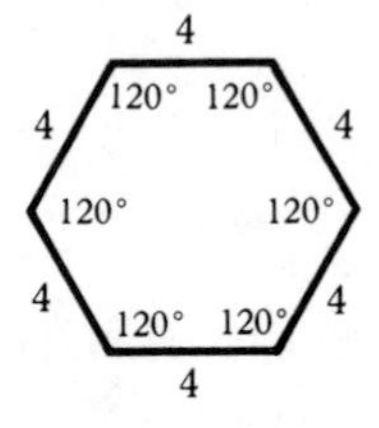

4 120° 4 120° 120° 2 2 120° 120° 120° 4 4

3.

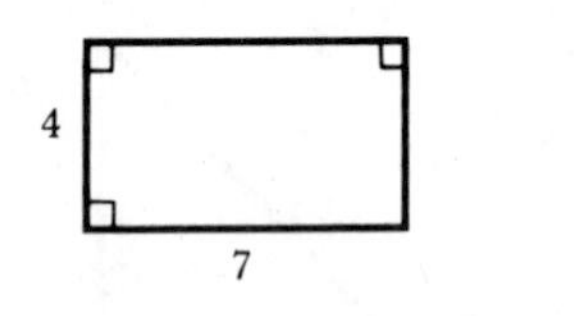

4.

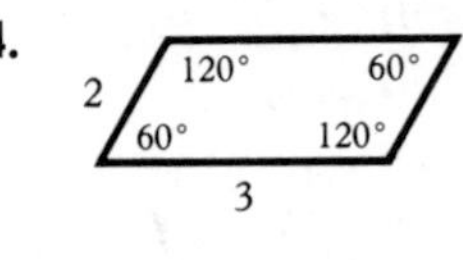

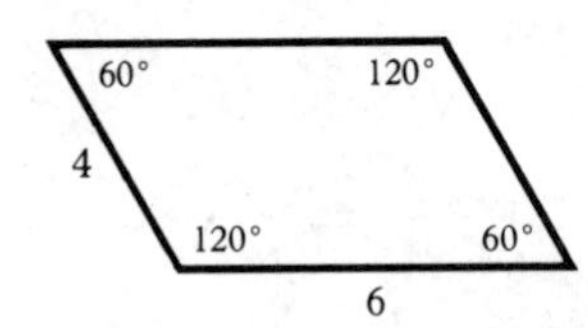

5. Suppose $\triangle HIJ \sim \triangle H'I'J'$. Name three pairs of corresponding angles that are congruent.

6. If $\triangle HIJ \sim \triangle H'I'J'$, complete this proportion in two different ways.

$$\frac{HI}{H'I'} = \underline{\ ?\ }$$

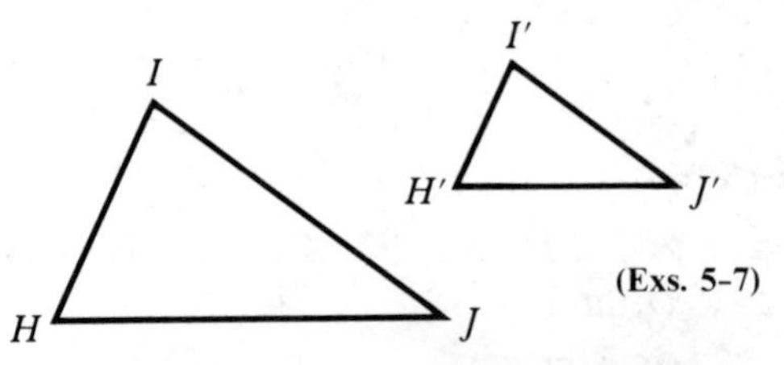

(Exs. 5–7)

7. Suppose $\triangle HIJ \sim \triangle H'I'J'$, and that $H'I' = 4$, $I'J' = 6$, $H'J' = 7$, and $HJ = 12$. Find lengths HI and IJ.

8. Using the scale indicated on this needlepoint pattern, find the length AB in the enlarged finished product.

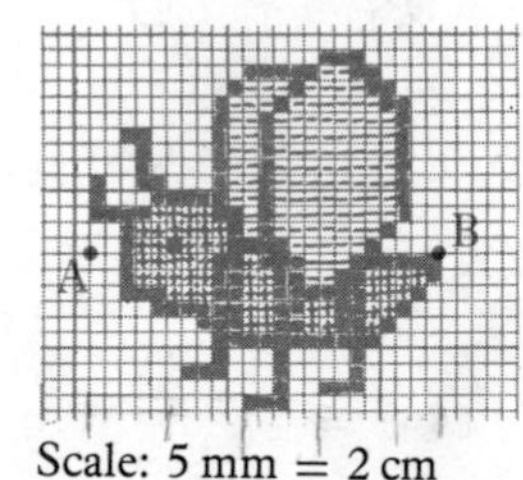

Scale: 5 mm = 2 cm

Activity

Here is a method of constructing a polygon similar to *ABCDE*.

a. Select a point *P* and draw $\overrightarrow{PA}$, $\overrightarrow{PB}$, $\overrightarrow{PC}$, $\overrightarrow{PD}$, and $\overrightarrow{PE}$.

b. Construct points A', B', C', D', E' as shown so that $AA' = 2PA$, $BB' = 2PB$, $CC' = 2PC$, $DD' = 2PD$, and $EE' = 2PE$.

1. Trace *ABCDE* and try the construction stated above.

2. Locate point *P* in a different position and repeat the construction.

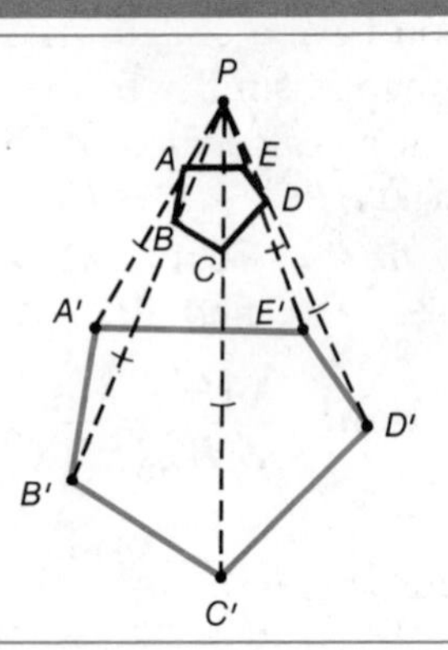

B.

In this figure $\overline{DE} \parallel \overline{BC}$.

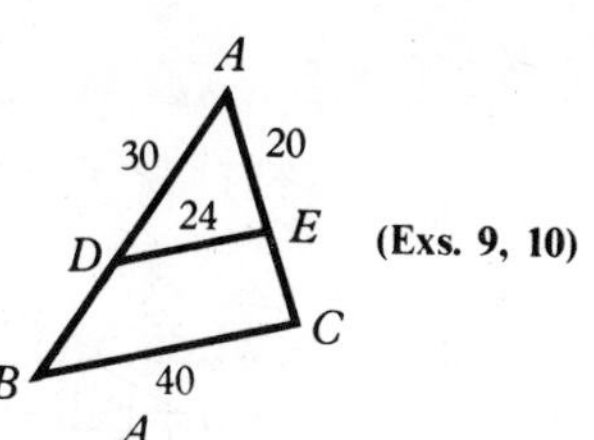

(Exs. 9, 10)

9. If $\dfrac{AD}{AB} = \dfrac{AE}{AC} = \dfrac{DE}{BC}$, prove that $\triangle ADE \sim \triangle ABC$.

10. If the length of segments are as shown, then find DB and EC. (*Hint:* Use exercise 9.)

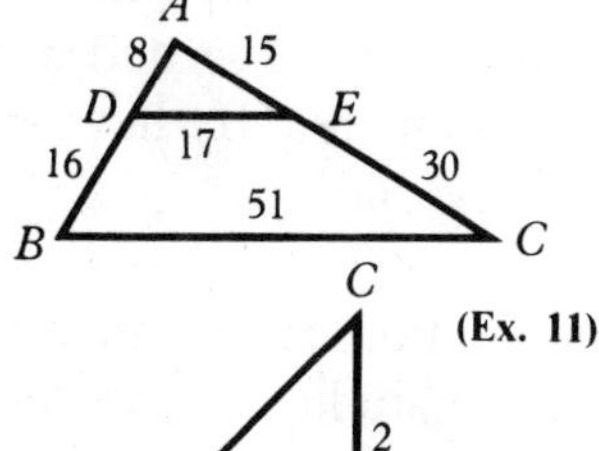

(Ex. 11)

11. If $\overline{DE} \parallel \overline{BC}$, and the lengths of segments are as shown, prove that $\triangle ADE \sim \triangle ABC$.

12. The lengths of the sides of a pentagon are 6, 8, 9, 12, and 15. If a similar pentagon has a longest side of 4, find the lengths of the remaining sides.

13. Construct a right triangle similar to $\triangle ABC$ with a leg of length $\sqrt{2}$.

(Ex. 13)

14. Construct a quadrilateral similar to $ABCD$, whose shortest side has length 9.

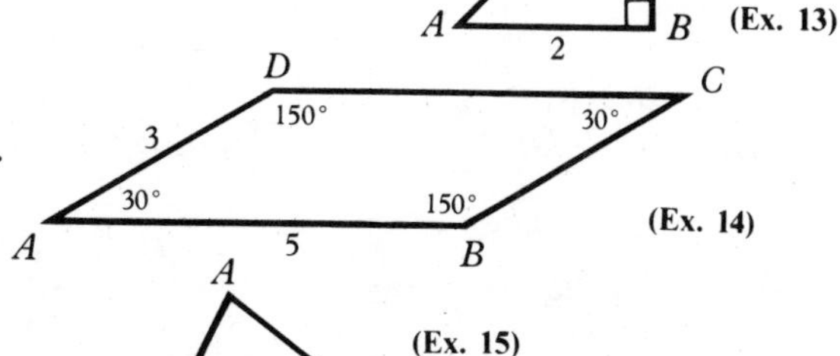

(Ex. 14)

C.

15. Suppose $\triangle ADE \sim \triangle ABC$. Prove that $\dfrac{DB}{AD} = \dfrac{EC}{AE}$. (This is the conclusion of the Side-Splitting Theorem.)

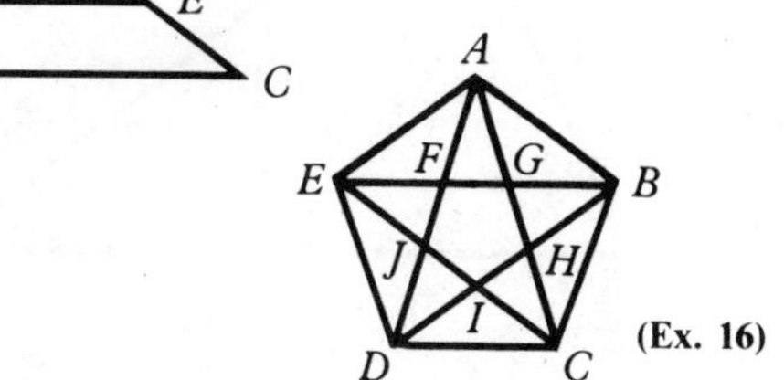

(Ex. 15)

(Ex. 16)

16. Given that $ABCDE$ is a regular pentagon, and that $\dfrac{BD}{DC} = \dfrac{BC}{DI} = \dfrac{DC}{CI}$, state several pairs of similar triangles. Justify your choices.

PROBLEM SOLVING

Use the problem solving method "Make a Table" (page 167) to solve this problem.

no subdivisions	one subdivision	two subdivisions	three subdivisions
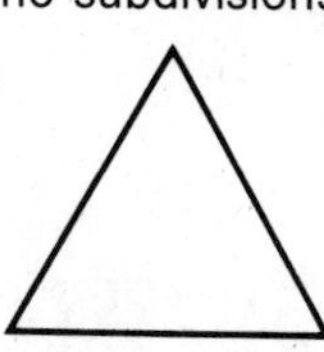	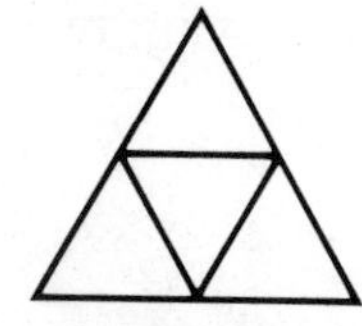	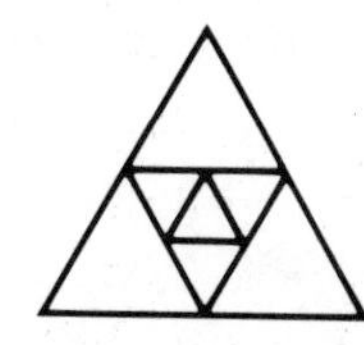	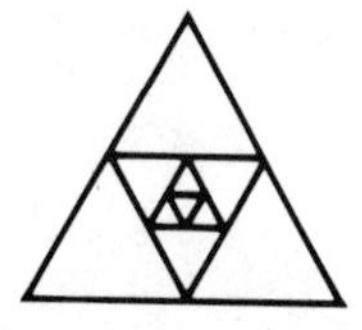
1 triangle	5 triangles	9 triangles	? triangles

If the equilateral triangle were subdivided ten times, how many triangles would result?

9–4 The AAA Similarity Postulate

In the sport of bowling, the bowler uses the sight marks to aim the ball. Suppose a bowler aims for the second mark and misses it by 2 centimeters. By how much will the ball miss the pin?

This question can be answered by applying the theorem studied in this lesson.

In $\triangle ABC$ and $\triangle DEF$, $\angle A \cong \angle D$, $\angle B \cong \angle E$, and $\angle C \cong \angle F$.

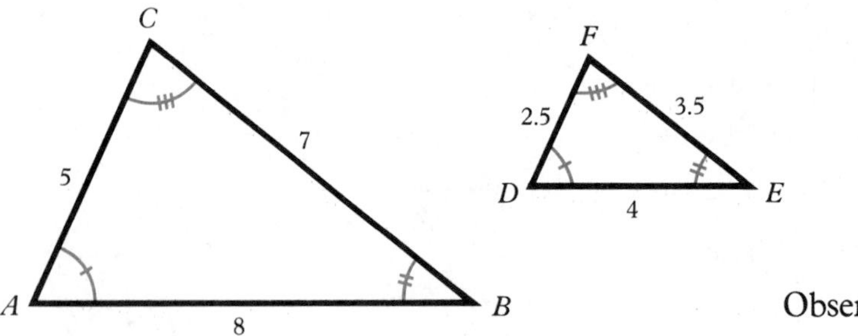

Observe that $\dfrac{AB}{DE} = \dfrac{BC}{EF} = \dfrac{CA}{FD}$.

It appears that whenever all three angles of one triangle are congruent to all three angles of another triangle, then the ratios of corresponding sides are also equal. We accept this as a postulate.

AAA Similarity Postulate

If three angles of one triangle are congruent to three angles of another triangle, then the triangles are similar.

The next theorem describes a simple method for proving two triangles similar.

Theorem 9–8 **AA Similarity Theorem.** If two angles of one triangle are congruent to two angles of another triangle, then the triangles are similar.

PROOF

Given: $\triangle ABC$ and $\triangle DEF$ with $\angle A \cong \angle D$, $\angle B \cong \angle E$
Prove: $\triangle ABC$ is similar to $\triangle DEF$.

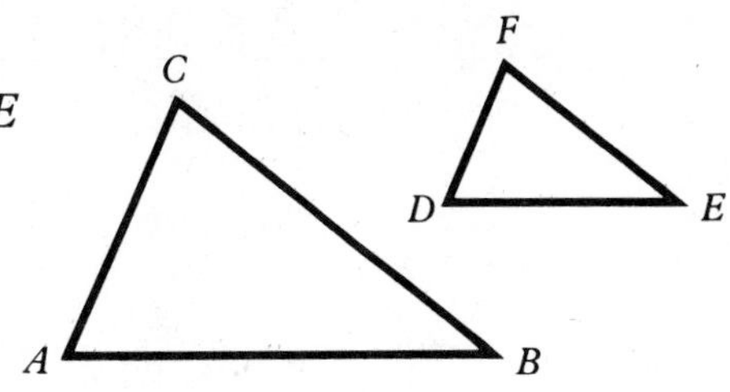

Statements	Reasons
1. $\angle A \cong \angle D$	1. Given
2. $\angle B \cong \angle E$	2. Given
3. $\angle C \cong \angle F$	3. Why ?
4. $\triangle ABC \sim \triangle DEF$	4. AAA Similarity

APPLICATION

When the bowler misses the mark by 2 cm, the ball misses the pin by how much? Consider triangles $\triangle ABC$ and $\triangle APD$. These triangles are constructed to be right triangles, and they have a common angle A. Therefore by Theorem 9–8, we conclude that $\triangle ABC \sim \triangle APD$.

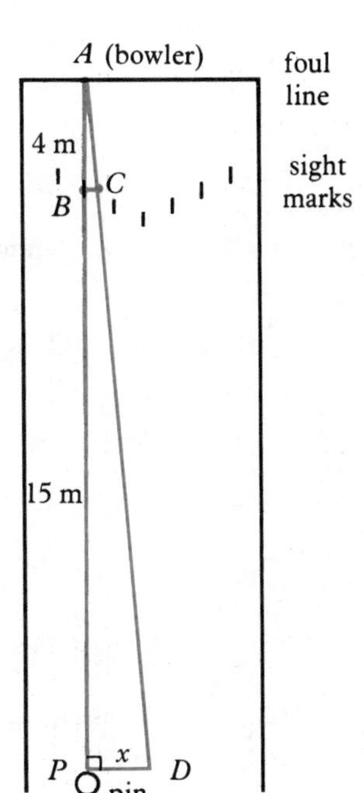

$$\frac{AB}{AP} = \frac{BC}{PD} \quad \text{or} \quad \frac{4 \text{ m}}{19 \text{ m}} = \frac{2 \text{ cm}}{x \text{ cm}}$$

$$\text{or} \quad x = \frac{38}{4} \text{ cm} = 9\frac{1}{2} \text{ cm}$$

Applying the AA Similarity Theorem to the case of right triangles gives this theorem.

Theorem 9–9 Two right triangles are similar if an acute angle of one triangle is congruent to an acute angle of the other triangle.

EXERCISES

A.

For exercises 1-4 $\triangle ABC$ and $\triangle XYZ$ are given. Complete the statement $\triangle ABC \sim$ _?_.

1. $m\angle A = 17$, $m\angle C = 49$, $m\angle X = 17$, $m\angle Z = 49$
2. $m\angle A = 23$, $m\angle B = 111$, $m\angle Y = 23$, $m\angle Z = 111$
3. $m\angle B = 68$, $m\angle C = 21$, $m\angle X = 21$, $m\angle Y = 91$
4. $m\angle C = 119$, $m\angle A = 24$, $m\angle X = 24$, $m\angle Y = 37$
5. Explain why $\triangle ABC \sim \triangle DBA$.

(Ex. 5)

6. Find x.

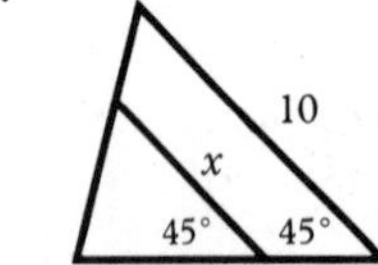

7. Find y.

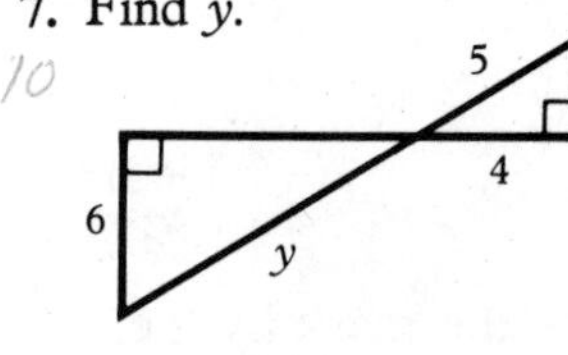

8. If a 6-foot man has a shadow of 9 feet, how long a shadow would a 20-foot pole have?
9. If $\overline{DE} \parallel \overline{BC}$, $AD = 3$, $AB = 8$, and $BC = 9$, what is the length of $\overline{DE}$?
10. Are all isosceles right triangles similar? Why?
11. Are all right triangles similar? Why?
12. If two isosceles triangles have their vertex angles congruent, are they similar? Why?
13. Are all 30°-60°-90° triangles similar? Why?
14. List as many similar triangles as you can in the figure shown.

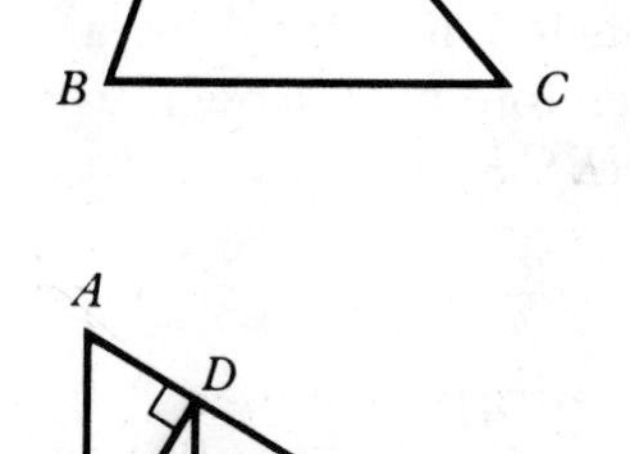

(Ex. 14)

B.

15. When a photograph is taken, the image formed on the film is similar to the object being photographed. Similar triangles help to explain this. If $\overline{AB}$ and $\overline{A'B'}$ are parallel, prove that $\triangle LAB$ and $\triangle LA'B'$ are similar.

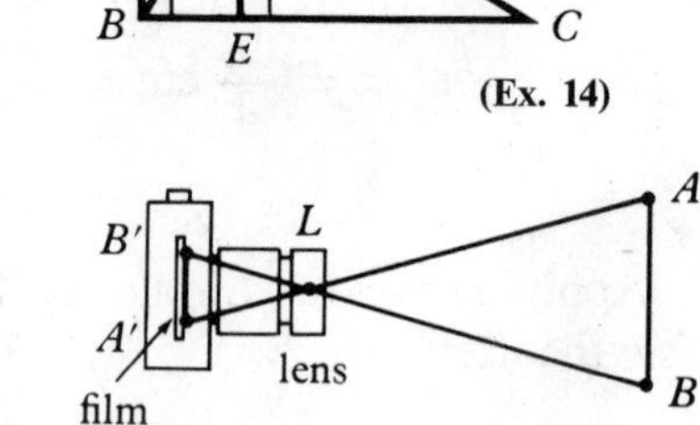

16. One method of finding the height of an object is to place a mirror on the ground and then position yourself so that the top of the object can be seen in the mirror. How high is a tower if a 150 cm tall person observes the top of the tower when the mirror is 120 m from the tower and the person is 6 m from the mirror?

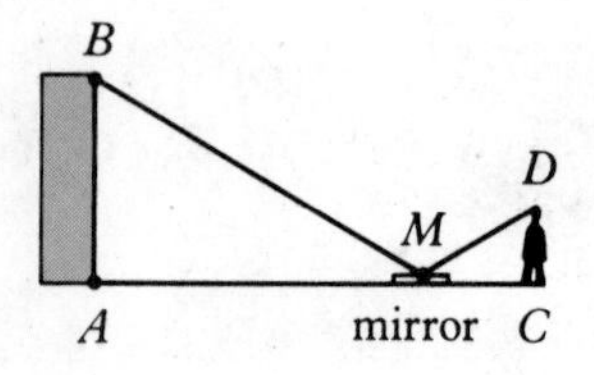

$\angle AMB \cong \angle CMD$

17. Given: $m\angle 1 = m\angle 2$
Prove: $\triangle ABC \sim \triangle EDC$

18. Given: $\overline{AB} \parallel \overline{DE}$
Prove: a. $\triangle ABC \sim \triangle EDC$

b. $\dfrac{AC}{CE} = \dfrac{AB}{DE}$

(Exs. 17, 18)

19. Given: $ABCD$ is a trapezoid
Prove: $\triangle AED \sim \triangle CEB$

(Ex. 19)

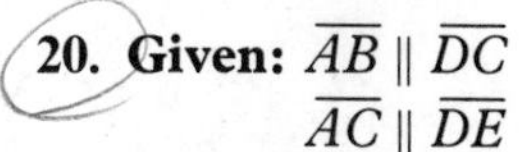

20. Given: $\overline{AB} \parallel \overline{DC}$
$\overline{AC} \parallel \overline{DE}$
Prove: $\triangle ABC \sim \triangle DCE$

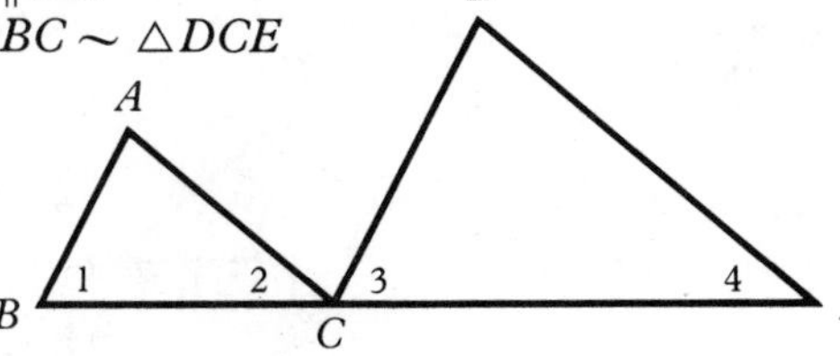

(Ex. 20)

21. Given: $\triangle ABC \sim \triangle DEF$
$\overline{AG}$ and $\overline{DH}$ are altitudes.
Prove: $\dfrac{AB}{DE} = \dfrac{AG}{DH}$

(Ex. 21)

22. Given: $\overline{NQ} \parallel \overline{OP}$
Prove: a. $\triangle MNQ \sim \triangle MOP$

b. $\dfrac{MN}{MO} = \dfrac{NQ}{OP}$

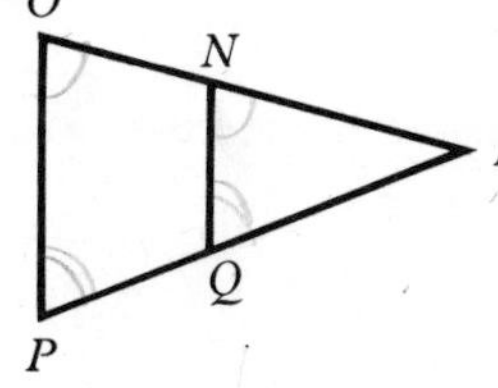

(Ex. 22)

23. Given: H, N, and Y are midpoints of $\overline{MA}$, $\overline{ME}$, and $\overline{AE}$.
Prove: $\triangle HNY \sim \triangle EAM$

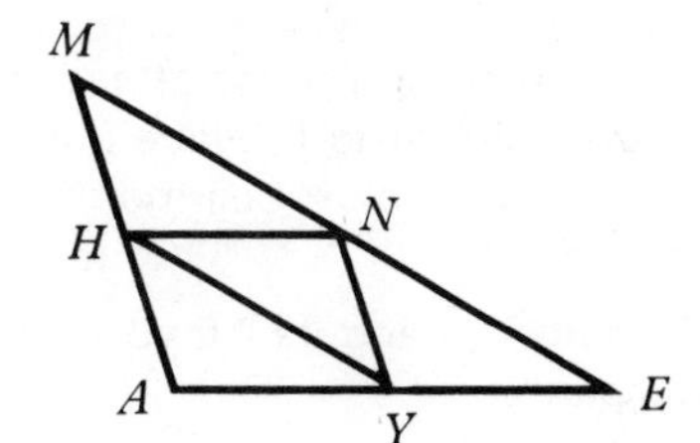

(Ex. 23)

24. Given: $\angle B \cong \angle C$, $\overline{DF} \perp \overline{AB}$, $\overline{DE} \perp \overline{AC}$
Prove: a. $\triangle BDF \sim \triangle CDE$

b. $\dfrac{FD}{ED} = \dfrac{BD}{CD}$

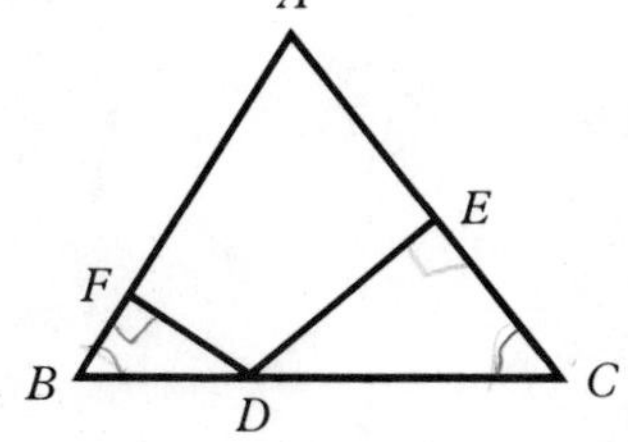

25. Given: $\angle RST$, $\angle 1$, and $\angle 2$ are right angles.
Prove: **a.** $\triangle RSU \sim \triangle RTS$
b. $\triangle UVT \sim \triangle RUS$

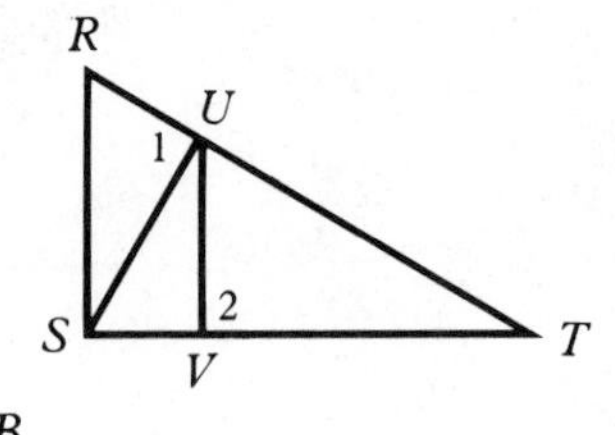

C.

26. Given: $ABCD$ is a trapezoid.
Prove: $AE \cdot DE = BE \cdot CE$

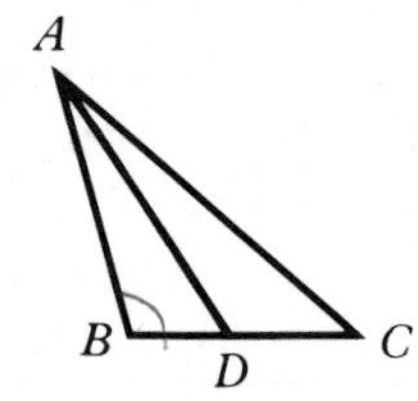

27. Given: $\triangle ABC \sim \triangle EFG$
$\overline{AD}$ bisects $\angle A$.
$\overline{EH}$ bisects $\angle E$.

Prove: $\dfrac{AB}{EF} = \dfrac{AD}{EH}$

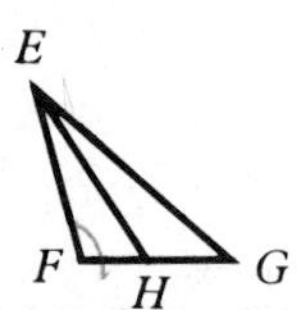

28. Given: $\overline{AD} \perp \overline{BC}$, $\overline{BE} \perp \overline{AC}$
Prove: **a.** $\dfrac{AD}{BE} = \dfrac{AC}{BC}$

b. $AD \cdot BC = AC \cdot BE$

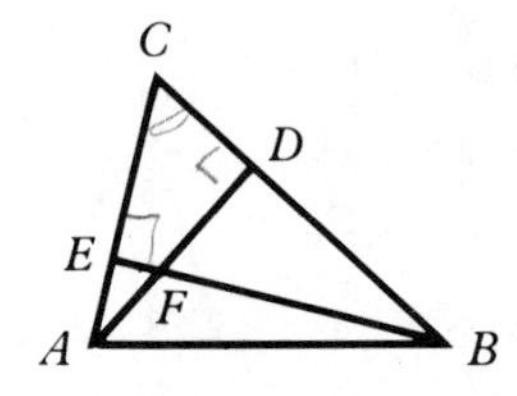

Activity

Set an overhead projector 10 feet from a screen and perpendicular to it. Place a cutout triangle *ABC* on the projector. Call the triangle on the screen *A′B′C′*.

1. Measure $\angle A$ and its image $\angle A'$. How do they compare?
2. Measure lengths *AB* and *A′B′*, *AC* and *A′C′*, *BC* and *B′C′*.

   How do the ratios $\dfrac{AB}{A'B'}$, $\dfrac{AC}{A'C'}$, and $\dfrac{BC}{B'C'}$ compare?

What do you conclude about $\triangle ABC$ and $\triangle A'B'C'$?

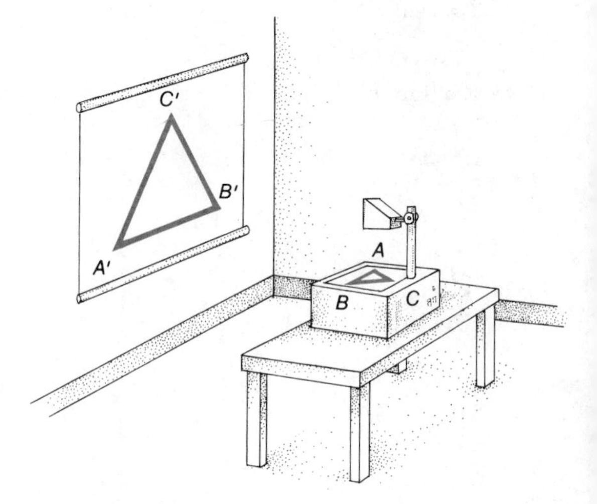

29. Given: $\overline{BE} \parallel \overline{CF} \parallel \overline{DG}$

Prove: $\frac{BC}{CD} = \frac{EF}{FG}$

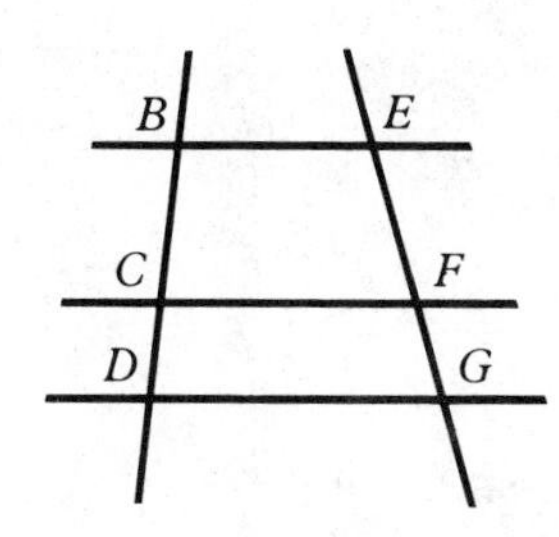

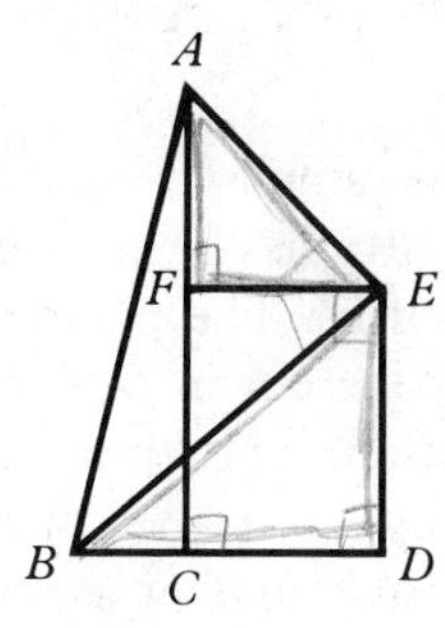

30. Given: $\overline{AC} \perp \overline{FE}$, $\overline{AC} \perp \overline{BD}$, $\overline{DE} \perp \overline{BD}$, $\overline{AE} \perp \overline{BE}$

Prove: $\triangle AFE \sim \triangle BDE$

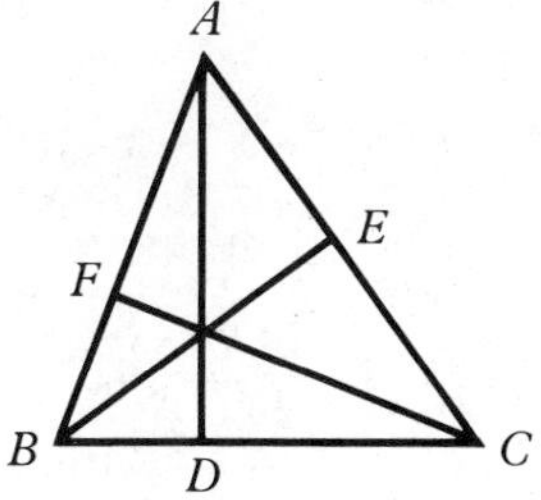

31. Given: $\overline{AD} \perp \overline{BC}$, $\overline{FC} \perp \overline{AB}$, $\overline{BE} \perp \overline{AC}$

Prove: $\frac{AF}{BF} \cdot \frac{BD}{CD} \cdot \frac{CE}{AE} = 1$

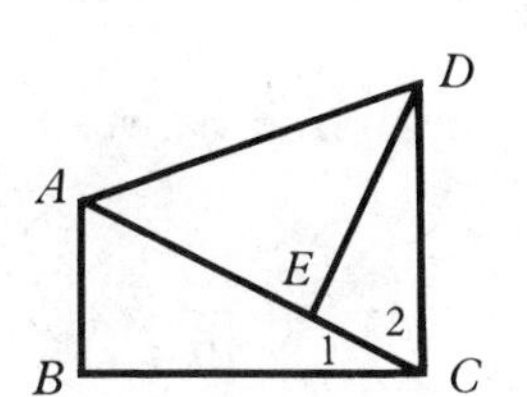

32. Given: $\overline{DE} \perp \overline{AC}$, $\overline{AB} \perp \overline{BC}$, $m\angle 1 + m\angle 2 = 90$

Prove: $BC \cdot CE = ED \cdot AB$

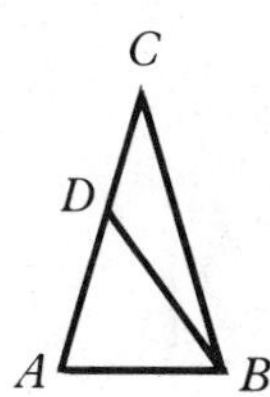

33. Given: $\overline{CA} \cong \overline{CB}$, $\overline{BA} \cong \overline{BD}$

Prove: $(AB)^2 = AC \cdot AD$

PROBLEM SOLVING

Suppose a slide projector and screen are set up as shown with the screen 20 feet from the projector. Assume $\triangle ABC$ is similar to $\triangle A'B'C'$.

1. If the triangular cutout $\triangle ABC$ is placed x feet in front of the projector, calculate the length $A'B'$ in terms of the length AB and the distance x.
2. If x is halved, what happens to $A'B'$?

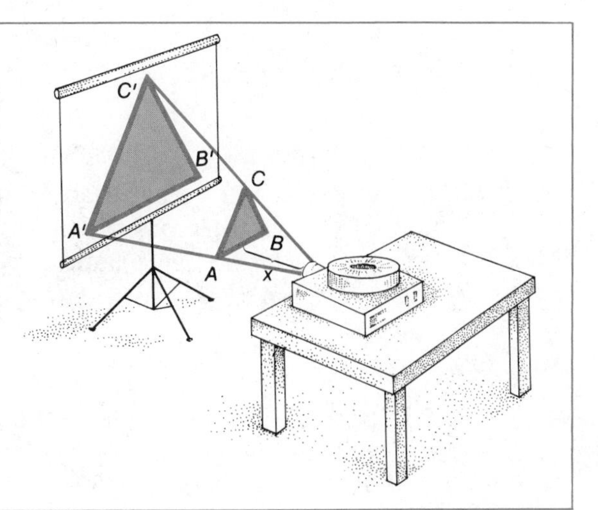

9–5 Right Triangles and Similar Triangles

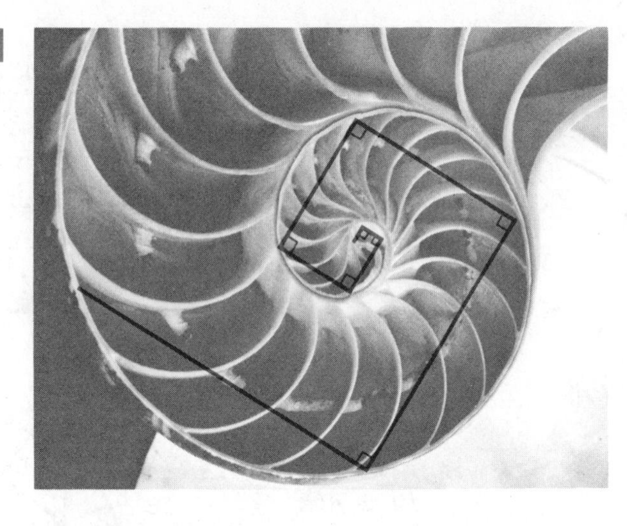

An interesting example of right triangle similarity in nature is the shell of the chambered nautilus. The photograph shows a shell that has been cut in half to reveal its spiral construction. This spiral can be approximated by a sequence of segments at right angles to one another as shown here. This spiral is related to the theorem of this lesson.

We begin with an example and a definition.
8 is the geometric mean between 4 and 16, since

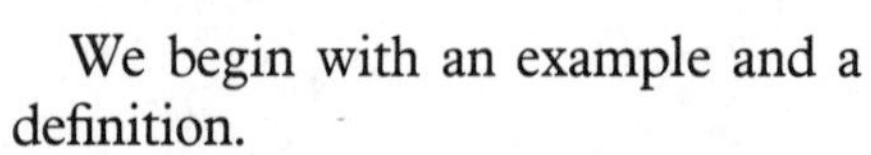

$$\frac{4}{8} = \frac{8}{16}.$$

Definition 9-3

A number x is a **geometric mean** between two numbers a and b if

$$\frac{a}{x} = \frac{x}{b},\ x \neq 0,\ b \neq 0.$$

The idea of geometric mean is used in the next theorem. Consider these right triangles.

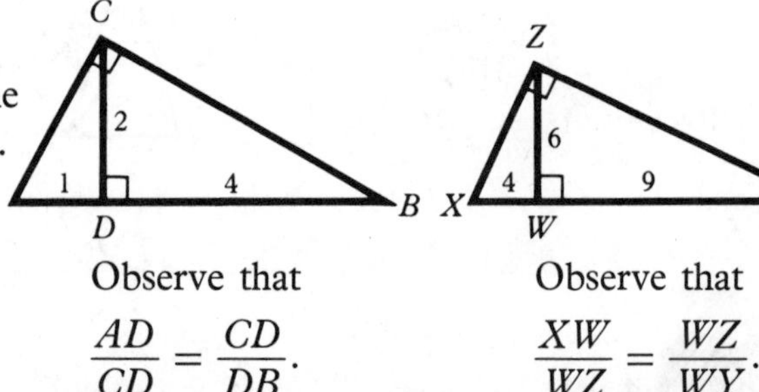

Observe that

$$\frac{AD}{CD} = \frac{CD}{DB}.$$

Observe that

$$\frac{XW}{WZ} = \frac{WZ}{WY}.$$

Theorem 9–10 In a right triangle, the length of the altitude to the hypotenuse is the geometric mean between the lengths of the two segments of the hypotenuse.

PROOF

Given: $\triangle ABC$ with $\angle C$ a right angle, $\overline{CD}$ an altitude

Prove: $\dfrac{AD}{DC} = \dfrac{DC}{DB}$

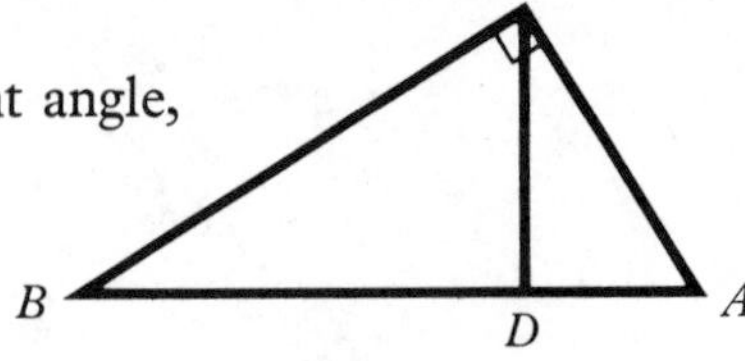

Statements	Reasons
1. $\angle ADC$ is a right angle.	1. $\overline{CD}$ is an altitude.
2. $\angle BDC$ is a right angle.	2. Why ?
3. $\angle C$ is a right angle.	3. Given
4. $\angle BCD$ is complementary to $\angle ACD$.	4. Why ?
5. $\angle CAD$ is complementary to $\angle ACD$.	5. Why ?
6. $\angle BCD \cong \angle CAD$.	6. Why ?
7. $\triangle ADC \sim \triangle CDB$.	7. Two right triangles are similar if an acute angle of one is congruent to an acute angle of the other.
8. $\frac{AD}{DC} = \frac{DC}{DB}$	8. Corresponding parts of similar triangles are proportional.

APPLICATION

The shell of the chambered nautilus is based on a geometric mean. Consider the sequence of radii
$\overline{OA}, \overline{OB}, \overline{OC}, \overline{OD}, \overline{OE}, \overline{OF}, \overline{OG}, \overline{OH}, \overline{OI}, \overline{OJ}, \overline{OK}$.
The length of each of these segments is a geometric mean between the lengths of the preceding segment and the succeeding segment.

Each three successive points, for example, G, H, and I, are vertices of a right triangle. Furthermore, $\overline{OH}$ is an altitude of $\triangle GHI$. Therefore, by Theorem 9–10, OH is the geometric mean between OG and OI.

This triangle illustrates Theorem 9–11. The proof of Theorem 9–11 is left as an exercise.

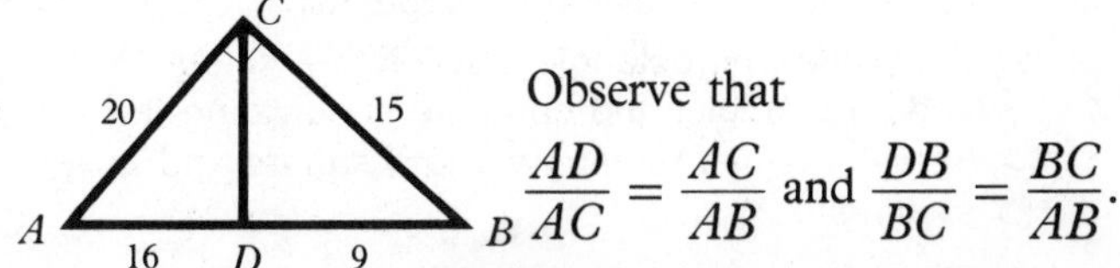

Observe that $\frac{AD}{AC} = \frac{AC}{AB}$ and $\frac{DB}{BC} = \frac{BC}{AB}$.

Theorem 9–11 Given a right triangle and the altitude to the hypotenuse, each leg is the geometric mean between the length of the hypotenuse and the length of the segment of the hypotenuse adjacent to the leg.

EXERCISES

A.

What is the geometric mean between the numbers in exercises 1–4?

1. 4 and 9 **2.** 9 and 16 **3.** 4 and 5 **4.** $\sqrt{3}$ and $\sqrt{5}$

5. The length of $\overline{CD}$ is the geometric mean between the lengths of which two segments?

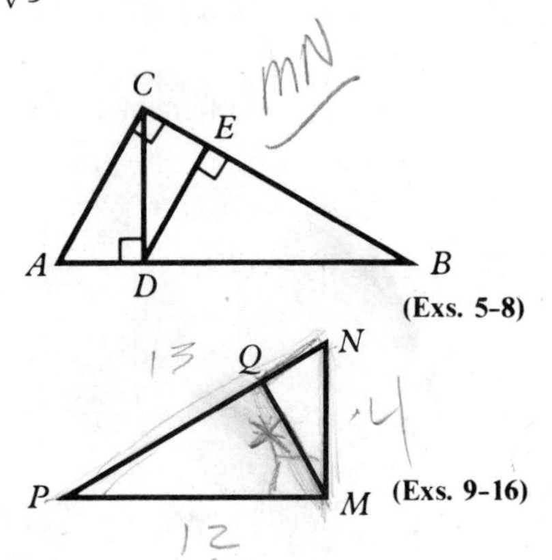

6. The length of $\overline{DE}$ is the geometric mean between the lengths of which two segments?

7. The length of $\overline{AC}$ is the geometric mean between the lengths of which two segments? (See Theorem 9–11.)

8. The length of $\overline{BC}$ is the geometric mean between the lengths of which two segments?

For exercises 9–16, use this figure in which $\angle PMN$ is a right angle and $\overline{MQ} \perp \overline{PN}$.

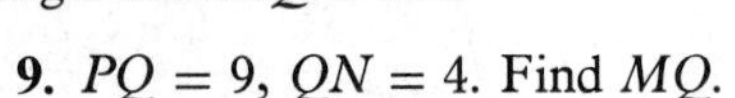

9. $PQ = 9$, $QN = 4$. Find MQ.

10. $QN = 3$, $MQ = 9$. Find PQ.

11. $PM = 12$, $PQ = 9$. Find PN.

12. $MN = 8$, $QN = 6$. Find PN.

13. $PN = 75$, $PQ = 72$. Find MN.

14. $MQ = 4$, $PN = 10$. Find QN.

15. $PN = 13$, $PM = 12$. Find MQ.

16. $PM = 16$, $MN = 12$. Find PQ.

Activity

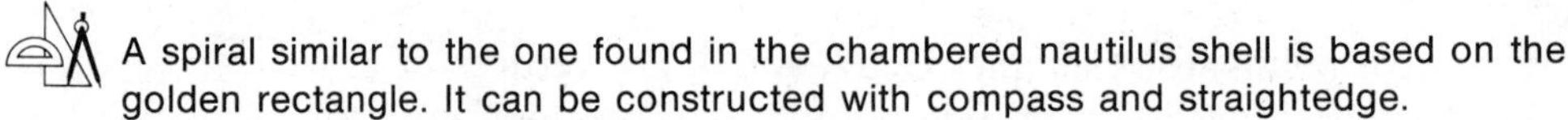

A spiral similar to the one found in the chambered nautilus shell is based on the golden rectangle. It can be constructed with compass and straightedge.

1. Construct a golden rectangle *ABCD* as shown in Geometry in Our World, page 301.
2. Subdivide the rectangle *BCEF* into a square and a rectangle, and continue subdividing the newly obtained rectangle into a square and a rectangle.
3. Construct in each square a circular arc as shown. The center of each circular arc is a vertex of the square.

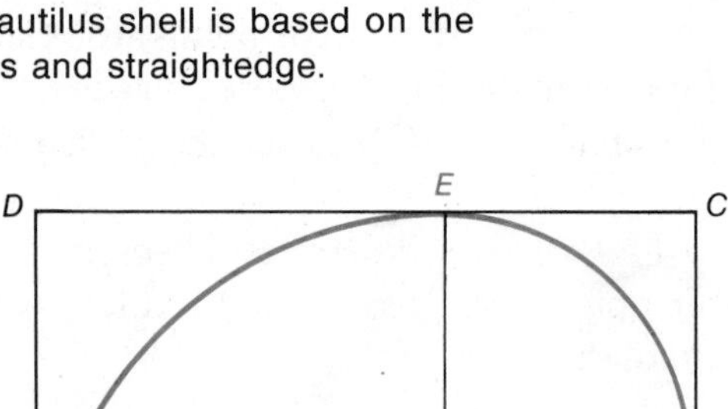

B.

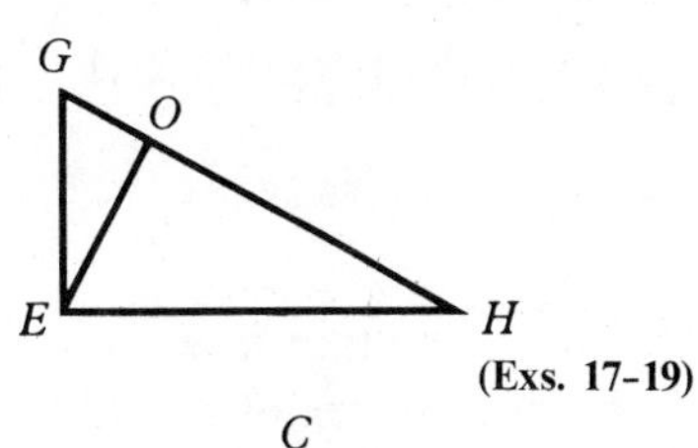

(Exs. 17–19)

17. Suppose $m\angle HEG = 90$ and $\overline{EO} \perp \overline{HG}$. If $HO = 6$ and $EG = 4$, find OG.

18. Suppose $m\angle HEG = 90$, $\overline{EO} \perp \overline{HG}$, $EO = 8$ and $\frac{HO}{OG} = \frac{2}{1}$.

Find HO.

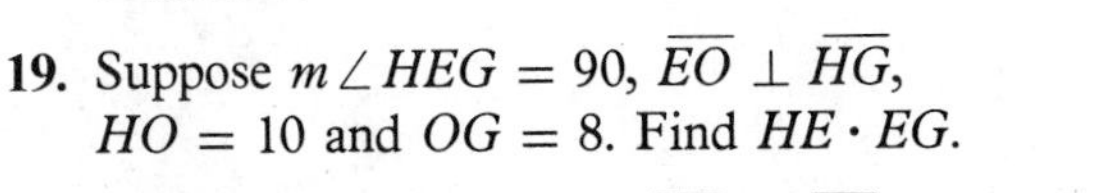

19. Suppose $m\angle HEG = 90$, $\overline{EO} \perp \overline{HG}$, $HO = 10$ and $OG = 8$. Find $HE \cdot EG$.

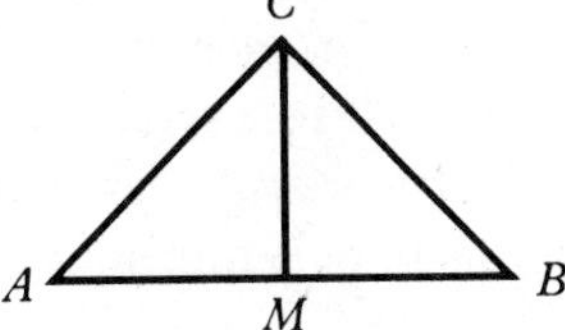

20. Given: $m\angle ACB = 90$, $\overline{CM} \perp \overline{AB}$, $AB \cdot CM = (AC)^2$
Prove: $AC = BC$

C.

21. Given: $m\angle TEM = 90$, $\overline{RE} \perp \overline{TM}$,
$TY = YM$, $ER = 4\frac{4}{5}$, $TE = 6$
Find: RY

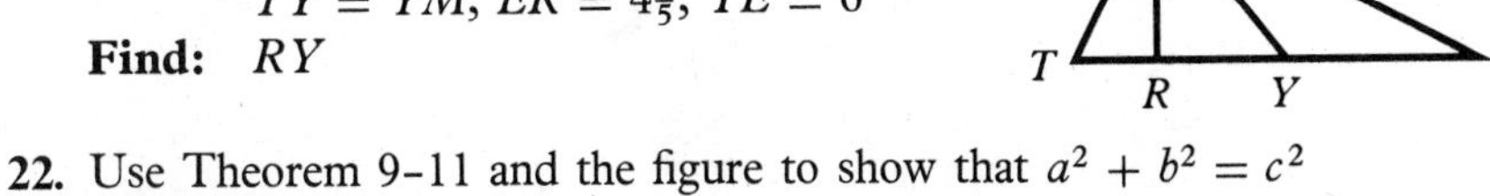

22. Use Theorem 9–11 and the figure to show that $a^2 + b^2 = c^2$ (Pythagorean Theorem).

23. Suppose $AFDB$ is a rectangle and $\overline{AD} \perp \overline{CE}$.
Show that the area of $AFDB = \sqrt{BC \cdot BA \cdot AF \cdot FE}$.

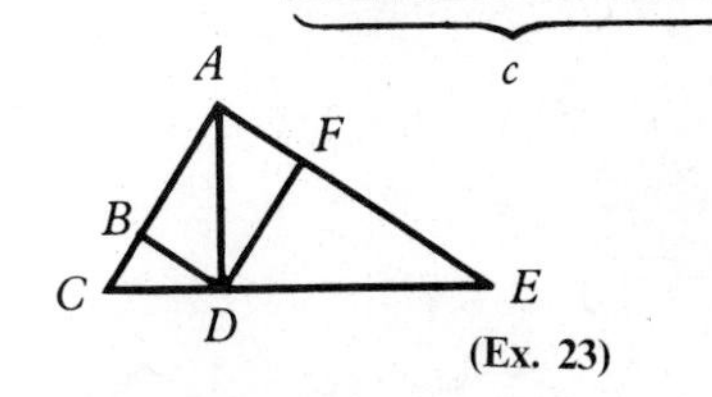

(Ex. 23)

24. Prove Theorem 9–11.

25. The geometric mean can be found in starfish in several ways. For example, in the five-pointed star shown here, AB is the geometric mean between BC and AC. Accept this fact and use it to show that AC is also the geometric mean between AB and AD. (*Hint*: Use Theorem 9–2.)

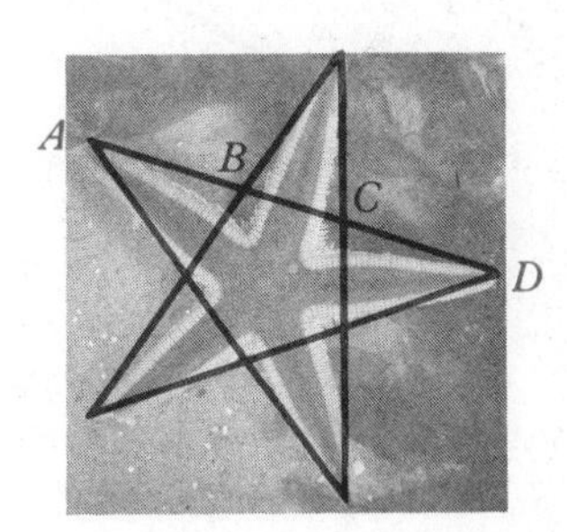

$AB = CD$

PROBLEM SOLVING

Show that the spiral constructed in the last activity is a spiral of the chambered nautilus.

That is, show that EX is the geometric mean between AE and XY. (*Hint:* Use the definition of golden rectangle found in the Architecture Geometry in Our World, page 300, together with the fact that $ABCD$ and $BCEF$ are both golden rectangles.)

9-6 The SSS and SAS Similarity Theorems

A water fountain is to be installed 32 feet from one corner of a building and 27 feet from another corner of the building. The building is 40 feet wide.

A set of working drawings for this project gives a scale of 5 mm to a foot. After the corners A' and B' of this building are located on the drawing, the point F' is drawn 160 mm from A' (5×32) and 135 mm from B' (5×27). Is $\triangle ABF$ similar to $\triangle A'B'F'$?

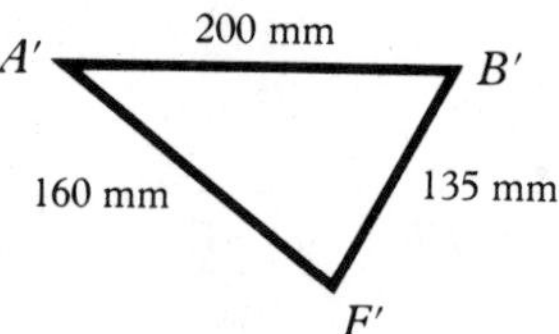

In the next example $\triangle XYZ$ and $\triangle X'Y'Z'$ are drawn so that

$$\frac{XY}{X'Y'} = \frac{YZ}{Y'Z'} = \frac{XZ}{X'Z'}.$$

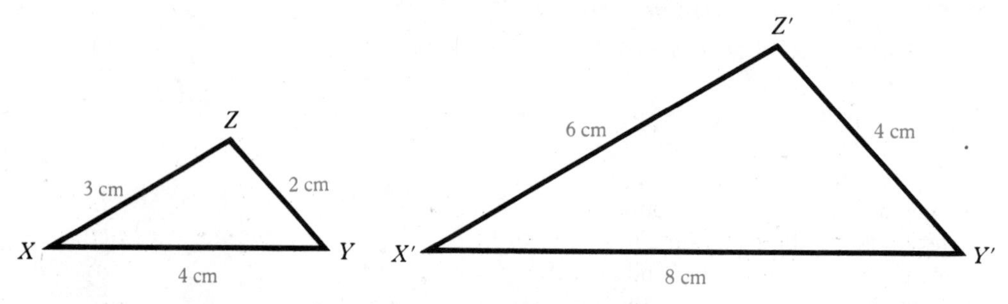

When the sides of the triangles are drawn proportionally then, $m\angle X = m\angle X' = 30$, $m\angle Y = m\angle Y' = 46$, and $m\angle Z = m\angle Z' = 104$.

These examples suggest the theorem called the SSS Similarity Theorem.

Theorem 9-12 **SSS Similarity Theorem.** If three sides of one triangle are proportional to the three sides of another triangle, then the triangles are similar.

Theorem 9–12 says

if $\frac{TJ}{PO} = \frac{JC}{OD} = \frac{TC}{PD}$,

then $\triangle TJC \sim \triangle POD$.

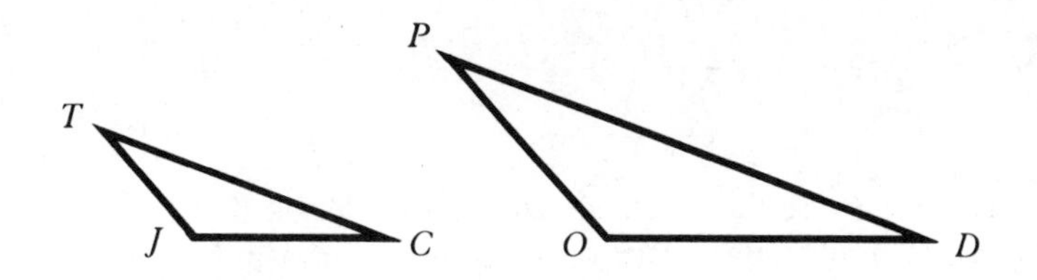

APPLICATION

In the example at the beginning of the lesson there is a triangle with sides of length 27 feet, 32 feet, and 40 feet, and a scale drawing with sides of length 135 mm, 160 mm, and 200 mm. Are these triangles similar?

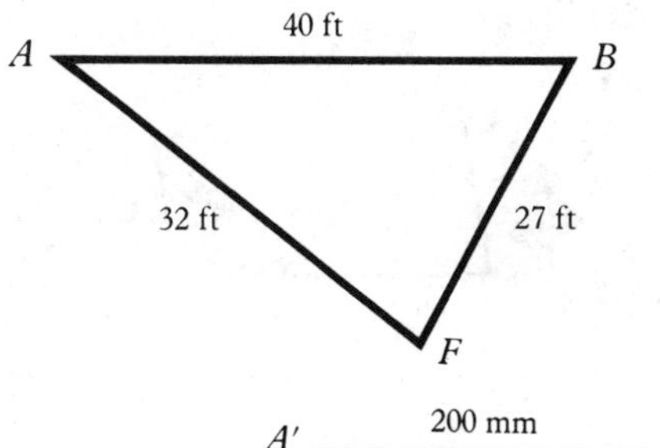

Since

$$\frac{40}{200} = \frac{32}{160} = \frac{27}{135} = \frac{1}{5},$$

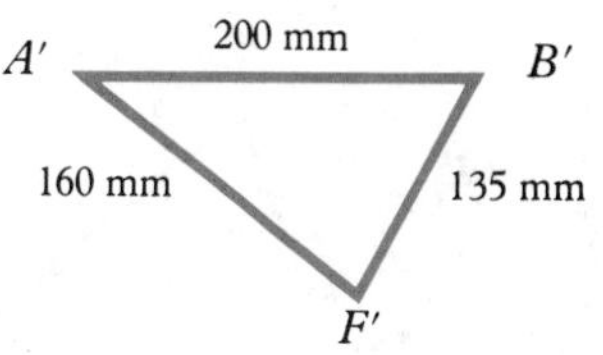

Theorem 9–12 answers the question. Yes, $\triangle ABF \sim \triangle A'B'F'$.

There is another way of showing two triangles are similar. $\triangle DEF$ and $\triangle GHI$ were constructed so that $\frac{DE}{GH} = \frac{EF}{HI}$ and $\angle E \cong \angle H$.

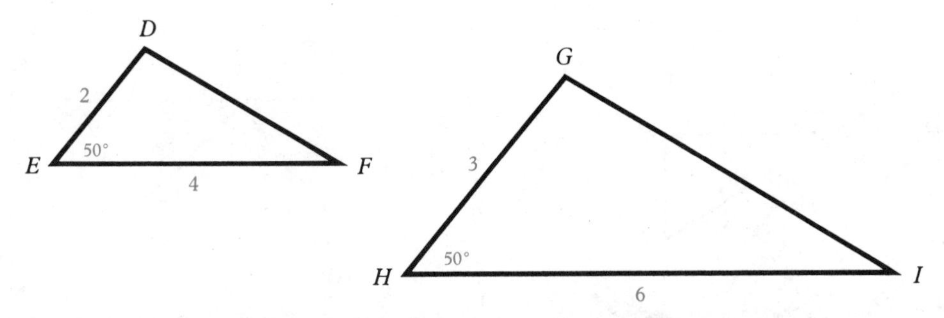

These conditions imply that $\angle F \cong \angle I$ and $\angle D \cong \angle G$. This example suggests the following theorem called the SAS Similarity Theorem.

Theorem 9–13 **SAS Similarity Theorem.** If two triangles have an angle of one triangle congruent to an angle of the other triangle, and if the corresponding sides including the angle are proportional, then the triangles are similar.

EXERCISES

A.

In exercises 1–4 use the given information to decide if the triangles are similar. Base your decision on the measurements given rather than the shape of the drawings. If the triangles are similar, state whether the AA, SAS, or SSS Similarity Theorem applies.

1.

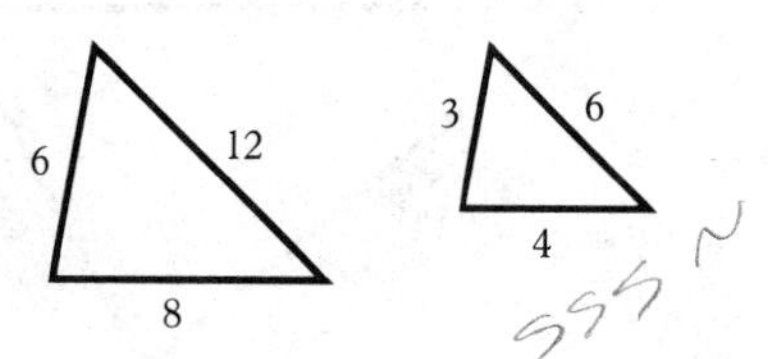

2.

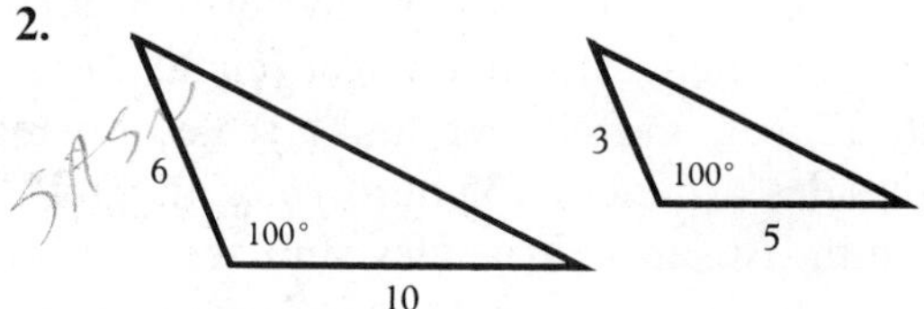

3.

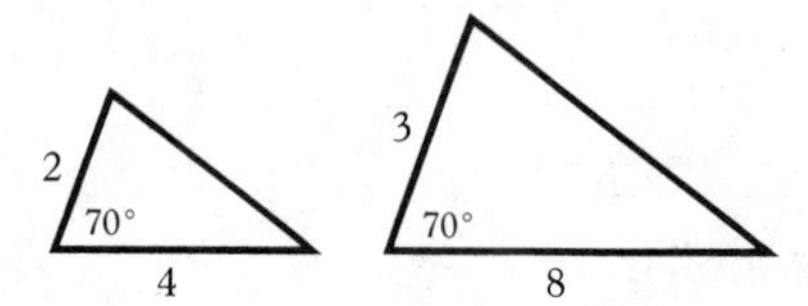

4.

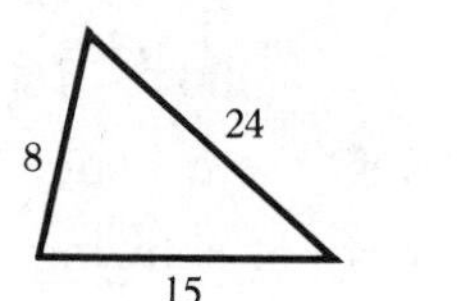

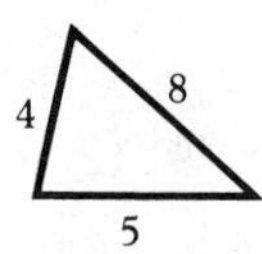

5. If $AB = 4$ and $BC = 7$, find $\frac{AD}{CE}$.

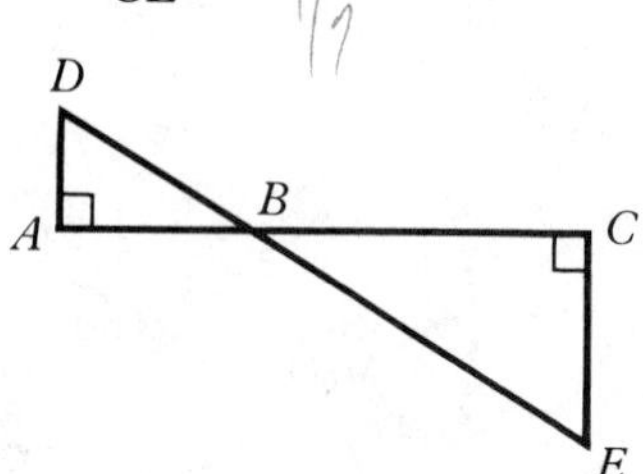

6. If point B divides $\overline{AC}$ and $\overline{DE}$ into thirds, how long is $\overline{CE}$?

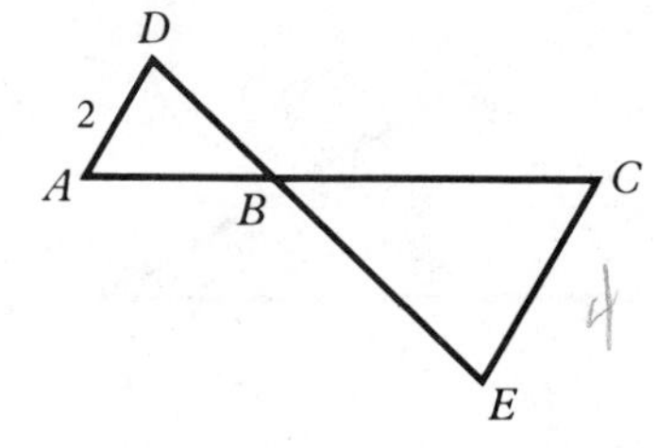

Activity

1. Construct a $\triangle ABC$ with sides 10 cm, 13 cm, and 17 cm long. Find the point of intersection of the perpendicular bisectors of the sides.
2. This point is the center of the circle that passes through the three vertices. This circle is called the circumscribed circle. Construct this circle.

3. Then construct the nine-point circle, as described on page 246.
4. How does the radius of the circumscribed circle compare to the radius of the nine-point circle?

B.

7. Given: Trapezoid $ABCD$, $\overline{AB} \parallel \overline{CD}$
Prove: $\triangle AOB \sim \triangle COD$

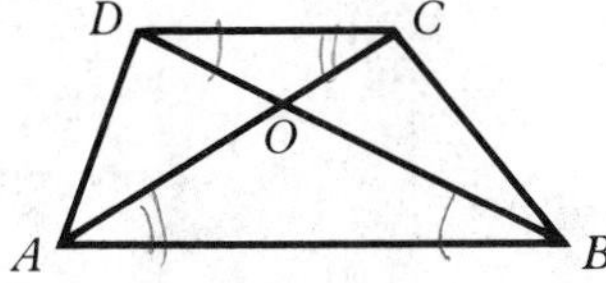

8. Given: $\overline{RU} \perp \overline{UV}$, $\overline{TV} \perp \overline{RT}$
Prove: $\triangle RSU \sim \triangle VST$

9. Given: $\triangle JKL \sim \triangle NMP$
$\overline{JI}$ and $\overline{NO}$ are medians.
Prove: $\dfrac{JI}{NO} = \dfrac{JK}{NM}$

(Ex. 9)

10. Given: T, U, and V are midpoints.
Prove: $\triangle QRS \sim \triangle VUT$

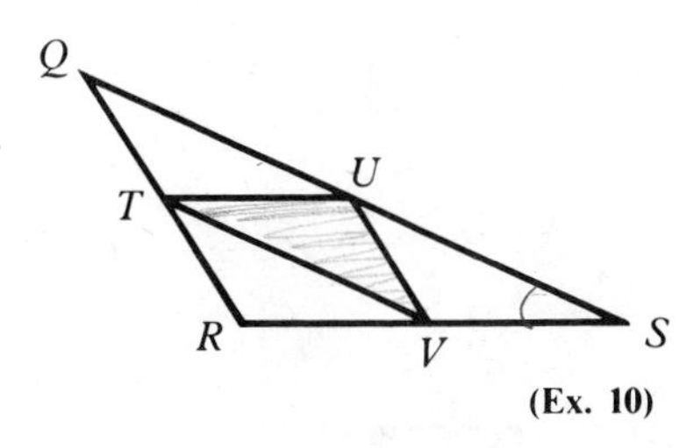

(Ex. 10)

11. Draw a counterexample for this statement.
If two sides of one triangle are proportional to two sides of another triangle and an angle of the first triangle is congruent to an angle of the second triangle, the triangles are similar.

C.

12. Prove: The corresponding diagonals of two similar quadrilaterals are in the same ratio as the corresponding sides.

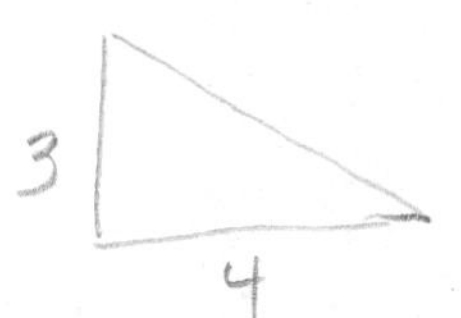

13. Prove: Two isosceles triangles with congruent vertex angles are similar.

14. Draw a triangle given two acute angles and the length of the altitude to the included side.

PROBLEM SOLVING

Identify as many different-shaped figures as possible for which you can find another figure that is similar.

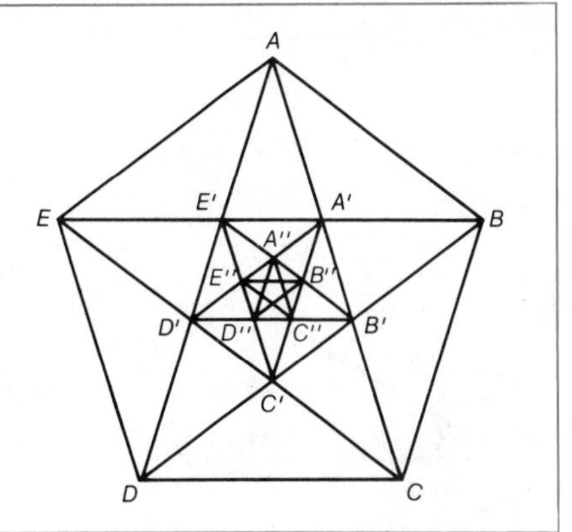

9–7 Trigonometric Ratios—An Application of Similar Triangles

The heights of very tall buildings can be determined with the aid of ratios in a right triangle.

If distance AC is known and if the angle measure of $\angle A$ is known, then height BC can be calculated using a method studied in this lesson.

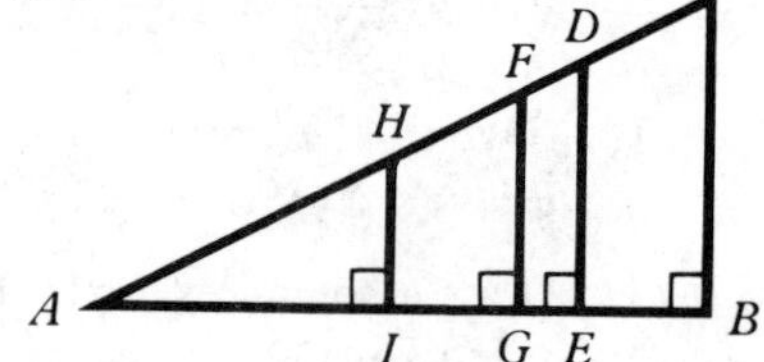
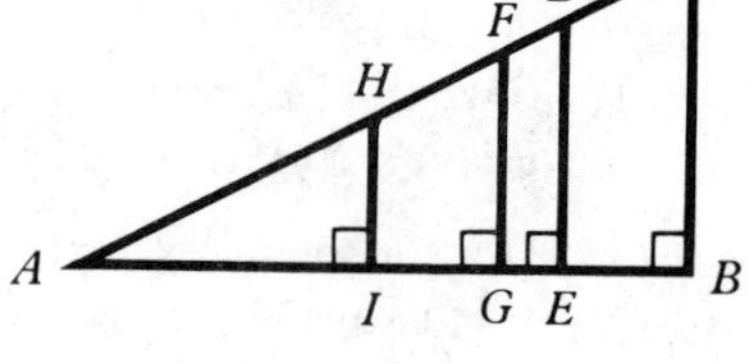

In this figure $\triangle ABC \sim \triangle AED \sim \triangle AGF \sim \triangle AIH$. Therefore, ratios of corresponding sides are equal.

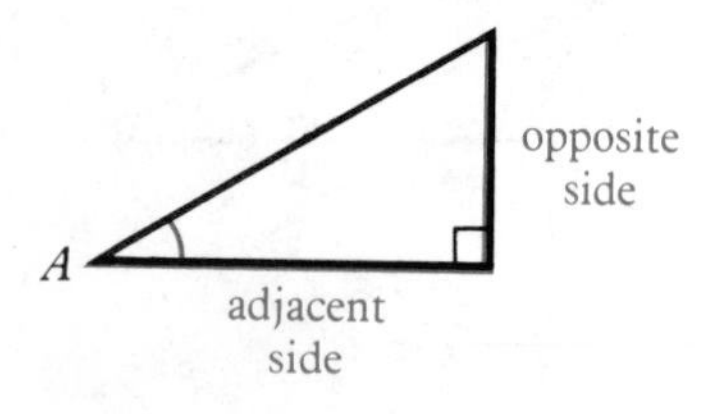

The ratios $\frac{BC}{AB}, \frac{DE}{AE}, \frac{FG}{AG}$, and $\frac{HI}{AI}$ in the figure above are all equal. These ratios are associated with $\angle A$ and are called the *tangent* of $\angle A$. This is abbreviated *tan A*.

Definition 9-4

The **tangent** of an acute angle of a right triangle is the ratio $\dfrac{\text{length of opposite side}}{\text{length of adjacent side}}$.

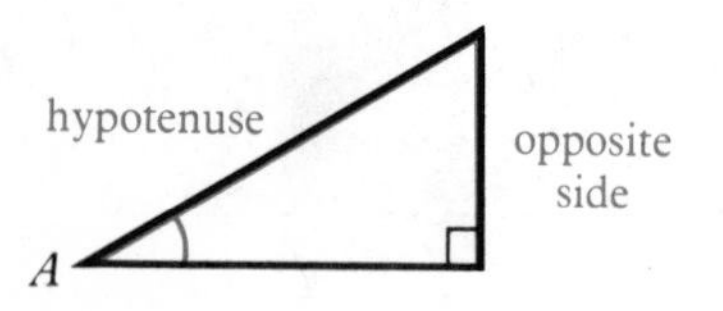

The ratios $\frac{BC}{AC}, \frac{ED}{AD}, \frac{GF}{AF}$, and $\frac{IH}{AH}$ are all equal. These ratios associated with $\angle A$ are called the *sine* of $\angle A$. This is abbreviated *sin A*.

Definition 9-5

The **sine** of an acute angle of a right triangle is the ratio $\dfrac{\text{length of opposite side}}{\text{length of hypotenuse}}$.

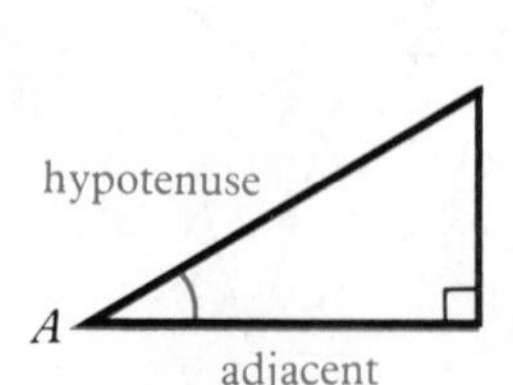

The ratios $\frac{AB}{AC}, \frac{AE}{AD}, \frac{AG}{AF}$, and $\frac{AI}{AH}$ are all equal. These ratios associated with $\angle A$ are called the *cosine* of $\angle A$. This is abbreviated *cos A*.

Definition 9-6

The **cosine** of an acute angle of a right triangle is the ratio $\dfrac{\text{length of adjacent side}}{\text{length of hypotenuse}}$.

Example 1

From the figure at the right we can see that

$$\tan 37^\circ = \frac{220}{292} \doteq 0.7534,$$

$$\sin 37^\circ = \frac{220}{365.6} \doteq 0.6018,$$

$$\cos 37^\circ = \frac{292}{365.6} \doteq 0.7986.$$

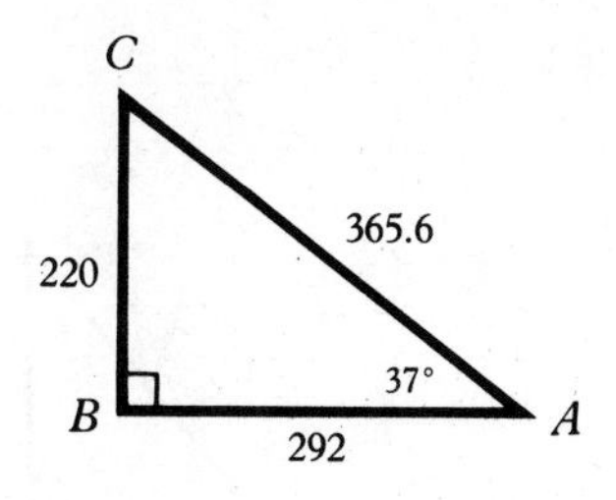

These trigonometric ratios can be found for various angles using either a table of values, as shown here, or by using a calculator that has the trigonometric functions.

$m\angle A$ in degrees	tan A	sin A	cos A
1	.0175	.0175	.9998
2	.0349	.0349	.9994
3	.0524	.0523	.9986
4	.0699	.0698	.9976
5	.0875	.0872	.9962
6	.1051	.1045	.9945
7	.1228	.1219	.9925
8	.1405	.1392	.9903
9	.1584	.1564	.9877
10	.1763	.1736	.9848
11	.1944	.1908	.9816
12	.2126	.2079	.9781
13	.2309	.2250	.9744
14	.2493	.2419	.9703
15	.2679	.2588	.9659
16	.2867	.2756	.9613
17	.3057	.2924	.9563
18	.3249	.3090	.9511
19	.3443	.3256	.9455
20	.3640	.3420	.9397
21	.3839	.3584	.9336
22	.4040	.3746	.9272
23	.4245	.3907	.9205
24	.4452	.4067	.9135
25	.4663	.4226	.9063
26	.4877	.4384	.8988
27	.5095	.4540	.8910
28	.5317	.4695	.8829
29	.5543	.4848	.8746
30	.5774	.5000	.8660
31	.6009	.5150	.8572
32	.6249	.5299	.8480
33	.6494	.5446	.8387
34	.6745	.5592	.8290
35	.7002	.5736	.8192
36	.7265	.5878	.8090
37	.7536	.6018	.7986
38	.7813	.6157	.7880
39	.8098	.6293	.7771
40	.8391	.6428	.7660
41	.8693	.6561	.7547
42	.9004	.6691	.7431
43	.9325	.6820	.7314
44	.9657	.6947	.7193
45	1.0000	.7071	.7071

Example 2

From the table of approximate values we see that

$$\tan 42^\circ = 0.9004,$$
$$\sin 42^\circ = 0.6691,$$
$$\cos 42^\circ = 0.7431.$$

APPLICATION

A person 1000 feet from the base of the Washington Monument finds the measure of $\angle A$ to be about 29°. About how high is the monument?

$$\tan 29^\circ = \frac{x}{1000} \quad \text{or} \quad x = 1000 \times \tan 29^\circ$$

$$= 1000 \times .5543 = 554.3 \text{ feet}$$

EXERCISES

A.

1. Complete the following:
$\tan A = \underline{?}$
$\sin A = \underline{?}$
$\cos A = \underline{?}$

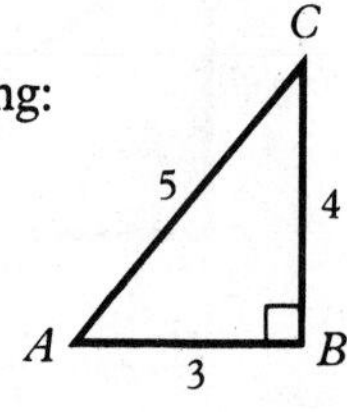

2. Complete the following:
$\tan M = \underline{?}$
$\sin P = \underline{?}$
$\cos P = \underline{?}$

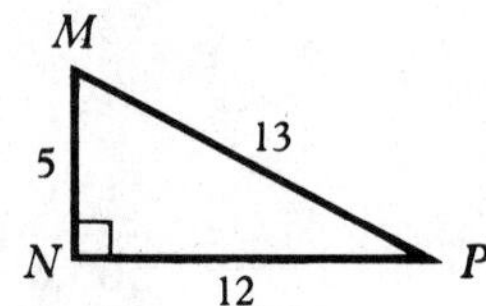

For exercises 3–14, use the trigonometric tables.

3. $\sin 17° = \underline{?}$
4. $\cos 43° = \underline{?}$
5. $\tan 21° = \underline{?}$
6. $\cos 13° = \underline{?}$
7. $\tan 35° = \underline{?}$
8. $\sin 37° = \underline{?}$

Find $m\angle A$ to the nearest degree given the following approximate measures:

9. $\tan \angle A = 0.7536.$
10. $\cos \angle A = 0.9985.$
11. $\sin \angle A = 0.2925.$
12. $\cos \angle A = 0.8290.$
13. $\sin \angle A = 0.0699.$
14. $\tan \angle A = 0.9658.$

B.

15. $\triangle ABC$ has $AB = AC = 10$ and $m\angle B = 40$. Find the length of $\overline{AD}$.

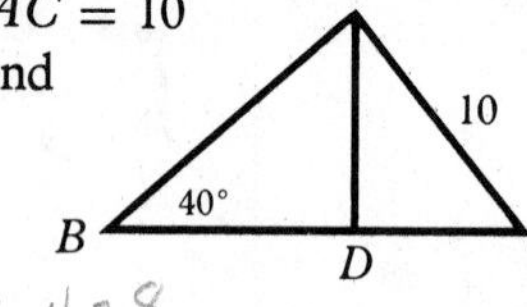

16. $\triangle ABC$ has $AB = AC = 10$ and $m\angle B = 40$. Find the length of $\overline{BD}$.

(Exs. 15, 16)

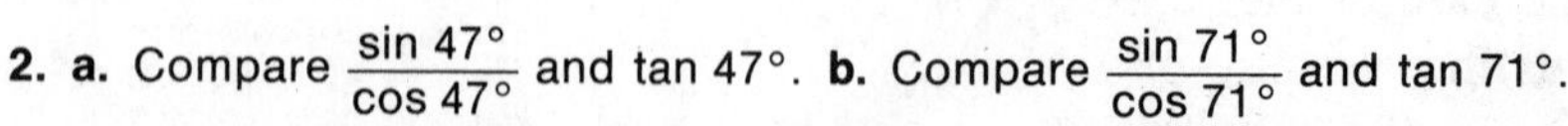

Use a calculator to determine the following.

1. a. $(\sin 57°)^2 + (\cos 57°)^2 = \underline{?}$ b. $(\sin 43°)^2 + (\cos 43°)^2 = \underline{?}$
   c. $(\sin 9°)^2 + (\cos 9°)^2 = \underline{?}$ d. $(\sin 24°)^2 + (\cos 24°)^2 = \underline{?}$
   e. What do you guess about $\sin^2 x + \cos^2 x$ for all x?

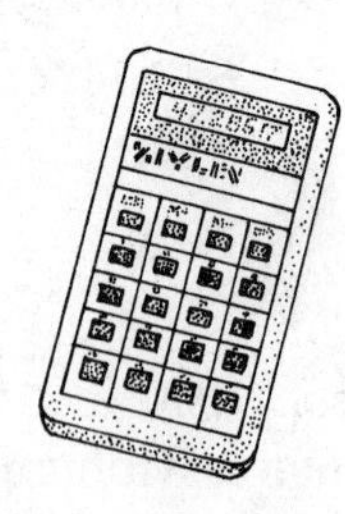

2. a. Compare $\frac{\sin 47°}{\cos 47°}$ and $\tan 47°$. b. Compare $\frac{\sin 71°}{\cos 71°}$ and $\tan 71°$.
   c. Compare $\frac{\sin 33°}{\cos 33°}$ and $\tan 33°$. d. Compare $\frac{\sin 66°}{\cos 66°}$ and $\tan 66°$.
   e. What do you guess about $\frac{\sin x}{\cos x}$ and $\tan x$?

17. $\sin F = \frac{7}{25}$

$FD = \underline{\ ?\ }$

$FE = \underline{\ ?\ }$

$\tan D = \underline{\ ?\ }$

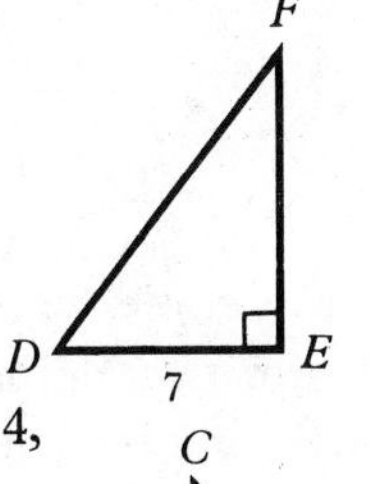

18. $\tan Z = \frac{8}{15}$

$XY = \underline{\ ?\ }$

$XZ = \underline{\ ?\ }$

$\cos X = \underline{\ ?\ }$

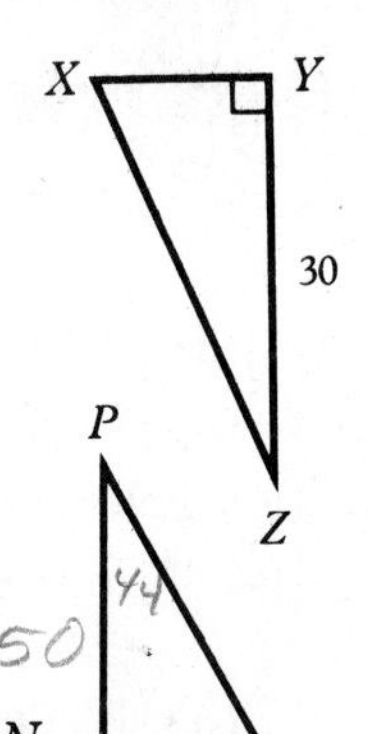

19. Suppose $AB = 3$, $BC = 4$, and $AC = 5$. Use the trig tables or a calculator to determine $m\angle A$ and $m\angle C$ to the nearest degree.

20. Suppose you want to find the distance across the pond QN. You measure to find that $PQ = 50$ m and determine $m\angle P = 44$. Find QN.

C.

21. Suppose you want to find the height of the building, that is, FN. The $m\angle FUN = 50$ at a distance 30 meters from N. What is the length of FN?

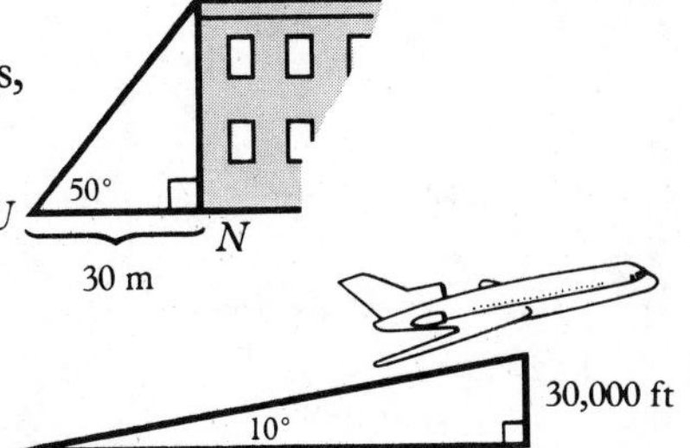

22. If an airplane takes off and climbs at a steady rate of 10° until an altitude of 30,000 feet is reached, what is the ground distance covered?

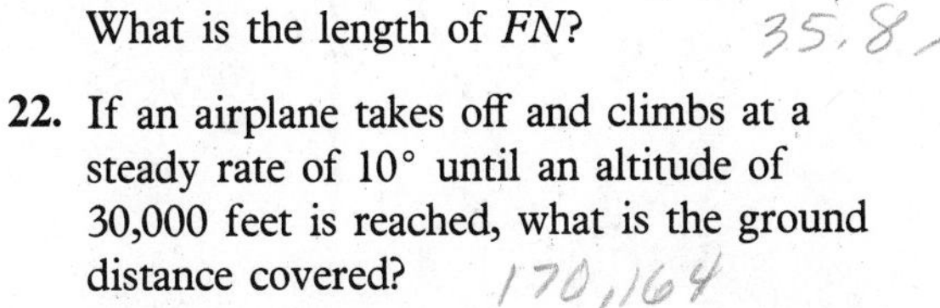

23. Melted gold is poured into a mold to form a brick. A box-like mold with inner slanting sides is used. The "draft angle" is the degree of slant of the walls. The draft angle is 2° and $BD = 6$ cm. How much wider is AB than CD?

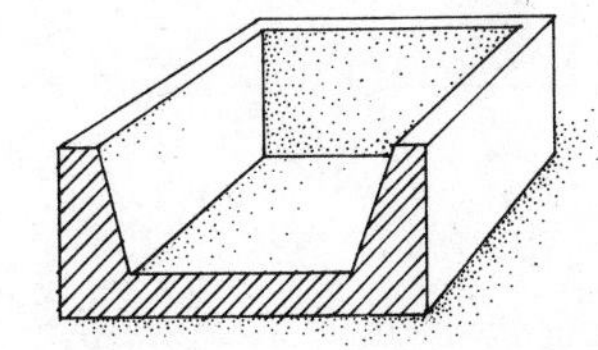

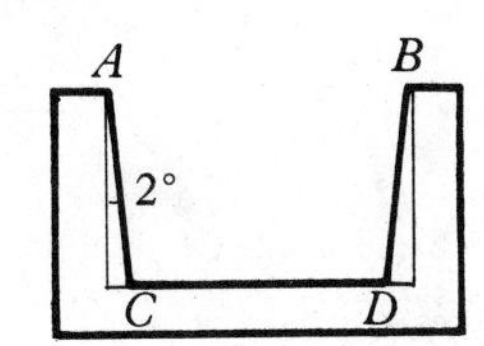

PROBLEM SOLVING

Suppose you want to find the height (DC) of a tower but you cannot measure distances AC and BC directly.

If $m\angle A = 40$, $m\angle DBC = 60$, and $AB = 200$ m, find height DC.

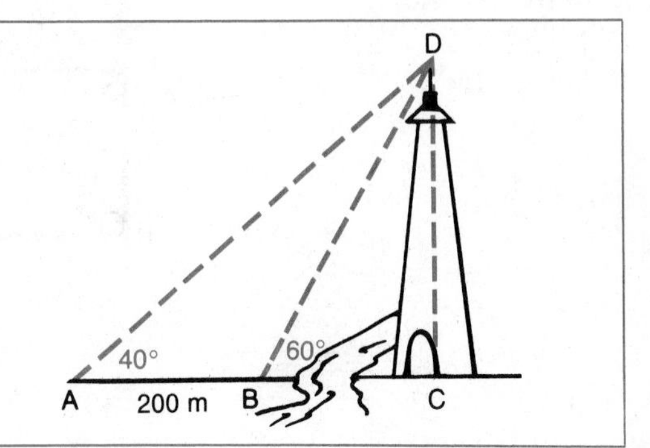

9–8 Trigonometric Ratios of Special Angles

Just as the 30°, 45°, and 60° angles are important to people who do drafting work, they are also important special angles in trigonometry. It is often helpful to know the trigonometric ratios of these angles without referring to tables of values or to a handheld calculator.

From Theorem 7–3 we conclude that the side lengths of a 45°-45°-90° triangle are in a ratio of $1:1:\sqrt{2}$.

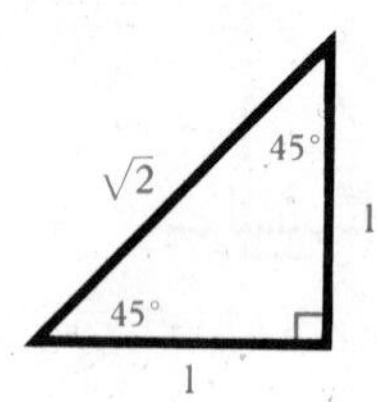

From Theorem 7–4 we conclude that the side lengths of a 30°-60°-90° triangle are in a ratio of $1:\sqrt{3}:2$.

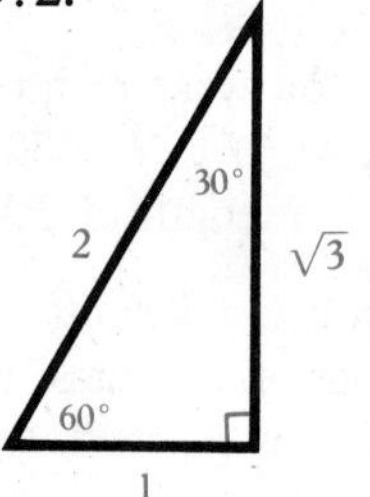

This table shows the trigonometric ratios for these special angles.

	30°	60°	45°
tan	$\frac{\sqrt{3}}{3}$	$\sqrt{3}$	1
sin	$\frac{1}{2}$	$\frac{\sqrt{3}}{2}$	$\frac{\sqrt{2}}{2}$
cos	$\frac{\sqrt{3}}{2}$	$\frac{1}{2}$	$\frac{\sqrt{2}}{2}$

Example 1

The diagonal of a square is 5 cm. Find the length of a side.

$$\sin \angle EHF = \frac{EF}{5}$$

$$\sin 45° = \frac{EF}{5}$$

$$\frac{\sqrt{2}}{2} = \frac{EF}{5}$$

$$EF = \frac{5\sqrt{2}}{2} \text{ cm}$$

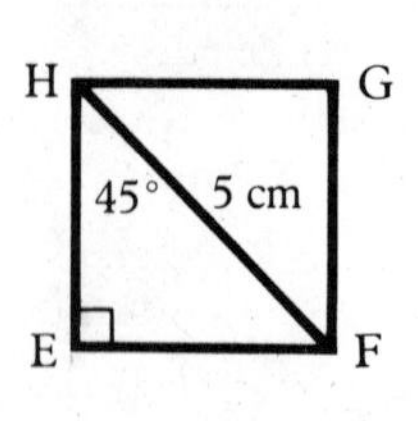

Example 2

In the triangle shown find XW and XZ.

$$\tan \angle Z = \frac{XW}{4}$$

$$\tan 30° = \frac{XW}{4}$$

$$\frac{\sqrt{3}}{3} = \frac{XW}{4}$$

$$XW = \frac{4\sqrt{3}}{3} \text{ ft}$$

X

30°

Z W

4 ft

Since XZ is $2XW$, then $XZ = \frac{8\sqrt{3}}{3}$ ft.

EXERCISES

A.

For exercises 1-6, complete the statement correctly without referring to the table on page 331.

1. $\sin 45° = \underline{?}$ **2.** $\cos 30° = \underline{?}$ **3.** $\tan 60° = \underline{?}$

4. $\cos 60° = \underline{?}$ **5.** $\sin 30° = \underline{?}$ **6.** $\tan 45° = \underline{?}$

For exercises 7-14, the right triangle shown is not drawn accurately. Accept the side lengths as shown. Complete the following statements correctly.

(Exs. 7-14)

7. $\sin A = \underline{?}$ **8.** $\cos A = \underline{?}$ **9.** $\tan A = \underline{?}$

10. $\cos B = \underline{?}$ **11.** $\tan B = \underline{?}$ **12.** $\sin B = \underline{?}$

13. $m\angle A = \underline{?}$ **14.** $m\angle B = \underline{?}$

B.

For exercises 15-18, evaluate each given expression. Identify those pairs of expressions that are equal. In each problem assume that $m\angle A = 30$.

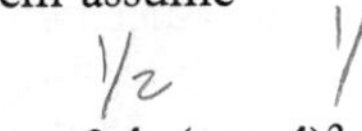

15. $2 \sin A$, $2 \sin A \cos A$, $\sin 2A$

16. $\cos 2A$, $(\cos A)^2 - (\sin A)^2$, $2(\cos A)^2 - 1$

17. $\tan 2A$, $2 \tan A$, $\dfrac{2 \tan A}{1 - (\tan A)^2}$

18. $2 \cos A$, $1 - 2(\sin A)^2$, $\cos 2A$

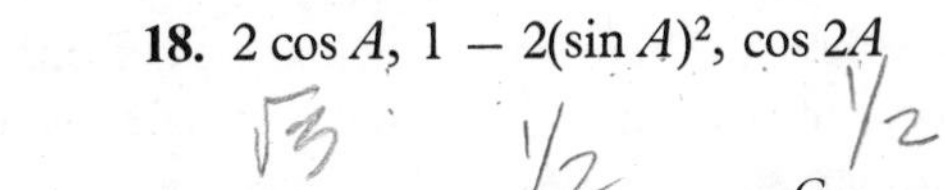

C.

19. If $m\angle GUS = 30$ and $US = 50$ m, how high is the building?

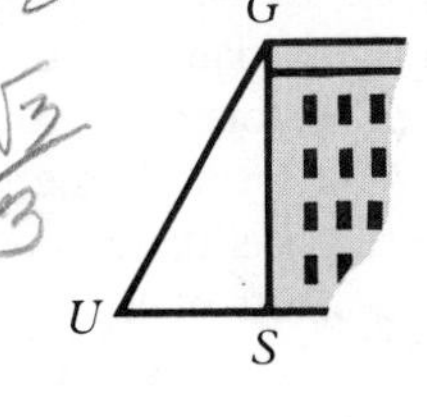

20. Quadrilateral $EASY$ is an isosceles trapezoid with $EA = SY$. If $EA = 10$ and $m\angle EAS = 45$, find the length of the altitude $\overline{EZ}$.

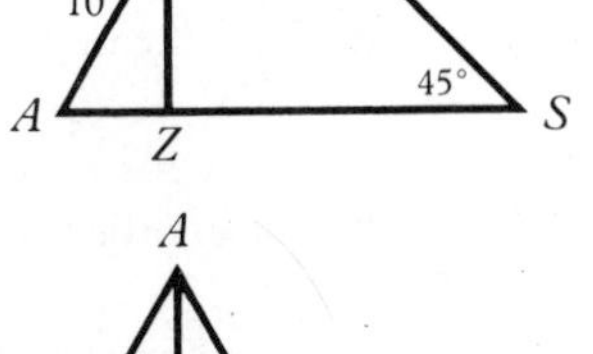

21. $\triangle ABC$ is equilateral. Find the length of the altitude $\overline{AD}$.

22. Show that, if $\triangle ABC$ has right angle $\angle C$, then $(\sin A)^2 + (\cos A)^2 = 1$.

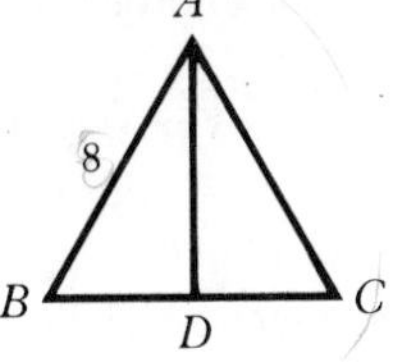

(Ex. 21)

Important Ideas—Chapter 9

Terms

Proportion (p. 304)
Similar polygons (p. 313)
Geometric mean (p. 322)
Tangent of an acute angle (p. 330)
Sine of an acute angle (p. 330)
Cosine of an acute angle (p. 330)

Postulate

AAA Similarity Postulate (p. 316)

Theorems

9-1 If $\frac{a}{b} = \frac{c}{d}$ then $a \times d = b \times c$.

9-2 If $\frac{a}{b} = \frac{c}{d}$, then $\frac{a+b}{b} = \frac{c+d}{d}$.

9-3 If $\frac{a}{b} = \frac{c}{d}$, then $\frac{a-b}{b} = \frac{c-d}{d}$.

9-4 If $\frac{a}{b} = \frac{c}{d}$, then $\frac{a}{c} = \frac{b}{d}$.

9-5 If $a \times d = b \times c$, then $\frac{a}{b} = \frac{c}{d}$.

9-6 **Side-Splitting Theorem.** If a line is parallel to one side of a triangle and intersects the other two sides, then it divides the two sides proportionally.

9-7 If a line intersects two sides of a triangle and divides them proportionally, then the line is parallel to the third side.

9-8 **AA Similarity Theorem.** If two angles of one triangle are congruent to two angles of another triangle, then the two triangles are similar.

9-9 Two right triangles are similar if an acute angle of one triangle is congruent to an acute angle of the other triangle.

9-10 In a right triangle, the length of the altitude to the hypotenuse is the geometric mean between the lengths of the two segments of the hypotenuse.

9-11 Given a right triangle and the altitude to the hypotenuse, each leg is the geometric mean between the length of the hypotenuse and the length of segment of the hypotenuse adjacent to the leg.

9-12 **SSS Similarity Theorem.** If three sides of one triangle are proportional to the three sides of another triangle, then the triangles are similar.

9-13 **SAS Similarity Theorem.** If two triangles have an angle of one triangle congruent to an angle of the other triangle, and if the corresponding sides including the angle are proportional, then the triangles are similar.

Chapter 9—Review

1. Indicate whether the following statements are true or false.

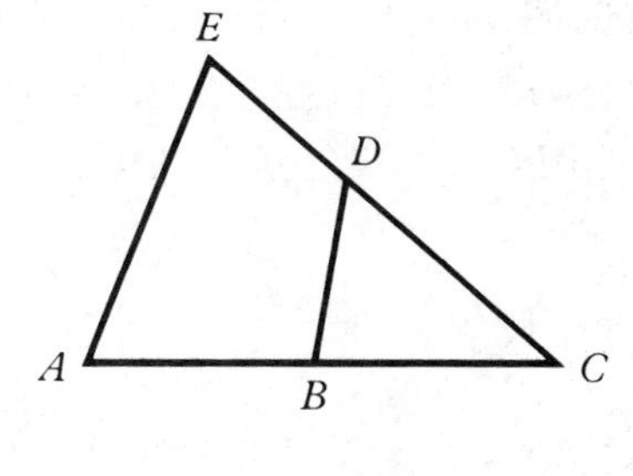

a. If $\overline{BD} \parallel \overline{AE}$, then $\frac{CD}{DE} = \frac{CB}{BA}$.

b. If $\frac{CD}{CE} = \frac{CB}{CA}$, then $\overline{BD} \parallel \overline{AE}$.

c. If $CD = 4$, $DE = 3$, $BC = 8$, then $AB = 6$.

d. If $\angle A \cong \angle DBC$, then $\triangle EAC \sim \triangle DBC$.

e. If $CD = DE = AB = BC$, then $\triangle EAC \sim \triangle DBC$.

2. Assume $\overline{DE} \parallel \overline{BC}$.

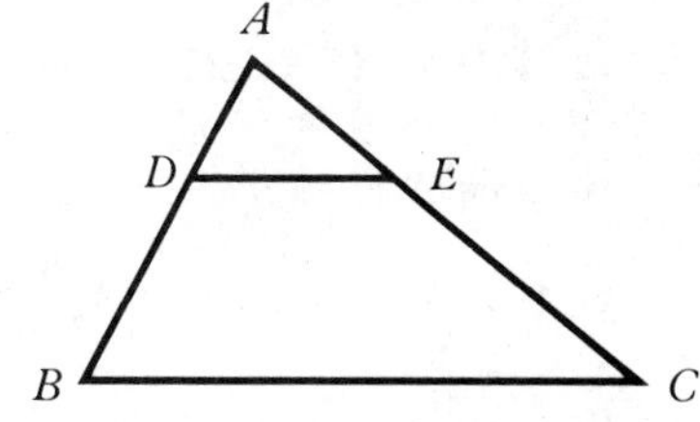

a. $AD = 4$, $BD = 6$, $AE = 5$. Find AC.

b. $AB = 10$, $BD = 7$, $AC = 12$. Find AE.

c. $AD = 3$, $BD = 4$, $BC = 6$. Find DE.

d. $AB = BC = AC = 6$, $AD = 2$. Find $AD + DE + AE$.

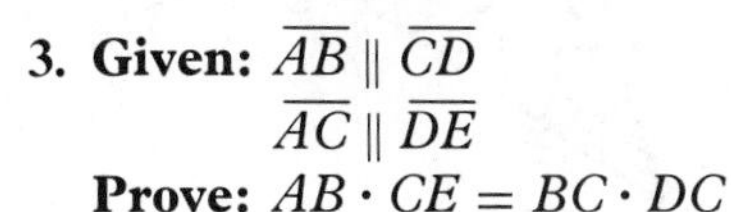

3. Given: $\overline{AB} \parallel \overline{CD}$
$\overline{AC} \parallel \overline{DE}$
Prove: $AB \cdot CE = BC \cdot DC$

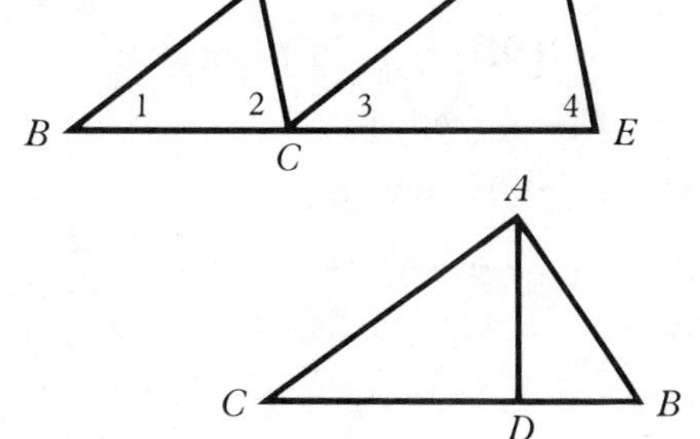

4. Assume $m\angle CAB = 90$ and $\overline{AD} \perp \overline{BC}$.

a. If $AB = 8$ and $BC = 12$, find BD.

b. If $AC = 6$ and $DC = 4$, find BC.

c. If $BD = 4$ and $AD = 6$, find DC.

5. Assume $m\angle D = 90$.

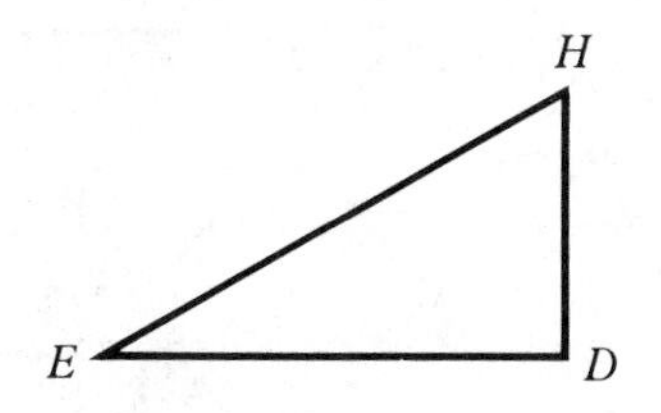

a. If $\sin \angle E = \frac{8}{17}$, find $\tan \angle E$.

b. If $\cos \angle H = \frac{9}{41}$, find $\cos \angle E$.

c. If $\tan \angle E = \frac{4}{3}$, find $\cos \angle H$.

6. If a 20-foot tree casts a shadow of 45 feet, how long a shadow would a 30-foot tree cast?

7. Given: Figure $ABCD$ is a parallelogram.
Prove: **a.** $\triangle ECB \sim \triangle EDF$
b. $\triangle EDF \sim \triangle BAF$
c. $\triangle ECB \sim \triangle BAF$

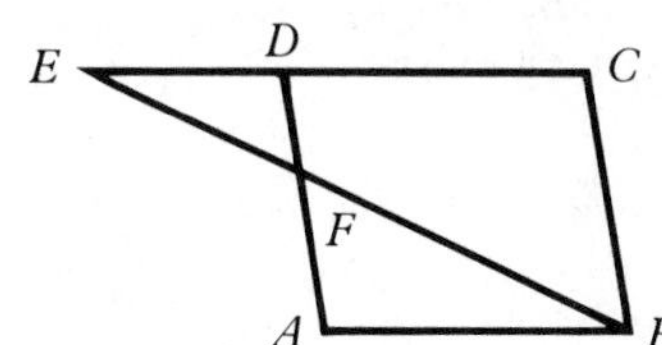

Chapter 9—Test

1. Indicate whether the following statements are true or false.

   a. If $\overline{DB} \parallel \overline{AE}$, then $CD \cdot DE = BC \cdot AB$

   b. If $\frac{EC}{DC} = \frac{AC}{BC}$, then $\triangle AEC \sim \triangle BDC$.

   c. If $\triangle AEC \sim \triangle BDC$, then $\frac{EC}{ED} = \frac{AC}{AB}$.

   d. If $\frac{EC}{DC} = \frac{AC}{BC}$, then $\triangle ACE \sim \triangle BCD$.

   e. If $DC \cdot AB = BC \cdot ED$, then $\overline{BD} \parallel \overline{AE}$.

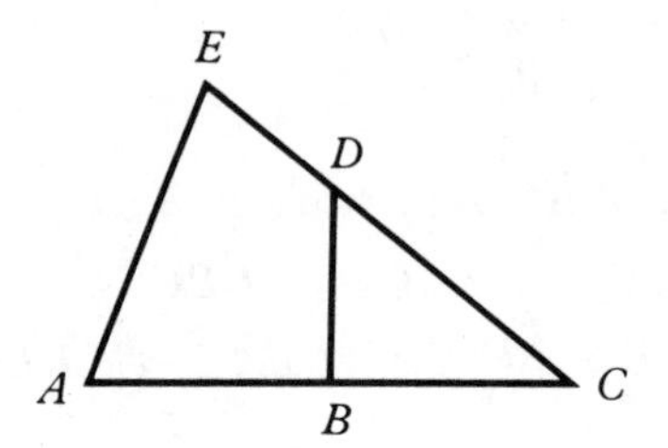

2. Assume $\overline{MN} \parallel \overline{CD}$.

   a. If $ME = 2ED$, find $\frac{NE}{EC}$.

   b. If $ME = 4$, $NE = 5$, and $EC = 3$, find ED.

   c. If $ME = 4$, $DE = 2$, and $NC = 9$, find EC.

   d. If $MN = ME = NE = 6$ and $CE = 4$, find $CE + CD + DE$.

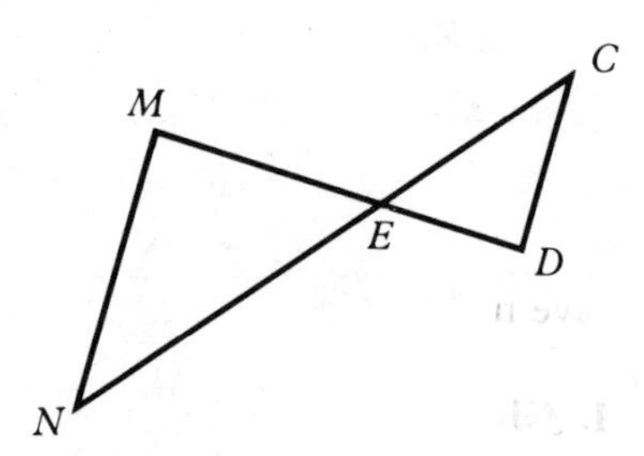

3. Assume $\triangle ABC$ and $\triangle ABD$ are right triangles.

   a. If $AC = 3$ and $AB = 4$, find AD.

   b. If $AB = 12$ and $BC = 13$, find DC.

   c. If $BD = 9$ and $BC = 15$, find AD.

   d. If $AC = 20$ and $BC = 40$, find DC.

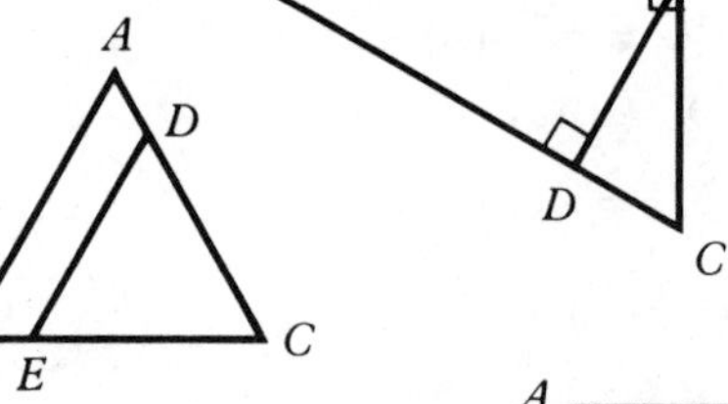

4. **Given:** $AB = AC$
   $DE = DC$
   Prove: $\triangle ABC \sim \triangle DEC$

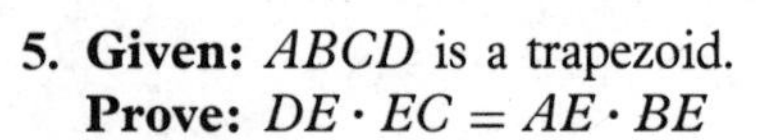

5. **Given:** $ABCD$ is a trapezoid.
   Prove: $DE \cdot EC = AE \cdot BE$

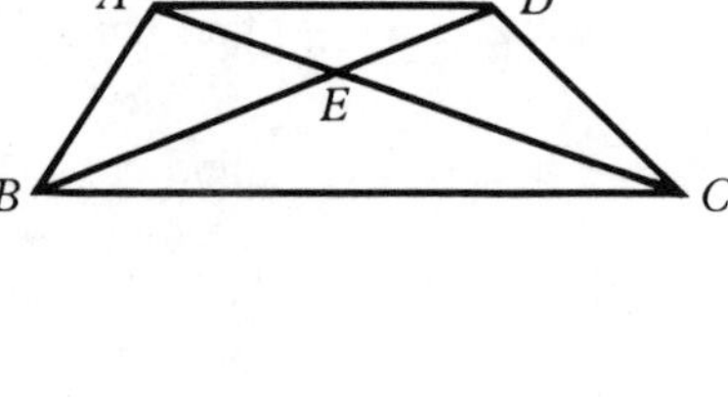

6. $ABCD$ is a square with diagonal $\overline{BD}$.

   a. Find tan $\angle 1$.

   b. Find cos $\angle 2$.

   c. Does cos $\angle 1 =$ sin $\angle 1$?

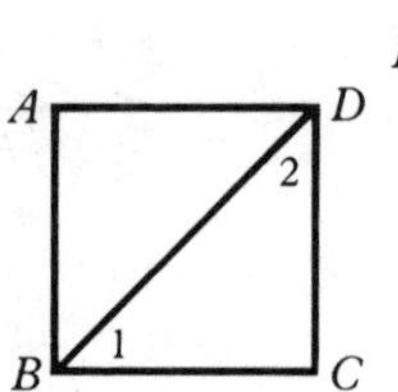

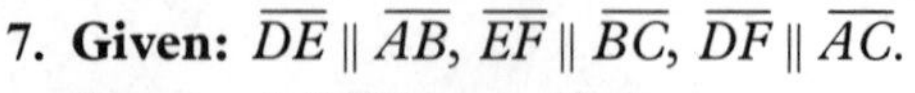

7. **Given:** $\overline{DE} \parallel \overline{AB}$, $\overline{EF} \parallel \overline{BC}$, $\overline{DF} \parallel \overline{AC}$.
   Prove: $\triangle DEF \sim \triangle ABC$

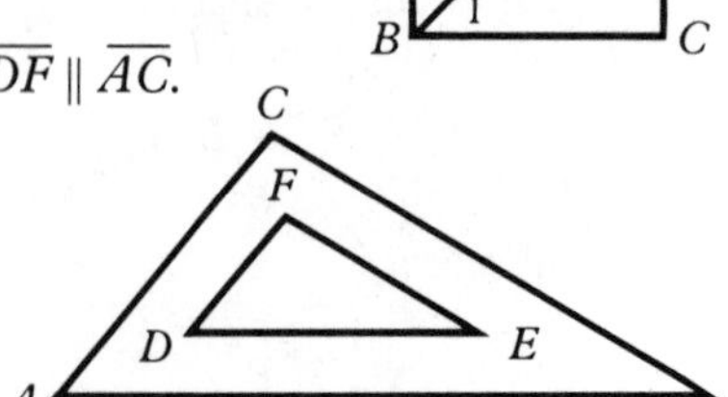

Problem Solving Techniques

Work Backwards

Sometimes when solving problems it is helpful to work backwards as well as forwards. Ask yourself, "What information do I need in order to reach the conclusion I want?"

Example

Consider the problem on the right. Use the questions and answers below to help solve the problem.

Given: $\angle 1 \cong \angle 2$, $\angle 3 \cong \angle 4$
$\overline{AB} \cong \overline{CD}$
Prove: $\triangle AGC \cong \triangle BED$

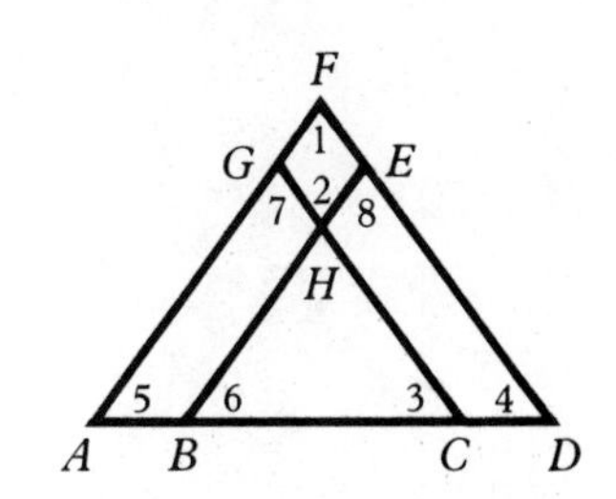

a. Question: How can I prove triangles congruent?

b. Question: Which segments are congruent?

c. Question: Which sides of the triangles can I prove congruent?

d. Question: Which angles of the triangles can I prove congruent?

PROBLEMS

Solve the problems by working backwards.

1. Given: $\overline{AD} \perp \overline{AB}$, $\overline{CB} \perp \overline{AB}$
$\overline{EF}$ bisects and is perpendicular to $\overline{DC}$.
Find: AF

D E C 8 6 A F B 8

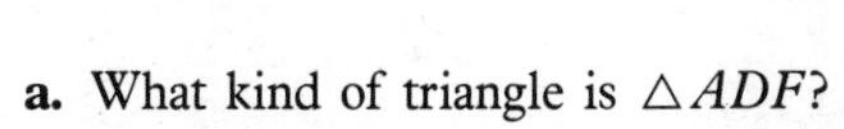

a. What kind of triangle is $\triangle ADF$?

b. Can I use the Pythagorean Theorem?

c. In order to find AF, which side of $\triangle ADF$ do I need to find?

d. What do I know about $\overline{DF}$?

2.

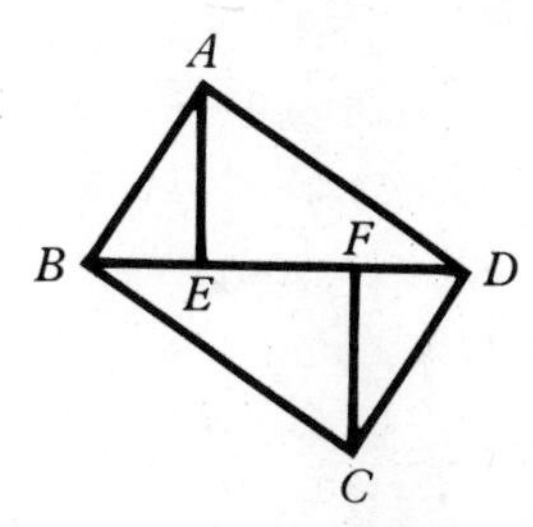

Given: $m\angle BAD = m\angle DCB = 90$,
$\overline{AE} \perp \overline{BD}$, $\overline{FC} \perp \overline{BD}$,
$AB = CD = 9$, $AD = BC = 12$
Find: EF

3. Suppose $\angle 1 \cong \angle 2$ and $\angle 3 \cong \angle 4$. What must be the measure of $\angle C$ so that $\overline{DE} \parallel \overline{GF}$?

a. Suppose $\overline{DE} \parallel \overline{GF}$. Then, $m\angle DEF + m\angle GFE = 180$.

b. Let $m\angle 1 = m\angle 2 = x$ and $m\angle 3 = m\angle 4 = y$. Find an expression for $m\angle 2 + m\angle 4$ and then for $m\angle C$.

c. Reverse this reasoning to prove that your answer assures that $\overline{DE} \parallel \overline{GF}$.

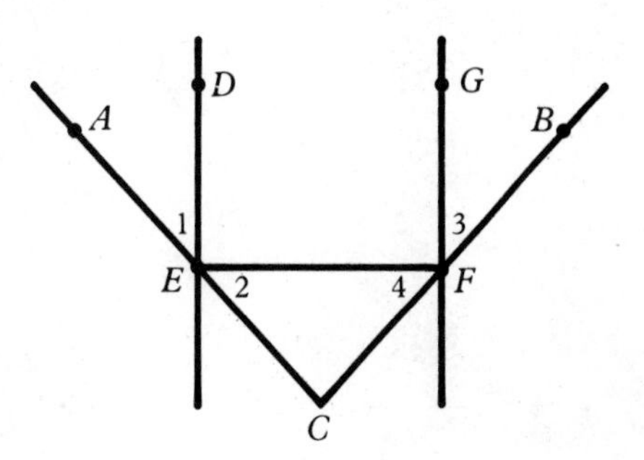

CHAPTER 10

Circles

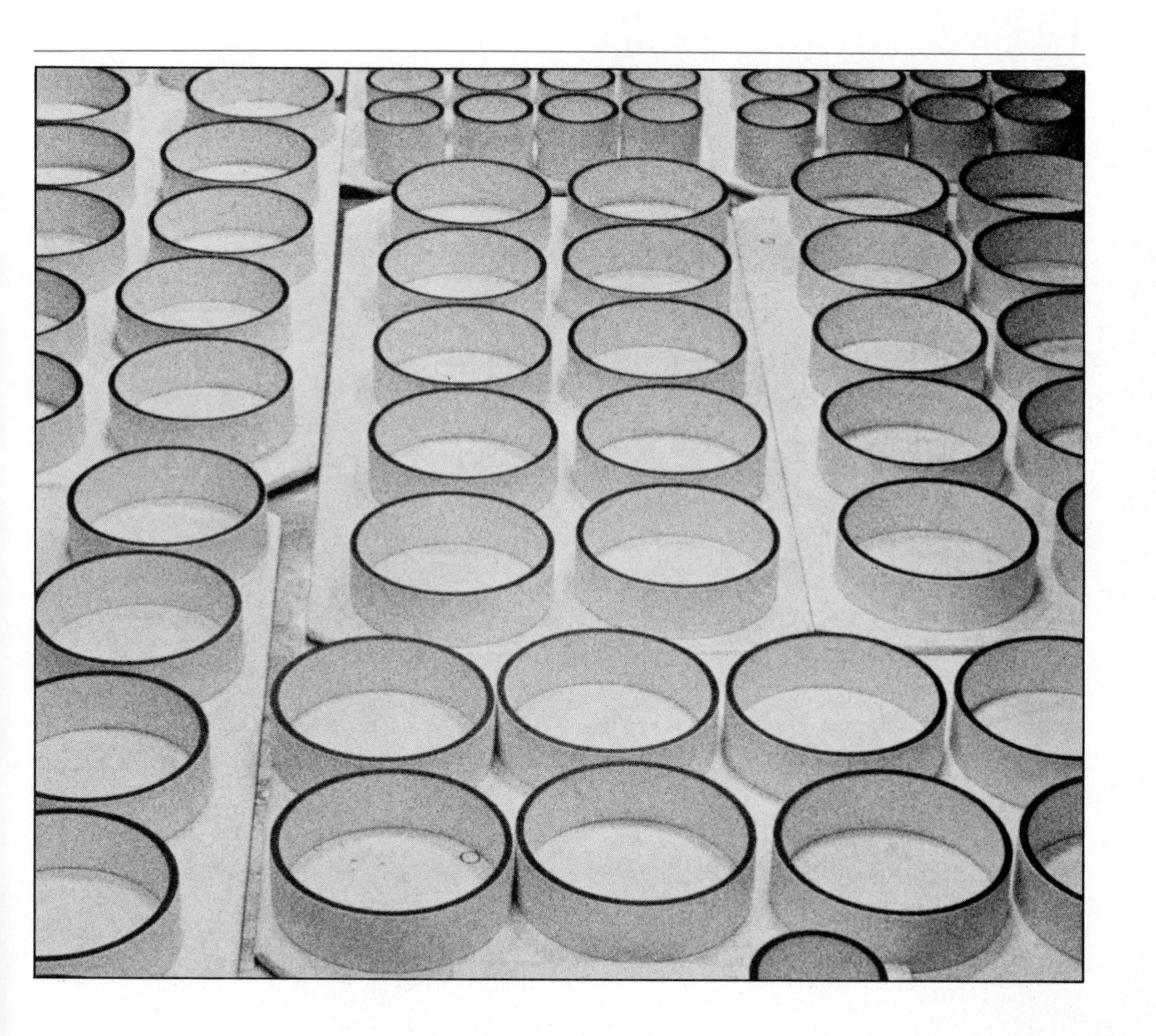

10–1 Basic Definitions

Recall that a circle is a set of points in a plane that are all an equal distance from a fixed point.

In this lesson we shall define terms related to circles.

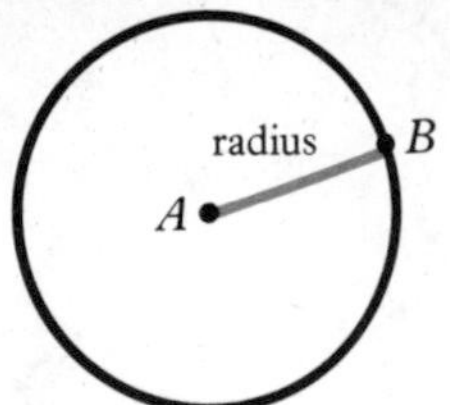

$\overline{AB}$ is a *radius* of $\odot A$. Each point on the circle is the endpoint of another radius.

Definition 10–1

A **radius** of a circle is a segment whose endpoints are the center and a point on the circle.

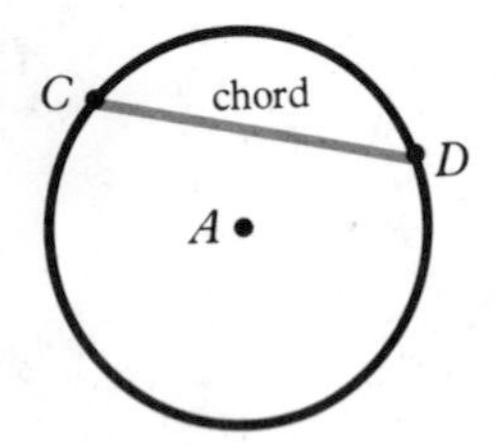

$\overline{CD}$ is a *chord* of $\odot A$. Each pair of points on the circle determines a chord of the circle.

Definition 10–2

A **chord** of a circle is a segment with endpoints on the circle.

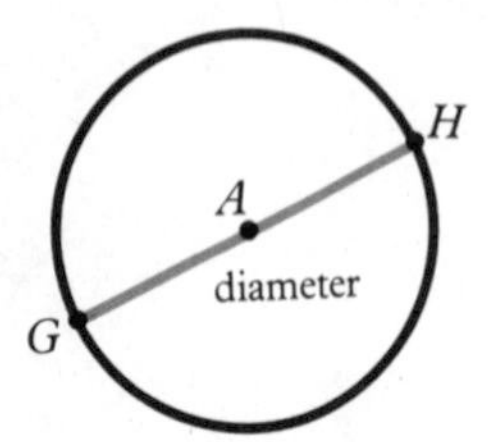

$\overline{GH}$ is a *diameter* of $\odot A$. Each pair of points on the circle that are collinear with A determine a diameter of the circle.

Definition 10–3

A **diameter** of a circle is a chord that contains the center of the circle.

Chords, radii, and diameters are segments associated with circles. The following definitions describe some lines and angles that are also associated with circles.

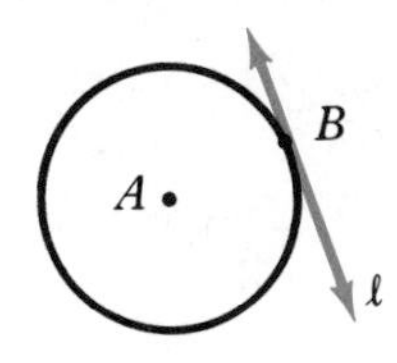

Line ℓ has only point B in common with $\odot A$.

Line ℓ is *tangent* to $\odot A$.

Point B is called the *point of tangency*.

Definition 10–4

A **tangent** to a circle is a line that intersects the circle in exactly one point.

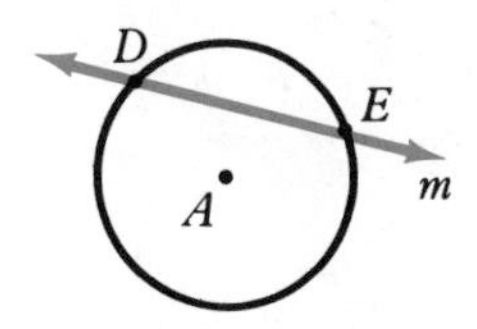

Line m has two points in common with $\odot A$.

Line m is a *secant* of $\odot A$.

Definition 10–5

A **secant** of a circle is a line that intersects the circle in exactly two points.

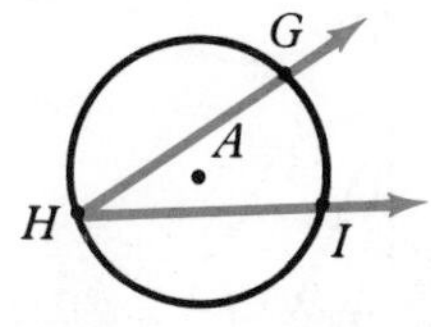

The vertex of $\angle GHI$ is on $\odot A$. The sides of $\angle GHI$ intersect $\odot A$ in points G and I.

$\angle GHI$ is an *inscribed angle.*

Definition 10–6

An **inscribed angle** is an angle with vertex on a circle and with sides that contain chords of the circle.

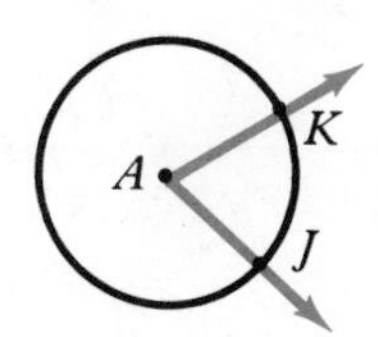

The vertex of $\angle KAJ$ is the center of $\odot A$.

$\angle KAJ$ is a *central angle.*

Definition 10–7

A **central angle** is an angle with vertex at the center of a circle.

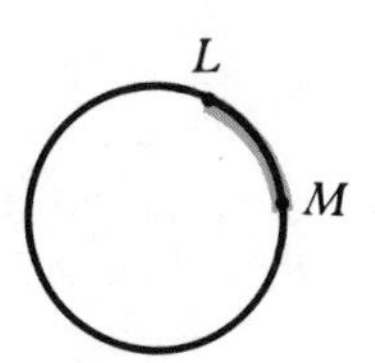

We think of an *arc* as a continuous part of a circle. We write $\widehat{LM}$ to symbolize *arc LM*. An *intercepted arc* is an arc with endpoints on the sides of inscribed or central angles.

EXERCISES

A.

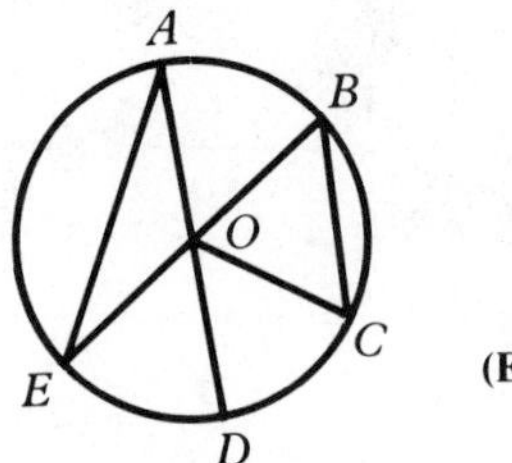

(Exs. 1-4)

1. Name all the chords shown in this figure.
2. Name the diameters in the figure.
3. Name at least four arcs in the figure.
4. Name all the radii shown.
5. Draw a circle with center T. Draw a line tangent to the circle at point B. Draw a secant line that intersects the circle in points F and G.

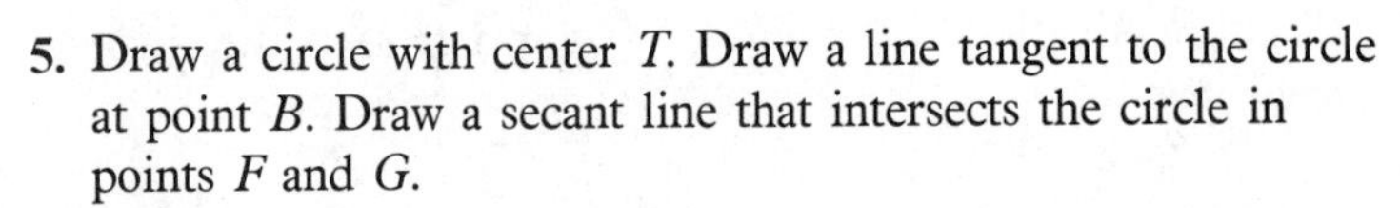

6. Draw a circle and an inscribed angle. If the arc intercepted by that angle is $\widehat{PQ}$, label it on the circle.
7. Draw a circle and a central angle. If the arc intercepted by that angle is $\widehat{XY}$, label it on the circle.
8. Draw a circle and label an arc as shown. Then draw an inscribed angle that intercepts $\widehat{AB}$.
9. Draw a circle and label an arc $\widehat{CD}$. Draw two different inscribed angles, both with intercepted arc $\widehat{CD}$.
10. Name all angles with intercepted arc AB; with intercepted arc CD.

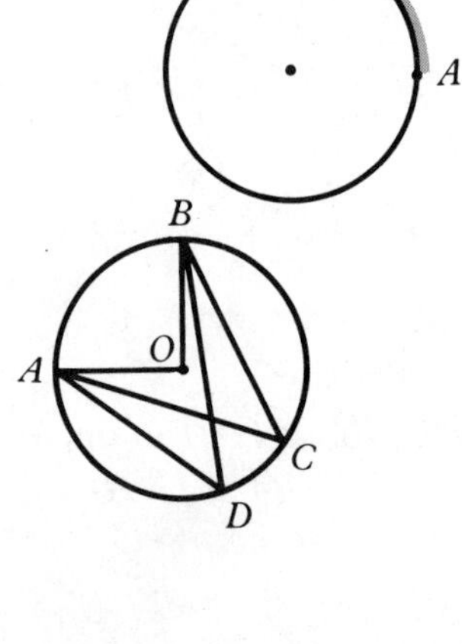

11. Name all the inscribed angles.

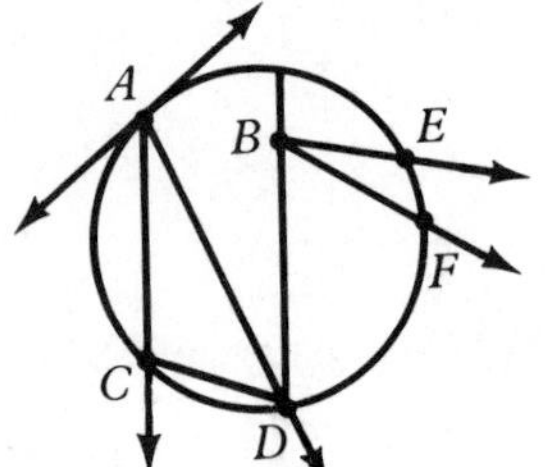

Activity

Use your compass to make larger examples of each *compass art* design below. Make some other designs of your own and color them in an interesting way.

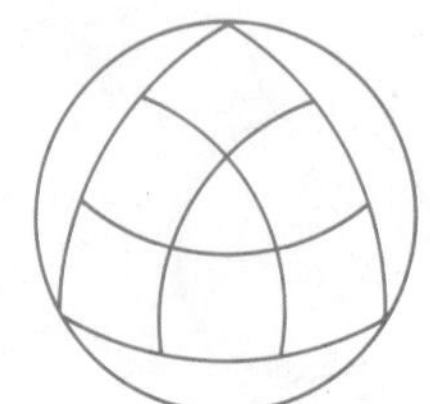

12. Name all angles with at least one side on a tangent line.

13. Name all the central angles.

(Exs. 12, 13)

B.

For exercises 14–16 draw a circle A.

14. Draw a segment that has one endpoint on the circle but is not a chord.

15. Draw a segment that is completely inside the circle but is not a chord.

16. Draw a segment that intersects the circle in two points, contains the center, but is not a radius, diameter, or chord.

For exercises 17–19 draw a circle B.

17. Draw a line that is neither a secant line or a tangent line.

18. Draw an angle that has its vertex on the circle and intersects the circle but is not an inscribed angle.

19. Draw an angle with two sides intersecting the circle and vertex not outside the circle, but which is not a central angle or an inscribed angle.

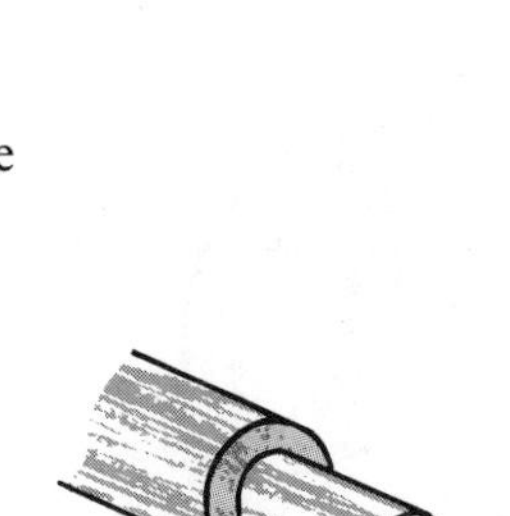

20. A handle 0.41 cm in diameter is reduced to a diameter of 0.34 cm. What is the depth of the cut?

21. Planes that fly from New York to Paris often fly over Ireland. Why is this route chosen? (*Hint:* Use a globe and a flexible ruler.)

PROBLEM SOLVING

This *star polygon* can be made by

a. marking five evenly spaced points on a circle. (You may want to use a protractor.)

b. starting at point S and connecting every second point as you go in a clockwise direction around the circle.

It is called star polygon $\begin{Bmatrix}5\\2\end{Bmatrix}$.

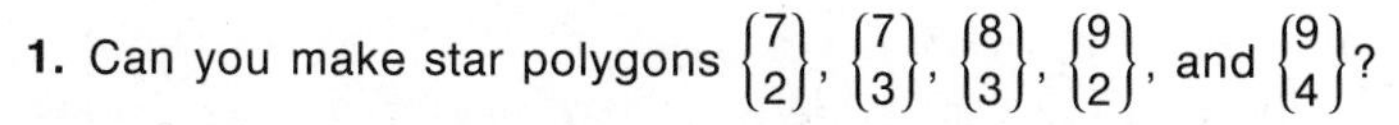

1. Can you make star polygons $\begin{Bmatrix}7\\2\end{Bmatrix}$, $\begin{Bmatrix}7\\3\end{Bmatrix}$, $\begin{Bmatrix}8\\3\end{Bmatrix}$, $\begin{Bmatrix}9\\2\end{Bmatrix}$, and $\begin{Bmatrix}9\\4\end{Bmatrix}$?

2. What can you say about star polygons $\begin{Bmatrix}7\\5\end{Bmatrix}$, $\begin{Bmatrix}7\\4\end{Bmatrix}$, $\begin{Bmatrix}8\\5\end{Bmatrix}$, etc.?

10–2 The Degree Measure of Arcs

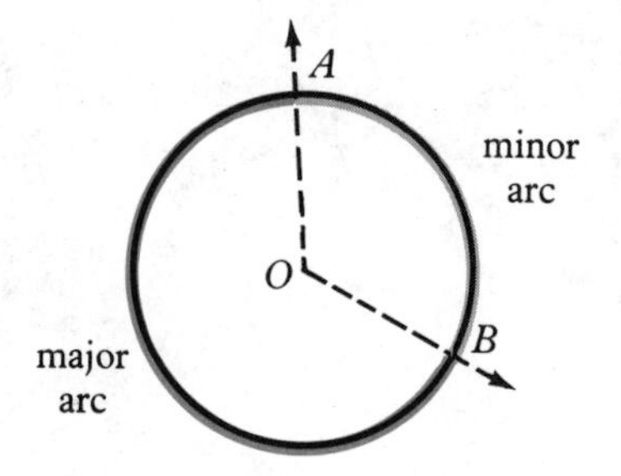

When two points (not endpoints of a diameter) are selected on a circle, two arcs are determined. One is called the *major arc*, the other the *minor arc*.

Definition 10–8

A **minor arc** is an arc that lies in the interior of a central angle. Otherwise it is called a **major arc.**

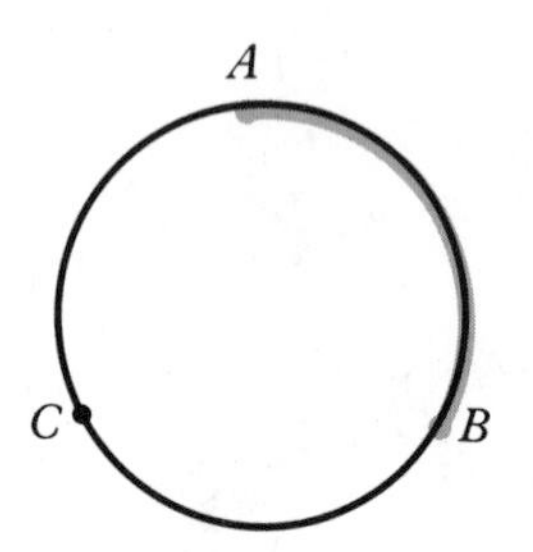

$\widehat{AB}$ will always denote the minor arc determined by points A and B. To denote the major arc a third point is included. $\widehat{ACB}$ denotes the major arc determined by points A and B.

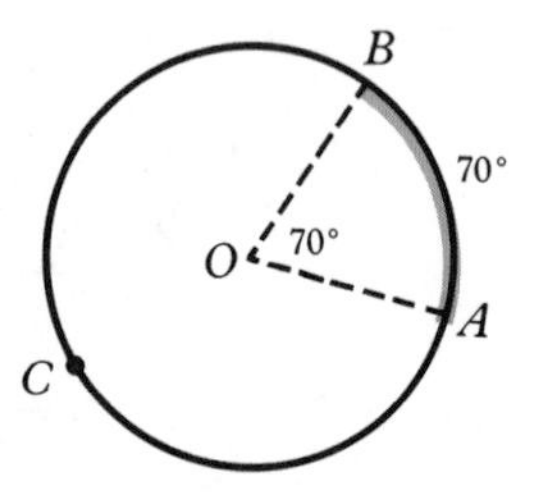

The measure of an arc is determined by the measure of its central angle. For example, $m\widehat{AB} = m\angle AOB = 70$, and $m\widehat{ACB} = 360 - 70 = 290$.

Definition 10–9

The **measure of a minor arc** is the measure of its associated central angle. The **measure of a major arc** is 360 minus the measure of its associated minor arc.

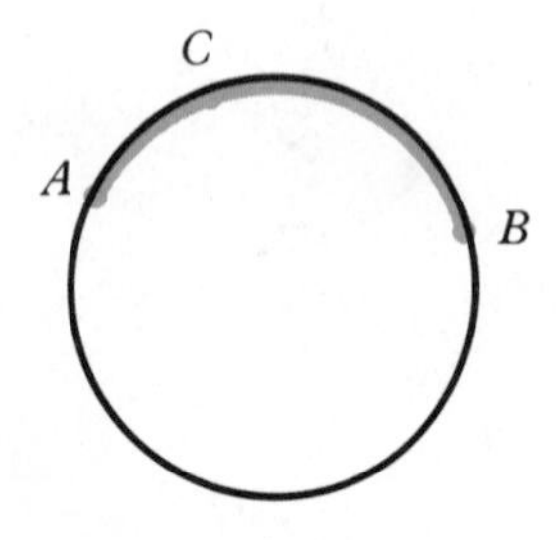

Point C is on arc AB. Two arcs, $\widehat{AC}$ and $\widehat{CB}$, are added to give arc AB.

Arc Addition Postulate

If C is on $\widehat{AB}$, then $m\widehat{AC} + m\widehat{CB} = m\widehat{AB}$.

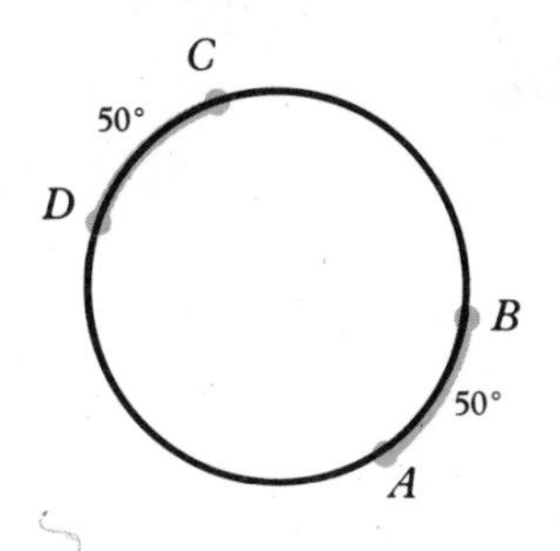

Arc DC and arc BA on this circle both have measure $50°$. We say that these *arcs are congruent.*

Definition 10–10

If two **arcs** of a circle have the same measure, they are called **congruent.** If $\widehat{AB}$ and $\widehat{CD}$ are congruent, we write $\widehat{AB} \cong \widehat{CD}$.

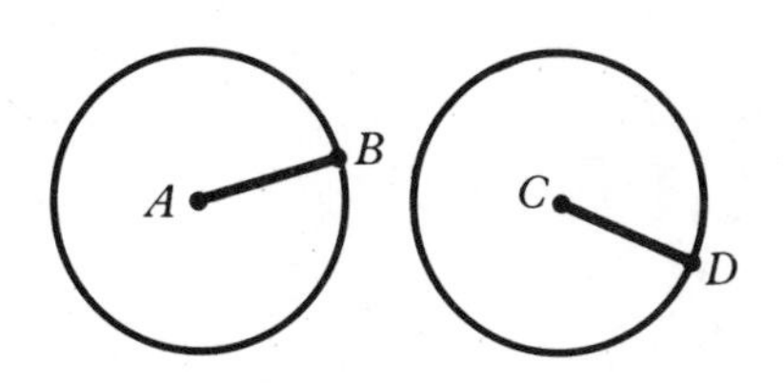

Radius AB and radius CD are the same length. The circles they determine are congruent.

Definition 10–11

Two **circles** are **congruent** if they have radii of equal length.

These two figures should focus your attention on the relationship between congruent chords and their arcs.

Given congruent chords $\overline{AB} \cong \overline{CD}$.

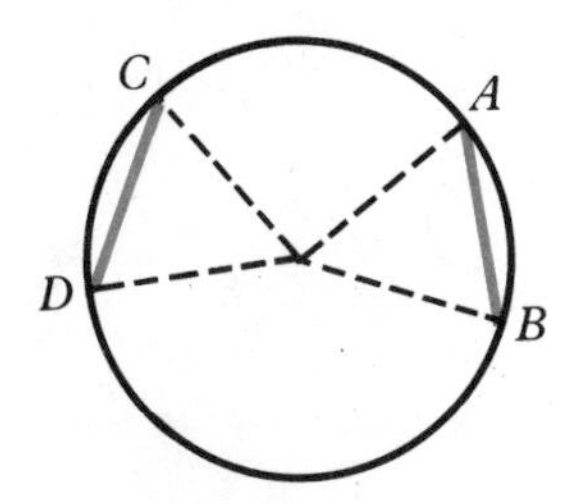

Is $\widehat{AB} \cong \widehat{CD}$?
Why?

Given congruent arcs $\widehat{AB} \cong \widehat{CD}$.

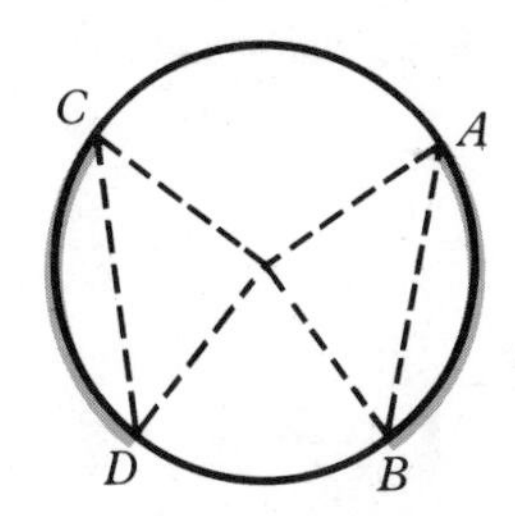

Is $\overline{AB} \cong \overline{CD}$?
Why?

These figures suggest the following theorems.

Theorem 10–1 In a circle or in congruent circles congruent chords have congruent minor arcs.

Theorem 10–2 In a circle or in congruent circles congruent minor arcs have congruent chords.

EXERCISES

A.

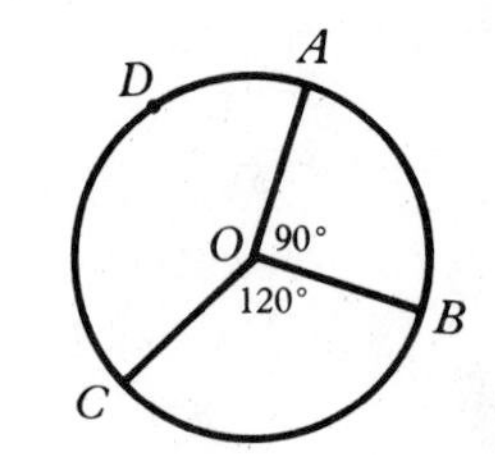

(Exs. 1-3)

1. Is point D on $\widehat{BAC}$? Is D on $\widehat{AB}$?
2. Name three minor arcs. Name three major arcs. Name three central angles.
3. Find each of these degree measures.
   a. $m\widehat{AB}$ b. $m\widehat{AC}$
   c. $m\widehat{BCA}$ d. $m\widehat{ABC}$

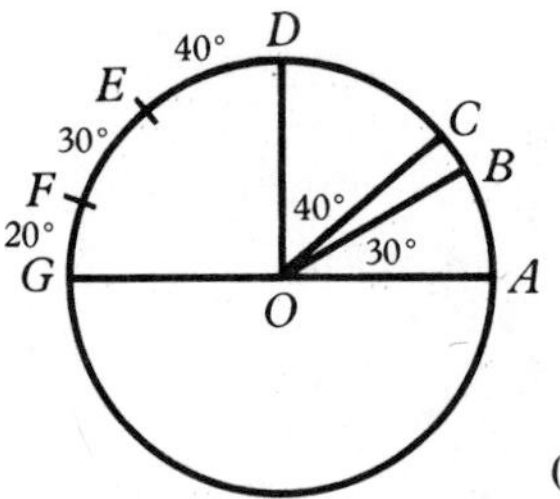

(Exs. 4-8)

4. Find each of these degree measures.
   a. $m\widehat{AB}$ b. $m\angle BOC$
   c. $m\widehat{BD}$ d. $m\angle COG$
5. Find each of these degree measures.
   a. $m\widehat{DF}$ b. $m\widehat{EG}$ c. $m\widehat{ECG}$
6. Name all the minor arcs containing point C.
7. Name three pairs of congruent minor arcs.
8. Name a pair of congruent major arcs.
9. Suppose $m\angle AOB = 40$, $m\angle BOC = 20$, and $m\angle COD = 40$. Name all pairs of congruent chords.

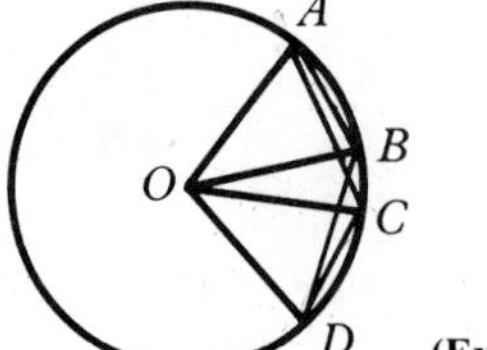

(Ex. 9)

Activity

1. Draw a circle with a radius of 4 cm and label a point A on the circle.
2. Using a protractor, draw points each 10° around the circle, beginning with point A.
3. Each of these points is the center of a circle through point A. Draw these circles. (Three such circles have been drawn.)
4. Guess what the final figure looks like.

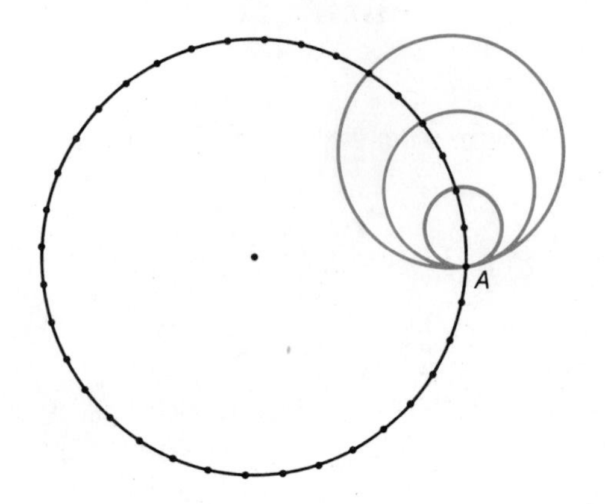

B.

For exercises 10–12, make accurate drawings and answer the questions.

10. In a circle, is the chord of a 90° arc twice as long as the chord of a 45° arc?

11. If the measure of a minor arc is doubled, is the measure of the central angle doubled?

12. Suppose in circle O, $\overline{OA}$ and $\overline{OB}$ are radii and $OA = OB = AB$. What is the measure of $\angle AOB$?

13. Prove Theorem 10–1.

14. Prove Theorem 10–2.

C.

15. Given: $ES = AY$
Prove: $EA = SY$

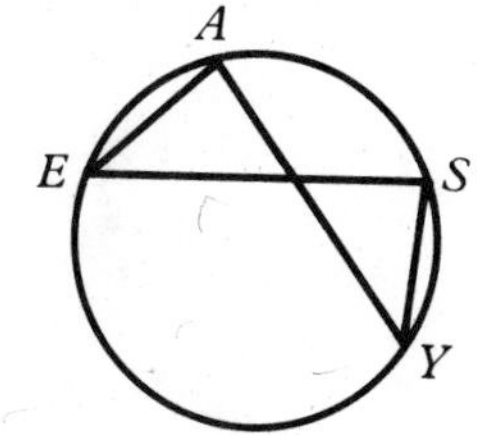

16. Given: $\widehat{HG} \cong \widehat{JI}$
Prove: $HJ = GI$

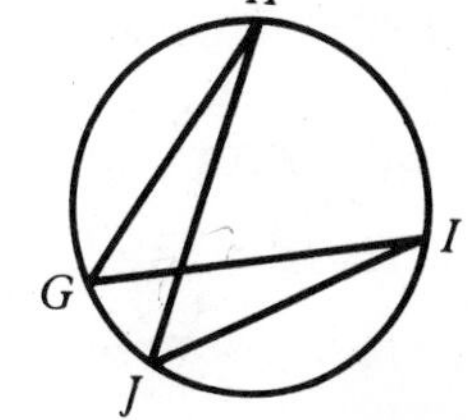

17. Given: $\overline{AB}$ and $\overline{CD}$ are diameters.
Prove: $ACBD$ is a parallelogram.

18. Prove that if the vertices of an equilateral triangle are on a circle, the circle is divided into three congruent arcs.

19. Given: $\overline{POS}$ is a diameter of $\odot O$.
$\overline{SR} \parallel \overline{OQ}$
Prove: $\widehat{RQ} \cong \widehat{QP}$

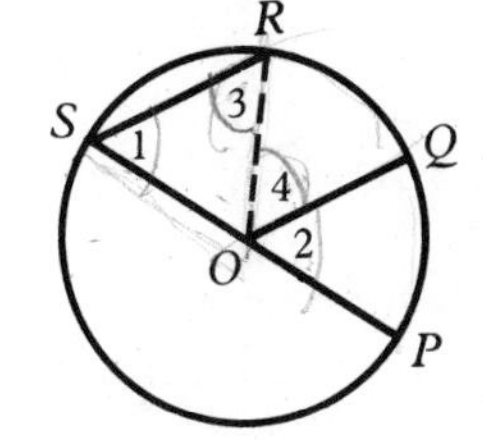

PROBLEM SOLVING

1. Draw circles C_1 and C_2 of two different sizes.
2. How many circles with collinear centers are there that touch both of the given circles at exactly one point? (One of them is drawn.)
3. Construct each one of these circles. (First construct the centers of these circles. No guessing is necessary.)

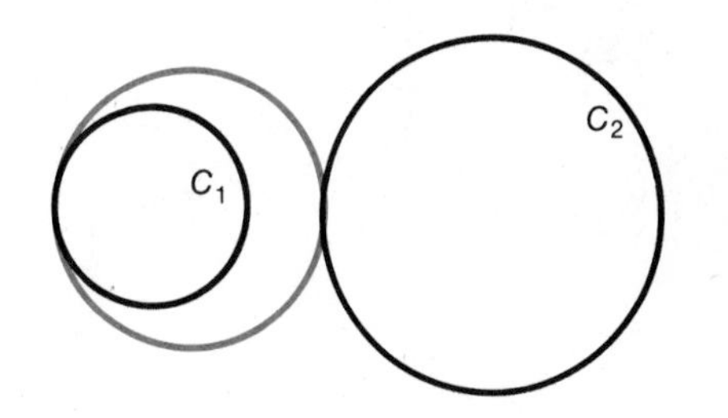

10–3 Chords and Distances from the Center

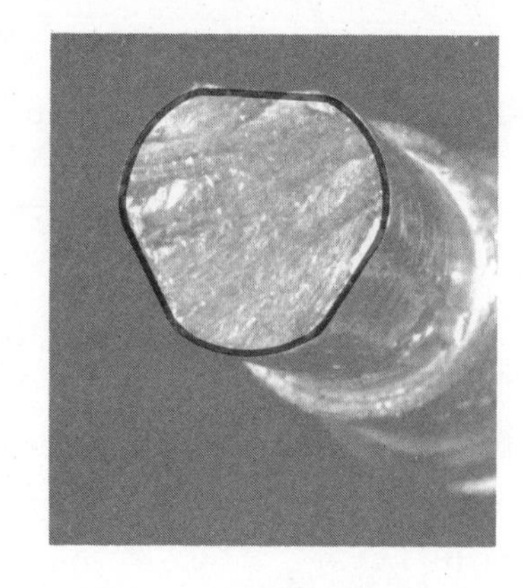

Pictured is an electrician's drill bit whose shank end has three flat surfaces. One necessary feature of this design is that these flat surfaces must be an equal distance from the rotating axis to ensure that the drill runs smoothly.

The theorem in this lesson describes a method for determining that this condition is satisfied.

In each figure a pair of congruent chords is given.

$CS = JN$

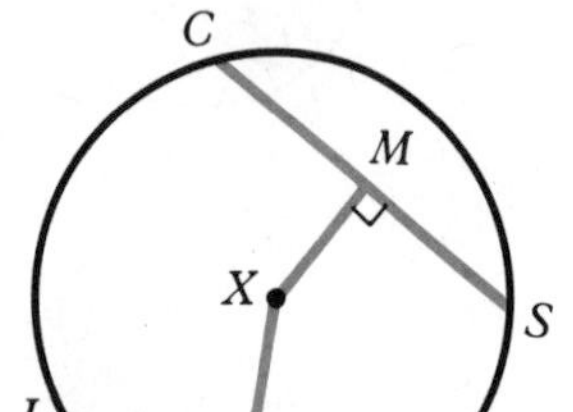

$VR = TH$

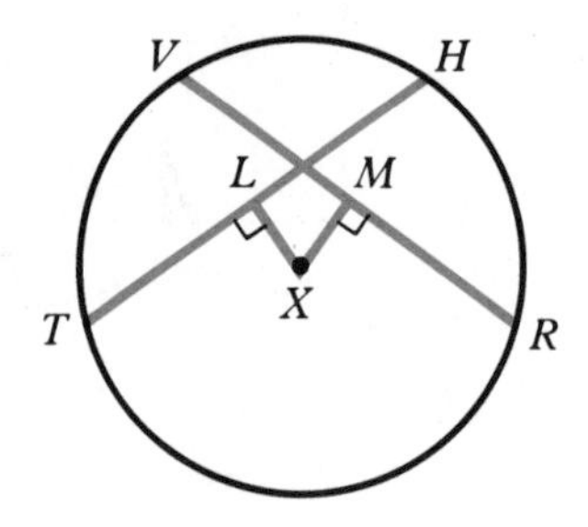

$FD = DN$

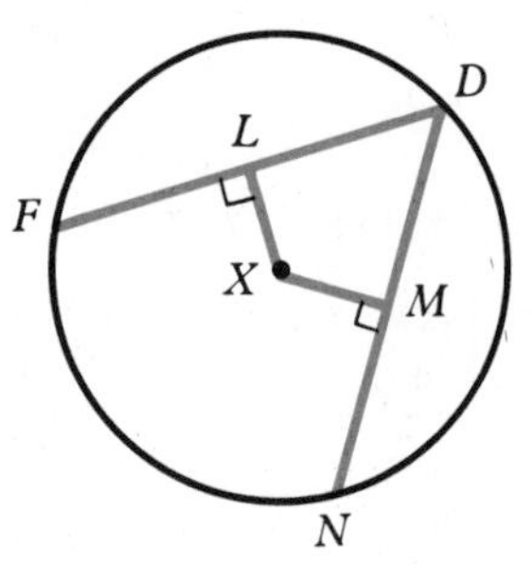

In each case does $XL = XM$?

These examples suggest the following theorem.

Theorem 10–3 In a circle or in congruent circles congruent chords are equidistant from the center.

PROOF

Given: $\odot O$, $\overline{AB} \cong \overline{CD}$, $\overline{OM} \perp \overline{AB}$, $\overline{OL} \perp \overline{CD}$
Prove: $OM = OL$

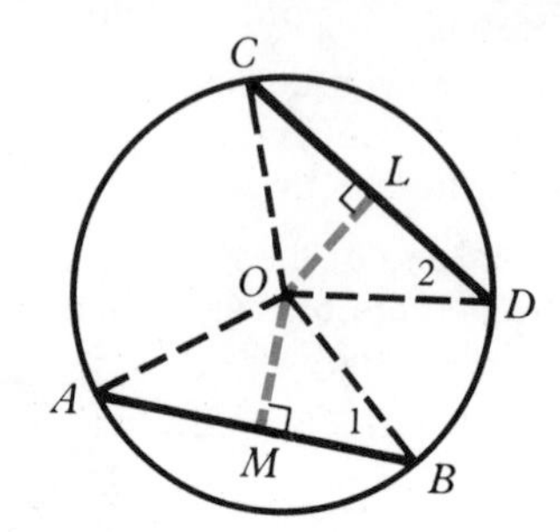

Statements	Reasons
1. $\overline{AB} \cong \overline{CD}$	**1.** Given
2. $OA = OB = OC = OD$	**2.** Definition of circle
3. $\overline{OA} \cong \overline{OB} \cong \overline{OC} \cong \overline{OD}$	**3.** Definition of congruent segments
4. $\triangle AOB \cong \triangle COD$	**4.** SSS Congruence
5. $\angle 1 \cong \angle 2$	**5.** CPCTC
6. $\overline{OM} \perp \overline{AB}$, $\overline{OL} \perp \overline{CD}$	**6.** Given
7. $\angle OMB \cong \angle OLD$, $\angle OMB$ and $\angle OLD$ are right angles.	**7.** Perpendicular lines form congruent right angles.
8. $\triangle OMB$ and $\triangle OLD$ are right triangles.	**8.** Definition of right triangles
9. $\triangle OMB \cong \triangle OLD$	**9.** HA Congruence
10. $\overline{OM} \cong \overline{OL}$	**10.** CPCTC
11. $OM = OL$	**11.** Definition of congruent segments

APPLICATION

The drill bit shown here must be balanced in order for the drill to run smoothly. How should the shank end be constructed so that the drill bit is balanced?

If the segments $\overline{AB}$, $\overline{CD}$, and $\overline{EF}$ are congruent, then Theorem 10–3 says that they are equidistant from the center of the circle containing arcs $\widehat{AB}$, $\widehat{CD}$, and $\widehat{EF}$. This will ensure that the drill bit is balanced.

The converse of Theorem 10–3 is also important. It is stated below.

Theorem 10–4 In a circle or in congruent circles chords equidistant from the center are congruent.

EXERCISES

A.

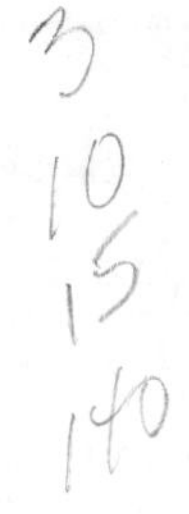

1. **Given:** $AB = CD$
   $\overline{OX} \perp \overline{AB}$, $\overline{OY} \perp \overline{CD}$
   $OX = 3$
   Find: OY.

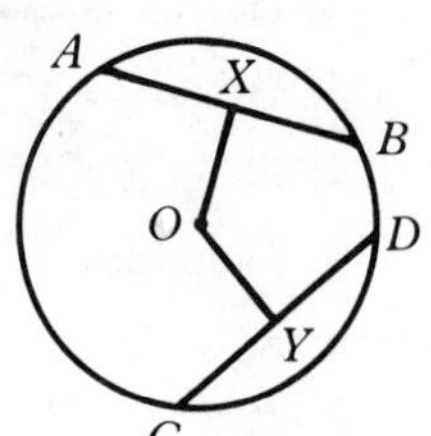

2. **Given:** $OX = OY$
   $\overline{OX} \perp \overline{AB}$, $\overline{OY} \perp \overline{CD}$
   $AB = 10$
   Find: CD

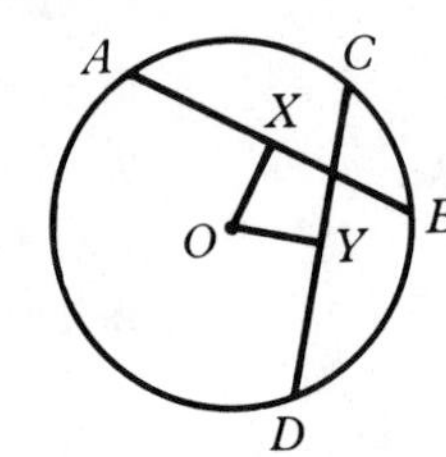

3. **Given:** $\overline{OM} \perp \overline{AB}$, $\overline{ON} \perp \overline{CD}$
   $AB = CD$
   $m\angle MON = 150$
   Find: $m\angle OMN$ (*Hint:* Does $OM = ON$?)

4. **Given:** $\overline{OM} \perp \overline{AB}$, $\overline{ON} \perp \overline{CD}$
   $AB = CD$
   $m\angle NMB = 70$
   Find: $m\angle MON$

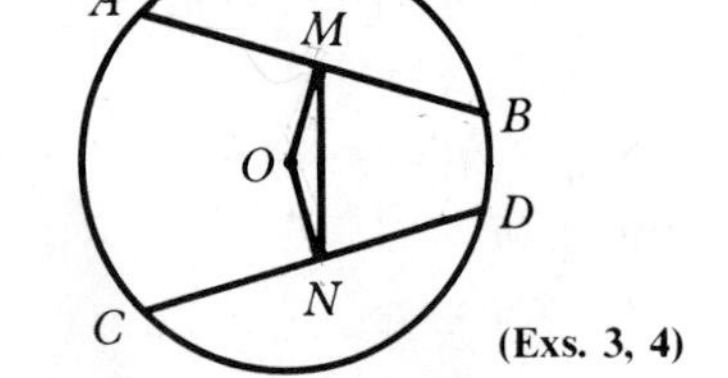

(Exs. 3, 4)

5. **Given:** $\overline{AB}$, $\overline{BC}$, and $\overline{CA}$ are equidistant from the center O.
   Prove: $\triangle ABC$ is equilateral.

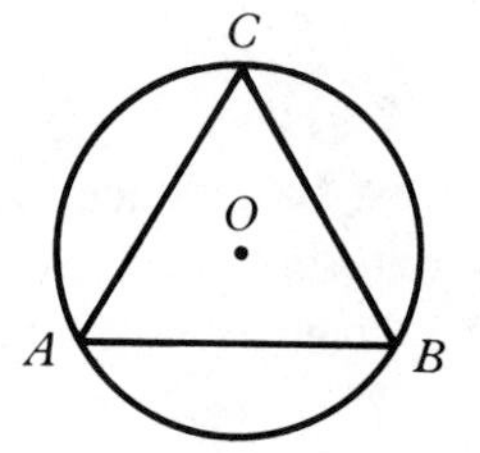

Activity

The path of a point B on a circle as that circle rolls around a fixed circle of the same radius is a curve called a *cardioid*.

A cardioid can also be drawn using a linkage as shown in the figure.

Follow these directions and draw a cardioid.

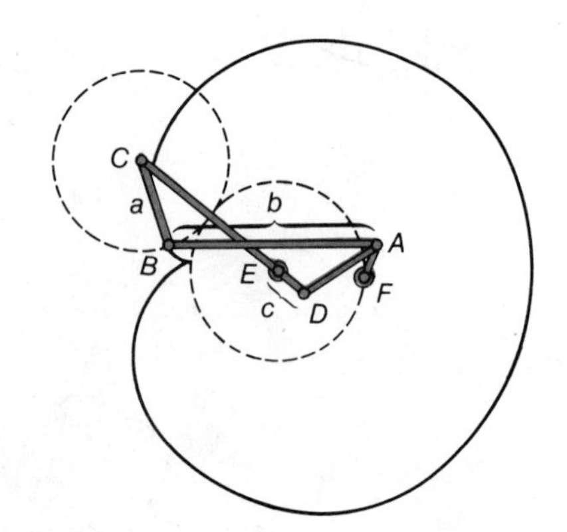

1. Construct a linkage out of stiff cardboard like the one shown in the figure. Note that $BC = AD = a$, $AB = CD = b$, $DE = AF = c$, and $a^2 = bc$. (Suggestion: Let $a = 6$ cm, $b = 32$ cm, and $c = 8$ cm.)
2. Attach your linkage to a bulletin board at points E and F.
3. Place your pencil at B and draw.

B.

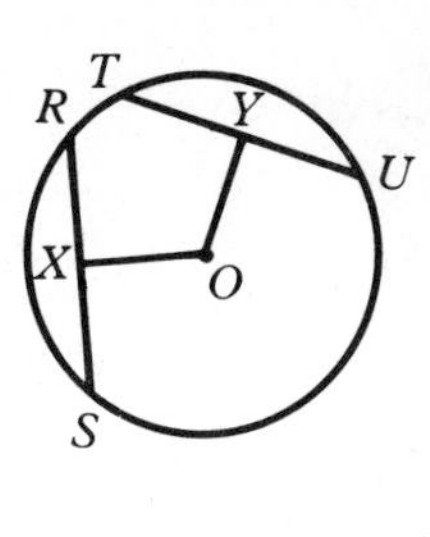

6. Given: $OX = OY$
$\overline{OX} \perp \overline{RS}$, $\overline{OY} \perp \overline{TU}$
Prove: $m\widehat{RS} = m\widehat{TU}$

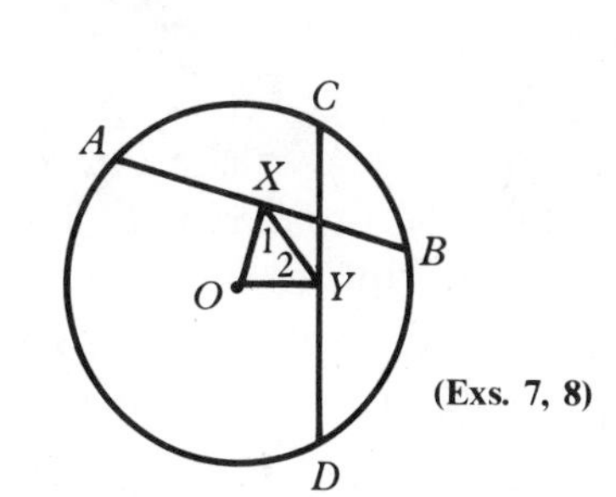

(Exs. 7, 8)

7. Given: In circle O, $\overline{OX} \perp \overline{AB}$,
$\overline{OY} \perp \overline{CD}$
$m\angle 1 = m\angle 2$
Prove: $AB = CD$

8. Given: In circle O, $\overline{OX} \perp \overline{AB}$,
$\overline{OY} \perp \overline{CD}$
$CD = AB$
Prove: $m\angle 1 = m\angle 2$

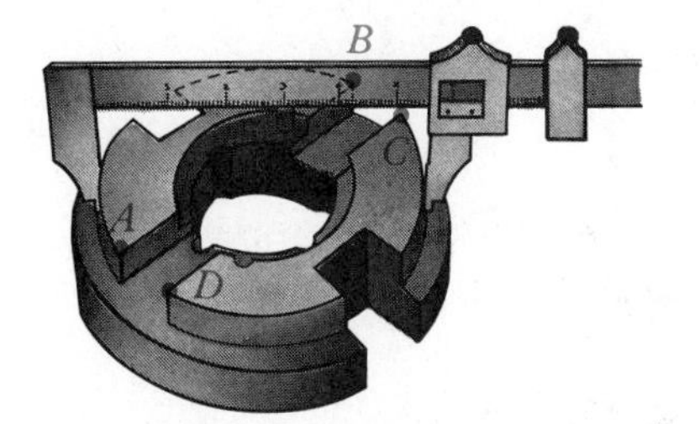

9. Often machines parts like the one shown here will work properly only if the groove is "centered." Why does measuring $\overline{AB}$ and $\overline{CD}$ tell you whether or not the groove is centered?

C.

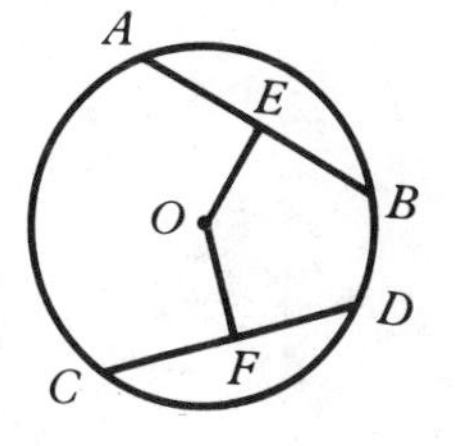

10. This exercise structures a proof of Theorem 10–4.
Given: Circle O, $OE = OF$
$\overline{OE} \perp \overline{AB}$, $\overline{OF} \perp \overline{CD}$
Prove: $AB = CD$
(*Hint:* Draw radii and use congruent triangles.)

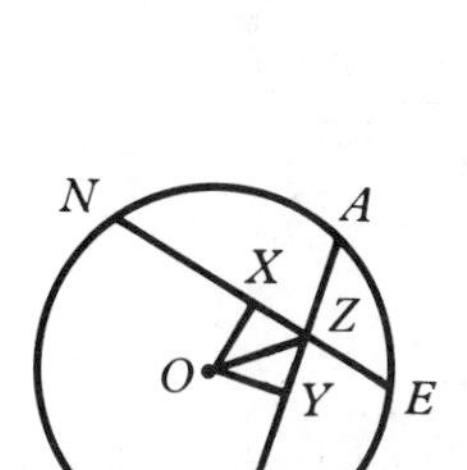

11. Given: In circle O, $\overline{OX} \perp \overline{NE}$,
$\overline{OY} \perp \overline{AT}$
$\angle XZO \cong \angle YZO$
Prove: $NE = AT$

PROBLEM SOLVING

The middle region of this string design appears to be circular. Explain why this is true. That is, explain why the midpoints of those segments that border on the middle region are equidistant from an imaginary center point. (You may assume that the nails at the ends of each piece of string are equally spaced around a circle.)

10–4 Perpendiculars to Chords

A carpenter's square can be used to find the center of a round table. The theorem in this section explains how this can be done.

These figures illustrate a property of the perpendicular bisector of a chord. In each figure ℓ is the perpendicular bisector of chord $\overline{AB}$.

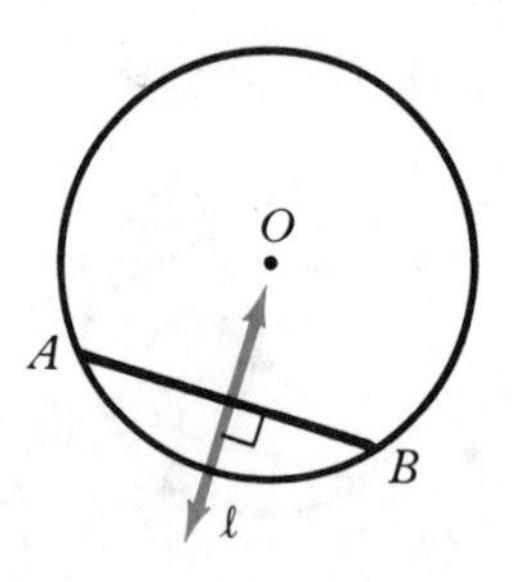

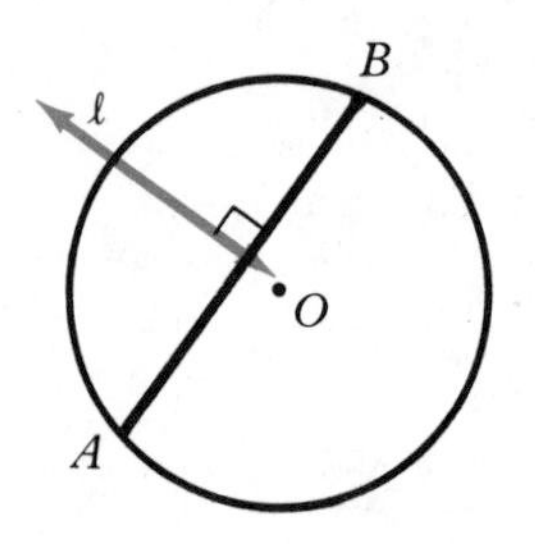

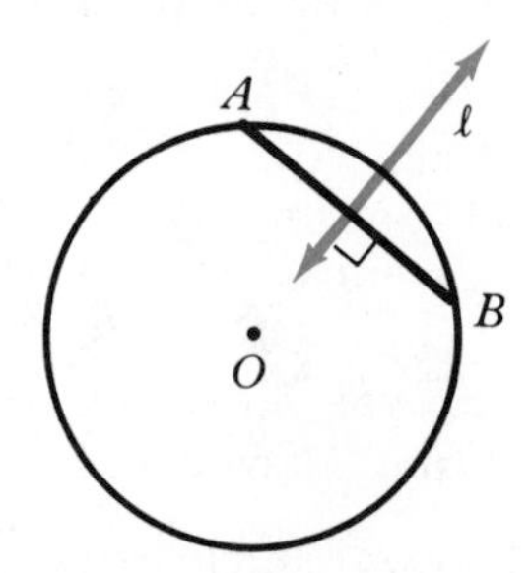

Does line ℓ pass through point O?

These three figures suggest the following theorem.

Theorem 10–5 The perpendicular bisector of a chord contains the center of the circle.

PROOF

Given: $\overline{AB}$ is a chord of circle O, and ℓ is the perpendicular bisector of $\overline{AB}$.
Prove: O is a point of ℓ.

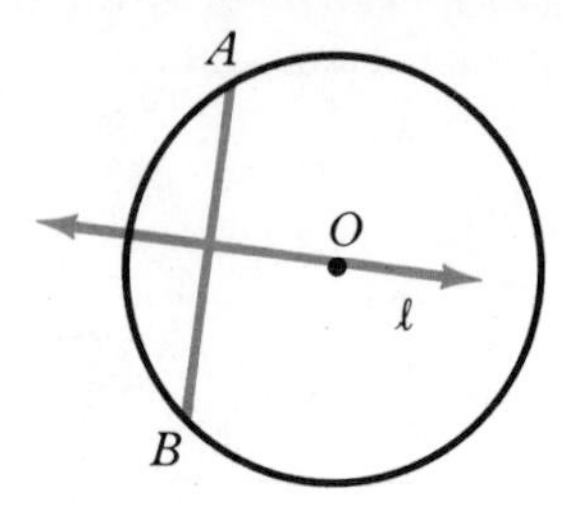

Statements	Reasons
1. ℓ is the perpendicular bisector of of $\overline{AB}$.	1. Given
2. $OA = OB$	2. Definition of circle
3. O lies on ℓ.	3. A point equidistant from points A and B belongs to the perpendicular bisector of $\overline{AB}$. (Theorem 6–10).

APPLICATION

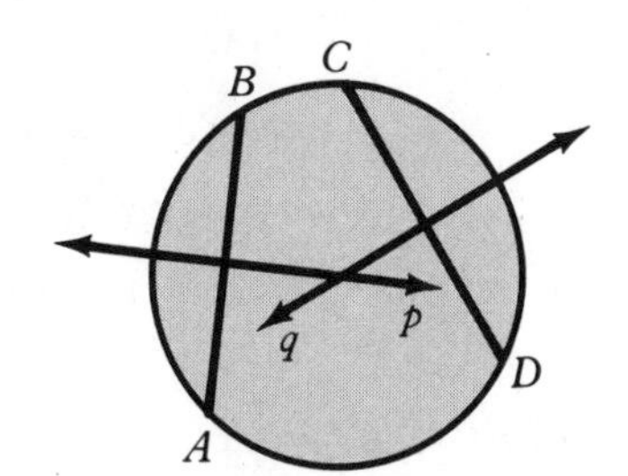

Find the center of a round table.

Step 1 Select any two chords $\overline{AB}$ and $\overline{CD}$.

Step 2 Draw the perpendicular bisector p of $\overline{AB}$, and the perpendicular bisector q of $\overline{CD}$.

Conclusion: By Theorem 10–5 the center lies on both lines p and q. Consequently, the center of the table must be the intersection of these lines.

Two other important theorems are the following.

Theorem 10–6 If a line through the center of a circle is perpendicular to a chord that is not a diameter, then it bisects the chord and its minor arc.

Theorem 10–7 If a line through the center of a circle bisects a chord that is not a diameter, then it is perpendicular to the chord.

Theorem 10–6 can be used to find missing information about circles.

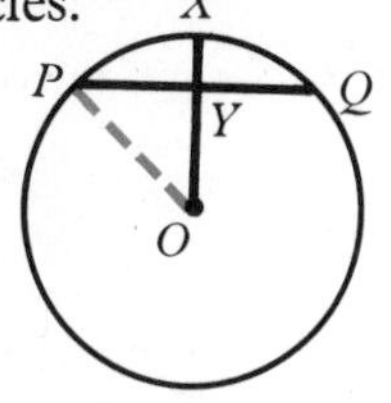

Example **Given:** $\odot O$ with radius 4 in. $\overline{OX} \perp \overline{PQ}$. Chord $\overline{PQ}$ is 1 inch from O.

Find: PQ

The given information tells us that $OP = 4$ (why?) and $OY = 1$ (why?). By applying the Pythagorean Theorem to $\triangle OPY$, we can determine that $PY = \sqrt{15}$. Theorem 10–6 tells us that $\overline{OX}$ bisects $\overline{PQ}$. Therefore $PQ = 2\sqrt{15}$.

EXERCISES

A.

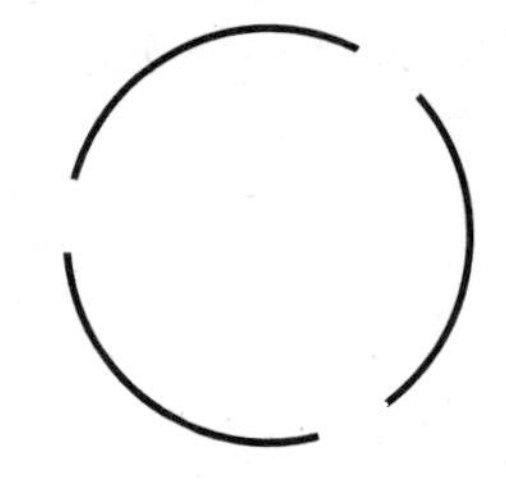

1. Trace the figure at the right. Then find the center of the arcs and complete the circle.

2. Using compass and straightedge, draw a figure that illustrates Theorems 10-6 and 10-7.

In the figure for exercises 3-4, O is the center of the circle.

3. If $\overrightarrow{OC} \perp \overline{AB}$, how is $m\widehat{AC}$ related to $m\widehat{CB}$?

4. If $AD = 3$ and $BD = 3$, what is $m\angle BDC$?

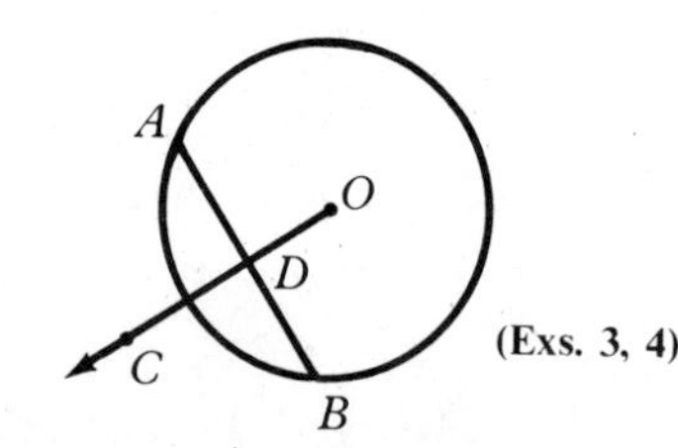

(Exs. 3, 4)

In exercises 5-7, state whether Theorem 10-5, 10-6, or 10-7 is used to reach the conclusion.

5. **Given:** $\odot O$ with $\overline{AOD}$ an altitude of $\triangle ABC$
Conclusion: $\overline{AD}$ bisects $\overline{BC}$.

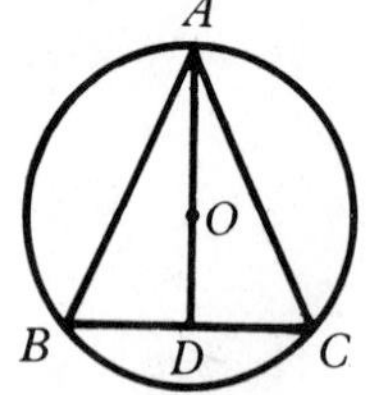

6. **Given:** Diameter $\overline{AB}$ bisects $\overline{CD}$.
Conclusion: $\overline{AB} \perp \overline{CD}$

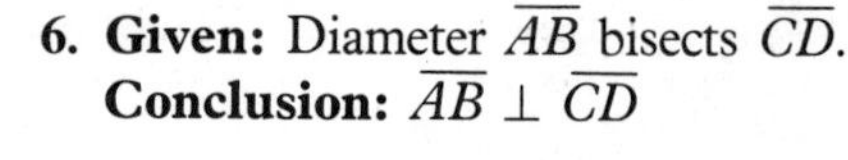

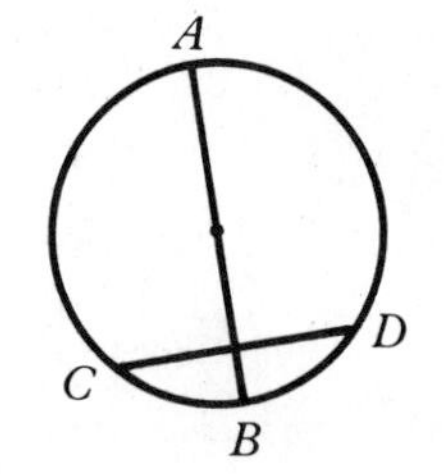

7. **Given:** ℓ_1 is the perpendicular bisector of $\overline{CD}$.
ℓ_2 is the perpendicular bisector of $\overline{AB}$.
ℓ_1 and ℓ_2 intersect at X.
Conclusion: X is the center of the circle.

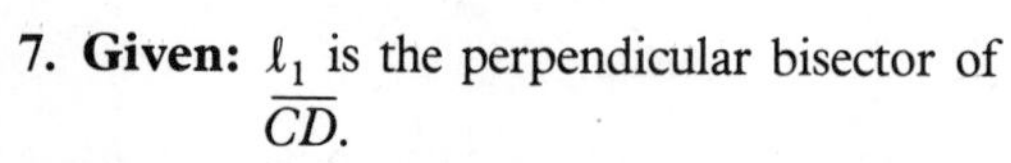

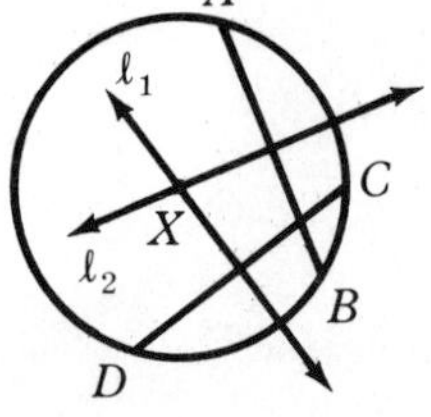

In exercises 8-10, find the missing information. O is the center of each circle.

8.

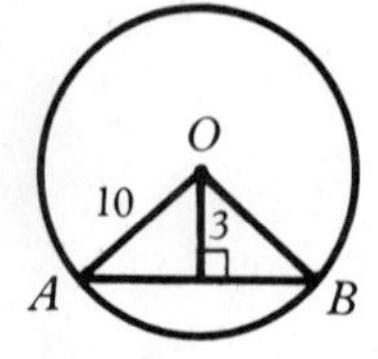

$AB = ?$

9.

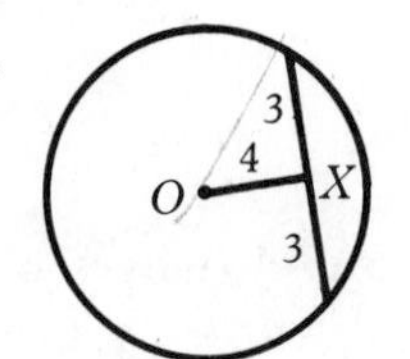

What is the length of the radius?

10.

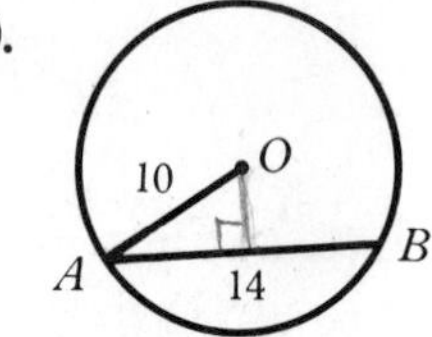

How far from the center is chord $\overline{AB}$?

B.

11. In a circle with radius 5 cm, $\overline{AB}$ is a chord that has length 8 cm. How far is $\overline{AB}$ from the center of the circle? (Draw a sketch to help you.)

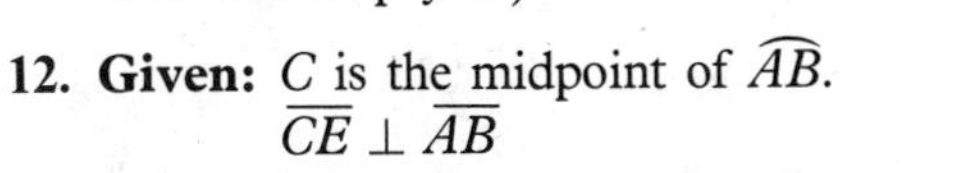

12. Given: C is the midpoint of $\widehat{AB}$.
$\overline{CE} \perp \overline{AB}$
$CE = 2$ inches, $AB = 16$ inches
Find: The length of a radius of the circle

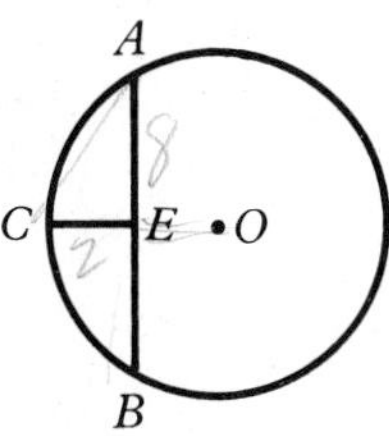

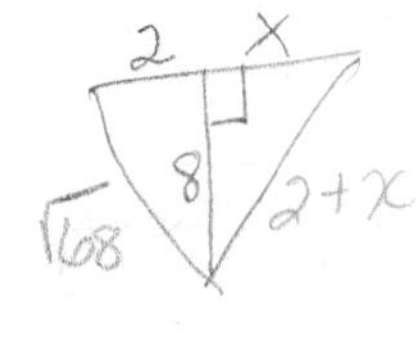

13. Given: $AM = MB = 6$ cm
$AO = 10$ cm
Find: OM.

14. Given: $\overline{OM} \perp \overline{AB}$
$OM = 5$, $AO = 13$
Find: AB.

15. Given: M is the midpoint of $\overline{AB}$.
$OM = MB$
$OB = \sqrt{2}$
Find: AB

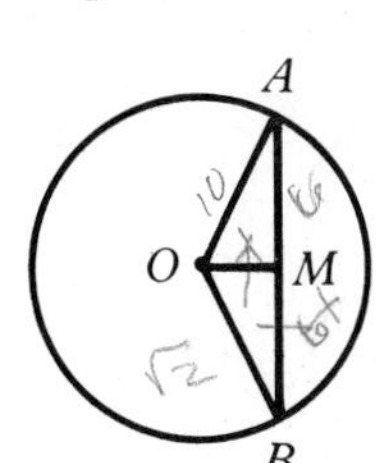

(Exs. 13-15)

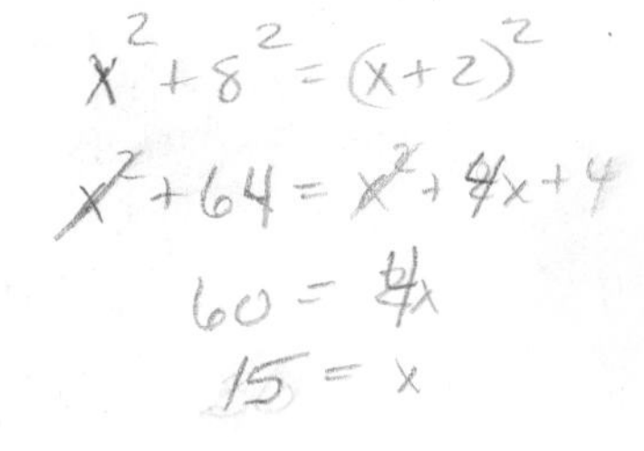

16. Two chords in a circle are equal in length. Their distances from the center can be represented by x^2 and $4x$ respectively. How far is each chord from the center?

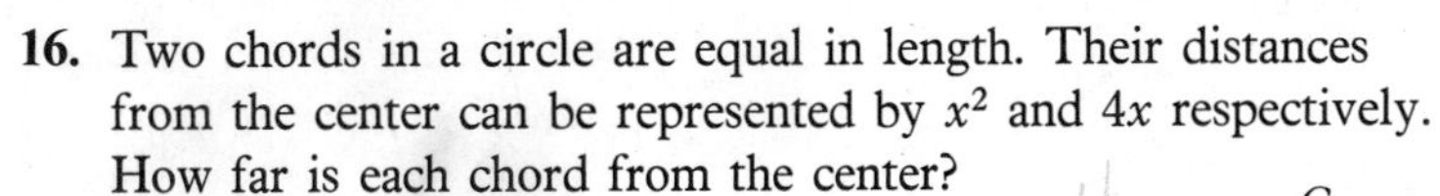

17. Given: A circle with $AB = 8$ ft
$m\angle ABC = 45$
Find: The distance from point O to $\overline{BC}$

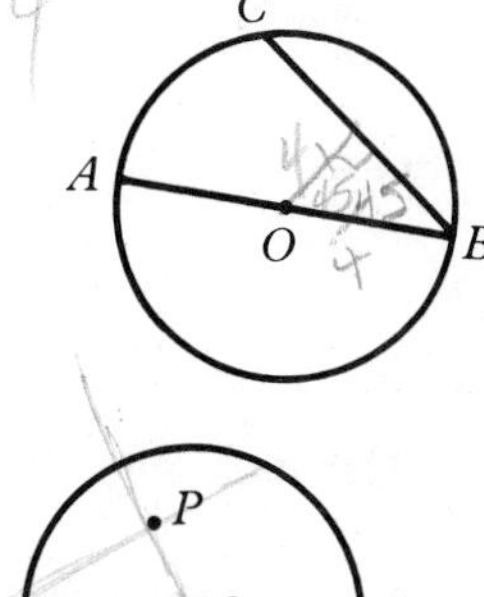

18. Draw a circle O and mark a point P inside the circle. Using your compass and straightedge, construct a chord that is bisected by P.

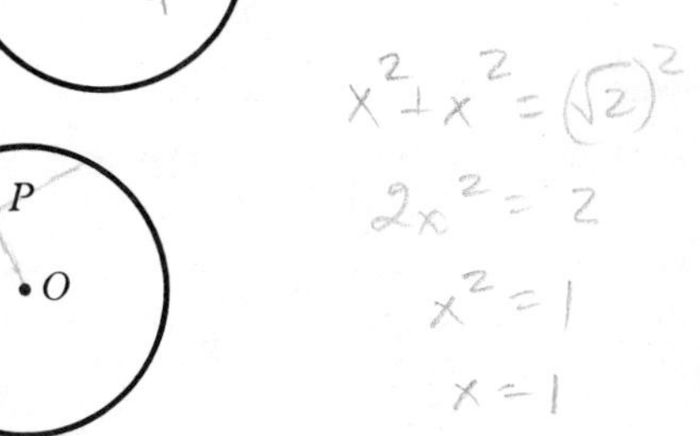

19. A part of an old wheel is found by an archeologist in a dig. The wheel can be reconstructed by determining the original radius. Explain how this can be accomplished.

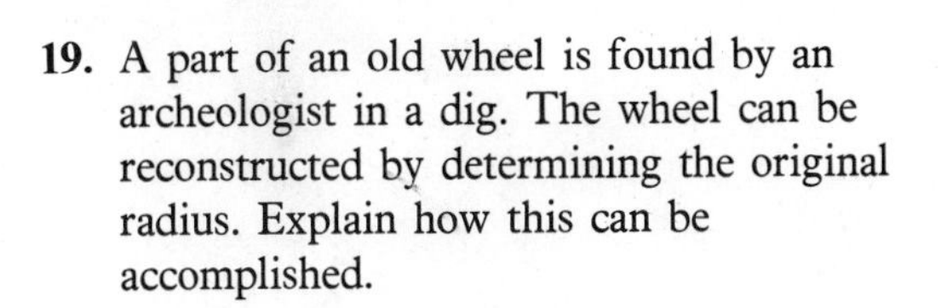

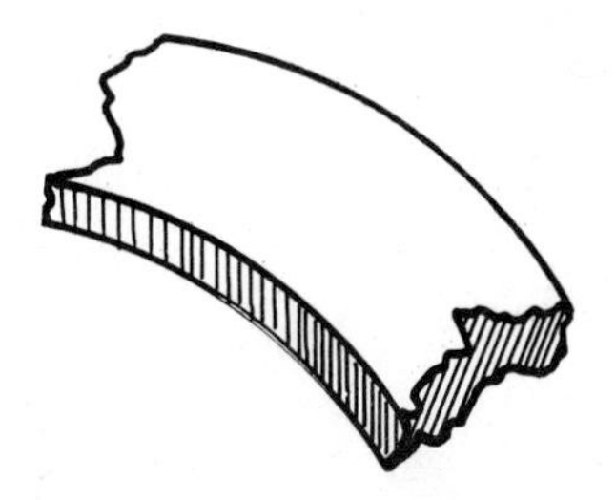

C.

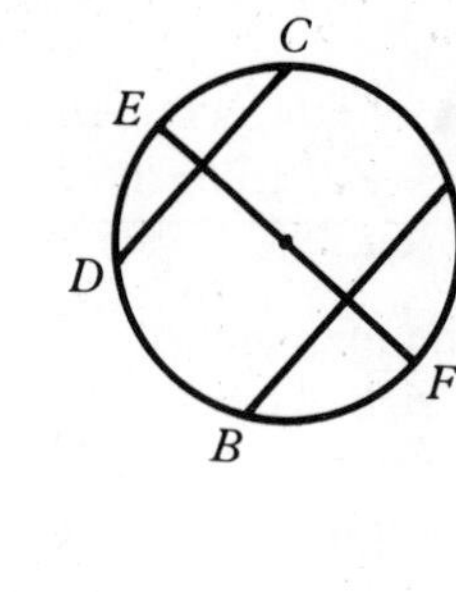

20. **Given:** $\overline{AB} \parallel \overline{CD}$
$\overline{EF}$ is the perpendicular bisector of $\overline{AB}$.
Prove: $\overline{EF}$ bisects $\overline{CD}$.

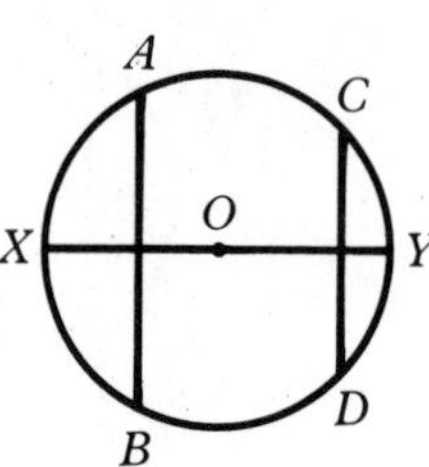

21. **Given:** $\overline{XY}$ is a diameter.
$\overline{XY}$ bisects $\overline{AB}$.
$\overline{XY}$ bisects $\overline{CD}$.
Prove: $\overline{AB} \parallel \overline{CD}$

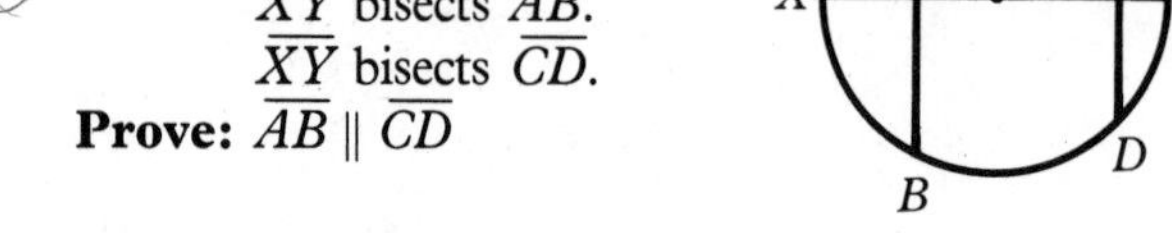

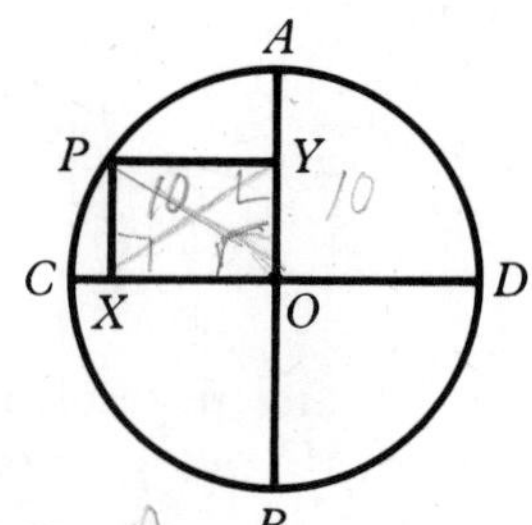

22. **Given:** $\overline{AB}$ and $\overline{CD}$ are diameters and $\overline{AB} \perp \overline{CD}$.
$AO = 10$ cm
$\overline{PX} \perp \overline{CD}$ and $\overline{PY} \perp \overline{AB}$
Find: XY

23. A circle O has a radius of 10 cm. Chords $\overline{AB}$ and $\overline{CD}$ are perpendicular and intersect at a point F inside the circle. If $AB = 16$, and $CD = 18$, find DF.

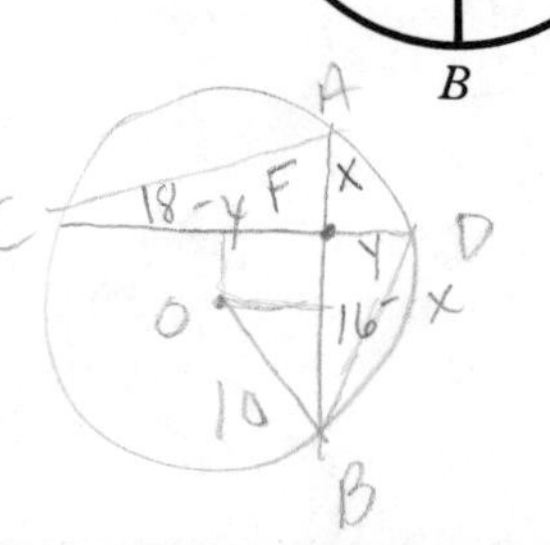

Activity

1. Trace this figure and cut out its pieces.
2. Arrange the pieces to form two egg-shaped regions with a missing center.
3. Draw this puzzle with a compass. (You will need to carefully determine the center of each arc. No guessing is necessary.)

24. Given: Two circles with center O
A, B, C, and D are collinear.
Prove: $AB = CD$

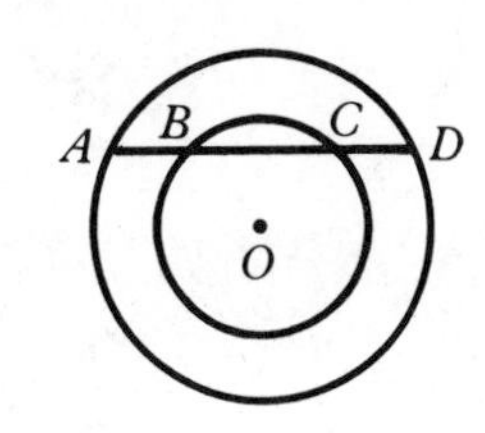

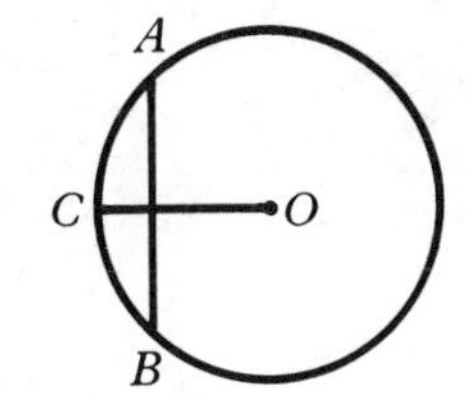

25. Given: $m\widehat{PM} = m\widehat{MQ}$
$\overline{XM} \perp \overline{OP}$
$\overline{YM} \perp \overline{OQ}$
Prove: $XM = YM$
(*Hint:* Draw $\overline{OM}$ and use congruent triangles.)

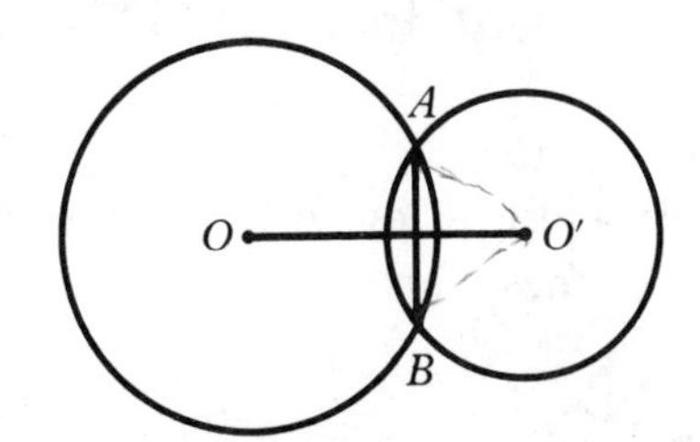

26. Given: $\overline{AB}$ is a common chord to circles O and O'.
Prove: $\overline{OO'}$ is the perpendicular bisector of $\overline{AB}$.

27. Given: $\overline{OC}$ bisects $\widehat{ACB}$.
Prove: $\overline{OC}$ bisects $\overline{AB}$.

A
C
O
B

PROBLEM SOLVING

A cardioid has been drawn using the method described in the activity on page 348.

Points B and C are centers of circles through A that meet again at point D.

Why are $\triangle ABC$ and $\triangle DBC$ congruent?

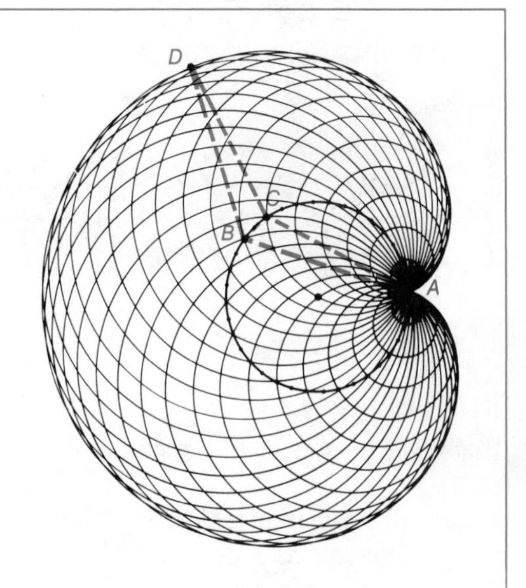

10–5 Tangents to Circles

REVIEW: A line is tangent to a circle if it intersects the circle in exactly one point.

Suppose you want to round off the corners of a piece of wood in order to make a small table. In order to do a neat job a way must be found to draw a circular arc. The edges of the board must be tangent to the circular arc. How can this arc be drawn?

A theorem in this lesson helps solve the problem.

In each of these figures $\overline{OA}$ is a radius and ℓ is perpendicular to $\overline{OA}$ at A.

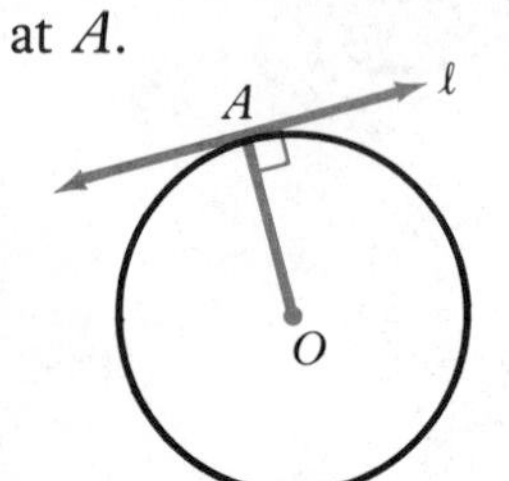

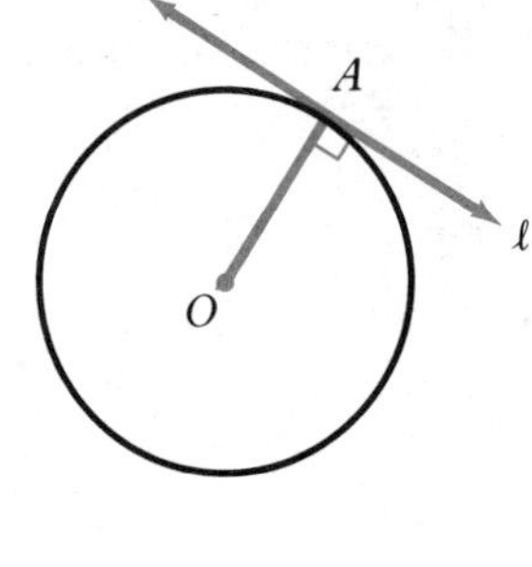

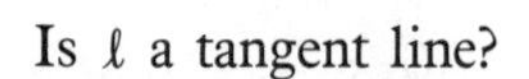

Is ℓ a tangent line?

Your observations suggest the following theorem.

Theorem 10–8 If a line is perpendicular to a radius at a point on the circle, then the line is tangent to the circle.

PROOF

Given: $\ell \perp \overline{OA}$

Prove: ℓ is tangent to the circle.

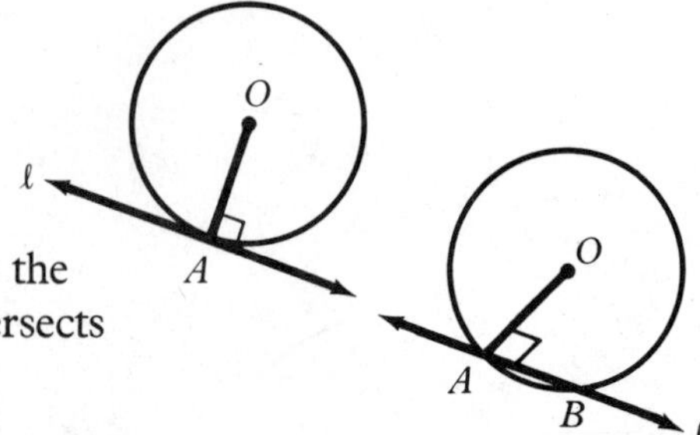

Plan: Use an indirect proof. Assume ℓ is not tangent to the circle. This means ℓ does not intersect the circle or ℓ intersects the circle in two places. We will investigate the latter assumption.

Statements	Reasons
1. ℓ intersects the circle at a second point B.	1. Indirect proof assumption
2. $\overline{OA} \perp \ell$	2. Given
3. $\overline{OB}$ is a hypotenuse of a right triangle.	3. Definition of hypotenuse
4. $OB > OA$	4. Length of the hypotenuse is greater than the length of either side.
5. $OB = OA$	5. Definition of circle

Statements 4 and 5 are contradictory. Hence the assumption is false and the line ℓ is tangent to the circle.

APPLICATION

We now solve the problem posed at the beginning of the lesson.

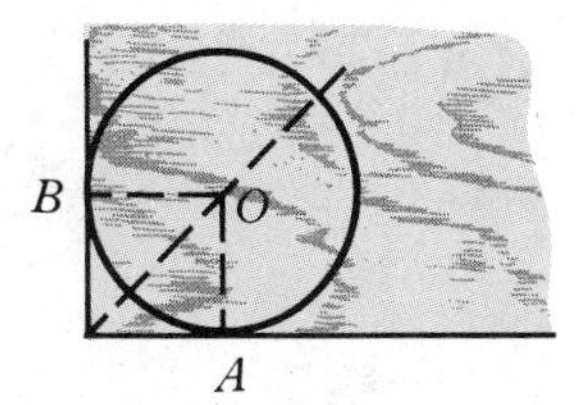

Step 1 Draw the angle bisector of the angle.

Step 2 Select a point O on the angle bisector and draw the perpendiculars $\overline{OA}$ and $\overline{OB}$ to the sides of the angle.

Step 3 Point O on the angle bisector is equidistant from the sides of the angles. Therefore $OA = OB$. Draw the circle centered at O through points A and B.

The edges of the board are tangent to the circle because of Theorem 10–8.

Here are two other theorems about tangents.

Theorem 10–9 If a line is tangent to a circle, then the radius drawn to the point of contact is perpendicular to the tangent.

Theorem 10–10 If a line is perpendicular to a tangent at a point on the circle, then the line contains the center of the circle.

EXERCISES

A.

1. Draw a circle O and mark a point P on the circle. Construct a tangent to the circle through P.

2. Trace the figure at the right in which ℓ and ℓ' are tangents at points P and Q, respectively. Find the center of the circle. (*Hint:* Use Theorem 10-10.)

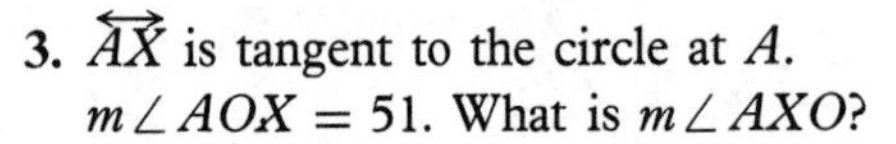

3. $\overleftrightarrow{AX}$ is tangent to the circle at A. $m\angle AOX = 51$. What is $m\angle AXO$?

4. $\overleftrightarrow{AX}$ is tangent to the circle at A. If $OA = 10$ and $AX = 24$, find OX.

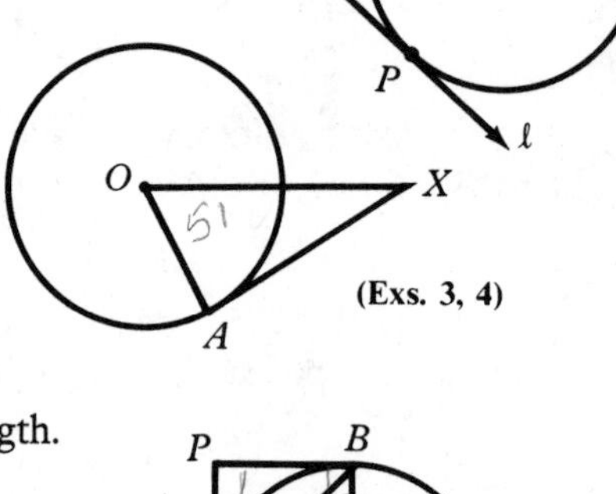

(Exs. 3, 4)

B.

5. **Given:** $\overline{PA}$ and $\overline{PB}$ are tangents.
   $\overline{OA}$ and $\overline{OB}$ are radii each 4 cm in length.
   $\overline{PA} \perp \overline{PB}$
   Prove: $AOBP$ is a square.

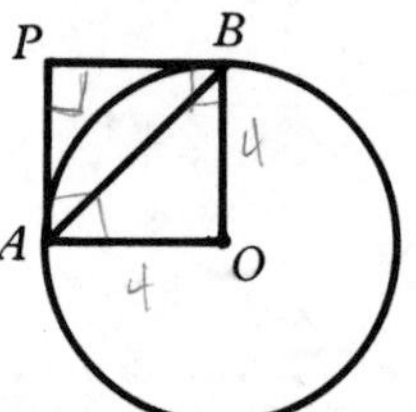

Activity

Draw, label, and cut out of cardboard this figure, sometimes called "the tomahawk."

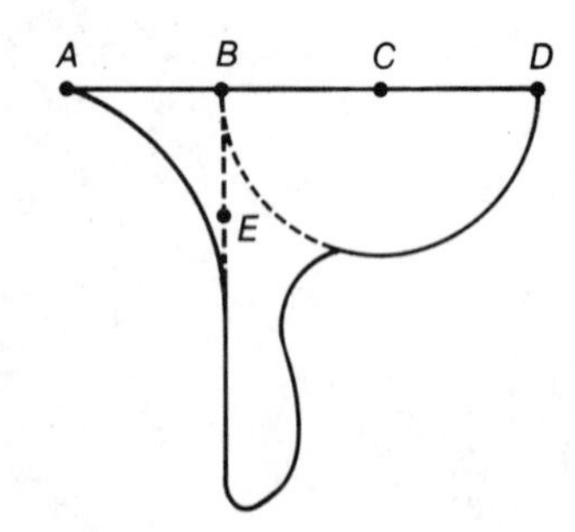

1. Draw $\overline{AD}$ so that $AB = BC = CD$.
2. Draw a semicircle on $\overline{BD}$.
3. Draw $\overline{BE} \perp \overline{AD}$ and complete the figure as shown.
4. Position the tomahawk on $\angle WXY$ so that
   a. X is on the handle edge $\overleftrightarrow{BE}$.
   b. A is on one ray of the angle.
   c. The semicircular edge of the tomahawk is tangent to the other edge of the angle.
5. Then $\overrightarrow{XC}$ is the angle trisector.

Use a tomahawk to trisect several angles.

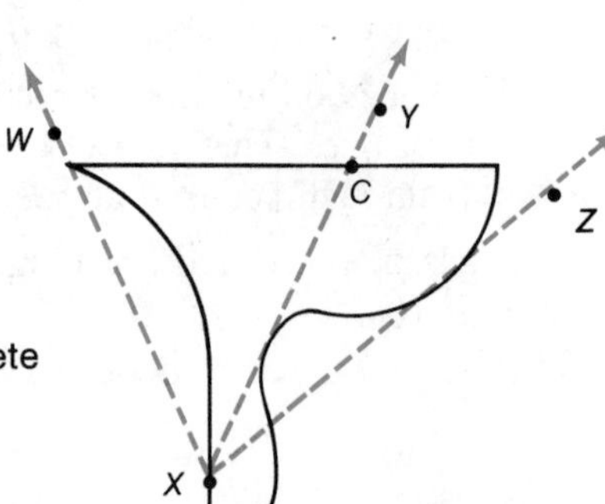

$m\angle YXZ = \frac{1}{3}m\angle WXZ$

6. **Given:** $\overline{PA}$ and $\overline{PB}$ are tangents.
   $\overline{PA} \perp \overline{PB}$
   $OB = 8$
   Find: OP

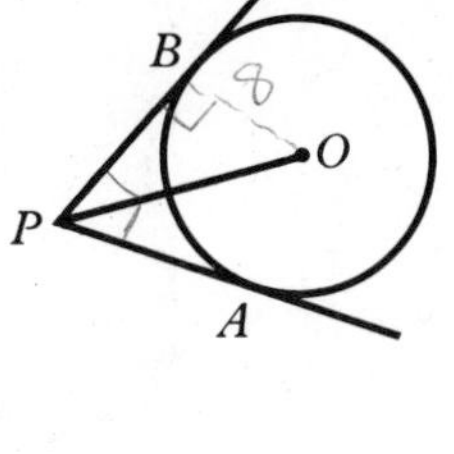

7. **Given:** $\overline{PA}$ and $\overline{PB}$ are tangents.
   $\overline{OA}$ and $\overline{OB}$ are radii.
   Prove: $\angle 1 \cong \angle 2$

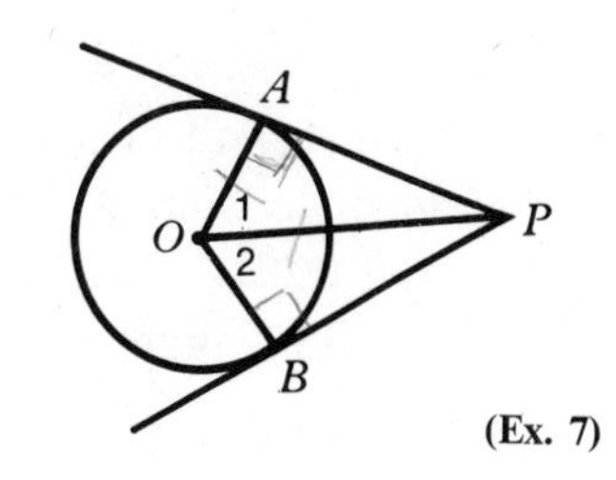

(Ex. 7)

8. **Given:** $\overline{PA}$ and $\overline{PB}$ are tangents.
   Prove: $m\angle 1 = m\angle 2$

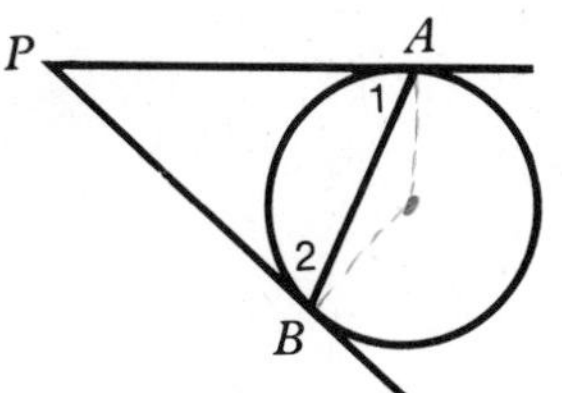

C.

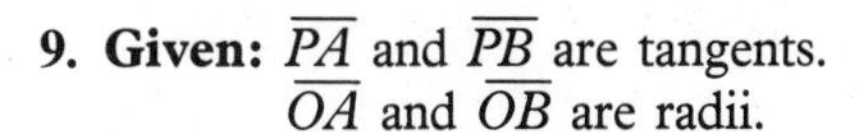

9. **Given:** $\overline{PA}$ and $\overline{PB}$ are tangents.
   $\overline{OA}$ and $\overline{OB}$ are radii.
   Prove: $\overline{OP}$ is the perpendicular bisector of $\overline{AB}$.

10. **Given:** $\overline{PA}$ and $\overline{PB}$ are tangents.
    $\overline{OA}$ and $\overline{OB}$ are radii.
    $m\angle APB = 80$
    Find: $m\angle ABO$ (Hint: Use the conclusion of exercise 9.)

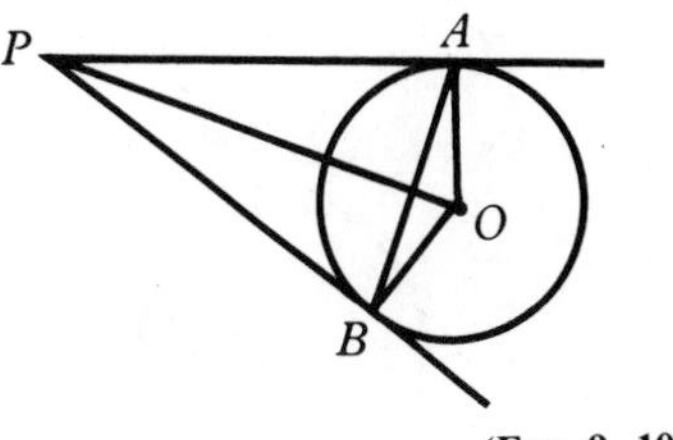

(Exs. 9, 10)

11. **Given:** $\overline{PA}$ and $\overline{PB}$ are tangents to circle O.
    $\overline{AC}$ is a diameter.
    Prove: $\overline{OP} \parallel \overline{BC}$.

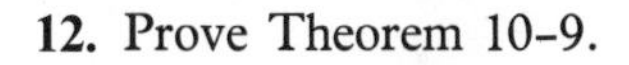

12. Prove Theorem 10–9.

13. Prove Theorem 10–10.

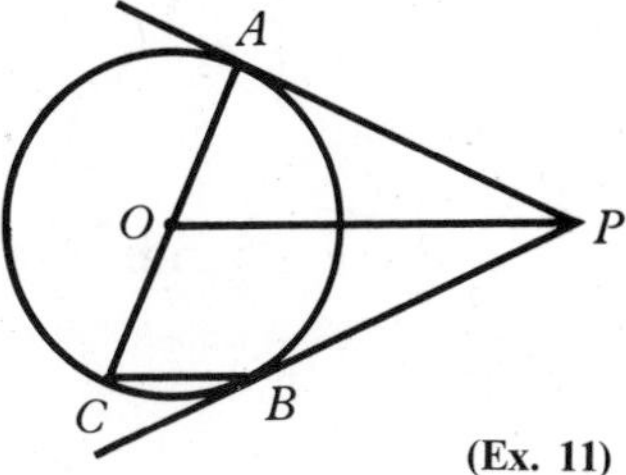

(Ex. 11)

PROBLEM SOLVING

Prove that the tomahawk method in the last activity does work by proving that $\angle 1$, $\angle 2$, and $\angle 3$ are congruent to each other.

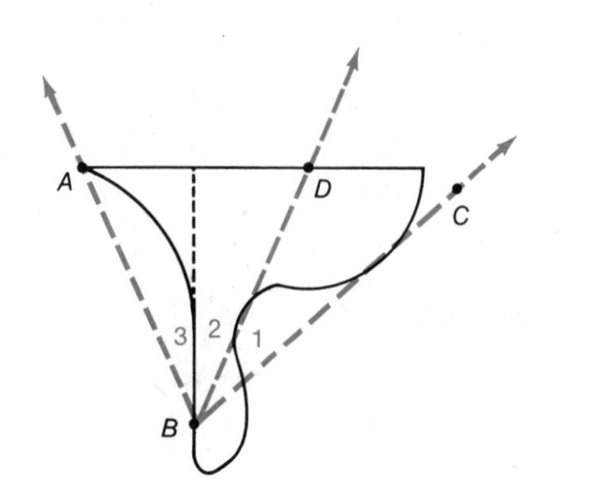

10–6 Tangents from a Point to a Circle

A surveyor is asked to find the center of a large circular wall of a fountain. A surveyor's pole and transits are available. A theorem in this lesson provides one method of finding the center using this equipment.

In each case, $\overrightarrow{PA}$ and $\overrightarrow{PB}$ are tangents at A and B. Measure with ruler or protractor to fill in each unknown length.

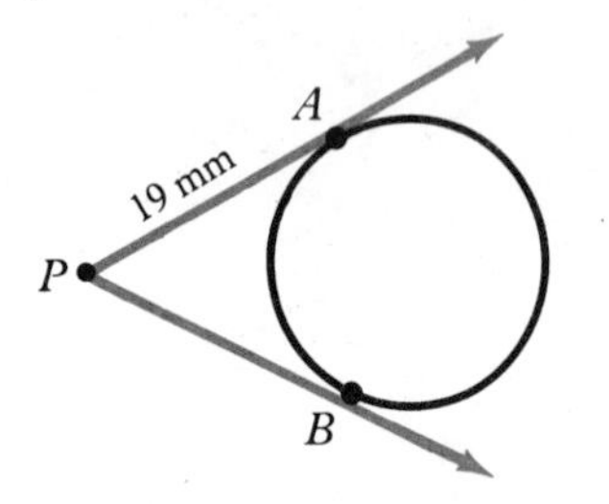

$PA = 19$ mm, $PB = \underline{\ ?\ }$

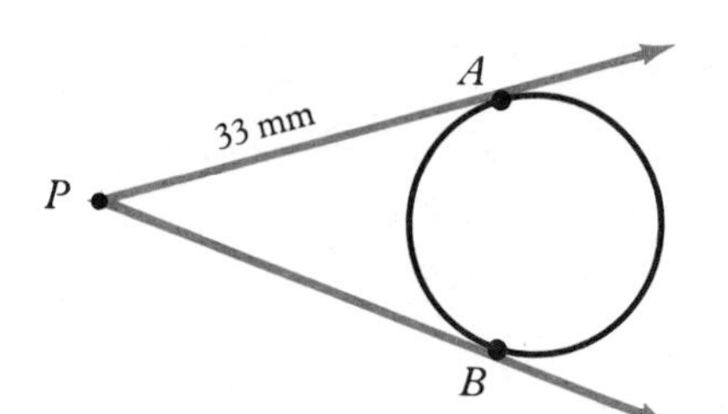

$PA = 33$ mm, $PB = \underline{\ ?\ }$

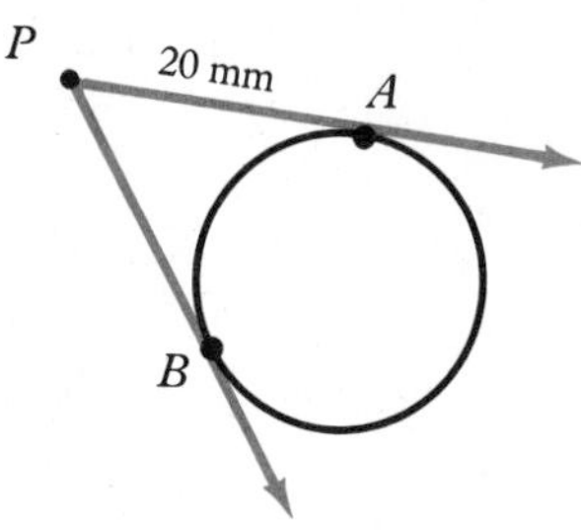

$PA = 20$ mm, $PB = \underline{\ ?\ }$

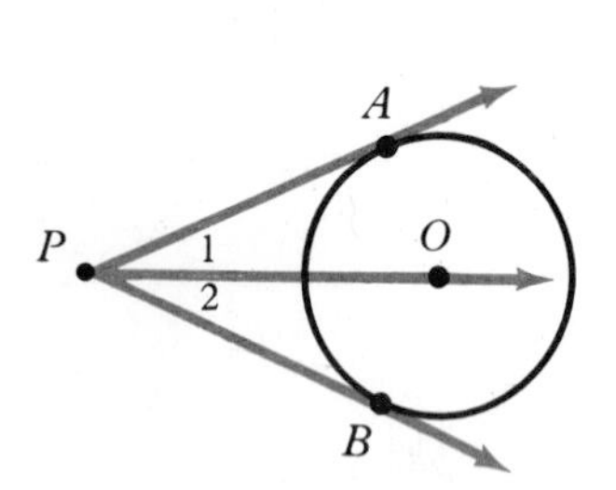

$m\angle 1 = 24$, $m\angle 2 = \underline{\ ?\ }$

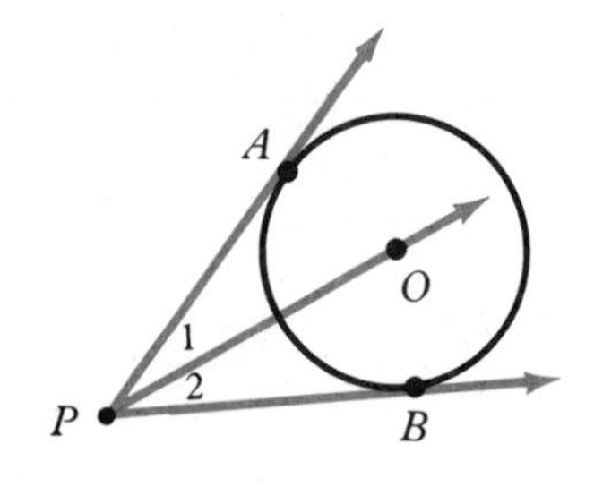

$m\angle 1 = 25$, $m\angle 2 = \underline{\ ?\ }$

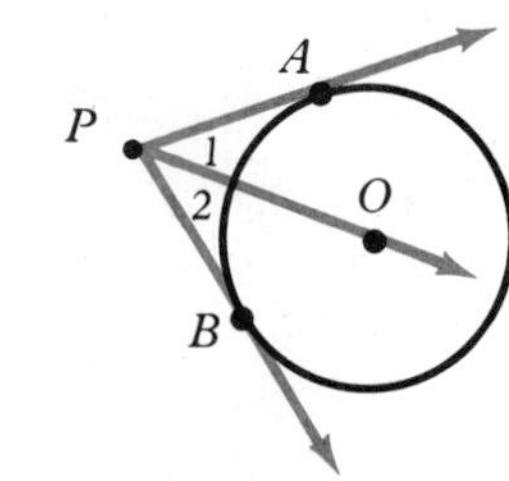

$m\angle 1 = 38$, $m\angle 2 = \underline{\ ?\ }$

Theorem 10–11 The tangent segments to a circle from a point outside the circle are congruent and form congruent angles with the line joining the center and the point.

PROOF

Given: $\overrightarrow{PA}$ and $\overrightarrow{PB}$ tangent at A and B
Prove: $\overline{PA} \cong \overline{PB}$ and $\angle 1 \cong \angle 2$

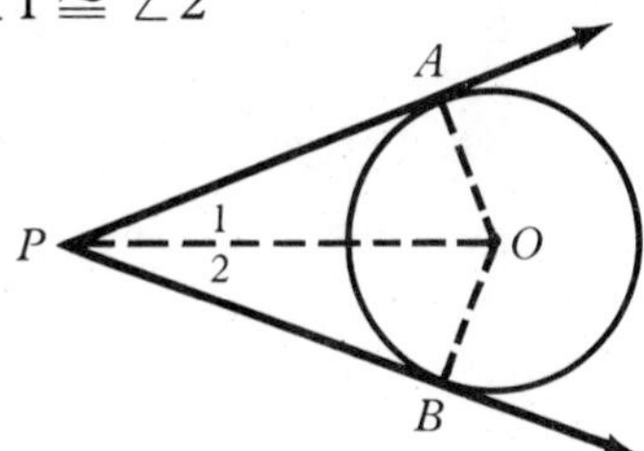

Statements	Reasons
1. Draw $\overrightarrow{PO}$ and radii $\overline{OA}$ and $\overline{OB}$.	**1.** Construction
2. $OA = OB$	**2.** Definition of radius
3. $PO = PO$	**3.** Why?
4. $\overline{OA} \perp \overrightarrow{PA}$ and $\overline{OB} \perp \overrightarrow{PB}$	**4.** Why?
5. $\triangle POA \cong \triangle POB$	**5.** Why?
6. $\overline{PA} \cong \overline{PB}$, $\angle 1 \cong \angle 2$	**6.** CPCTC

APPLICATION

The surveyor's problem introduced at the beginning of the lesson can be solved using Theorem 10–11 and the fact that the bisector of an angle is unique.

Step 1 Set up two transits and determine in each case the position of the tangent rays.

Step 2 Set the telescope of both transits in the position of the bisector of the angle formed by the tangents.

Step 3 A pole placed in the "line of vision" of both telescopes must be in the center of the circle.

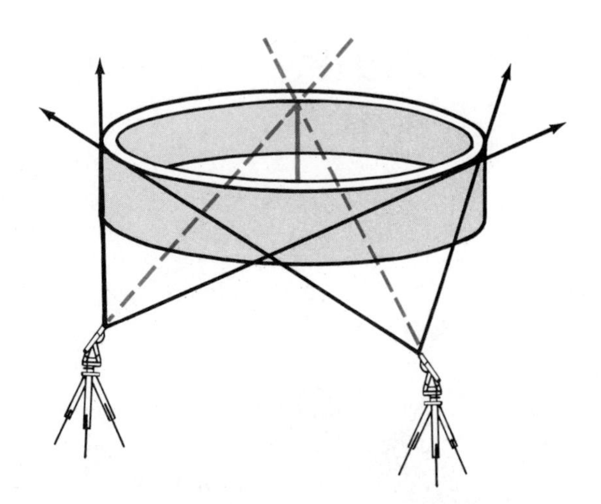

NOTE: Not drawn to scale

EXERCISES

A.

Given: $\overline{PA}$ and $\overline{PB}$ are tangents.
$PA = 5$ cm, $m\angle BPO = 17$

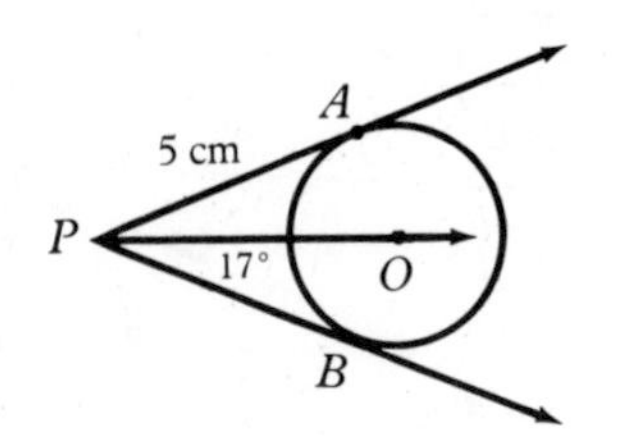

1. Find PB. **2.** Find $m\angle APB$.

3. Given: $\overline{PA}$, $\overline{PB}$, and $\overline{PC}$ are tangents.
$PA = 10$ cm
Find: PC.

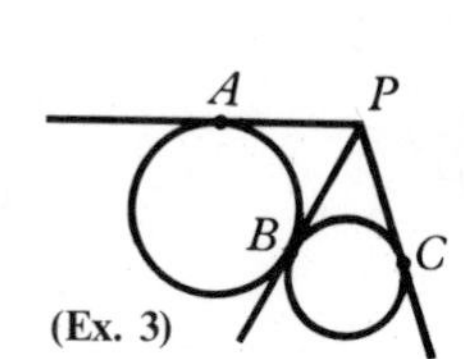

(Ex. 3)

B.

4. Given: $\overline{HA}$, $\overline{AR}$, $\overline{RD}$, and $\overline{DH}$ are tangents.
Find: Lengths x and y.

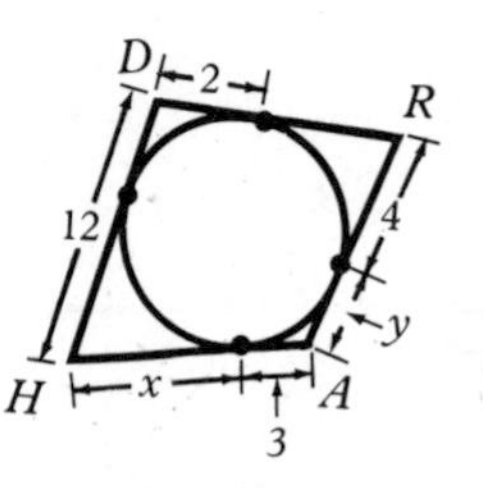

5. Given: $\overline{PA}$ and $\overline{PB}$ are tangents to $\odot O$.
$OA = 10$
$m\angle APB = 60$
Find: OP.

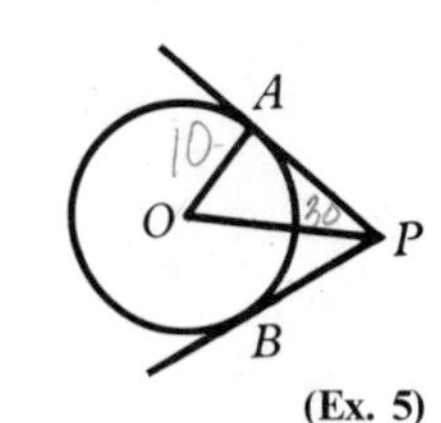

(Ex. 5)

6. Given: $\overline{AB}$, $\overline{AD}$, and $\overline{BC}$ are tangents to $\odot O$.
Prove: $AD + BC = AB$

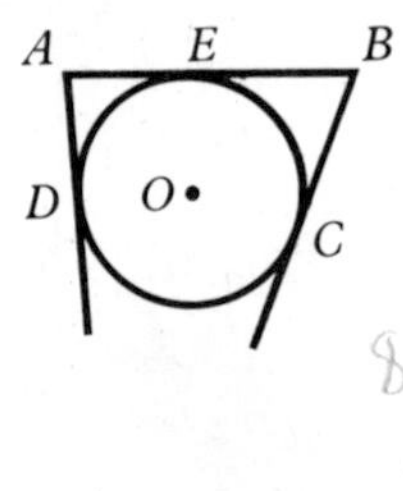

7. Given: Right triangle ABC
$\overline{AB}$, $\overline{BC}$, and $\overline{AC}$ are tangents.
$AB = 6$, $BC = 8$ and $AC = 10$
Find: The length of radius $\overline{OX}$

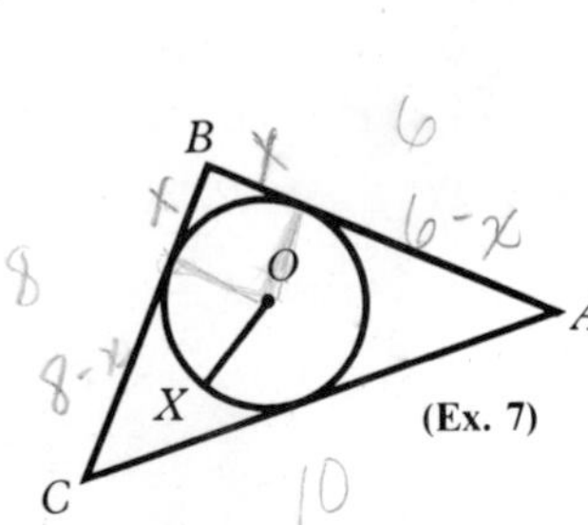

(Ex. 7)

Activity

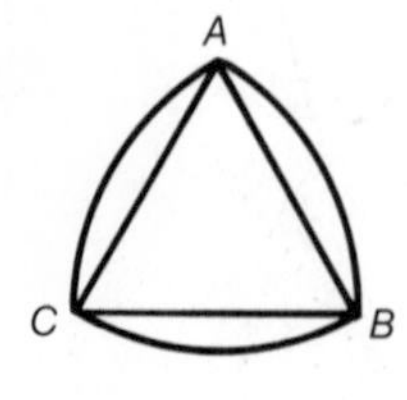

The Wankel engine is designed around a curve called a curve of constant width.

Construct several identical curved shapes from cardboard using the following procedure.

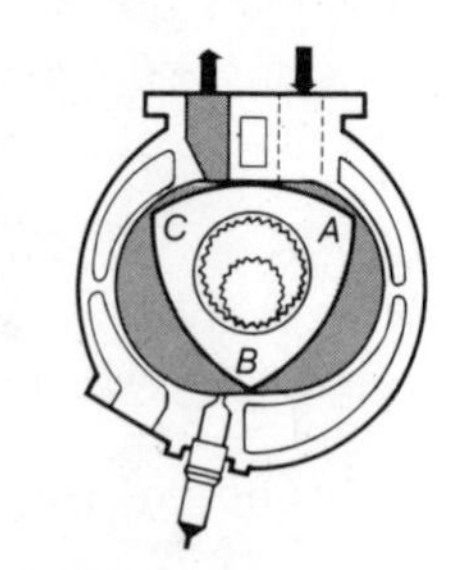

1. Construct an equilateral triangle $\triangle ABC$.

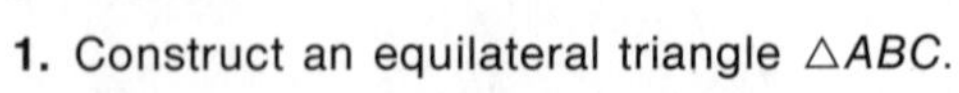

2. Construct arcs $\widehat{AB}$, $\widehat{AC}$, and $\widehat{BC}$ each centered at the opposite vertex.
3. Use these curves as "rollers" as shown in this diagram to demonstrate that they have the same width.

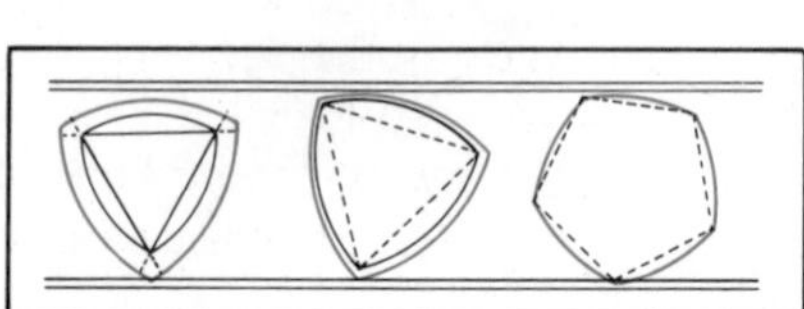

8. Given: $\overline{CP}$, $\overline{CD}$, and $\overline{PB}$ are tangents.
$CD = 4$, $CP = 9$
$m\angle APB = 60$
Find: AB.

(Ex. 8)

C.

9. Given: $\overline{AB}$ and $\overline{CD}$ are common tangents as shown.
Prove: $AB = CD$.

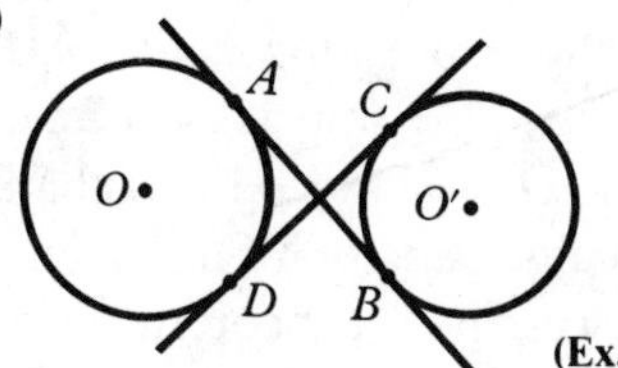

(Ex. 9)

10. Given: Circle $O \cong$ circle O'
$\overline{AB}$ is a common internal tangent.
Prove: $\overline{AB}$ bisects $\overline{OO'}$.

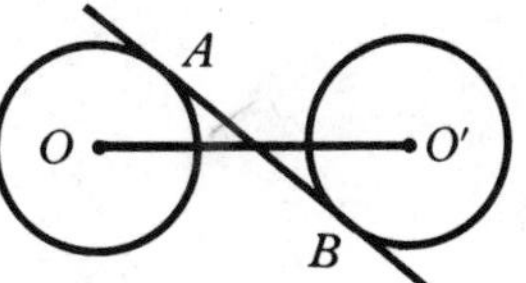

11. Quality control in the manufacturing of machine parts often requires unusual methods of measurement. For example, in order to check that the angles A and B are correct on a part called a dovetail, circular plugs are inserted as shown. Then the distance X is measured with a micrometer. For the dovetail shown here, what should this distance equal?

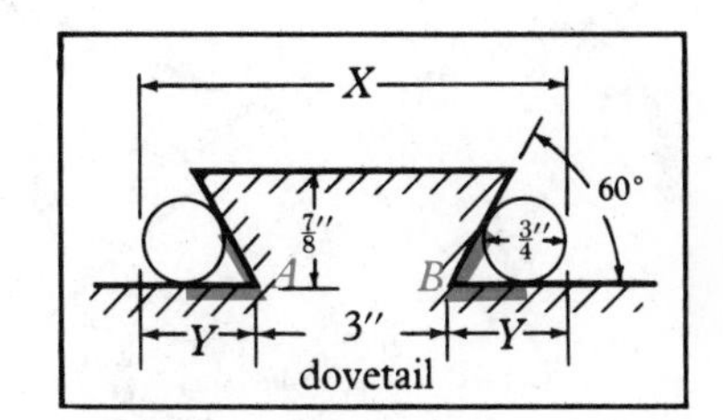

12. Three metal discs each with a radius of 10 cm are tangent to each other. The discs are enclosed by a metal frame that forms an equilateral triangle. What is the length of one side of the frame?

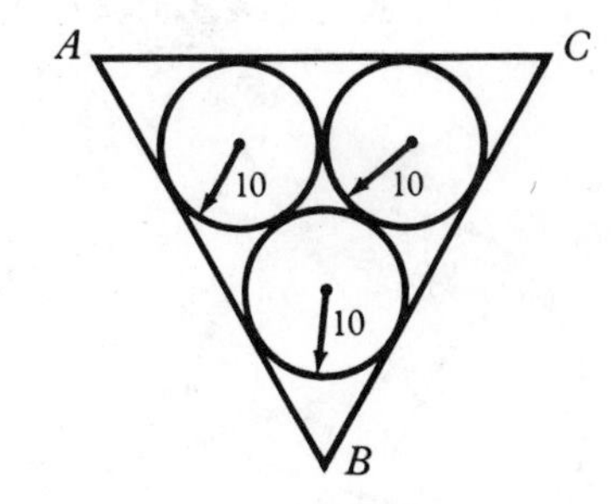

PROBLEM SOLVING

Suppose ℓ is a line tangent to an arc of the curve constructed in the Activity on page 366 and ℓ' is parallel to ℓ through an opposite vertex.

How does the distance d between these lines compare to length AB?

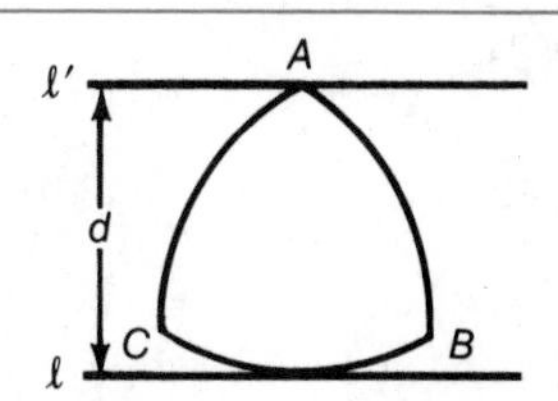

10–7 Measures of Inscribed Angles

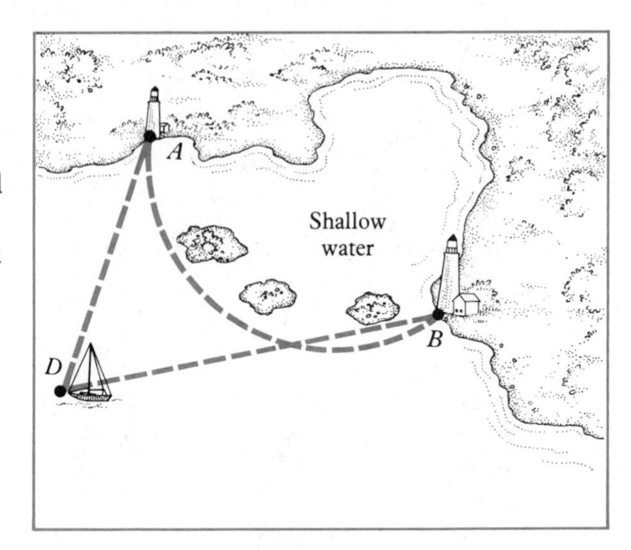

Two lighthouses can serve as a navigation aid for a ship sailing near coastlines and shallow water. If a ship is positioned at point D, then $\angle ADB$ should be less than a published "danger angle." This navigation technique is based upon a theorem developed in this section.

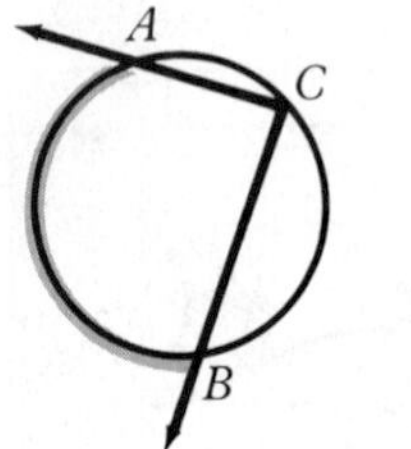

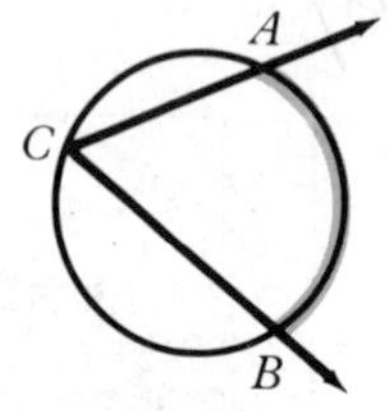

An inscribed angle determines an arc called the *intercepted arc.*

Definition 10–12

The **intercepted arc** for an inscribed $\angle ACB$ is the arc AB lying in the interior of the angle.

In each figure $m\widehat{AB}$ and $m\angle ACB$ and $m\angle ADB$ are given.

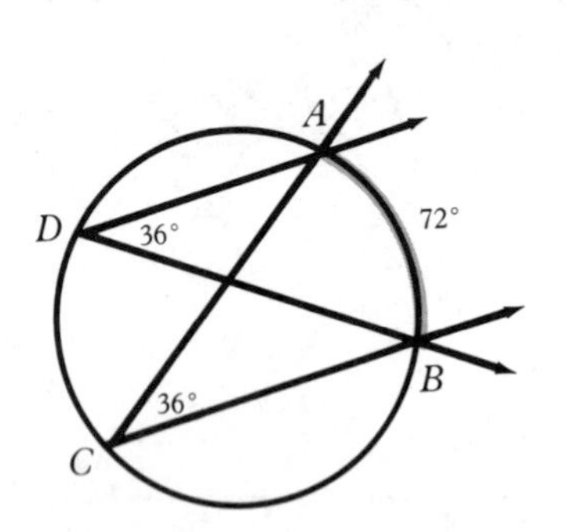

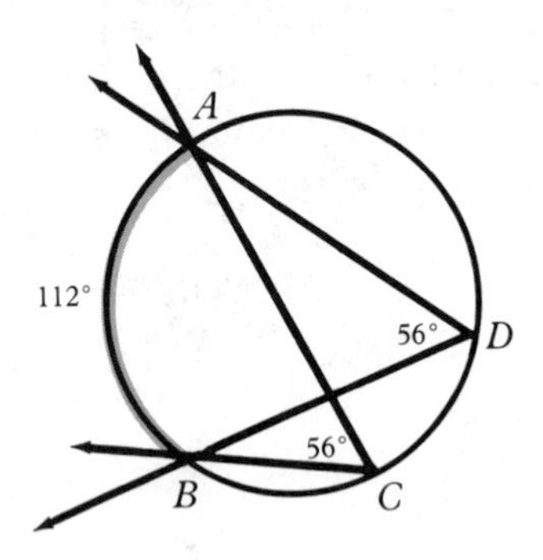

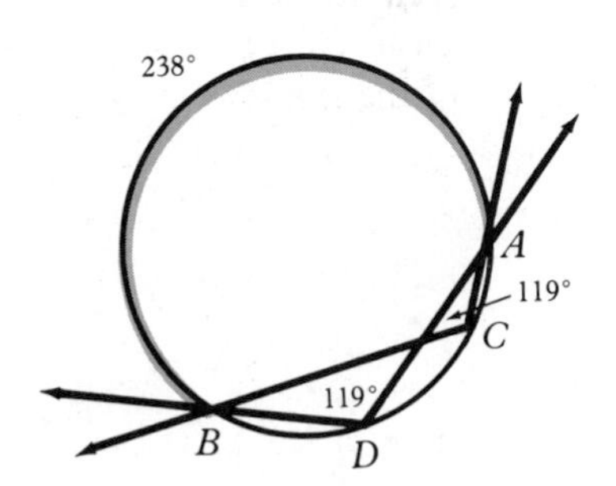

These figures suggest the following theorem.

Theorem 10–12 The measure of an inscribed angle is one half the measure of its intercepted arc.

APPLICATION 1

The navigation technique on page 368 is based upon Theorem 10–12. If a point C lies on a circle such that arc AB has measure twice the "danger angle," then $m\angle ACB$ equals the danger angle.

If D were on this same circle or inside it, then $m\angle ADB$ would be equal to or greater than the danger angle. When D is outside the circle, $m\angle ADB$ is less than the danger angle and a ship at point D is in a safe position.

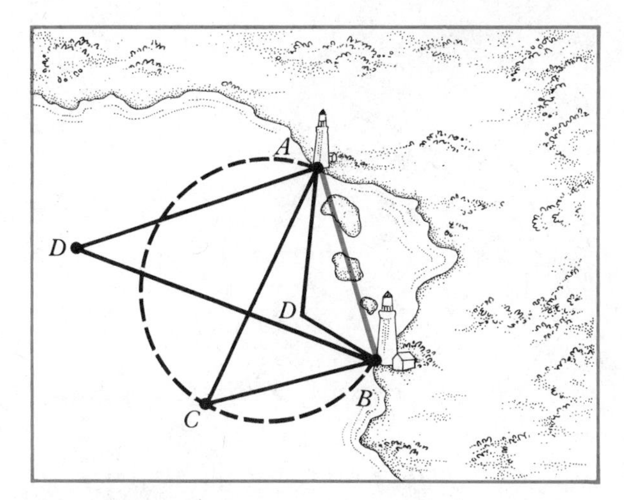

The second application is based upon a special case of Theorem 10–12, which is stated as Theorem 10–13.

APPLICATION 2

A draftsman often needs to draw from a given point outside a circle two tangent lines to the circle. Here is one way that it can be done.

Step 1 From a point P outside a given circle with center O, draw $\overline{OP}$ and its midpoint M.

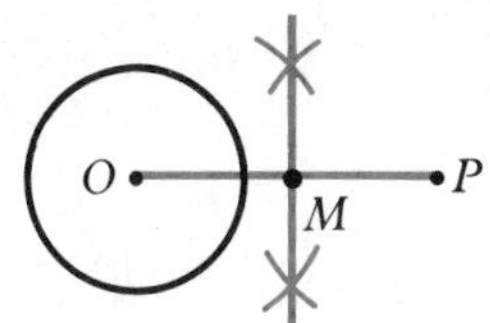

Step 2 Draw the circle with diameter $\overline{OP}$ intersecting the given circle at points A and B. Draw $\overrightarrow{PA}$ and $\overrightarrow{PB}$. Theorem 10–12 tells us that $\angle OAP$ and $\angle OBP$ are right angles.

Step 3 Theorem 10–8 tells us that $\overrightarrow{PA}$ and $\overrightarrow{PB}$ are tangent to the given circle.

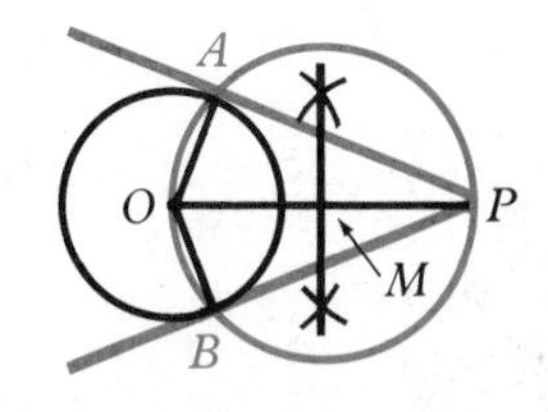

Theorem 10–13 An angle inscribed in a semicircle is a right angle.

EXERCISES

A.

In exercises 1-4 $m\widehat{AB} = 50$, $m\widehat{AOC} = 230$.

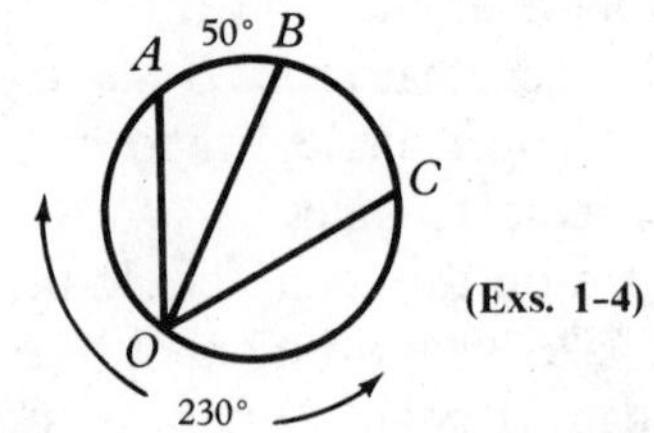

(Exs. 1-4)

1. $m\angle AOB = \underline{\ ?\ }$ **2.** $m\angle BOC = \underline{\ ?\ }$

3. $m\angle AOC = \underline{\ ?\ }$ **4.** $m\widehat{AC} = \underline{\ ?\ }$

5. Find the measures of each angle of $\triangle ABC$.

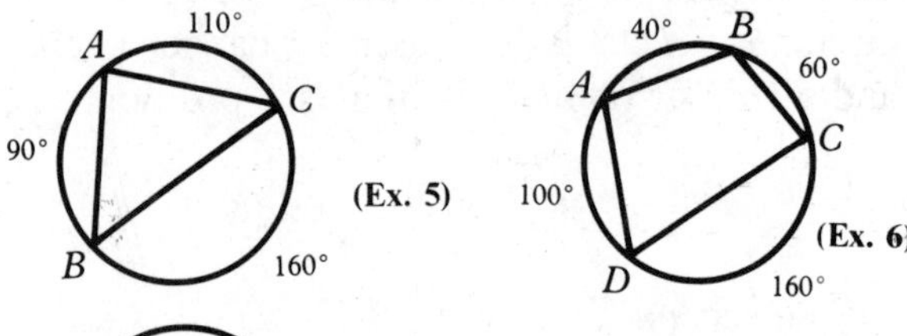

6. Find the measure of each angle of $ABCD$.

7. Find $m\widehat{AB}$, $m\widehat{AC}$, and $m\widehat{BC}$.

(Ex. 7)

8. Given: $XY = YZ$

$m\angle Y = 40$

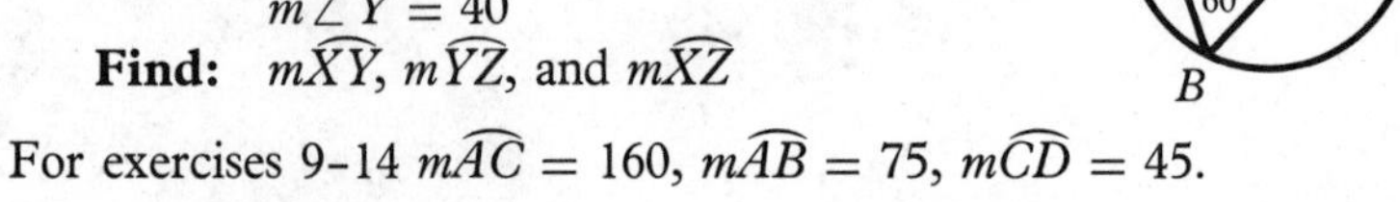

Find: $m\widehat{XY}$, $m\widehat{YZ}$, and $m\widehat{XZ}$

For exercises 9-14 $m\widehat{AC} = 160$, $m\widehat{AB} = 75$, $m\widehat{CD} = 45$.

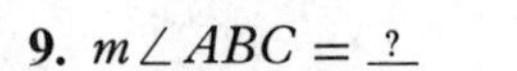

9. $m\angle ABC = \underline{\ ?\ }$ **10.** $m\angle ADC = \underline{\ ?\ }$

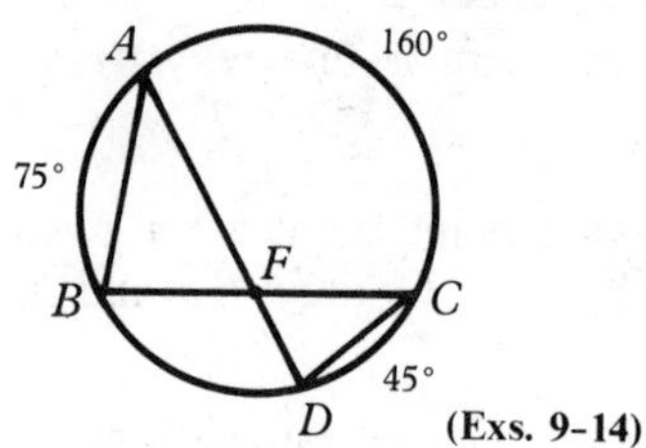

(Exs. 9-14)

11. $m\widehat{BD} = \underline{\ ?\ }$ **12.** $m\angle BAD = \underline{\ ?\ }$

13. $m\angle BCD = \underline{\ ?\ }$ **14.** $m\angle AFB = \underline{\ ?\ }$

B.

15. Given: $\overline{BC}$ is a diameter.

$AB = 8$, $AC = 6$

Find: BC

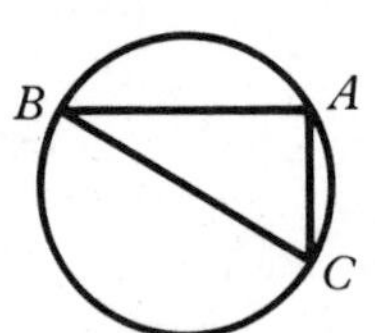

For exercises 16-19, $\overline{AC}$ is a diameter, $m\widehat{CD} = 66$, and $m\angle CDB = 60$.

16. $m\angle ADB = \underline{\ ?\ }$ **17.** $m\widehat{BC} = \underline{\ ?\ }$

18. $m\angle BCA = \underline{\ ?\ }$ **19.** $m\angle BCD = \underline{\ ?\ }$

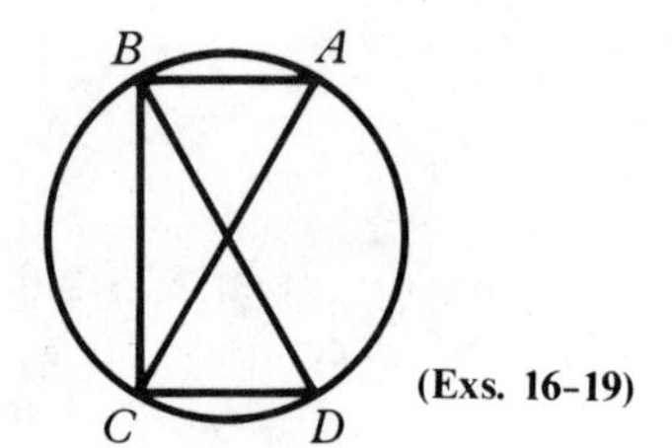

(Exs. 16-19)

20. Given: $\frac{m\widehat{MN}}{m\widehat{NP}} = \frac{2}{3}$ and $\frac{m\widehat{NP}}{m\widehat{MP}} = \frac{3}{4}$

Find: $m\angle M$, $m\angle N$, and $m\angle P$.

21. Given: $m\widehat{BC} = 100$, $m\widehat{AB} = 80$

$\overline{AC}$ is a diameter.

$\overline{BD} \perp \overline{AC}$

Find: **a.** $m\angle BAC$ **b.** $m\angle ACB$

c. $m\angle EBC$ **d.** $m\widehat{AD}$

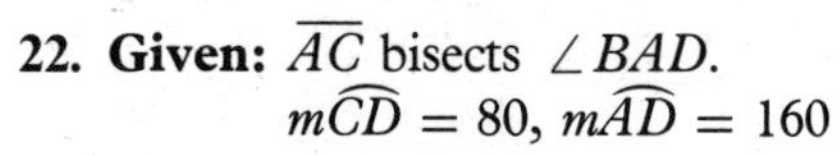

22. Given: $\overline{AC}$ bisects $\angle BAD$.

$m\widehat{CD} = 80$, $m\widehat{AD} = 160$

Find: **a.** $m\angle BAC$ **b.** $m\angle BDC$

c. $m\angle AEB$ **d.** $m\angle ADB$

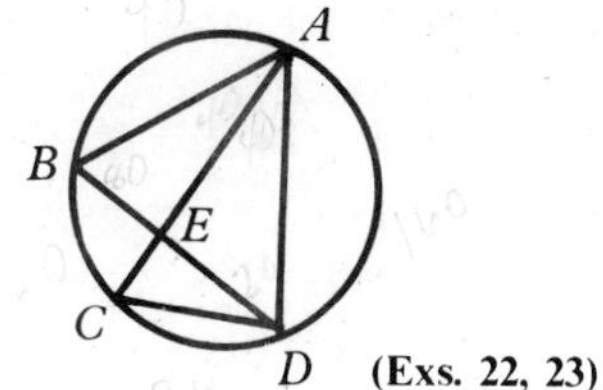

(Exs. 22, 23)

23. Given: $\overline{AC}$ bisects $\angle BAD$.

Prove: Three angles of $\triangle ABE$ are congruent to three angles of $\triangle DCE$.

24. How can a carpenter's square be used to find the center of a circular disc? Why does your method work?

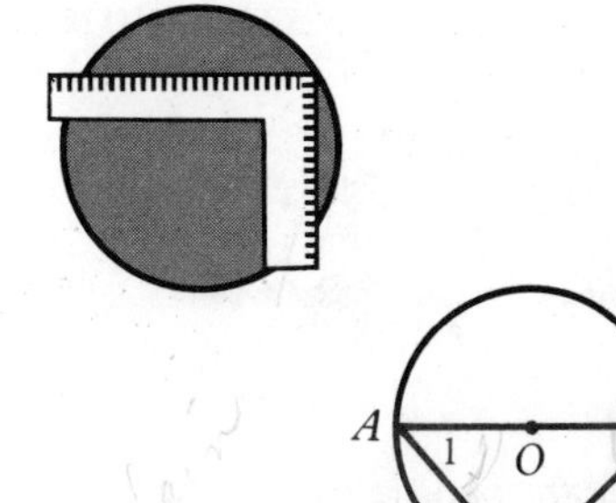

25. Given: $\overline{AB}$ is a diameter of circle O.

$\overline{BC}$ is a diameter of circle O'.

Circle O is tangent to circle O' at B.

Prove: $m\angle 1 = m\angle 2$.

26. Prove that all inscribed angles with the same or congruent intercepted arcs are equal in measure.

27. Draw a circle and a point P not in or on the circle. Construct two lines through P that are tangent to the circle.

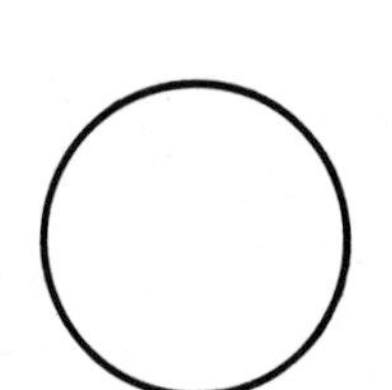

C.

28. A curve of constant width like the one in a Wankel engine consists of three circular arcs, AB, BC, and AC. What is the measure of each of these arcs? (Review the construction shown in the activity on p. 366.)

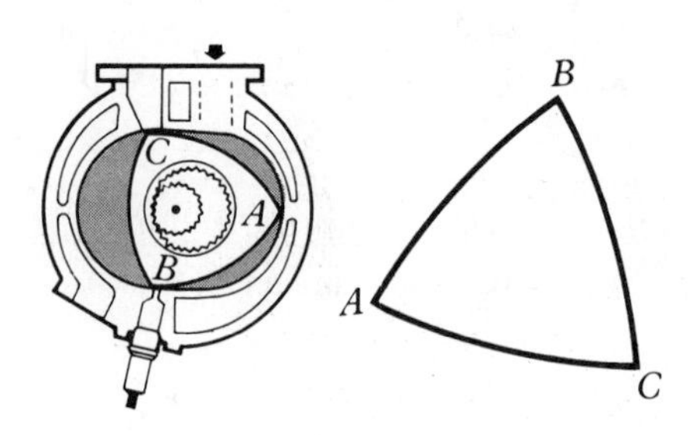

29. Prove that if a quadrilateral is inscribed in a circle, its opposite angles are supplementary.

30. If $ABCD$ is a quadrilateral inscribed in a circle and $m\angle A = 3x + 50$, $m\angle B = 4x + 25$, and $m\angle C = 7x + 30$, find $m\angle D$.

31. Prove that a parallelogram inscribed in a circle is a rectangle.

32. In the figure $\angle BAD$ and $\angle BCD$ are inscribed angles. Prove that $\triangle ABE$ is similar to $\triangle CDE$.

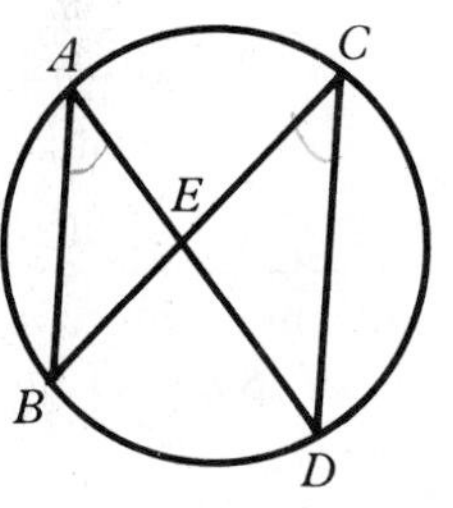

(Ex. 32)

Activity

A carpenter's square can be used to draw a circle.

1. Hold the square against a pair of nails and a pencil at the right angle.
2. Rotate the square, always keeping the arms of the square against the nails. The pencil will draw the semicircle with diameter determined by the nails. Why?

Draw a circle using this method.

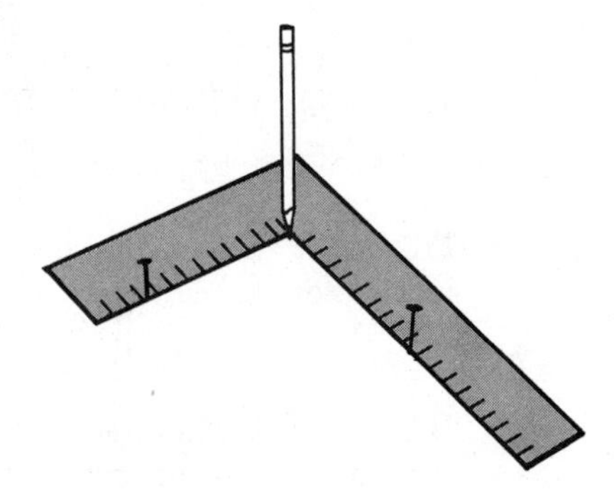

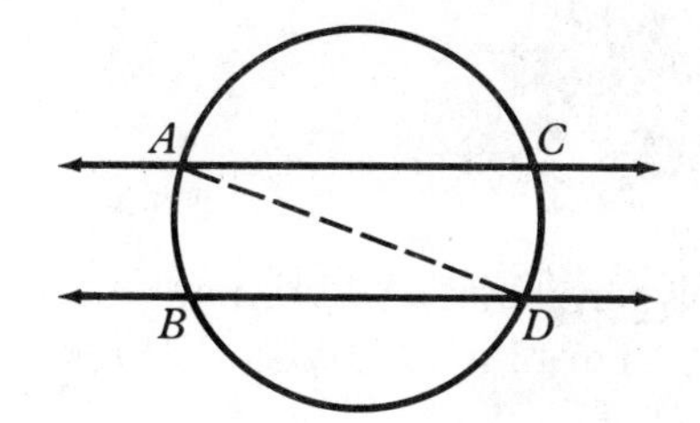

33. Prove that if two parallel lines intersect a circle, then they intercept congruent arcs.

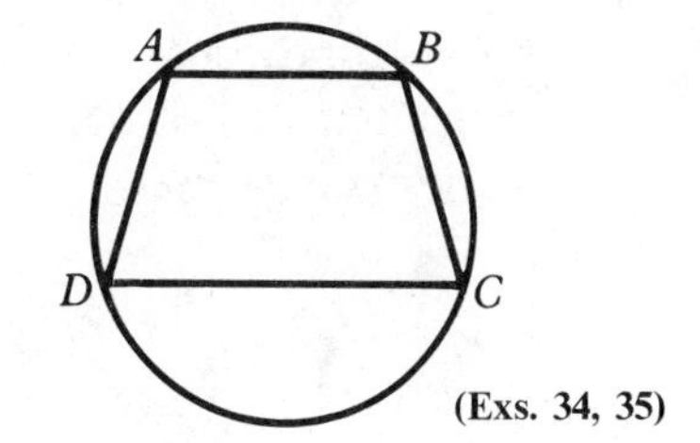

(Exs. 34, 35)

34. Given: *ABCD* is an inscribed trapezoid.
Prove: *ABCD* is an isosceles trapezoid.

35. Given: *ABCD* is an inscribed quadrilateral and $\overline{AD} \cong \overline{BC}$.
Prove: *ABCD* is a trapezoid.

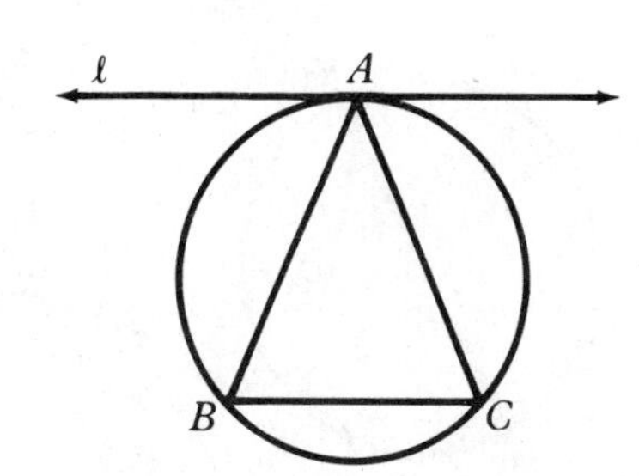

36. Given: ℓ is tangent to the circle at A.
$\overline{BC} \parallel \ell$
Prove: $\triangle ABC$ is an isosceles triangle.

The figure at the right shows one circle rolling around another circle and generating a cardioid.

If $m\angle AOX = t$, why is $m\angle OAP = \frac{t}{2}$?

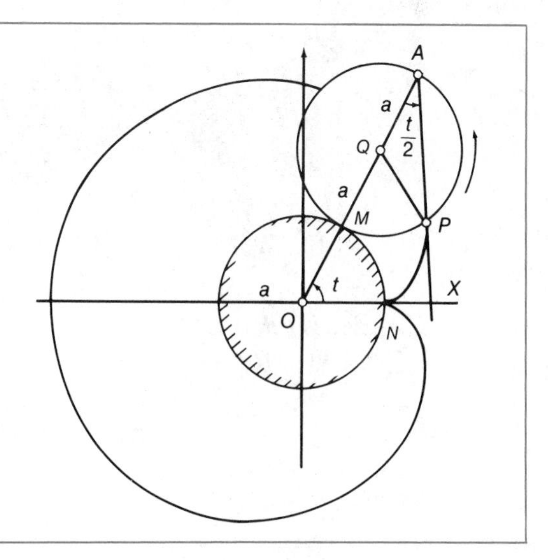

10–8 Angles Formed by Chords

The star polygon is drawn by joining every fourth point from nine evenly spaced points on a circle. (See Problem Solving, p. 345.) There are many angles in this star design that appear to be congruent. In this lesson we study a theorem that can be used to prove these angles congruent.

In each figure $m\widehat{AB} + m\widehat{CD} = 80$.

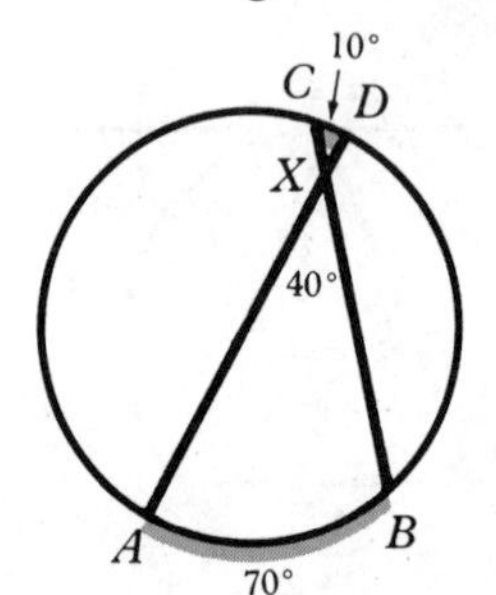

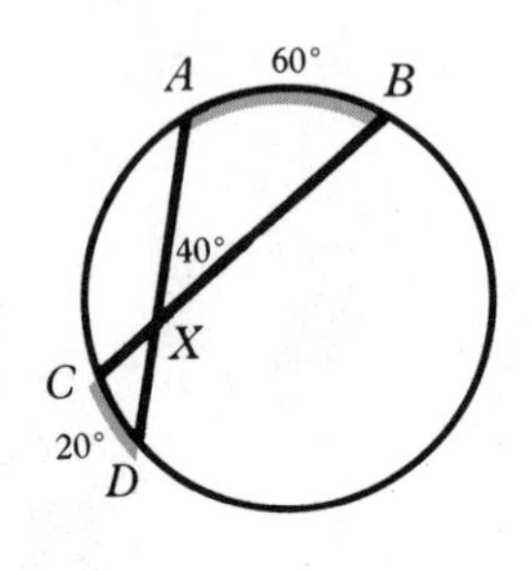

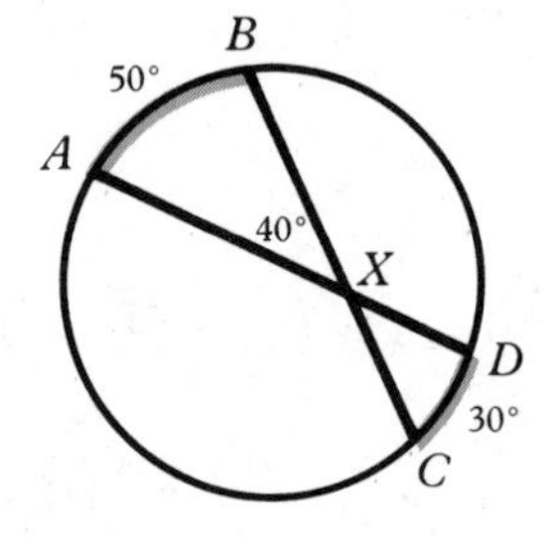

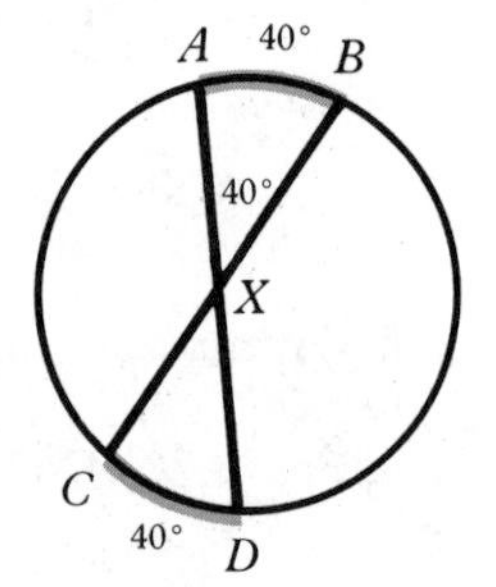

These figures suggest the following theorem.

Theorem 10–14 An angle formed by two chords intersecting inside a circle has a measure equal to one half the sum of the intercepted arcs.

PROOF

Given: Chords $\overline{AD}$ and $\overline{BC}$ intersecting in point X

Prove: $m\angle AXB = \frac{1}{2}(m\widehat{AB} + m\widehat{CD})$

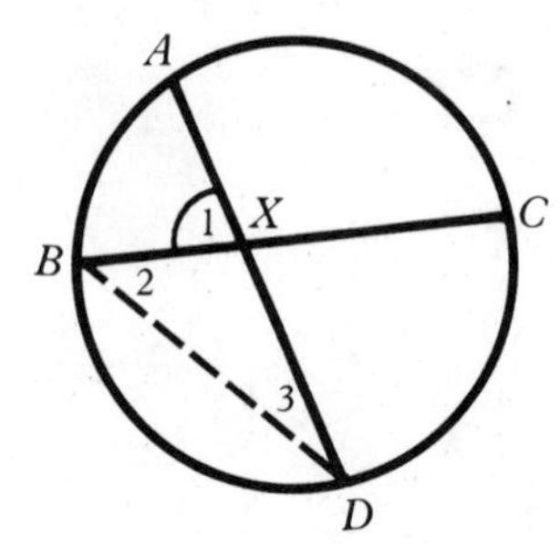

Statements	Reasons
1. Construct $\overline{BD}$.	**1.** Construction
2. $m\angle 2 = \frac{1}{2}m\widehat{CD}$	**2.** The measure of an inscribed angle is one half its intercepted arc.
3. $m\angle 3 = \frac{1}{2}m\widehat{AB}$	**3.** Why?
4. $m\angle AXB = m\angle 2 + m\angle 3$	**4.** Why?
5. $m\angle AXB = \frac{1}{2}m\widehat{AB} + \frac{1}{2}m\widehat{CD}$	**5.** Substitution (Statements 2, 3, 4)
6. $m\angle AXB = \frac{1}{2}(m\widehat{AB} + m\widehat{CD})$	**6.** Distributive Property

APPLICATION

Determine the angle measures of angles in this star polygon. We shall use Theorem 10–14.

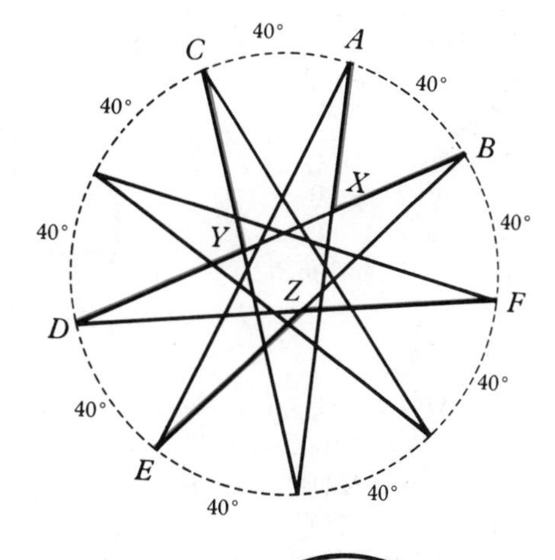

1. $m\angle AXB = \frac{1}{2}(40 + 80) = 60$

2. $m\angle CYD = \frac{1}{2}(80 + 120) = 100$

3. $m\angle EZF = \frac{1}{2}(120 + 160) = 140$

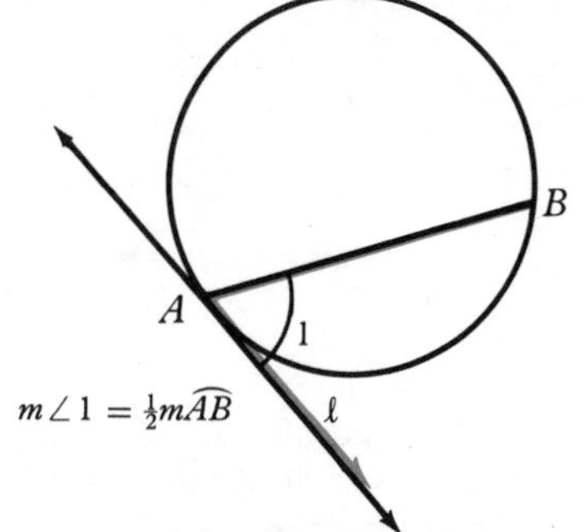

There is a special case of Theorem 10–14 that involves a tangent line. It is stated below.

Theorem 10–15 The measure of an angle formed by a tangent and a chord drawn to the point of contact is one half the intercepted arc.

EXERCISES

A.

1. **Given:** $m\widehat{AB} = 30$
   $m\widehat{CD} = 20$
   Find: $m\angle 1$

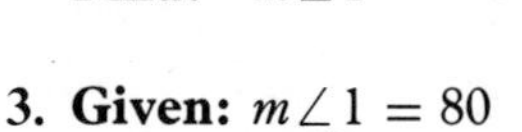

2. **Given:** $m\widehat{AXB} = 190$
   $m\widehat{CD} = 25$
   Find: $m\angle 1$

3. **Given:** $m\angle 1 = 80$
   $m\widehat{AB} = 100$
   Find: $m\widehat{CD}$

4. **Given:** $\overleftrightarrow{AB}$ is tangent to circle O.
   $m\widehat{ADC} = 300$
   Find: $m\angle 1$ and $m\angle 2$

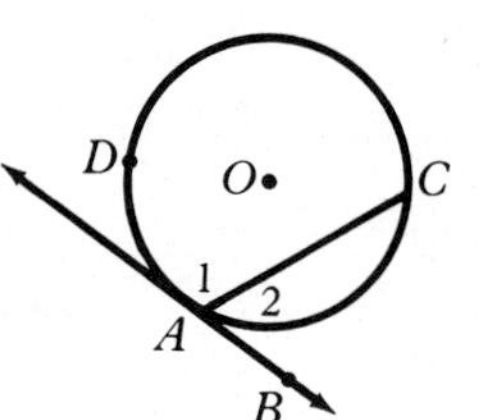

5. **Given:** $\overleftrightarrow{AB}$ is tangent to circle O.
   $m\widehat{AE} = 160$, $m\widehat{AD} = 50$, $m\widehat{DC} = 60$
   Find: $m\angle 1$ and $m\angle 2$

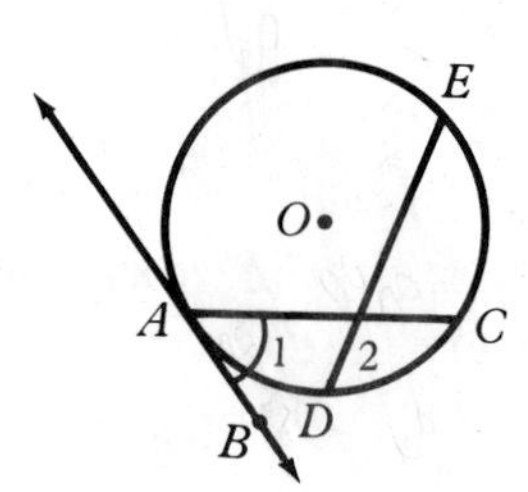

6. **Given:** $\overline{AB} \perp \overline{CD}$
   $m\widehat{BD} = 20$
   $m\widehat{AD} = 80$
   Find: $m\widehat{AC}$ and $m\widehat{BC}$.

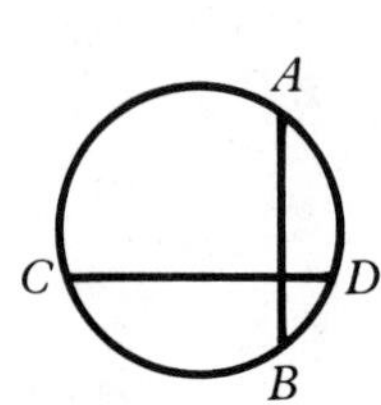

B.

7. **Given:** $\overleftrightarrow{MN}$ is tangent to circle O.
   $m\widehat{PQ} = 100$, $m\widehat{MXQ} = 150$
   Find: **a.** $m\angle NMP$ **b.** $m\angle PQM$
   c. $m\angle MPQ$ **d.** $m\angle PMQ$
   e. $m\angle MNP$

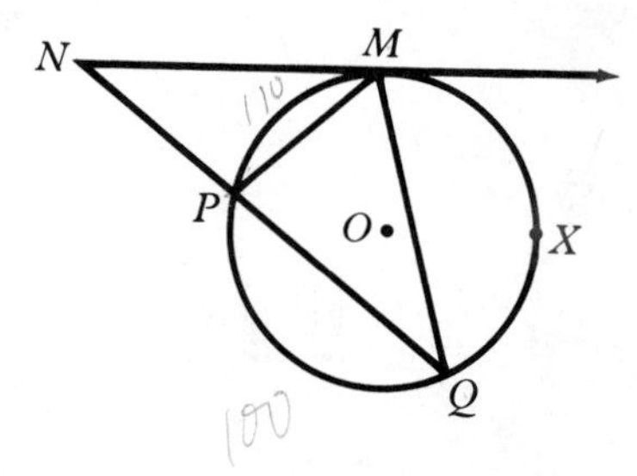

Activity

Using a compass and straightedge construct 15 points evenly spaced around a circle. Then draw two star polygons, one by joining every fourth point and the other by joining every seventh point. (*Hint*: Construct a regular pentagon and an equilateral triangle with a common vertex. Then $m\widehat{XY} = 24 = \frac{1}{15}(360)$. The method for constructing a regular pentagon is described on page 274.)

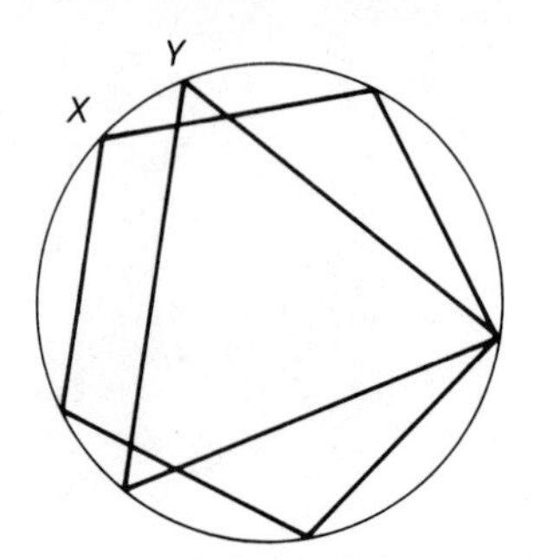

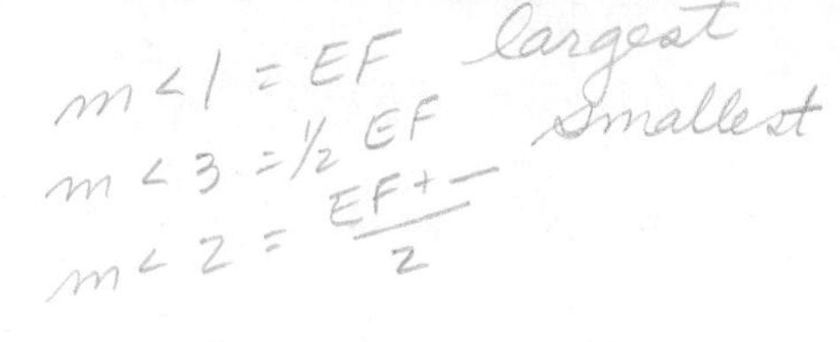

8. The three circles shown are all congruent, with $m\widehat{AB} = m\widehat{CD} = m\widehat{EF}$. $\angle 1$ is a central angle and $\angle 3$ is an inscribed angle. Which of the three angles is the largest? the smallest? Why?

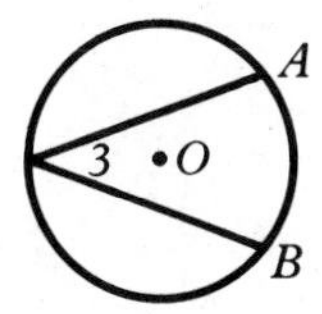

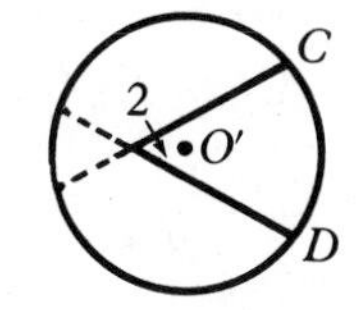

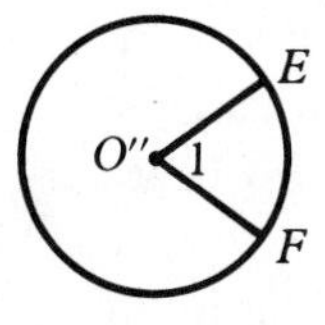

9. Given: $\overline{AB} \perp \overline{CD}$
Prove: $m\widehat{AD} + m\widehat{BC} = m\widehat{AC} + m\widehat{BD}$

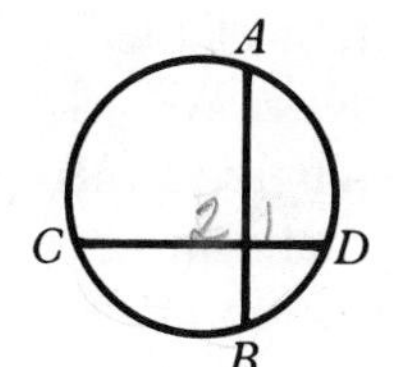

C.

10. Given: $\overline{AB}$ is a common external tangent to circles O and O'. $\overline{CD}$ is a common internal tangent.
Prove: $\angle ADB$ is a right angle.

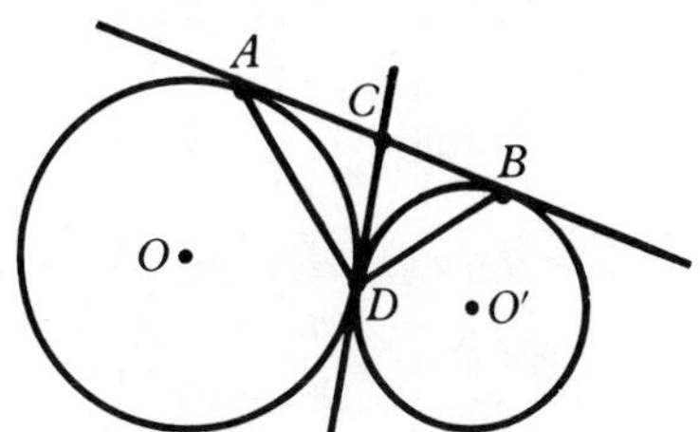

11. Given: $\overline{AD} \perp \overline{CE}$
$\overline{BE} \perp \overline{AC}$
Prove: $m\widehat{BC} = m\widehat{CD}$.

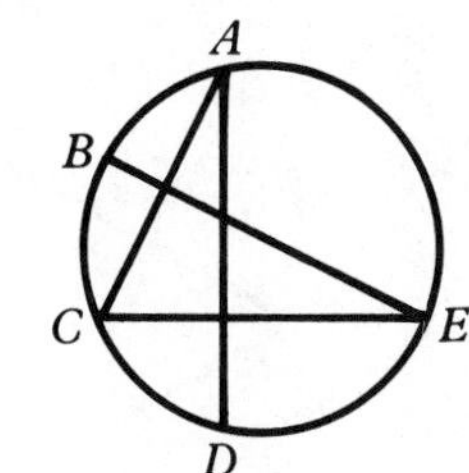

PROBLEM SOLVING

In the star polygon at the right five angles have been highlighted in color.

Without using a protractor find each of the following:

$m\angle 1 = \underline{?}$ $m\angle 4 = \underline{?}$

$m\angle 2 = \underline{?}$ $m\angle 5 = \underline{?}$

$m\angle 3 = \underline{?}$

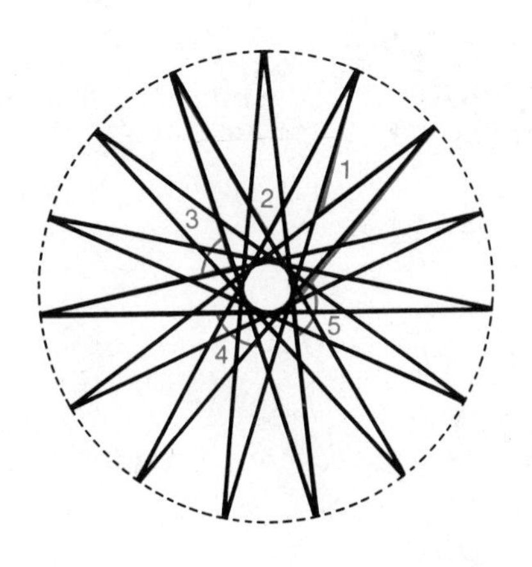

10–9 Angles and Segments Formed by Tangents and Secants

When engineers design radio towers, they need to know what fraction of the earth's surface will be covered by the radio beams from the tower.

In this section we simplify the problem by considering a circular cross section of the earth through the base of the tower. We ask: If we know the measure of the angle formed by the top of the tower and the tangent rays to the circle, can we find the fraction of the circumference of the circle covered by the radio beams?

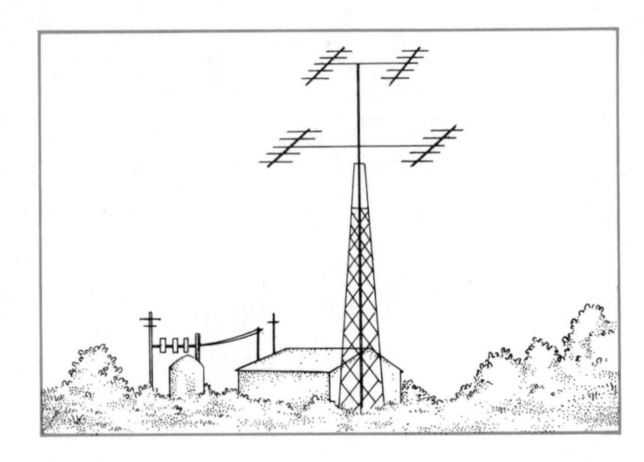

In each case $\overrightarrow{TA}$ and $\overrightarrow{TB}$ are tangent rays.

$m\widehat{ACB} - m\widehat{AB} = 180$

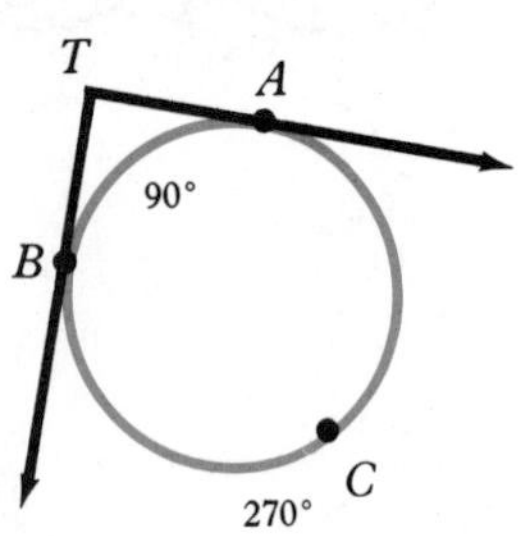

$m\widehat{ACB} - m\widehat{AB} = 112$

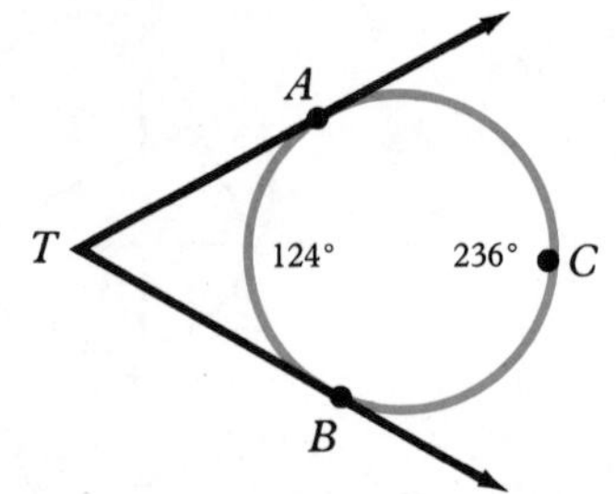

$m\widehat{ACB} - m\widehat{AB} = 216$

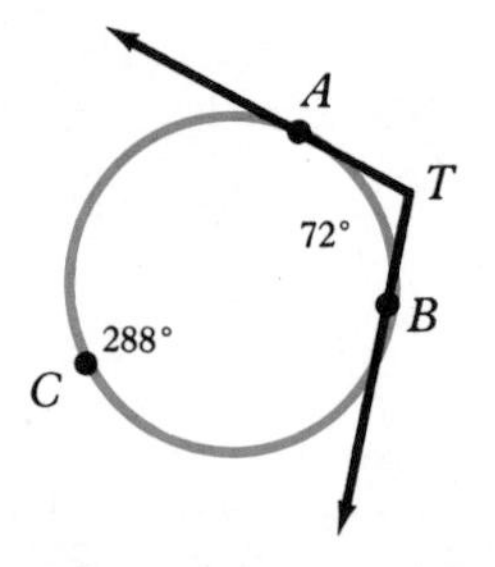

Measure $\angle ATB$ with a protractor. What do you find?

Theorem 10–16 The measure of an angle formed by two intersecting tangents to a circle is one half the difference of the measures of the intercepted arcs.

PROOF

Given: $\overrightarrow{TA}$ and $\overrightarrow{TB}$ are tangent rays to a circle, $m\widehat{AB} = x$, and $m\widehat{ACB} = y$.

Prove: $m\angle ATB = \frac{1}{2}(y - x)$

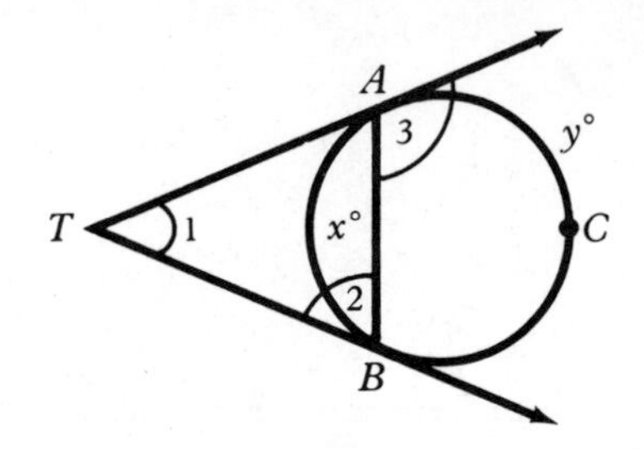

Statements	Reasons
1. $m\angle 2 = \frac{1}{2}x$	1. The measure of an angle formed by a tangent and a chord is one half the intercepted arc.
2. $m\angle 3 = \frac{1}{2}y$	2. Why?
3. $m\angle 3 = m\angle 1 + m\angle 2$	3. The measure of an exterior angle equals the sum of the measures of the two remote interior angles.
4. $m\angle 1 = m\angle 3 - m\angle 2$	4. Why?
5. $m\angle 1 = \frac{1}{2}y - \frac{1}{2}x$	5. Substitution
6. $m\angle 1 = \frac{1}{2}(y - x)$	6. Why?

APPLICATION

Suppose the angle formed by the two tangent rays from the top of the radio tower has a measure of 160°. What fraction of the circle do the radio waves cover?

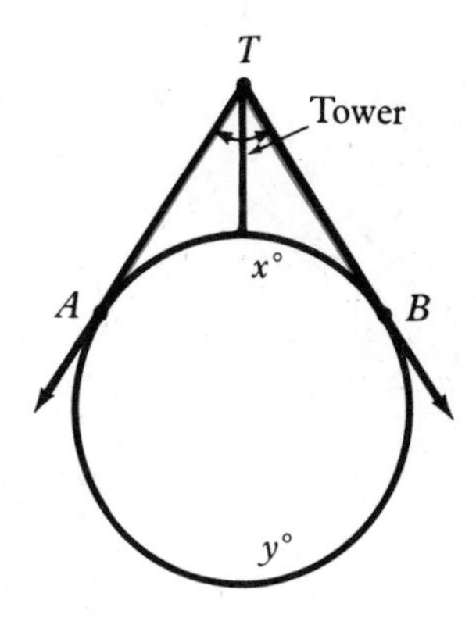

$\frac{1}{2}(y - x) = 160$ (1)
$(y + x) = 360$ (2)

Answer: 1. Theorem 10–16 results in equation (1) on the right and equation (2) expresses a property of a circle.
2. Solving the system of equations, we find that $x = 20$.
3. $\frac{x}{360} = \frac{20}{360} = \frac{1}{18}$

The radio waves cover $\frac{1}{18}$ of the circumference of the circle.

These figures suggest an additional theorem.

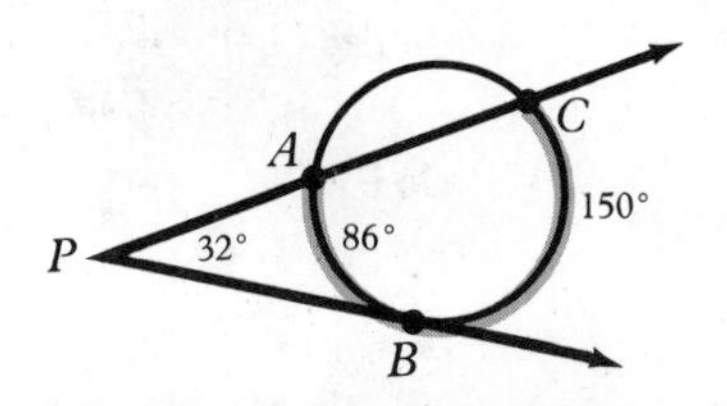

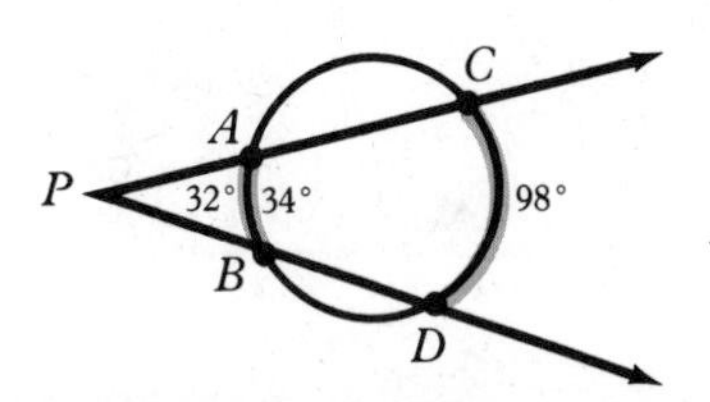

Theorem 10–17 The measure of an angle formed by a tangent and a secant or two secants from a point exterior to a circle is one half the difference of the measures of the intercepted arcs.

On page 378 we asked what fraction of the earth's surface will be covered by the radio beams from the tower. An equally important question is how far do the radio beams reach? The theorem on this page will give a good approximation to the answer.

In order to proceed with the next theorem we need to introduce some more terms.

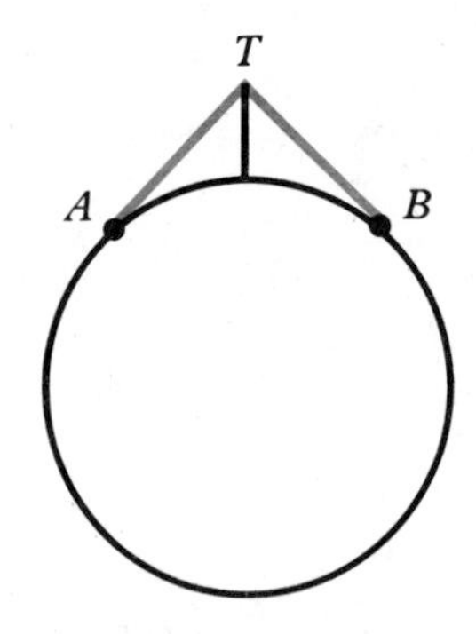

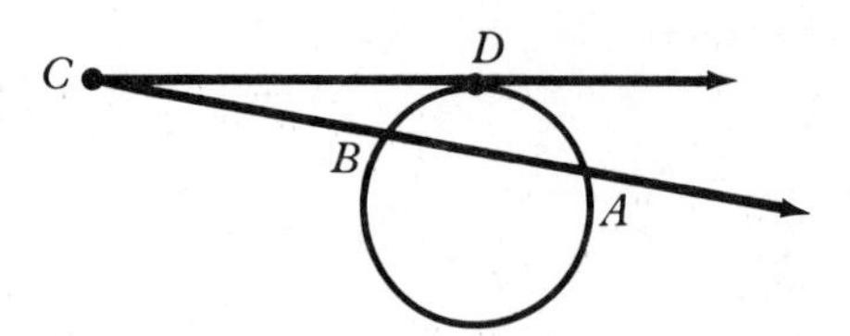

Recall that $\overleftrightarrow{AC}$ is a secant. We call $\overline{CA}$ a *secant segment.* $\overline{BC}$ is called an *external secant segment.* $\overline{CD}$ is a *tangent segment.*

Consider the following examples of circles with a tangent and a secant. What relationship can you find that is common to all three examples?

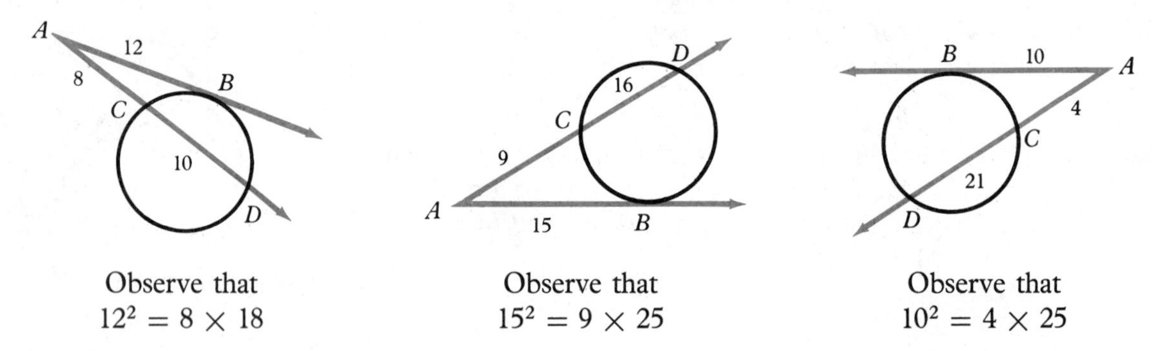

Observe that $12^2 = 8 \times 18$

Observe that $15^2 = 9 \times 25$

Observe that $10^2 = 4 \times 25$

This relationship is stated as Theorem 10–18.

Theorem 10–18 If a tangent segment and a secant segment are drawn to a circle from an exterior point, then the square of the length of the tangent segment equals the product of the lengths of the secant segment and its external secant segment.

PROOF

Given: $\odot O$ with tangent segment $\overline{PT}$.
Prove: $(PT)^2 = PS \cdot PR$
Plan: Draw in $\overline{ST}$ and $\overline{TR}$. Use similar triangles.

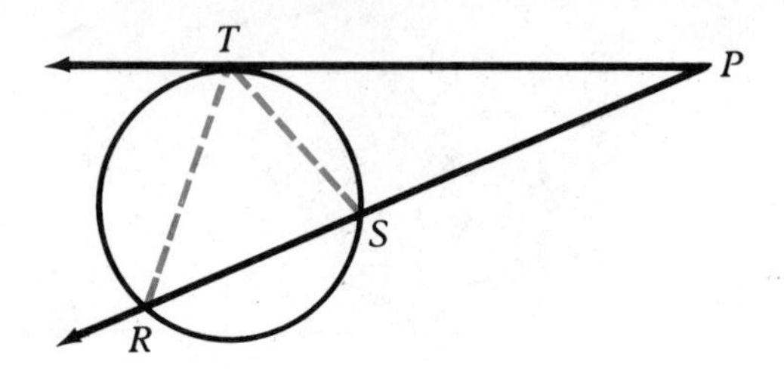

Statements	Reasons
1. Draw $\overline{ST}$ and $\overline{TR}$	1. Construction
2. $\angle P \cong \angle P$	2. Reflexive property
3. $m\angle PTS = \frac{1}{2}m\widehat{TS}$	3. Why?
4. $m\angle SRT = \frac{1}{2}m\widehat{TS}$	4. Why?
5. $\angle PTS \cong \angle SRT$	5. Substitution, Definition of congruence
6. $\triangle PTS \sim \triangle PRT$	6. AA Similarity Theorem
7. $\frac{PT}{PR} = \frac{PS}{PT}$	7. Definition of similar triangles
8. $(PT)^2 = PS \cdot PR$	8. Theorem 9–1

APPLICATION

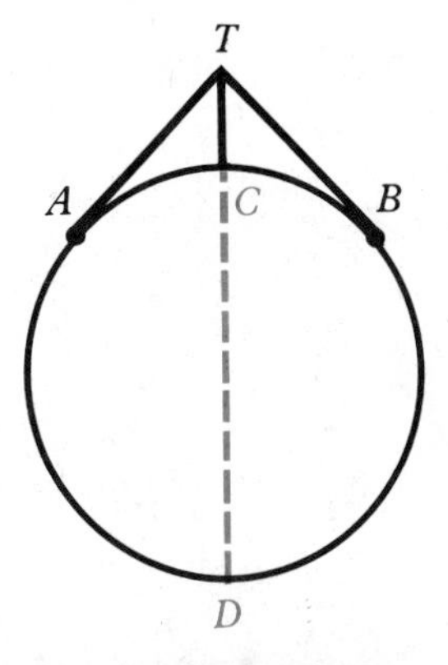

At the top of the previous page we asked how far the rays reach from the tower. The length TA is a good approximation. Theorem 10–18 says that $(TA)^2 = (TC)(TD)$ or $TA = \sqrt{(TC)(TD)}$.

Suppose the tower is 800 feet tall. We will assume that the diameter $\overline{CD}$ of the earth is 8000 miles $\times$ 5280 feet/mile or 42,240,000 feet. Then

$$TA = \sqrt{800 \text{ ft} \times 42{,}240{,}800 \text{ ft}} \doteq 183{,}827.7 \text{ ft} \doteq 34.8 \text{ miles.}$$

The following two theorems also involve segments related to circles.

Theorem 10–19 If two chords intersect in a circle, then the product of the lengths of the segments of one chord equals the product of the lengths of the second chord.

Theorem 10–20 If two secant segments are drawn to a circle from an exterior point, then the product of the lengths of one secant segment and its external secant segment equals the product of the lengths of the other secant segment and its external secant segment.

Example 1 **Find:** BE

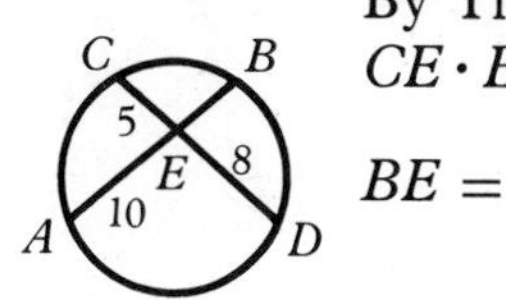

By Theorem 10–19,
$CE \cdot ED = BE \cdot AE$

$$BE = \frac{CE \cdot ED}{AE} = \frac{5 \cdot 8}{10} = 4$$

Example 2 **Find:** PD

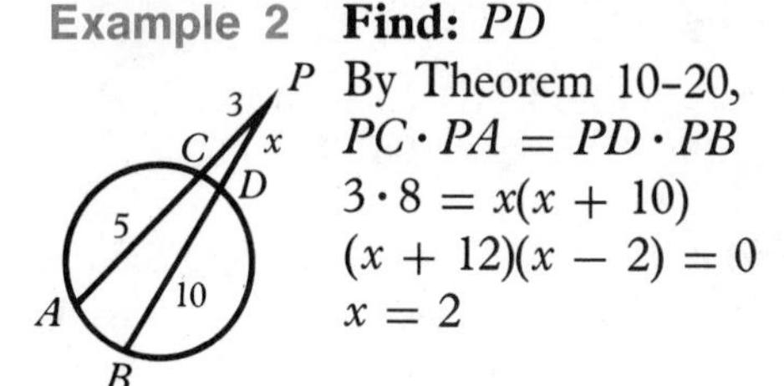

By Theorem 10–20,
$PC \cdot PA = PD \cdot PB$
$3 \cdot 8 = x(x + 10)$
$(x + 12)(x - 2) = 0$
$x = 2$

EXERCISES

A.

In exercises 1–12, find x. You may assume that lines that appear to be tangents are tangents.

1.

2.

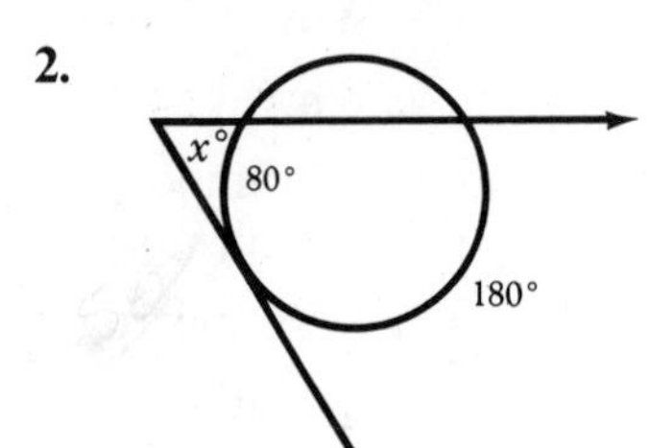

3.

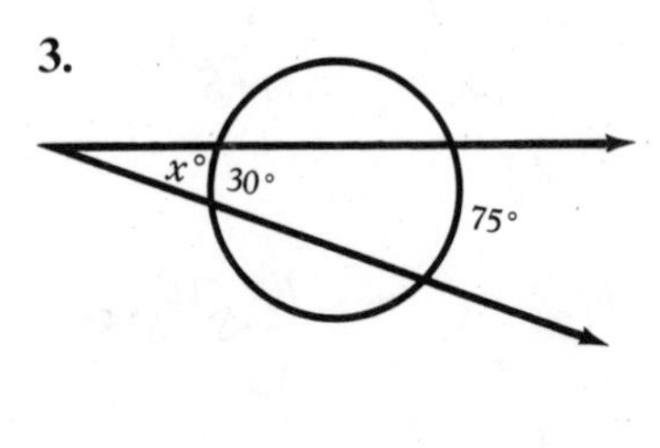

4.

5.

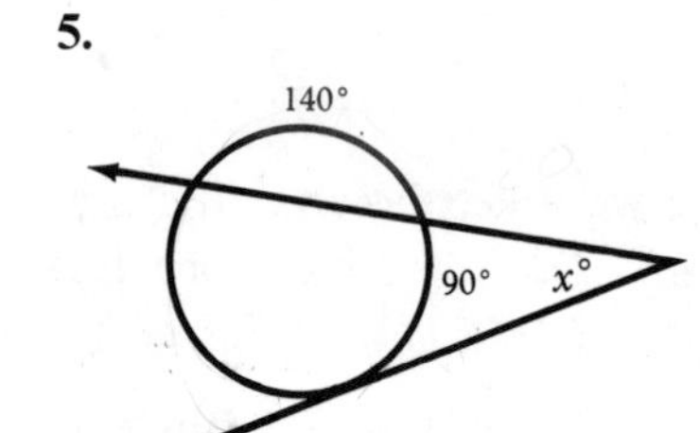

6.

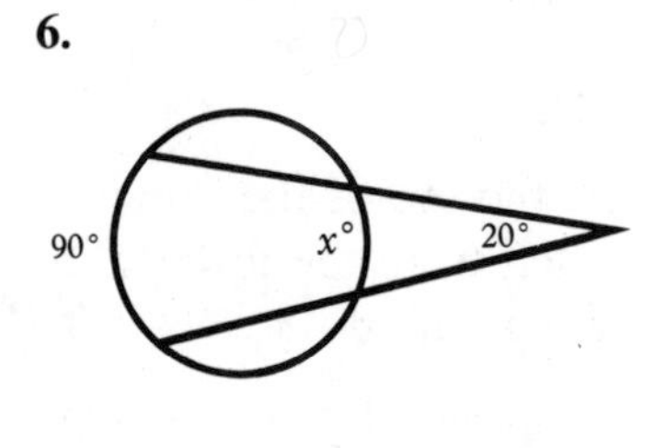

7.

8.

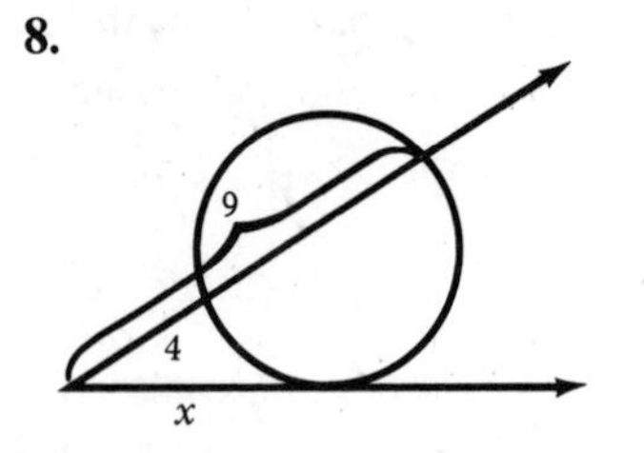

9.

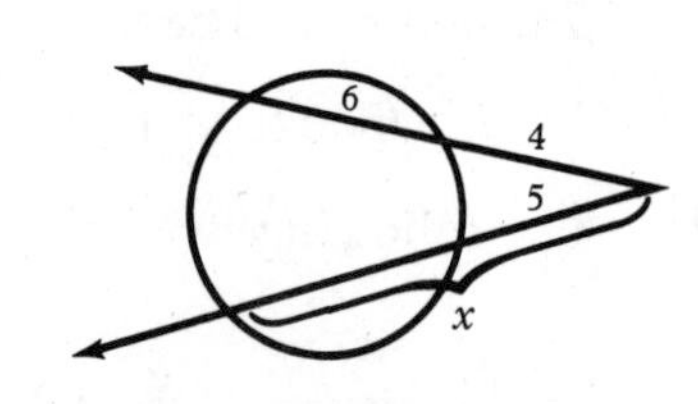

10.

11.

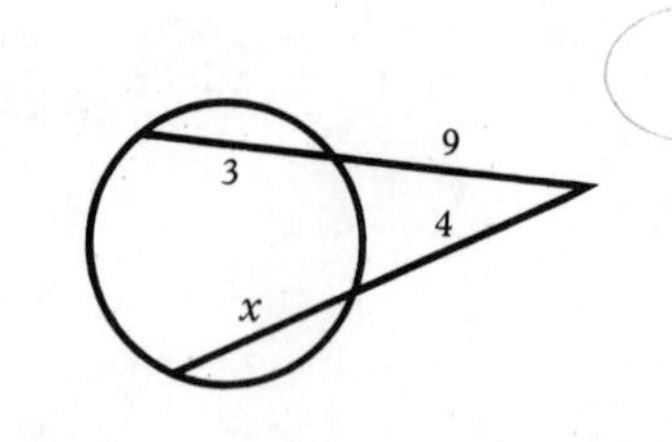

12.

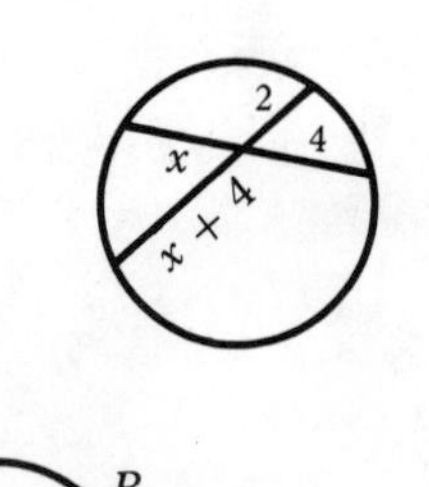

(Exs. 13–15)

B.

For exercises 13–15, $ABCD$ is an inscribed quadrilateral. $m\widehat{AB} = 100$, $m\widehat{AD} = 30$, $m\widehat{BC} = 90$.

13. Find $m\angle P$.

14. Find $m\angle BAD$.

15. Find $m\angle ABC$.

For exercises 16–19, $ABCD$ is a circumscribed quadrilateral. $m\widehat{FG} = 60$, $m\widehat{GH} = 70$, $m\widehat{HE} = 80$.

16. Find $m\widehat{EF}$.

17. Find $m\angle A$.

18. Find $m\angle B$.

19. Find $m\angle C$ and $m\angle D$.

20. Find the values of x and y.

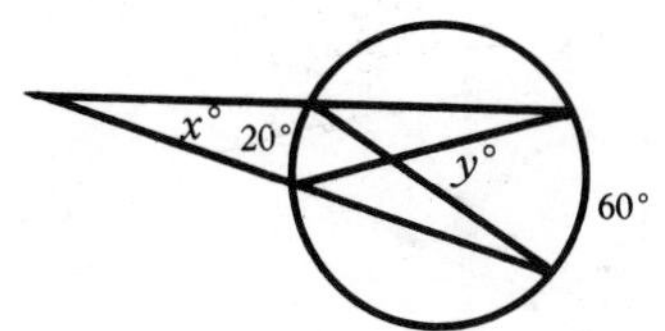

21. Find the values of x and y.

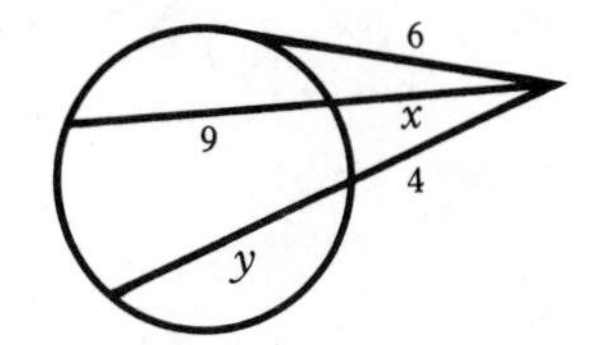

22. Find the values of x and y.

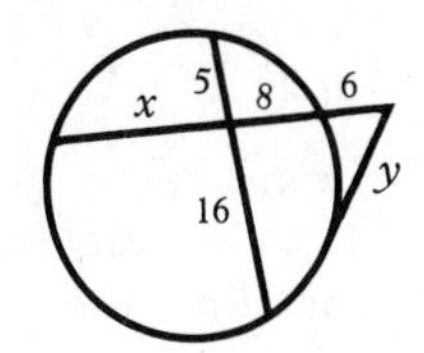

For exercises 23–25, $\overline{EC}$, $\overline{EB}$, $\overline{AD}$, and $\overline{AC}$ are all secants. $m\angle E = 40$, $m\widehat{BC} = 120$, and $m\widehat{BF} = 80$.

23. Find $m\widehat{DF}$.

24. Find $m\widehat{DC}$.

25. Find $m\angle A$.

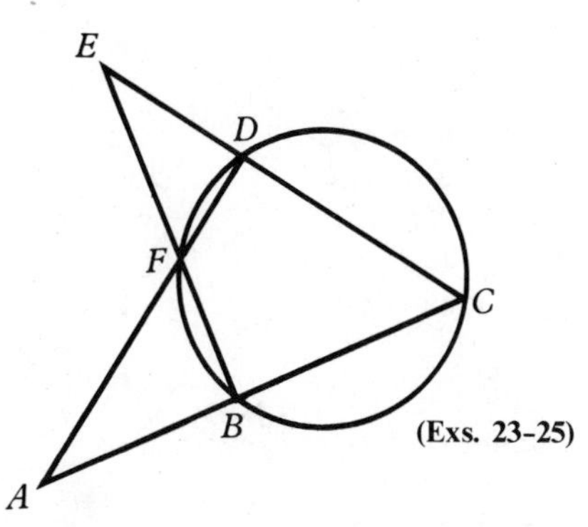

(Exs. 23-25)

For exercises 26–29, $m\widehat{AB} = 55$, $m\widehat{BD} = 40$, $\overline{AC}$ is a diameter, and $\overline{PB}$ is tangent to the circle at B.

26. Find $m\angle P$.

27. Find $m\angle 2$.

28. Find $m\angle 1$.

29. Is $\overline{AD} \parallel \overline{PB}$? Explain.

(Exs. 26-29)

30. Given: $\overline{AD} \perp \overline{BE}$ and $m\angle C = 40$
Find: $m\widehat{BD}$

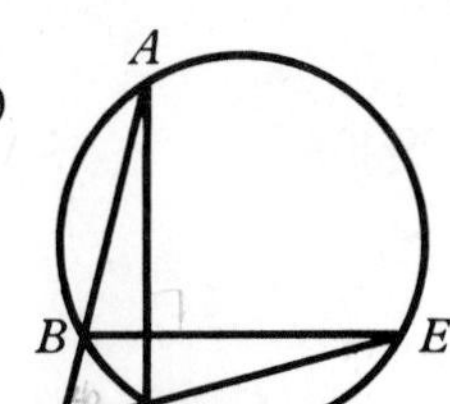

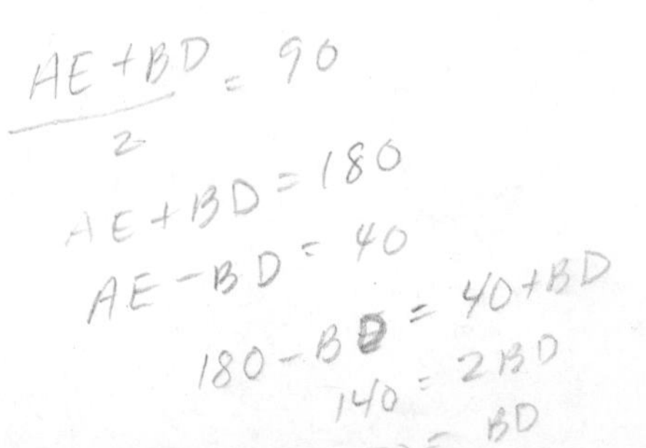

31. Find AB and CD.

C.

32. In the figure, O is the center of both circles. $\overline{RS}$ is a tangent to the smaller circle. If $RX = 5$ and $RS = 30$, find XY.

33. In this figure ℓ_2 is tangent to both circles, ℓ_1 and ℓ_3 are tangent to the circles at A and B respectively. Prove that $\ell_1 \parallel \ell_3$.

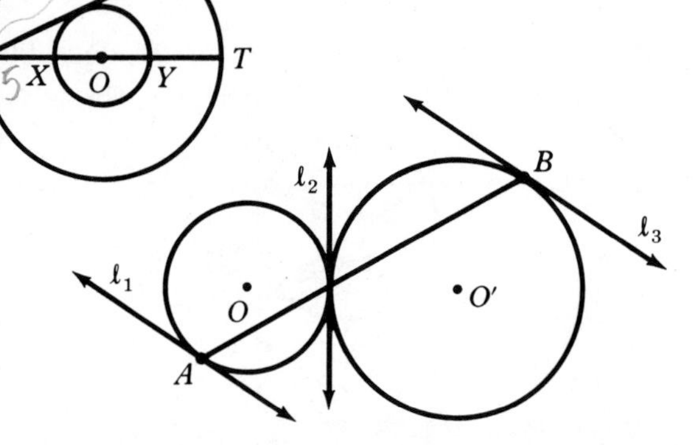

Activity

When a circle is rolled along the inside of a larger circle, a point P on the rolling circle moves on a path (shown in red) called a *deltoid,* provided that the radius of the rolling circle is $\frac{1}{3}$ or $\frac{2}{3}$ the larger radius. Draw a deltoid as outlined below.

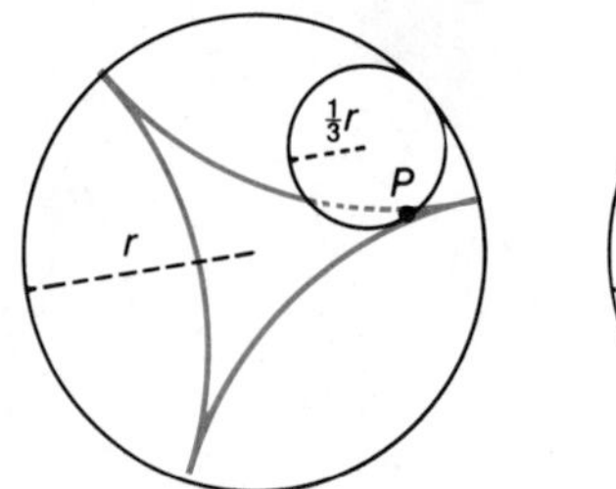

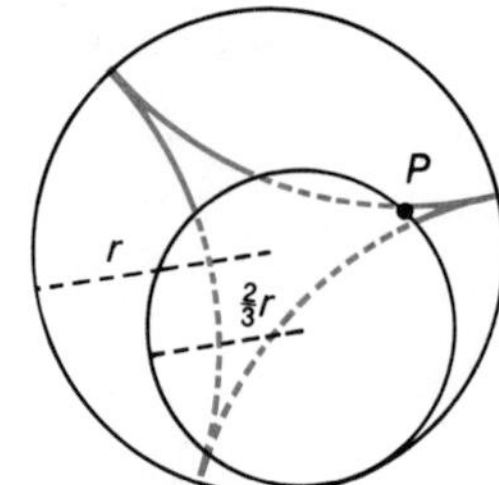

1. Draw a circle with a 3 cm radius in the middle of a notebook size sheet of paper. Mark points at 5° intervals. Number the points 0, 1, 2, . . . in a counterclockwise manner (shown in black.)
2. Begin with 36 (shown in black) and number alternate points 0, 1, 2, . . . in a clockwise manner (shown in red.)
3. Draw a ray *from* a point with a *red* number *through* a point with the same number shown in *black*. Do this for all numbers 0 through 71.
4. Outline the deltoid figure surrounding the circle.

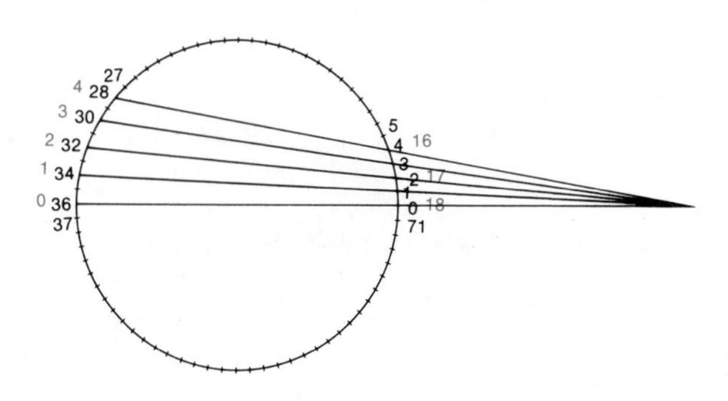

34. If $\overline{PB}$ and $\overline{PD}$ are secant segments and $PB = PD$, prove that $PA = PC$.

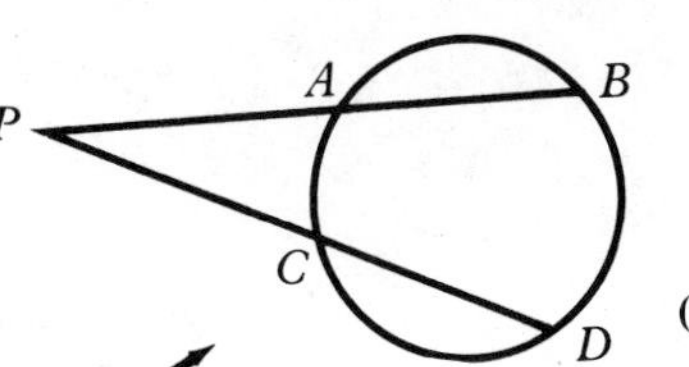

(Ex. 34)

35. Prove Theorem 10–17 for the case of a tangent and a secant.

36. Prove Theorem 10–19.

37. Prove Theorem 10–20.

(Ex. 35)

38. If two circles are tangent internally and the diameter of the smaller circle is the radius of the larger circle, then any chord of the larger circle drawn to the point of tangency will be bisected by the smaller circle.

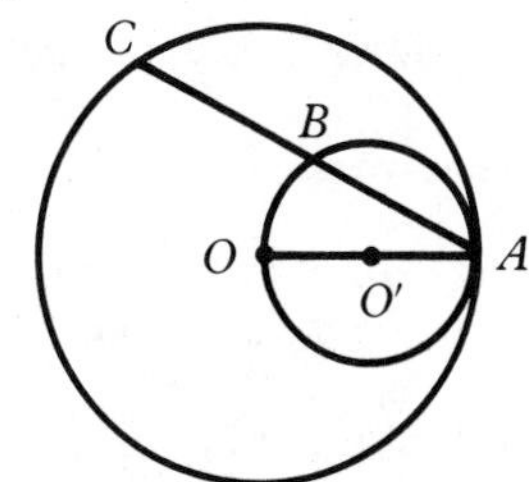

Given: $O'A = \frac{1}{2}OA$ and the circles are tangent at A.
Prove: B is the midpoint of $\overline{AC}$.

PROBLEM SOLVING

A deltoid is drawn with the method described in the last activity using 10° intervals. Each point has two rays emanating from it. Why are the two rays perpendicular to each other?

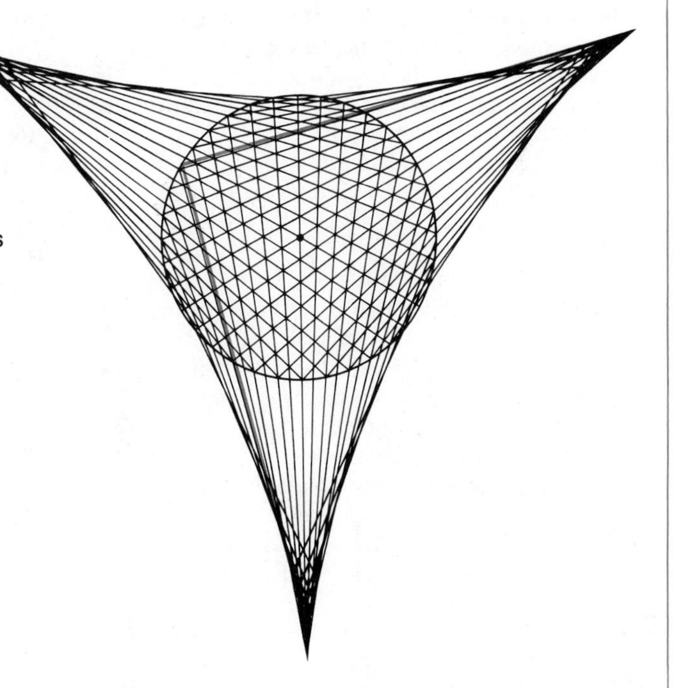

Important Ideas—Chapter 10

Terms

Radius (p. 342)
Chord (p. 342)
Diameter (p. 342)
Tangent (p. 343)
Secant (p. 343)
Inscribed angle (p. 343)
Central angle (p. 343)
Minor arc (p. 346)
Major arc (p. 346)
Measure of a minor arc (p. 346)
Measure of a major arc (p. 346)
Congruent arcs (p. 347)
Congruent circles (p. 347)

Postulate

Arc Addition Postulate (p. 346)

Theorems

10-1 In a circle or in congruent circles congruent chords have congruent minor arcs.

10-2 In a circle or in congruent circles congruent minor arcs have congruent chords.

10-3 In a circle or in congruent circles congruent chords are equidistant from the center.

10-4 In a circle or in congruent circles chords equidistant from the center are congruent.

10-5 The perpendicular bisector of a chord contains the center of the circle.

10-6 If a line through the center of a circle is perpendicular to a chord that is not a diameter, then it bisects the chord and its minor arc.

10-7 If a line through the center of a circle bisects a chord that is not a diameter, then it is perpendicular to the chord.

10-8 If a line is perpendicular to a radius at a point on the circle, then the line is tangent to the circle.

10-9 If a line is tangent to a circle, then the radius drawn to the point of contact is perpendicular to the tangent.

10-10 If a line is perpendicular to a tangent at a point on the circle, then the line contains the center of the circle.

10-11 The tangent segments to a circle from a point outside the circle are congruent and form congruent angles with the line joining the center and the point.

10-12 The measure of an inscribed angle is one half the measure of its intercepted arc.

10-13 An angle inscribed in a semicircle is a right angle.

10-14 An angle formed by two chords intersecting inside a circle has a measure equal to one half the sum of the intercepted arcs.

10-15 The measure of an angle formed by a tangent and a chord drawn to the point of contact is one half the intercepted arc.

10-16 The measure of an angle formed by two intersecting tangents to a circle is one half the difference of the measures of the intercepted arcs.

10-17 The measure of an angle formed by a tangent and a secant or two secants from a point exterior to a circle is one half the difference of the measures of the intercepted arcs.

10-18 If a tangent segment and a secant segment are drawn to a circle from an exterior point, then the square of the length of the tangent segment equals the product of the lengths of the secant segment and its external secant segment.

10-19 If two chords intersect in a circle, then the product of the lengths of the segments of one chord equals the product of the lengths of the second chord.

10-20 If two secant segments are drawn to a circle from an exterior point, then the product of the lengths of one secant segment and its external secant segment equals the product of the lengths of the other secant segment and its external secant segment.

Chapter 10—Review

For exercises 1-4 indicate on your paper whether the following statements are true or false. If a statement is false, draw a counterexample.

1. If a triangle is inscribed in a circle with one side as a diameter, then the triangle is a right triangle.
2. If a line bisects two chords which are not diameters, then the chords are parallel.
3. If a line is perpendicular to a chord, then it contains the center of the circle.
4. If $\overleftrightarrow{PA}$ and $\overleftrightarrow{PB}$ are tangents to the same circle at points A and B respectively, then $PA = PB$.
5. **Given:** $m\angle AOB = 120$, $m\widehat{AD} = 150$, $\overline{AC}$ is a diameter.
   Find: **a.** $m\angle ADB$
   b. $m\angle BAC$
   c. $m\angle CED$
   d. $m\widehat{BCD}$

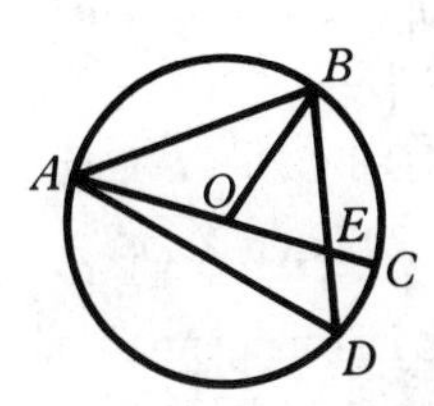

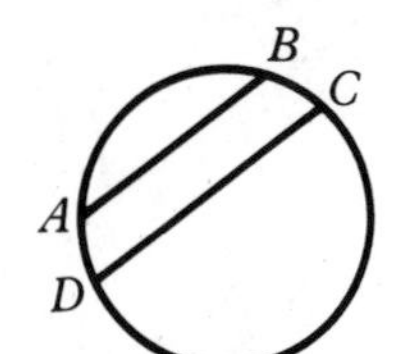

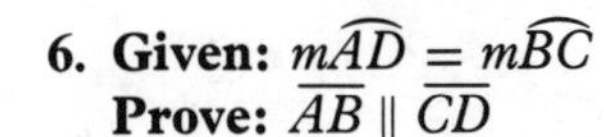

6. **Given:** $m\widehat{AD} = m\widehat{BC}$
   Prove: $\overline{AB} \parallel \overline{CD}$

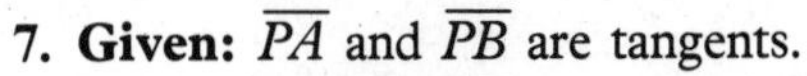

7. **Given:** $\overline{PA}$ and $\overline{PB}$ are tangents.
   O is the center of a circle.
   $\overline{AC}$ is a diameter.
   $m\angle APO = 20$
   Find: **a.** $m\angle DPB$
   b. $m\widehat{AD}$
   c. $m\widehat{BC}$
   d. $m\widehat{AE}$
   e. $m\angle CAB$

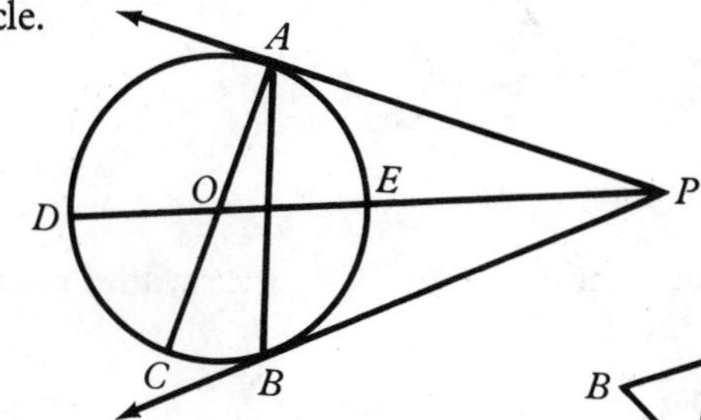

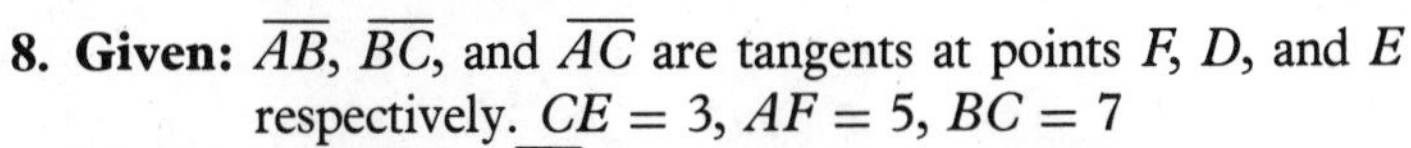

8. **Given:** $\overline{AB}$, $\overline{BC}$, and $\overline{AC}$ are tangents at points F, D, and E respectively. $CE = 3$, $AF = 5$, $BC = 7$
   Find: **a.** length of $\overline{BD}$.
   b. perimeter of $\triangle ABC$.

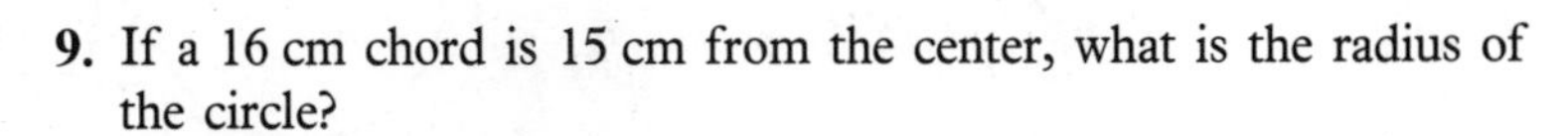

9. If a 16 cm chord is 15 cm from the center, what is the radius of the circle?
10. $\overline{SZ}$ is tangent to the circle in the figure shown. Find SZ and WY.

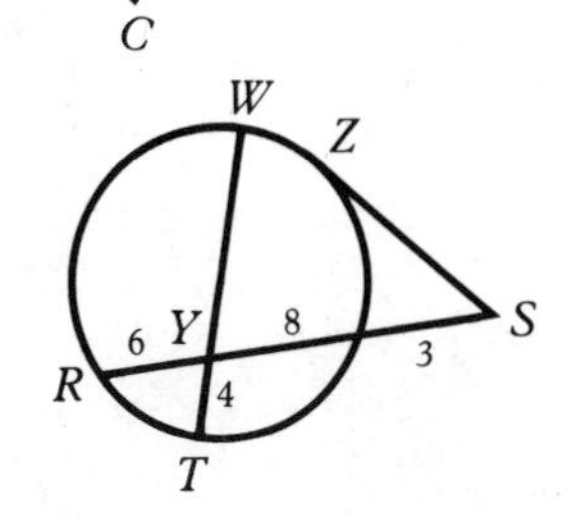

Chapter 10—Test

For exercises 1–4 indicate on your paper whether the following statements are true or false. If a statement is false, draw a counterexample.

1. In two different circles, if two chords are the same length, they are the same distance from their centers.

2. If a triangle is inscribed in a circle and the intercepted arcs have measures of 200°, 90°, and 70°, then triangle is an obtuse triangle.

3. If a line bisects the minor arc of a chord, it bisects the chord's major arc also.

4. If two tangents are parallel, then their points of tangency determine a diameter.

5. **Given:** $\overline{AB} \parallel \overline{CD}$, $\overline{EF}$ is the perpendicular bisector of $\overline{AB}$.

   Prove: $\overline{EF}$ bisects $\overline{CD}$.

(Ex. 5)

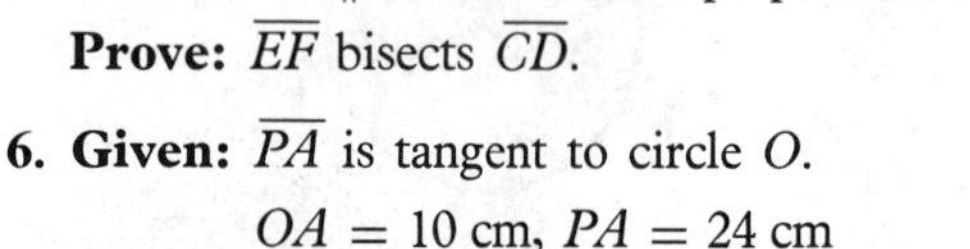

6. **Given:** $\overline{PA}$ is tangent to circle O.

   $OA = 10$ cm, $PA = 24$ cm

   Find the length of $\overline{PC}$.

(Ex. 6)

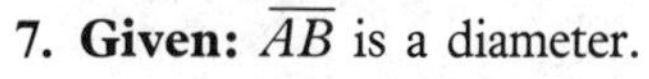

7. **Given:** $\overline{AB}$ is a diameter.

   $m\angle CAB = 50$

   $m\widehat{BD} = 20$

   Find: **a.** $m\widehat{BC}$

   b. $m\widehat{AC}$

   c. $m\angle ADC$

   d. $m\angle BED$

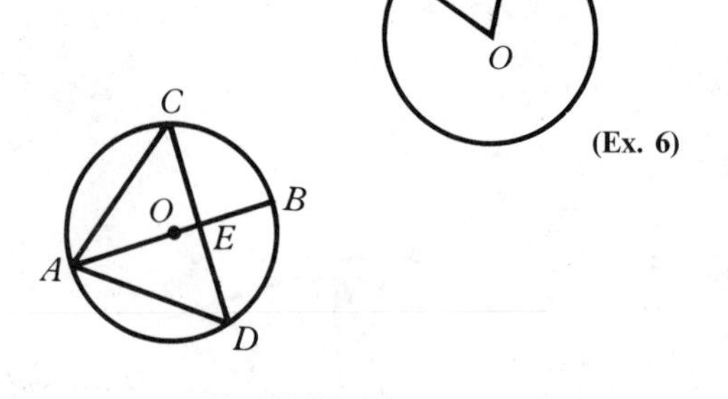

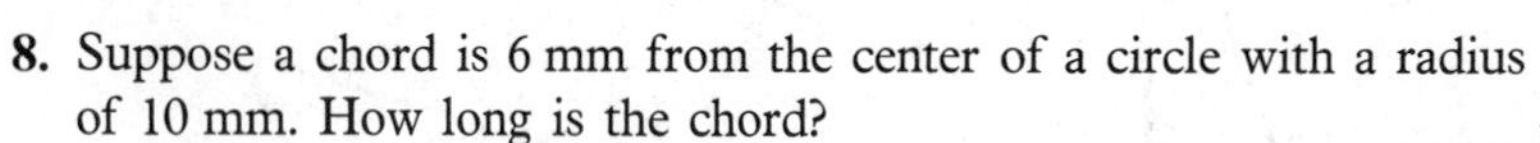

8. Suppose a chord is 6 mm from the center of a circle with a radius of 10 mm. How long is the chord?

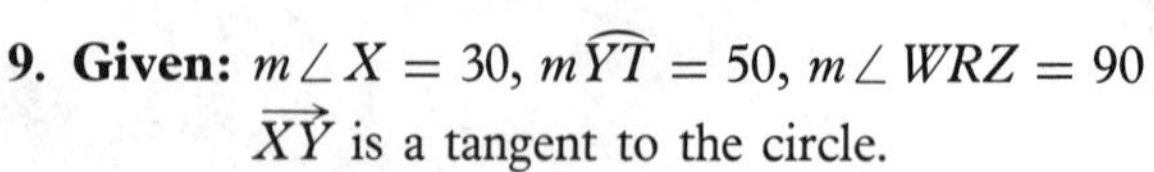

9. **Given:** $m\angle X = 30$, $m\widehat{YT} = 50$, $m\angle WRZ = 90$

   $\overrightarrow{XY}$ is a tangent to the circle.

   Find $m\widehat{YZ}$, $m\widehat{WZ}$, and $m\widehat{TW}$.

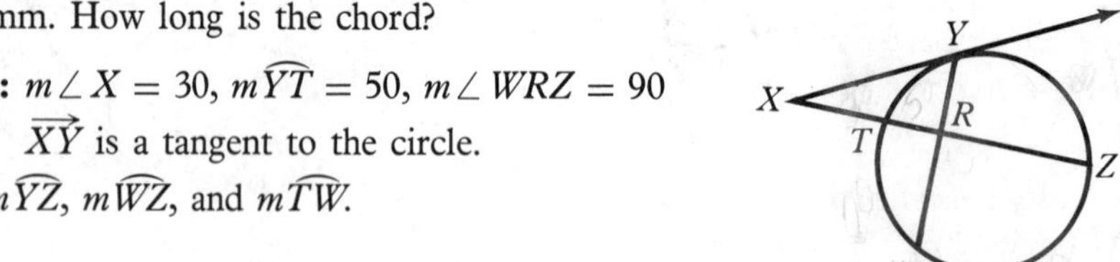

10. $\overline{FH}$ is tangent to the circle in the figure shown. Find JI and FH.

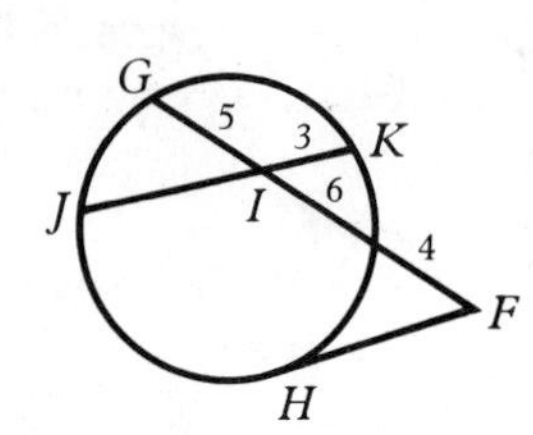

Cumulative Review—Chapters 8–10

1. Indicate on your paper whether the following statements are true or false.

   a. If a parallelogram is inscribed in a circle, it is a rectangle.

   b. If $ABCD$ is a parallelogram, then its diagonals are congruent.

   c. If $m\angle A = 40$ in right triangle ABC and $m\angle D = 50$ in right triangle DEF, then the triangles are similar.

   d. All rectangles are similar polygons.

2. $\overline{AB}$ is a diameter and $\overline{CD}$ is perpendicular to $\overline{AB}$.

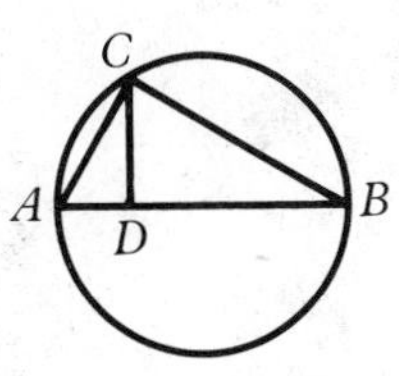

   a. If $AD = 4$ and $AB = 12$, find CD.

   b. If $AB = 13$ and $CD = 6$, find AD.

   c. If $CB = 12$ and $AB = 13$, find BD.

   d. Prove $\triangle ABC \sim \triangle CBD$.

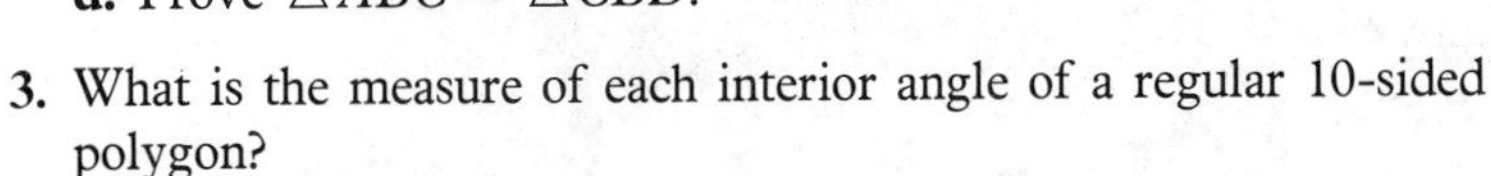

3. What is the measure of each interior angle of a regular 10-sided polygon?

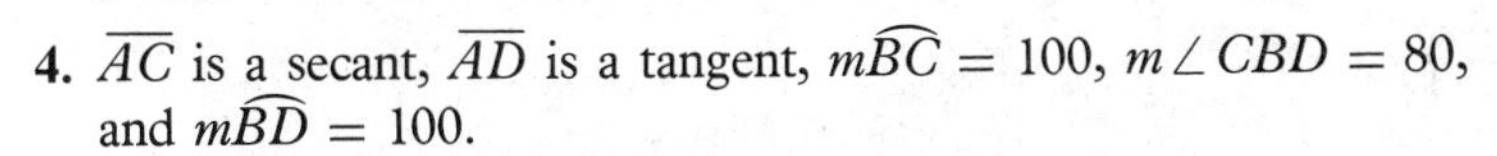

4. $\overline{AC}$ is a secant, $\overline{AD}$ is a tangent, $m\widehat{BC} = 100$, $m\angle CBD = 80$, and $m\widehat{BD} = 100$.

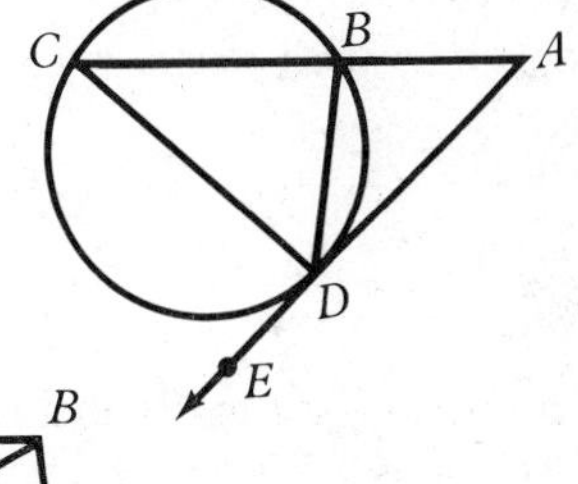

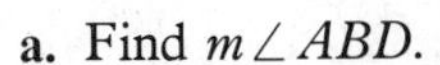

   a. Find $m\angle ABD$.

   b. Find $m\angle BCD$.

   c. Find $m\angle CAD$.

   d. Find $m\angle EDC$.

5. **Given:** $ABCD$ is a trapezoid with $\overline{AB} \parallel \overline{DC}$.
   Prove: $NB \cdot NC = NA \cdot ND$

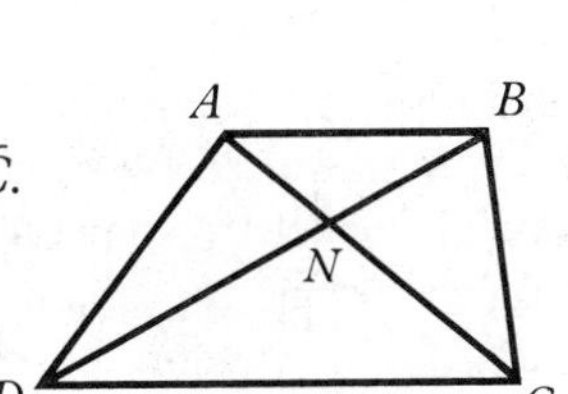

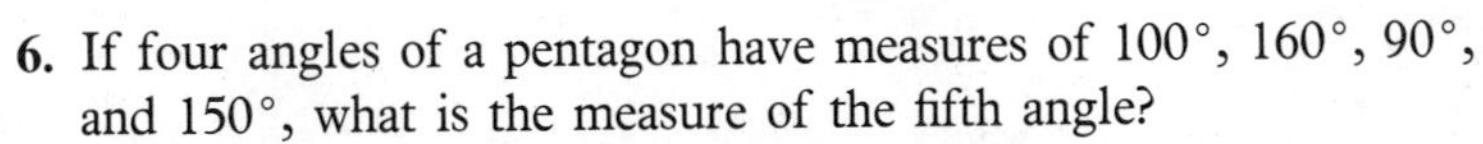

6. If four angles of a pentagon have measures of 100°, 160°, 90°, and 150°, what is the measure of the fifth angle?

7. **Given:** $MNPQ$ is a trapezoid with $MP = QN$.
   A, B, C, and D are midpoints as shown.
   Prove: $ABCD$ is a rhombus

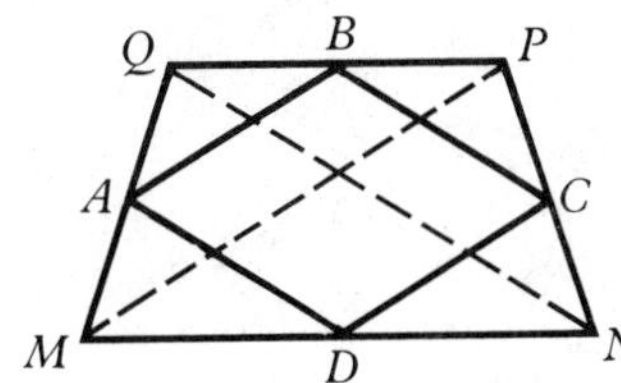

Surveying: The Transit

A surveyor is involved in the construction of buildings, roads, dams, and bridges. One of the surveyor's responsibilities is to establish exact land boundaries. All the necessary information is recorded at the site. Later, at the office, drawings or maps are made of the surveyed land.

The transit is probably the surveyor's most valuable tool. It is used to measure both angles and distances.

The transit can be used both to measure angles between objects and angles of elevation. An angle between objects is measured by sighting the first object and then moving the telescope to the right or left to the second object. An angle of elevation is measured by tilting the telescope up to sight the top of the object. There are two scales on the transit, one to measure horizontal angles and one to measure vertical angles.

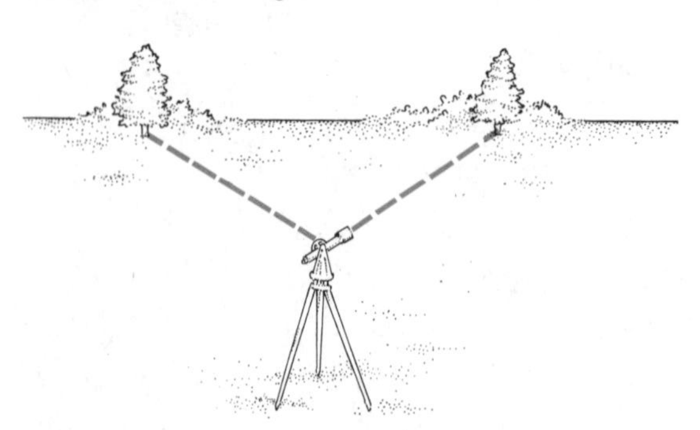

Measuring angle between two objects (horizontal angle)

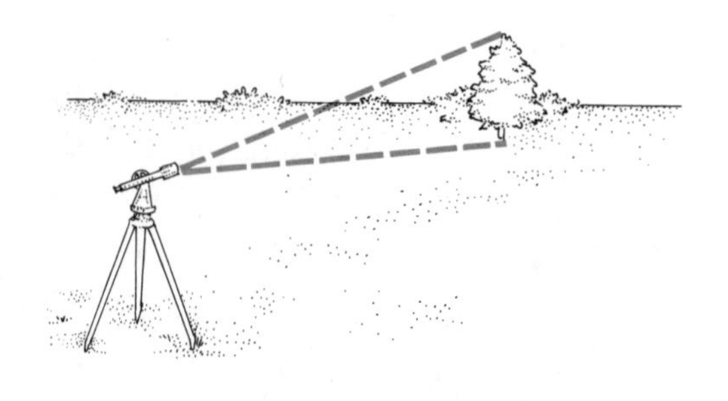

Measuring angle of elevation (vertical angle)

The transit is also used to measure distances. The optical properties of a transit telescope cause light rays to cross to form a pair of similar triangles.

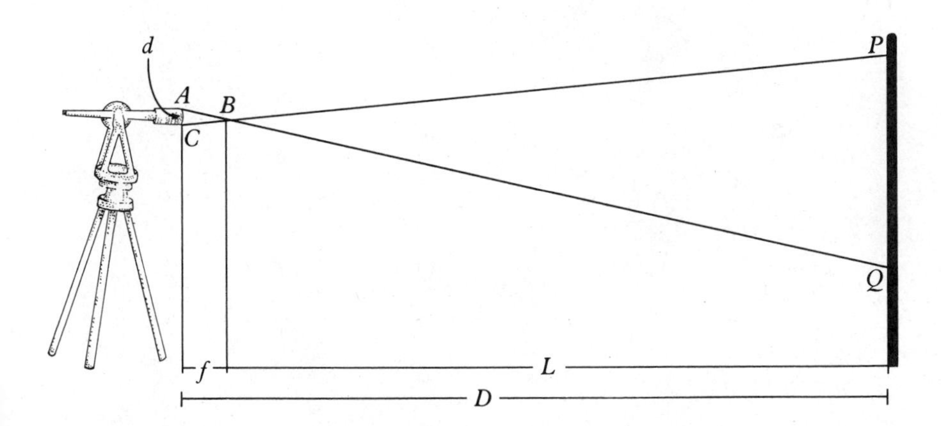

Two people are usually involved in finding distances. One person stands at the transit, and the other stands at the second location, holding a scaled rod perpendicular to the ground. The following steps show how to find the desired distance D.

Step 1 Look through the telescope. Read the numbers on the rod to determine the distance PQ.

Step 2 Find L by using a proportion based on similar triangles.

Step 3 Add f to L to find D.

1. Why is $\triangle ABC$ similar to $\triangle QBP$?
2. f and L are lengths of the altitudes of the two triangles. We can prove that

$$\frac{f}{L} = \frac{d}{PQ}.$$

   Use this proportion to find an expression for $\frac{f}{d}$.

3. f is called the focal distance of the telescope. The telescope is constructed so that the light rays will always cross at the same distance. d is also fixed for a given telescope. Therefore the ratio f/d is fixed.
   Suppose $f = 1$ meter, $d = 1$ centimeter, and $PQ = 0.836$ meters. Find L and D (see Step 3 above).

CHAPTER 11

Area and Perimeter

11–1 Area Postulates

When a house is built, siding is nailed in place. Later it must be painted or stained. The roof is often covered with plywood sheets which must be covered with shingles. House construction provides many applications of the postulates and definitions introduced in this section.

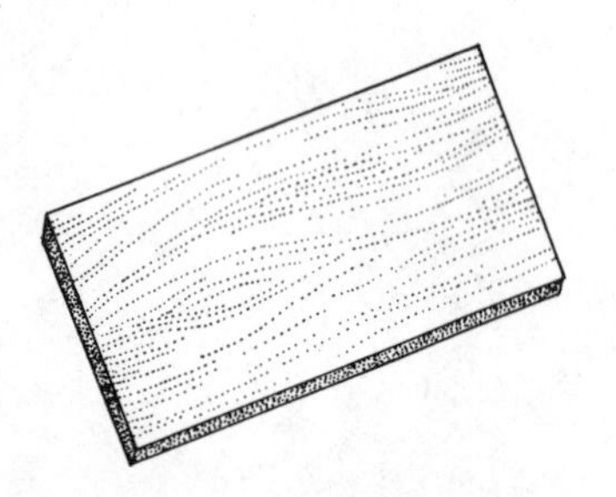

The edges of a sheet of siding represent a polygon called a rectangle. The surface of the sheet represents a subset of a plane called a *polygonal region.*

Definition 11-1

A **polygonal region** is a subset of a plane bounded by a polygon (or polygons).

Here are three examples of polygonal regions.

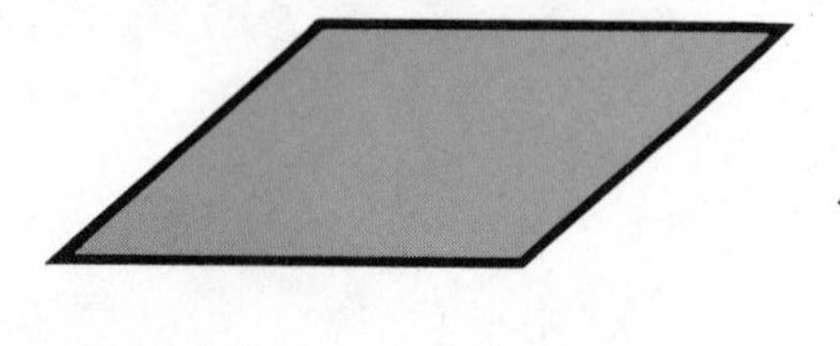

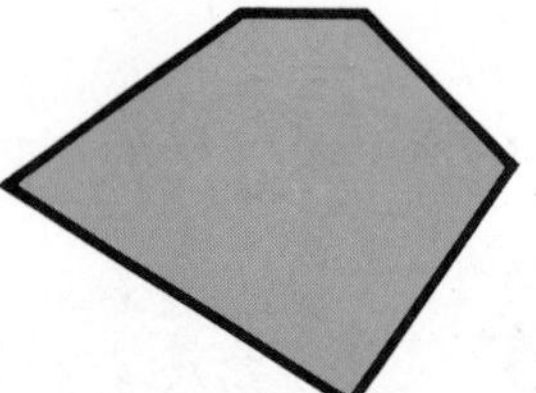

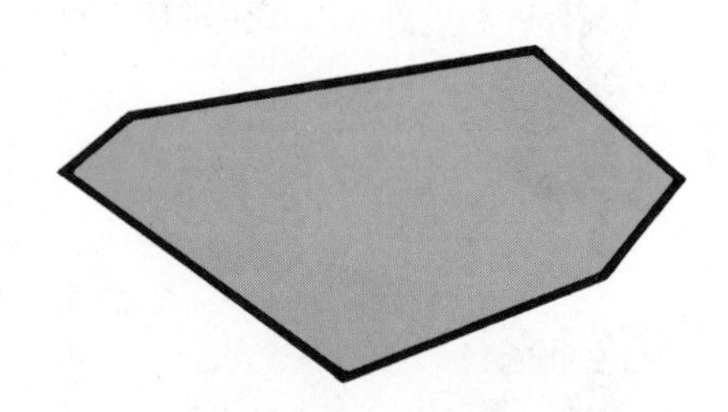

How much stain is needed for a sheet of siding?

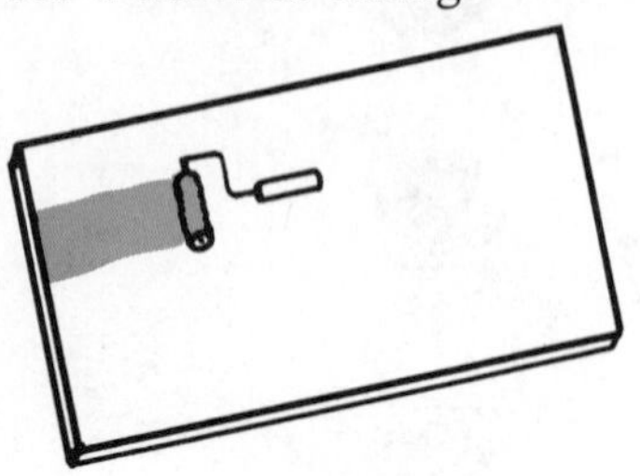

The amount of stain needed for a sheet of siding depends upon its size. A number called the *area* is used to describe this size.

Area Postulate

A unique positive number called the **area** can be assigned to each polygonal region. The area of region R is denoted by $A(R)$.

Properties of area are described by several postulates.

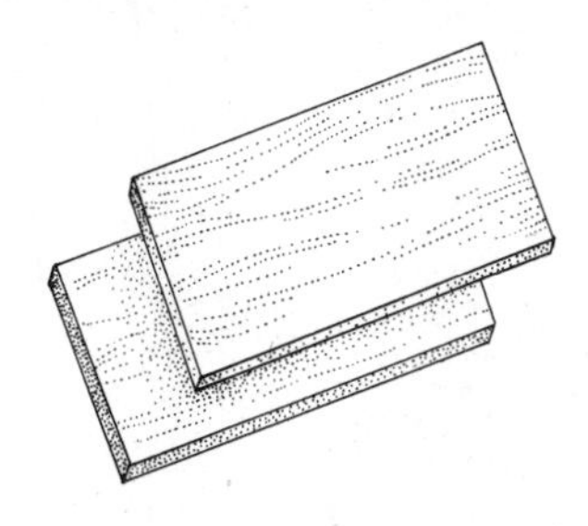

Two sheets the same size have the same area and should take the same amount of stain.

This fact is the subject of a postulate.

Area of Congruent Regions Postulate

If two rectangles or two triangles are congruent, then the regions they bound have the same area.

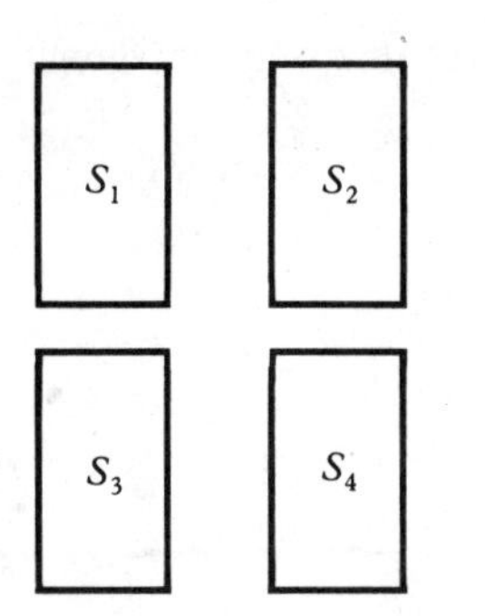

Four sheets of siding S_1, S_2, S_3, S_4 are often joined together.

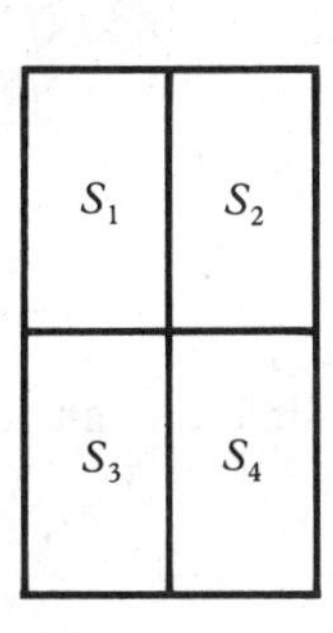

The area of this four-piece section is equal to the sum of the areas of each piece. That is,
$A(4 \text{ pieces}) = A(S_1) + A(S_2) + A(S_3) + A(S_4)$.

Area Addition Postulate

If a polygonal region is the union of n non-overlapping polygonal regions, then its area is the sum of the areas of these n-regions.

To count the number of plywood sheets that are needed for a house, we need to be able to calculate the area of rectangular regions.

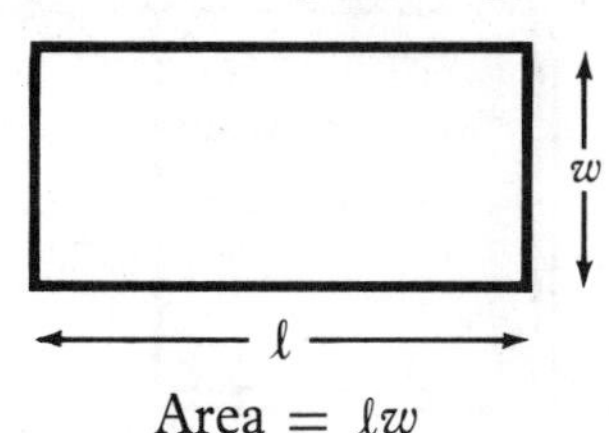

Area $= \ell w$

This last postulate in combination with the Area Postulate, the Area of Congruent Regions Postulate, and the Area Addition Postulate makes it possible to calculate area.

Rectangle Area Postulate

The area of a rectangle with length ℓ and width w is given by the formula ℓw.

EXERCISES

A.

1. Draw a polygon and shade in the polygonal region determined by it.
2. Is the interior of a circle a polygonal region?
3. Is a rectangle a polygonal region?
4. If two rectangles have the same area, are they necessarily congruent?
5. Which postulate says that every polygonal region must have area?
6. Do the postulates say that only polygonal regions have area?
7. Draw a counterexample to this statement:
   If two polygonal regions have the same area, then they have the same number of sides.

Find the area of these regions. You may assume that angles appearing to be right angles are right angles.

8.

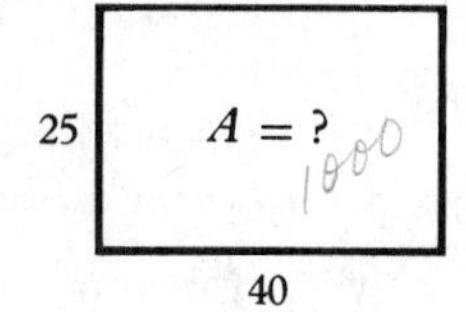

9. 14, 45, $A = ?$

10. 5, 11, $A = ?$

B.

For exercises 11–16 assume the area of the shaded area is 1. Find the area of each region by using the area postulates. (*Hint:* Look for rectangles and halves of rectangles.)

11.

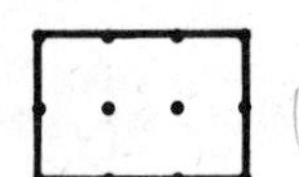

12.

13.

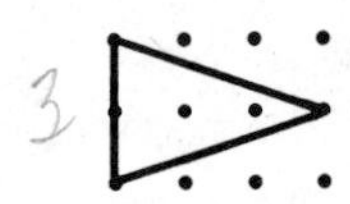

Activity

The area of the small shaded square on this geoboard is 1.

Construct on a geoboard or draw on dot paper triangles with areas of $\frac{1}{2}$, 1, $1\frac{1}{2}$, 2, $2\frac{1}{2}$, and 3.

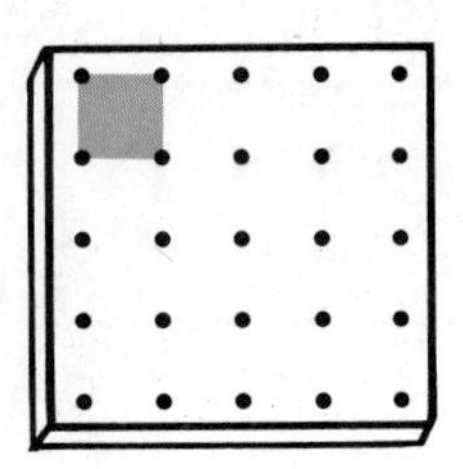

14. 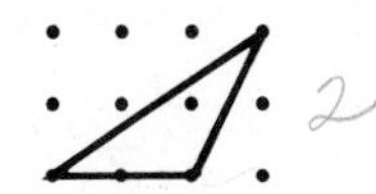

15. 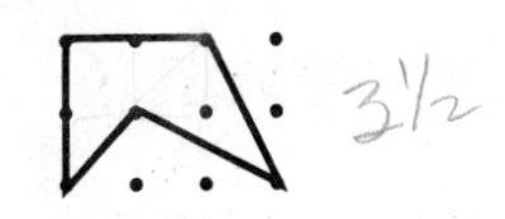

16. 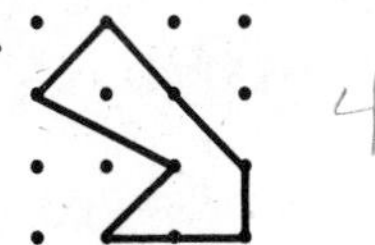

Find the area of these regions.

17. 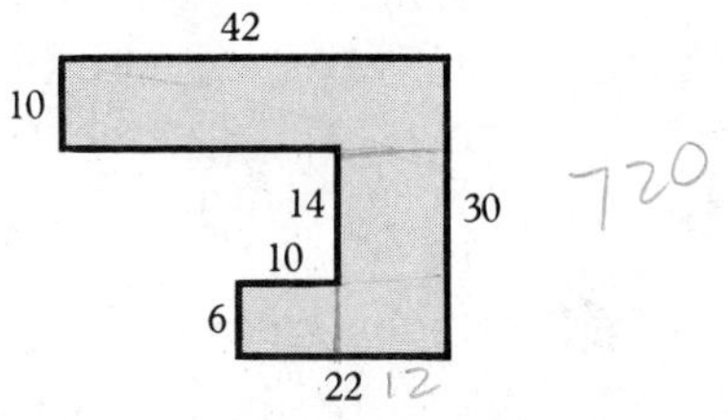

18. 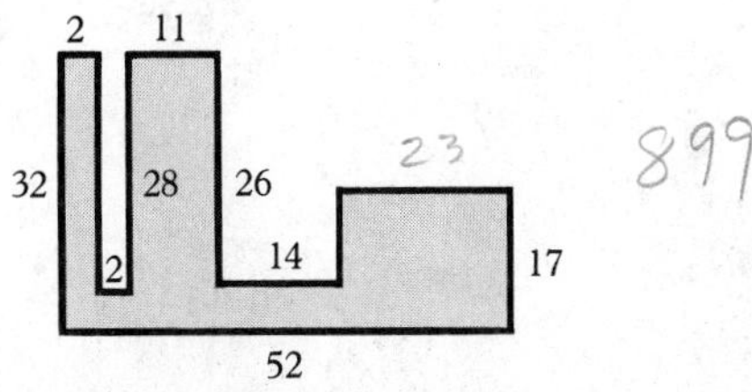

19. Find the area of the roof of the building shown. If you assume that 10% of the materials ordered are wasted, how many 4 × 8 sheets of plywood are needed for this roof?

20. Prove that the diagonal of a rectangle divides the rectangle into two triangles equal in area.

21. *ABIH*, *IDEF*, and *ACEG* are all rectangles. Explain why the areas of R_1 and R_2 are equal. (*Hint:* $A(\triangle ACE) = A(\triangle AGE)$.)

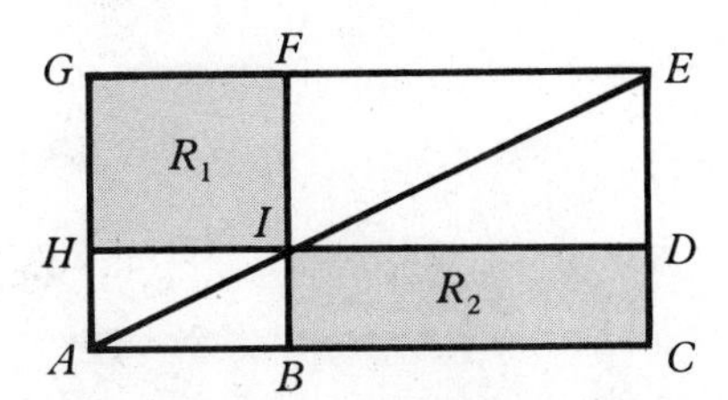

22. The area of *MBNX* is $\frac{1}{3}$ the area of *ABCD* and *M* is the midpoint of $\overline{AB}$. How does the length of $\overline{BN}$ compare to the length of $\overline{BC}$?

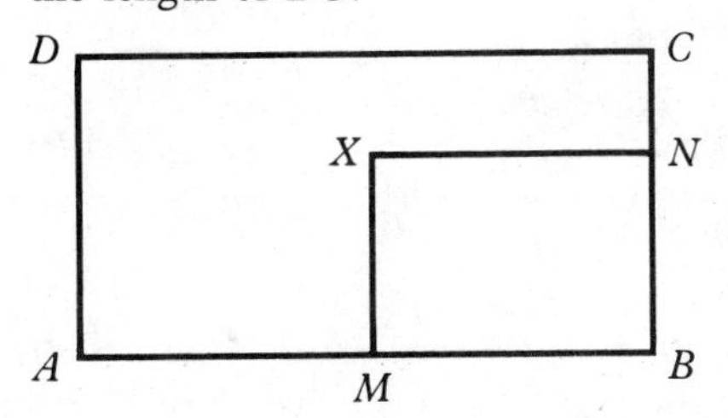

PROBLEM SOLVING

In the figure at the right, *D* is the center of the smaller of the two squares. The larger square overlaps the smaller square in quadrilateral *ABDE*. Find the area of this quadrilateral. Is it important that *B* trisects $\overline{AC}$?

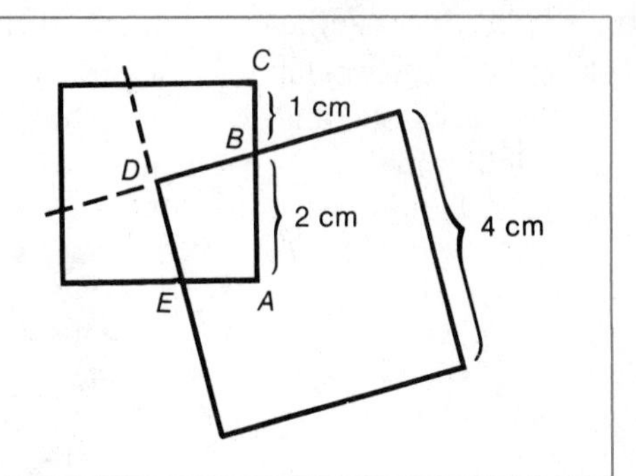

11–2 Area of Parallelograms

There are situations in which it is important to find the area of regions that are not rectangular. For example, if a parking lot is to have slant parking, each parking spot is a parallelogram region. The amount of asphalt required for one spot depends upon the area of that parallelogram region.

1 centimeter

1 square centimeter

A unit of area must be chosen when measuring the area of regions like the one described above.

The most commonly used units of area are square inches, square feet, square yards, square centimeters, and square meters.

Definition 11-2

A **square unit** is a square region in which the length of a side is one unit of length.

The area of a region can be determined by counting the number of square units that are required to exactly cover the region.

By fitting together the square units and the congruent triangular regions, and using several area postulates, we conclude that the parallelogram on the right has an area of 10 square centimeters.

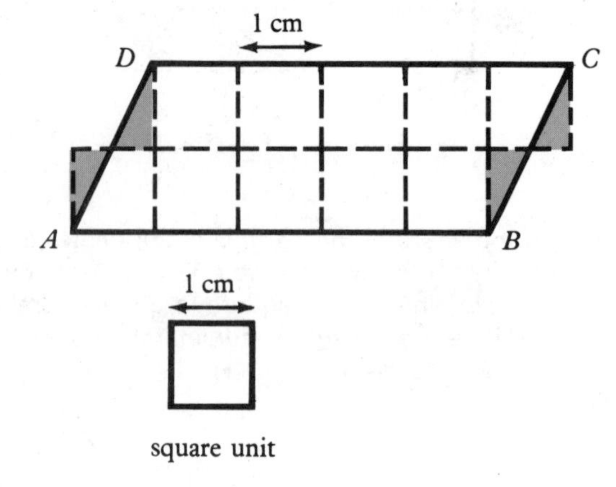

We write: $A(ABCD) = 10\ \text{cm}^2$

Another way to find the area of a parallelogram is to imagine that the triangular piece on one end is cut off and moved to the other end to form a rectangle. Using the Area of Congruent Regions Postulate and the Area Addition Postulate, we conclude that the areas of the parallelogram and rectangle are the same. Therefore, since the area of a rectangle is length times width, it follows that the area of a parallelogram is also "length" times "width."

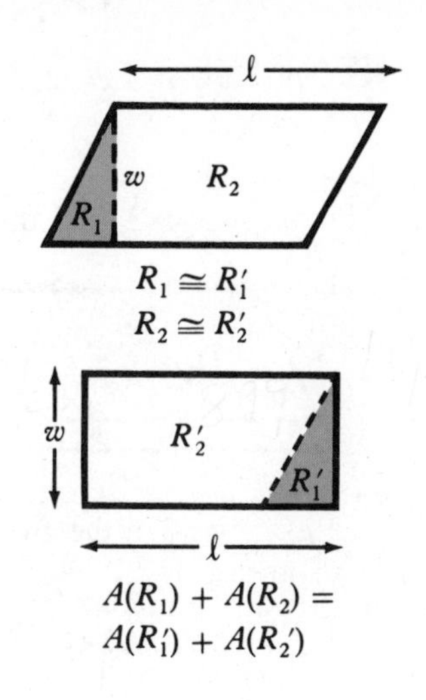

In a parallelogram we will use the terms "base" and "altitude" instead of length and width. Any side of a parallelogram can be called the base. Once we choose a base, a segment perpendicular to that base, with endpoints on the base and its opposite side, is called a corresponding altitude. Notice that a parallelogram has two pairs of parallel bases.

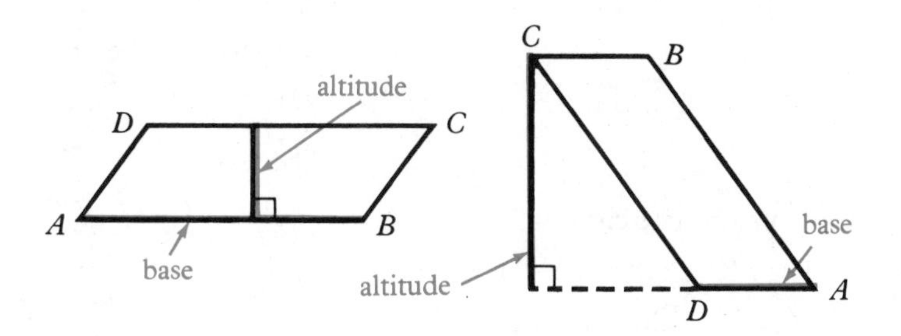

Definition 11-3

An **altitude of a parallelogram** is a segment perpendicular to a pair of parallel sides with endpoints on those parallel sides. The **height** is the length of an altitude.

Theorem 11–1 Given a parallelogram with base b and corresponding height h, the area A is given by the formula $A = bh$.

APPLICATION

The standard slant parking spot is 9 feet wide and 24 feet long. What is the surface area of the asphalt that covers one parking spot?

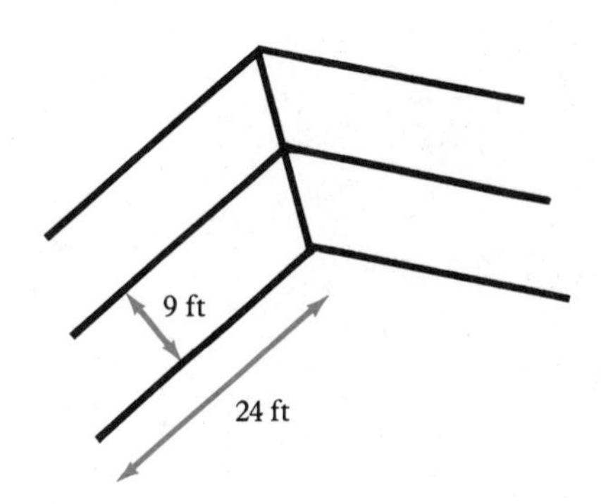

Answer. A parking spot is a parallelogram with base 24 feet and altitude 9 feet. Applying Theorem 11-1 we calculate the area:

$$\text{area} = 24 \text{ ft} \times 9 \text{ ft} = 216 \text{ sq ft}$$

EXERCISES

A.

In exercises 1–3, find the area of the parallelogram.

1.

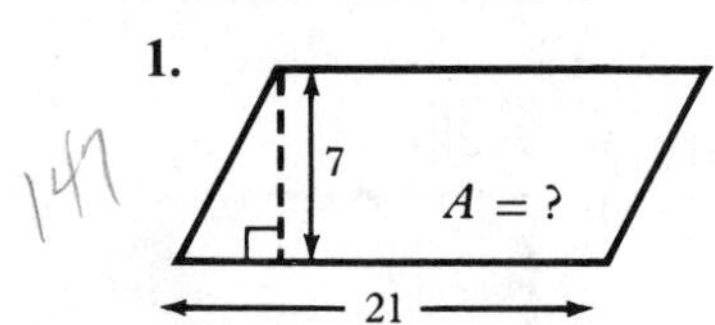

2.

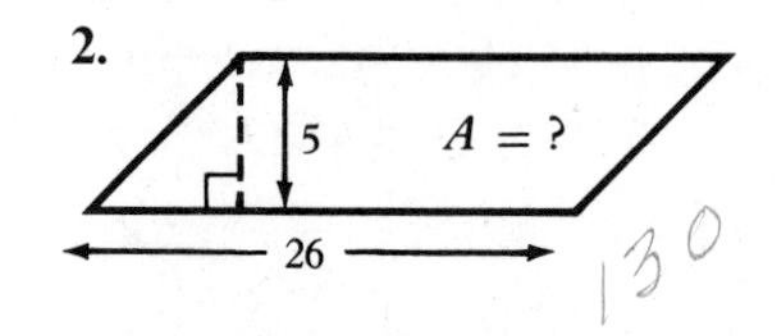

3.

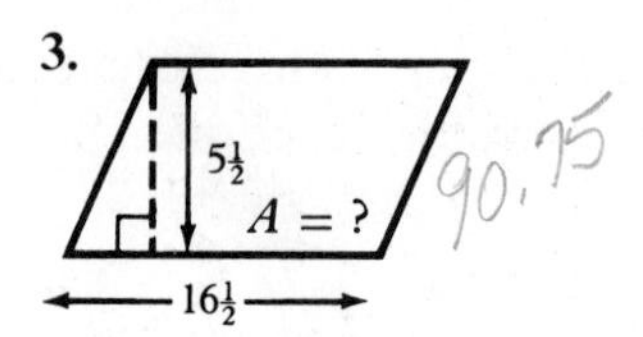

In exercises 4–6 the area of the parallelogram is given. Find the unknown part.

4.

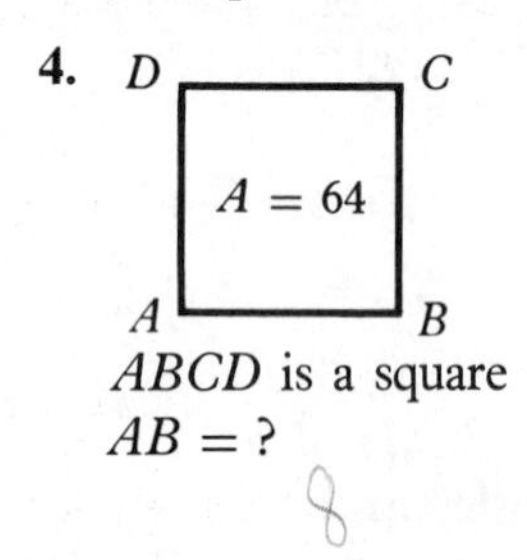

ABCD is a square
$AB = ?$

5.

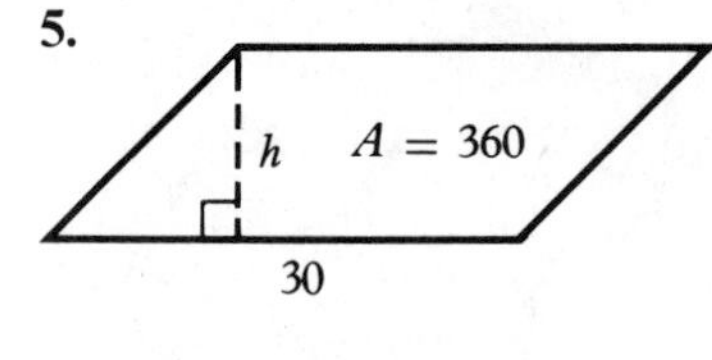

$h = ?$

6.

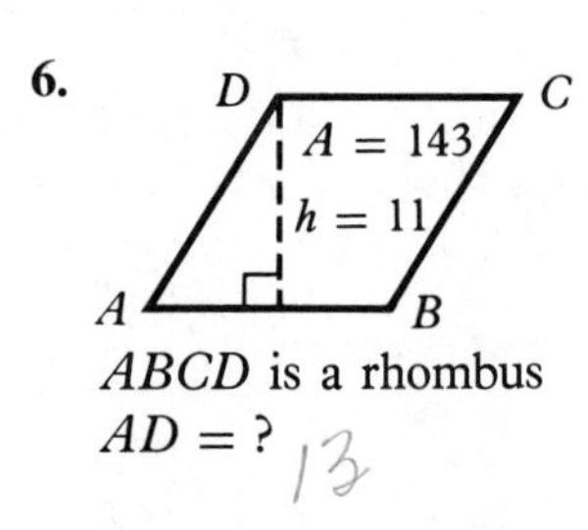

ABCD is a rhombus
$AD = ?$

B.

Find the area of each of the parallelograms in exercises 7–9.

7.

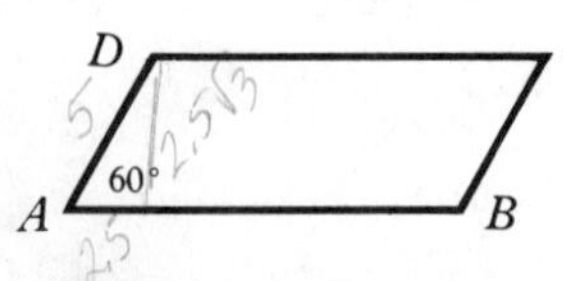

$AB = 14$, $AD = 5$

8.

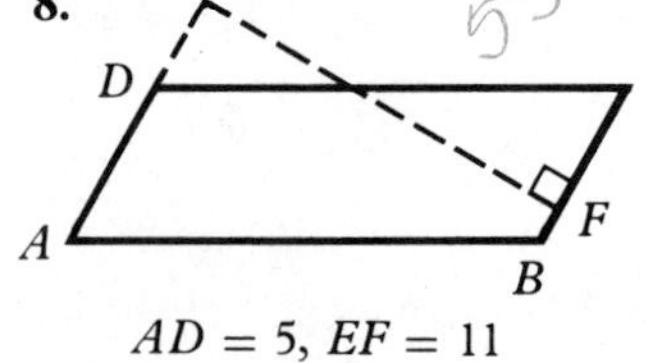

$AD = 5$, $EF = 11$

9.

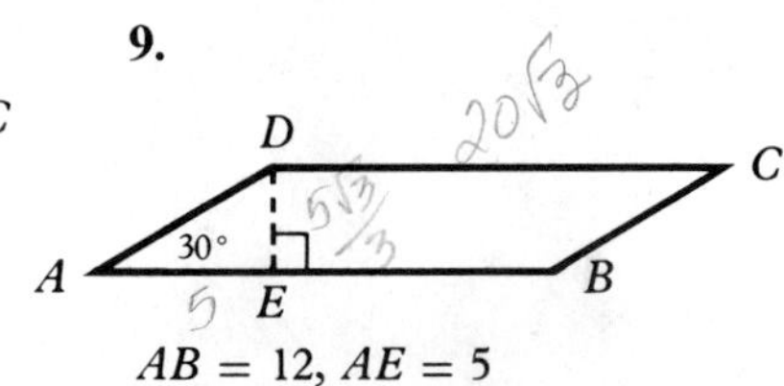

$AB = 12$, $AE = 5$

Activity

Draw this 8-inch square. Then cut and rearrange the pieces as shown.

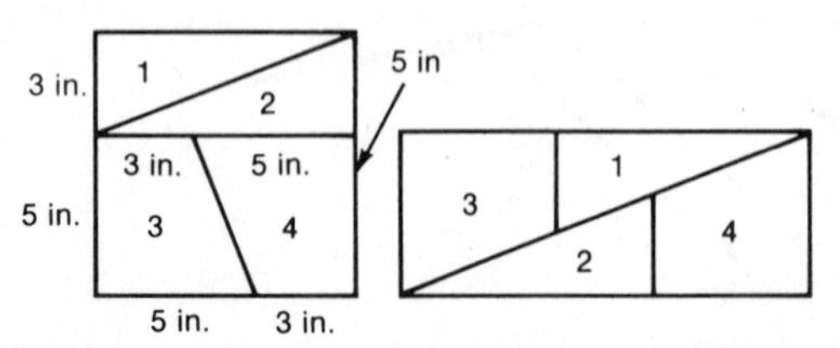

1. Which of the three situations indicated occurs?
2. Use area concepts to determine which one of the three actually happens.

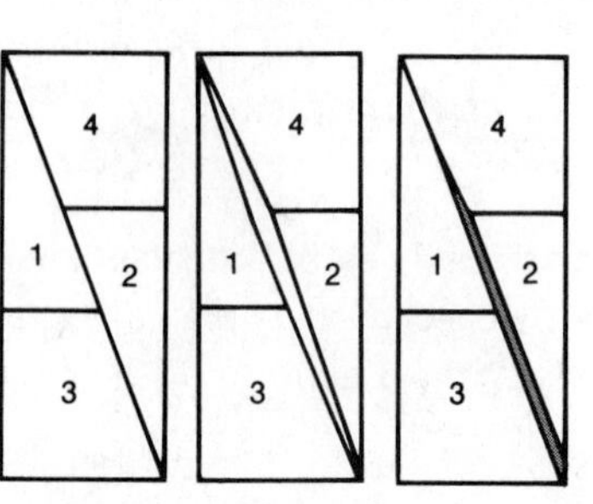

In exercises 10–12 find the unknown part. Each quadrilateral is a parallelogram.

10.

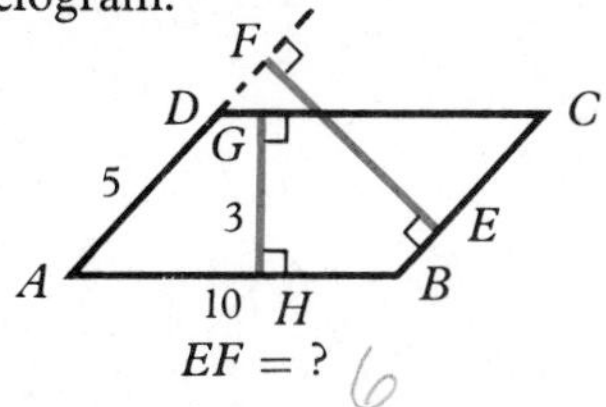

11.

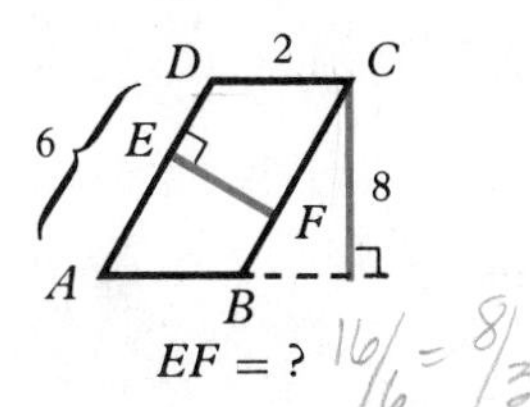

12.

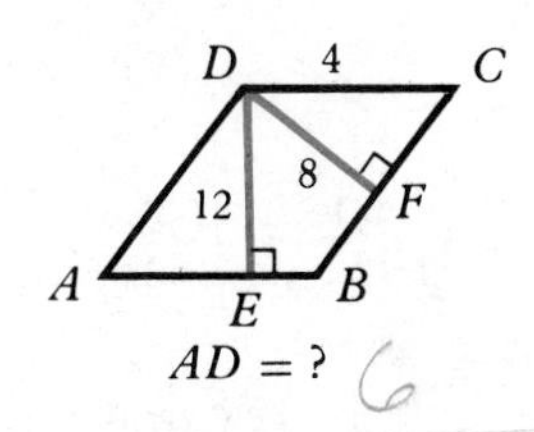

13. If the lengths of the sides of a parallelogram are doubled, what happens to the area of the parallelogram?

14. A parallelogram has sides of length 12 and 8 and one of the angle measures 120°. What is its area?

C.

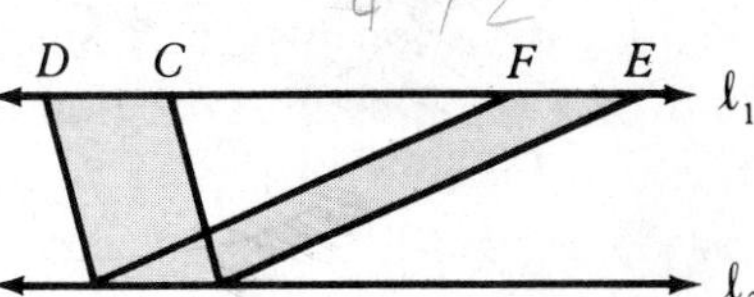

15. Lines ℓ_1 and ℓ_2 are parallel. Compare the area of parallelograms $ABEF$ and $ABCD$.

16. Given parallelograms $ABCD$ and $EFGH$ with $m\angle A = m\angle E$ and $h_2 = \sqrt{3}\,h_1$. If the area of $EFGH$ is twice the area of $ABCD$, how does AB compare with EF?

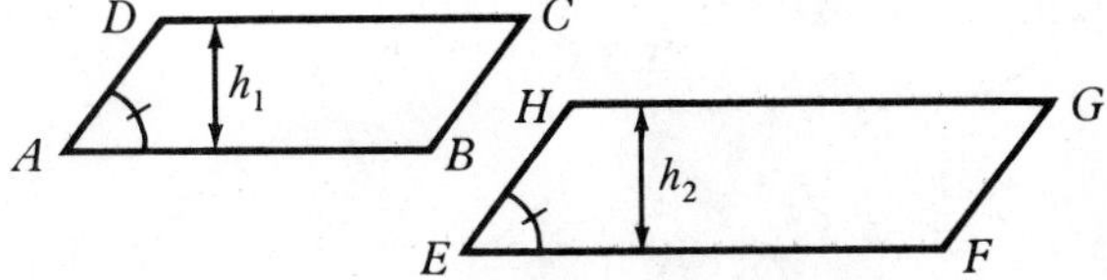

Find the areas of the regions in exercises 17 and 18. Assume that segments that appear perpendicular or parallel are related in this way.

17.

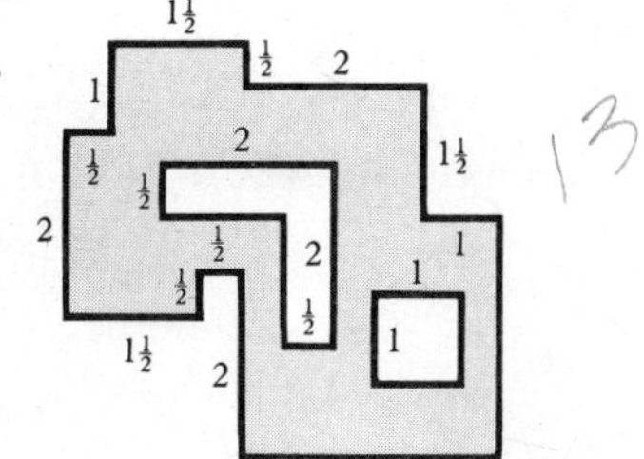

18.

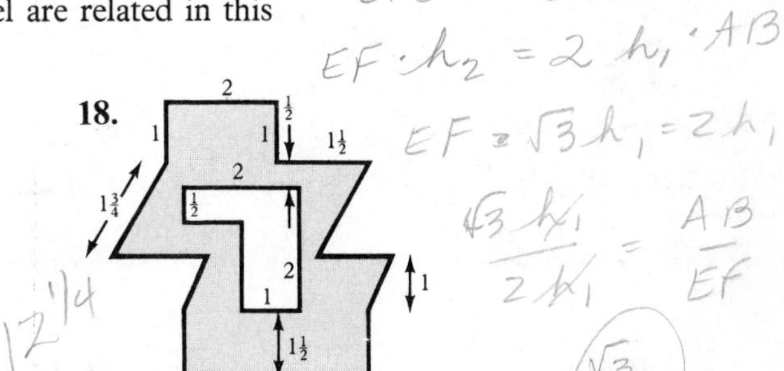

PROBLEM SOLVING

The ancient Babylonians used the formula $\frac{(a + c)(b + d)}{4}$ for the area of a quadrilateral with sides of length *a*, *b*, *c*, and *d*.

1. Does this formula work for rectangles?

2. Does this formula work for parallelograms?

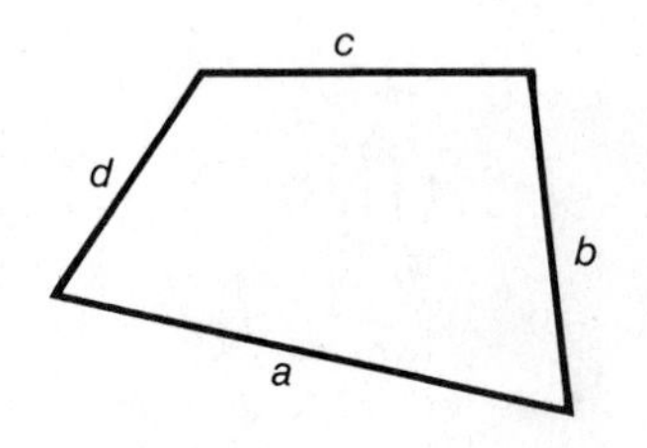

11–3 Areas of Triangles and Trapezoids

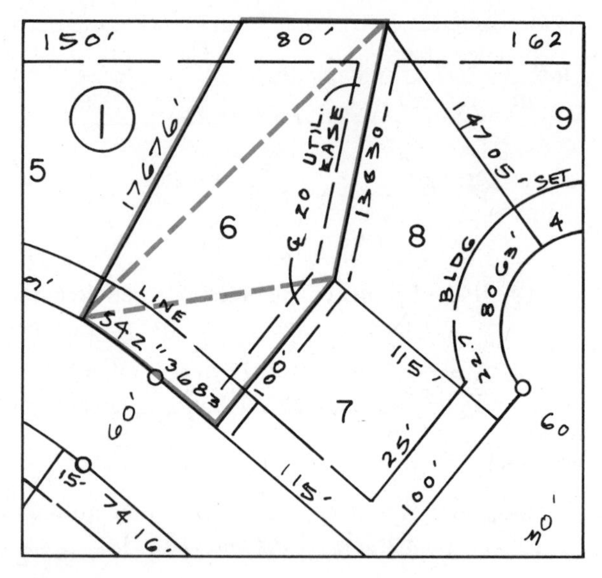

A civil engineer needs to find the area of an irregularly shaped lot in a housing subdivision like lot #6 shown here. This can be done by dividing the region into triangular regions and calculating the area of each triangular region.

The figures below illustrate that a triangular region may be thought of as one half of a parallelogram region. Therefore, the formula for finding the area of a parallelogram leads to an area formula for triangles.

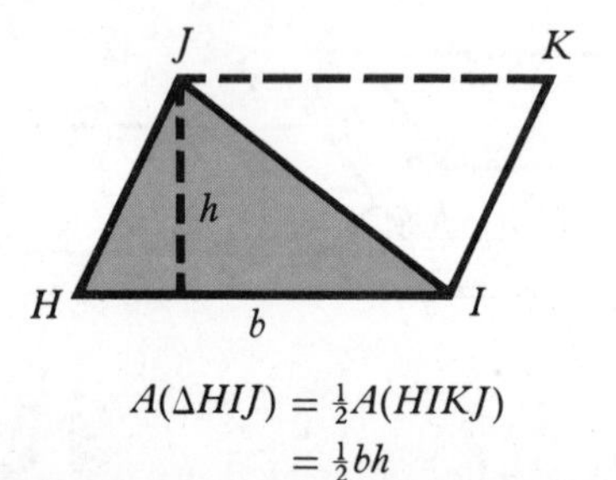

$A(\triangle HIJ) = \frac{1}{2}A(HIKJ)$
$= \frac{1}{2}bh$

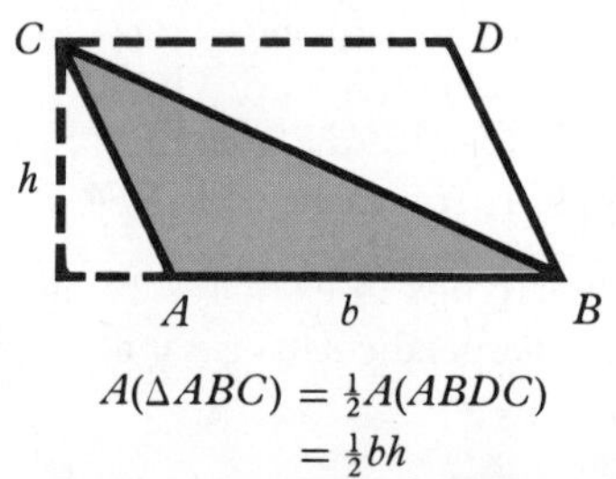

$A(\triangle ABC) = \frac{1}{2}A(ABDC)$
$= \frac{1}{2}bh$

Theorem 11–2 Given a triangle with base b and corresponding altitude h, the area A is given by the formula $A = \frac{1}{2}bh$.

Sometimes the lengths of all three sides of a triangle may be known, but an altitude may not be. In that case a formula, known to Heron of Alexandria in the first century, is useful.

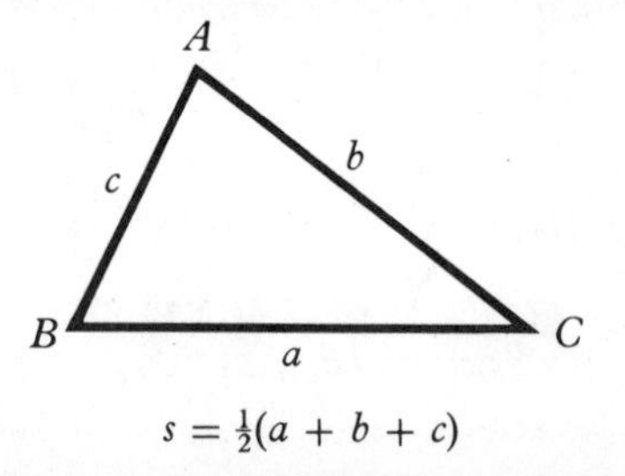

$s = \frac{1}{2}(a + b + c)$

Theorem 11–3 **Heron's Formula.** If $\triangle ABC$ has sides of length a, b, and c, then $A(\triangle ABC) = \sqrt{s(s-a)(s-b)(s-c)}$ where $s = \frac{1}{2}(a + b + c)$.

APPLICATION

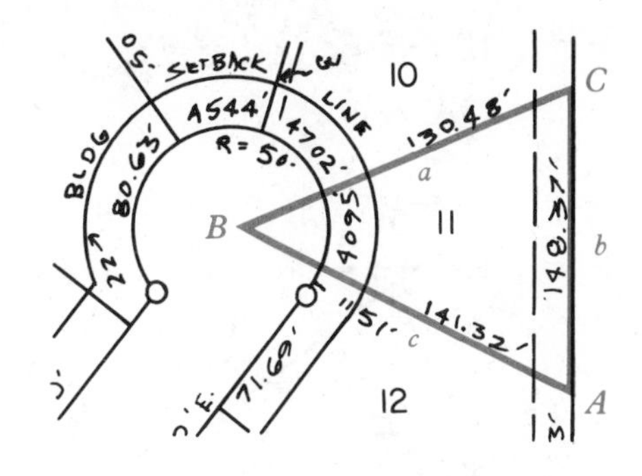

One method of finding the area of lot #11 requires finding the area of $\triangle ABC$ first. By using Heron's formula and a hand calculator, this is a manageable task. (Note that the radius of the circle is 50 feet.)

$a = 130.48 + 50 = 180.48 \qquad b = 148.37$

$c = 141.32 + 50 = 191.32$

$s = \frac{1}{2}(a + b + c) = 260.09$

$s - a = 79.61,\ s - b = 111.72,\ s - c = 68.77$

By Heron's Formula $A(\triangle ABC) \doteq \sqrt{(260.09)(79.61)(111.72)(68.77)} \doteq 12{,}613$.

A trapezoid may also be viewed as one half of a parallelogram. The area of the trapezoid is one half the area of that parallelogram.

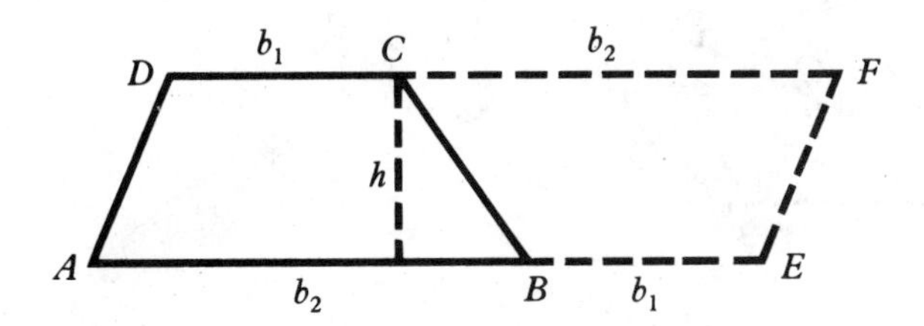

base of $\square AEFD = b_1 + b_2$
$A(\square AEFD) = h(b_1 + b_2)$

Theorem 11-4 Given a trapezoid with bases b_1 and b_2 and altitude h, the area A is given by the formula $A = \frac{1}{2}h(b_1 + b_2)$.

APPLICATION

A dam often has a trapezoidal cross section. The designer of a dam must determine the area of this trapezoidal cross section. If the dam is 180 meters tall and has bases 10 meters and 60 meters long, what is the area of the cross section? By using Theorem 11-4 we calculate the area:

$$\text{area} = \tfrac{1}{2} \cdot 180(10 + 60)\ \text{m}^2 = 6300\ \text{m}^2$$

EXERCISES

A.

Calculate the area of each region in exercises 1–11.

1.

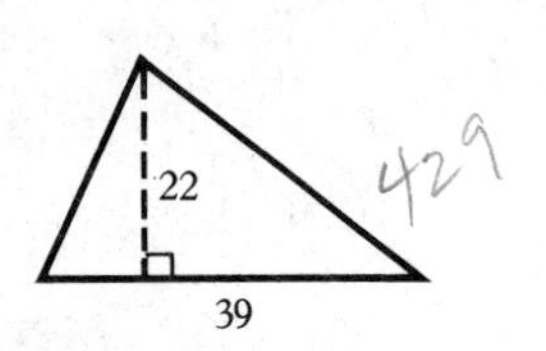

2.

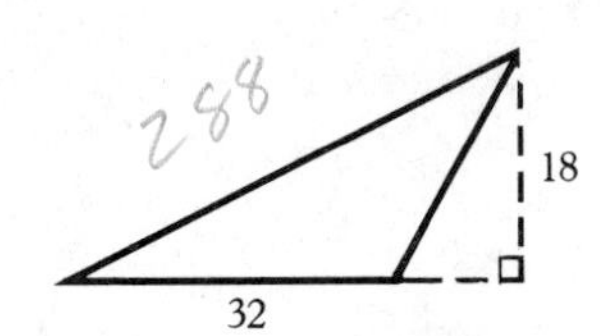

3.

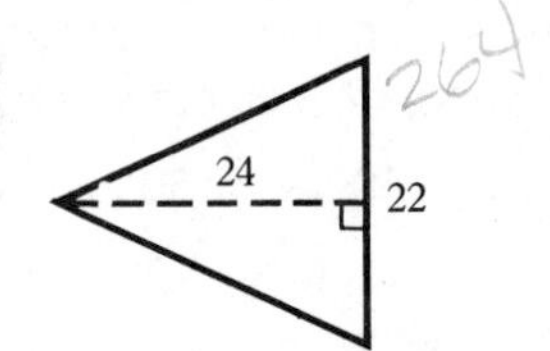

4.

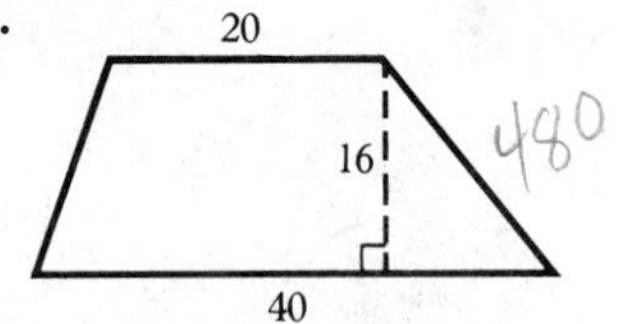

5.

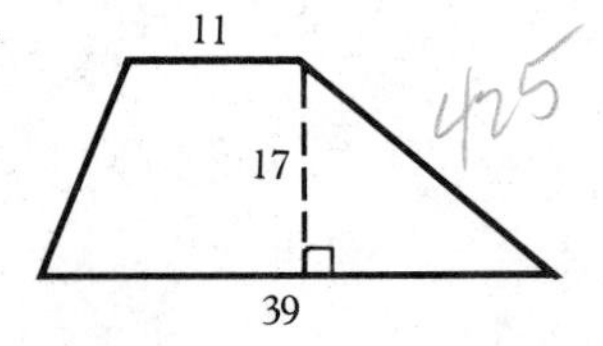

6.

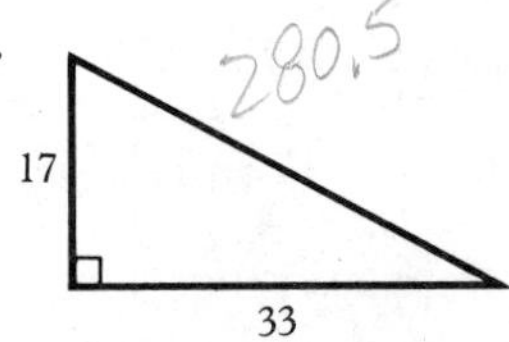

7.

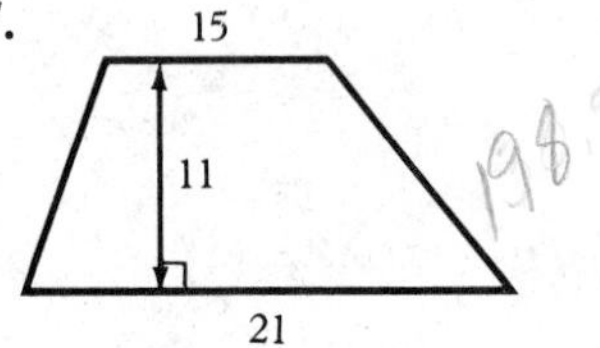

8.

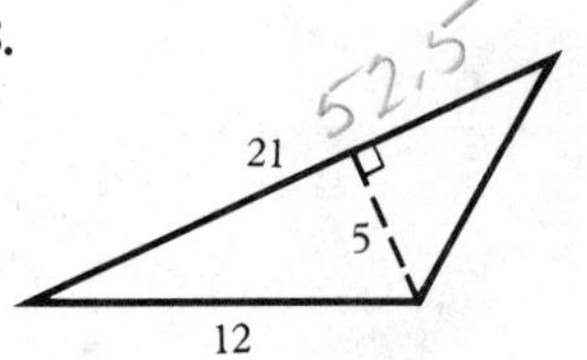

9.

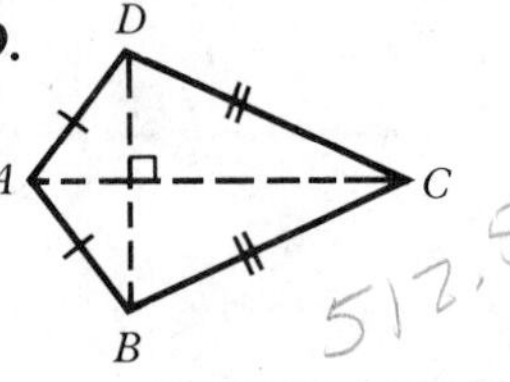

$AC = 41 \quad BD = 25$

10.

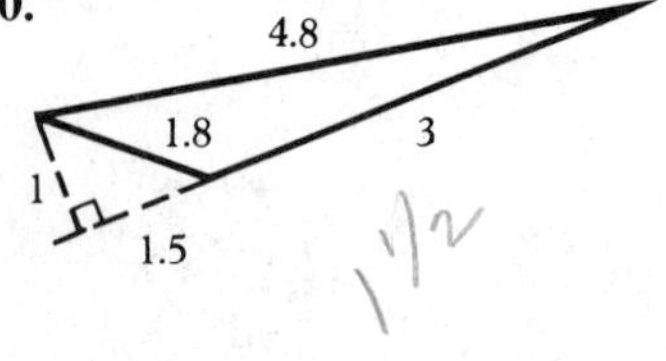

11.

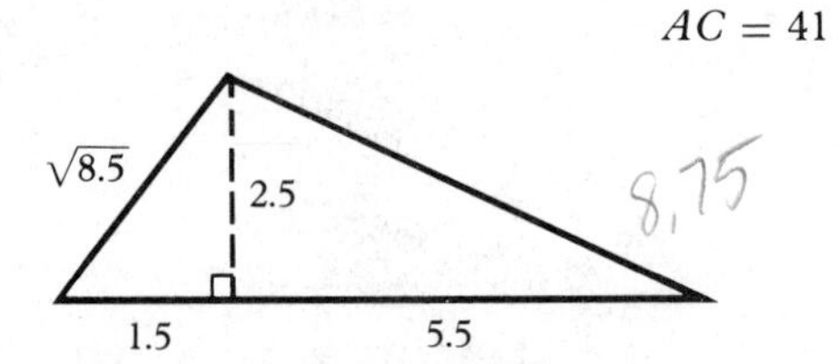

B.

12. The area of $\triangle ABC$ is 48 cm² and $AB = 6$ cm. What is the length of the altitude on $\overline{AB}$?

13. A trapezoid with base lengths 14 ft and 21 ft has an area of $87\frac{1}{2}$ sq ft. What is its altitude?

14. What is the area of the shaded region?

15. What is the area of the unshaded region?

16. What is the ratio of the area of the shaded region to the area of $\triangle ABE$?

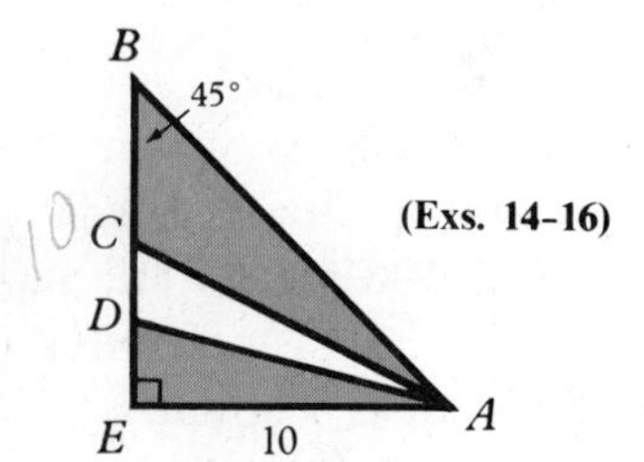

(Exs. 14–16)

C is the midpoint of $\overline{BE}$.
D is the midpoint of $\overline{CE}$.

For exercises 17–18 find the area of the shaded region.

17. *ABCD* is a rectangle.

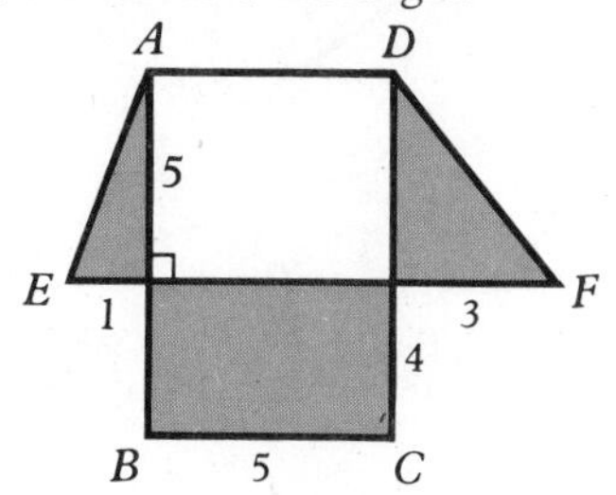

18. *ABCD* is a parallelogram.

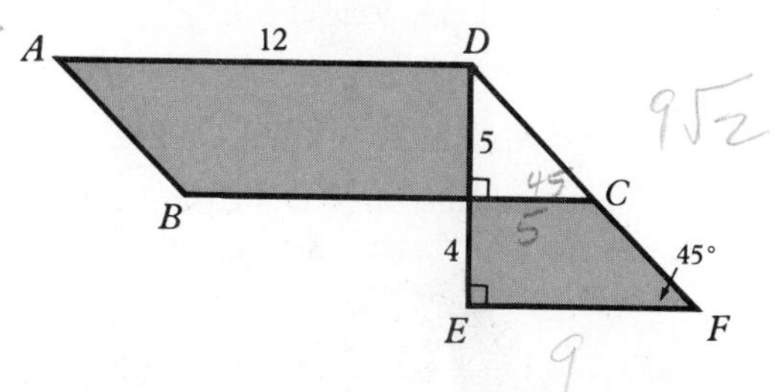

19. *ABCD* is a trapezoid and *E* is the midpoint of $\overline{AB}$. Show that the area of *AECD* is equal to the area of *EBCD*.

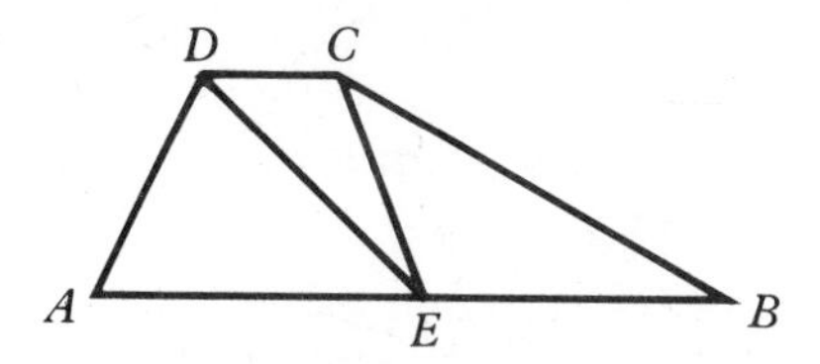

20. *ABCD* is a parallelogram whose area is 60 square units. Find the area of the kite *ABED*. (*Hint:* Find the area of $\triangle ABD$.)

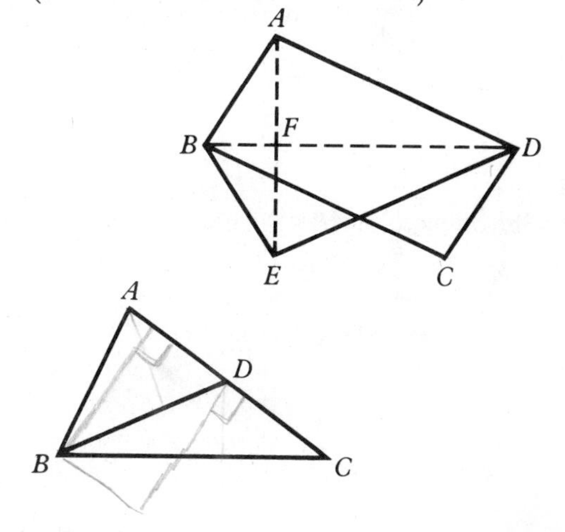

21. Show that a median divides a triangle into two regions of equal area. That is, if $\overline{BD}$ is a median of $\triangle ABC$, show that the area of $\triangle ABD$ is equal to the area of $\triangle BDC$.

22. *ABCD* is a parallelogram. Find the length *BE*.

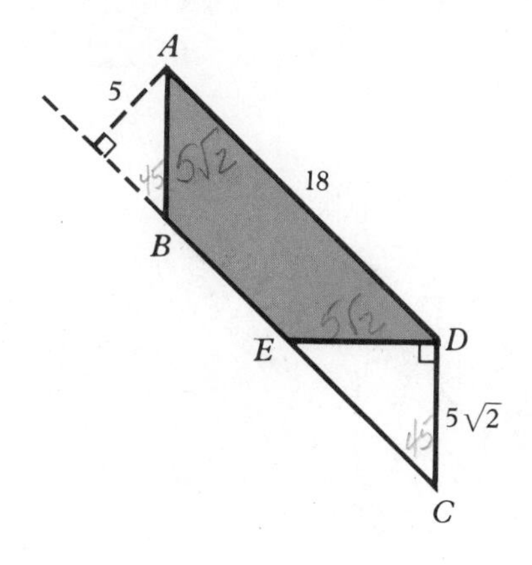

23. *ABCD* is a parallelogram and *X* is any point inside. Show that the area of the shaded region is one half the area of the parallelogram. (*Hint:* $h_1 + h_2$ is the altitude of *ABCD*.)

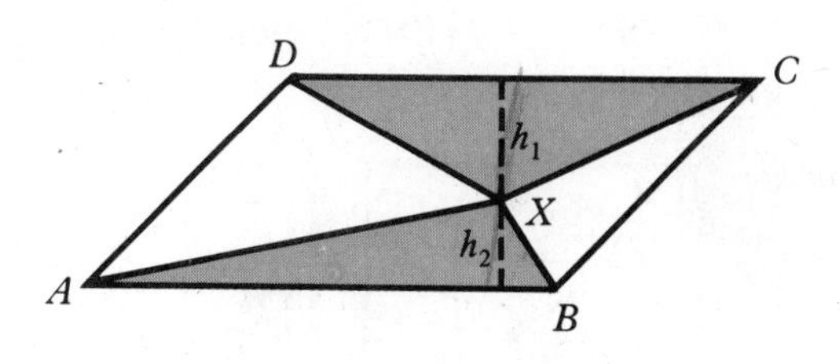

24. Use Heron's Formula to find the area of a triangle with sides of these lengths.

a. 3 cm, 4 cm, 5 cm **b.** 17 cm, 18 cm, 19 cm (Use a calculator.)

c. 25 cm, 36 cm, 41 cm (Use a calculator.)

25. Show that the three medians of a triangle divide the triangle into six regions that are equal in area.

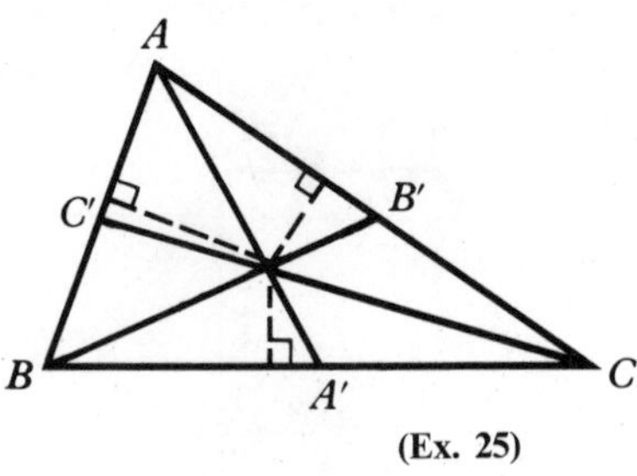

(Ex. 25)

26. A developer bought a piece of land which formed an irregular pentagon. Find the area of this land if $AF = 10$ m, $FG = 40$ m, $GH = 15$ m, $HC = 20$ m, $EF = 20$ m, $DG = 30$ m, and $HB = 35$ m.

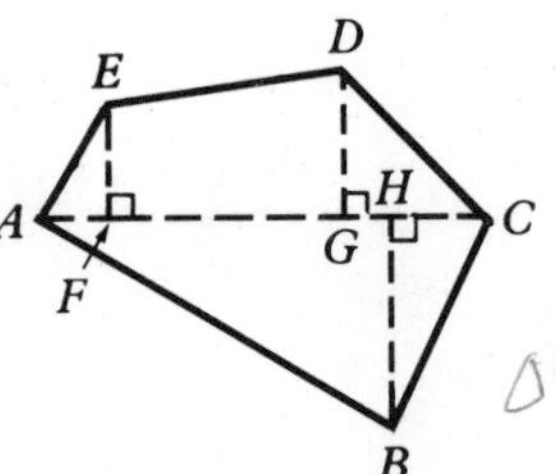

27. $ABCD$ is a trapezoid and E is the midpoint of $\overline{BC}$. Show that the area of $\triangle ADE$ is one half the area of $ABCD$.

28. Suppose $\triangle ABC$ is an equilateral triangle with altitude h. Let X be any point in the interior of the triangle, and let a, b, and c be the lengths of the perpendiculars to the sides of $\triangle ABC$. Prove that $a + b + c = h$. (*Hint:* Use area.)

Activity

On this geoboard the area of square A is 1, and the area of each of figures B and C is $1\frac{1}{2}$.

1. Draw the figures below on dot paper or construct on a geoboard.
2. Find the area of each region below without using any area formulas.

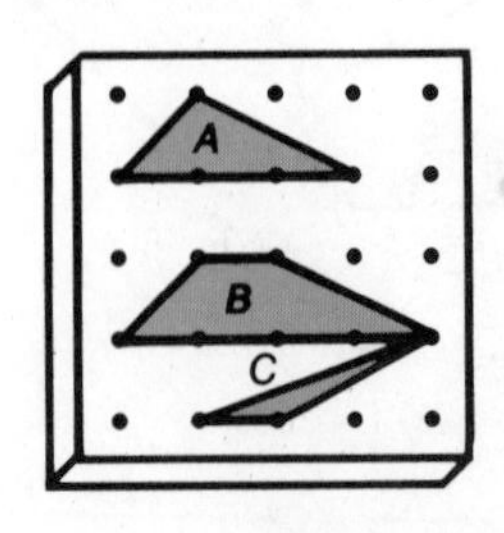

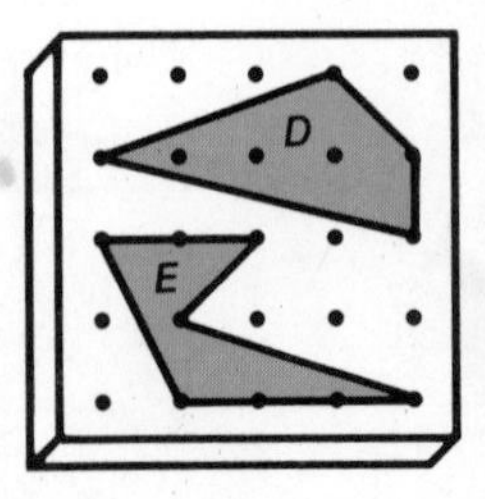

29. Given $\triangle ABC$ with medians $\overline{BD}$ and $\overline{CE}$. Show that the areas of the shaded regions are equal.

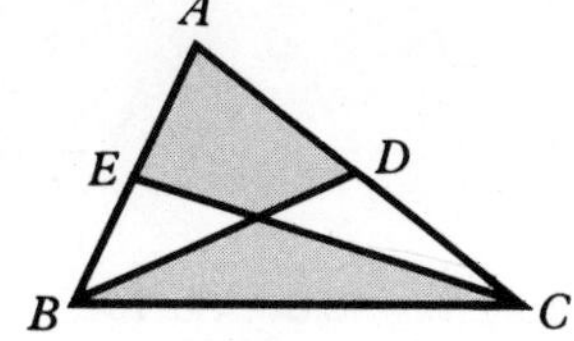

30. Prove that the area of an equilateral triangle whose sides have length s is $s^2\sqrt{3}/4$.

31. Consider the square $ABCD$.
If triangles are cut off each corner, an octagon results. If $AB = 3$, show that $x = \dfrac{3}{2 + \sqrt{2}}$ if the resulting octagon is a regular octagon.

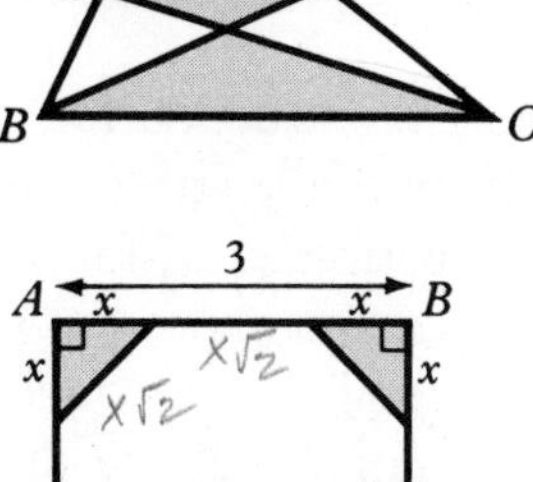

(Exs. 31, 32)

32. What is the area of a regular octagon whose side length is 2?

33. Consider the equilateral triangle $\triangle ABC$. Points D, E, F, and G are selected as shown so that $\overline{ED} \perp \overline{AB}$, $\overline{FG} \perp \overline{BC}$, $DE = FG = 1$, and $EF = 2$. Show that the area of $\triangle CFG$ is $\dfrac{1}{2\sqrt{3}}$ or $\dfrac{\sqrt{3}}{6}$.

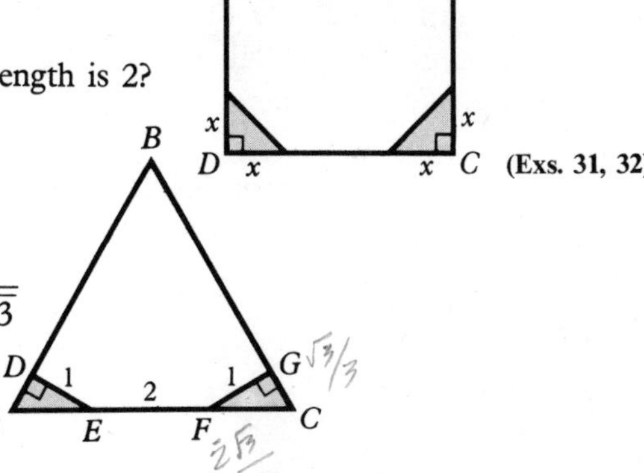

34. Show that the area of a regular 12-gon with side length 2 is $6(4 + 2\sqrt{3})$. (*Hint:* The figure on the right shows pentagon $BDEFG$ is $\frac{1}{6}$ of a regular 12-gon, side length 2. Find the length AC, then use it to find the area of $\triangle ABC$. Then subtract the areas of triangles $\triangle ADE$ and $\triangle CFG$.)

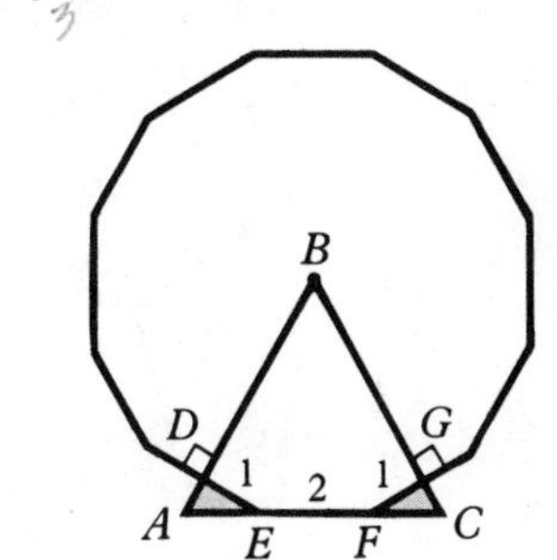

PROBLEM SOLVING

The length of the edges of the cube are all 1.

1. Find the length of $\overline{BE}$.
2. Find the length of $\overline{BH}$.
3. Find the area of $\triangle BEG$.
4. Find the area of rectangle $BCHE$.
5. Find the area of $\triangle BIC$.

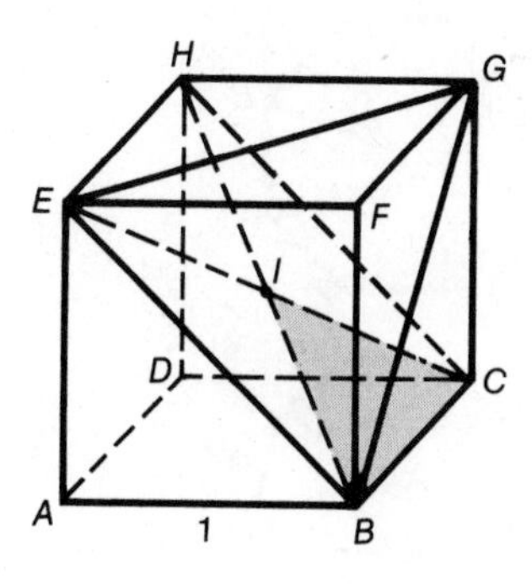

11-4 Area of Regular Polygons

The cost of construction for a building is influenced by the length of the outside walls—the perimeter of the building. A large perimeter requires more brick, siding, and window materials. Consequently, in designing a building, an architect might ask, "what regular polygonal shape will provide the most area for a given perimeter?"

There are two definitions needed.

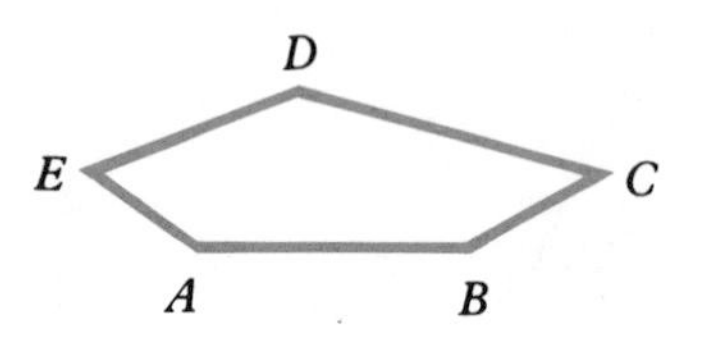

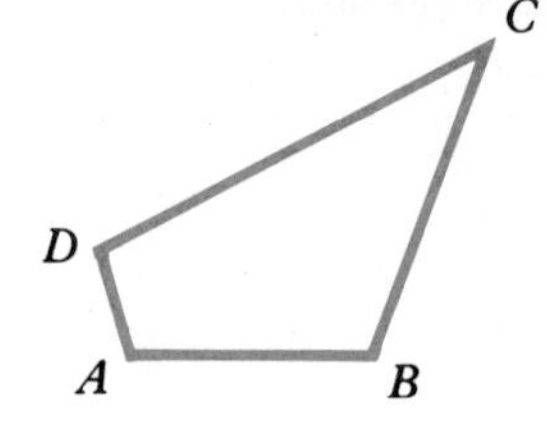

Definition 11-4

The **perimeter (p) of a polygon** is the sum of the lengths of the sides of the polygon.

$p = AB + BC + CD + DE + AE$ $\quad$ $p = AB + BC + CD + AD$

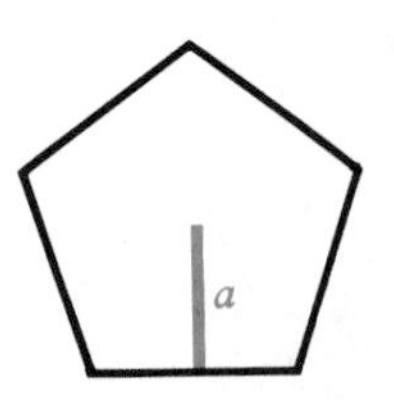

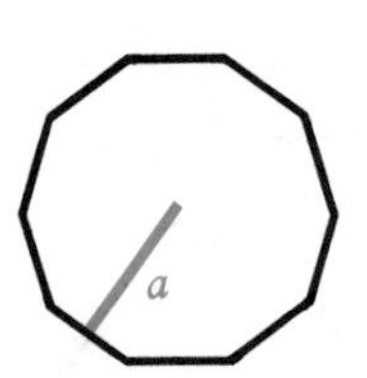

Definition 11-5

The **apothem (a) of a regular polygon** is the distance from its center to a side.

These two definitions are used to develop a formula for the area of a regular polygon with n sides. The table shown here helps analyze two examples.

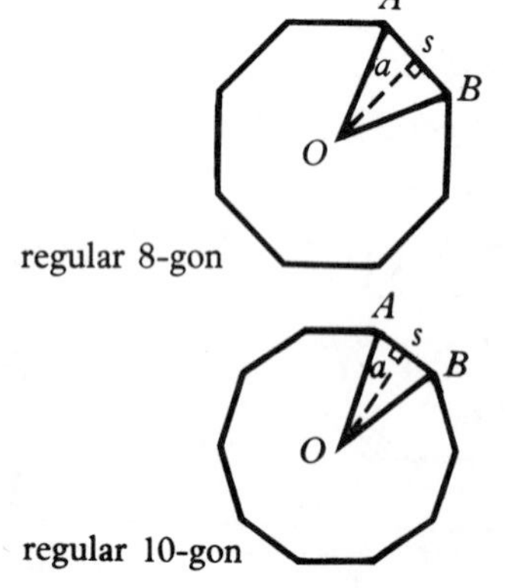

	Area of $\triangle ABO$	Perimeter (p)	Area of Polygon
8-gon (octagon)	$\frac{1}{2}as$	$p = 8s$	$8 \times \frac{1}{2}as = \frac{1}{2}a(8s)$ $= \frac{1}{2}ap$
10-gon (decagon)	$\frac{1}{2}as$	$p = 10s$	$10 \times \frac{1}{2}as = \frac{1}{2}a(10s)$ $= \frac{1}{2}ap$

Theorem 11–5 Given a regular n-gon with sides of length s and apothem a, the area A is given by the formula $A = \frac{1}{2}ans = \frac{1}{2}ap$ where perimeter $p = ns$.

Example

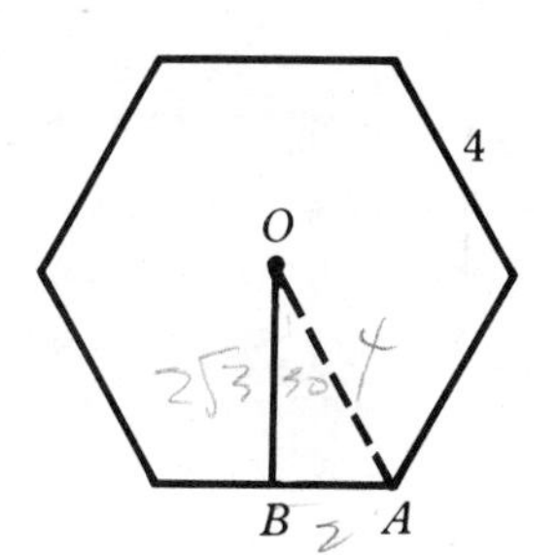

The side length of a regular hexagon is 4. Find the apothem and the area of the regular hexagon.

$\triangle OAB$ is a 30°-60°-90° triangle. Therefore,

$AB = 2,\ OA = 4$

$a = OB = 2\sqrt{3}.$

Applying Theorem 11–5, area $= \frac{1}{2}(2\sqrt{3}) \cdot 6 \cdot 4 = 24\sqrt{3}.$

$$\underset{a}{\uparrow} \quad \underset{n}{\uparrow} \quad \underset{s}{\uparrow}$$

APPLICATION

If a square building and a regular hexagon building have the same perimeter (p), how do their areas compare?

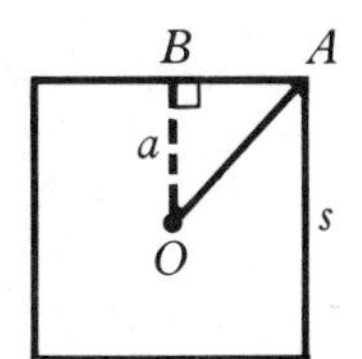

1. $\triangle OAB$ is a 45°-45°-90° triangle.

   Therefore the apothem $a = AB$

   $$= \frac{1}{2}s = \frac{1}{2}\left(\frac{p}{4}\right) = \frac{p}{8}.$$

   Area of square $= \frac{1}{2} \cdot \frac{p}{8} \cdot p.$

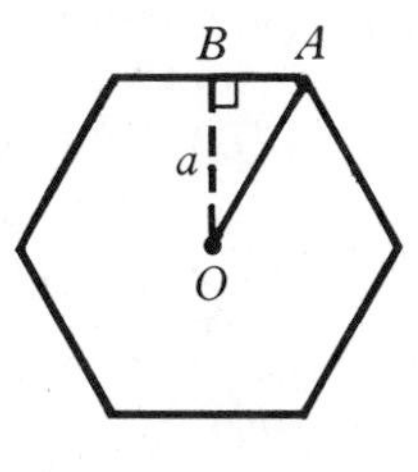

2. $\triangle OAB$ is a 30°-60°-90° triangle.

   The apothem $a = \sqrt{3}AB = \sqrt{3}(\frac{1}{2}s)$

   $$= \sqrt{3}\left(\frac{1}{2} \cdot \frac{p}{6}\right) = \frac{\sqrt{3}p}{12}.$$

   Area of hexagon $= \frac{1}{2} \cdot \frac{\sqrt{3}}{12}p \cdot p.$

Since $\frac{\sqrt{3}}{2 \times 12} > \frac{1}{2 \times 8}$, the area of the hexagon is greater than the area of the square. Therefore a hexagonal building provides more area than a square building with the same perimeter.

EXERCISES

A.

For exercises 1-6, find the perimeter of the given figure.

1.

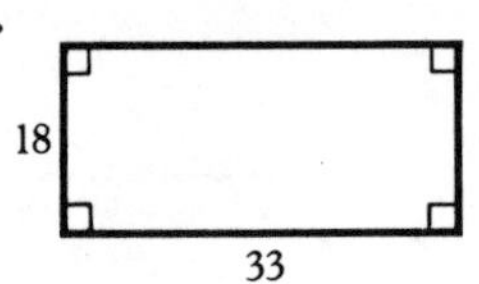

2.

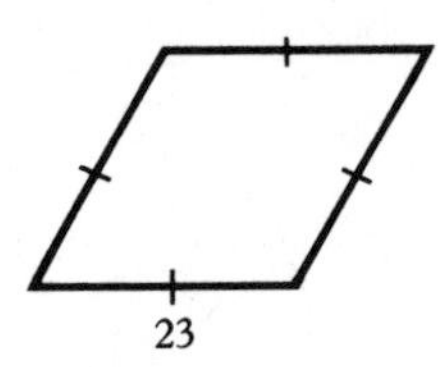

3.

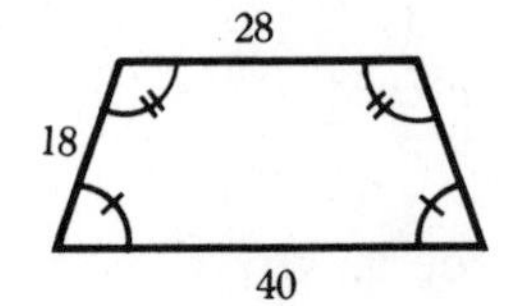

4.

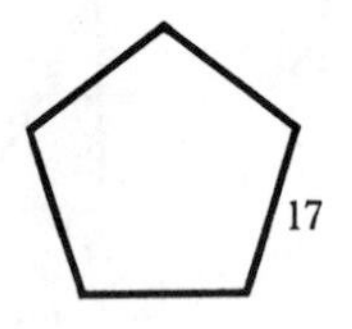

5.

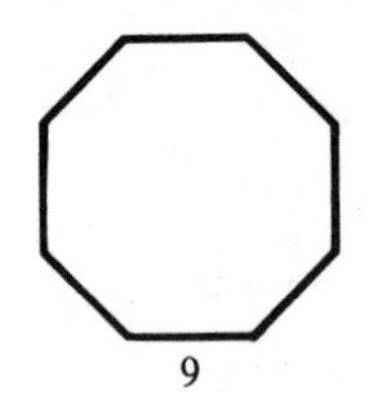

6.

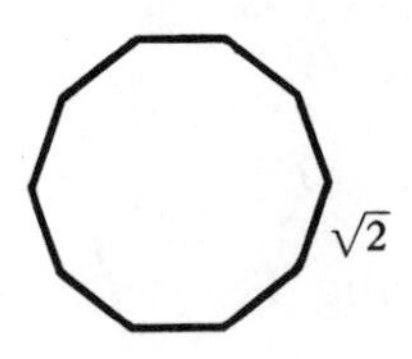

For exercises 7-9, find the apothem and the area of the given regular polygon.

7.

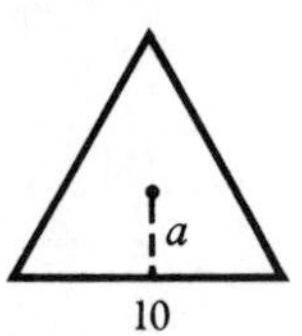

8.

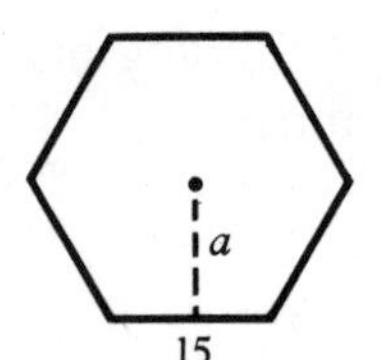

9.

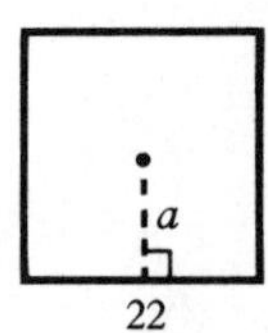

Activity

In the activity on page 406 you found the area of some regions on a geoboard without using any area formulas. Complete the table below. Look for a formula for the area of these polygons in terms of the number of nails on the boundary of the figure (d) and the number of interior points (i).

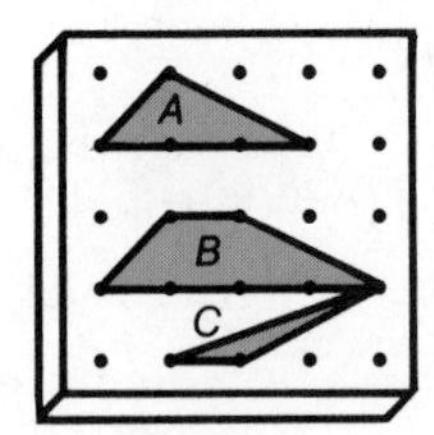

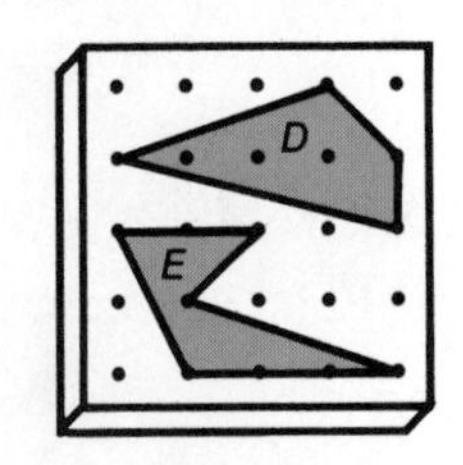

Figure	Number of nails on boundary (d)	Number of interior points (i)	$\frac{d}{2} + i$	Area of polygon
A	?	?	?	?
B	7	0	$\frac{7}{2} + 0$	$\frac{5}{2}$
C	?	?	?	?
⋮				

B.

10. Find the area of a regular hexagon with apothem $3\sqrt{3}$.

11. Find the area of a regular octagon with side length 5 and apothem k.

12. If the area of a regular hexagon is $36\sqrt{3}$ cm^2, what is its apothem and the length of its side?

13. If the apothem of a regular hexagon is 5 m, what is its perimeter? Its area?

C.

14. If an equilateral triangle and a regular hexagon have equal perimeters, prove that the ratio of their areas is 2 to 3.

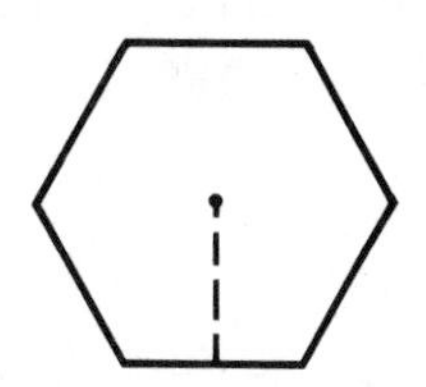

15. The area of a regular hexagon is $50\sqrt{3}$ sq ft. What is its perimeter? Its apothem?

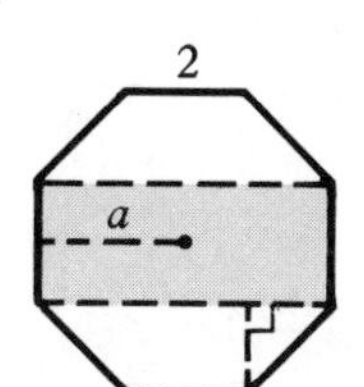

16. The side length of a regular octagon is 2. What is its apothem?

17. A farmer is to enclose a rectangular pen with 100 meters of fence. He is trying to decide what shape the pen should have. Fill out this table and see if you have any recommendation for the farmer.

length	width	perimeter	area
48 m	? 2	100 m	? 96
45 m	? 5	100 m	? 225
40 m	? 10	100 m	? 400
35 m	? 15	100 m	? 525
30 m	? 20	100 m	? 600
25 m	? 25	100 m	? 625

PROBLEM SOLVING

Find the perimeter of each polygon on these geoboards. Note that $AB = 1$.

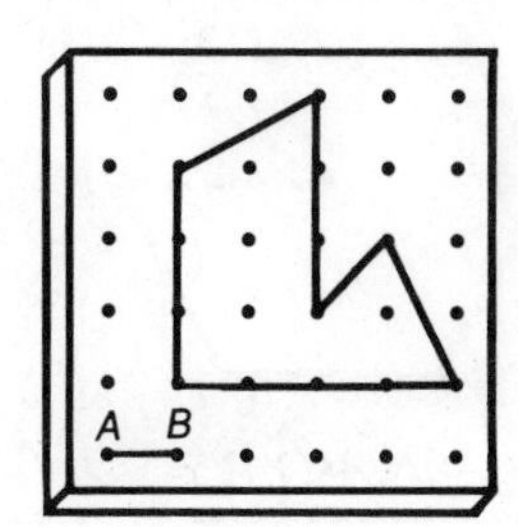

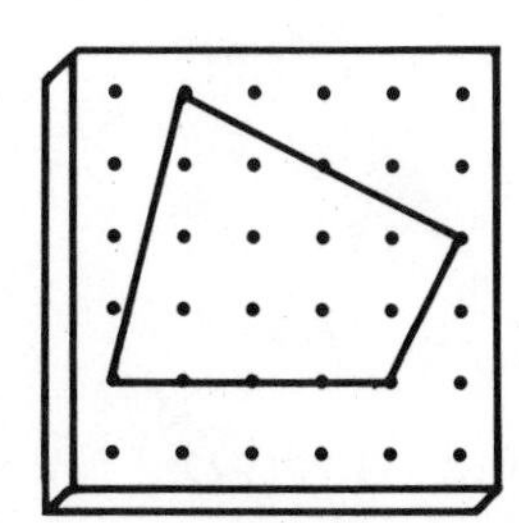

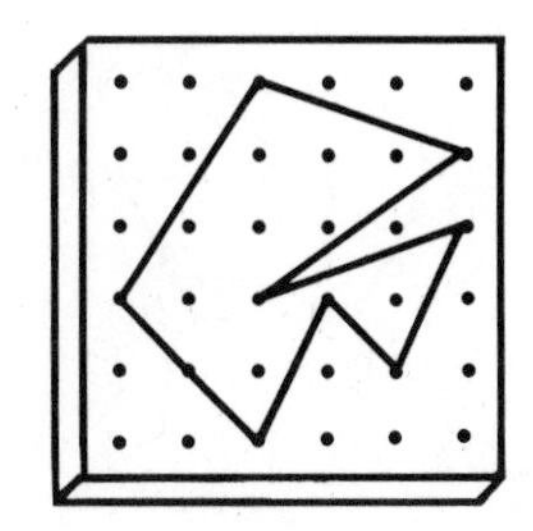

11–5 Comparing Perimeters and Areas of Similar Polygons

An engineer designing the heating-cooling system for a building must be able to answer the following types of questions.

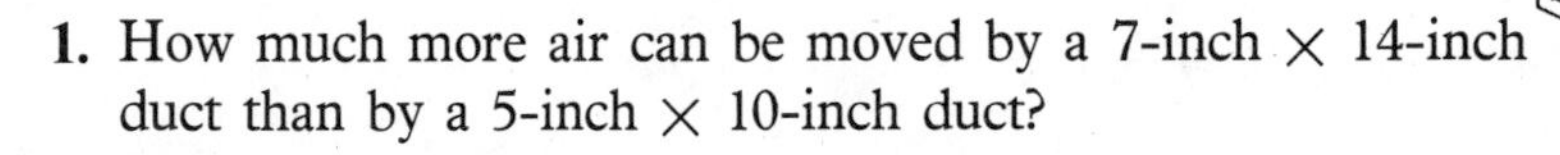

1. How much more air can be moved by a 7-inch × 14-inch duct than by a 5-inch × 10-inch duct?

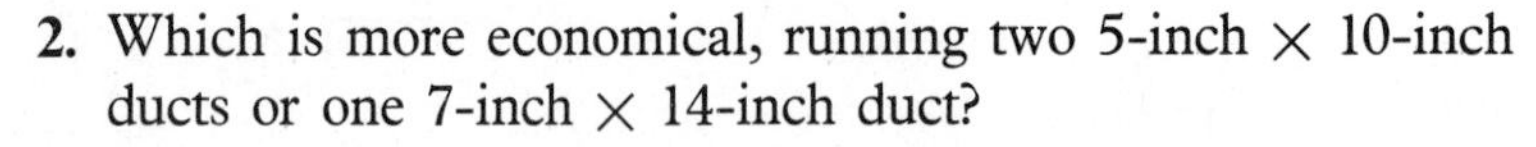

2. Which is more economical, running two 5-inch × 10-inch ducts or one 7-inch × 14-inch duct?

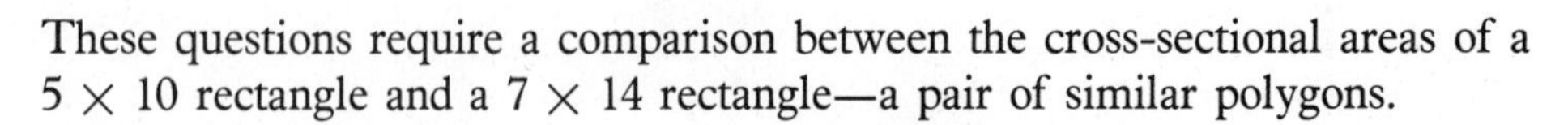

These questions require a comparison between the cross-sectional areas of a 5 × 10 rectangle and a 7 × 14 rectangle—a pair of similar polygons.

Study these two examples. We are comparing the areas of a pair of similar triangles and a pair of similar hexagons.

Example 1 $\triangle A'B'C' \sim \triangle ABC$ with $\frac{A'B'}{AB} = \frac{A'C'}{AC} = \frac{B'C'}{BC} = \frac{5}{3}$

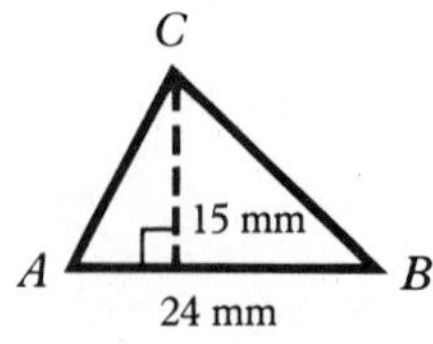

C′, 25 mm, A′, B′, 40 mm

$$\frac{\text{perimeter } \triangle A'B'C'}{\text{perimeter } \triangle ABC} = \frac{5}{3} \qquad \frac{\text{area } \triangle A'B'C'}{\text{area } \triangle ABC} = \frac{\frac{1}{2}(40)(25)}{\frac{1}{2}(24)(15)} = \frac{500}{180} = \frac{25}{9} = \left(\frac{5}{3}\right)^2$$

Example 2 $A'B'C'D'E'F' \sim ABCDEF$ with $\frac{A'B'}{AB} = \frac{2}{1}$

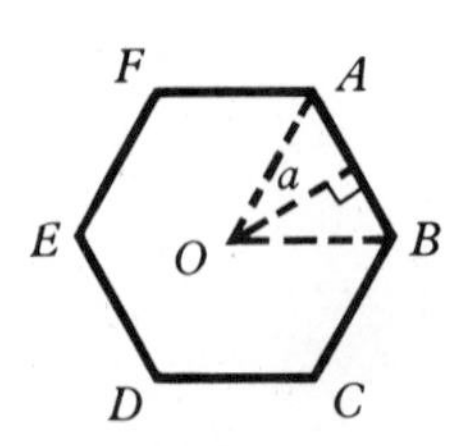

F′, A′, a′, E′, O′, B′, D′, C′

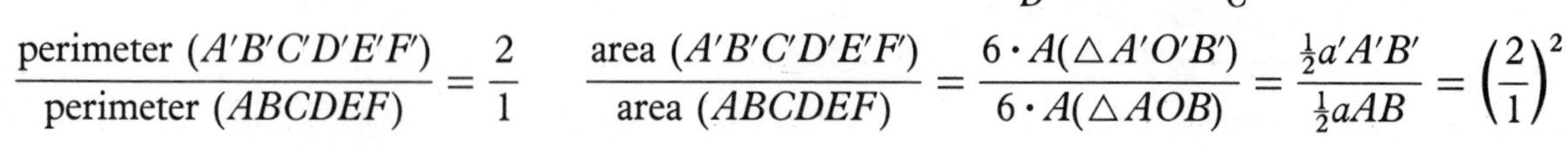

$$\frac{\text{perimeter } (A'B'C'D'E'F')}{\text{perimeter } (ABCDEF)} = \frac{2}{1} \qquad \frac{\text{area } (A'B'C'D'E'F')}{\text{area } (ABCDEF)} = \frac{6 \cdot A(\triangle A'O'B')}{6 \cdot A(\triangle AOB)} = \frac{\frac{1}{2}a'A'B'}{\frac{1}{2}aAB} = \left(\frac{2}{1}\right)^2$$

We summarize these examples in this table.

	Ratio of Corresponding Sides	Ratio of Perimeters	Ratio of Areas
Example 1	$\frac{A'B'}{AB} = \frac{40}{24} = \frac{5}{3}$	$\frac{5}{3}$	$\left(\frac{5}{3}\right)^2$
Example 2	$\frac{A'B'}{AB} = \frac{2}{1}$	$\frac{2}{1}$	$\left(\frac{2}{1}\right)^2$

These examples suggest the following theorems.

Theorem 11–6 The ratio of the perimeters of two similar polygons is equal to the ratio of the lengths of any pair of corresponding sides.

Theorem 11–7 The ratio of the areas of two similar polygons is equal to the square of the ratio of the lengths of any pair of corresponding sides.

APPLICATION

We shall answer the two questions asked at the beginning of the lesson by comparing the area and perimeter of the rectangular cross sections of the two ducts.

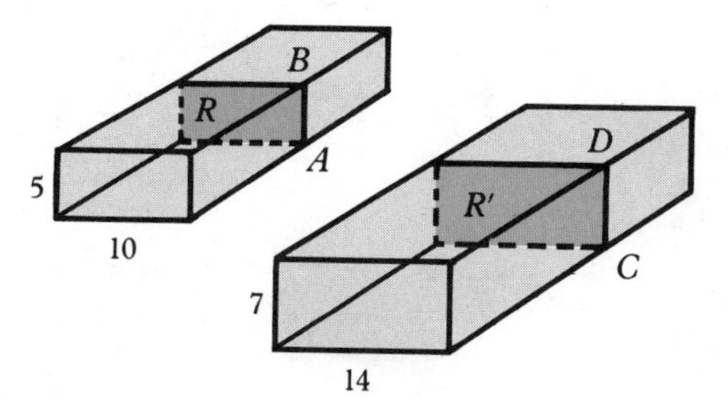

$$\frac{CD}{AB} = \frac{7}{5} \quad \frac{\text{area}(R')}{\text{area}(R)} = \left(\frac{7}{5}\right)^2 = \frac{49}{25} \doteq \frac{2}{1} \quad \frac{\text{perimeter}(R')}{\text{perimeter}(R)} = \frac{7}{5}$$

Conclusion: The cross-section area (and hence the amount of air moved) is nearly twice as great for the larger duct. Yet its cross-section perimeter is only $\frac{7}{5}$ as great as the smaller duct. Consequently less material would be required to build it than two of the smaller ducts.

EXERCISES

A.

Suppose the lengths of the sides of two squares are 4 and 8 respectively.

1. What is the ratio of their perimeters?
2. What is the ratio of their areas?

Two regular pentagons have side lengths in a ratio of 13:20.

3. What is the ratio of the perimeters of these pentagons?
4. What is the ratio of the areas of these two pentagons?

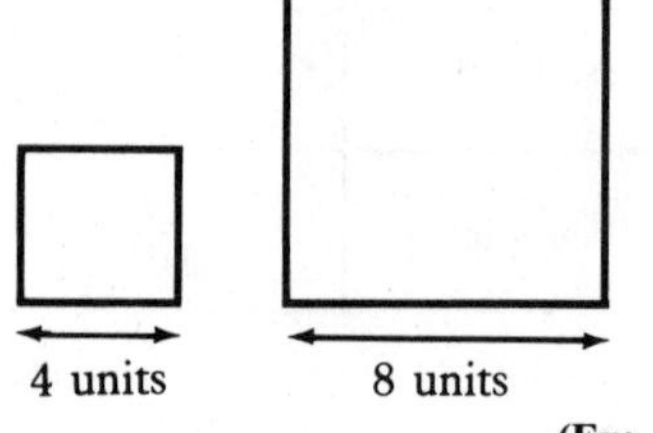

(Exs. 1,2)

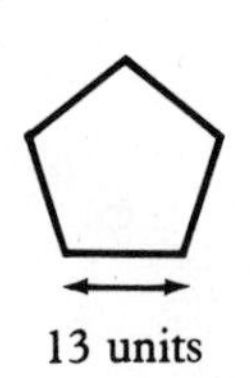

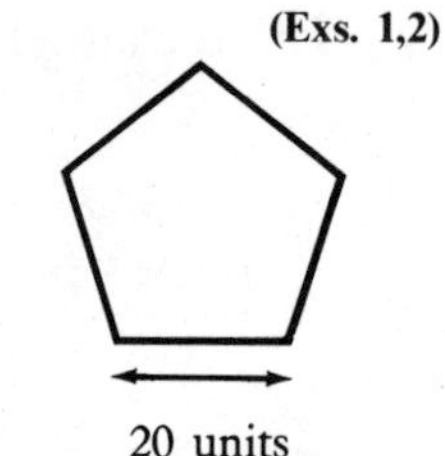

(Exs. 3,4)

B.

5. The ratio of the perimeters of two similar polygons is $\frac{\sqrt{3}}{2}$. What is the ratio of their areas?
6. If the ratio of the areas of two similar n-gons is $\frac{36}{25}$, what is the ratio of their perimeters?
7. The ratio of the areas of two similar polygons is $\frac{25}{9}$ and the sum of the two areas is 272. Find the areas of the two polygons.

Activity

An equilateral triangle is called a "reptile" (an abbreviation for "repeating tile") because four equilateral triangles can be arranged to form a larger equilateral triangle. Which of these figures are "reptiles?"

Answer this question by either drawing on dot paper or cutting out four copies of each figure and trying to arrange them.

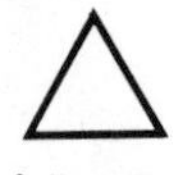

A "reptile"

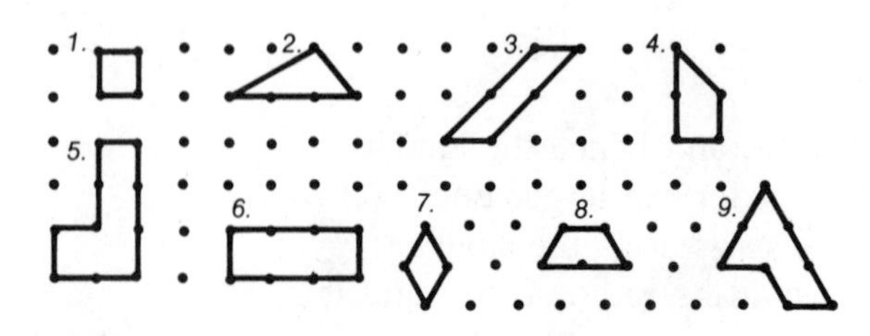

8. Suppose $\triangle ABC$ is a right triangle and $\overline{CD} \perp \overline{AB}$. If $CD = 8$, $AD = 16$, and $BD = 4$, find these ratios of areas.

a. $\dfrac{A(\triangle ACD)}{A(\triangle CBD)}$ **b.** $\dfrac{A(\triangle ACD)}{A(\triangle ABC)}$

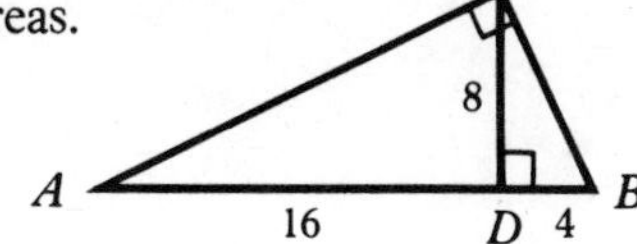

C.

9. Suppose points X, Y, and Z are the midpoints of the sides of $\triangle ABC$. Find the ratio $A(\triangle XYZ):A(\triangle ABC)$.

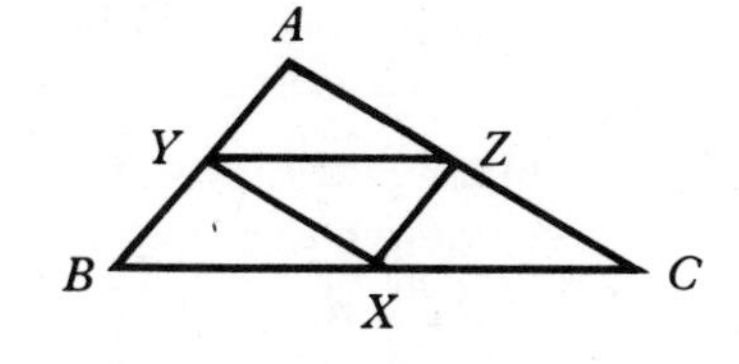

10. Suppose $\triangle ABC$ is a right triangle with hypotenuse c and legs a and b. Construct equilateral triangles on the sides of $\triangle ABC$ as shown. If the areas of these triangles are A_1, A_2, and A_3 as shown, show that $\dfrac{A_2}{A_1} + \dfrac{A_3}{A_1} = 1$.

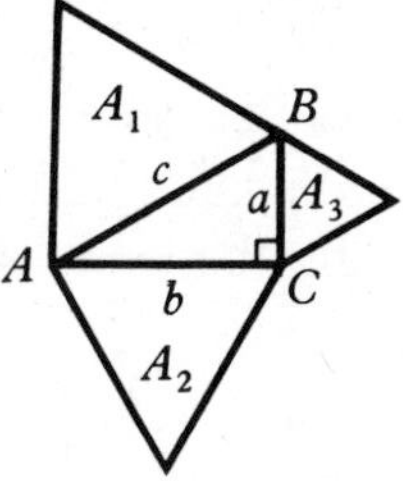

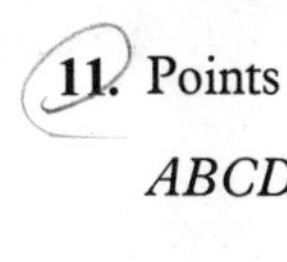

11. Points W, X, Y, and Z are midpoints of the sides of square $ABCD$. Find $\dfrac{A(ABCD)}{A(WXYZ)}$.

12. Points R, S, T, U, V, and W are midpoints of the sides of regular hexagon $ABCDEF$. Find $\dfrac{A(ABCDEF)}{A(RSTUVW)}$.

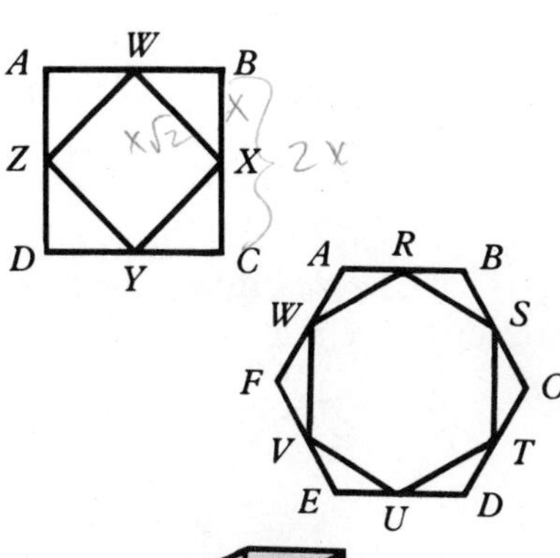

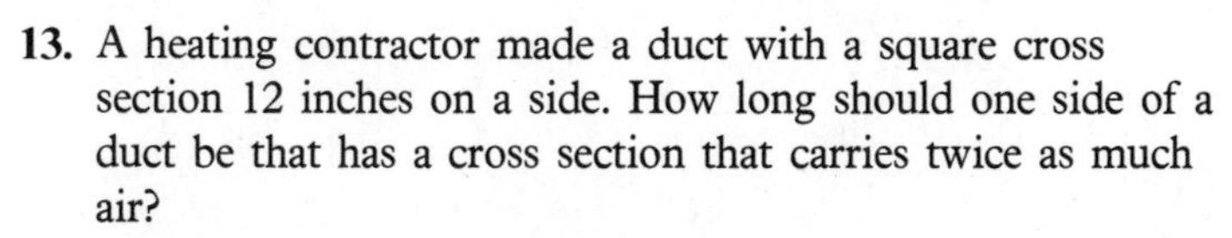

13. A heating contractor made a duct with a square cross section 12 inches on a side. How long should one side of a duct be that has a cross section that carries twice as much air?

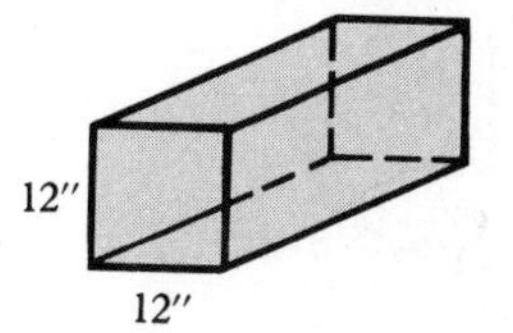

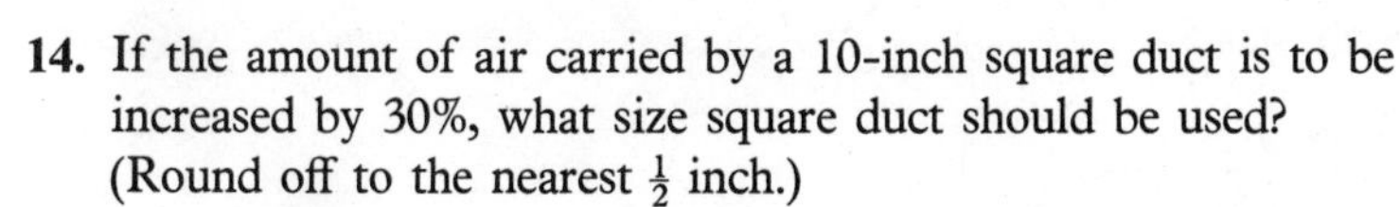

14. If the amount of air carried by a 10-inch square duct is to be increased by 30%, what size square duct should be used? (Round off to the nearest $\frac{1}{2}$ inch.)

PROBLEM SOLVING

A square-based pyramid is sliced by a plane passing through edge $\overline{AB}$ and point C. If the plane is parallel to the square base, a square cross section results.

If $\dfrac{AC}{CB} = \dfrac{1}{3}$, find $\dfrac{A(S)}{A(S')}$.

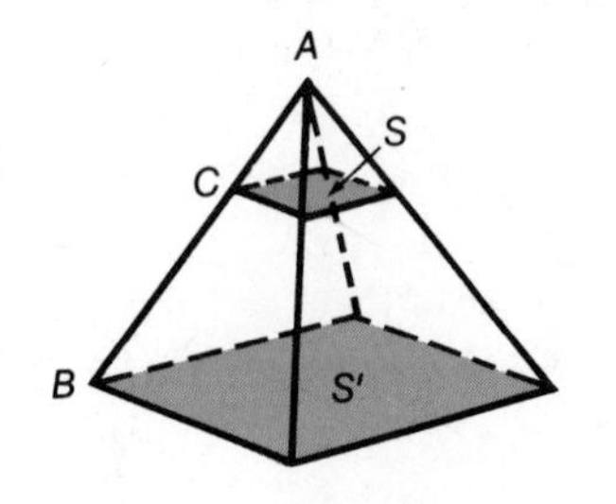

11–6 Ratio of Circumference and Diameter of a Circle

In computer graphics the plotter of the computer draws what appears to be curved lines. Actually the pen of the plotter draws successive straight line segments that are so short that the overall effect is a curved line. This same concept is used in finding the circumference of a circle.

These figures show a sequence of regular polygons that get closer and closer to a circle.

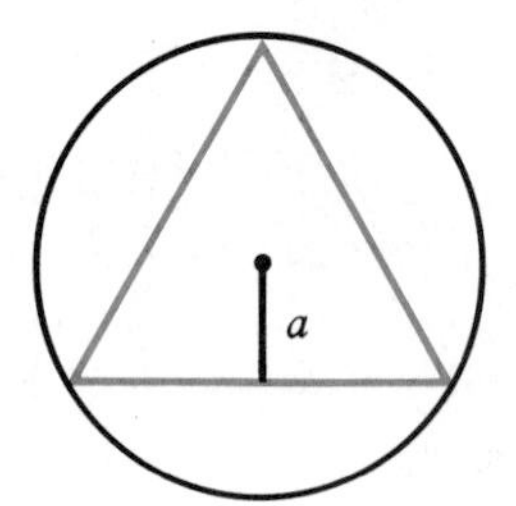

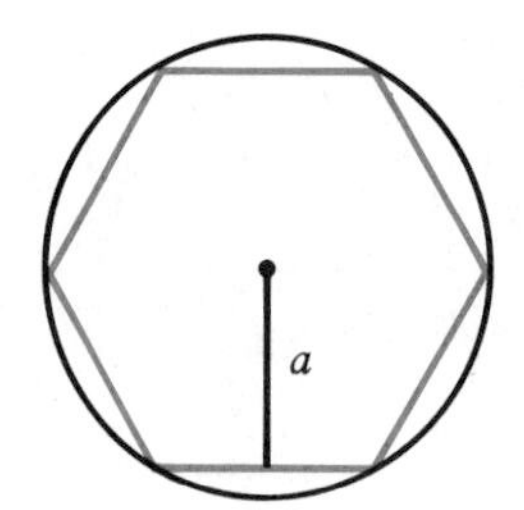

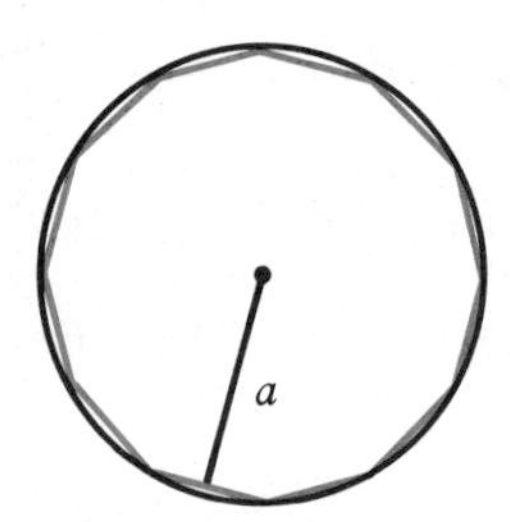

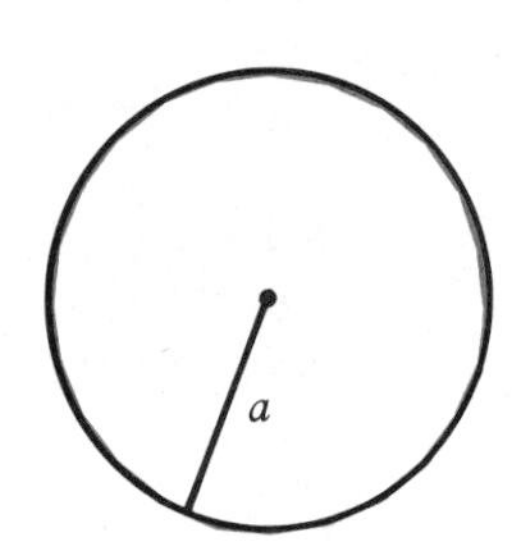

As the number of sides of the regular polygon increases, the polygon is nearly identical to its circumscribed circle. Also, the perimeter becomes close to a fixed number called the *circumference* of the circle, and the apothem becomes close to the radius of the circumscribed circle.

The following theorem is basic to the theory of circles.

Definition 11-6

The **circumference of a circle** is the number approached by the perimeters of the inscribed regular polygons as the number of sides of the regular polygons increases.

Theorem 11–8 The ratio of the circumference to the diameter is the same for all circles.

OUTLINE OF PROOF

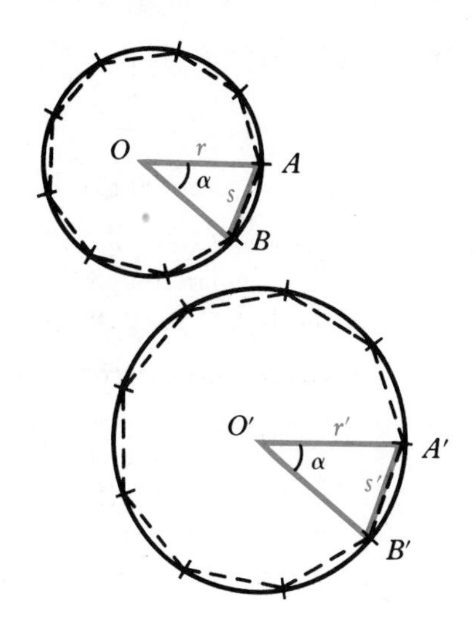

1. Select any two circles and inscribe in each a regular n-gon.
2. A pair of similar isosceles triangles $\triangle AOB$ and $\triangle A'O'B'$ are determined by one side of each n-gon.
3. Therefore, the ratios $\frac{s}{r}$ and $\frac{s'}{r'}$ are equal and $\frac{ns}{r} = \frac{n's'}{r'}$.
4. The numbers ns and $n's'$ equal the perimeters p and p' of the two regular n-gons. Therefore,
$$\frac{p}{r} = \frac{p'}{r'}.$$
5. As the number of sides n increases, the perimeters p and p' approach the circumferences C and C'. Therefore
$$\frac{C}{r} = \frac{C'}{r'} \text{ and } \frac{C}{2r} = \frac{C'}{2r'}.$$

The ratio $\frac{C}{d}$ is an irrational number, which means it cannot be written exactly as a decimal. Some approximations of this number are 3.14, $3\frac{1}{7}$, 3.14159.

Definition 11–7

The **ratio** $\frac{C}{d}$, which is the same real number for any circle, is denoted by π (the Greek letter pi).

Theorem 11–9 Given a circle with radius r and diameter d, the circumference C is given by the formula $C = \pi d = 2\pi r$.

APPLICATION

A cheerleader wants to make a pattern for a megaphone. This pattern is a portion of a circle bounded by a central angle and its intercepted arc. If the sides of the pattern are 15 inches and the central angle has a measure of 120°, find the length of the intercepted arc.

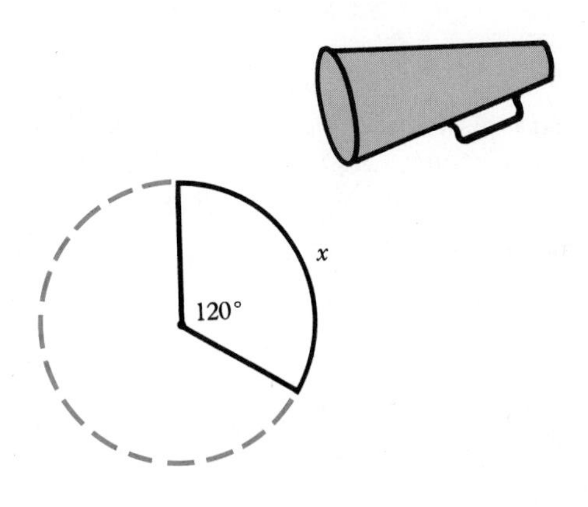

Solution. We can set up a proportion between the arc length, the circumference of the circle, the measure of the central angle, and the degree measure of the circle.

$$\frac{120}{360} = \frac{x}{\text{circumference}} = \frac{x}{2\pi 15}$$

$$\frac{1}{3} = \frac{x}{30\pi \text{ in.}} \quad \text{or} \quad x = 10\pi \doteq 31.4 \text{ in.}$$

EXERCISES

A.

1. If a regular 100-gon is inscribed in a circle, the perimeter of the 100-gon is nearly equal to the _?_ of the circle.
2. If a regular 100-gon is inscribed in a circle, the apothem of the 100-gon is nearly equal to the _?_ of the circle.
3. Give several approximations for the value π.

For exercises 4–8, find the missing numbers.

	radius	*diameter*	*circumference*
4.	2	?	4π
5.	?	6	?
6.	$7/\pi$	?	?
7.	?	?	8π
8.	?	?	16

B.

9. In a circle what does the ratio $\frac{C}{\pi}$ equal?

Activity

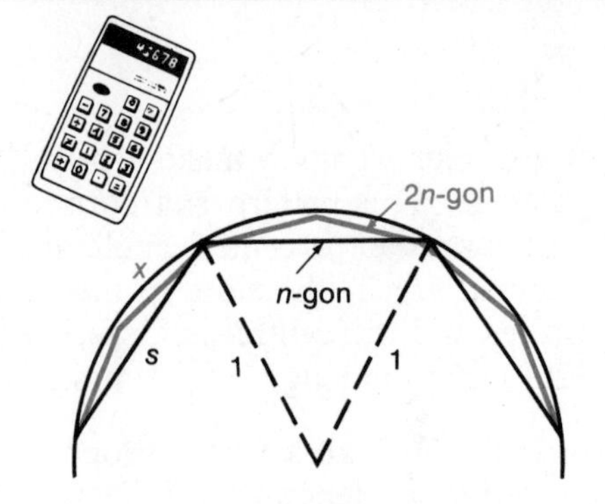

Finding an approximate value of π. (Use a calculator.)
The following formula can be proved.

$x = \sqrt{2 - \sqrt{4 - s^2}}$ $\quad s =$ length of side of the regular n-gon inscribed in a circle of radius 1.

Complete this table and approximate the value of π.

$x =$ length of a side of the corresponding $2n$-gon.

Continue the table for $n = 48, 96, 192, 384,$ and 768.

Number of sides (n)	Length of side (s)	Perimeter ($n \cdot s$)	Perimeter ÷ diameter	Side length of $2n$ gon (x)
6	1	6	3	$\sqrt{2 - \sqrt{4 - (1)^2}} = 0.517638$
12	0.517638	6.211656	3.105828	$\sqrt{2 - \sqrt{4 - (.517638)^2}} = 0.261052$
24	0.261052	?	?	

10. Find the length of an arc intercepted by a $60°$ central angle in a circle with radius 10. (Leave your answer in terms of π.)

11. A rectangular piece of cardboard is bent to form a tube 12 inches long and 3 inches in diameter. What is the area of this piece of cardboard?

12. If a gallon of paint covers 400 square feet, how many gallons are required to paint a silo (excluding the roof) that is 10 feet in diameter and 50 feet high?

13. On a large machine the centers of two pulleys are 16 feet apart and the radius of each pulley is 24 inches. How long a belt is needed to wrap around both pulleys?

14. The large sprocket on the pedals of a bicycle has 50 teeth and the small sprocket on the rear wheel has 20 teeth. When the pedals make two complete revolutions, how many revolutions does the wheel make?

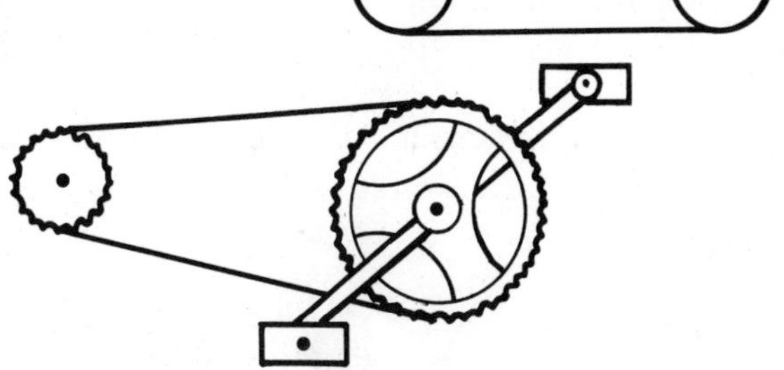

C.

15. A round tower with a 10-meter circumference is surrounded by a fence that is 2 meters from the tower. How long is the fence?

16. How far does a bicycle travel with each 25 revolutions of a wheel if the outside diameter of a tire is 29 inches?

17. Assume the earth's equator is a perfect circle with radius 4000 miles, and that a rope is tied tightly around the equator. Suppose a 40-foot piece of rope has been spliced into the rope and the rope has been propped up to form a fence. What would be the distance between the fence and the earth?

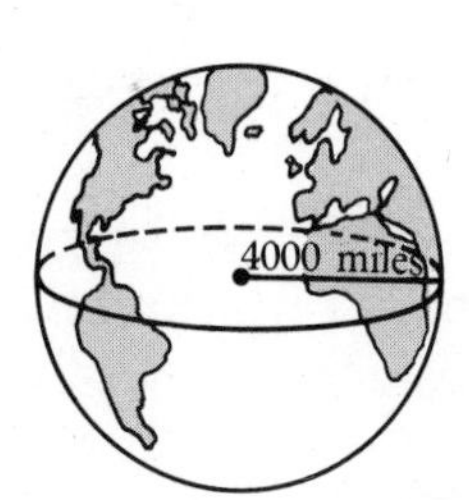

PROBLEM SOLVING

Use the Pythagorean Theorem twice to prove the formula that you used in the Activity on the opposite page.

Given: $OC = 1$

$AB = s$, $AC = x$

$AD = \frac{s}{2}$

Find: OD, CD, and x.

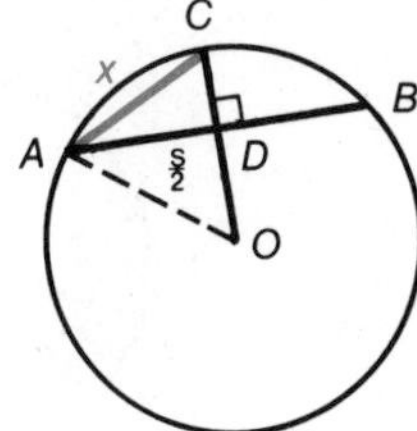

11–7 Area of Circles

A city building inspector must be sure that the water mains are large enough to meet the water demand in each part of the building. How much more water does a 6-inch water main carry than a 4-inch water main?

To show that the greater volume is $2\frac{1}{4}$ times the lesser volume, you must compare the area of the circular cross section of the larger pipe to the area of the circular cross section of the smaller pipe.

This figure helps explain the definition of area of a circle.

The area of an inscribed regular n-gon is a good approximation of the area of the circumscribed circle when n has a large value.

Definition 11-8

The **area of a circle** is the number approached by the areas of the inscribed regular n-gons as n gets larger and larger.

An inscribed regular polygon can be cut into triangles, which can be rearranged to form a parallelogram.

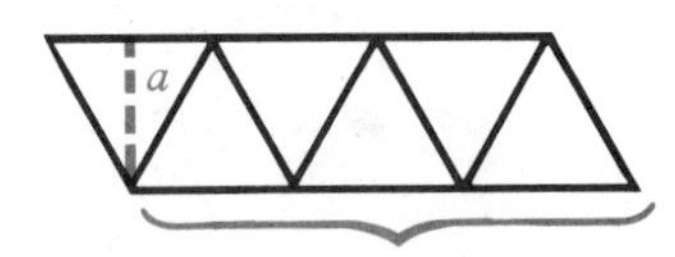

The area of the parallelogram is closely approximated by $\frac{1}{2}Ca$, $\frac{1}{2}(2\pi r)a$, or πra.

This approximation improves when the number of sides of the regular polygon is increased.

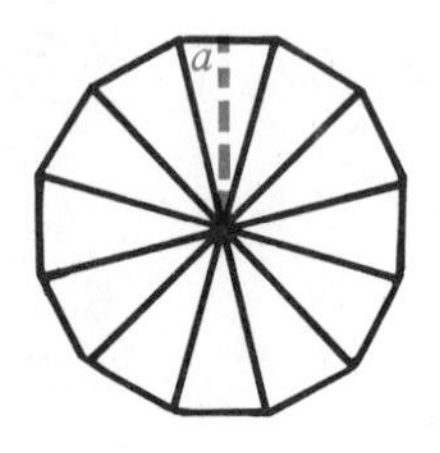

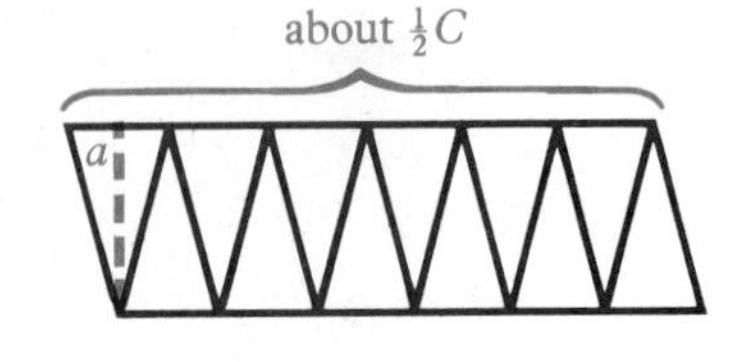

As the number of sides increases, the number of triangles making up the parallelogram increases.

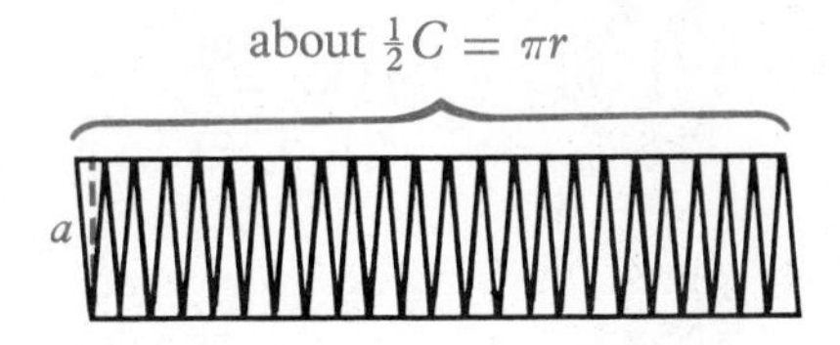

The apothem a approaches the radius r and the area πra approaches πr^2.

Theorem 11-10 Given a circle with radius r, the area A is given by the formula $A = \pi r^2$.

APPLICATION

The amount of water that a 6-inch pipe can carry can be compared to the water carried by a 4-inch pipe. We can do this by forming a ratio of the areas.

$A(C_1) = \pi(3)^2 = 9\pi$

$A(C_2) = \pi(2)^2 = 4\pi$

$\frac{A(C_1)}{A(C_2)} = \frac{9\pi}{4\pi} = 2.25$ or $2\frac{1}{4}$ times as much.

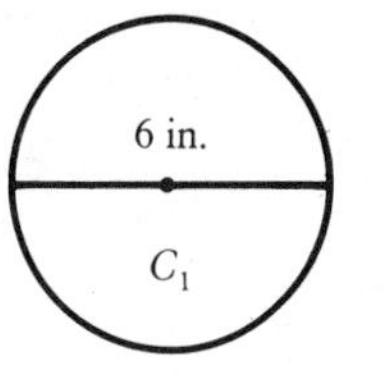

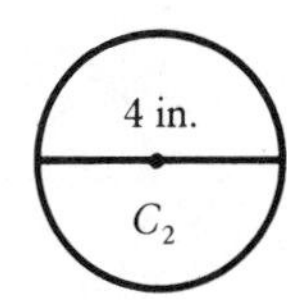

The formula for the area of a circle can be used to find the area of a region called a sector.

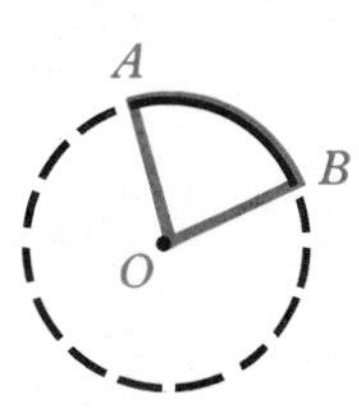

AOB is a sector of $\odot O$.

Definition 11-9

A **sector** is a region bounded by a central angle and its intercepted arc.

The ratio $\frac{\text{area of a sector}}{\text{area of the circle}}$ is equal to the ratio $\frac{\text{degree measure of the central angle}}{360°}$.

APPLICATION

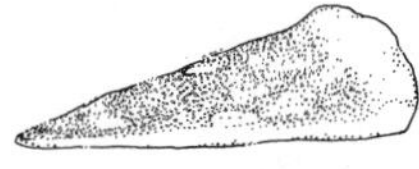

If a 16-inch pizza is cut into eight congruent pieces, what is the area of one piece?

$\frac{\text{area of one piece}}{64\pi \text{ sq in.}} = \frac{45°}{360°}$

Area(one piece) $= \frac{1}{8} \times 64\pi$ sq in. $= 8\pi$ sq in.

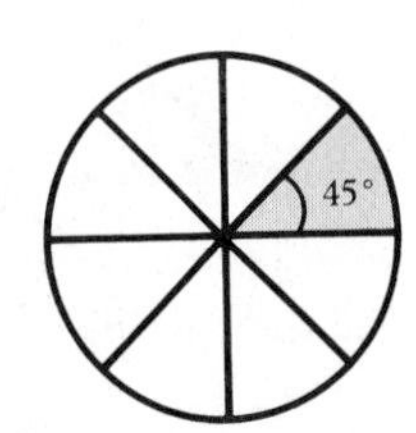

EXERCISES

A.

For exercises 1–4, express the answers as an exact number (use the number π).

1. Find the area of a circle with radius

a. 2 **b.** $5\frac{1}{2}$ **c.** π **d.** $\sqrt{3}$

2. Find the area of a circle with diameter

a. 6 **b.** $7\frac{1}{2}$ **c.** 3π **d.** $4\sqrt{2}$

3. Find the area of a circle whose circumference is

a. 2π **b.** 6π **c.** $\sqrt{6}\pi$ **d.** 10

4. Find the radius of a circle whose area is

a. 144π **b.** 225π **c.** 12π **d.** 100

For exercises 5–8, find the area of the shaded sectors. Give answers in terms of π.

5.

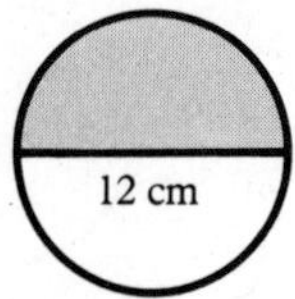

6.

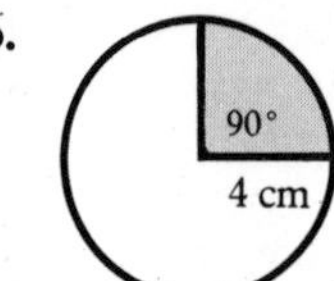

7.

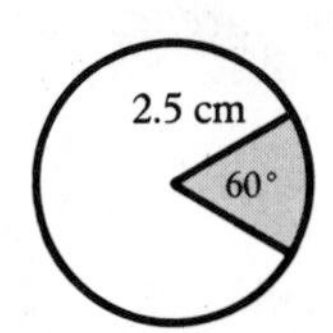

8.

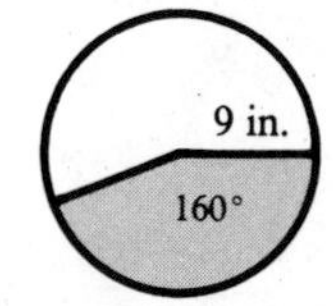

9. Find the approximate area of the following sectors. Use 3.14 for π.

a. Central angle, 50°
Radius, 3 cm

b. Central angle, 75°
Radius, 3 m

c. Central angle, 15°
Radius, 10 in.

10. If the area of a sector is one tenth the area of the circle, what is the central angle of the sector?

B.

11. Two circles have radii of 4 cm and 5 cm, respectively. What is the ratio of their areas?

12. The areas of two circles have a ratio of 9 to 4. What is the ratio of their radii?

13. The areas of two circles have a ratio of 8 to 5. What is the ratio of their radii?

14. Find the area of the inscribed and circumscribed circles of a square whose side is 4 cm.

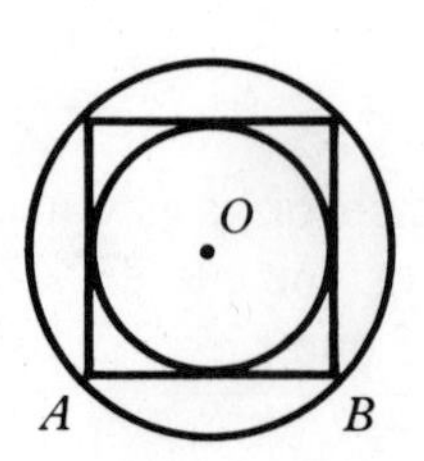

$AB = 4$ cm

For exercises 15–17, find the area of the shaded region. The length of one side of the square is 3.

15.

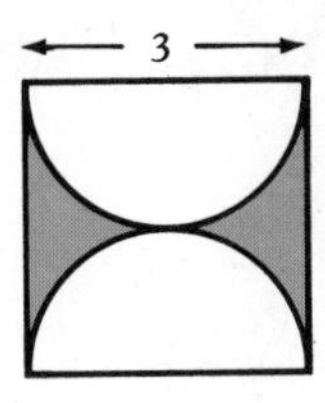

16.

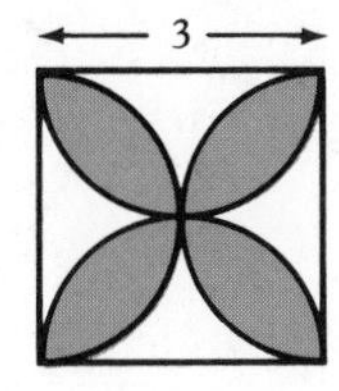

17.

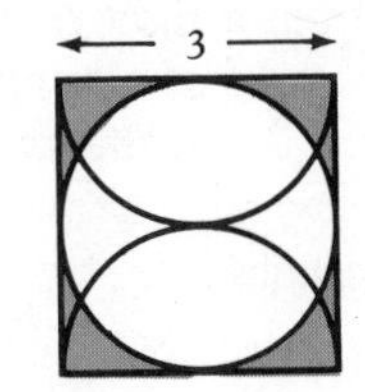

The shaded areas in the figures for exercises 18–20 are called **segments of the circle.** Find the area of each segment of the circle.

18.

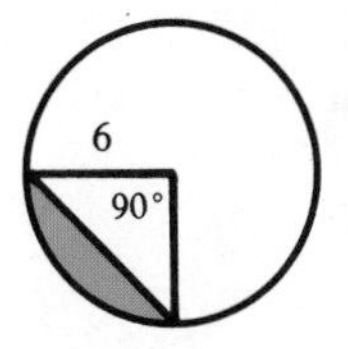

19.

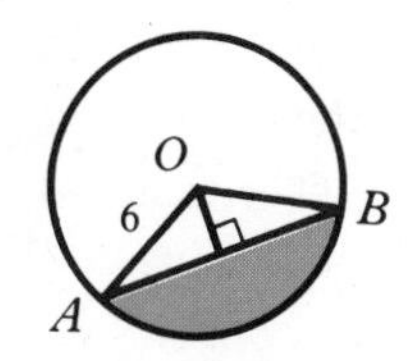

$m\angle AOB = 120$

20.

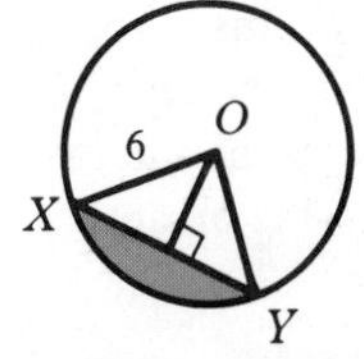

$m\angle XOY = 60$

C.

21. Circles of equal radii are packed in a rectangle as shown. What fraction of the rectangular region is shaded?

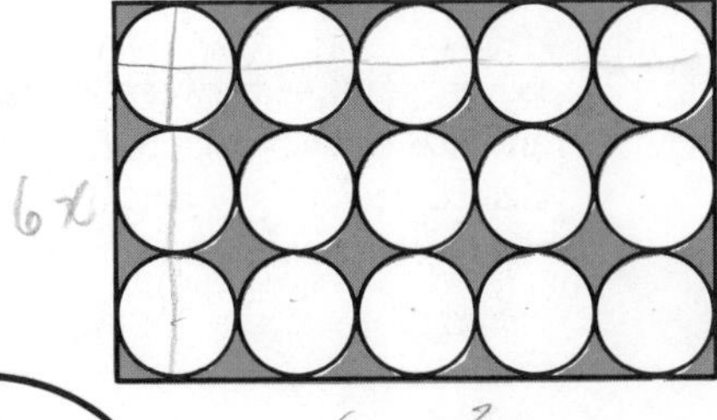

22. A pipe 12 inches in diameter carries how many times as much water as a pipe 10 inches in diameter?

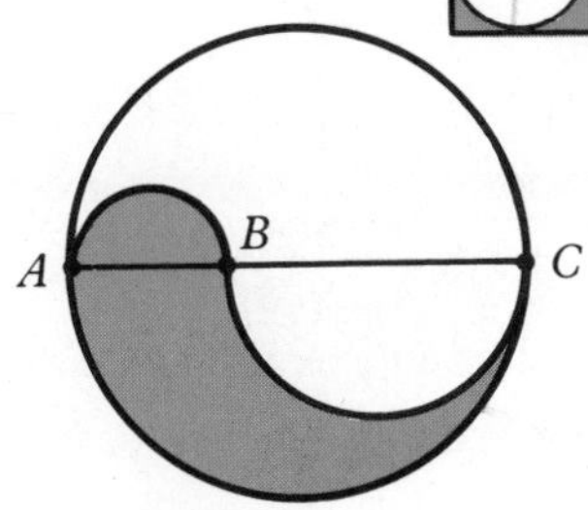

23. If $BC = 2AB$, what fraction of the circle is shaded?

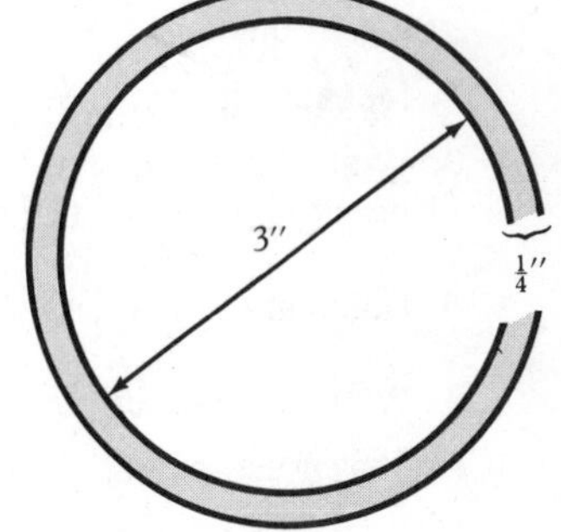

24. The figure at the right represents the cross section of a pipe $\frac{1}{4}$ inch thick that has an inside diameter of 3 inches. Find the area of the shaded region.

25. Given a right triangle $\triangle ABC$, show that the area of a semicircle on the hypotenuse is equal to the sum of the areas of the semicircles on the two legs of the triangle.

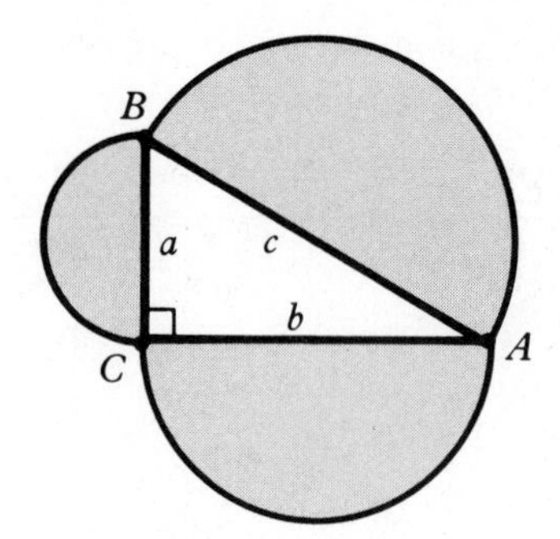

26. Given a right triangle $\triangle ABC$, its circumscribed circle, and semicircles on the two legs, show that the sum of the areas of the two shaded regions is equal to the area of $\triangle ABC$.

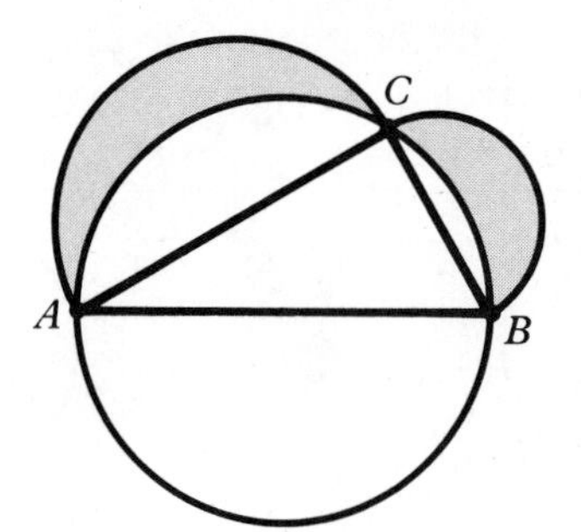

27. Given point C between A and B, and semicircles on $\overline{AC}$, $\overline{CB}$, and $\overline{AB}$ as shown. If $\overline{CD} \perp \overline{AB}$, show that the area of the shaded region is equal to the area of the circle with $\overline{CD}$ as diameter. (*Hint:* Consider the right triangle $\triangle ADB$.)

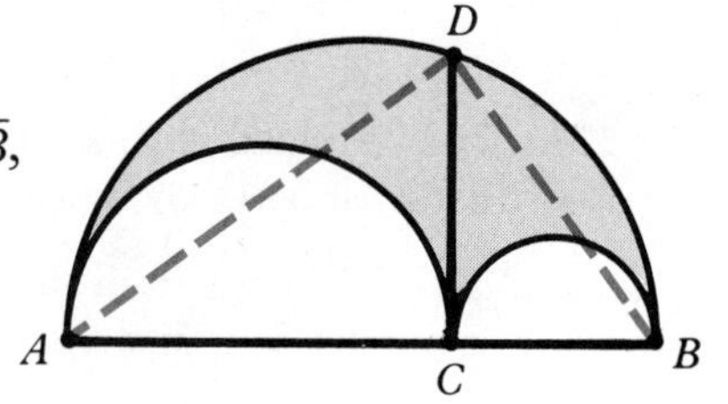

Activity

Estimate the value of π through direct measurement.

1. Select a circular object about the size of the top of a round waste basket.
2. Measure its diameter (d) to the nearest millimeter.
3. Wrap a string around the object and measure its length to find its circumference (C) to the nearest millimeter.
4. Calculate $\frac{C}{d}$. How accurate is your estimate of π?
5. What things can you do to improve your estimate?

Repeat these same five steps using a tin can and a bicycle wheel.

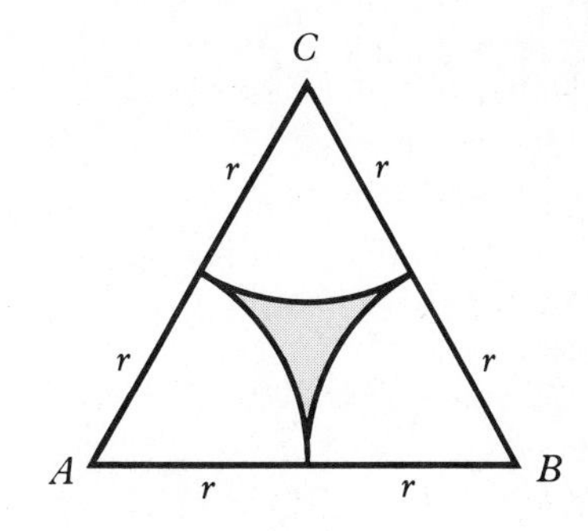

28. If $\triangle ABC$ is an equilateral triangle, what fraction of the triangle is shaded?

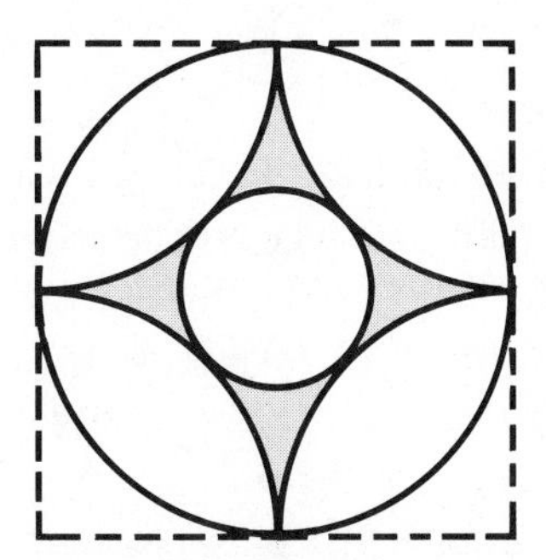

29. In the figure the small circle is tangent to four circular arcs. What fraction of the large circle is shaded?

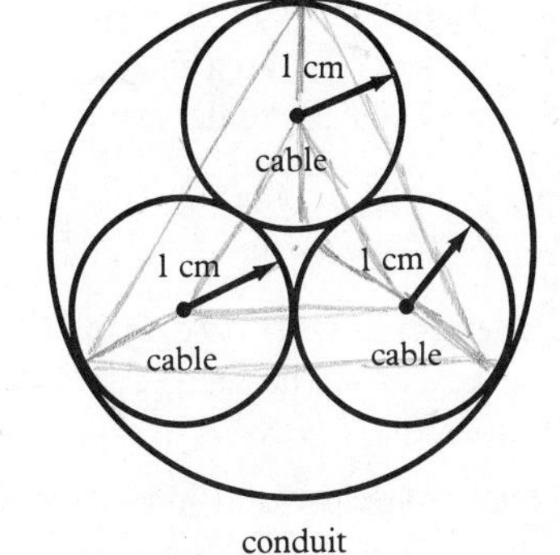

30. Conduit for telephone cable is sized so that it carries three cables (each circular and tangent to the conduit and to each other) that are each 1 cm in radius. What fraction of the conduit is filled?

PROBLEM SOLVING

Points A', B', and C' are points of trisection of the sides of $\triangle ABC$. The area of the shaded triangular region is _?_ the area of $\triangle ABC$.

Use a grid of small squares or a measurement technique to decide whether the blank should be filled in with the fraction $\frac{1}{5}$, $\frac{1}{6}$, $\frac{1}{7}$, or $\frac{1}{8}$.

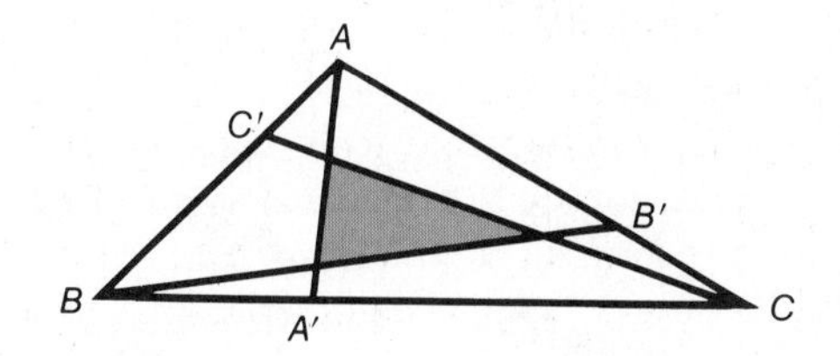

Important Ideas—Chapter 11

Terms

Polygonal region (p. 394)
Square unit (p. 398)
Altitude of a parallelogram (p. 399)
Perimeter of a polygon (p. 408)
Apothem of a regular polygon (p. 408)
Circumference of a circle (p. 416)
Pi(π) (p. 417)
Area of a circle (p. 420)
Sector (p. 421)
Segment of a circle (p. 423)

Postulates

Area Postulate. A unique positive number called the area can be assigned to each polygonal region. The area of region R is denoted by $A(R)$.

Area of Congruent Regions Postulate. If two rectangles or two triangles are congruent, then the regions they bound have the same area.

Area Addition Postulate. If a polygonal region is the union of n non-overlapping polygonal regions, then its area is the sum of the areas of these n-regions.

Rectangle Area Postulate. The area of a rectangle with length ℓ and width w is given by the formula ℓw.

Theorems

11-1 Given a parallelogram with base b and corresponding height h, the area A is given by the formula $A = bh$.

11-2 Given a triangle with base b and corresponding altitude h, the area A is given by the formula $A = \frac{1}{2}bh$.

11-3 If $\triangle ABC$ has sides of length a, b, and c, then $A(\triangle ABC) = \sqrt{s(s-a)(s-b)(s-c)}$ where $s = \frac{1}{2}(a+b+c)$.

11-4 Given a trapezoid with bases b_1 and b_2 and altitude h, the area A is given by the formula $A = \frac{1}{2}h(b_1 + b_2)$.

11-5 Given a regular n-gon with sides of length s and apothem a, the area A is given by the formula $A = \frac{1}{2}ans = \frac{1}{2}ap$ where perimeter $p = ns$.

11-6 The ratio of the perimeters of two similar polygons is equal to the ratio of the lengths of any pair of corresponding sides.

11-7 The ratio of the areas of two similar polygons is equal to the square of the ratio of the lengths of any pair of corresponding sides.

11-8 The ratio of the circumference to the diameter is the same for all circles.

11-9 Given a circle with radius r and diameter d, the circumference C is given by the formula $C = \pi d = 2\pi r$.

11-10 Given a circle with radius r, the area A is given by the formula $A = \pi r^2$.

Chapter 11—Review

1. Find the area of the figures below. Assume that segments are parallel or congruent if they appear so.

a.

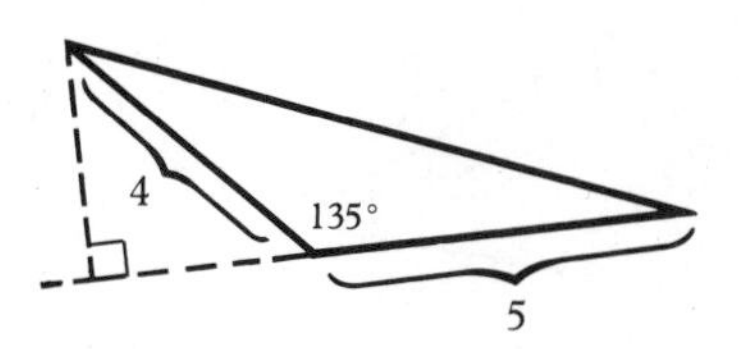

b.

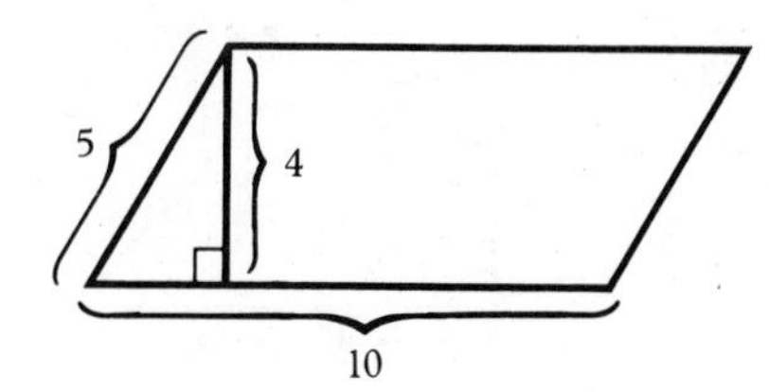

c.

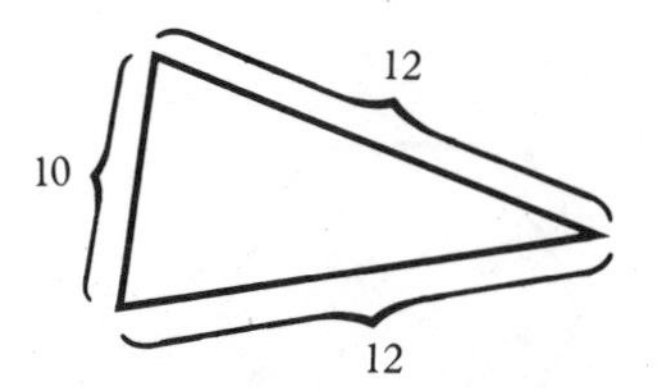

d.

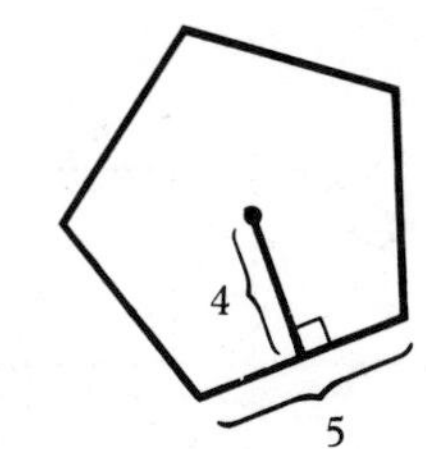

2. Given: $\triangle ABC \sim \triangle DEF$, area$(\triangle ABC) = 3$

a. Find the length of the altitude to $\overline{AB}$.

b. Find the area of $\triangle DEF$.

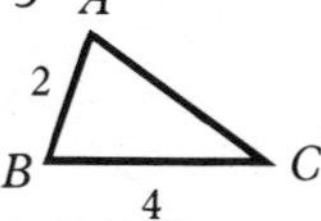

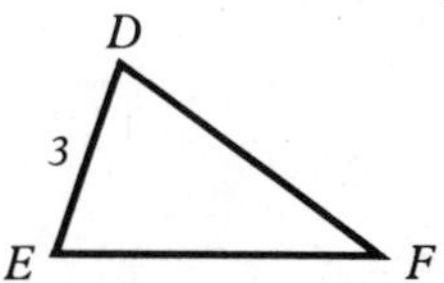

3. The circumference of circle O' is twice that of circle O. What is the ratio of the lengths of their diameters?

4. Find the area of a regular hexagon inscribed in a circle with a diameter of 6 cm.

5. In $\triangle ABC$, $\overline{AE}$ is an altitude, $\overline{AF}$ is an angle bisector, and $\overline{AD}$ is a median. Which segment divides $\triangle ABC$ into two triangles of equal area?

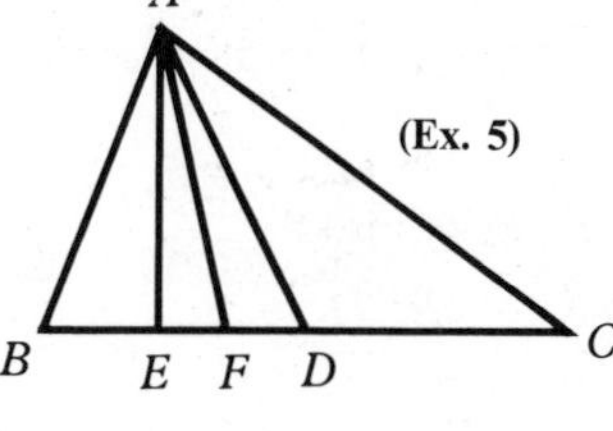

6. Find the area of the shaded portions. Assume segments are congruent if they appear so.

(Ex. 6)

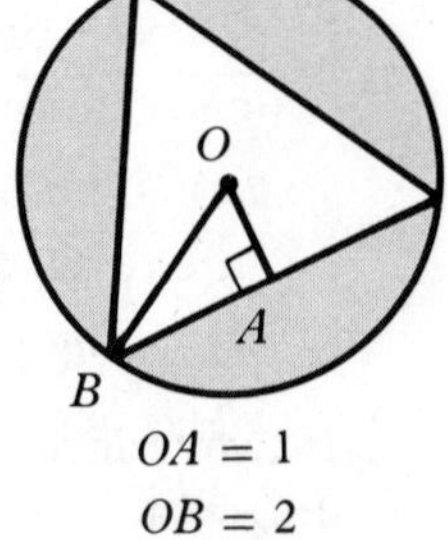

7. In $\triangle ABC$, D, E, and F are midpoints.

Find the ratio $\dfrac{\text{area}(\triangle DEF)}{\text{area}(\triangle ABC)}$.

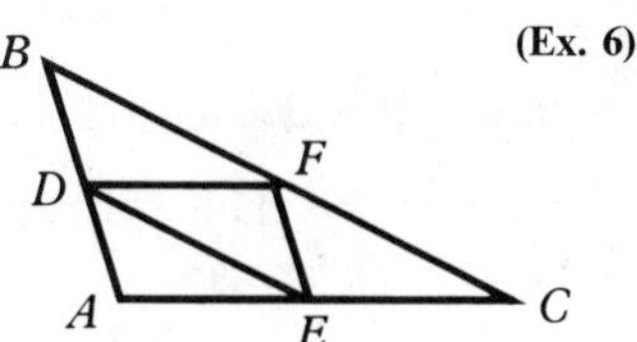

8. Find the area of a circle that is inscribed in a square whose area is 16 square units.

Chapter 11—Test

1. Find the area of the figures below. Assume that segments are parallel or congruent if they appear so.

a.

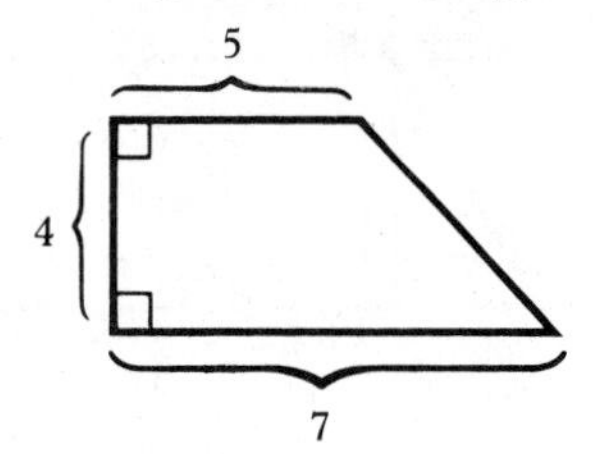

b.

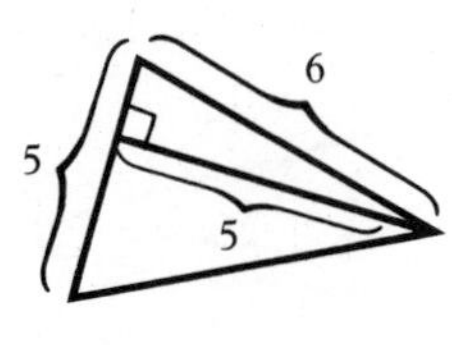

c.

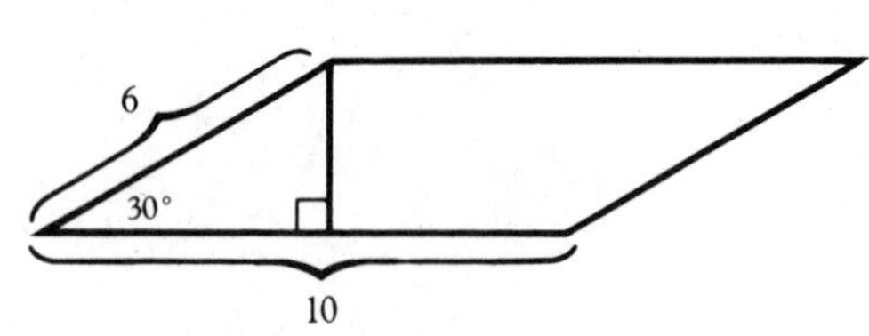

d.

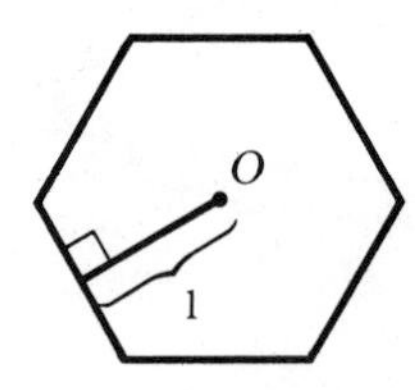

2. **Given:** $\triangle ABC \sim \triangle DFE$

   a. Find the perimeter of $\triangle ABC$.

   b. Find the area of $\triangle ABC$.

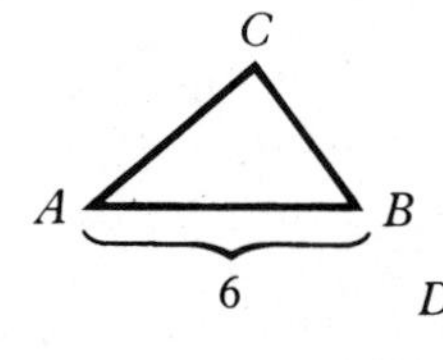

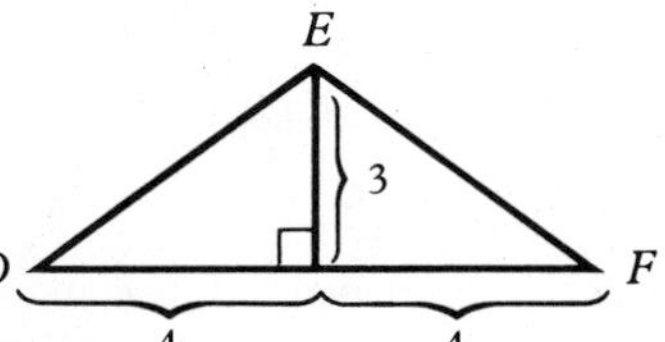

3. Find the area of the shaded portions, where $AB = 10$ and $BC = 26$.

4. If each side of a regular polygon is doubled, how is the perimeter affected? How is the area affected?

5. Find the following two ratios.

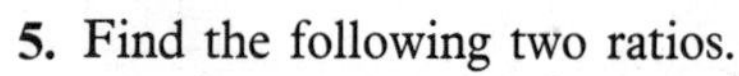

   a. $\dfrac{\text{perimeter of square } ABCD}{\text{circumference of circle } O}$

   b. $\dfrac{\text{area}(ABCD)}{\text{area}(\odot O)}$

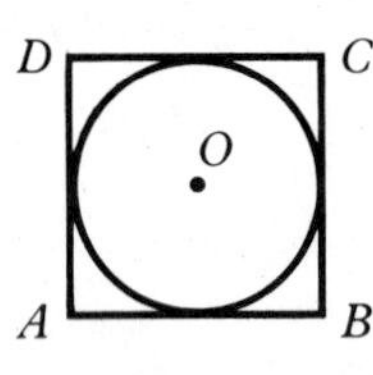

   c. Do the answers to **a** and **b** depend on the size of the figure?

6. If two triangles are similar and their perimeters are in a ratio of 2 : 1, what is the ratio of their areas?

7. Find the circumference and area of a circle with diameter of 4 cm. How are they different?

8. Find the area of the regular polygon.

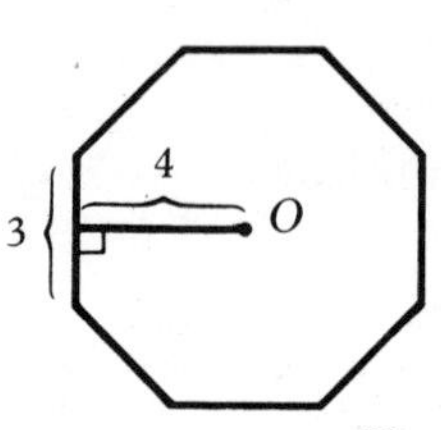

(Ex. 8)

Algebra Review

Evaluate each formula for the letter indicated.

1. $A = bh$; for A if $b = 6$ cm, $h = 4$ cm
2. $A = \frac{1}{2}h\,(b_1 + b_2)$; for A if $h = 7$ cm, $b_1 = 9$ cm, $b_2 = 15$ cm
3. $C = 2\pi r$; for C if $r = 14$ cm (use $\pi \doteq 3.14$).
4. $A = 4\pi r^2$; for A if $r = 14$ cm
5. $V = \frac{4}{3}\pi r^3$; for V if $r = 14$ cm
6. $V = \frac{1}{3}Bh$; for h if $V = 100\text{ cm}^3$, $B = 30\text{ cm}^2$
7. $A = \frac{1}{2}h\,(b_1 + b_2)$; for h if $A = 36\text{ cm}^2$, $b_1 = 12$ cm, $b_2 = 8$ cm
8. $A = 4\pi r^2$; for r if $A = 100\pi\text{ m}^2$
9. $A = \pi r\ell + \pi r^2$; for A if $r = 4\frac{1}{2}$ in., $\ell = 8\frac{1}{2}$ in.
10. $A = \dfrac{s^2\sqrt{3}}{4}$; for s if $A = 6\sqrt{3}$ sq yd

Solve for x.

11. $(x + 2)(x - 3) = 0$
12. $x^2 - 9 = 0$
13. $x^2 + 4x + 4 = 0$
14. $x^2 - 6x + 9 = 0$
15. $x^2 + 5x = -6$
16. $x^2 + x - 2 = 0$
17. $x(x - 1) = 90$
18. $6x^2 - 7x = 5$
19. $1 - 8x + 15x^2 = 0$
20. $x^2 - 11x = 180$
21. $x(x - 5) + 6 = 0$
22. $0 = 5x - 3x^2 + 2$

Solve.

23. Find the area of a rectangular field whose length is 100 yards and width is 79 yards.
24. Find the area of a square whose perimeter is 20 cm.
25. The perimeter of a rectangle is 40 cm and its length is 5 cm more than its width. Find its area.
26. A circular pond has a diameter of 48 meters. What is its area?
27. The base of a triangle is 3 times as long as its height. If together they measure 72 mm, what is the area of the triangle?
28. The length and width of a rectangle together measure 100 yards. Their difference is 7 yards. What is the area of the rectangle?
29. The dimensions of a rectangular flower garden are 40 meters by 24 meters. There is a walk around the garden. The area of the garden and the walk is 1232 square meters. Find the width of the walk.
30. The width of a rectangle is 16 cm. The diagonal is 4 cm more than the length. Find the length of the rectangle.

Geometry In Our World

Computer Graphics: Transformations

An important use of computer graphics is the analysis of shapes. First we will discuss the idea of moving a shape in a plane. The computer can be programmed to move a figure to different positions on the screen. These movements are called transformations.

One of the transformations that may be used is the translation. In a program the following command will cause the point (x, y) to be moved 50 units to the right and 70 units up. It is one line in a program that causes a figure to be translated.

```
HPLOT X,Y TO X+50, Y+70
```

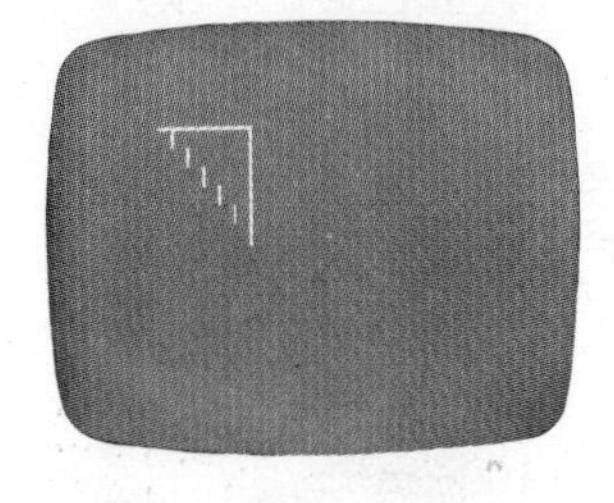

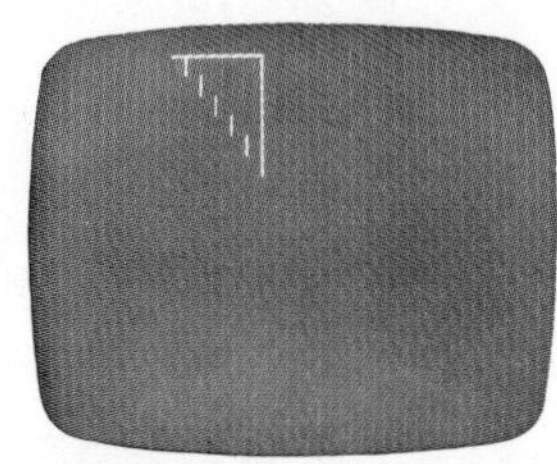

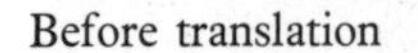

Before translation

After translation

In a program the following command will cause a point (x, y) to be rotated 90° counterclockwise about the origin. It could be one line in a program that causes a figure to be rotated.

```
HPLOT X, Y TO -Y,X
```

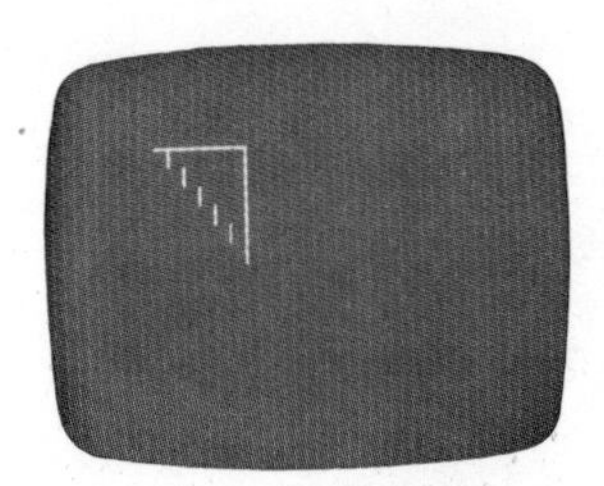

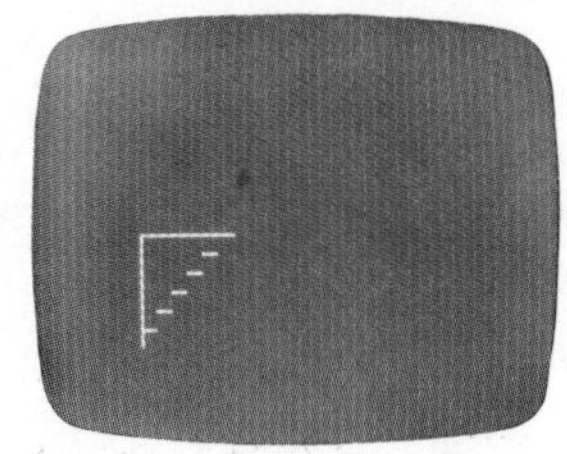

Before rotation

After rotation

In a program the following command will cause a point (x, y) to be reflected in the y-axis. It could be one line in a program that causes a figure to be reflected.

```
HPLOT X,Y TO -X,Y
```

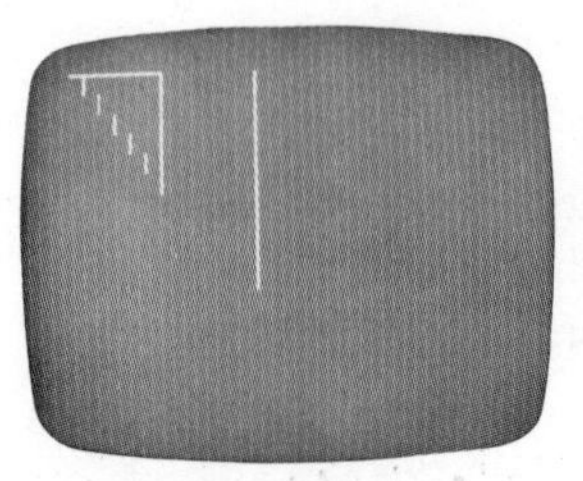

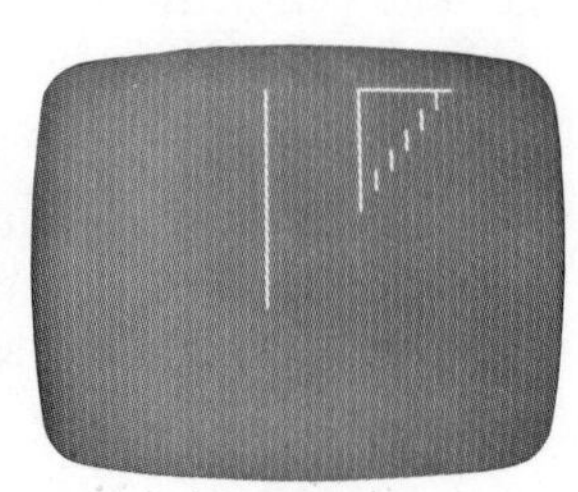

Before reflection

After reflection

The benefit for using the computer to show different views of an object is particularly great for 3-dimensional solids. Here we see an example of such a solid.

Below we see how a computer can help show different views of this solid.

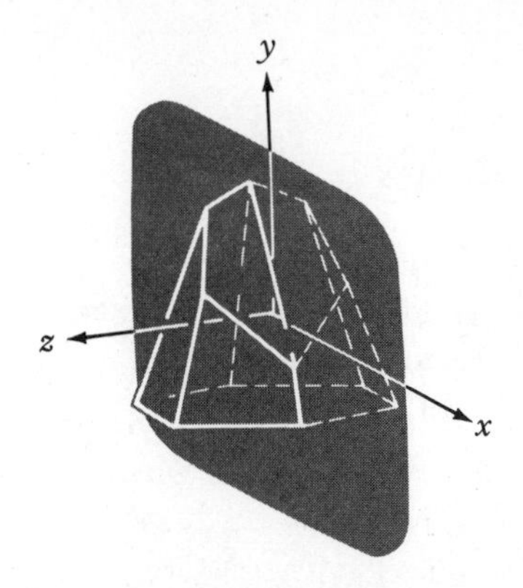

In each of these figures the computer screen shows the solid as you look at the *xy*-plane.

A view onto the *xy*-plane

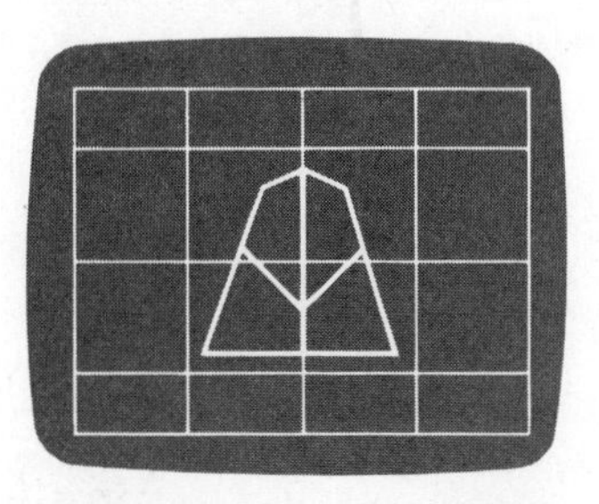

A view after a 90° rotation about the *y*-axis

A view after a 90° rotation about the *x*-axis

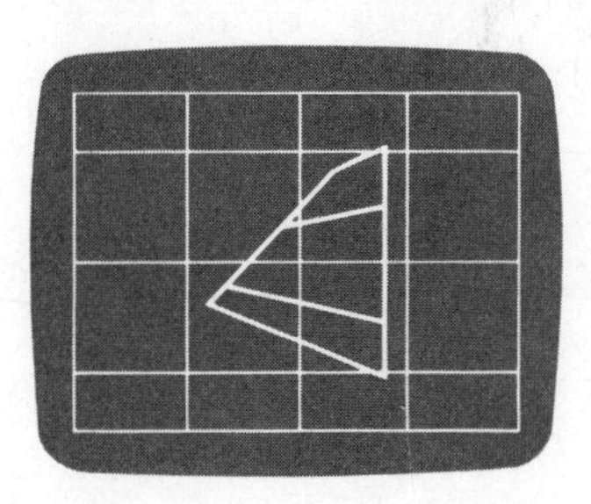

A view after a 90° rotation about the *z*-axis

1. Sketch the same four views as shown above for the solid shown here.

2. Draw a 3-dimensional sketch of your own. Draw the same four views as shown above for your solid.

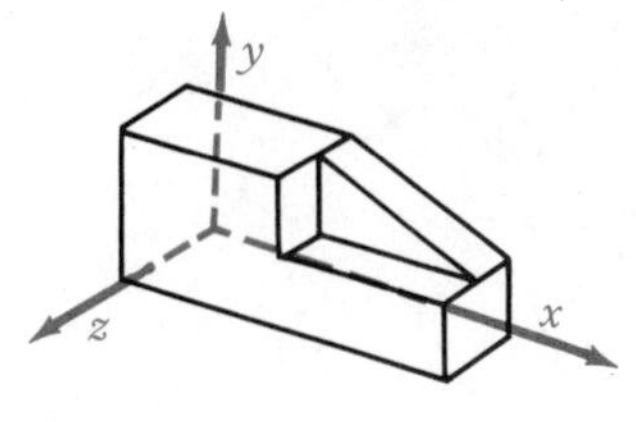

CHAPTER 12

Solids

12–1 Pyramids and Prisms

The pyramid shape was used by many ancient civilizations. These pyramids were built by Egyptians. They are examples of *polyhedra*.

A *polyhedron* is a 3-dimensional object made up of polygonal regions called *faces*. The sides and vertices of the faces are called *edges* and *vertices* of the polyhedron.

This triangular prism is a special kind of polyhedron.

Definition 12–1

A **polyhedron** consists of a finite number of polygonal regions. Each edge of a region is the edge of exactly one other region. If two regions intersect, then they intersect in an edge or a vertex.

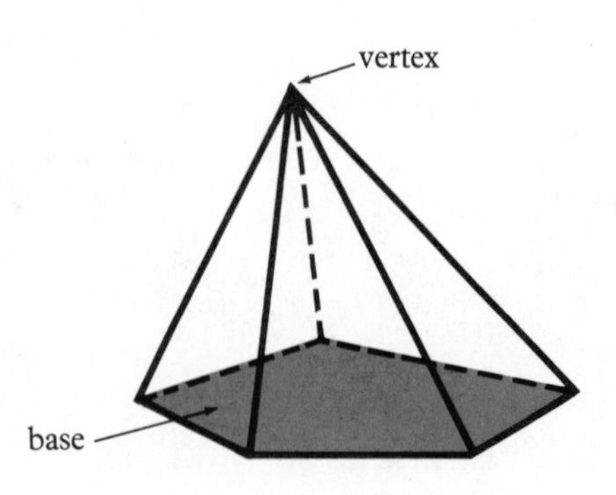

Definition 12–2

A **pyramid** is a polyhedron in which all faces but one have a vertex in common.

That common vertex is called *the vertex* of the pyramid, and the face that does not contain the vertex is called the *base* of the pyramid.

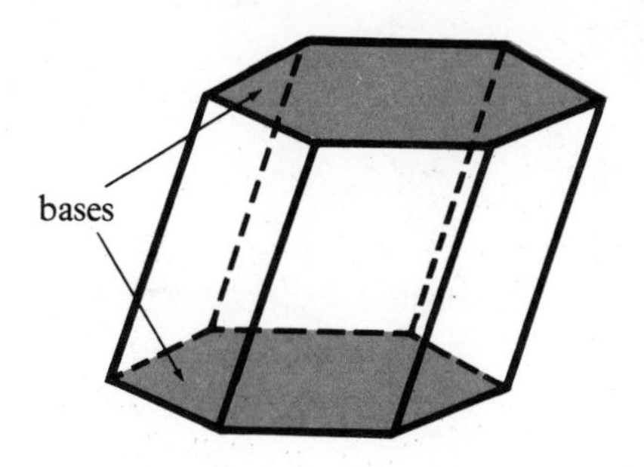

Definition 12–3

A **prism** is a polyhedron that satisfies these properties:

1. There is a pair of congruent faces that lie in parallel planes (*bases*).
2. All other faces are parallelograms.

For both pyramids and prisms, the faces that are not bases are called *lateral faces* and the non-base edges are called *lateral edges*. A segment between the bases of a prism perpendicular to the bases is an *altitude*. A segment from the vertex to the base of a pyramid perpendicular to the base is an *altitude*.

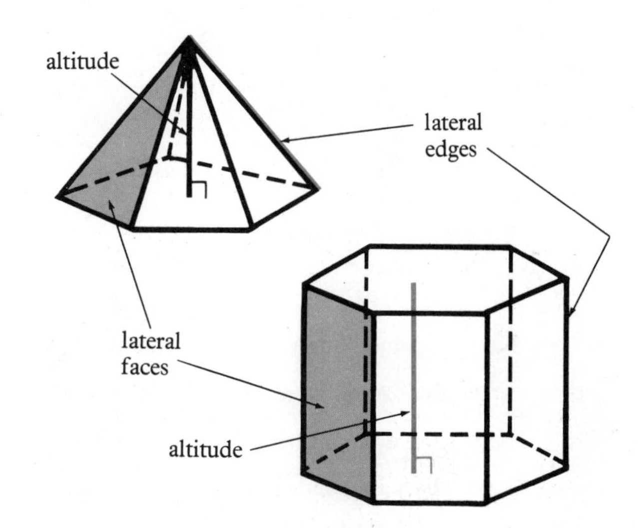

A pyramid is *regular* if its base is a regular polygon and its lateral edges are congruent.

A prism is a *right prism* if its lateral edges are perpendicular to its bases.

regular pyramid   slant height   right prism

This theorem states an important characteristic of prisms.

Theorem 12–1 The lateral edges of a prism are parallel and congruent.

EXERCISES

A.

1. Which one of these figures is **not** a pyramid? Why?

a.

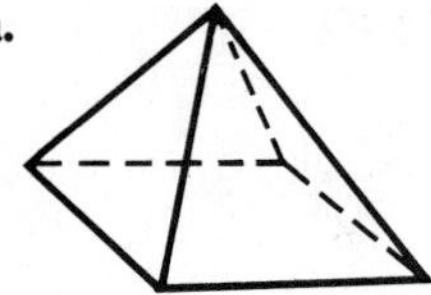

b.

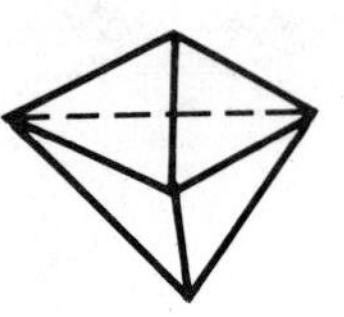

c.

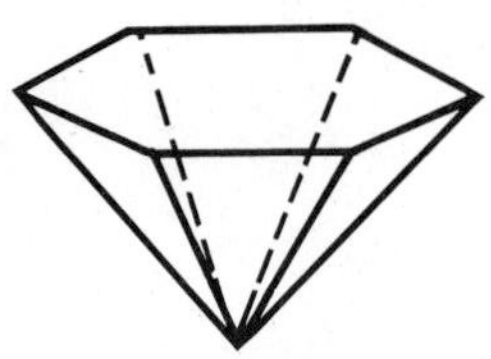

2. Which one of these figures is a prism? Why?

a.

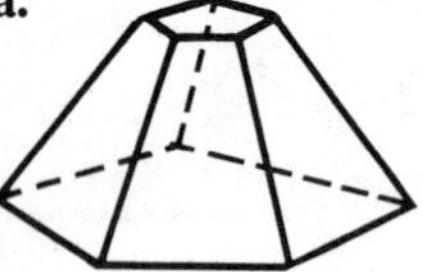

b.

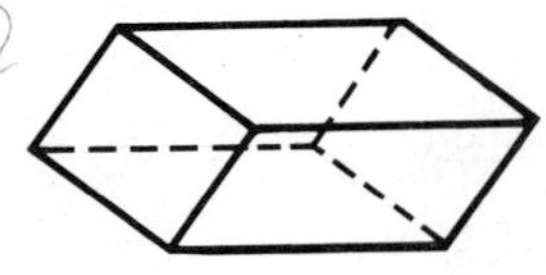

c.

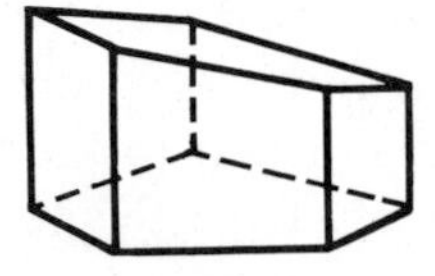

3. Name five base edges in this pyramid.
4. Name five lateral edges in this pyramid.
5. Identify five lateral faces in this pyramid.

(Exs. 3–5)

6. Name the base edges in this prism.
7. Name the lateral edges in this prism.
8. Identify the lateral faces in this prism.
9. In any pyramid how do the number of base edges compare to the number of lateral edges? same
10. In any prism how do the number of base edges compare to the number of lateral edges? same

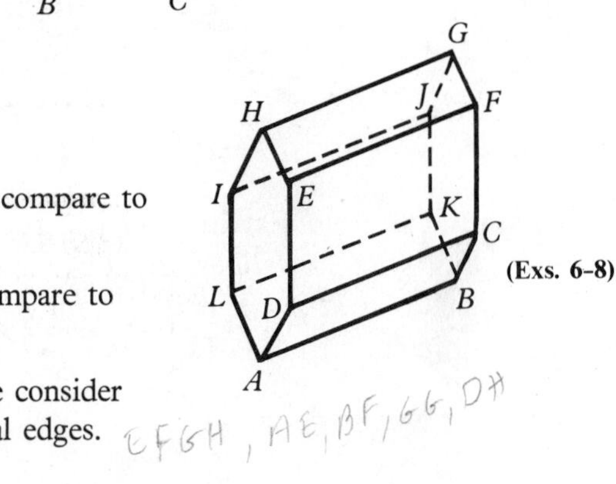

(Exs. 6–8)

11. If we view the cube at the right as a prism and we consider $ABCD$ a base, name the second base and the lateral edges. EFGH, AE, BF, GG, DH
12. If for the cube at the right we consider $ABFE$ a base, name the second base and the lateral edges.

CDHG
BC, AD, EH, FG

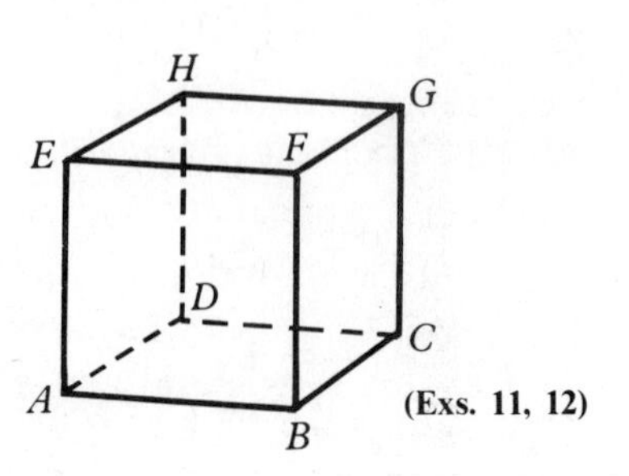

(Exs. 11, 12)

If the bases of a prism are a parallelogram, the prism is called a parallelepiped. Exercises 13–19 are about a parallelepiped.

(Exs. 13–19)

13. If $BCGF$ is one base of the prism, name the second base.

14. If $ABFE$ is one base of the prism, name the second base.

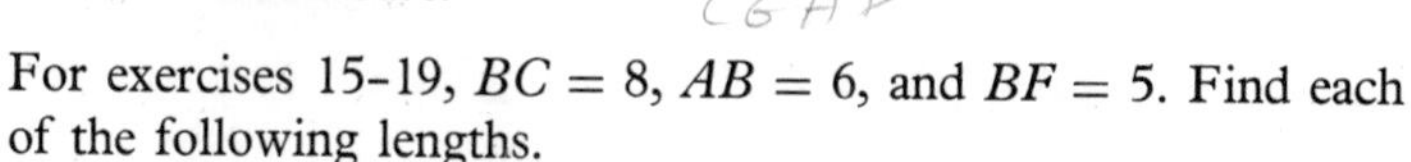

For exercises 15–19, $BC = 8$, $AB = 6$, and $BF = 5$. Find each of the following lengths.

15. $AE = \underline{?}$ 16. $EH = \underline{?}$

17. $CD = \underline{?}$ 18. $DH = \underline{?}$

19. Name the four diagonals of this parallelepiped.

20. Sketch a pyramid with a quadrilateral base. Hidden edges should be represented by drawing dashed lines. (*Hint:* First draw the base, then choose the vertex, then connect the vertex to the vertices of the base.)

21. Sketch a pyramid with a hexagonal base.

22. Sketch a prism with a hexagonal base.

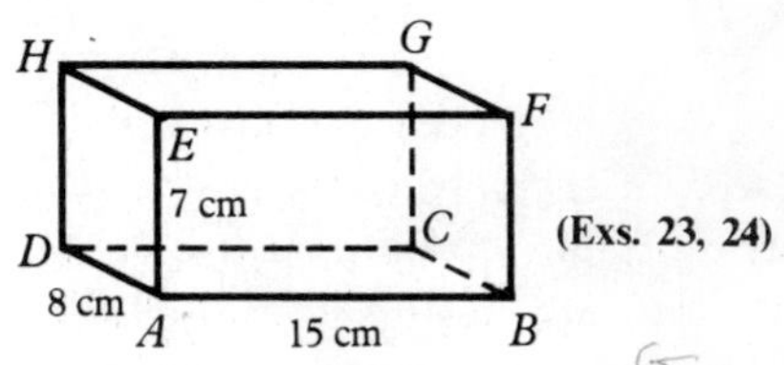

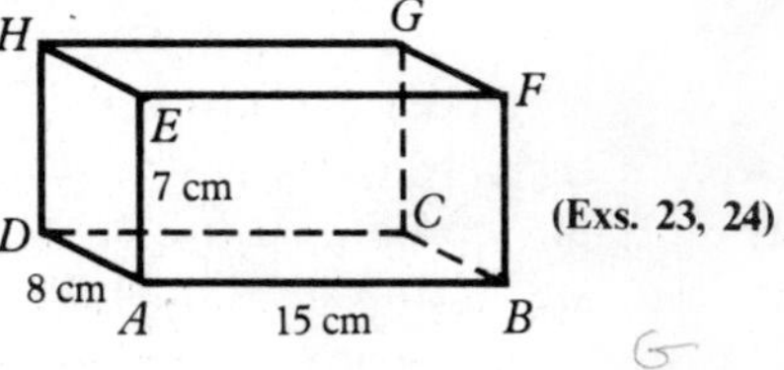

(Exs. 23, 24)

23. Suppose all faces of a parallelepiped are rectangles and $AB = 15$ cm and $AD = 8$ cm. Show that $AC = 17$.

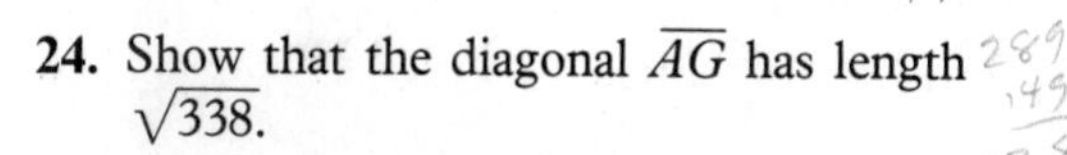

24. Show that the diagonal $\overline{AG}$ has length $\sqrt{338}$.

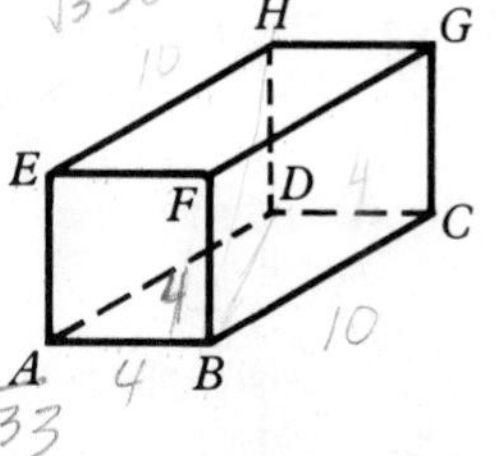

25. Given a parallelepiped with all rectangular faces as shown. If $EH = 10$, $DC = 4$, and $FB = 4$, find the length of diagonal $\overline{HB}$.

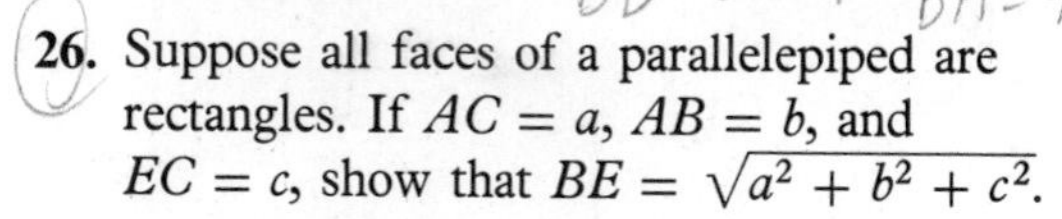

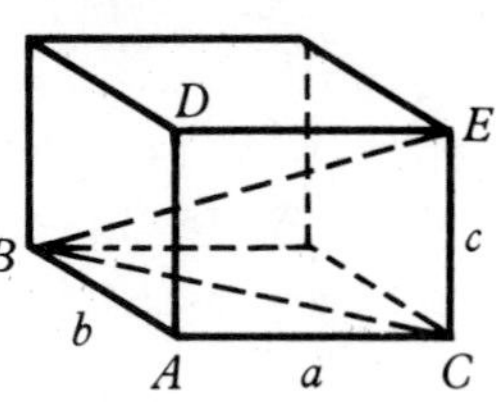

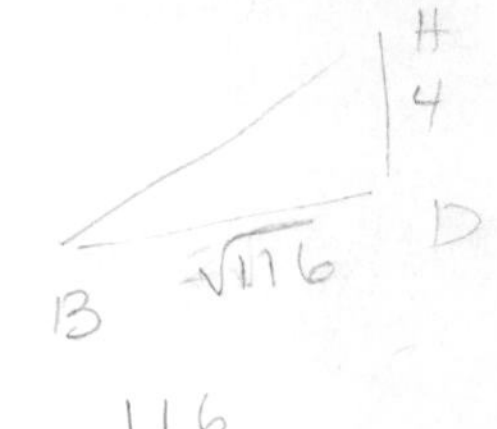

26. Suppose all faces of a parallelepiped are rectangles. If $AC = a$, $AB = b$, and $EC = c$, show that $BE = \sqrt{a^2 + b^2 + c^2}$.

27. In the cube shown, $AB = 5$. Find the length of diagonal $\overline{AC}$.

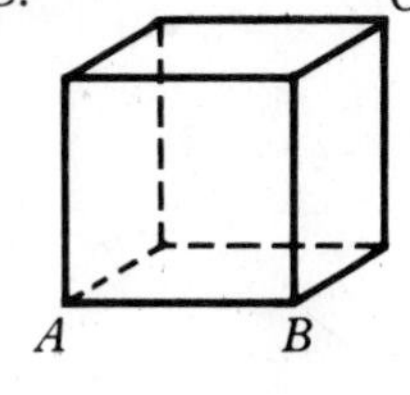

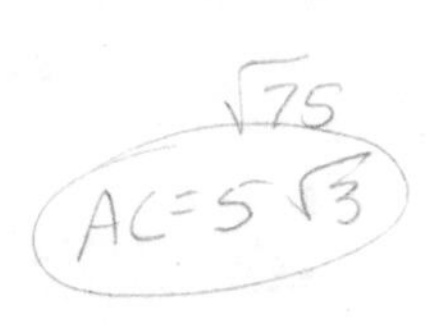

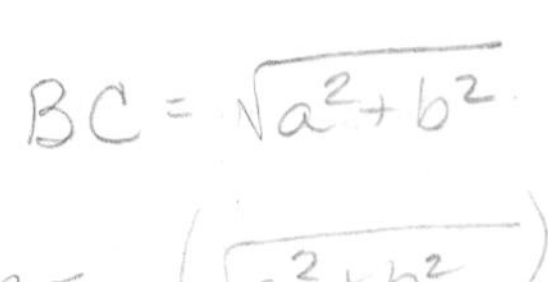

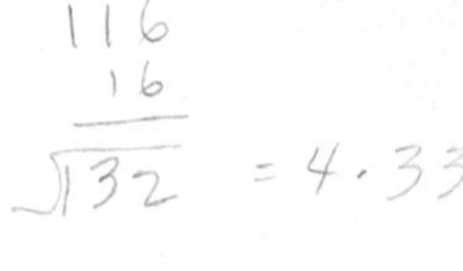

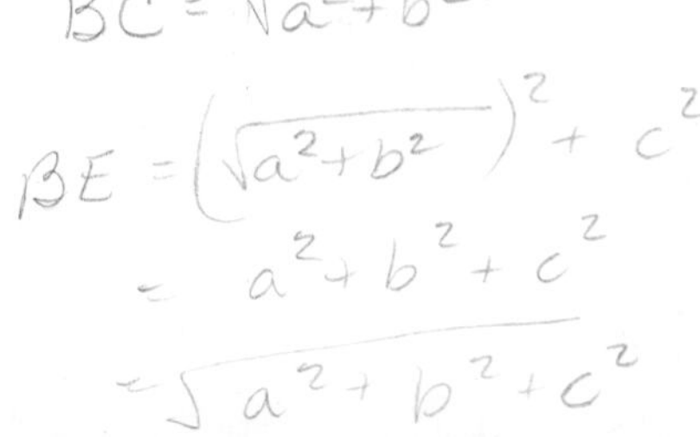

C.

28. In this figure the polyhedron with vertices $ABCDP$ is what type of polyhedron?

29. The segments from P to each of the vertices of the cube divide the cube into how many pyramids?

(Exs. 28-30)

30. Name the base of each of the pyramids counted in Exercise 29.

31. Suppose a cube is sliced by a plane ACF as shown, forming a pyramid $ABCF$. Explain why this pyramid is a regular pyramid. (Recall that the edges of a cube are all the same length.)

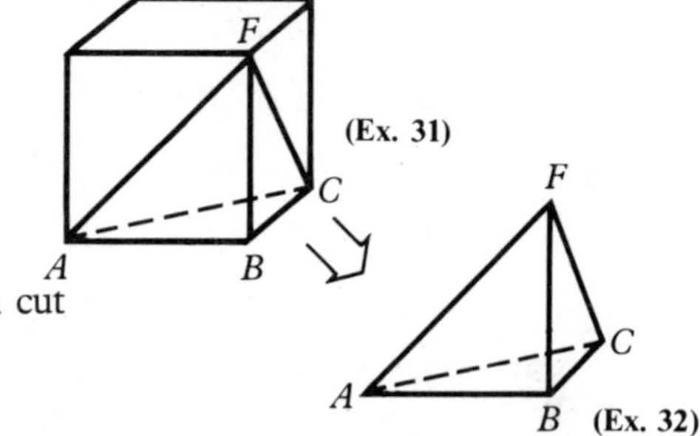

(Ex. 31)

(Ex. 32)

32. What is the base of the regular pyramid that has been cut from the cube?

33. How many regular pyramids like $ABCF$ can be sliced from the cube? Name them.

34. After four of the pyramids like $ABCF$ have been removed from the cube shown, the polyhedron $ACHF$ remains. Name all the faces of $ACHF$, and explain why they are all equilateral triangles.

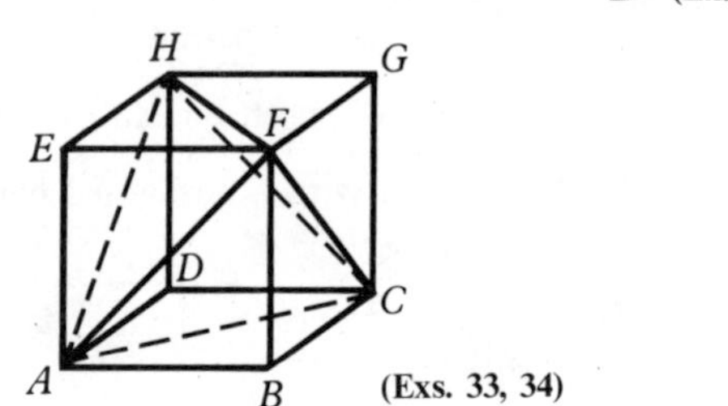

(Exs. 33, 34)

Activity

Outlined below is a method for constructing a triangular-based pyramid from a sealed envelope. Complete the construction.

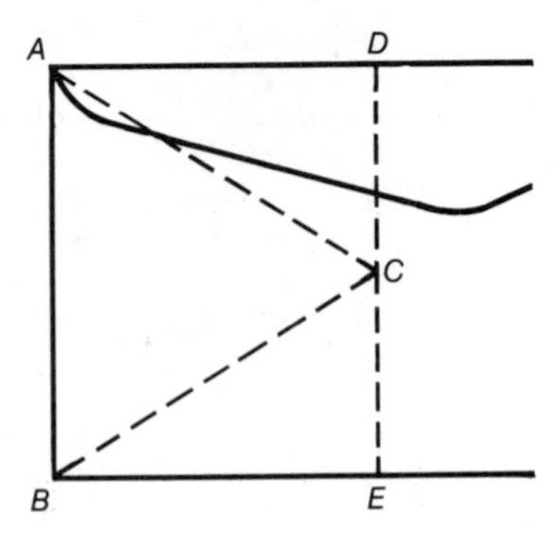

1. Construct point C so that $\triangle ABC$ is an equilateral triangle.
2. Cut along $\overline{DE}$, through C, and parallel to $\overline{AB}$.
3. Fold along $\overline{AC}$ and $\overline{BC}$ back and forth in both directions.
4. Let C' be the point on the reverse side corresponding to point C.
5. Open and pinch the envelope so that points D and E are joined and C and C' are separated. Tape along segment $\overline{CC'}$ and the pyramid is complete.

Construct a solid using this method.

35. In this parallelepiped explain why point O is the midpoint of $\overline{AG}$ and $\overline{BH}$.

36. The segments $\overline{CE}$ and $\overline{AG}$ are the diagonals of what parallelogram?

37. Explain why point O is the midpoint of $\overline{CE}$.

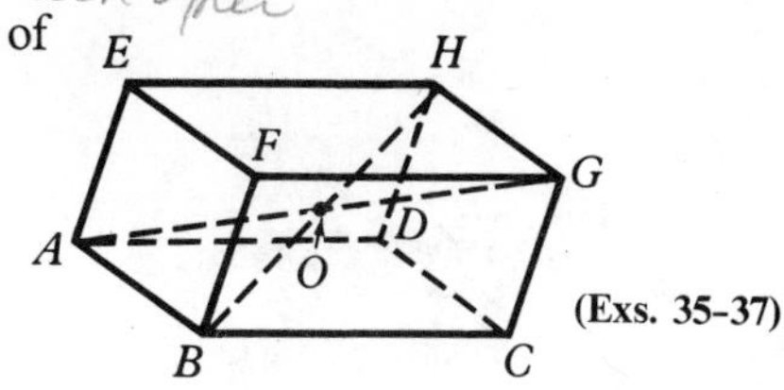

(Exs. 35–37)

38. A school hall 9 feet high and 9 feet wide turns a corner as shown. (This can be viewed as a pair of intersecting parallelepipeds with rectangular faces.) Can a pole 12 feet long (like one used in pole vaulting) be carried down the hall and around the corner? Explain.

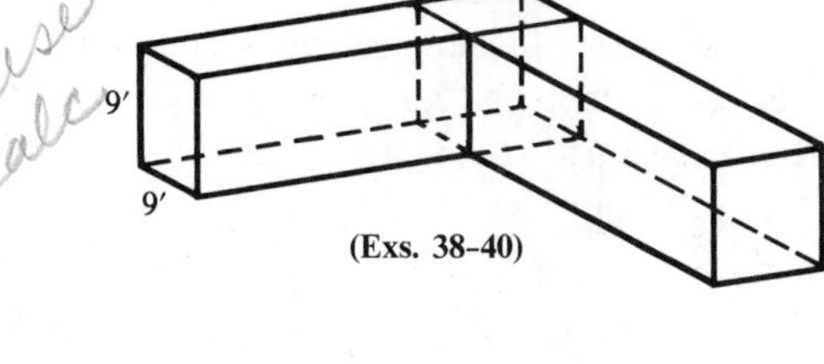

(Exs. 38–40)

39. A top view of the hall is shown. If $\overline{AB} \parallel \overline{CD}$, verify that $CD = 18\sqrt{2}$.

40. Could a pole slightly longer than $18\sqrt{2}$ feet be carried down the hall and around the corner? Explain.

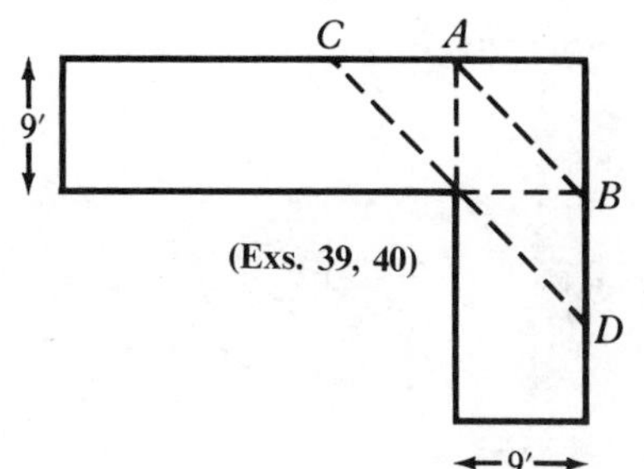

(Exs. 39, 40)

PROBLEM SOLVING

A box with dimensions 2 by 4 by 8 can be wrapped in either of two methods. How much ribbon is required in each case? (*Hint:* Think of cutting the box open to calculate the ribbon length for method 2. In the diagram some faces are shown twice.)

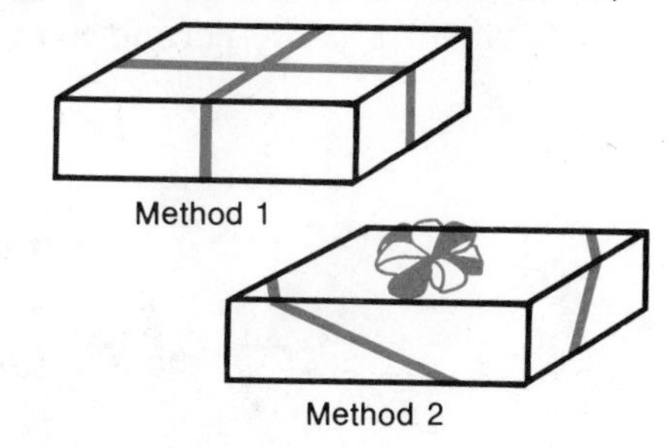

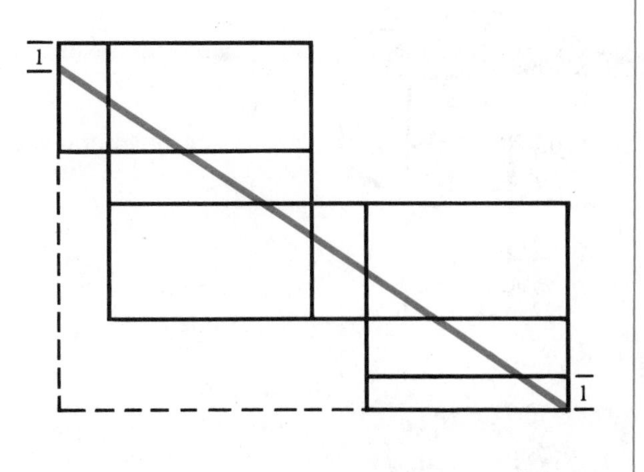

12–2 Surface Area of Prisms and Pyramids

Professional interior decorators and do-it-yourself remodelers need to determine the quantity of materials required to decorate surfaces. Sometimes familiar objects, such as end tables or cabinets, have prism shapes. It is often necessary to calculate surface areas of these shapes.

The areas of the surfaces of prisms and pyramids can be found using the following rule:

> Surface Area = Sum of the areas of the lateral faces
> + Area of the bases

Consider a prism with altitude h, rectangular lateral faces, and pentagonal bases.

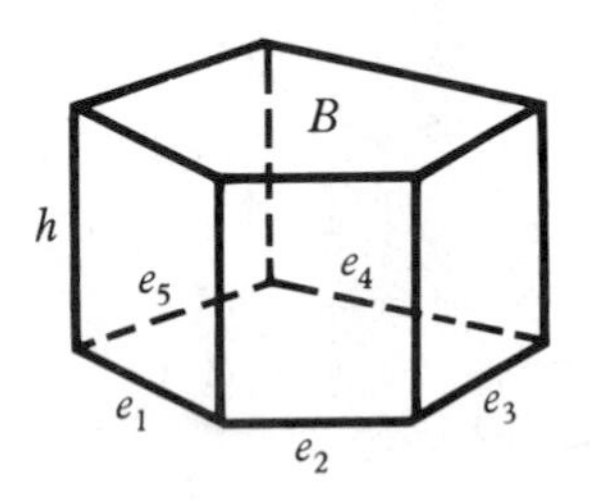

If the area of each base is B and the base edges have lengths e_1, e_2, e_3, e_4, and e_5, then

$$\begin{aligned}\text{Area of lateral faces} &= e_1h + e_2h + e_3h + e_4h + e_5h \\ &= h(e_1 + e_2 + e_3 + e_4 + e_5) \\ &= hp, \text{ where } p \text{ is the perimeter of the base.}\end{aligned}$$

Theorem 12–2 Given a prism with rectangular lateral faces. If the altitude of the prism is h and the bases have area B and perimeter p, then the surface area S is found by the formula $S = hp + 2B$.

The surface area of a pyramid is equal to the sum of the areas of the lateral faces plus the area of the base.

Consider a regular pyramid with pentagon base, slant height ℓ, and base edges with lengths $e_1 = e_2 = e_3 = e_4 = e_5$.

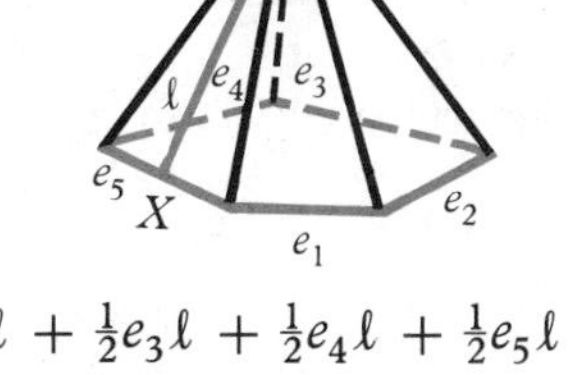

Sum of areas of the lateral faces

$$= \tfrac{1}{2}e_1\ell + \tfrac{1}{2}e_2\ell + \tfrac{1}{2}e_3\ell + \tfrac{1}{2}e_4\ell + \tfrac{1}{2}e_5\ell$$
$$= \tfrac{1}{2}\ell(e_1 + e_2 + e_3 + e_4 + e_5)$$
$$= \tfrac{1}{2}\,\ell p, \text{ where } p \text{ is the perimeter of the base.}$$

This information is summarized in the following theorem.

Theorem 12–3 Given a regular pyramid with slant height ℓ and a base with area B and perimeter p, the surface area S is found by the formula

$$S = \tfrac{1}{2}\ell p + B.$$

APPLICATION

Sometimes formulas need to be adapted to be applied to a given physical object. For example, consider the plumb (a weight used in construction) shown here. Its shape is that of a hexagonal prism with a regular hexagon base attached to a hexagonal pyramid at the bottom. A manufacturer needs to know its surface area.

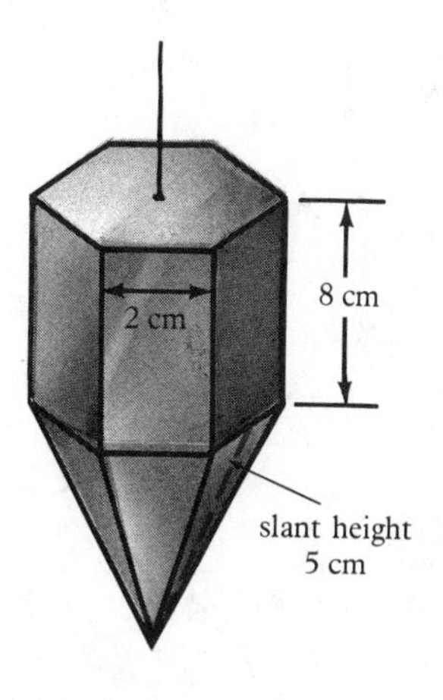

From the drawing we can calculate that the area of the base is $6\sqrt{3}\text{ cm}^2$. Using Theorems 12–2 and 12–3, we find the surface area of the prism and pyramid:

$$\text{Surface area of prism} = (12)(8)\text{ cm}^2 + 12\sqrt{3}\text{ cm}^2,$$
$$\text{Surface area of pyramid} = \tfrac{1}{2}(5)(12)\text{ cm}^2 + 6\sqrt{3}\text{ cm}^2.$$

But one base of the prism and the base of the pyramid are joined. Because neither base is part of the surface of the plumb, we must subtract the base area twice. Therefore,

Surface area of plumb

$$= (12)(8) + 12\sqrt{3} + \tfrac{1}{2}(5)(12) + 6\sqrt{3} - 2(6\sqrt{3})$$
$$= (126 + 6\sqrt{3})\text{cm}^2.$$

EXERCISES

A.

For exercises 1 and 2, select the correct formula for finding the surface area. p is the perimeter of the base, h is the altitude, ℓ is the slant height, and B is the area of the base(s).

1.

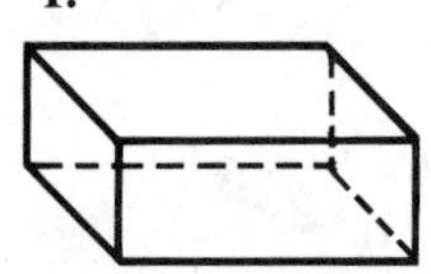

a. $S = \frac{1}{2}ph + 2B$

b. $S = ph + B$

c. $S = ph + 2B$

d. $S = p\ell + 2B$

2.

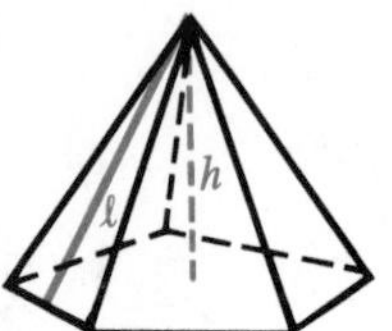

a. $S = \frac{1}{2}ph + B$

b. $S = p\ell + B$

c. $S = \frac{1}{2}p\ell + 2B$

d. $S = \frac{1}{2}p\ell + B$

For exercises 3–5, find the surface area of these right prisms and a regular pyramid.

3.

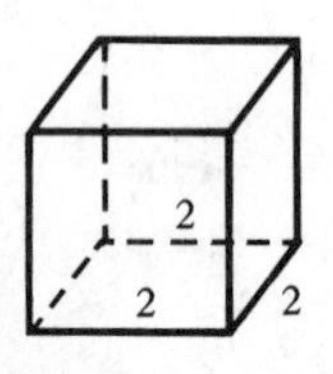

4.

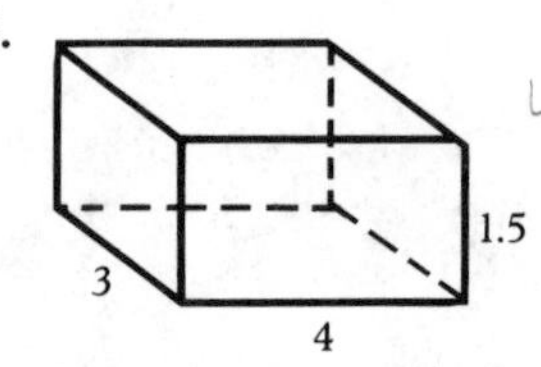

5.

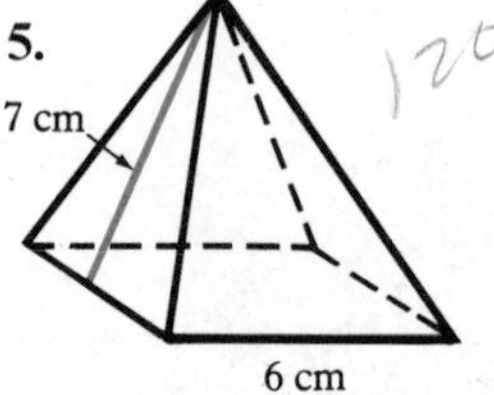

6. Find the surface area of a box with no top that is 5 units long, 3 units wide, and 2 units high.

7. Find the surface area of a right prism with equilateral triangle bases if all edges are 2 units long.

B.

Find the surface area of these regular pyramids.

8.

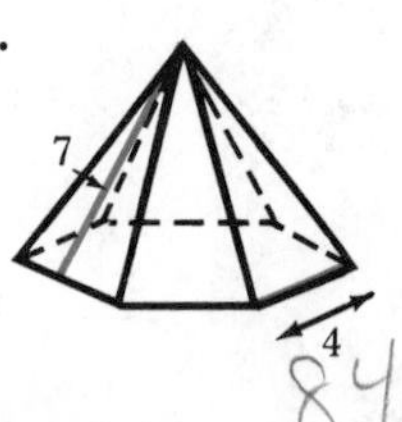

9.

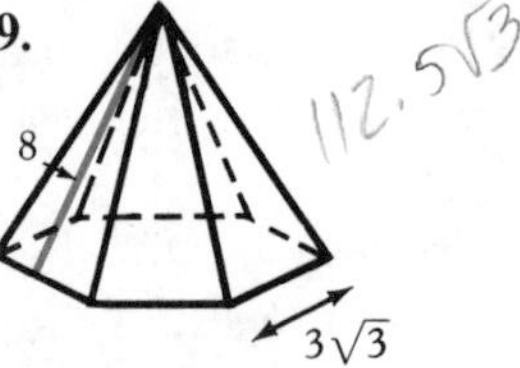

10.

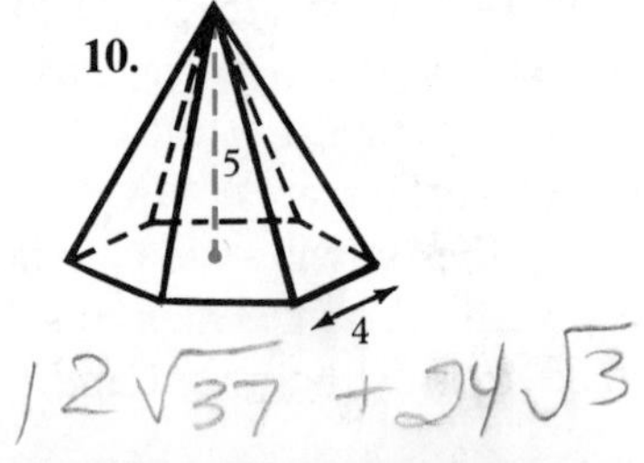

Activity

A deltahedron is a polyhedron with triangular faces. Make models of the deltahedra by gluing toothpicks together. Which of the deltahedra are pyramids?

11. The surface of a square-based prism is 360 cm² and the height is twice the length of a base edge. What are the lengths of the edges of this prism?

6, 12

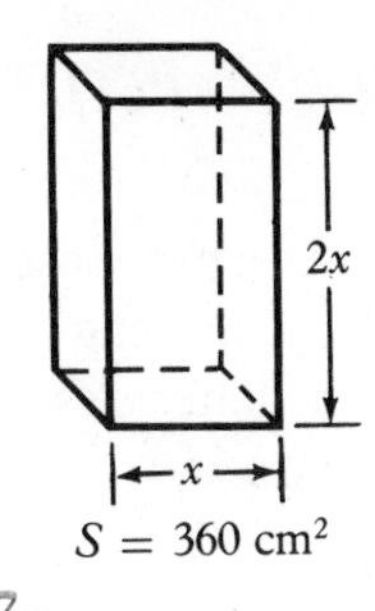

$S = 360 \text{ cm}^2$

12. The surface area of a square-based pyramid is 48 cm². If the slant height is equal to the base edge, what is the area of the base?

B = 16 cm²

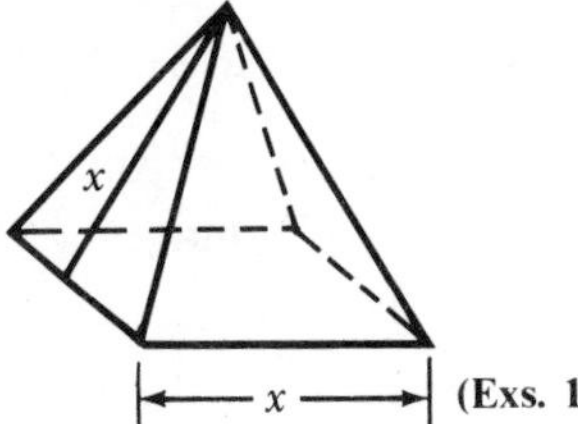

(Exs. 12, 13)

13. What is the length of the altitude of the pyramid in exercise 12?

2√3

14. If the length of each edge of a prism is doubled, how does the surface area change?

quad

C.

15. Square cake pans 20 cm on an edge and 6 cm deep are to be coated on the inside with a non-stick material. If the amount of non-stick material available covers 100 square meters, how many pans can be coated?

1136

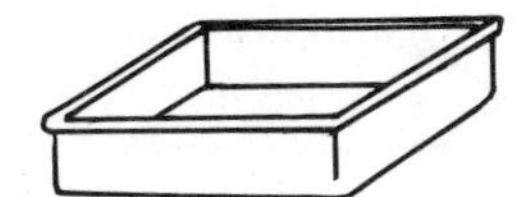

16. A large container shaped like a regular pyramid has an open top. The top is a regular hexagon with dimensions as shown. If one hundred of these containers are to be painted, both inside and out, with a paint that covers 450 square feet per gallon, how many gallons of paint are needed?

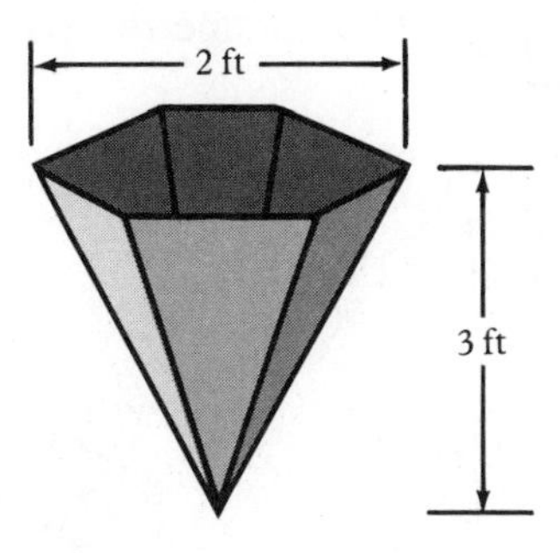

PROBLEM SOLVING

In the figure at the right 14 cubes have been stacked to form a solid whose surface area (including the base) is 42 units.

1. How can the surface area be changed to 44 units by moving only one block?
2. How can the surface area be changed to 40 units by moving only one block?

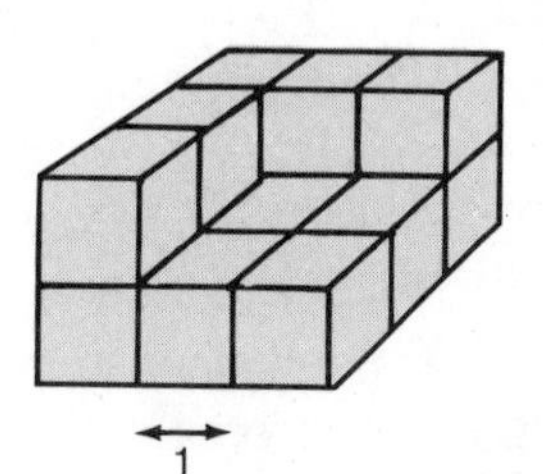

12–3 Volume of Prisms

A civil engineer estimates construction costs. At this highway construction site the engineer determines the amount of earth material to be moved in reshaping the terrain by calculating the volume.

There are postulates that characterize the concept of volume. We shall study these postulates in this lesson.

Intuitively, we think of volume as a measure of the amount of space occupied by a solid.

Volume Postulate

Each solid is assigned a unique positive number called its **volume**.

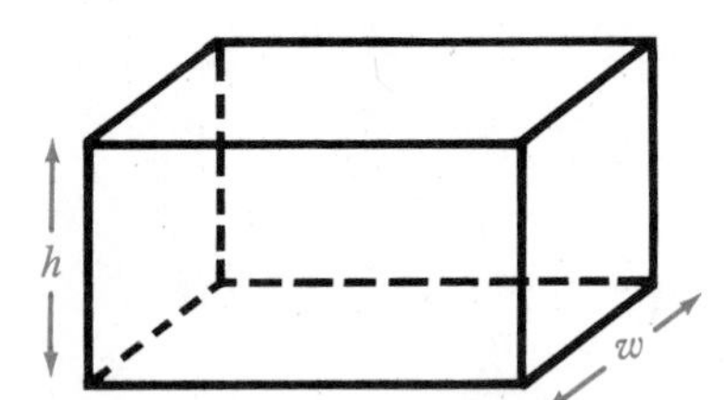

We begin our study of volume by considering a solid commonly referred to as a "box" shape which we define to be a *rectangular solid.*

Definition 12–4

A **rectangular solid** is a prism with rectangular bases whose lateral edges are perpendicular to the bases.

A rectangular solid has length, width, and height.

Rectangular Solid Volume Postulate

The **volume of a rectangular solid** is equal to the product of its length ℓ, width w, and height h.

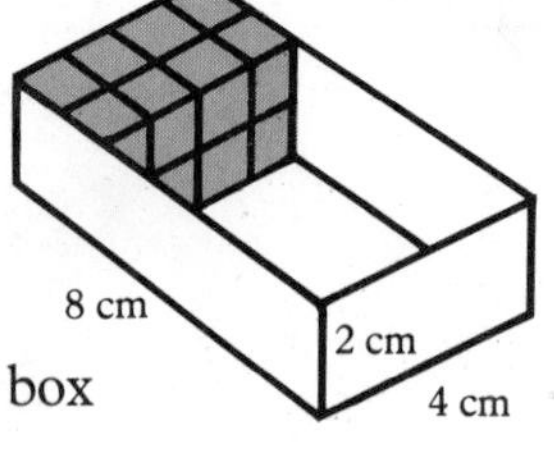

Example Find the volume (V) of a box 8 cm by 4 cm by 2 cm.
$V = 2\text{ cm} \times 4\text{ cm} \times 8\text{ cm} = 64\text{ cm}^3$
(Read 64 cubic centimeters.)

This is equivalent to counting the number of cubes 1 cm on a side that fit into the box.

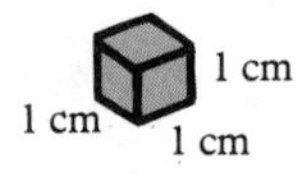

Volume Addition Postulate

If a solid is the union of two solids that have no common interior points, then its volume is the sum of the volumes of the two solids.

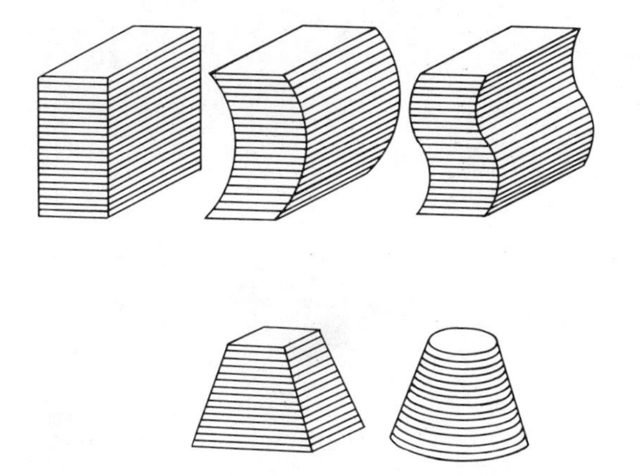

Imagine that a rectangular solid has been sliced into thin layers and that the layers shift to form irregular-shaped solids. The volume of the solid remains the same.

Similarly, suppose that two solids can be sliced into thin layers so that the tops of corresponding layers have equal areas. Intuition suggests that the volumes of the two solids are equal.

Definition 12-5

A **cross section** of a solid is a region common to the solid and a plane that intersects the solid.

These examples lead to a postulate known as Cavalieri's Principle, named after the seventeenth century Italian mathematician Bonaventura Cavalieri (1598–1647).

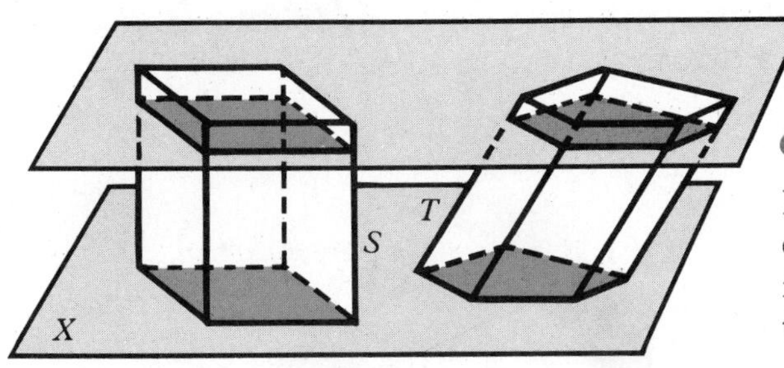

Cavalieri's Postulate

Let S and T be two solids and X be a plane. If every plane parallel to X that intersects S or T intersects both S and T in a cross section having the same area, then

$$\text{Volume } S = \text{Volume } T.$$

The postulates from this lesson can be combined to prove the following theorem.

Theorem 12–4 The volume of any prism is the product of the length of an altitude and the area of the base.

EXERCISES

A.

Find the volume of each of these boxes.

1.

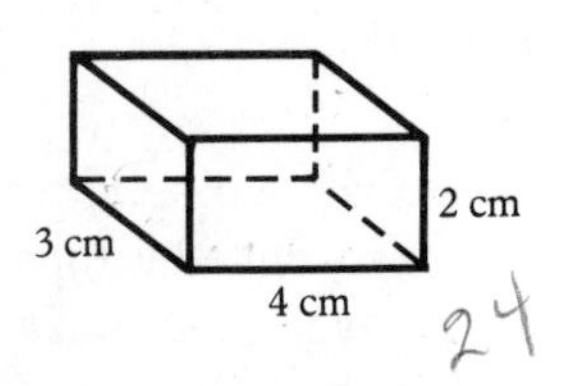

2.

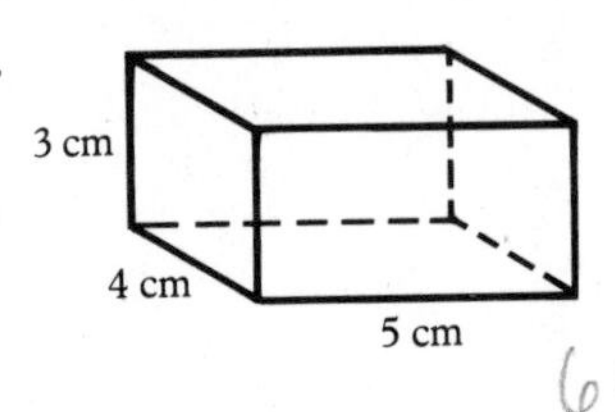

3.

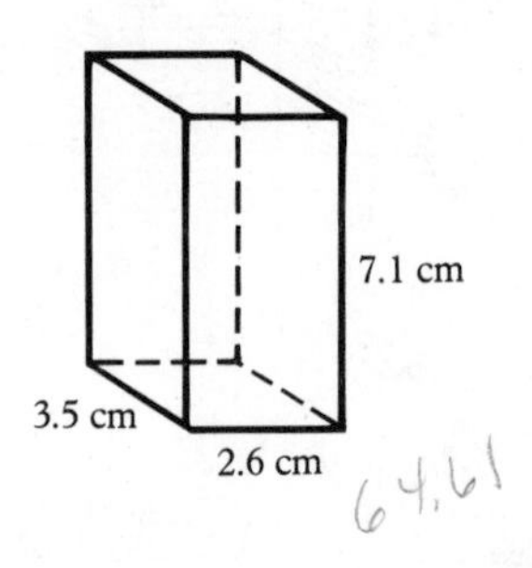

4. How many cubes 1 cm on a side will fit into the box in exercise 1?

5. How many cubes 2 cm on a side will fit into the box in exercise 1?

6. How many cubes 1 cm on a side will fit into the box in exercise 2?

7. How many cubes 1 cm on a side will fit into the box in exercise 3?

8. How many cubic inches are there in one cubic foot?

Find the volume of the prisms in exercises 9–11.

9.

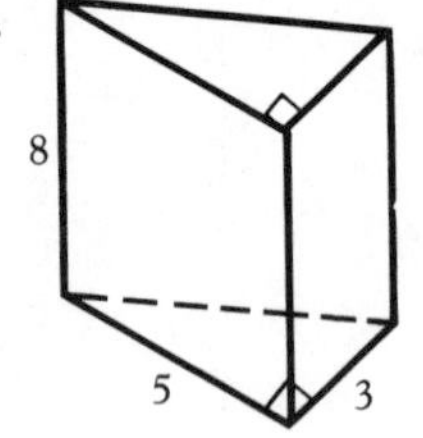

10.

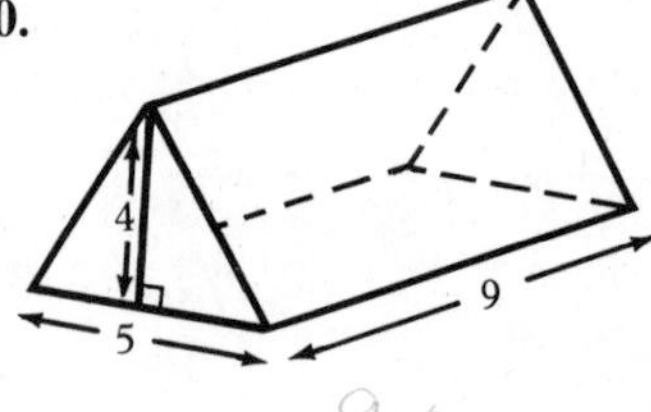

11.

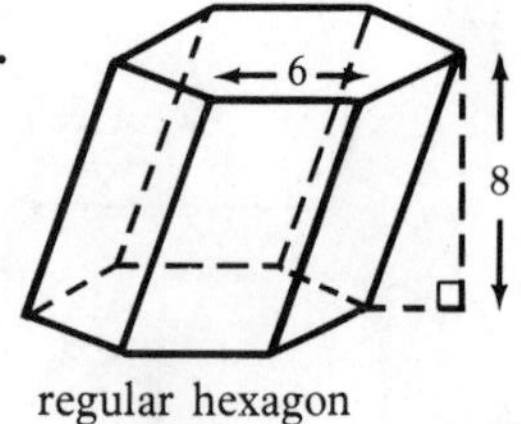

regular hexagon base

B.

12. If the area of the base of a prism is doubled and the height remains the same, how much does the volume increase?

Activity

Draw two copies of this figure and make two solid figures.

Fit those two solids together to form a prism. (When drawing this figure, make sure that polygon 1 is a regular hexagon and polygons 2 are 45-45-90 triangles.)

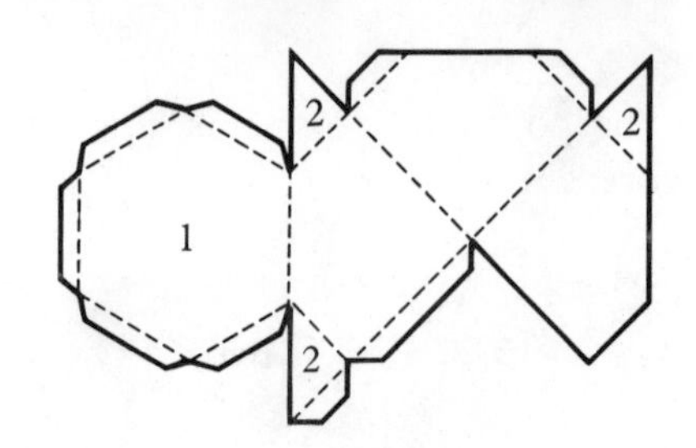

13. If the lengths of all sides of a box are doubled, how much is the volume increased?

14. Silver ingots are molded in bars shaped as shown. The ends are parallel isosceles trapezoids. What is the volume?

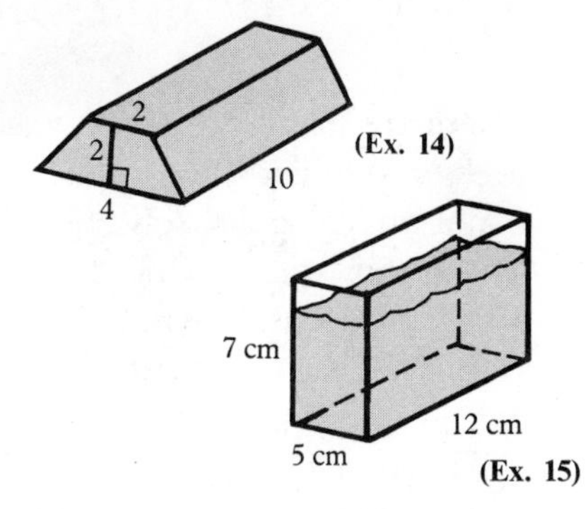

(Ex. 14)
(Ex. 15)

15. A rectangular container is 5 cm wide and 12 cm long and contains water to a depth of 7 cm. A stone is placed in the water and the water rises 1.7 cm. What is the volume of the stone?

16. A heating engineer needs to find the volume of a building in order to design its heating system. Find the volume of the building pictured.

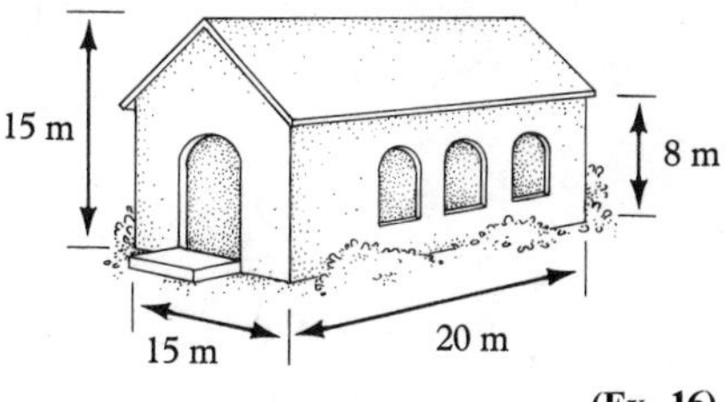

(Ex. 16)

17. If a rectangular container with a square base is 2 feet high and has a volume of 50 cubic feet, find the length and width of the base.

18. Suppose the area of a base of a prism is x square feet and its height is $2x$ feet. If the volume of the prism is 54 cubic feet, how tall is the prism?

C.

19. An engineer's plan shows a canal with a trapezoid cross section, 8 feet deep and 14 feet across at the bottom, and walls sloping outward at an angle of 45°. The canal is 620 feet long. A contractor estimates that it will cost $1.50 per cubic yard to excavate the canal. If the contractor adds 10% for profit, what should the bid be?

20. A concrete retaining wall is 80 feet long with ends shaped as shown. How many cubic yards of concrete are used in constructing this wall?

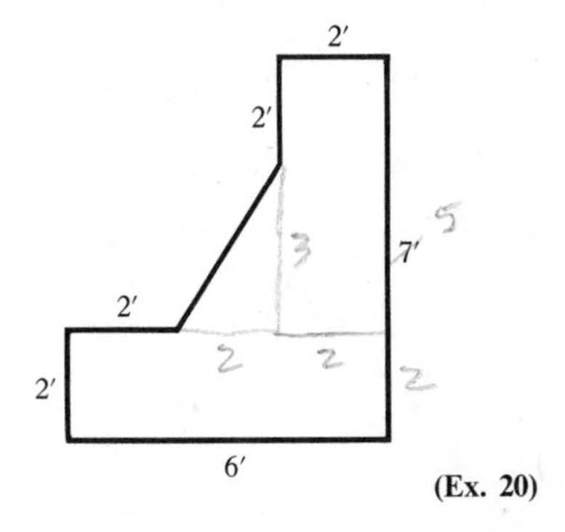

(Ex. 20)

PROBLEM SOLVING

How many cubic yards of concrete are needed for the steps shown in the diagram?

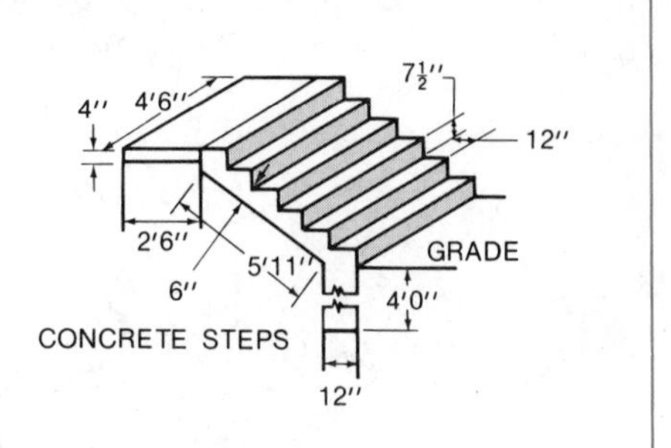

12–4 Volume of Pyramids

There are many occasions when it is necessary to find the volume of an object that is not a rectangular solid or a prism. This sketch shows a dairy product container that is a triangular-based pyramid. Knowing the volume of the container is essential to the dairy company.

Theorem 12–7 gives the formula for the volume of a pyramid. First we must state two other theorems. These theorems are used in the development of the formula.

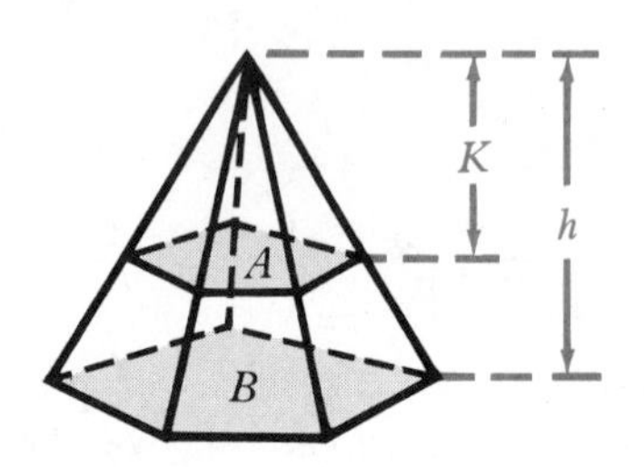

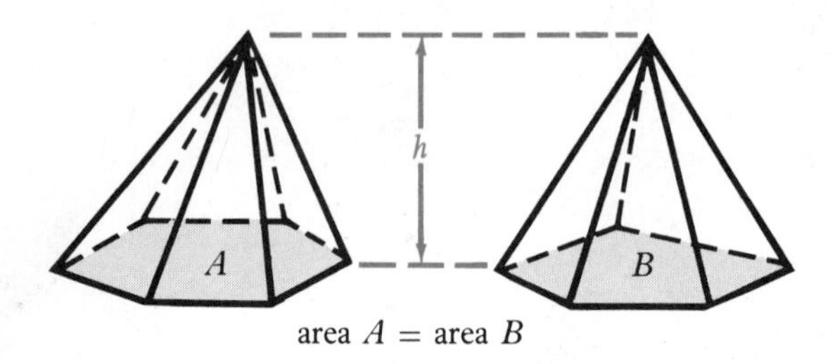

area A = area B

Theorem 12–5

Given a pyramid with base B and altitude h. If A is a cross section parallel to the base and the distance from the vertex to the cross section is K, then

$$\frac{\text{area } A}{\text{area } B} = \left(\frac{K}{h}\right)^2.$$

Theorem 12–6

Two pyramids with equal altitudes and bases of equal area have the same volume.

Suppose we want to find the volume of pyramid $WXYZ$. We shall do this by finding the volume of a right pyramid $ABCD$ with base area equal to the area of base $\triangle XYZ$ and altitude equal to h. Use Theorem 12–6.

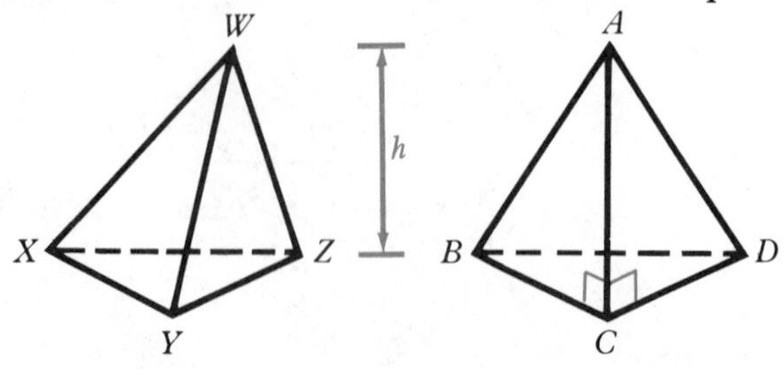

Next consider a right prism with the same base and altitude as pyramid *ABCD*.

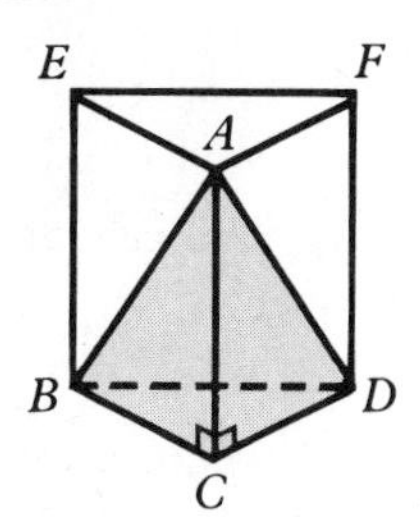

Make the following two cuts in the prism:

1. Cut from A through BD.
2. Cut from A through ED.

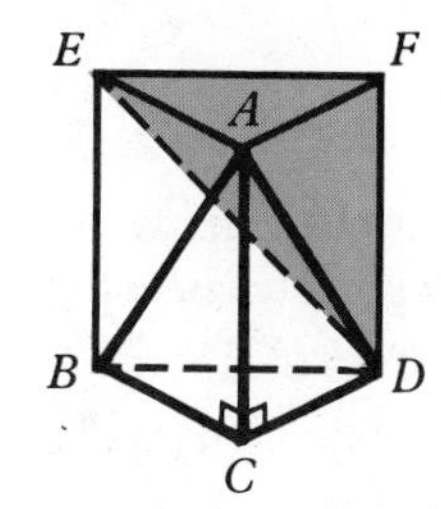

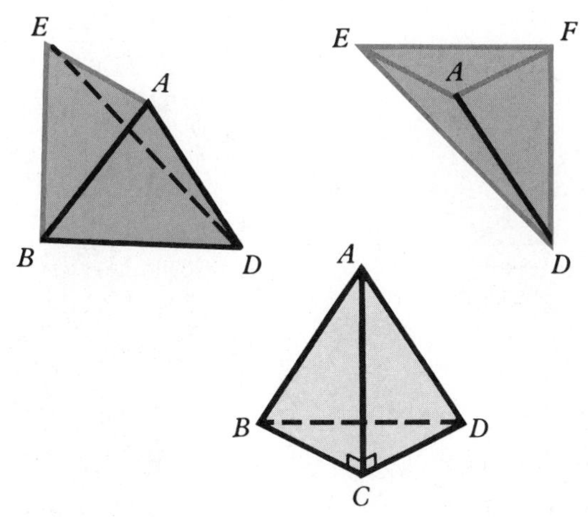

Then

1. Volume of $ABCD$ = Volume $ADEF$. Bases $\triangle BCD$ and $\triangle AEF$ have equal area, and altitudes AC and DF are equal in length. Therefore Theorem 12-6 implies the equality of volume.
2. Volume of $ADEF$ = Volume of $ABDE$. These two pyramids have bases $\triangle BDE$ and $\triangle FDE$ that have equal areas since they are each half of rectangle $BDFE$. The altitudes for both pyramids are formed by a perpendicular segment from A to the opposite base and so the altitudes are equal. Theorem 12-6 states that the volumes are equal.

Therefore, the volume of pyramid $ABCD = \frac{1}{3}$ the volume of prism $ABCDEF$

$$= \tfrac{1}{3}hB.$$

Theorem 12–7 Given a pyramid with altitude h and base area B, the volume is found by the formula $V = \frac{1}{3}hB$.

EXERCISES

A.

Answer exercises 1–5 true or false.

1. If two pyramids of equal altitudes have congruent bases, then their volumes are equal.
2. If two pyramids have equal volumes, then their altitudes are necessarily equal.
3. If two pyramids have equal volumes and equal altitudes, then their bases are necessarily congruent.
4. If two pyramids have equal volumes and bases equal in area, then their altitudes are necessarily equal.
5. A pyramid with a square base can never have a volume equal to a pyramid with a triangular base.

Find the volume of these pyramids.

6. 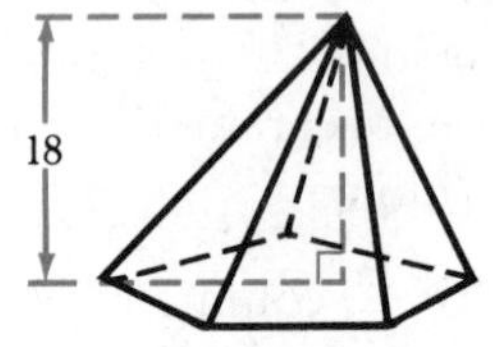

7. 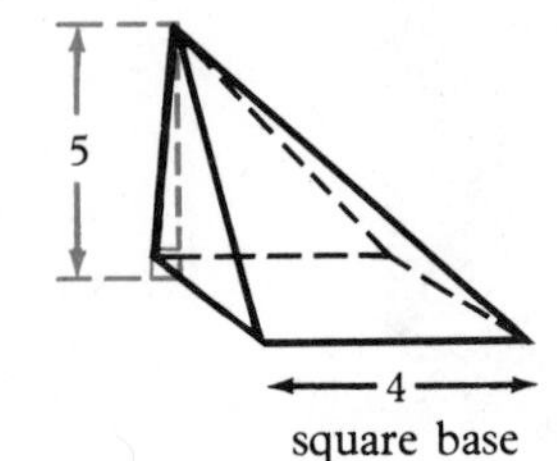

8. 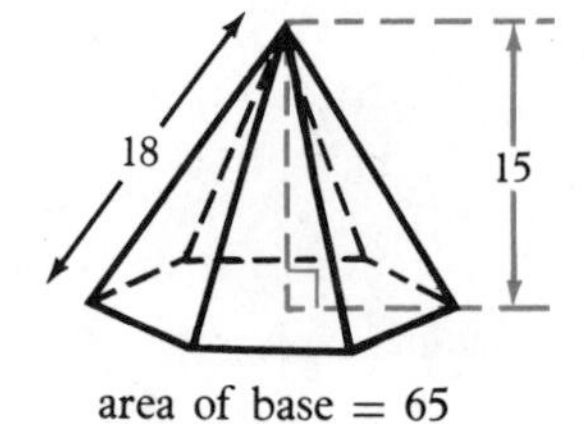

B.

In exercises 9–11, find the volume of the given regular pyramid.

9. 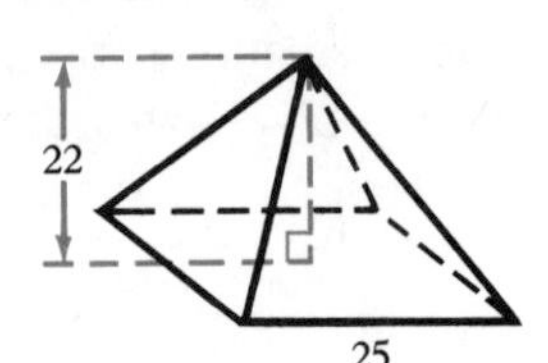

10. 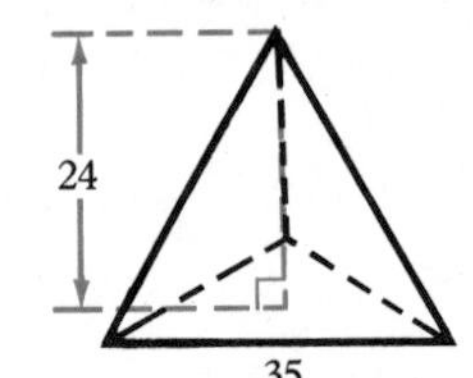

11. 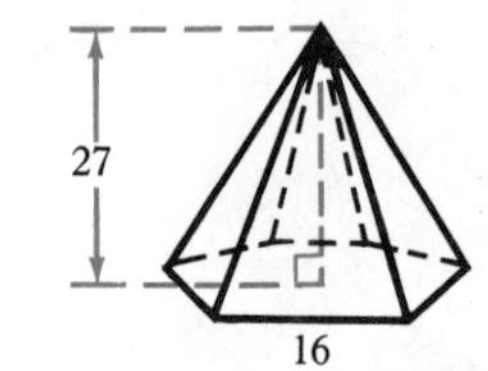

Activity

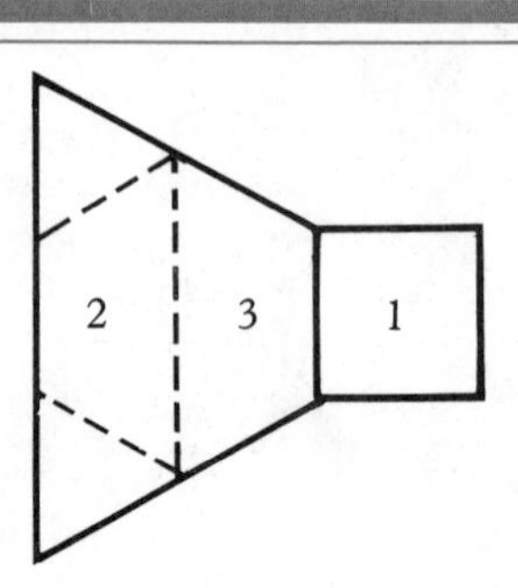

Draw an enlargement of this figure, cut out two copies, fold, and tape together to make two polyhedra.

Can you put the two polyhedra together to form a pyramid?

(When drawing this figure make sure polygon 1 is a square and that polygons 2 and 3 taken together form a regular hexagon.)

12. The bases of these two pyramids have equal area. How do their volumes compare?

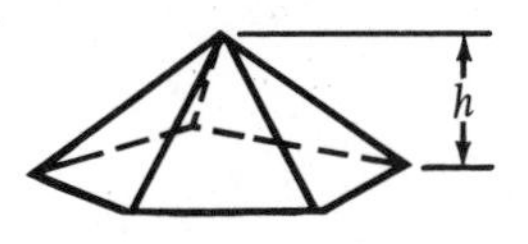

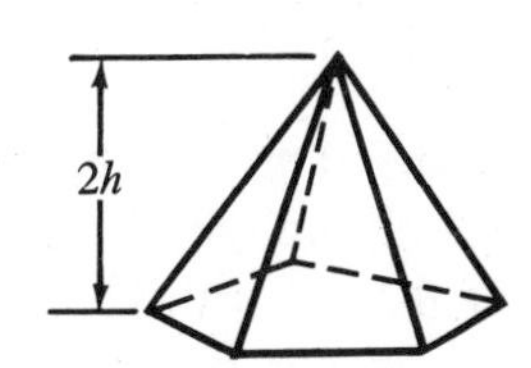

13. These two pyramids have equal altitudes and square bases. How do their volumes compare?

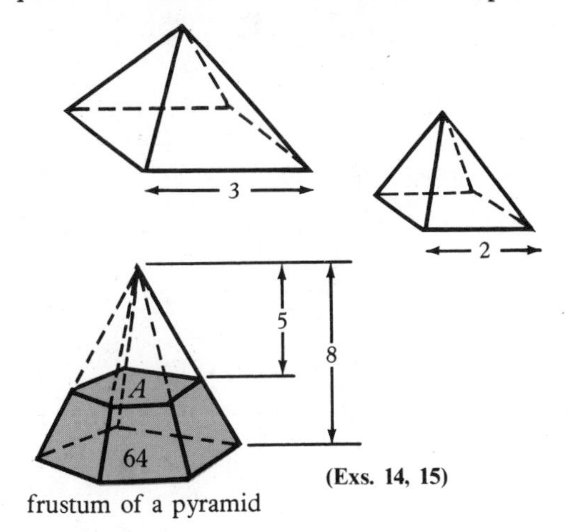

frustum of a pyramid

(Exs. 14, 15)

C.

14. What is the area of the cross section A of this pyramid?

15. What is the volume of the shaded portion of this pyramid?

16. What is the volume of a regular octahedron whose edge lengths are 3?

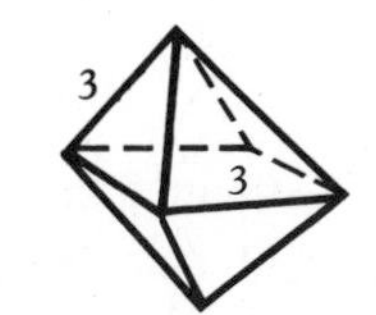

regular octahedron

17. A water retention basin is located along side of a parking lot. The basin begins at point A and deepens as it widens. The top edge $\overline{BC}$ of the deep end is 8 meters wide. Point B is 40 meters from A. The deepest point D is 1.5 meters below $\overline{BC}$. There is a drain at D that drains 50 liters per minute. Given that 1 m^3 holds 1000 liters, how many hours will it take for the basin to drain when it is full? (Assume that $ABCD$ is a pyramid.)

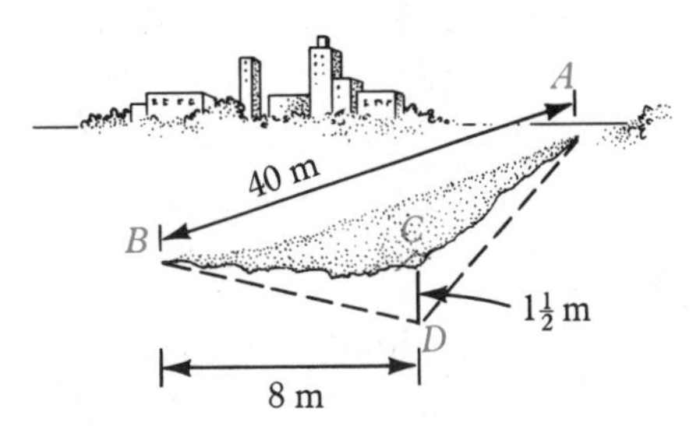

PROBLEM SOLVING

Many blueprint drawings show the top, side, and front views of objects. Notice the use of dashed lines to show cuts hidden from view.

Sketch two "cut blocks" that have the same top and front views but different side views.

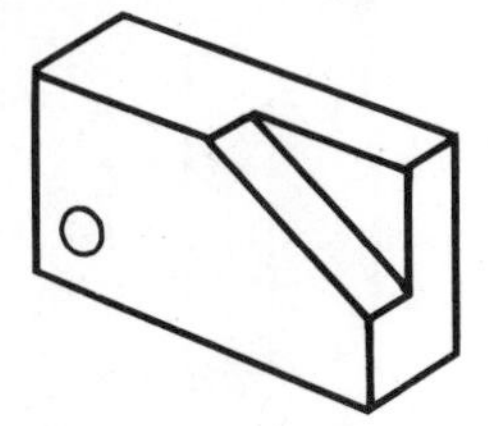

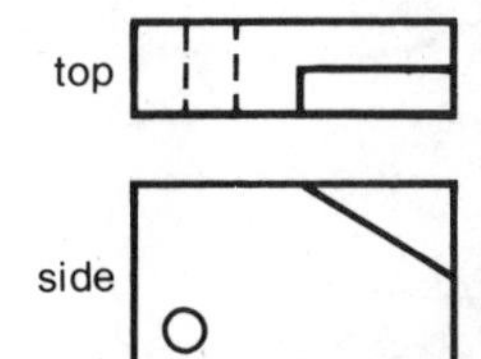

12–5 Surface Area and Volume of Cylinders

Many familiar objects are examples of the cylindrical shape. These pictures show some of them. In this lesson we define a circular cylinder and describe formulas for calculating its surface area and volume.

A *cylinder* is like a prism in that it has congruent bases in a pair of parallel planes. The bases are congruent circular regions.

The segment joining the centers of the two bases is called the *axis* of the cylinder. A cylinder is a *right cylinder* if its axis is perpendicular to the bases. The *height* of the cylinder is the length of the axis.

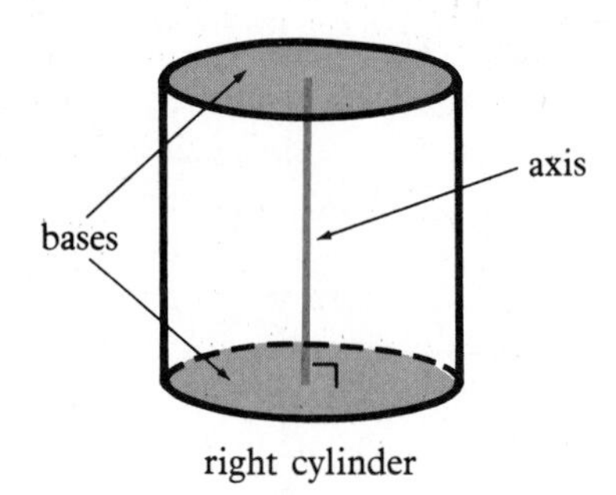

A cylinder can be thought of as a prism with an infinite number of sides. The lateral surface and the circumference of the bases of a cylinder correspond to the lateral faces and perimeter, respectively, of a prism.

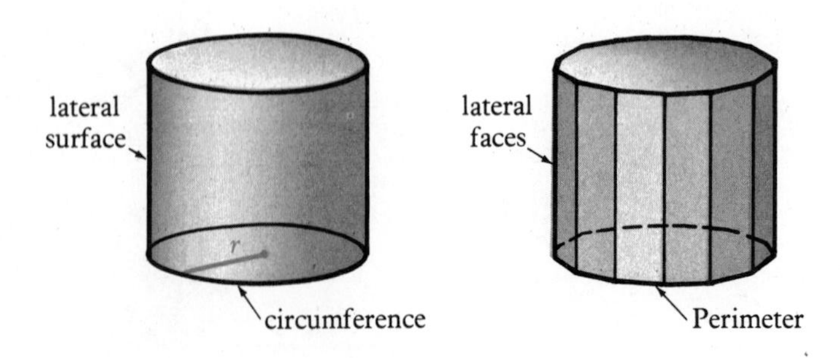

The next two theorems describe the surface area and volume of a right circular cylinder.

Theorem 12–8 Given a right circular cylinder with altitude h. If the circumference of the base is C, and the area of the base is B, then the surface area S is found by the formula

$$S = Ch + 2B = 2\pi rh + 2\pi r^2.$$

Theorem 12–9 Given a right circular cylinder with base area B and height h, the volume is found by the formula

$$V = Bh = \pi r^2 h.$$

Example 1

A container in the shape of a right circular cylinder is 35 cm tall and 16 cm in diameter. Find the surface area and the volume of this container.

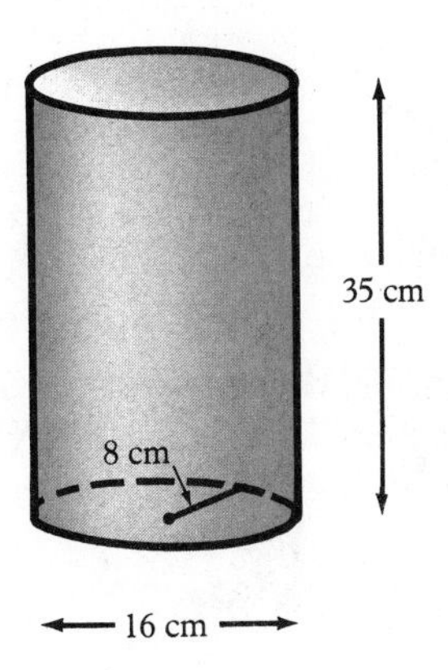

$$\begin{aligned} S &= 2\pi(8) \cdot 35 + 2\pi(8)^2 \\ &= 560\pi + 128\pi \\ &= 688\pi \text{ cm}^2 \end{aligned}$$

$$\begin{aligned} V &= \pi(8)^2 \cdot 35 \\ &= 2240\pi \text{ cm}^3 \end{aligned}$$

Example 2

If the radius and height of a cylinder double, how much do the surface area and volume change?

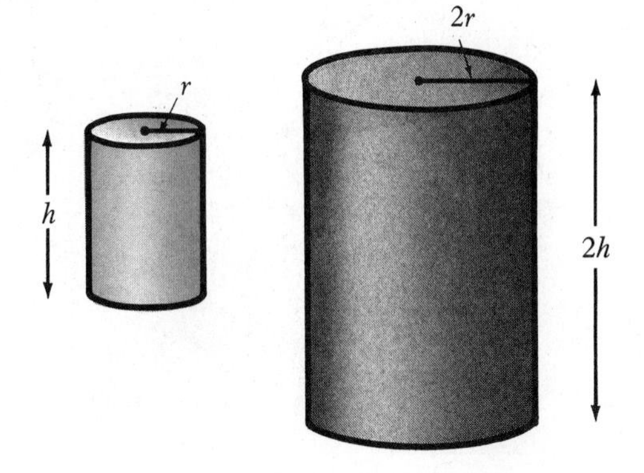

$$\begin{aligned} S(\text{large cylinder}) &= 2\pi(2r)(2h) + 2\pi(2r)^2 \\ &= 4(2\pi rh) + 4(2\pi r^2) \\ &= 4S \text{ (small cylinder)} \end{aligned}$$

$$\begin{aligned} V(\text{large cylinder}) &= \pi(2r)^2(2h) \\ &= 8\pi r^2 h \\ &= 8V \text{ (small cylinder)} \end{aligned}$$

EXERCISES

A.

Find the surface area and volume of the cylinders in exercises 1–3.

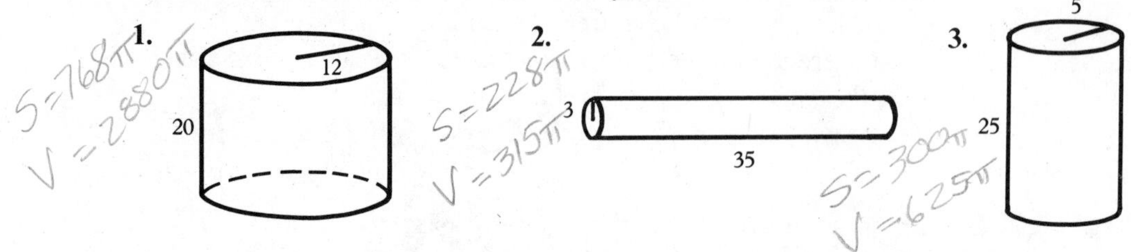

4. A cylindrical tank is 17 feet high and has a base radius of 10 feet. How many cubic feet are contained in the tank?

5. How many cubic yards are contained in the tank in exercise 4?

B.

6. A marble column in the shape of a right circular cylinder is 9 meters high and 80 cm in diameter. If 1 m^3 of marble weighs 300 kg, find the weight of the column.

7. The volume of a right circular cylinder is 972 cm^3. If the height is 12 cm, what is the radius of the base?

8. Two right circular cylinders with the same height have radii with a ratio of 2:1. What is the ratio of the volumes of the two cylinders?

Activity

Make a solid out of clay, wood, or other material that completely plugs up each of these holes and can be pushed through each with no change in shape.

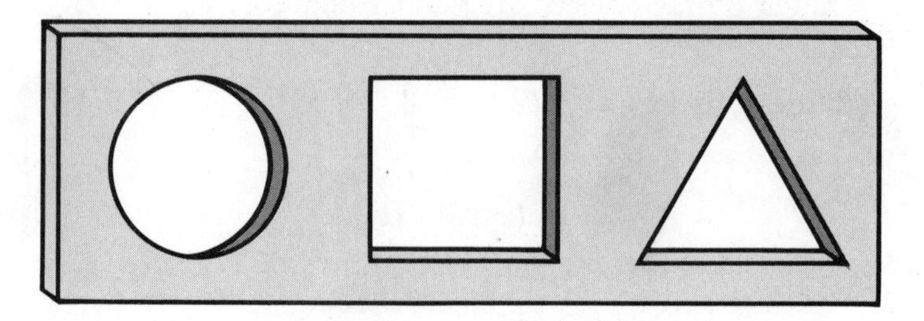

9. A cylindrical hole with diameter 8 inches is cut through a cube. The edge of the cube is also 8 inches. Find the volume and the surface area of this hollow solid.

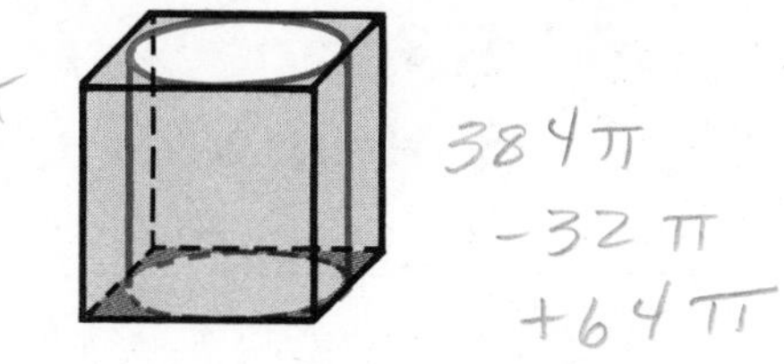

10. A 4 × 7 rectangle is rotated about the long side to generate a cylinder and is also rotated about the short side to generate a cylinder. What is the ratio of the volumes of these cylinders?

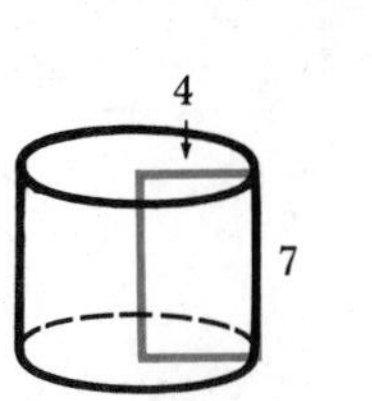

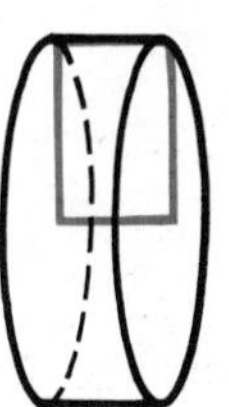

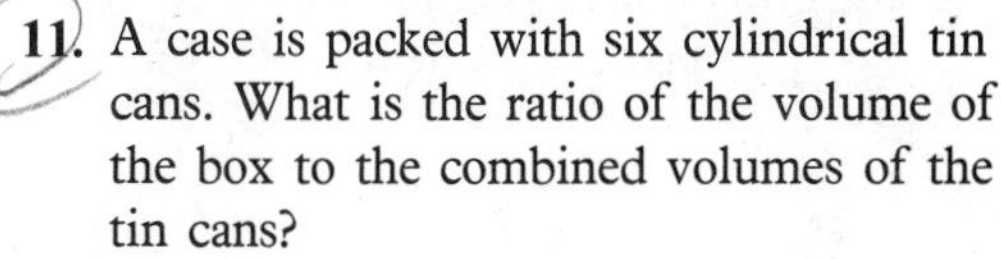

11. A case is packed with six cylindrical tin cans. What is the ratio of the volume of the box to the combined volumes of the tin cans?

12. Find the surface area and the volume of this solid steel casting.

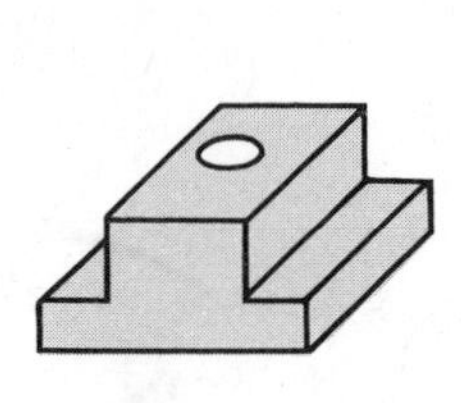

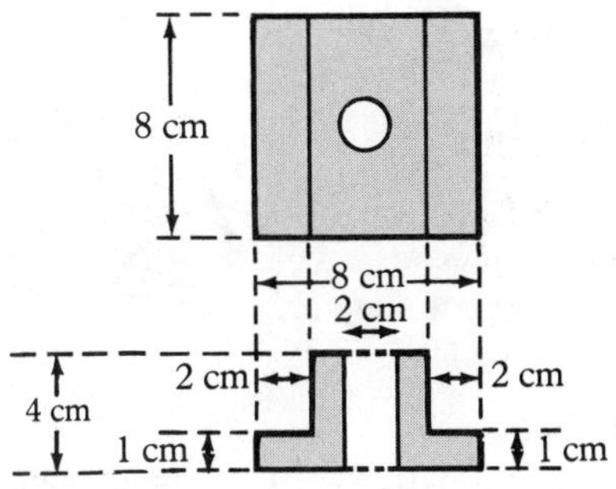

PROBLEM SOLVING

Find the volume and surface area of this bearing washer.

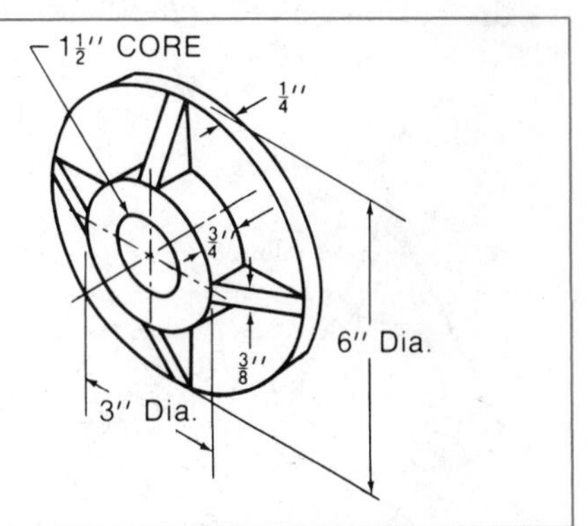

12–6 Surface Area and Volume of Cones

The cone shape is often found in the physical world in combination with the cylinder shape. For example, the top of storage bins, the tip of a pencil, and the tip of a nail can all be viewed as a cone mounted on a cylinder. A child might make a sand castle by combining these shapes.

The figure on the right is a *right circular cone*. It has a circular *base* and a *vertex*.

Its *axis* is the segment joining the vertex to the center of the base. The cone is called a *right cone* since the axis is perpendicular to the base.

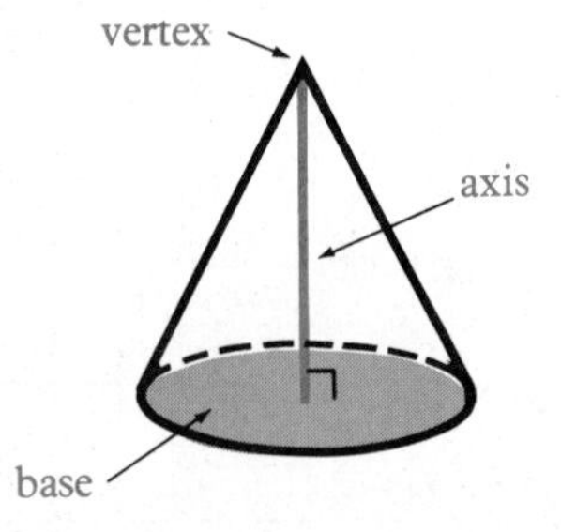

A cone can be thought of as a pyramid with an infinite number of lateral faces. The lateral surface of a cone corresponds to the lateral faces of a pyramid. The slant height (ℓ) of a cone corresponds to the slant height (ℓ) of a pyramid, and the circumference (C) of the base of a cone corresponds to the perimeter (p) of the base of a pyramid.

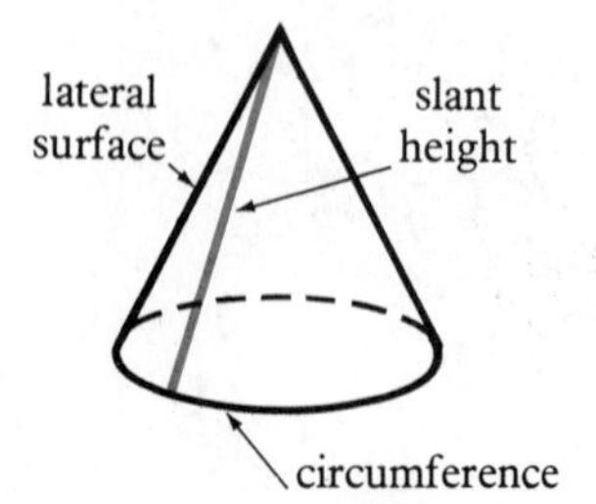

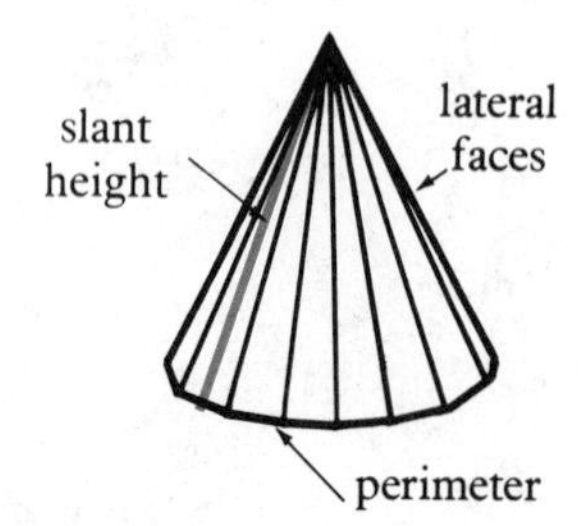

The next theorem describes the surface area of a cone.

Theorem 12–10 Given a right circular cone with slant height ℓ. If the circumference of the base is C, and the area of the base is B, then the surface area S is given by the formula

$$S = \tfrac{1}{2}\ell C + B = \pi r\ell + \pi r^2.$$

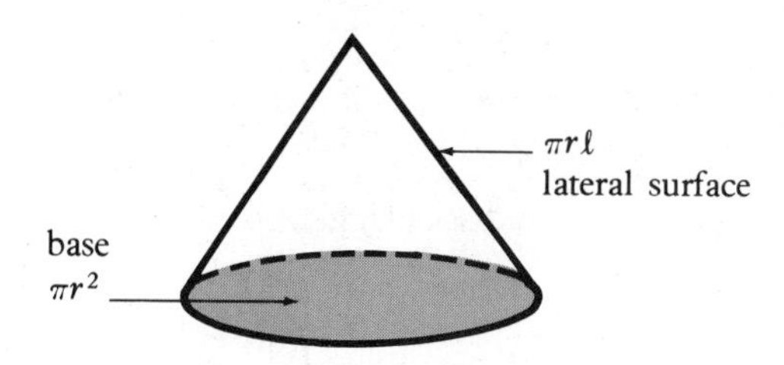

The formula for volume given in this next theorem is similar to the formula for the volume of a pyramid.

Theorem 12–11 Given a right circular cone with height h and base area B, the volume is found by the formula

$$V = \tfrac{1}{3}hB = \tfrac{1}{3}\pi r^2 h.$$

Example

A right circular cone has height 15 and base radius of 8. Find the slant height, the surface area, and the volume.

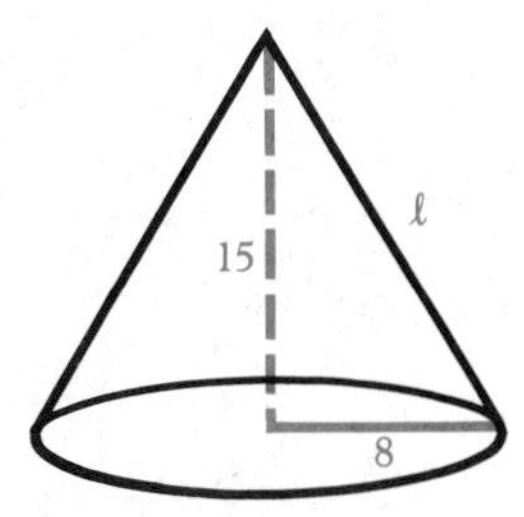

a. slant height:
   $\ell^2 = 64 + 225 = 289$
   $\ell = 17$
b. $S = \pi(8)(17) + \pi 64 = 200\pi$
c. $V = \frac{1}{3}\pi(8)^2 15 = 320\pi$

EXERCISES

A.

For exercises 1–3, find the volume and surface area of the right cones shown.

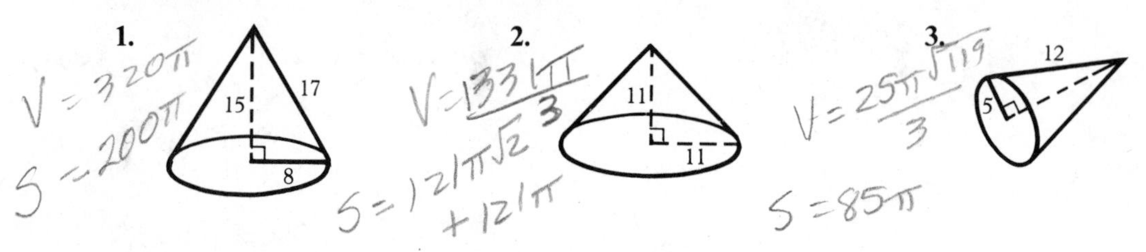

4. The radius of a cone is 5 cm and its altitude is 12 cm. Find its surface area and volume.
5. If the volume of a cone is 72π, find its height and radius if they are equal.

B.

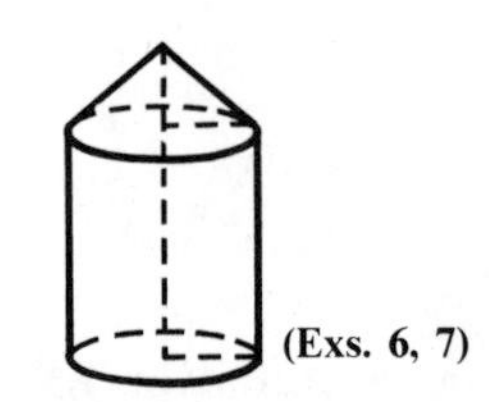

6. A container is composed of a right circular cylinder of diameter 4 cm and height 8 cm surmounted by a cone of height 6 cm. Find the volume of this container.
7. Find the surface area of this container.

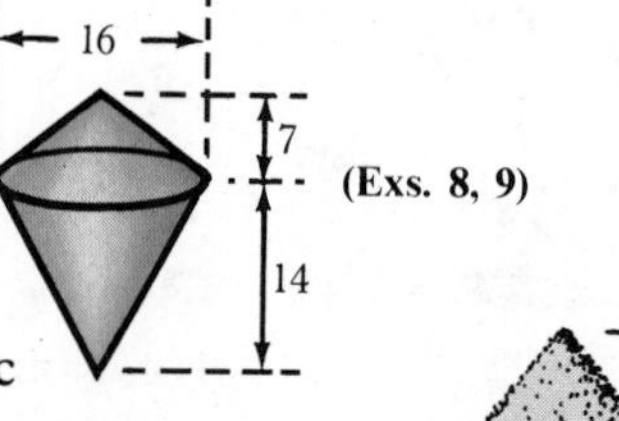

8. Find the volume of this toy top.
9. Find the surface area of this top.
10. A sand pile is shaped like a cone as shown. How many cubic yards of sand are in this pile? (Large quantities of sand are purchased by the cubic yard.)

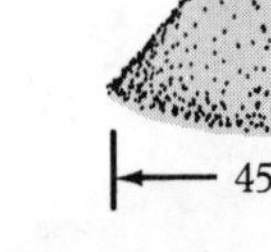

Activity

Make, or otherwise obtain, models of a cone and a cylinder with an open top that have equal radii and height.

Fill the cone to the top with sand and dump the sand into the cylinder.

How many cones of sand are required to fill the cylinder?

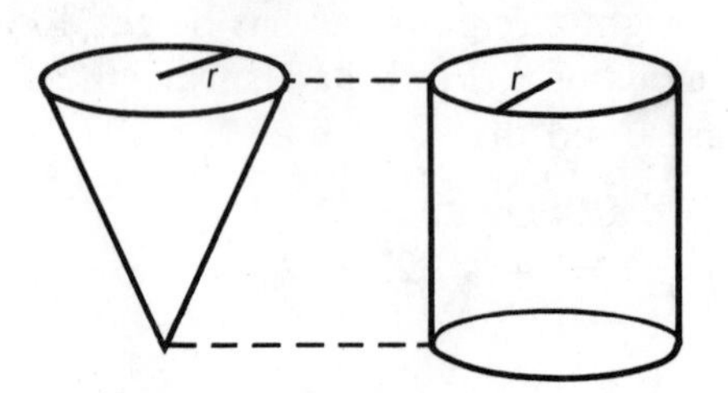

11. How many cubic inches of lead are there in the sharpened tip of this pencil? (Use a calculator.)

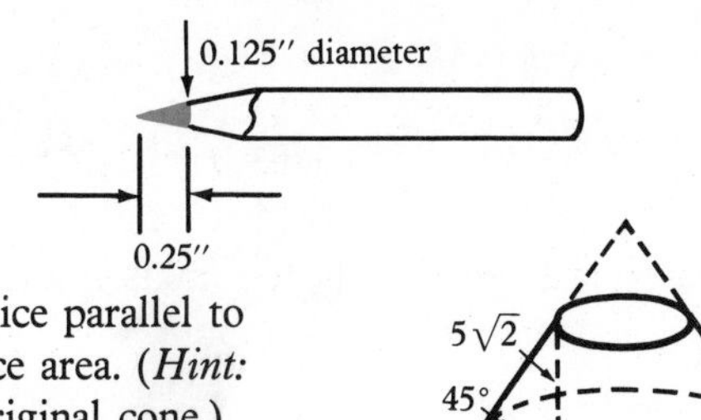

12. This solid is formed by cutting a cone with a slice parallel to the base of the cone. Find its volume and surface area. (*Hint:* Use similar triangles to find the height of the original cone.)

13. The legs of a right triangle have lengths of 2 and 3. Cones are formed by revolving the triangles about the shorter and longer sides. Find the ratio of volumes and the ratio of surface areas of these two solids.

14. This solid is formed by cutting a cone with a slice parallel to the base, and then boring a cone-shaped cut into the resulting solid. Find the volume of this solid.

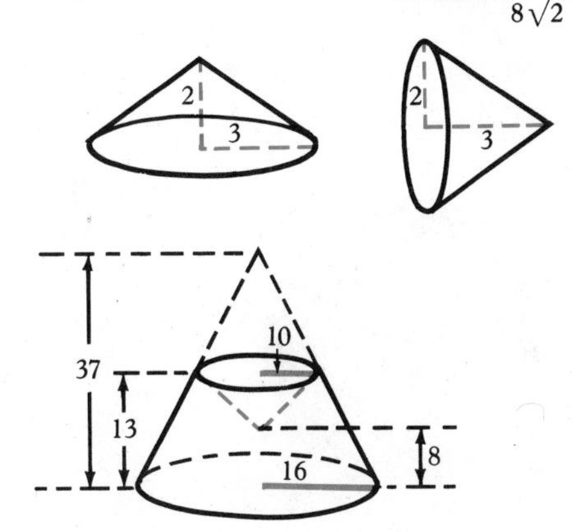

PROBLEM SOLVING

Match the object in Set 1 with its correct view (top or side) from Set 2.

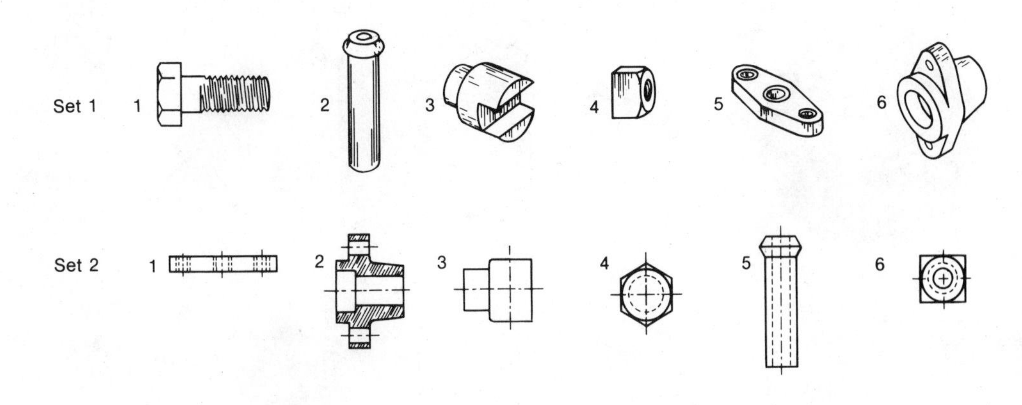

12–7 Surface Area and Volume of Spheres

In this lesson we shall study formulas for the volume and surface area of a sphere.

Definition 12-6

A **sphere** is the set of all points that are a given distance from a given point.

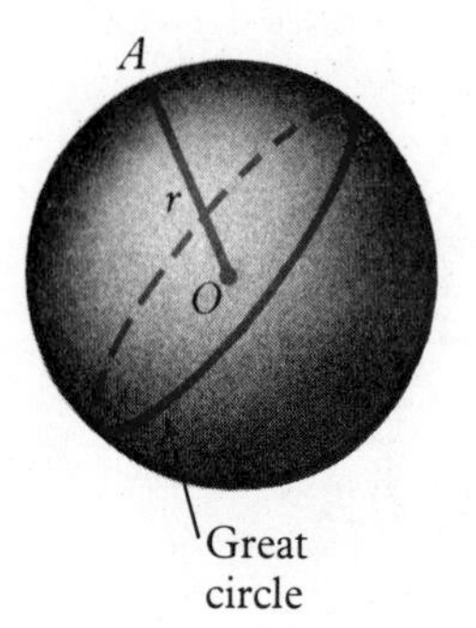

The given point O is called the *center* of the sphere. A *radius* of a sphere is a segment determined by the center and a point on the sphere. The intersection of a sphere and a plane containing the center of the sphere is called a *great circle* of the sphere.

The explanation of the formula in Theorem 12–12 is based upon a comparison between a sphere and a cylinder that has had a double cone carved out of it. The radii of the sphere and cylinder are equal in length. The height of the cylinder is twice the radius.

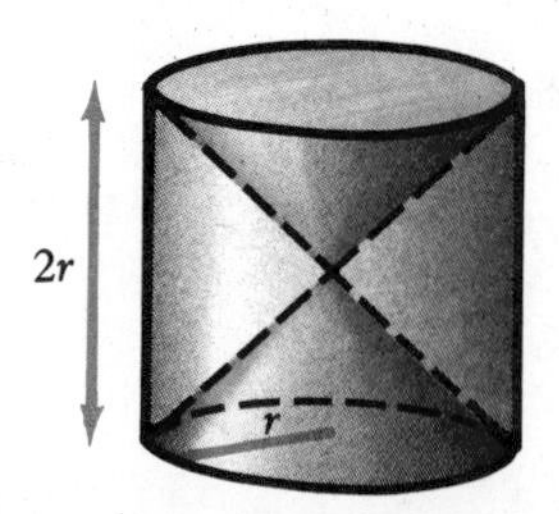

Theorem 12–12 Given a sphere of radius r, the volume is found by the formula

$$V = \frac{4}{3}\pi r^3.$$

Consider a cross section of both the sphere and the carved out cylinder that is a distance b from the center of the sphere. We conclude from the Pythagorean Theorem that the distance a in the figure is $a^2 = r^2 - b^2$.

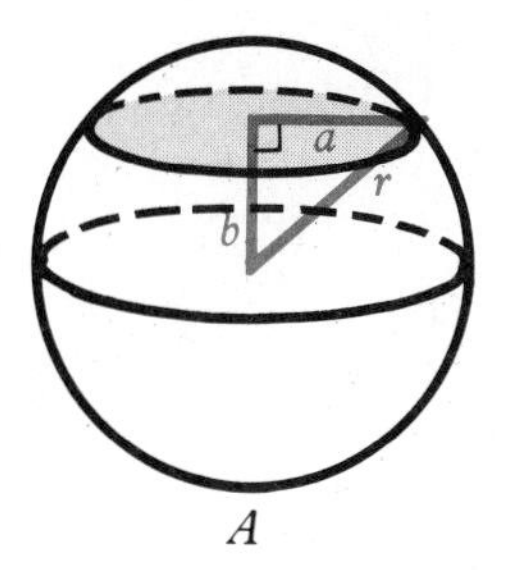

A

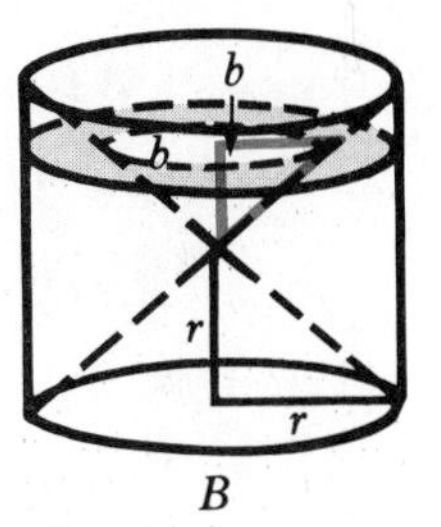

B

The triangle in red is an isosceles triangle.

Compare the areas of the two cross sections.

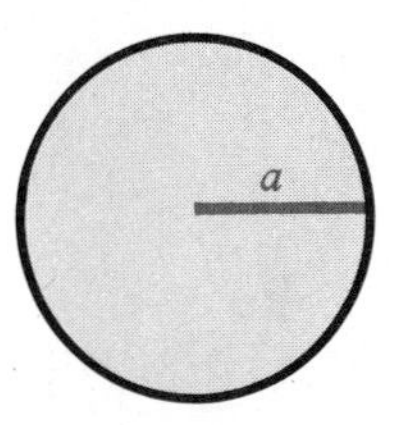

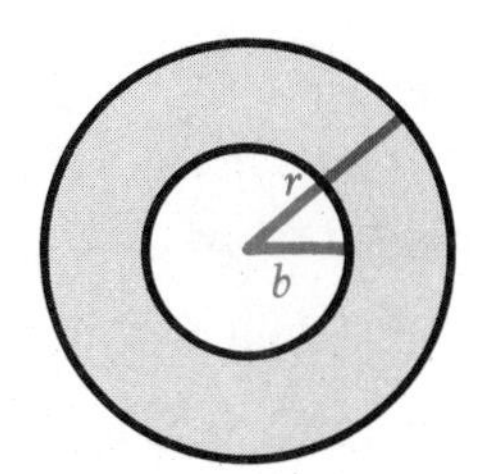

Area $= \pi a^2$

$$\text{Area} = \pi r^2 - \pi b^2 = \pi(r^2 - b^2) = \pi a^2$$

Since the areas of each cross section are equal, we conclude from Cavalieri's Principle (page 445) that the volume of the sphere A is equal to the volume of the solid B from which two cones are carved.

The volume of solid B can be calculated as:

$$\pi r^2(2r) - 2(\tfrac{1}{3}\pi r^2)(r) = 2\pi r^3 - \tfrac{2}{3}\pi r^3 = \tfrac{4}{3}\pi r^3.$$

Then the volume of sphere A with radius r is also $\frac{4}{3}\pi r^3$.

Theorem 12–13 gives a formula for the surface area of a sphere.

Theorem 12–13 Given a sphere of radius r, the surface area S is found by the formula

$$S = 4\pi r^2.$$

EXERCISES

A.

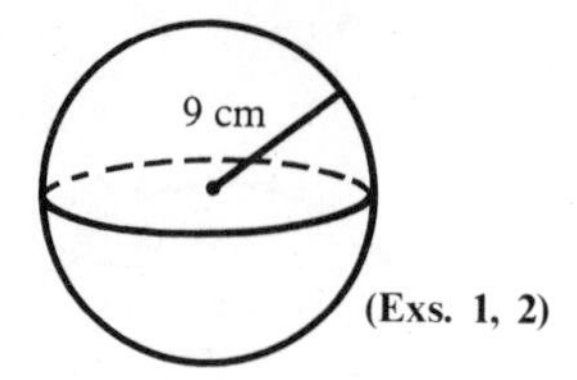

(Exs. 1, 2)

1. Find the volume of a sphere of radius 9 cm.
2. Find the surface area of a sphere of radius 9 cm.
3. Find the volume of a sphere of radius 2π.
4. Find the surface area of a sphere of radius 2π.
5. If the surface area of a sphere is 36π, find the radius.
6. If the volume of a sphere is 36π, find the radius.
7. If the surface area of a sphere is 8π, find the radius.
8. If the volume of a sphere is $4\pi\sqrt{3}$, find the radius.

B.

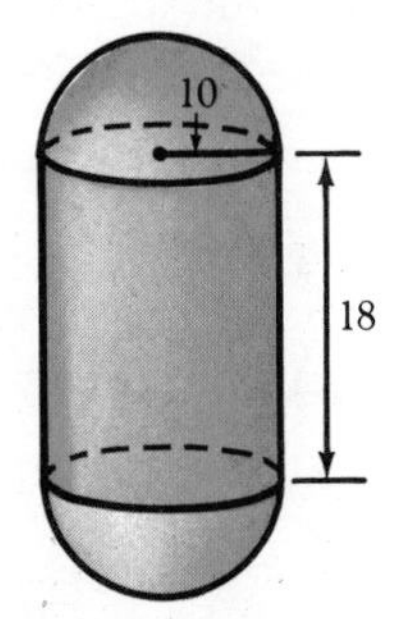

For exercises 9 and 10 assume the solid is a right cylinder capped by two hemispheres.

9. Find the volume of the solid shown.

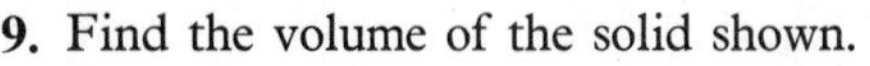

10. Find the surface area of the solid shown.
11. Find the volume of a sphere whose surface area is 144π square units.
12. Find the surface area of a sphere whose volume is 36π cubic units.
13. If the number of square feet of surface area of a sphere is equal to the number of cubic feet of volume of the sphere, what is the radius of the sphere?

Activity

Obtain a hemispherical container and a cylindrical container whose base diameter and height equal the diameter of the sphere.

Using sand or other material, measure how many cupfuls are required to fill the cylinder.

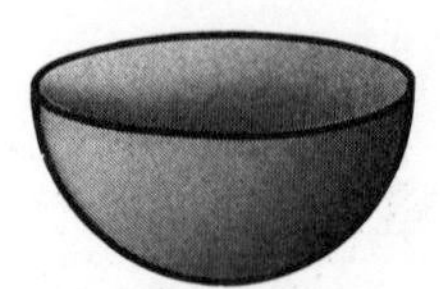

14. The radius of one sphere is twice the radius of another sphere. What are the ratios of their volumes and surface areas?

C.

15. A sphere is inscribed in a cylinder. Show that the surface area of the sphere is equal to the lateral surface area of the cylinder.

16. A spherical tank whose radius to the outer surface is 15 feet is made of steel $\frac{1}{2}$ inch thick. How many cubic feet of steel are used in the construction of this tank?

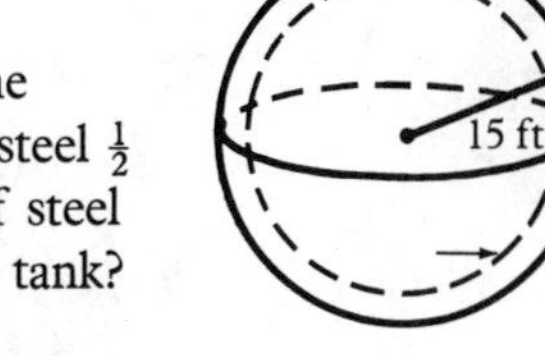

17. How does the volume of a cone whose height is twice its radius compare to the volume of a sphere whose radius equals the radius of the cone base?

18. The shape of the Earth is an oblate spheroid and not a perfect sphere. Determine the average radius of the Earth given that the Polar radius is 6357 km and the Equatorial radius is 6378 km. Assume that the Earth is a perfect sphere and determine its volume and surface area.

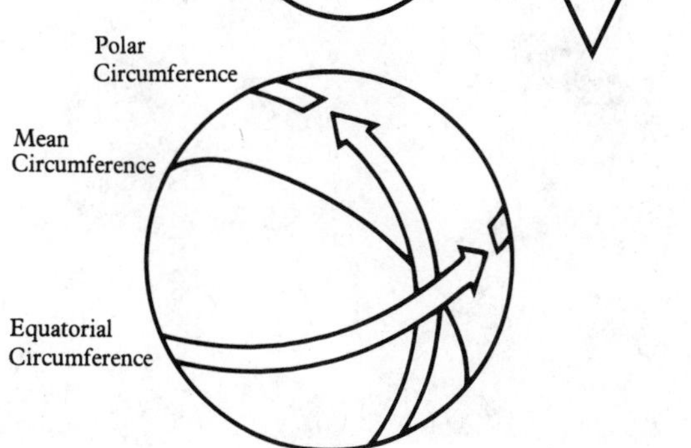

PROBLEM SOLVING

If a sphere is sliced with a plane a portion of a sphere with a circular base is formed as shown.

Fact: If the radius of this circular base is r_1, and its height is h, then the volume of this solid cap is

$$V = \frac{1}{2}\pi r_1^2 h + \frac{1}{6}\pi h^3.$$

If a hole 3 cm in radius is drilled through the center of a sphere of radius 9 cm, find the volume of this bead-like solid.

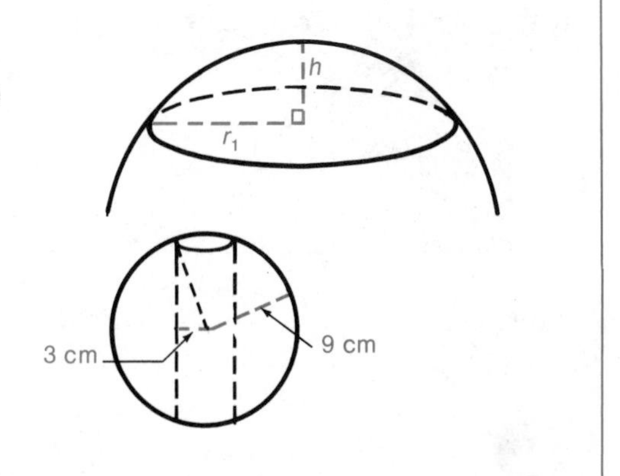

12–8 Regular Polyhedra

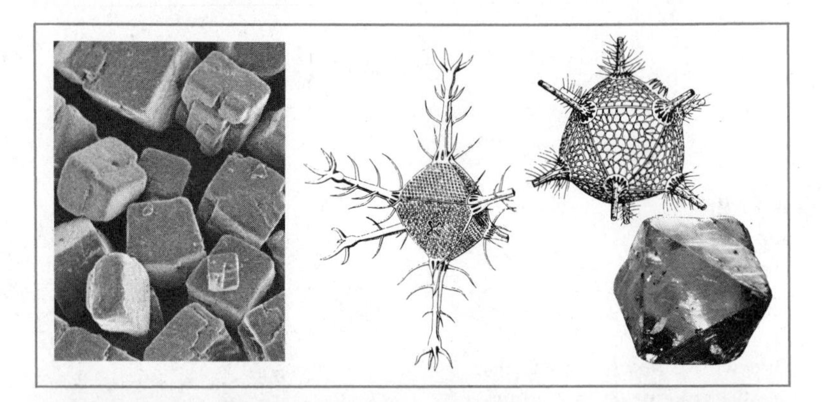

Some naturally occurring minerals and skeletons of tiny sea creatures are models of solids that we study in this lesson. These solids are called polyhedra.

Definition 12–7

A **regular polyhedron** is a polyhedron whose faces are all regular polygons with the same number of edges and whose vertices are each surrounded by the same number of faces.

A cube is an example of a regular polyhedron. The method of constructing a cube described here by forming a "roof" is instructive in our analysis of the theorem below.

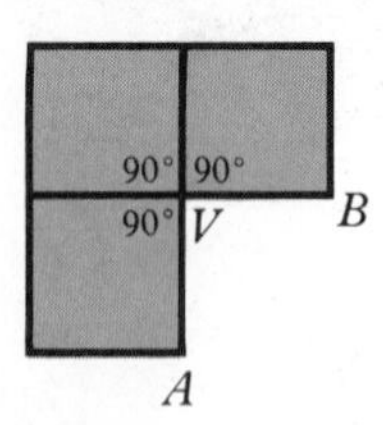

Surround a vertex (V) with three squares.

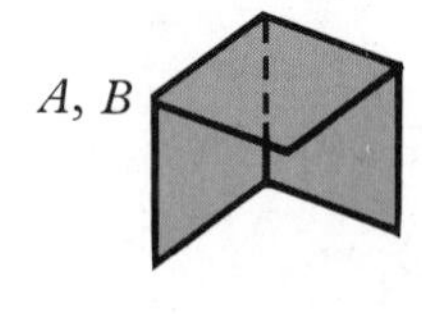

Fold, join A and B to form a 3-dimensional "roof."

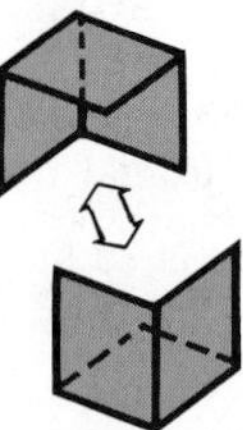

Join two "roofs" to form a cube.

Theorem 12–14 There are exactly five regular polyhedra that are convex solids.

This table summarizes the five convex regular polyhedra. There are only five types of "roofs" that can be constructed with regular polygons. Each one results in a regular polyhedron.

Polygon Face	Number of faces at a vertex (V)	Join $\overline{AV}$ and $\overline{BV}$ to form a 3 dimensional "roof."	The "roof" fits over each vertex of a complete regular polyhedron.
equilateral triangle	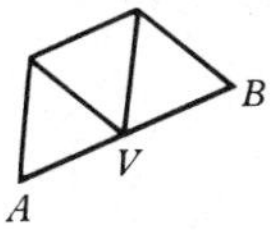		 regular tetrahedron
equilateral triangle	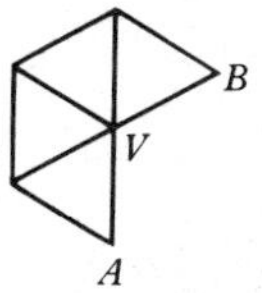		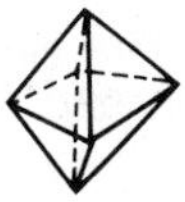 regular octahedron
equilateral triangle	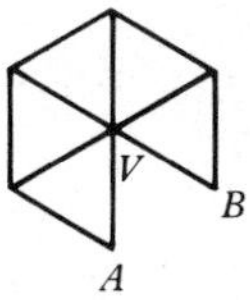	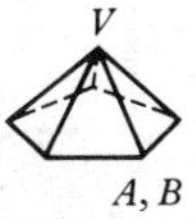	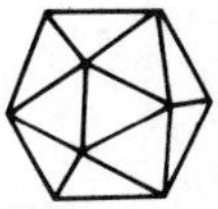 regular icosahedron
square	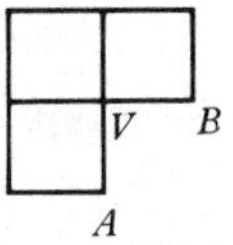	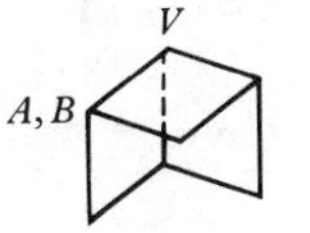	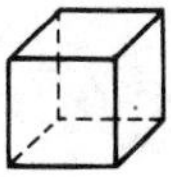 cube
regular pentagon	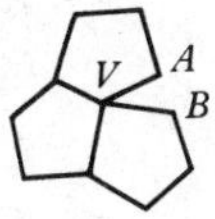	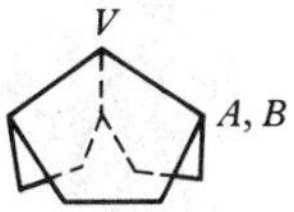	 regular dodecahedron

The prefix used in the name of each regular polyhedron tells the number of faces for that polyhedron. This information is summarized in this table.

Polyhedron Name	Prefix and Prefix Meaning	Number of Faces
tetrahedron	tetra—4	4
cube (hexahedron)	hexa—6	6
octahedron	octa—8	8
dodecahedron	dodeca—12	12
icosahedron	icosa—20	20

EXERCISES

A.

1. Name the three regular polyhedra with equilateral triangular faces.
2. Which regular polyhedron has 20 faces?
3. Why can a regular hexagon *not* be the face of a regular polyhedron?
4. Why can there *not* be six faces at a vertex in a regular polyhedron?
5. Which regular polyhedron is a pyramid?
6. Which regular polyhedron is a prism?

B.

Use stiff paper to construct a model of each regular polyhedron. The patterns shown below should be enlarged. Cut on solid lines, fold on dotted lines.

7. Tetrahedron

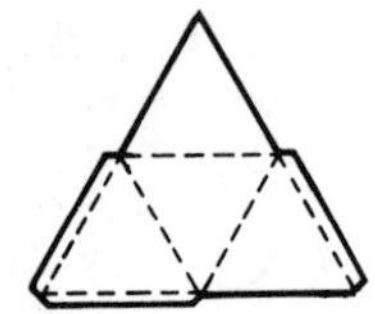

8. Cube

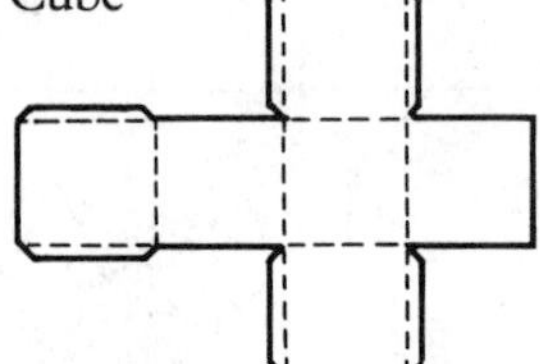

9. Octahedron

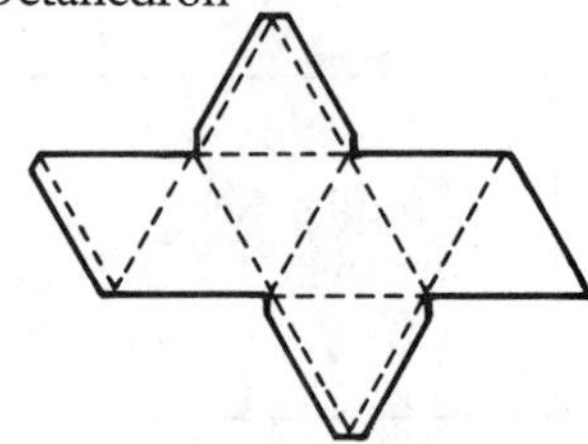

Activity

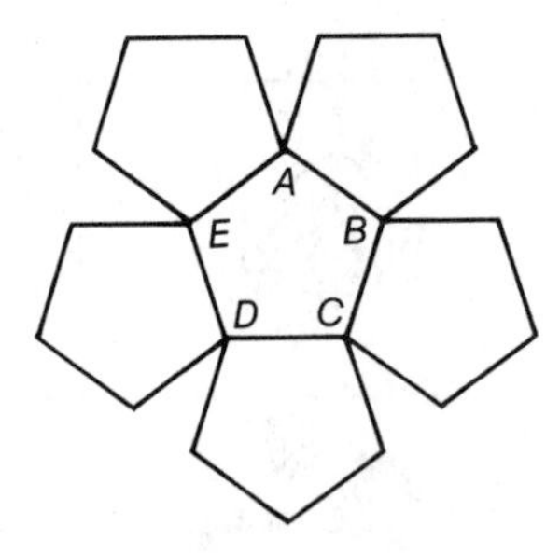

1. Cut from posterboard two large patterns like the one above.
2. Crease sharply along edge *ABCDE*.
3. Place one pattern upon the other one rotated 36°. While holding the patterns in place, weave an elastic band alternately above and below the corners.
4. When you raise your hand, you will see a dodecahedron.

10. Dodecahedron

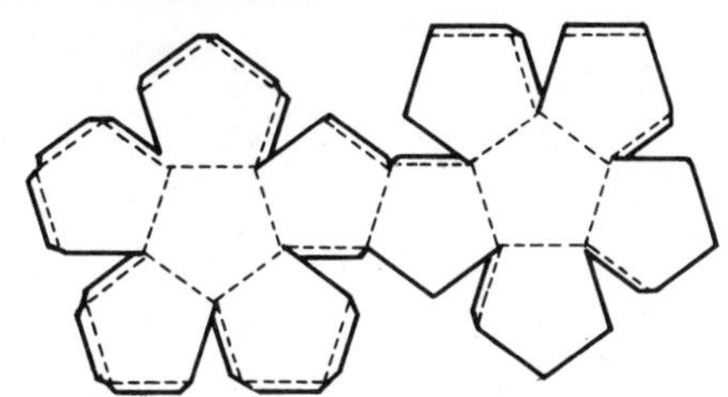

11. Icosahedron

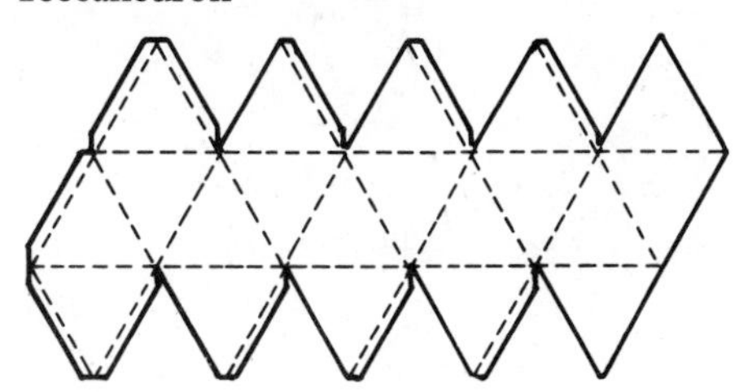

C.

The number of faces (F), the number of edges (E), and the number of vertices (V) of a polyhedron satisfy one of the formulas below.

12. Which one formula below is satisfied by the regular tetrahedron and regular octahedron?

a. $F + E + V = 26$ **b.** $F - V + E = 10$

c. $F - E + V = 2$ **d.** $F - E + V = 0$

The correct answer to this exercise is called *Euler's Formula.*

For which of these polyhedra does Euler's Formula hold?

13.

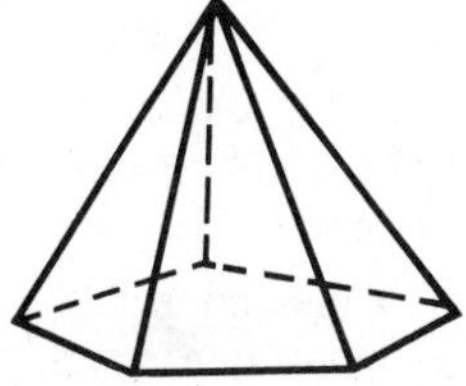

14.

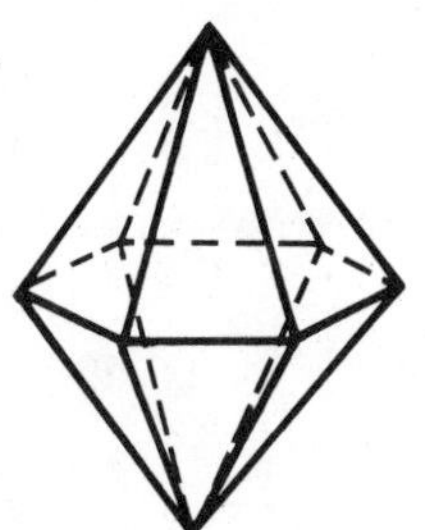

15.

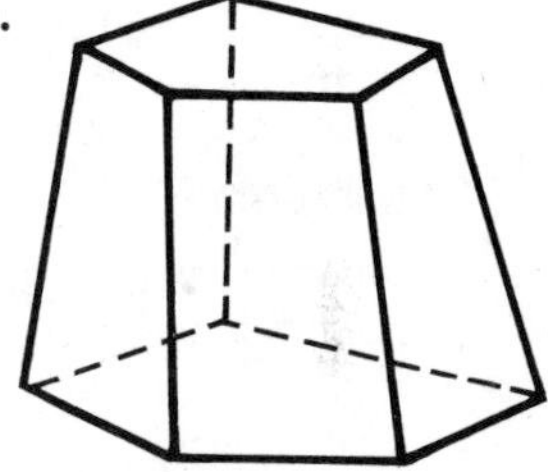

PROBLEM SOLVING

Let F be the number of faces of a polyhedron, E be the number of edges of a polyhedron, and V be the number of vertices of a polyhedron. $F \times$ (number of edges per face) $= 2E$ because each edge of a polyhedron is an edge of two faces.

1. How many edges does a regular octahedron possess?

2. How many edges does a regular dodecahedron possess?

3. How many edges does a regular icosahedron possess?

4. In a regular dodecahedron $F \times$ (number of vertices/face) $= 3V$ because each vertex of a regular dodecahedron is a vertex of 3 faces. How many vertices does a regular dodecahedron possess?

Important Ideas—Chapter 12

Terms

Polyhedron (p. 434)
Pyramid (p. 434)
Prism (p. 435)
Rectangular solid (p. 444)
Cross section (p. 445)
Circular cylinder (p. 452)
Right circular cone (p. 456)
Sphere (p. 460)
Regular polyhedron (p. 464)

Postulates

Volume Postulate (p. 444)
Rectangular Solid Volume Postulate (p. 444)
Volume Addition Postulate (p. 445)
Cavalieri's Postulate (p. 445)

Theorems

12-1 The lateral edges of a prism are parallel and congruent.

12-2 Given a prism with rectangular lateral faces. If the altitude of the prism is h and the bases have area B and perimeter p, then the surface area S is found by the formula $S = hp + 2B$.

12-3 Given a regular pyramid with slant height ℓ and a base with area B and perimeter p, the surface area S is found by the formula $S = \frac{1}{2}\ell p + B$.

12-4 The volume of any prism is the product of the altitude and the area of the base.

12-5 Given a pyramid with base B and altitude h. If A is a cross section parallel to the base and the distance from the vertex to the cross section is K, then

$$\frac{\text{area } A}{\text{area } B} = \left(\frac{K}{h}\right)^2.$$

12-6 Two pyramids with equal altitudes and bases of equal area have the same volume.

12-7 Given a pyramid with altitude h and base area B, the volume is found by the formula $V = \frac{1}{3}hB$.

12-8 Given a right circular cylinder with altitude h. If the circumference of the base is C, and the area of the base is B, then the surface area S is found by the formula $S = Ch + 2B = 2\pi rh + 2\pi r^2$.

12-9 Given a right circular cylinder with base area B and height h, the volume is found by the formula $V = Bh = \pi r^2 h$.

12-10 Given a right circular cone with slant height ℓ. If the circumference of the base is C, and the area of the base is B, then the surface area S is given by the formula $S = \frac{1}{2}\ell C + B = \pi r\ell + \pi r^2$.

12-11 Given a right circular cone with height h and base area B, the volume is found by the formula $V = \frac{1}{3}Bh = \frac{1}{3}\pi r^2 h$.

12-12 Given a sphere of radius r, the volume is found by the formula $V = \frac{4}{3}\pi r^3$.

12-13 Given a sphere of radius r, the surface area S is found by the formula $S = 4\pi r^2$.

12-14 There are exactly five regular polyhedra that are convex solids.

Careers in Computers

Companies that design and build computers have become a vital part of the economy. The computer revolution has caused many new companies to grow, literally from the inventors' garages. Numerous companies offer personal computers, accessories, and software (the programs that make the computers run). But it is people who must invent, design, test, refine, and market this equipment. These pages show a few of the careers centered in the computer industry.

1 **A computer engineer uses a small computer to test circuits in a mainframe computer.**

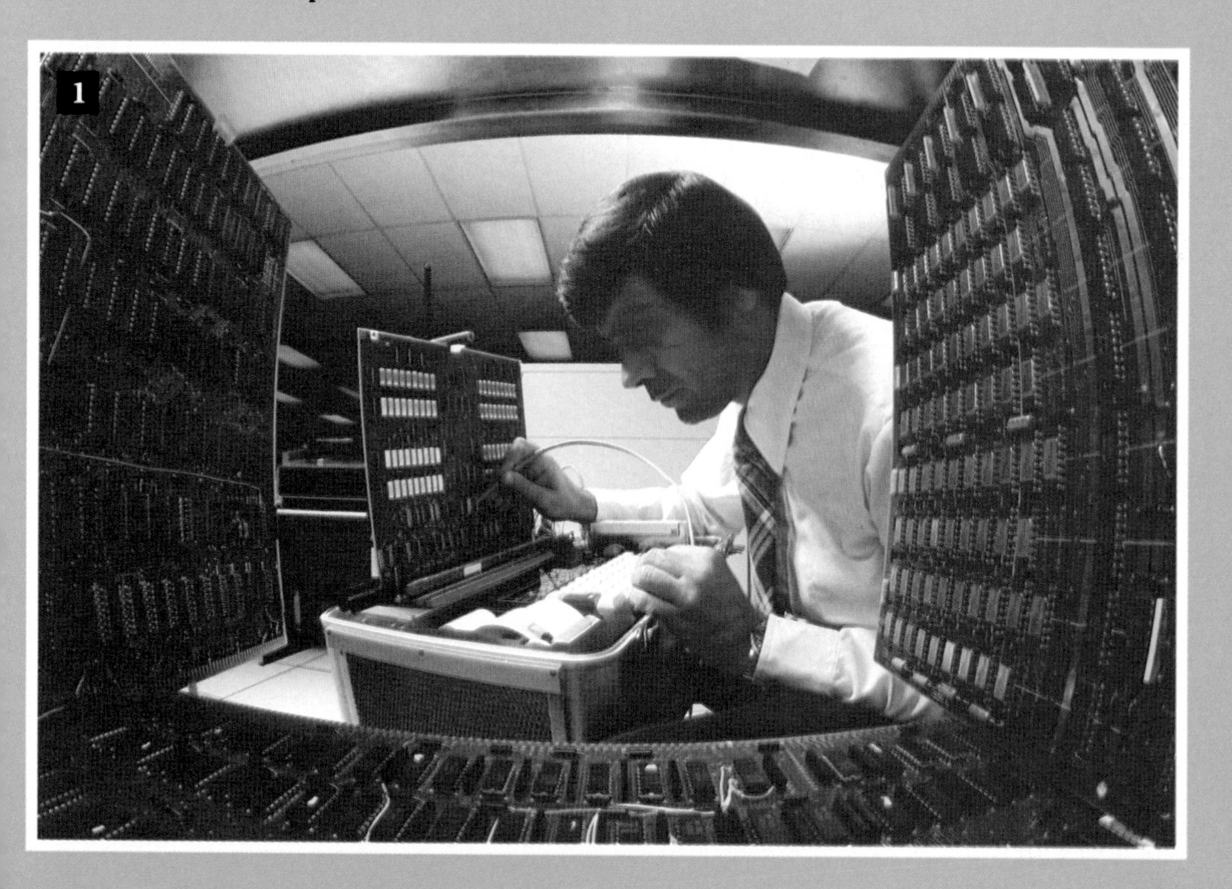

2 A prototype is a handmade sample showing how all parts of a new computer fit together. These technicians discuss a problem with a cable prototype.

3 Testing is a continuous activity.

4 Industrial designers work to make the computer system attractive and functional. Pleasing shapes, balance between horizontal and vertical, and pleasing ratios of width to height are geometric factors to consider.

5 Customer service personnel make sure the computer operates correctly.

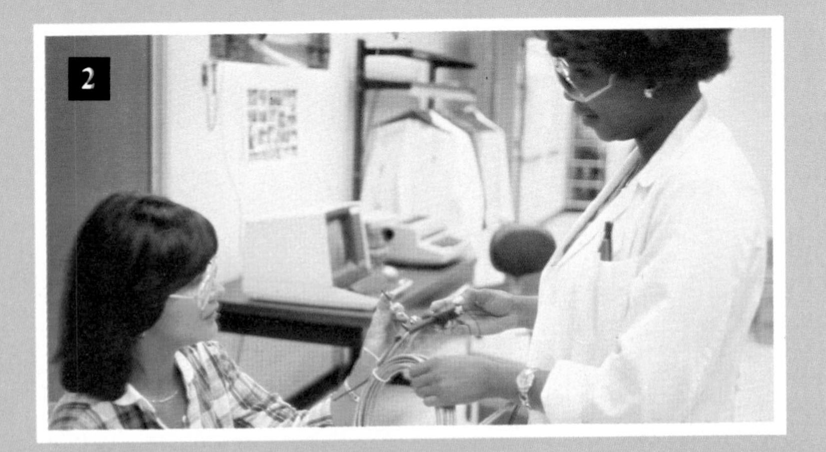

IBM
370168

PRIME
Computer

Computers in Industry

Computers are used in many industries for many different purposes. Often they monitor the work of other machines. This insures accuracy in manufacture, especially in repetitive jobs. Computers also control machines to achieve critical measurements and exact fit. Although some jobs have been taken over by computers, many others have been created or enriched by computer technology. For people in these industries, geometric ideas, concepts, and skills are important in their training.

1 **Computer-guided robots assemble body parts in an automobile plant. Geometric concepts of angle and distance play an important part in robot design.**

2 TV control room operators must view scenes from a variety of angles and select the one most appropriate for the situation.

3 Computerized drafting machines can draw simultaneously in four colors. Geometric visualization skills are necessary for the programmer.

4

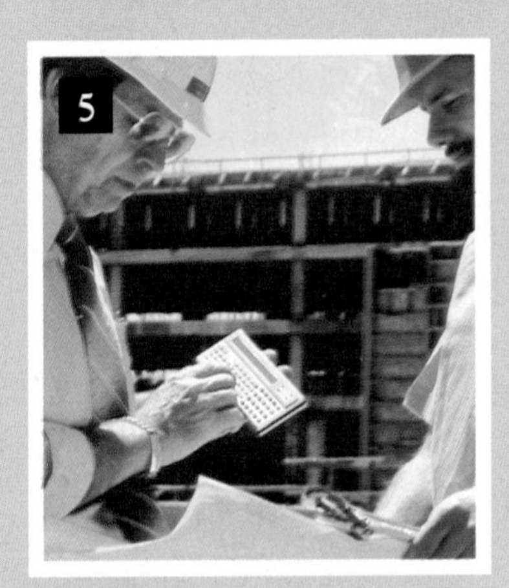
5

6

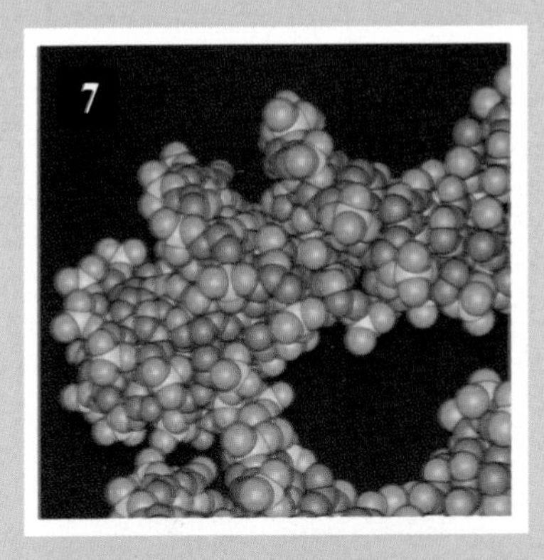
7

8
Deposit Envelopes

9
IMPORTANT
NTROL
MODULES
EM MASTER
BILL OF MATERIAL
PURCHA

4 Microfilm, viewed through microfiche viewers, is used to catalog parts lists and show three-dimensional drawings of parts.

5 Pocket computers help in measurement.

6 Air traffic controllers use concentric circles, angles, and distance to determine plane location near an airport.

7 A computer drawing of a DNA molecule aids in biological research.

8 Special geometric figures on a bank credit card enable the automatic teller to identify the customer and complete the transaction.

9 The designer of a printed page uses a geometric "sixth sense" to determine the proper balance between type sizes and styles.

10 Bar code scanners give customers better information and help store managers control the inventory.

11 Microcomputers are used for many small business tasks.

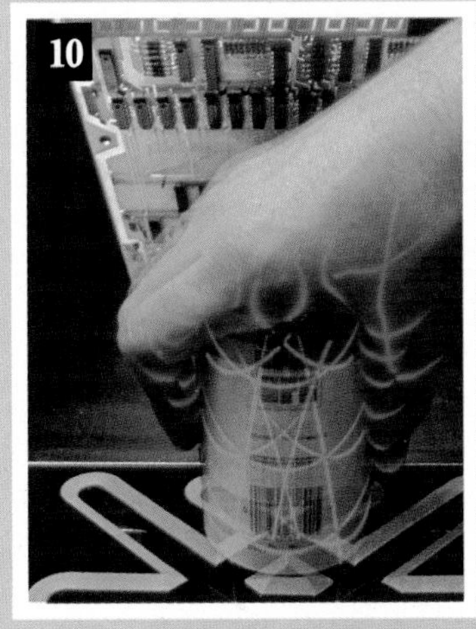

12 Trains, buildings, bridges, and other human creations employ a wide variety of geometric ideas for their design and construction.

13 A printed "hardcopy" uses different colors to show different automotive systems. These three-dimensional diagrams help mechanic trainees visualize the systems.

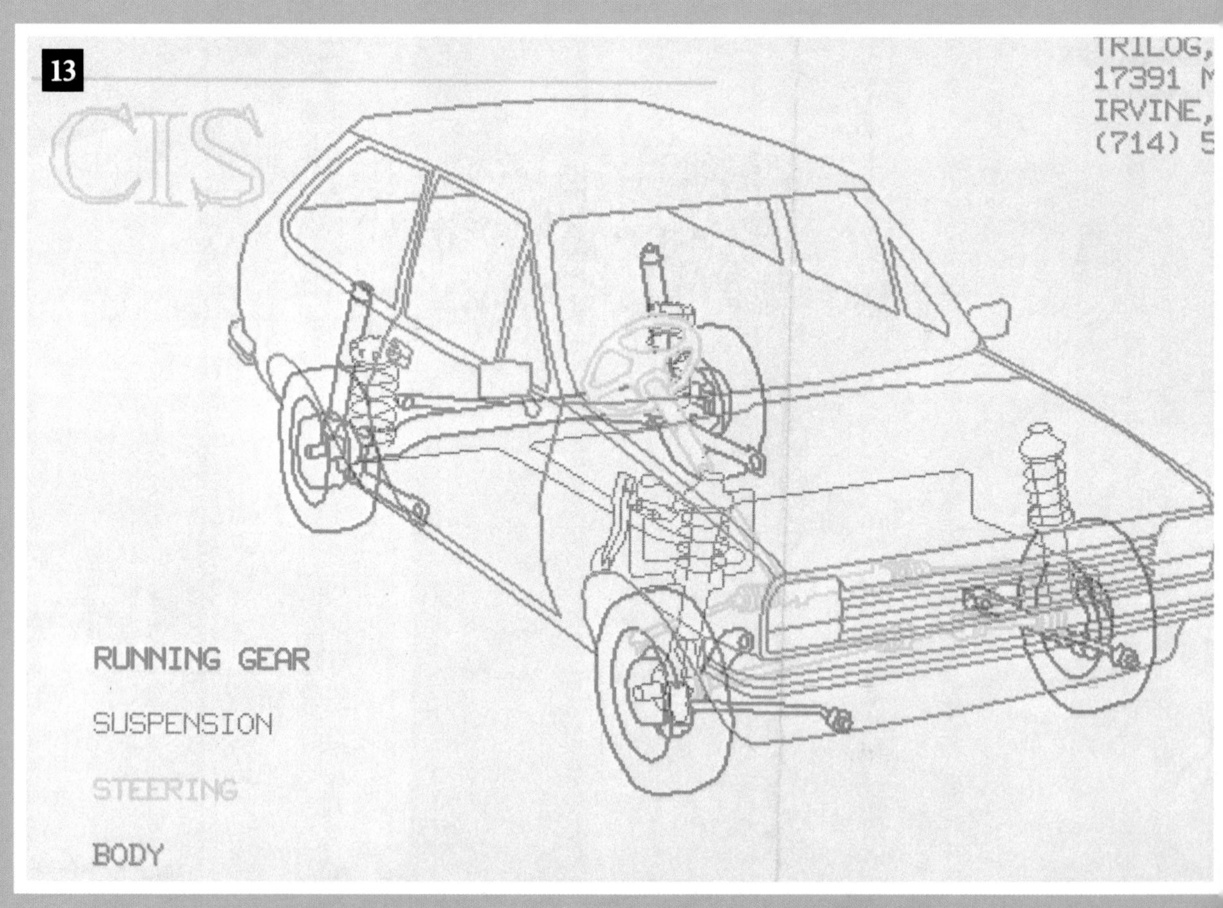

Chapter 12—Review

1. Find the surface area and volume of a cube in which each edge is 4 cm.

2. Find the surface area of the regular pyramid and regular prism shown.

a.

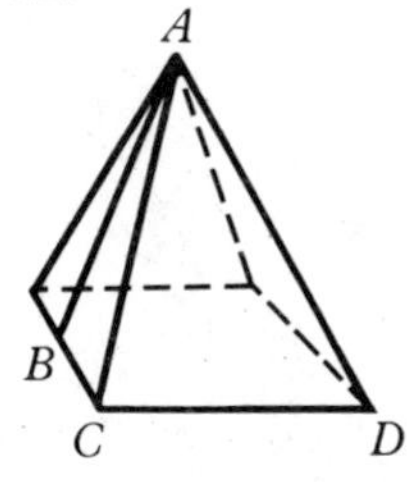

$AB = 10$ cm, $CD = 6$ cm

b.

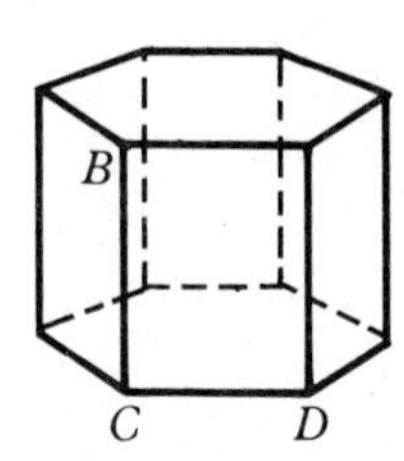

$BC = 6$ cm, $CD = 2$ cm

3. Find the volumes of the regular pyramid and regular prism shown.

a.

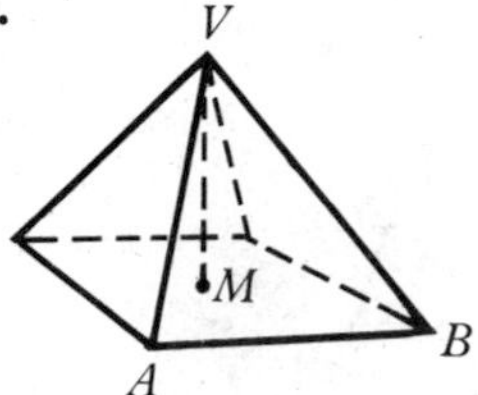

$VM = 8$ cm, $AB = 5$ cm

b.

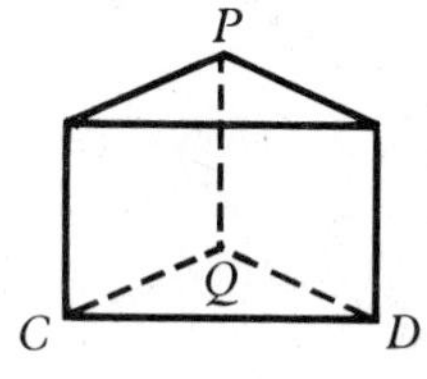

$PQ = 8$ cm, $CD = 4$ cm

4. How many square centimeters of paper would it take for a label on a cylindrical can 10 cm high and with a circular base of 6 cm in diameter.

5. Find the volume of the cylindrical can described in exercise 4.

6. The volume of a right circular cylinder is 160π. If the height is 10, what is the diameter of the base?

7. Find the volume of the circular cone, where $PA = 12$ cm and $AB = 3$ cm.

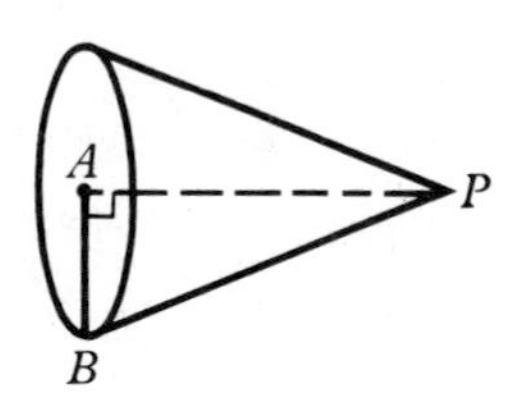

8. If the height of a right circular cone is doubled, how is the volume affected?

9. A sphere has a volume of 36π cm^3. What is its radius?

10. Find the surface area of a sphere with radius 10 cm.

Chapter 12—Test

1. How many cubes with an edge of 2 cm can fit into a box with dimensions 3 cm × 10 cm × 16 cm?
2. Find the diagonal of a cube if each edge is 1 cm long.
3. Find the surface area of the regular pyramid and right circular cylinder shown.

a.

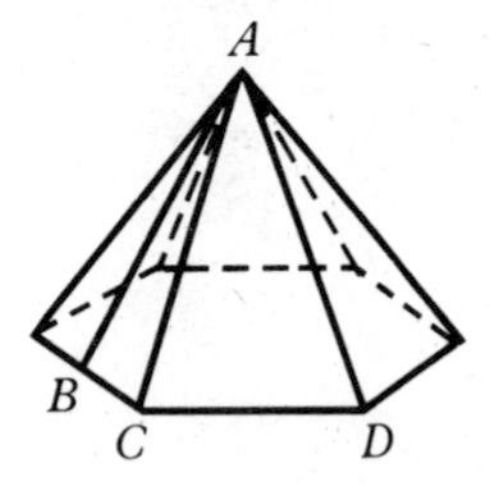

$AB = 6$ cm, $CD = 2$ cm

b.

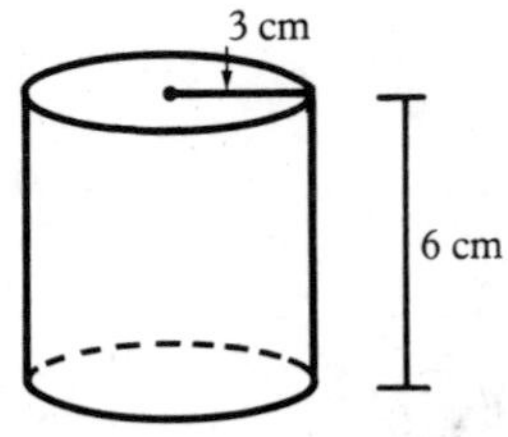

4. Find the volume of the prism and trapezoid-based pyramid shown.

a.

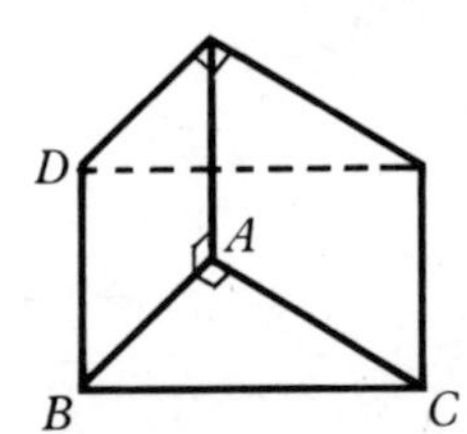

$AB = 4$ cm, $AC = 6$ cm, $BD = 12$ cm

b.

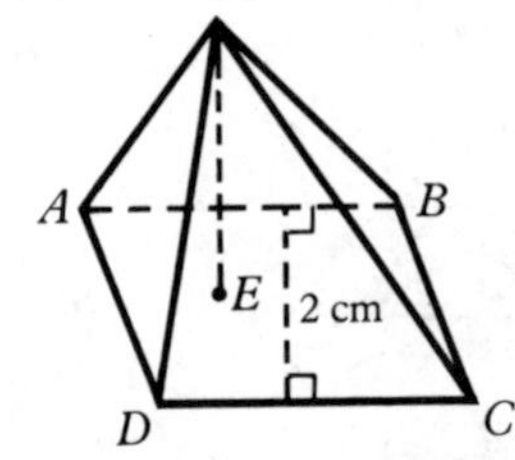

$AB = 4$ cm, $DC = 3$ cm, $FE = 5$ cm

5. How many cubic centimeters of liquid could be in a right circular cone if its height is 8 cm and its base has a radius of 3 cm?
6. Find the surface area of a right circular cone if the base has a radius of 2 cm and its altitude is 6 cm.
7. Find the volume of the cone described in exercise 6.
8. Find the volume of a sphere with a radius of 3 cm.
9. Find the radius of a sphere if its volume is 288π cm^3.
10. How is the surface area of a sphere affected if the diameter is doubled?
11. How is the volume of a sphere affected if the radius is doubled?

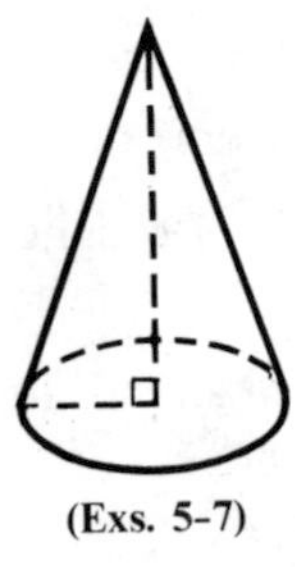

(Exs. 5-7)

Problem Solving Techniques

Make an Accurate Drawing

Sometimes an answer to a problem can be found by making an accurate drawing or a scale drawing. Study the example below in which a scale drawing is used to solve a problem.

Example

An 8-foot by 12-foot pool table has a ball in the corner. Suppose the ball is struck and travels at a 45° angle with a side until it hits a side. The ball then rebounds off that side and travels at a 45° angle until it hits and rebounds off another side. How many times will the ball hit a side before it reaches a corner? The scale drawing shows it will have three hits.

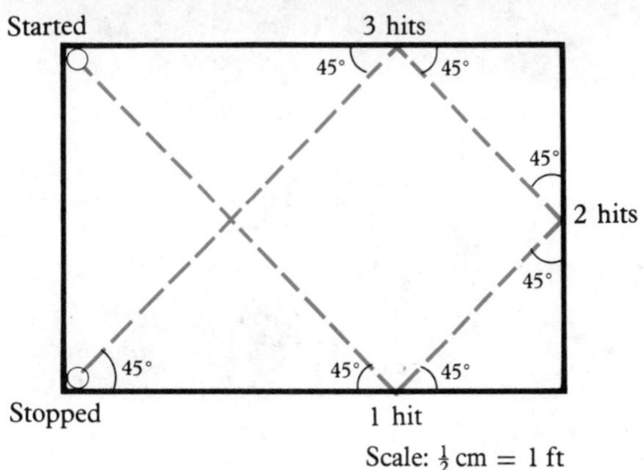

PROBLEMS

Use an accurate drawing or a scale drawing to solve the problems below.

1. Suppose a ball travels as described in the example above on an 8-foot by 10-foot table. How many times will the ball hit a side before it reaches a corner?
2. Answer the same question for a 6-foot by 8-foot pool table.
3. O is the intersection of the perpendicular bisectors of the sides of $\triangle ABC$, G is the intersection of the medians, and H is the intersection of the altitudes. Observe that O, G, and H are collinear. What fraction of OH is OG? Try several triangles.

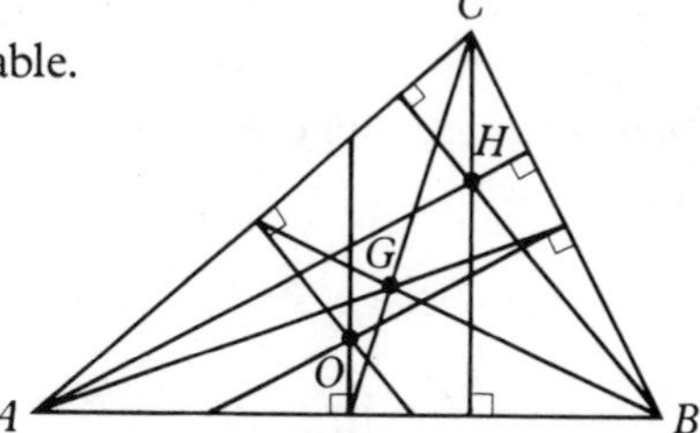

4. A pilot in a small plane maintains a constant ground speed of 120 mi/hr. She travels due north for 30 minutes, then northeast for 10 minutes, then southeast for 45 minutes, then southwest for 30 minutes. At that point how long will it take to fly straight home?

Navigation

Traveling in a pleasure boat can be an adventurous way to see the world. But someone on board needs to know about navigation.

Generally speaking, navigation means safely finding your way from one place to another and knowing where you are along the way. Someone who pilots a boat must be constantly aware of the location of the craft, the direction the boat is traveling, and the distance traveled.

Two important tools available to a navigator are a compass and nautical charts. Nautical charts are scaled-down maps of areas of water. They include information about water depth, location of landmarks and ports, and any dangers to navigation in the area.

Two Navigation Techniques

1 Determining the position of a craft by sighting one object.

To determine the position of a craft, it is often useful to find the distance D from the craft to a sighted object. (Fig. 1)

As the boat travels in the direction of $\overrightarrow{P_1P_2}$, a sighting is made of the lighthouse from P_1. Later, when the angle of sight has doubled, the sighting is made from P_2. The distance, d, that the boat travels from P_1 to P_2 is found using speed and time. The desired distance D is equal to d.

Why is this true? What theorem(s) did you use?

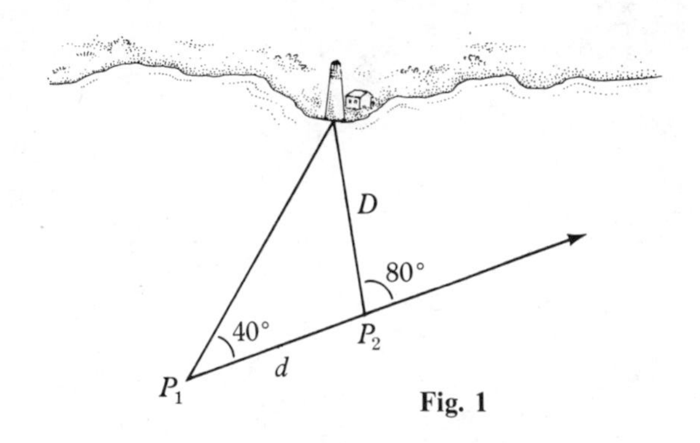

Fig. 1

2

Determining the position of a craft by sighting three objects.

To determine a boat's position, a pilot sights three actual objects represented by A, B, and C on a nautical chart (Fig. 2). Then the pilot measures the angles between the lines of sight. Lines from point P showing these angles are drawn on a sheet of red-tinted plastic. When the plastic is positioned on the chart so that the lines go through A, B, and C, the position of the boat is shown by point P.

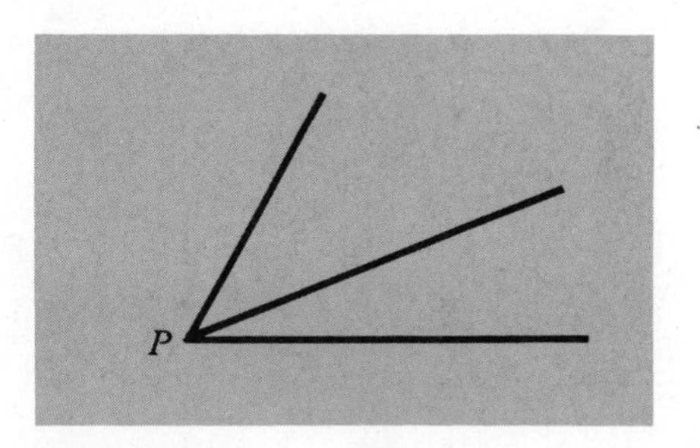

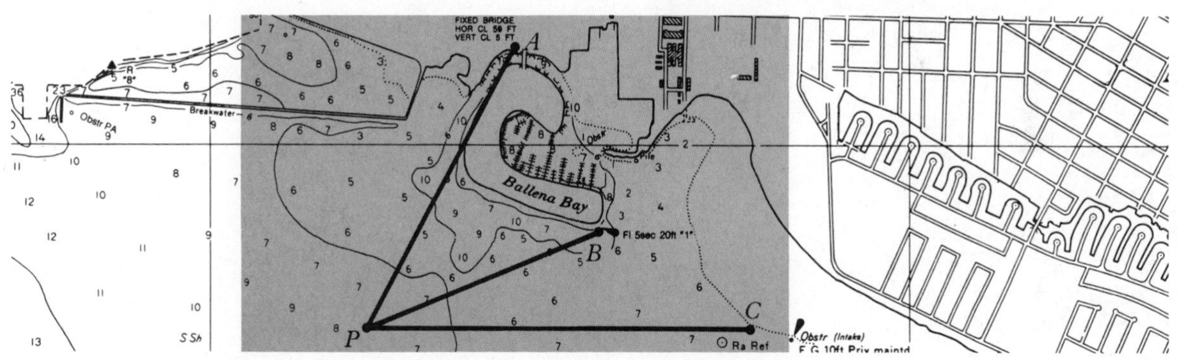

Fig. 2

U.S. Dept. of Commerce

The method described above will not work, however, when P is on a circle containing A, B, and C. In this picture, for example, the boat could have been at position R, S, or another location on the circle. What theorem can be used to show that this is true?

B C A 12° 30° R S P

CHAPTER 13

Transformations and Symmetry

13–1 Line Reflections

The word transformation implies that an object is being changed in some way. In a geometric transformation there are three things to consider:

1. the original figure,
2. a rule or operation that describes the change, and
3. the figure that results after that change.

Drawing by W. Miller;

The object prior to the change is called the *preimage*, and the object after the change is called the *image*.

In this chapter we shall study the three types of transformations called *line reflections*, *translations*, and *rotations*. The first of these transformations, a line reflection, can be described by using a MIRA.

Suppose a MIRA is placed on a line ℓ as shown. Points A' and B' are the reflection images of A and B.

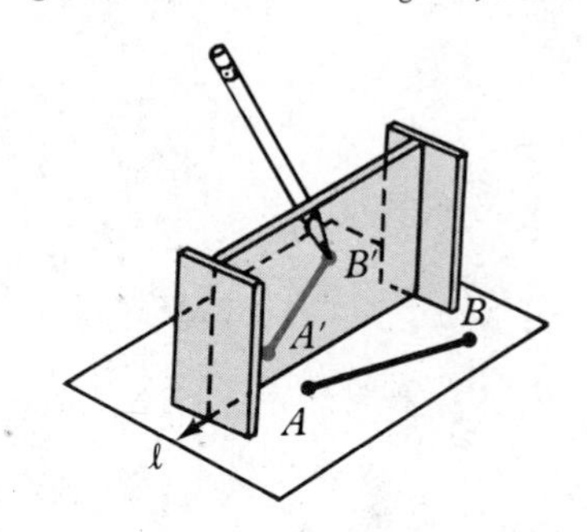

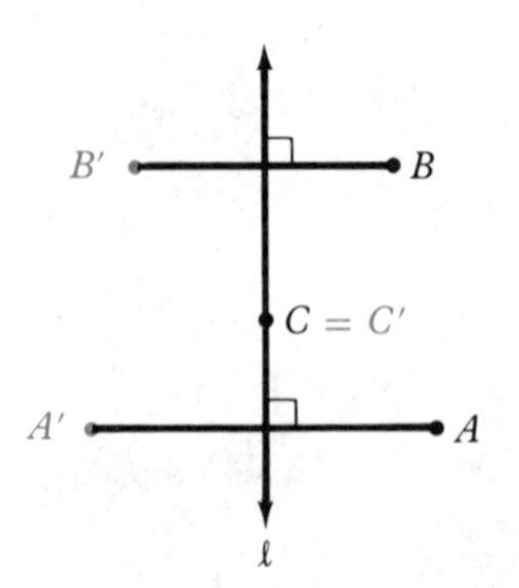

Notice that ℓ is the perpendicular bisector of $\overline{AA'}$ and $\overline{BB'}$. This is true for any segment connecting a point and its reflection image. Point C, because it is on ℓ, is its own image.

Definition 13–1

In a plane, a **reflection** over line ℓ is a transformation that maps each point P of the plane onto the point P' as follows:

a. If P is on ℓ, $P' = P$.

b. If P is not on ℓ, then ℓ is the perpendicular bisector of $\overline{PP'}$.

P' is called the **image** of P and P is the **preimage** of P'.

When each point of a figure is reflected over a line ℓ, the set of all image points form a figure called the reflection image of the figure. Two examples are shown.

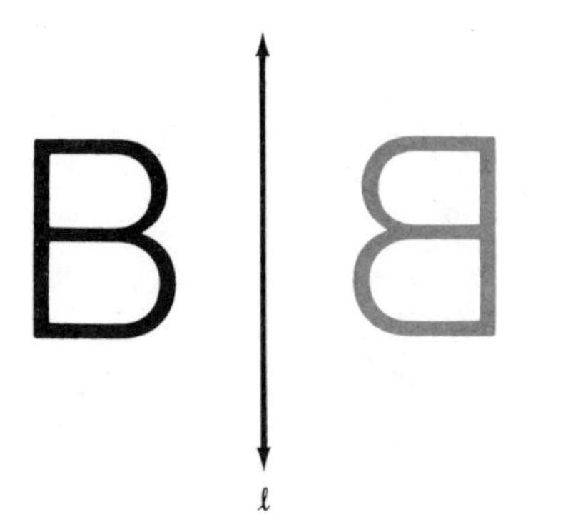

A letter "B" and its reflection over line ℓ.

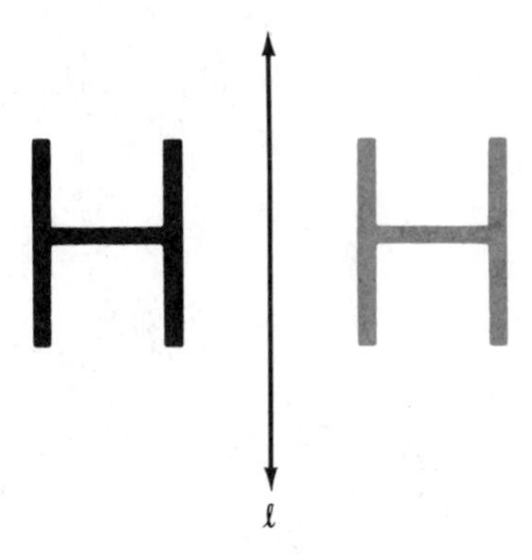

A letter "H" and its reflection over line ℓ.

The transformation called a line reflection satisfies several important properties as stated in this theorem.

Theorem 13–1 Given a line reflection:

a. the reflection image of a segment is a segment of equal length;

b. the reflection image of an angle is an angle of equal measure.

Below is the plan for proving part a of Theorem 13–1.

PROOF

Given: $\overline{AB}$ is the reflection image of $\overline{A'B'}$.
Prove: $AB = A'B'$

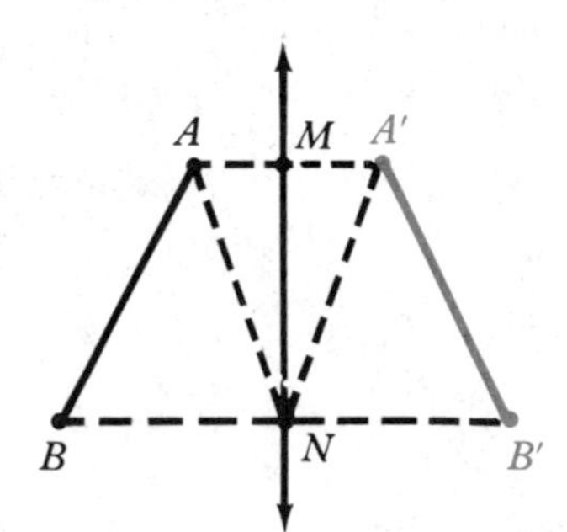

Plan: ℓ is the perpendicular bisector of $\overline{AA'}$ and $\overline{BB'}$. Draw in auxiliary segments AN and $A'N$ and use congruent triangles.

The proof is left as an exercise.

EXERCISES

A.

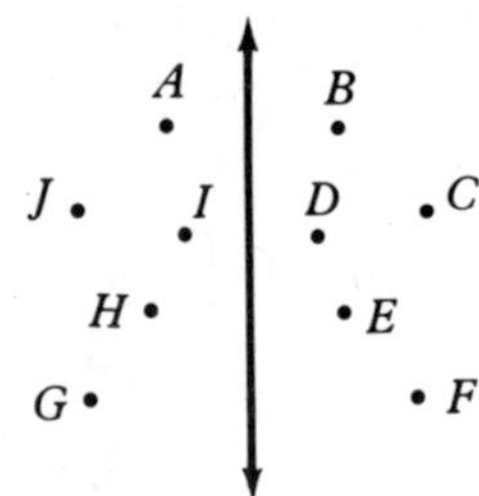

1. The reflection image over line ℓ
   a. of B is ?. b. of I is ?.
   c. of D is ?. d. of F is ?.

2. Trace line ℓ and the red figure. Use a compass or a MIRA to construct the reflection image of the red figure.

a. 

b. 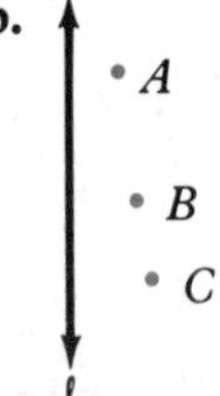

c. 

Copy the following figures. Use a MIRA, tracing paper, or a compass to draw as accurately as possible the reflection image of each figure over line ℓ.

3. 

4. 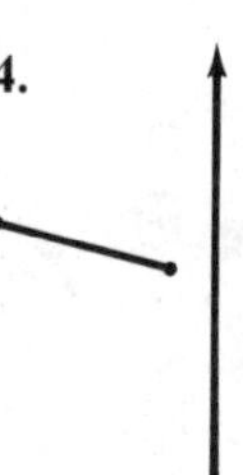

5. 

6. 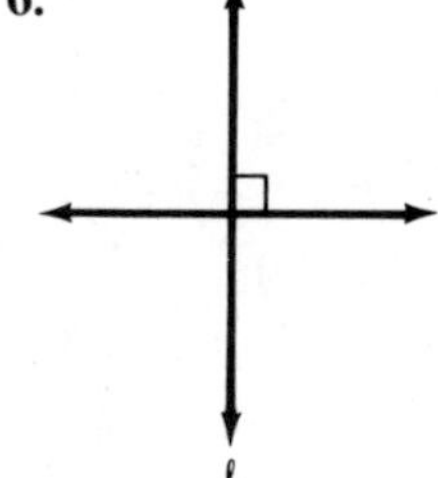

Activity

Obtain a pair of rectangular mirrors and hinge them together with tape. You can see different regular polygons by using graph paper and construction paper and changing the angle θ between the mirrors. First, tape together a half sheet of graph paper and a half sheet of dark construction paper. Position the mirrors so that one mirror is at a right angle to a line on the graph paper (see photo). Swing the second mirror to form different regular polygons.

Experiment to determine what values of θ will create a picture of a regular polygon. For example, in the photo an equilateral triangle is formed. What is the value of θ? What value of θ will create a square? a regular pentagon? a regular hexagon? Can you find a relationship between the angle θ and the number of sides?

B.

For exercises 7–14, trace the given figure. Make a freehand sketch of the reflection image over line ℓ of the given figure. Check your work with a compass, MIRA, or mirror.

7.

8.

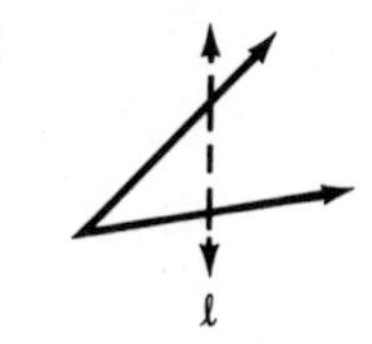

9.

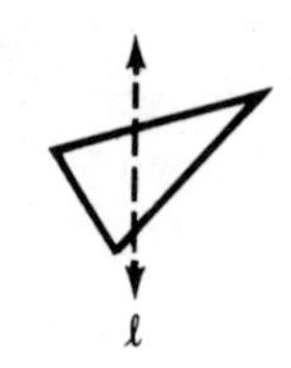

10.

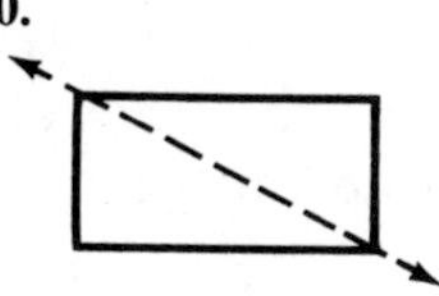

11.

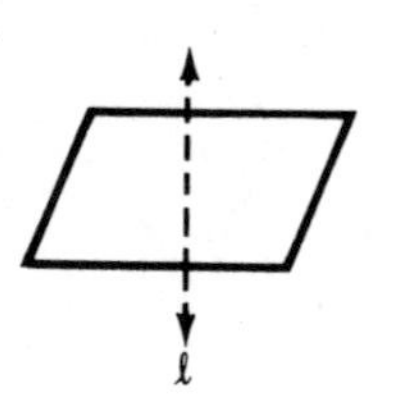

12.

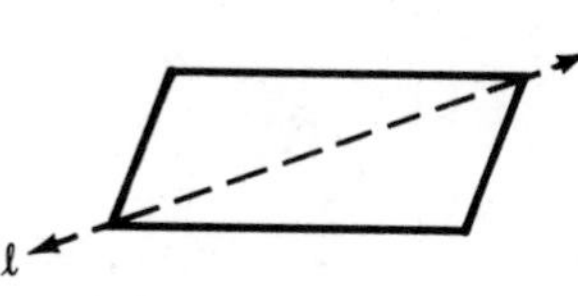

13.

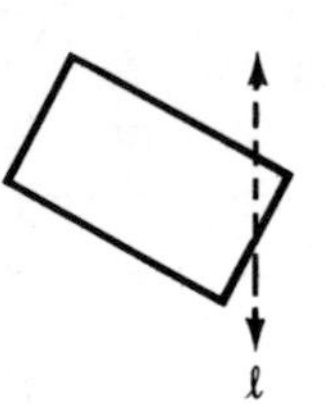

14.

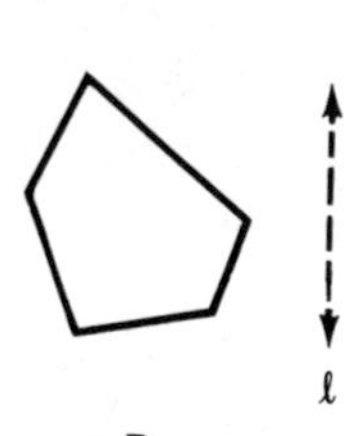

C.

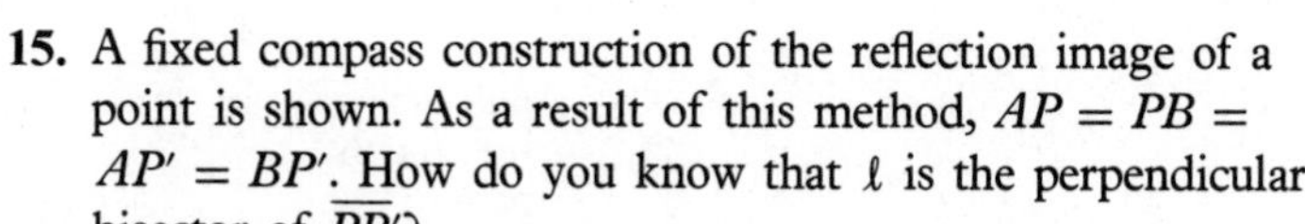

15. A fixed compass construction of the reflection image of a point is shown. As a result of this method, $AP = PB = AP' = BP'$. How do you know that ℓ is the perpendicular bisector of $\overline{PP'}$?

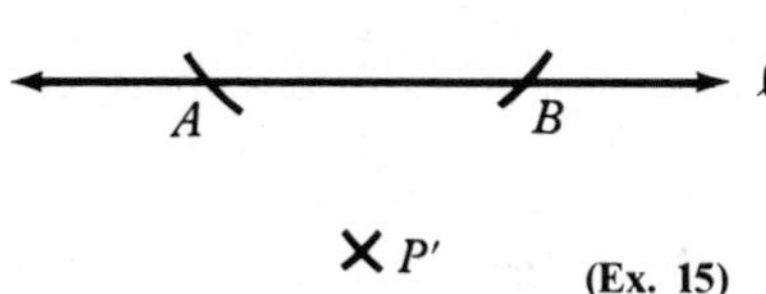

(Ex. 15)

16. Trace this figure in which A' is the reflection image of A. Using only a straightedge, construct the reflection of point B.

17. Write a complete two-column proof that shows that your construction in exercise 16 is correct.

18. Write a two-column proof of Theorem 13-1.

19. Prove that a triangle and its reflection image are congruent.

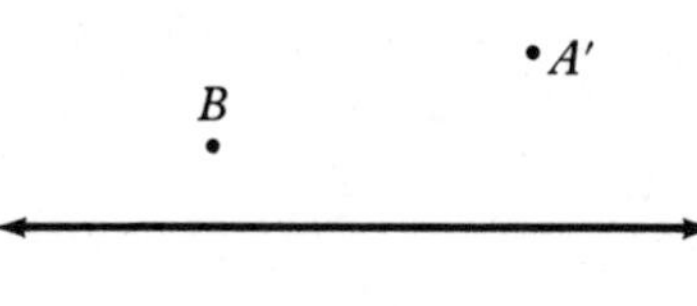

(Ex. 16)

PROBLEM SOLVING

1. Can you decode this message?

The reason this looks
so strange is that it was
written using a mirror.

2. Is this sum correct?

3414
340
74813
43374813

13–2 Using Line Reflections in Problem Solving

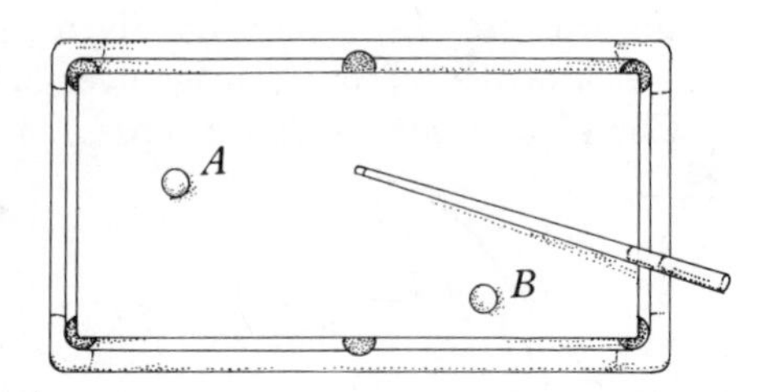

The geometry of line reflections can be used to solve everyday problems. Two examples are included here, one centering around a billiard table problem.

Problem 1

On a billiard table a cue ball is to be banked off cushion $\overline{AB}$ to hit the eight ball E. Assuming that the cue ball has no spin, at what point of $\overline{AB}$ should the cue ball strike?

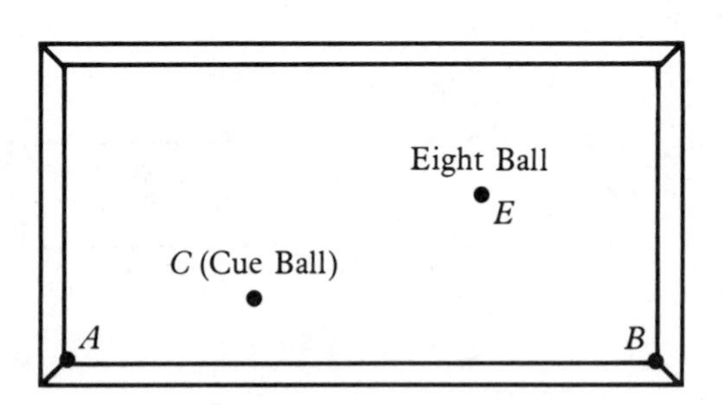

Solution. The answer to this question uses the following fact. *The ball rebounds along a path that is the reflection* (in the line of the cushion) *of the straight path through the cushion.*

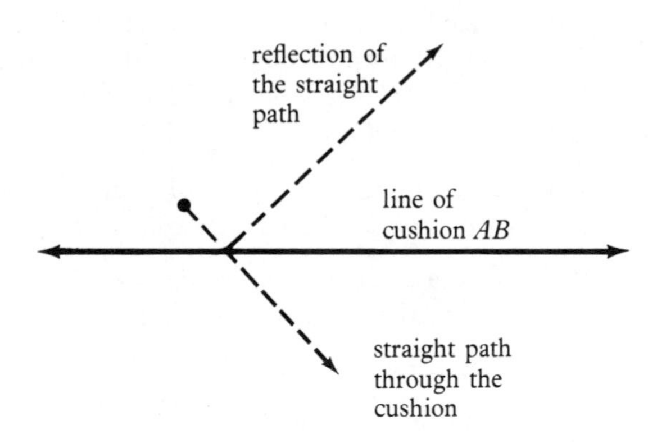

Step 1 Reflect E over the line AB to point E'.

Step 2 Draw the line CE'. Let X be the point where $\overleftrightarrow{CE'}$ intersects the cushion.

Step 3 A ball hit with no spin at the point X will rebound and hit the eight ball E. Why?

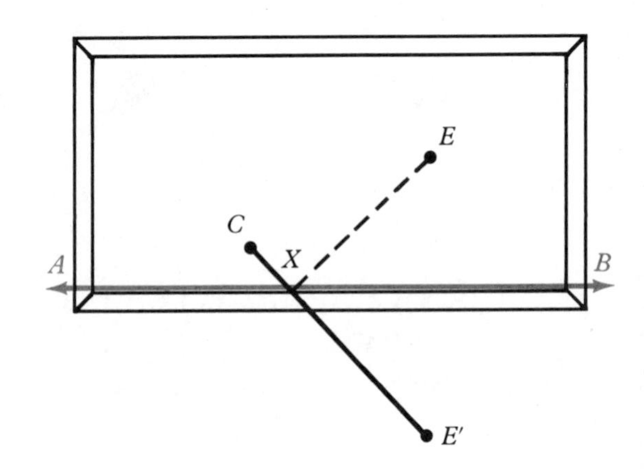

In the first problem we used a line reflection to determine the location of a point that satisfied a necessary condition. The second problem also involves determining the location of a point. In Problem 2 we will use the definition of betweenness for points together with a line reflection to determine a location for a bridge that is to be built.

Problem 2

Two cities are positioned on the same side of a river across which a bridge is to be built. Where should the bridge (B) be built so that the length of the highway $AB + BC$ is as short as possible?

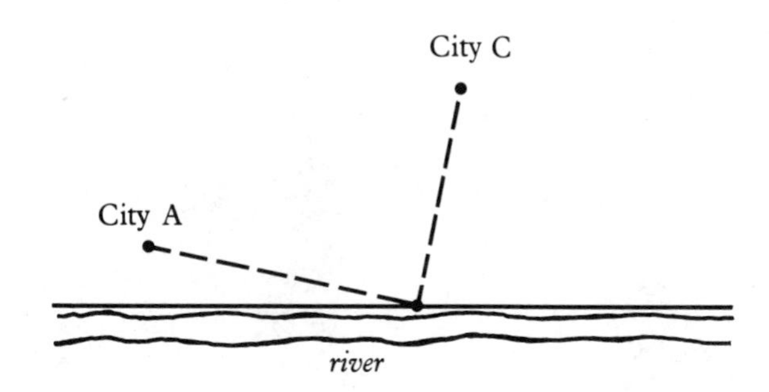

Solution

Step 1 Imagine that the river is line ℓ and reflect point C over line ℓ to point C'.

Step 2 From Theorem 13–1 we can conclude that $BC = BC'$. Therefore $AB + BC = AB + BC'$.

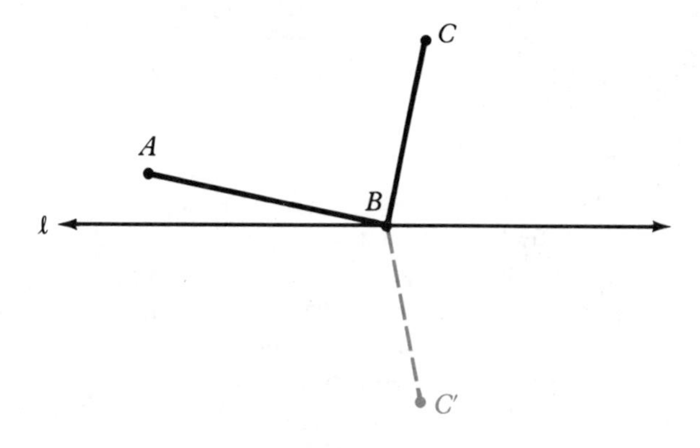

Step 3 But the shortest path from A to C' is a straight path. Therefore, in order for path A-B-C to be a minimum length, the bridge B should be built so that A, B, and C' are collinear.

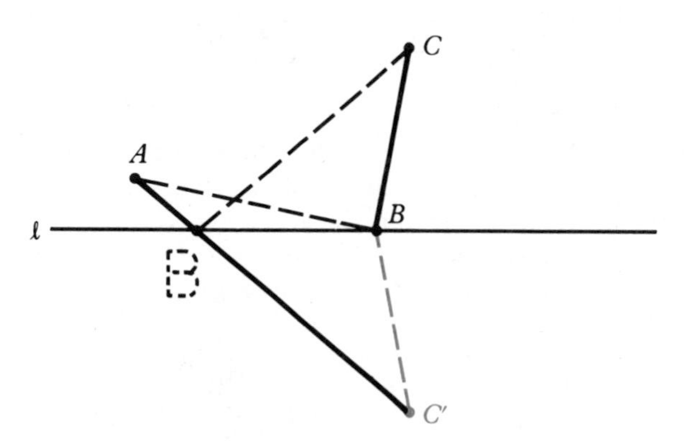

EXERCISES

A.

1. Use a millimeter ruler to measure each of the distances in this figure and record the distances in a table as shown on the right.

Point P_i	AP_i	BP_i	$AP_i + BP_i$
P_1			
P_2			
P_3			
P_4			
P_5			

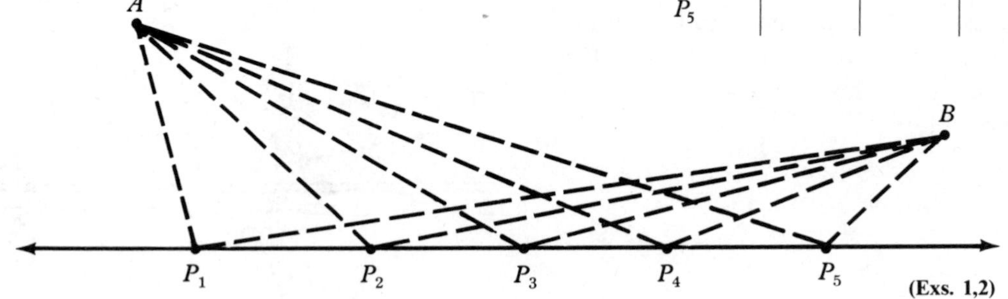

(Exs. 1,2)

2. In the figure which point, P_1, P_2, P_3, P_4, or P_5, makes $AP_i + P_iB$ a minimum?

B.

3. Trace the figure of a billiard table with cue ball C and a second ball B. Complete constructions to find a point on each of the four cushions that the cue ball should strike to rebound and hit the ball. (*Hint:* Reflect B in each of the four sides of the table.)

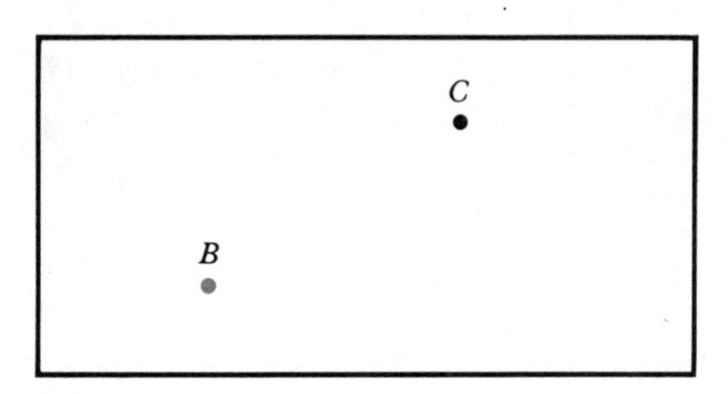

4. The cue ball C is to rebound off of one cushion and strike ball 5 before striking any other ball. Determine by completing a construction the cushion and the point on that cushion that the cue ball should strike.

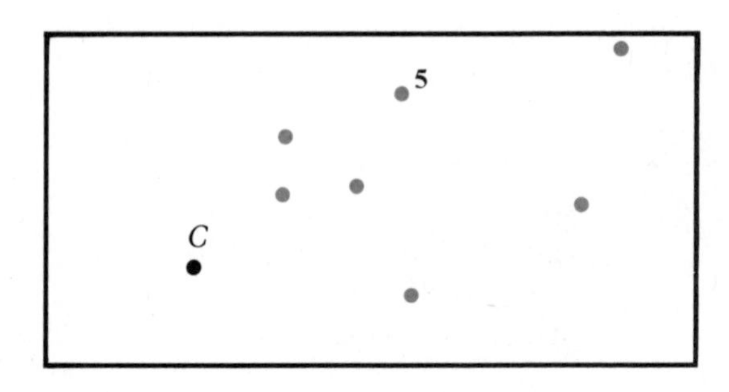

5. In this figure two cities are shown on the same side of the river. Locate the position (B) where a bridge should be built in order to minimize the length of a highway $AB + BC$.

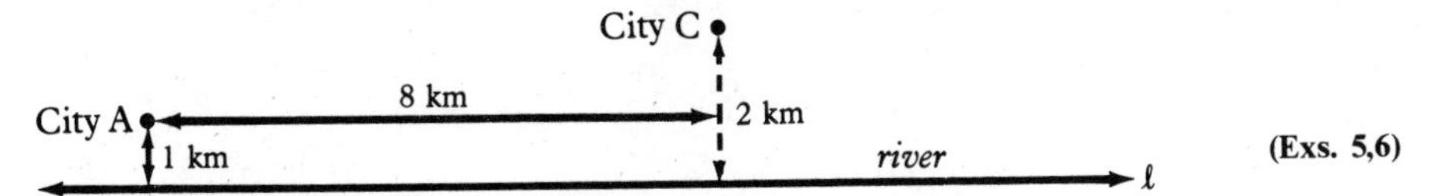

(Exs. 5,6)

6. After constructing the point B in exercise 5, use the Pythagorean Theorem to calculate the minimum length $AB + BC$.

C.

7. Suppose a path from A to B must first touch line s and then line t. Trace this figure and construct points X on s and Y on t so that $AXYB$ is the shortest of all such paths. (*Hint:* Reflect point A over line s and point B over line t.)

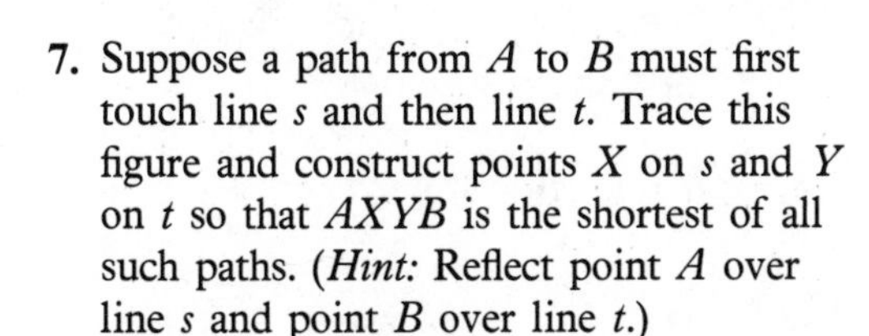

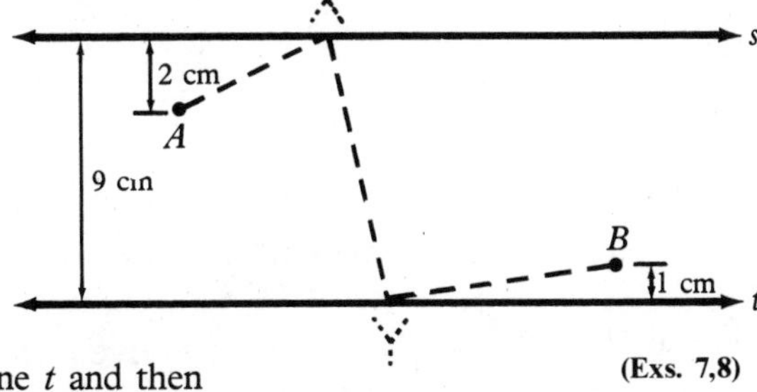

(Exs. 7,8)

8. Suppose a path from A to B must first touch line t and then line s. Trace the figure and construct points X on t and Y on s so that $AYXB$ is the shortest of all such paths. How does the length of this path compare to the length of the one found in exercise 7?

9. The figure illustrates how to determine the point on cushion EF that the cue ball C should strike in order to rebound off of *two* cushions and strike ball A.

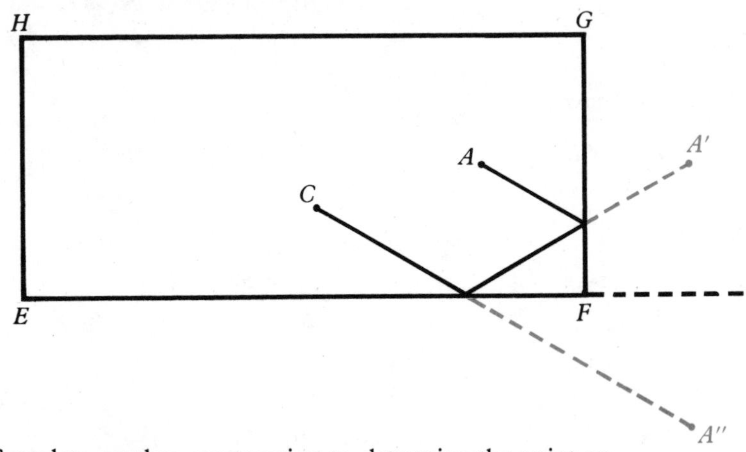

Complete another construction to determine the point on cushion GH that the cue ball should strike in order to rebound off two cushions and strike ball A.

13–3 Translations

Mirrors can often be found in department stores and shops. They are important for both decorative and security purposes.

Sometimes these mirrors can be found on opposite walls of a room. They have certainly produced an interesting effect in the barbershop in this cartoon.

The theorem in this lesson relates to this reflection of a reflection. However, we begin with a definition.

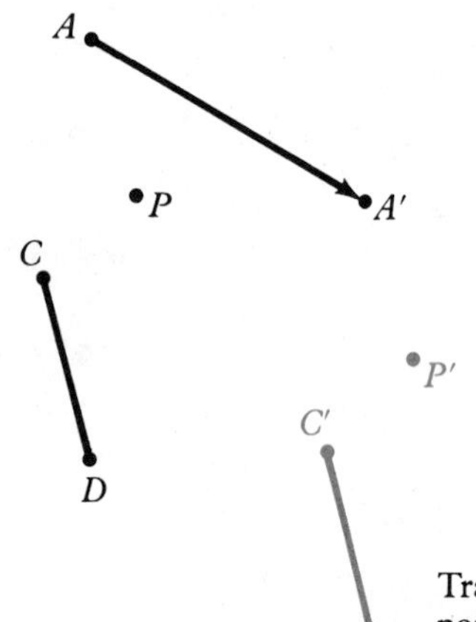

Translation image of points P, C, D and segment CD

Given an arrow AA', we imagine sliding a figure in the direction of the arrow through a distance AA'.

Definition 13-2

Given an arrow AA', the **translation image** of a point P for the arrow AA' is the point P' where:

a. $AA' = PP'$, and

b. arrows AA' and PP' have the same direction.

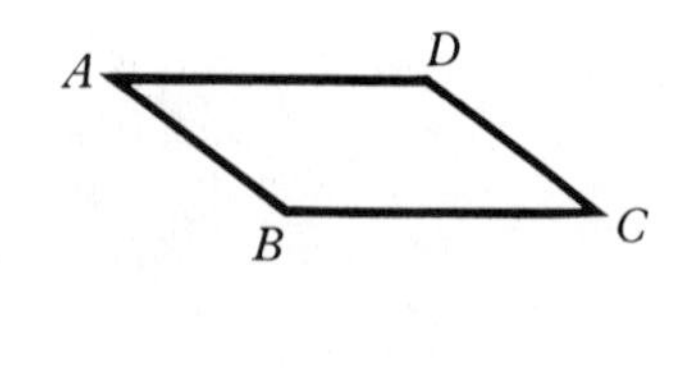

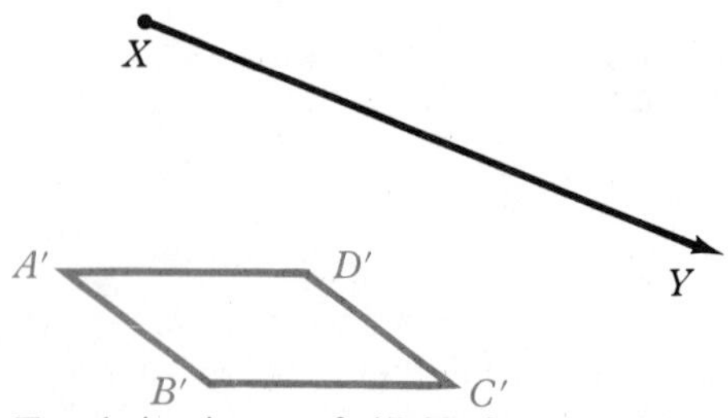

Translation image of $ABCD$ for arrow XY

We can accomplish a translation by following one reflection by another. Complete this four-step construction for yourself.

Step 1

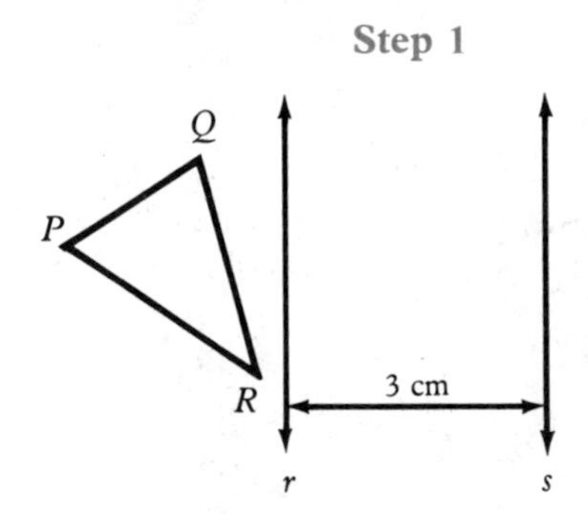

Start with lines r and s parallel and 3 cm apart.

Step 2

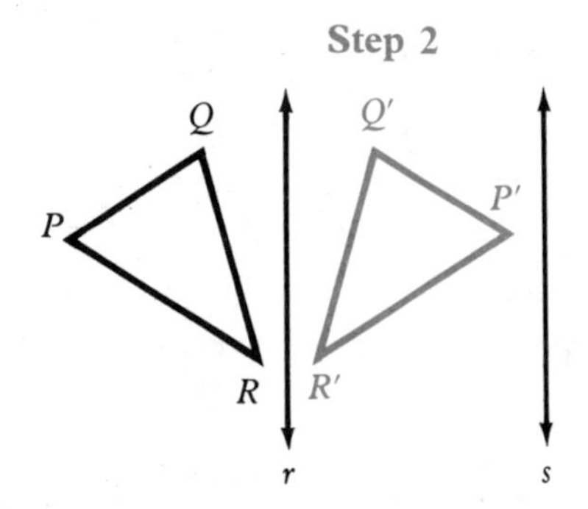

First find the reflection of $\triangle PQR$ over line r.

Step 3

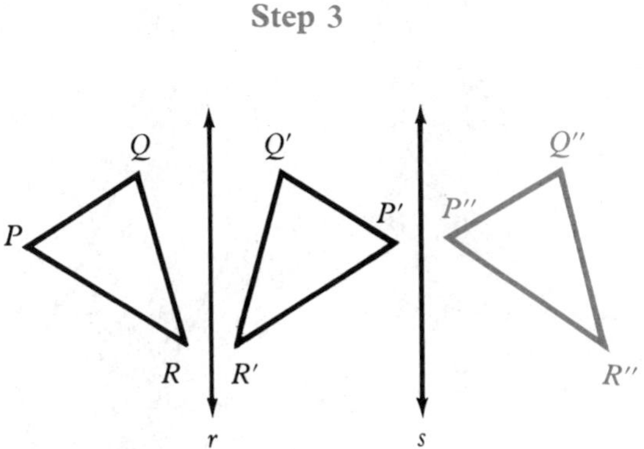

Then find the reflection of $\triangle P'Q'R'$ over line s.

Step 4

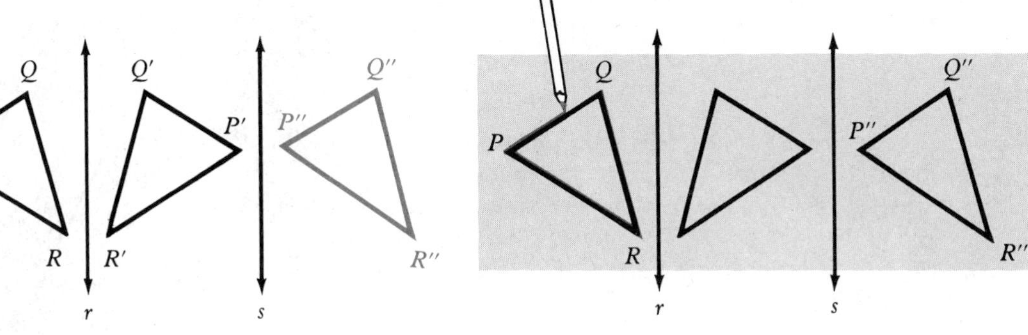

Trace $\triangle PQR$ and show that it can be translated 6 cm in a direction perpendicular to r and s and that $\triangle PQR \cong \triangle P''Q''R''$.

Theorem 13-2 If lines r and s are parallel, then a reflection over line r followed by a reflection over line s is a translation. Furthermore, if A'' is the image of A, then

a. $\overline{AA''} \perp r$,

b. $AA'' = 2d$ where d is the distance between the lines r and s.

EXERCISES

A.

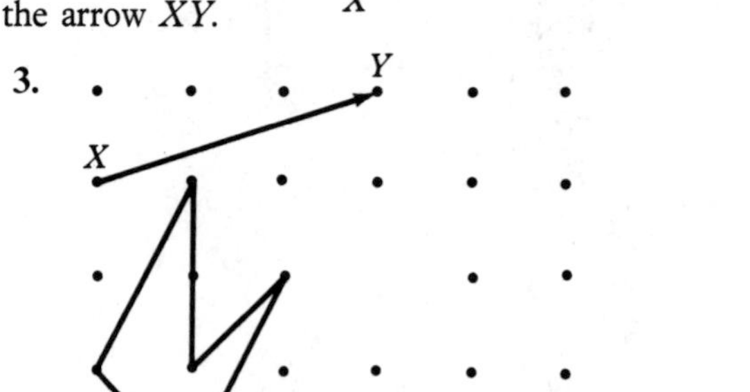

1. For the translation arrow XY the translation image of:

   a. C is _?_. b. E is _?_.

   c. D is _?_. d. B is _?_.

For exercises 2 and 3, draw the given figure on dot paper or graph paper. Then draw its translation image for the arrow XY.

2. 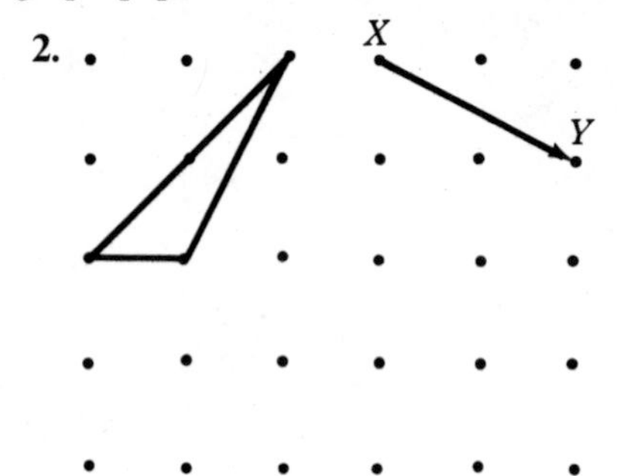

3. 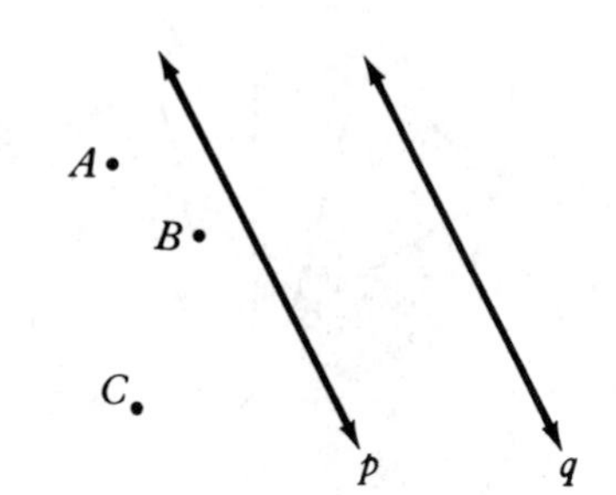

B.

4. Draw a pair of parallel lines and three points A, B, and C as shown in this figure. Construct the images of A, B, and C for the reflection over line p followed by the reflection over line q. Call these points A'', B'', and C''. Measure $\overline{AA''}$, $\overline{BB''}$, and $\overline{CC''}$. Convince yourself that these segments are parallel and equal in length.

Activity

Cover the front and back inside faces of a box, preferably nearly a cube in shape, with mirrors. Cover the other faces with black construction paper.

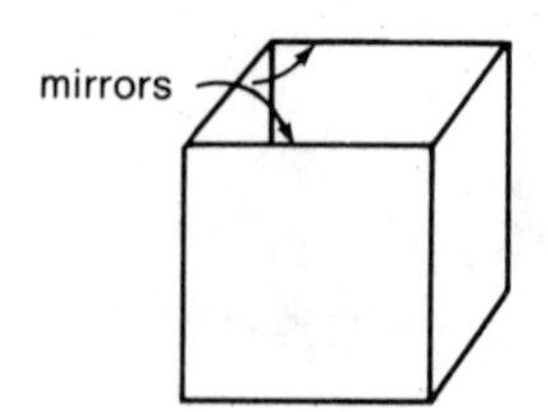

Dangle an object by a string into the box and look into the box over the front edge. What will you see?

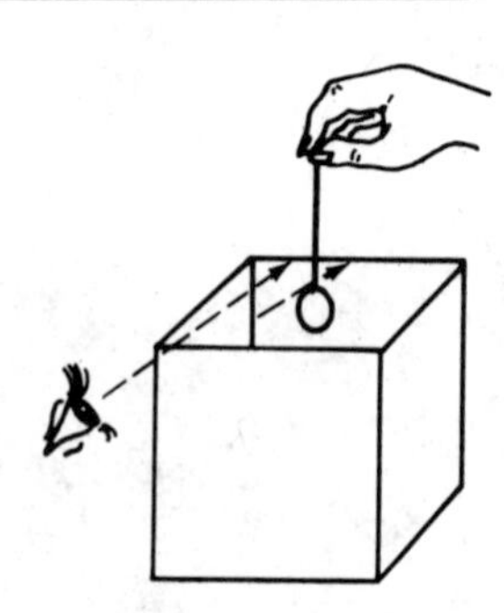

How does the view in this box relate to the cartoon on page 484?

5. Draw a pair of parallel lines p and q that are 3 cm apart and $\triangle ABC$ as shown. Construct the image of $\triangle ABC$ for the reflection over line p followed by the reflection over line q.

6. Which arrow in the figure describes the translation that is the reflection over line p followed by the reflection over line q?

   a. arrow DE **b.** arrow FG

   c. arrow HI **d.** arrow JK

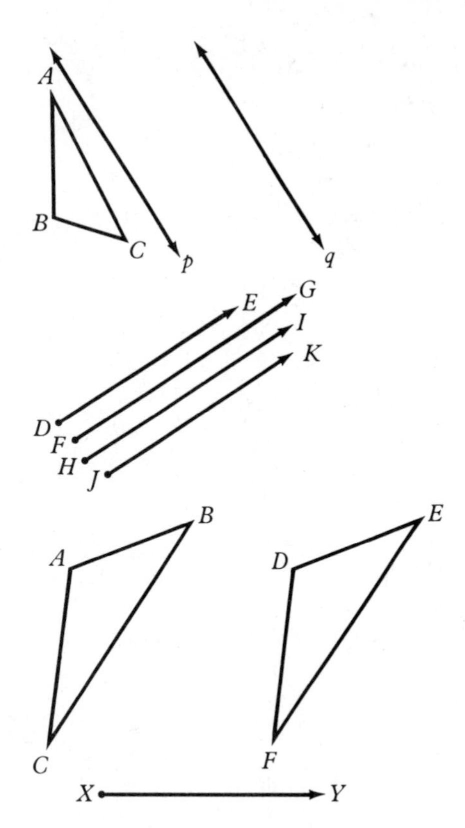

C.

7. In this figure $\triangle DEF$ is the translation image of $\triangle ABC$ for the translation of arrow XY.

   a. Trace the figure on a sheet of paper.

   b. Draw any line p perpendicular to line XY.

   c. Draw a line q so that the reflection over line p followed by the reflection over line q is the translation with arrow XY.

PROBLEM SOLVING

What fraction of the square region is shaded? (Assume that the indicated process of shading is continued indefinitely.)

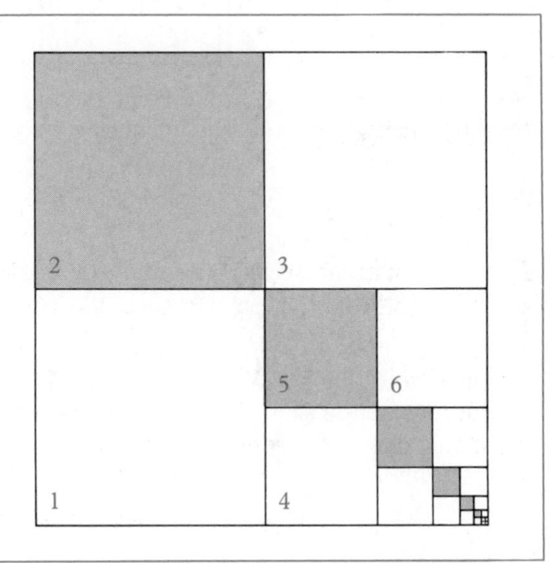

13–4 Rotations

"*You're fired!*"

Drawing by Richter;
© 1957 The New Yorker Magazine, Inc.

There are many situations in which we encounter a "turning situation," often called a "rotation." Failure to recognize the need for this motion may have had serious consequences for the gentleman in the cartoon!

You can investigate the properties of a rotation as shown below.

Step 1

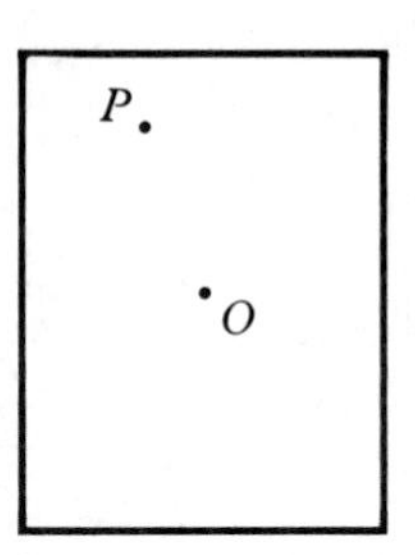

Mark a center point O and another point P on a sheet of paper.

Step 2

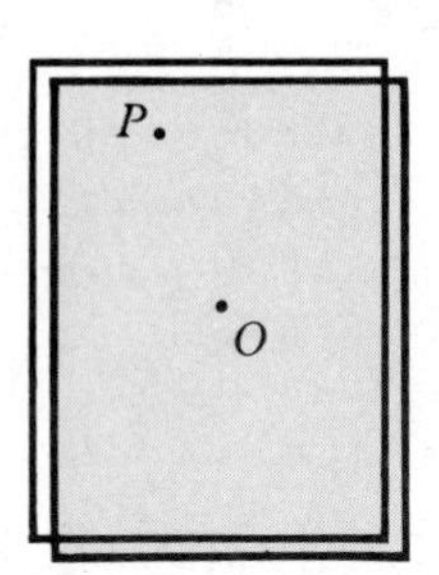

Trace point P on a sheet of tracing paper.

Step 3

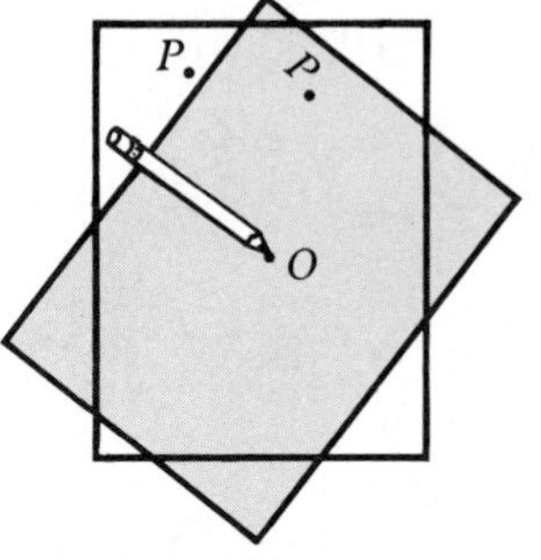

Keep point O from moving and turn the tracing paper.

Step 4

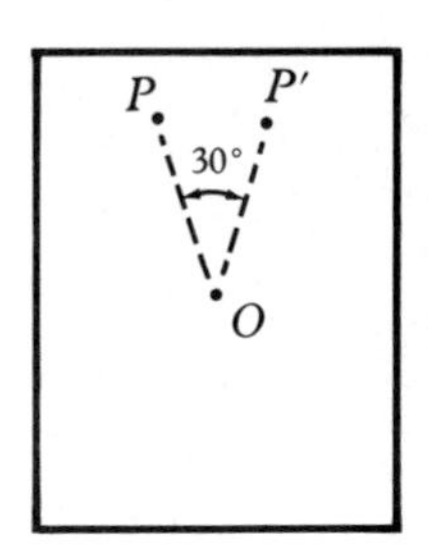

Mark the new position of P as P'.

P' is the rotation image of point P. O is the center of the rotation. In this case, the angle of rotation is 30°.

These ideas suggest the accompanying definition of a rotation. Note that a rotation can be clockwise or counterclockwise.

Definition 13-3

A **rotation** with center O and angle α is a transformation that maps each point P of the plane onto a point P' as follows:

a. If P is the center point O, $P' = P$.

b. If $P \neq O$, then $P'O = PO$ and $m\angle POP' = \alpha$.

P' is called the **rotation image** of point P.

Like translations, rotations can be accomplished by following one reflection by another. This time the lines of reflection are not parallel. Complete this four-step construction for yourself.

Step 1

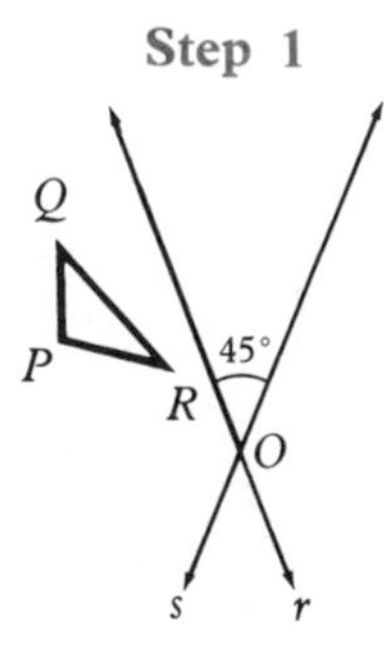

Start with lines r and s, passing through O and intersecting at a 45° angle, and $\triangle PQR$.

Step 2

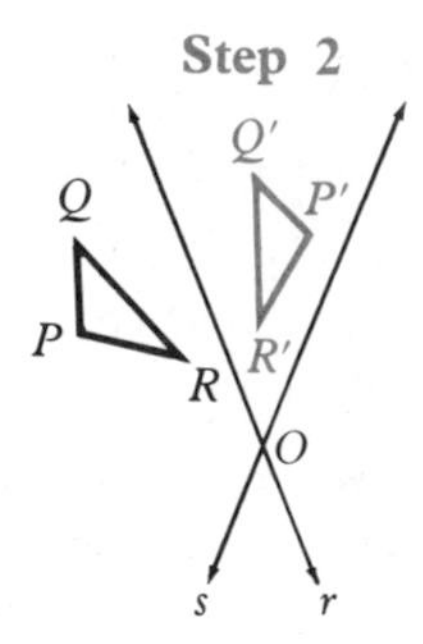

First find the reflection of $\triangle PQR$ over line r.

Step 3

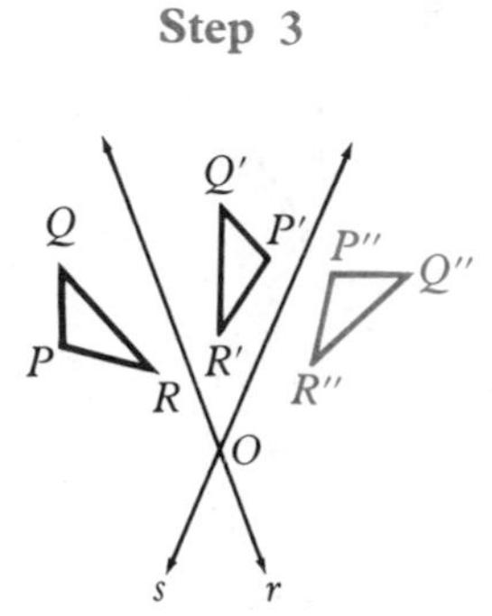

Then find the reflection of $\triangle P'Q'R'$ over line s.

Step 4

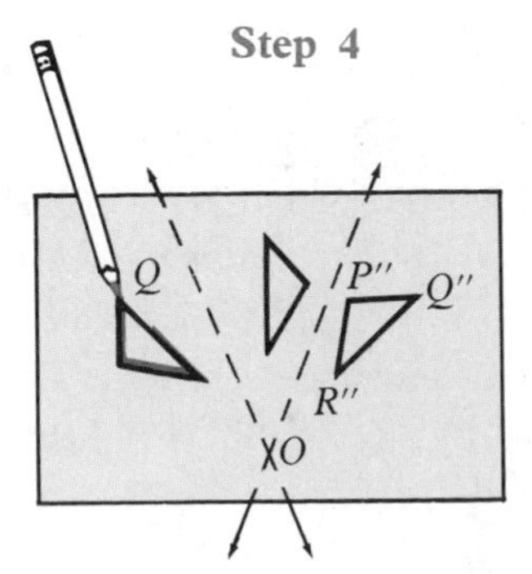

Trace $\triangle PQR$ and show that it can be rotated through a 90° angle around point O and that $\triangle PQR \cong \triangle P''Q''R''$.

Two reflections over intersecting lines will always result in a rotation through an angle twice the angle between the lines. This suggests the theorem below.

Theorem 13–3 If lines r and s intersect in point O, then a reflection over r followed by a reflection over s is a rotation. Point O is the center of the rotation and the angle of rotation is 2α, where α is the measure of the acute or right angle between lines r and s.

EXERCISES

A.

1. Find the image of B under a 45° clockwise rotation.
2. Find the image of H under a 90° counterclockwise rotation.
3. Find the image of B under a 135° clockwise rotation.
4. Find the image of $\triangle DEF$ under a 45° counterclockwise rotation.

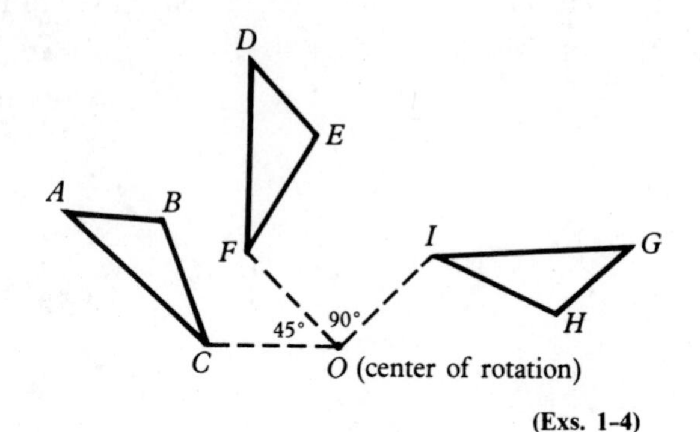

(Exs. 1-4)

5. Draw on your paper points O and A. Draw the image A' of A for a 60° clockwise rotation as follows.
   a. Draw ray $\overrightarrow{OA}$. Use a protractor to draw $\overrightarrow{OX}$ so that $m\angle AOX = 60$.
   b. Use a compass to draw an arc with center O and radius OA. This arc intersects the side of the angle at point A'.

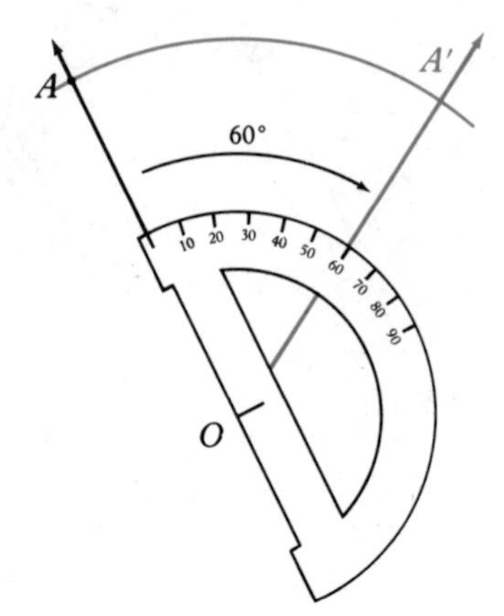

6. Draw a segment $\overline{XY}$ and a point O on your paper. Use a protractor and compass to draw the image of $\overline{XY}$ for a 40° counterclockwise rotation.

7. Draw a triangle ABC and a point O on your paper. Use a protractor and compass to draw the image of $\triangle ABC$ for a 50° clockwise rotation.

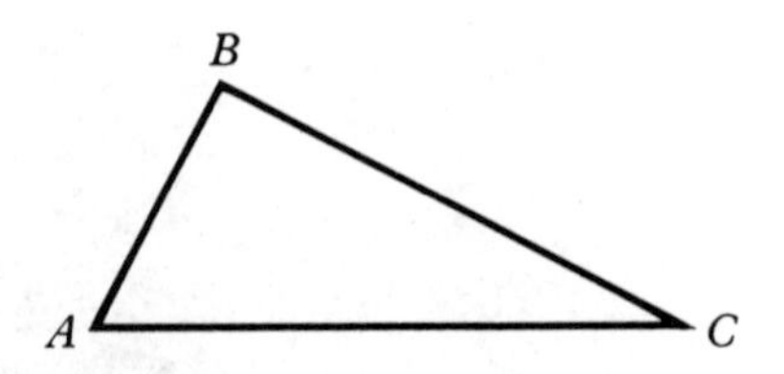

O

8. Draw a triangle ABC and a point O. Draw the image of $\triangle ABC$ for a 135° counterclockwise rotation.

B.

9. If $\overline{A'B'}$ is the image of $\overline{AB}$ for a rotation with center O, which angle should be measured to find the angle of rotation?

a. $\angle AOB$

b. $\angle AA'O$

c. $\angle A'B'O$

d. $\angle BOB'$

B

A

O

10. If $\overline{A'B'}$ is the image of $\overline{AB}$ after a rotation, which one of the four points could be the center of rotation? (Recall that if O is the center, $OA = OA'$ and $OB = OB'$.)

a. W

b. X

c. Y

d. Z

A' B'

X W
Y
Z

11. Trace $\overline{RS}$ and $\overline{VW}$. If $\overline{VW}$ is the image of $\overline{RS}$ under a rotation, locate the center of rotation, and find the angle of rotation.

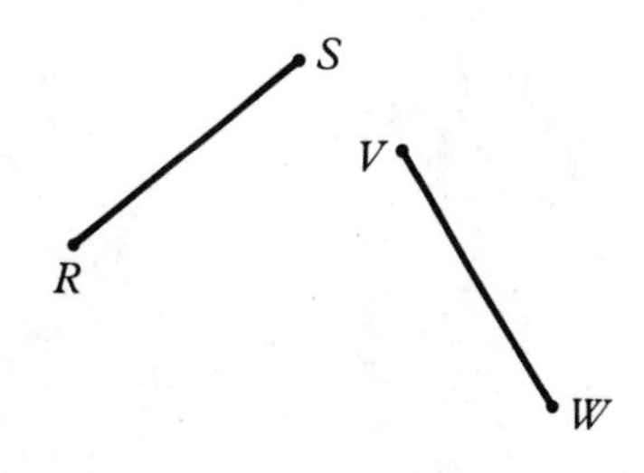

12. In each of the figures shown, the red figure is the image of the black figure under a turn. Label the center of the turn and indicate the angle measure for each turn. (Tracing paper may be helpful.)

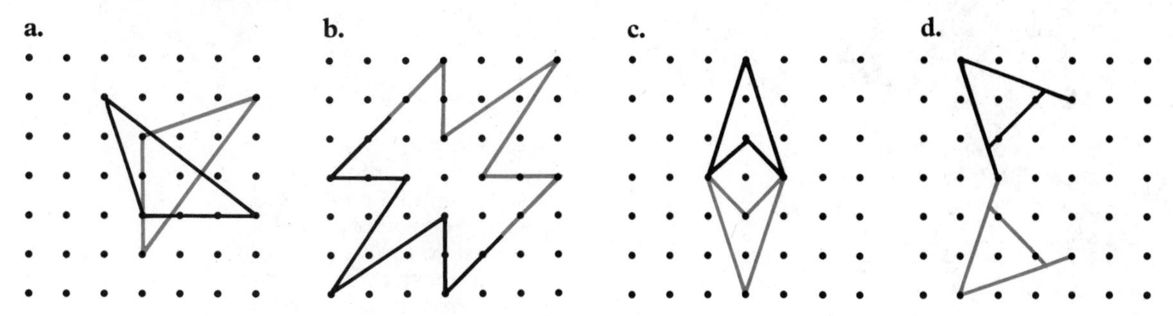

C.

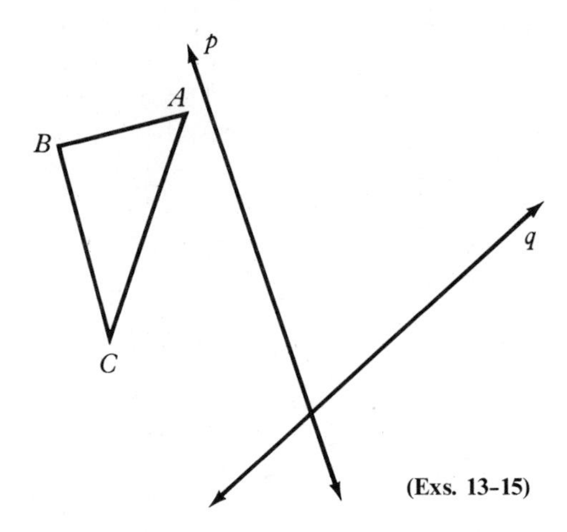

13. Draw a pair of intersecting lines p and q and a triangle ABC as shown. Draw the image of $\triangle ABC$ for the reflection over line p followed by the reflection over line q. Call this image $\triangle A''B''C''$.

14. Use tracing paper to check that $\triangle A''B''C''$ that you drew in exercise 13 is the rotation image of $\triangle ABC$.

15. Measure with a protractor the acute angle formed by the lines p and q in your drawing from exercise 13. How does this angle compare in size with the angle of rotation?

16. A $180°$ rotation about a point is called a *half-turn*. $\triangle A'B'C'$ is the half-turn rotation image of $\triangle ABC$. Trace these figures and find the center of the half-turn.

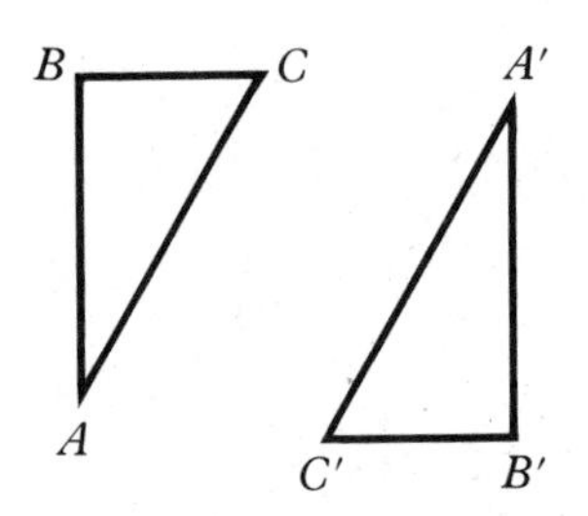

Activity

Hinge two mirrors at a 90° angle and look into them as shown. Are you surprised by what you see? Can you explain your observation?

Hinge two mirrors at a 90° angle and look into them as shown in this photo. The reflection shown is one of three that you will see. How is one of these three images different from the other two?

17. Mark points X and Y on your paper and draw $\triangle RST$.

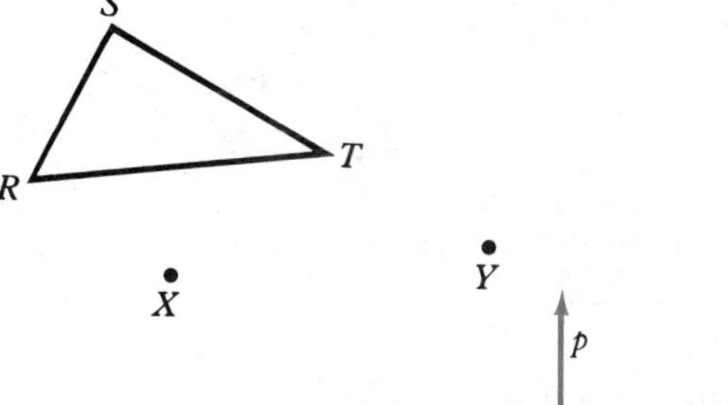

a. Draw the half-turn image of $\triangle RST$ around X. Using the image of this turn, draw a half-turn around Y.

b. What single motion has the same effect as a half-turn about X followed by a half-turn about Y? Be as specific as possible in describing this motion.

18. $\triangle A'B'C'$ is the image of $\triangle ABC$ under a rotation about center Q. Trace these figures. Can you construct line q so that a reflection over line p followed by a reflection over line q will have the same effect as the turn?

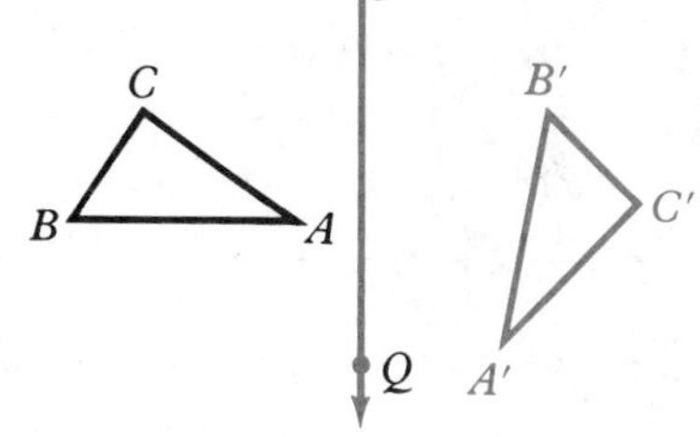

PROBLEM SOLVING

Trace the pattern below on tracing paper. Rotate the tracing 60° about point A and notice that the tracing matches the pattern (assuming that the pattern and its tracing are both extended in all directions to cover the entire plane).

1. What other angles of rotation centered at A will make the pattern fit back on itself?
2. What are the angles of rotation centered at points B and C that will make the pattern fit back on itself?

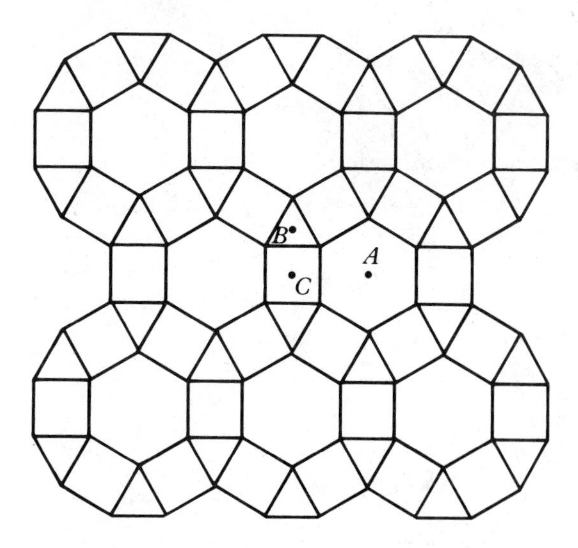

13–5 Symmetry

The butterfly and crab shown here possess a natural beauty related to their shape. One half appears identical to the other half. The match seems so perfect that a mirror could be placed so that one half is reflected giving the entire specimen.

We say that the shapes possess *reflectional symmetry* and that the line on which the mirror is placed is a *line of symmetry*.

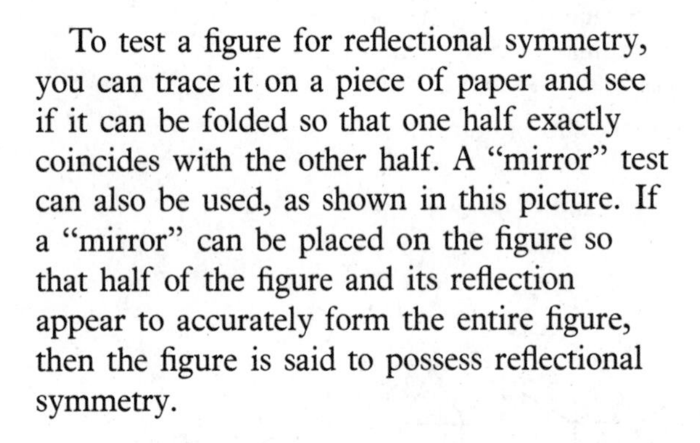

To test a figure for reflectional symmetry, you can trace it on a piece of paper and see if it can be folded so that one half exactly coincides with the other half. A "mirror" test can also be used, as shown in this picture. If a "mirror" can be placed on the figure so that half of the figure and its reflection appear to accurately form the entire figure, then the figure is said to possess reflectional symmetry.

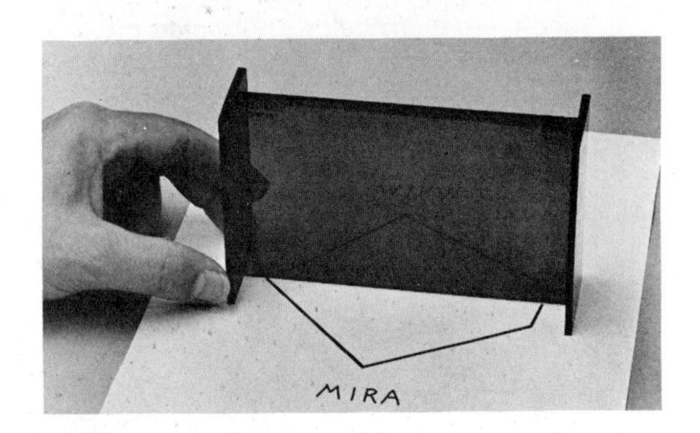

We present the following definition, aided by this illustration.

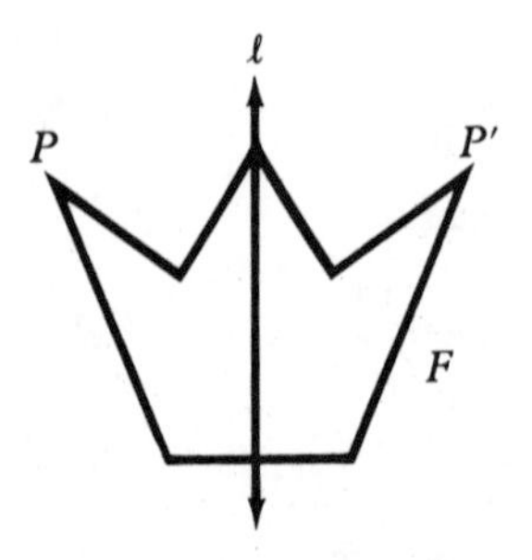

Definition 13–4

A figure F has **reflectional symmetry** if there is a line ℓ such that the reflection image over ℓ of each point P of F is also a point of F. The line ℓ is called a **line of symmetry** for F.

This flower possesses another kind of symmetry. It can be turned about a fixed center to new positions so as to appear almost identical to the way it appeared originally.

We say that the shape possesses *rotational symmetry* and that the fixed center is the *center of rotational symmetry*.

To test a figure for rotational symmetry, you can trace the figure on a piece of tracing paper or a piece of plastic. Place the tracing directly on top of the original figure. Then, while holding the center fixed, turn the tracing until the tracing and the original again coincide, as shown.

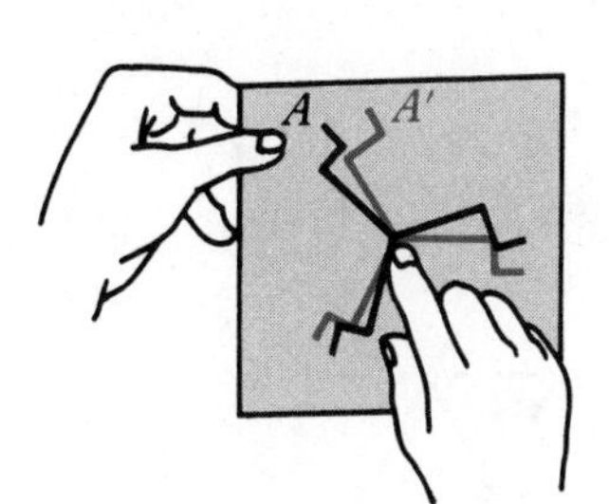

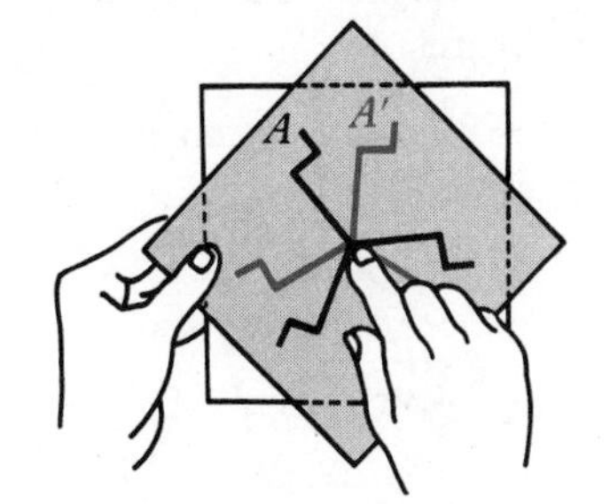

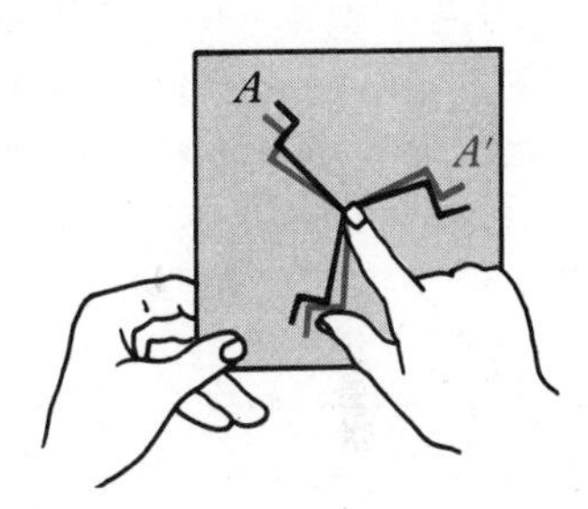

Checking for rotational symmetry—the "trace and turn test."

We present the following definition, aided by this illustration.

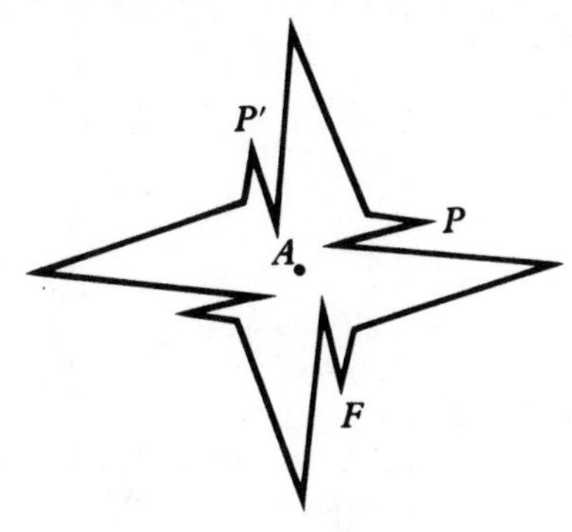

Definition 13–5

A figure F has **rotational symmetry** if there is a rotation about a center A such that the rotation image of each point P of figure F is also a point of F. The center, A, of the rotation is called the **center of rotational symmetry** for F.

EXERCISES

A.

In which of the following figures is ℓ a line of symmetry? Check your answers using the "mirror" test for reflectional symmetry.

1.

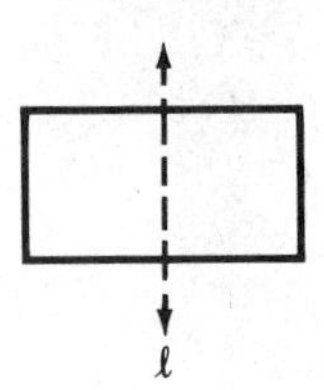

2.

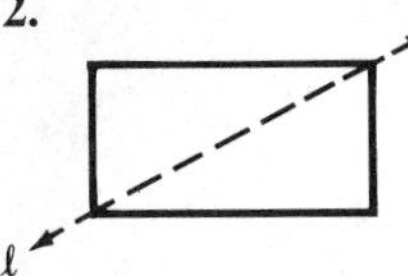

3.

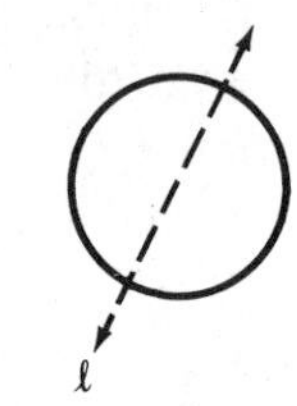

4.

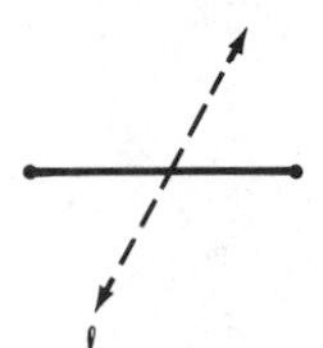

5.

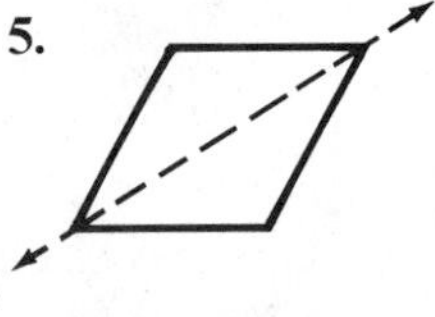

6.

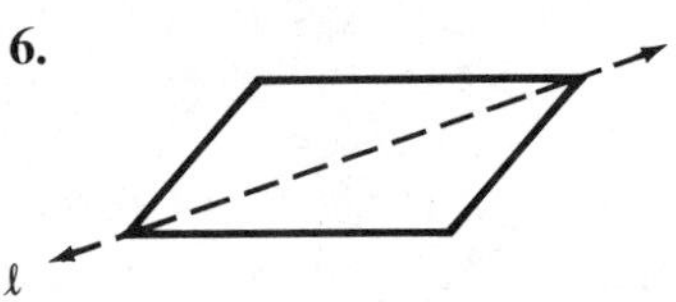

7. Draw a square, a rhombus, a rectangle, a trapezoid, a regular pentagon, and a regular hexagon and show all lines of reflectional symmetry for each figure.

The statement "This figure possesses rotational symmetry." is true for which of the figures in exercises 8–10?

8.

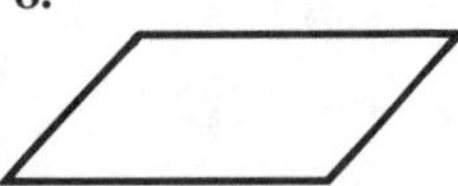

9.

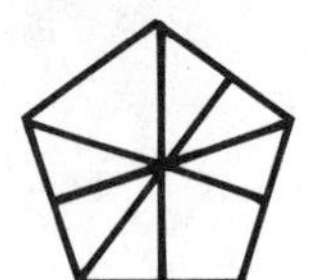

10.

Activity

Pictured is a figure with 90° rotational symmetry (can be rotated 90° to fold back on itself) on a 5 × 5 geoboard. The figure is constructed by drawing four identical paths that satisfy these conditions.

1. All paths begin at the center nail and move from nail to nail until reaching an outside boundary nail.
2. None of the four paths touch or cross each other or themselves.
3. Once a path reaches an outside boundary it stops.

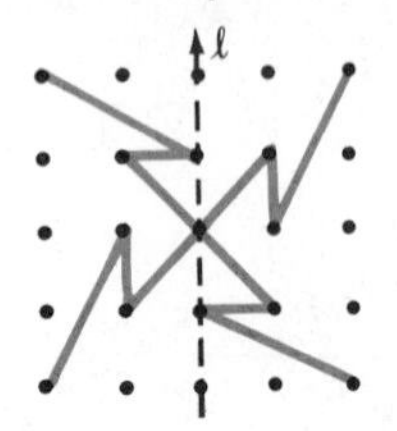

Draw on 5 × 5 dot paper at least 20 different patterns with 90° rotational symmetry that satisfy the conditions above.
Note that the figure at the left is not considered to be "different" from the one above, since it is the figure above reflected over line ℓ. Figures that can be reflected or rotated to match each other are not considered different.

B.

Draw figures satisfying each of the following conditions.

11. Nonconvex quadrilateral with a line of symmetry

12. A hexagon with exactly two lines of symmetry

13. A hexagon with exactly three lines of symmetry

14. A pentagon with exactly one line of symmetry

15. A figure with an infinite number of lines of symmetry

16. Sketch a polygon that possesses rotational symmetry but does not possess reflectional symmetry.

17. Sketch a polygon which possesses both rotational and reflectional symmetry.

C.

For exercises 18 and 19, assume that the pattern has been extended to cover the entire plane. In each problem which of the lines p, q, and r are lines of symmetry?

18.

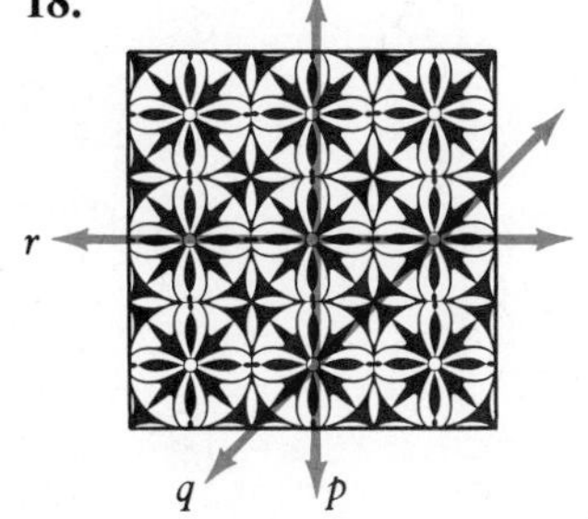

19.

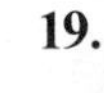

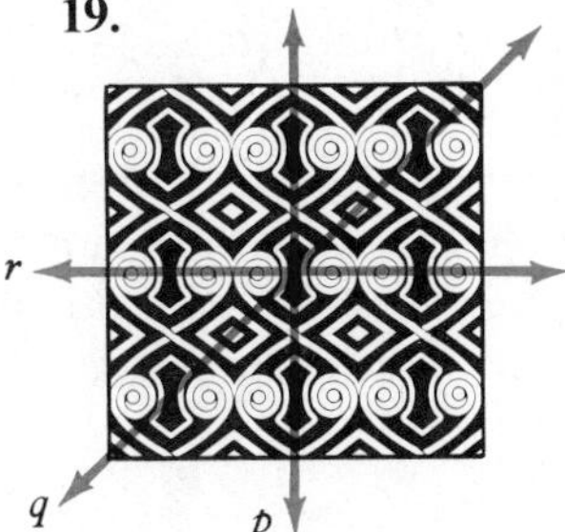

PROBLEM SOLVING

NOW NO
SWIMS
ON MON

A sign like this appeared beside a public swimming pool. Turn this card 180°. What do you notice?

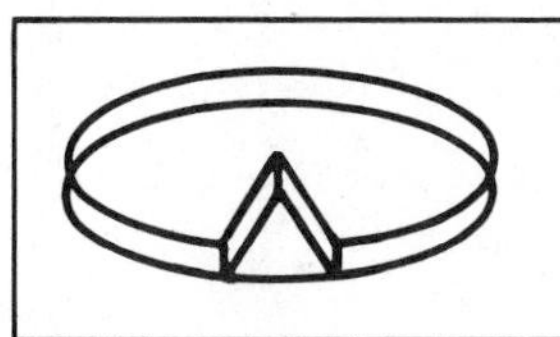

A slice is missing from this cake. Can you turn the card in such a way as to find the slice?

337-31770

Oliver Lee asked that the above number appear on his license plate. Turn the card 180°. Can you explain why he made this request?

Important Ideas—Chapter 13

Terms

Reflection (p. 476)
Translation image (p. 484)
Rotation (p. 488)
Reflectional symmetry (p. 494)
Line of symmetry (p. 494)
Rotational symmetry (p. 495)
Center of rotational symmetry (p. 495)

Theorems

13–1 Given a line reflection:
a. the reflection image of a segment is a segment of equal length;
b. the reflection image of an angle is the angle of equal measure.

13–2 If lines r and s are parallel, then a reflection over line r followed by a reflection over line s is a translation. Furthermore, if A'' is the image of A, then
a. $\overline{AA''} \perp r$,
b. $AA'' = 2d$ where d is the distance between the lines r and s.

13–3 If lines r and s intersect in point O, then a reflection over t followed by a reflection over s is a rotation. Point O is the center of rotation and the angle of rotation is 2α, where α is the measure of the acute angle between lines r and s.

Chapter 13—Review

1. Indicate on your paper whether the following statements are true or false.

   a. Every reflection is a transformation.

   b. If P' is the image of P for a given reflection over line ℓ, then ℓ is the perpendicular bisector of PP'.

   c. A rotation can be represented as two reflections.

   d. A square has exactly two lines of symmetry.

   e. An isosceles trapezoid has rotational symmetry.

2. Name two capital letters that have exactly two lines of symmetry? Are there any others?

3. Name two capital letters that have rotational symmetry but no line symmetry. Are there any others?

4. How many lines of symmetry does a regular octagon have?

5. Trace the triangles ABC and $A'B'C'$. Construct line ℓ so that $\triangle A'B'C'$ is the reflection image of $\triangle ABC$ over ℓ.

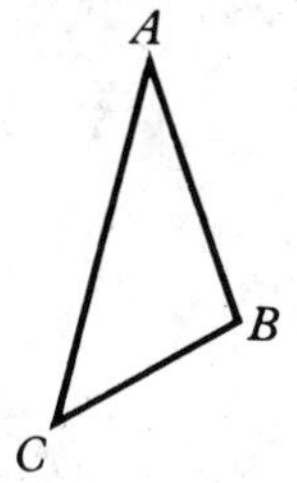

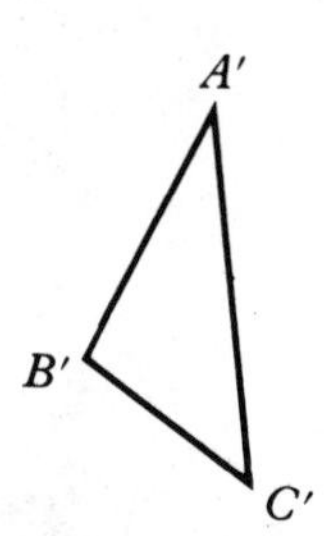

6. Trace $\overline{AB}$ and $\overline{A'B'}$. Find the center of rotation and the angle of rotation if $\overline{A'B'}$ is the image of $\overline{AB}$ under a rotation.

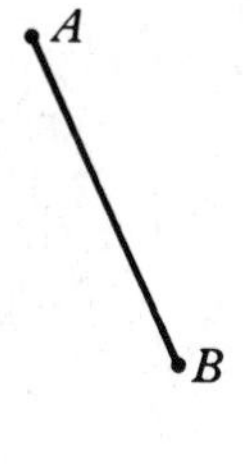

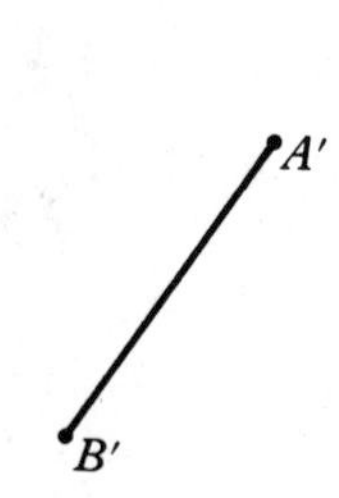

Chapter 13—Test

1. Indicate on your paper whether the following statements are true or false.

   a. Every translation is a transformation.

   b. If $\overline{A'B'}$ is the image of $\overline{AB}$ under a rotation about center O, then $m\angle AOA' = m\angle BOB'$.

   c. A translation can be represented as two reflections.

   d. A parallelogram has exactly two lines of symmetry.

   e. A rhombus has rotational symmetry.

2. Name two capital letters that have exactly one line of symmetry. Are there any others?

3. Name two capital letters that have both rotational and reflectional symmetry. Are there any others?

4. Does a regular polygon have to have both rotational and reflection symmetry? Explain.

5. Trace the triangle ABC, lines p and q, and the translation arrow $\overrightarrow{XY}$. Reflect $\triangle ABC$ over p and over q. How does the distance between p and q relate to XY?

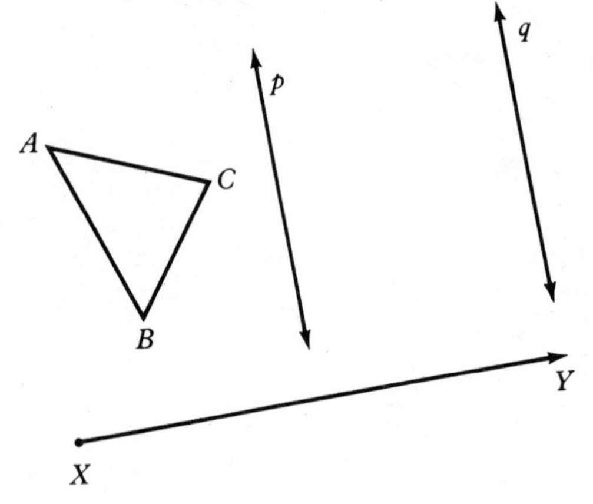

6. Trace $\triangle ABC$. Using C as the center of rotation, rotate $\triangle ABC$ through an angle of 120°.

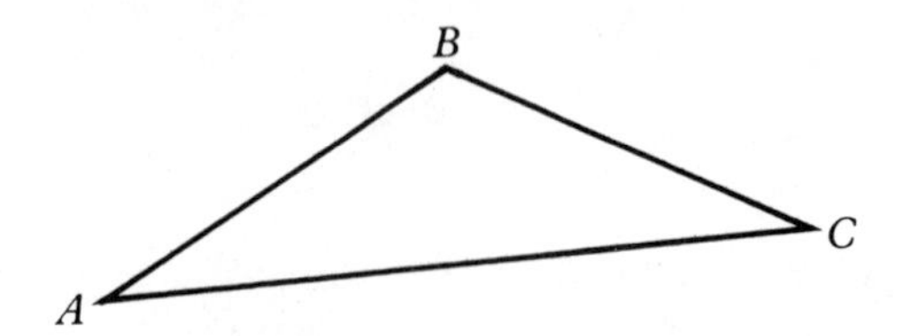

Examine Special Cases

Sometimes it is helpful to consider special cases when solving problems. Study the example below.

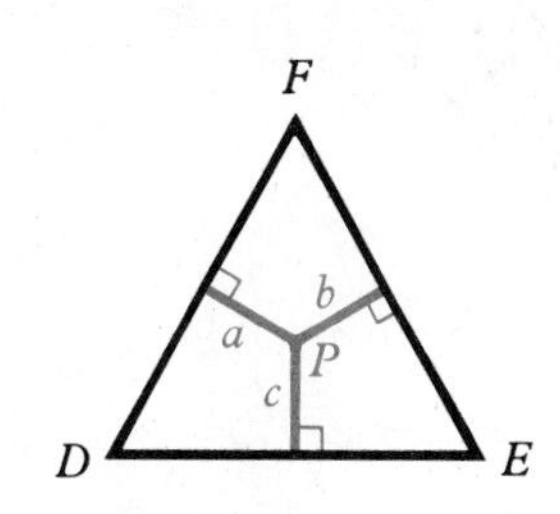

Example

Let P be any point on or inside an equilateral triangle. If a, b, and c are the lengths of the perpendicular segments from P to the sides of the triangle, how does the sum $a + b + c$ compare with the length of an altitude?

Consider these special cases.

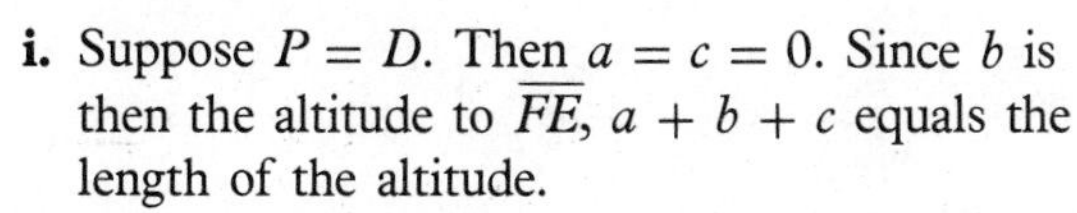

i. Suppose $P = D$. Then $a = c = 0$. Since b is then the altitude to $\overline{FE}$, $a + b + c$ equals the length of the altitude.

ii. Suppose P is at the center of $\triangle DEF$. Then $a = b = c = \frac{1}{3}FH$ (the altitude). Then $a + b + c = FH$ or the length of the altitude.

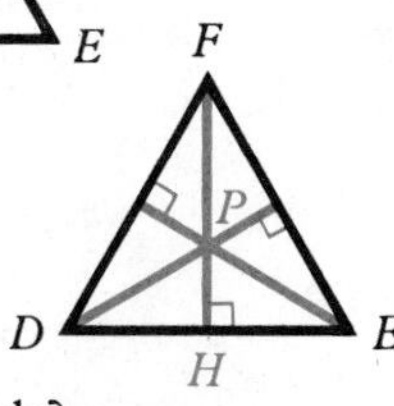

Does it appear that $a + b + c$ is equal to the length of the altitude?

PROBLEMS

1. In the example above try the special case when P is the midpoint of a side. Does $a + b + c$ equal the length of the altitude for this case also?

2. $\triangle ABC$ is an equilateral triangle inscribed in a circle. P is any point on the circle. How are PA, PB, and PC related? (*Hint:* Consider these cases: **i.** $P = A$, **ii.** $P = C$, and **iii.** $PA = PC$.)

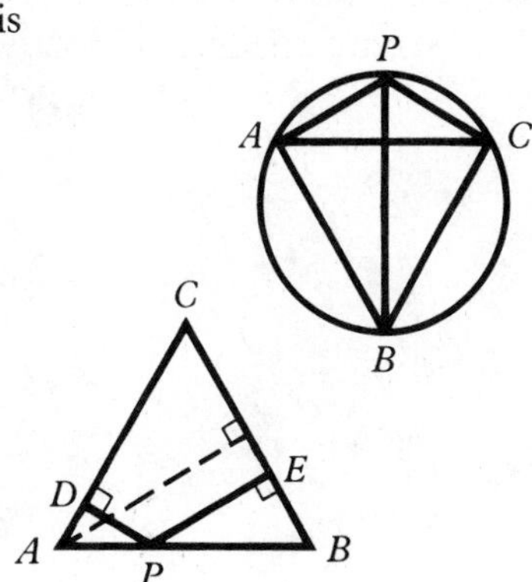

3. **Given:** $AB = BC = AC = 4$ cm. P is any point on $\overline{AB}$. $\overline{DP} \perp \overline{AC}$, $\overline{PE} \perp \overline{BC}$.
   Find: $DP + PE$
   (*Hint:* Consider the relationship among DP, PE, and AF using the special cases when $P = A$ and $PA = PB$.)

4. **Given:** Square $ABCD$ with each side 1 unit in length.
   Find: A point P such that $PA + PB + PC + PD$ is a minimum.

   (*Hint:* Consider these cases: **i.** $P = A$, **ii.** P is the midpoint of $\overline{AB}$, **iii.** P is intersection of the diagonals, and **iv.** Use a ruler to find $PA + PB + PC + PD$ when P is in the interior of $ABCD$ but not at the point of intersection of the diagonals.)

   Which position seems to produce a minimum for $PA + PB + PC + PD$?

CHAPTER 14

Coordinate Geometry

14–1 Cartesian Coordinate System

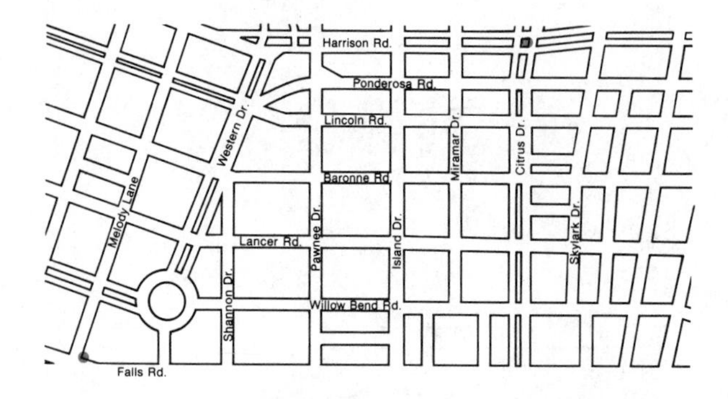

How would you tell someone to get from one point to another? When giving directions we often say to go a certain distance in one direction and then go a certain distance in a different direction.

To give directions for getting from point A to point B on the grid at the right, you could say:

"Go one block east, eight blocks north, five blocks east, and then two blocks south."

Can you give two simpler ways to get from A to B?

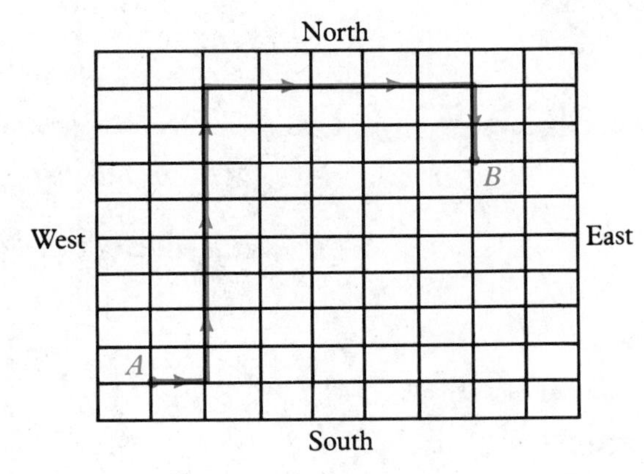

In mathematics we use two perpendicular number lines to create a method of locating points. The point of intersection of the lines is called the *origin*.

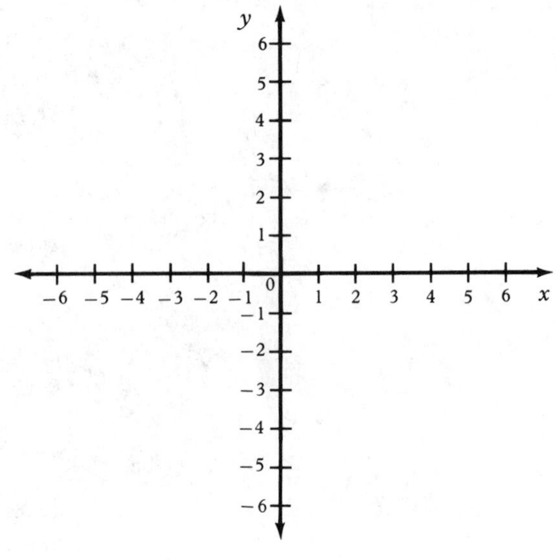

A pair of numbers called *coordinates* name the location of each point. Point A, below, is "over 2" and "up 1" from the origin. We say that A has coordinates (2, 1). The first number is called the x-coordinate and the second is the y-coordinate. In general, a point is represented by the coordinates (x, y). We will use the notation $P(x, y)$ to represent the point P with coordinates (x, y). This method of determining points is called the *Cartesian coordinate system* and is named after the famous mathematician René Descartes.

Study the examples below.

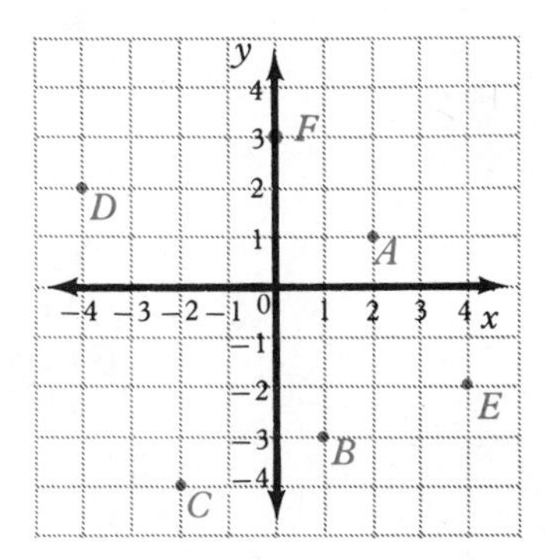

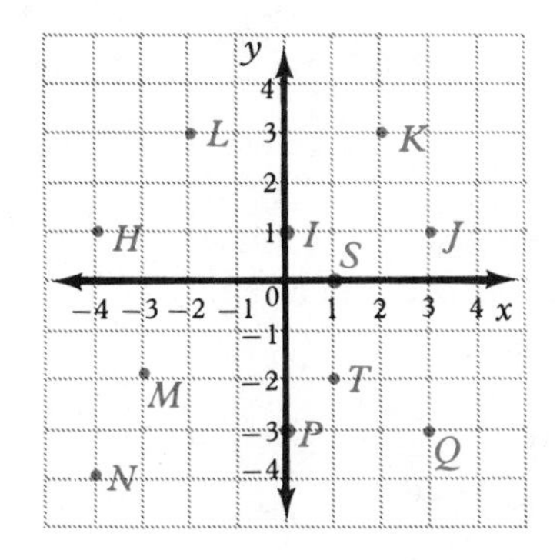

Point	*Coordinates*
A	(2, 1)
B	$(1, -3)$
C	$(-2, -4)$
D	?
E	?
F	?

Point	*Coordinates*
J	(3, 1)
H	$(-4, 1)$
I	(0, 1)
?	$(-3, -2)$
?	(1, 0)
?	$(0, -3)$

The examples below show that the coordinates do not have to be integers. Study each example.

Point	*Coordinates*
A	$(3, \frac{2}{3})$
B	$(-1\frac{4}{5}, -\frac{7}{3})$
C	$(-2, \sqrt{2})$
D	$(\pi, -2)$

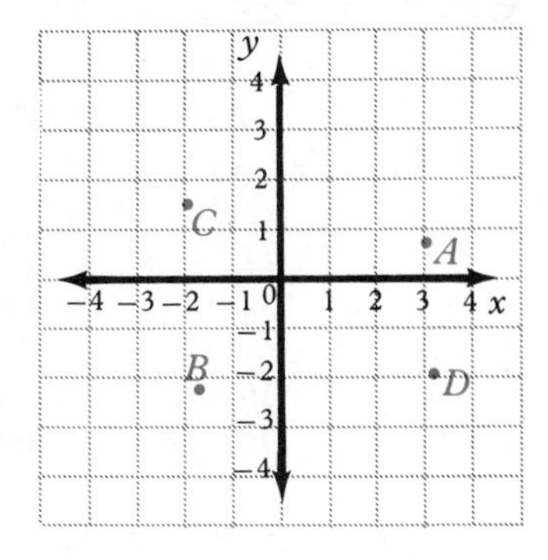

EXERCISES

A.

In exercises 1-4, plot the following sets of points on graph paper. Use a different set of axes for each exercise.

1. $(-4, 2)$, $(6, -1)$, $(-5, -4)$, and $(-3, -2)$
2. $(6, 2)$, $(-2\frac{1}{2}, \frac{2}{3})$, $(-5, \frac{8}{3})$, and $(-\sqrt{6}, \sqrt{3})$
3. $(-4, 0)$, $(5, 0)$, $(0, 0)$, and $(2\frac{1}{2}, 0)$
4. $(0, -2\frac{1}{2})$, $(0, 6)$, $(0, -3)$, and $(0, \sqrt{2})$

In exercises 5-8, draw lines that contain the following pairs of points.

5. $(0, 0)$ and $(-5, -5)$
6. $(4, 0)$ and $(0, -3)$
7. $(-4, 2)$ and $(-2, -6)$
8. $(5, -3)$ and $(4, -3)$

In exercises 9-11, draw triangles with the following coordinates as vertices. Tell whether the triangles are acute, right, or obtuse.

9. $(-2, 3)$, $(4, 1)$, and $(7, -2)$
10. $(3, 3)$, $(-4, 0)$, and $(4, 6)$
11. $(-4, 2)$, $(-4, -3)$, and $(3, -3)$

In exercises 12-14, draw quadrilaterals with the following coordinates as vertices.

12. $(-5, -3)$, $(-1, -3)$, $(-5, 1)$, and $(-1, 1)$
13. $(0, 6)$, $(6, 0)$, $(0, -6)$, and $(-6, 0)$
14. $(-1, 5)$, $(3, 2)$, $(2, -5)$, and $(-4, -1)$

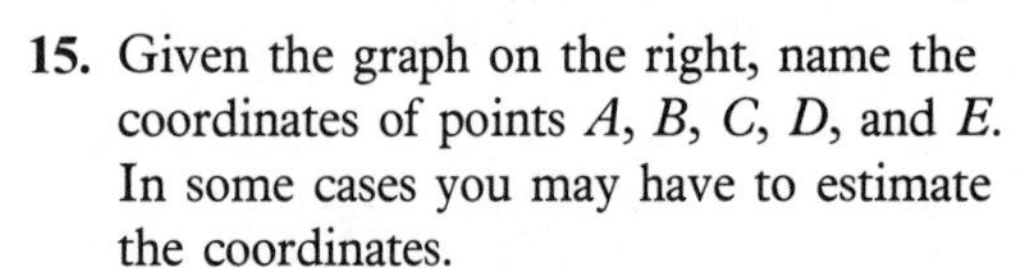

15. Given the graph on the right, name the coordinates of points A, B, C, D, and E. In some cases you may have to estimate the coordinates.

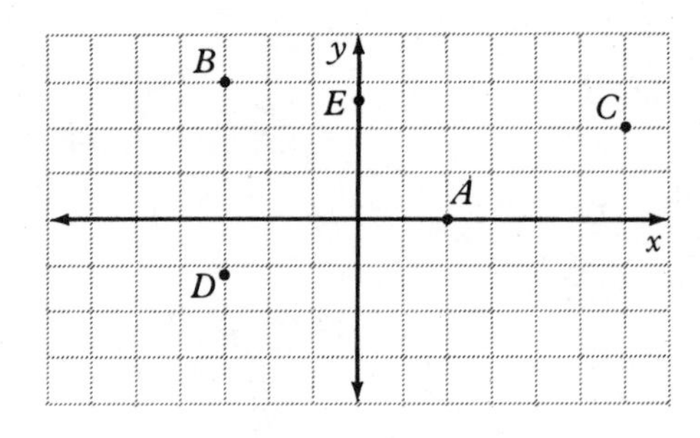

Activity

On a coordinate grid start at (0, 0) and draw a continuous sequence of segments going from point to point. Read down each column.

WHAT OBJECT IS REPRESENTED?

Start →	(0, 0)	(6, 24)	(6, 39)	(4, 39)	(4, 24)
	(10, 0)	(6, 35)	(7, 39)	(4, 37)	(0, 22)
	(12, 2)	(7, 35)	(6, 39)	(3, 37)	(0, 17)
	(12, 8)	(6, 35)	(6, 42)	(4, 37)	(2, 14)
	(8, 14)	(6, 37)	(4, 42)	(4, 35)	(−2, 8)
	(10, 17)	(7, 37)	(4, 39)	(3, 35)	(−2, 2)
	(10, 22)	(6, 37)	(3, 39)	(4, 35)	(0, 0) ← Stop

B.

In exercises 16–18, the coordinates of three vertices of a rectangle are given. Find the coordinates of the fourth vertex. (*Hint:* You may want to graph the three coordinates.)

16. $(0, 0)$, $(-4, 0)$, and $(0, -2)$

17. $(-4, 3)$, $(-4, -1)$, and $(5, -1)$

18. $(1, -3)$, $(1, 5)$, and $(4, 5)$

In exercises 19–21, the coordinates of three vertices of a square are given. Find the coordinates of the fourth vertex.

19. $(0, 0)$, $(3, 0)$, and $(0, -3)$

20. $(-1, 2)$, $(2, 2)$, and $(2, -1)$

21. $(-3, 2)$, $(-3, 5)$, and $(0, 5)$

In exercises 22 and 23, the coordinates of three vertices of a parallelogram are given. Find the coordinates of the fourth vertex. (There is more than one correct answer.)

22. $(0, 0)$, $(4, 4)$, and $(6, 4)$

23. $(1, 1)$, $(4, 1)$, and $(0, -1)$

24. Plot several points in which the product of the coordinates equals 12. Draw a smooth line through the points.

25. Plot several points in which the y-coordinate is twice the x-coordinate. Draw a line through the points.

26. Find a third point that lies on the line through the two points $(3, -2)$ and $(-1, 2)$.

27. Graph the points $(2, 0)$ and $(0, 4)$ and draw a line through the points. If the coordinates $(0, 0)$ and $(3, n)$ determine a line parallel to the first line, what is the value of n?

PROBLEM SOLVING

Two vertices of a figure are (0, 0) and (6, 0).

1. What are the coordinates of the third vertex if the figure is an equilateral triangle? (There are two solutions.)
2. What are the coordinates of the other two vertices if the figure is a square? (There are three solutions.)
3. What are the coordinates of the other two vertices if the figure is a parallelogram with height 4?

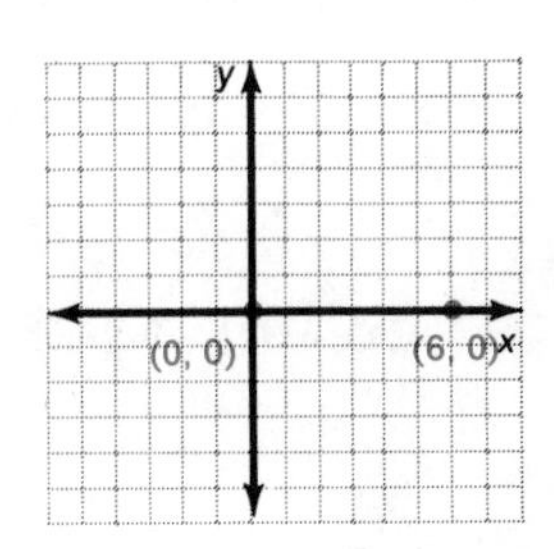

14–2 Midpoint of a Segment

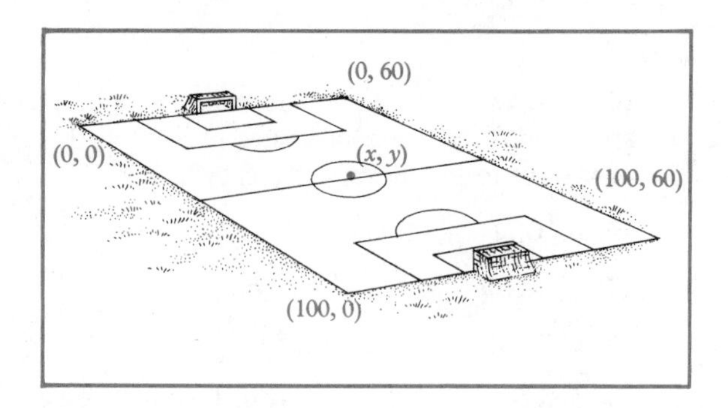

A soccer field is usually about 100 yards long and 60 yards wide. Suppose coordinates are assigned to the corners of the soccer field as shown. What are the coordinates of the center of the field?

Observe the midpoints of the segments at the right.

Observe that for the horizontal segment $\overline{MN}$, the x-coordinate of the midpoint is one half the sum of the x-coordinates of the endpoints. For the vertical segment $\overline{PQ}$, the y-coordinate of the midpoint is one half the sum of the y-coordinates of the endpoints.

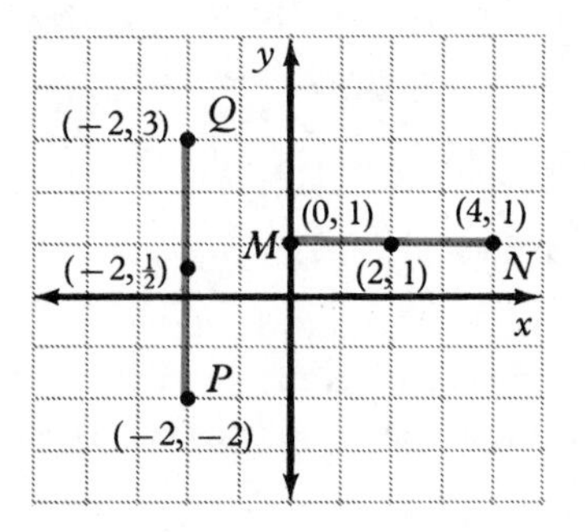

This same idea can be used for other line segments. Let (x_1, y_1) be the coordinates of one endpoint and (x_2, y_2) be the coordinates of the other endpoint in the figure below.

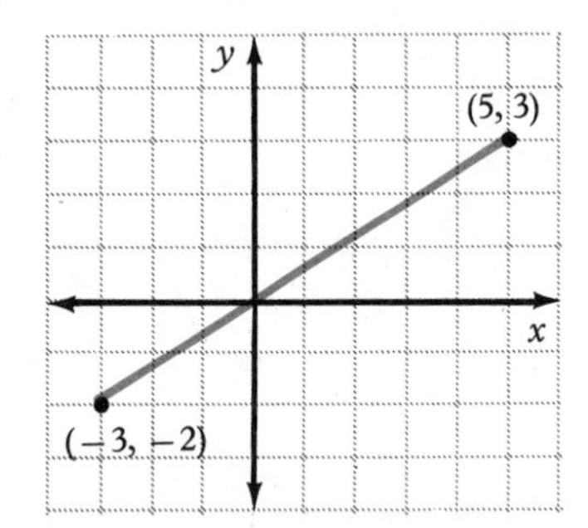

$(x_1, y_1) = (-3, -2)$; $(x_2, y_2) = (5, 3)$

$$\frac{x_1 + x_2}{2} = \frac{-3 + 5}{2} = 1$$

$$\frac{y_1 + y_2}{2} = \frac{-2 + 3}{2} = \frac{1}{2}$$

The coordinates of the midpoint are $(1, \frac{1}{2})$.

This example suggests the following theorem.

Theorem 14–1 If the coordinates of the endpoints of the segment $\overline{P_1P_2}$ are (x_1, y_1) and (x_2, y_2), then the coordinates of the midpoint of $\overline{P_1P_2}$ are $\left(\frac{x_1 + x_2}{2}, \frac{y_1 + y_2}{2}\right)$.

The following questions suggest how we might prove Theorem 14–1. The proof is left as an exercise.

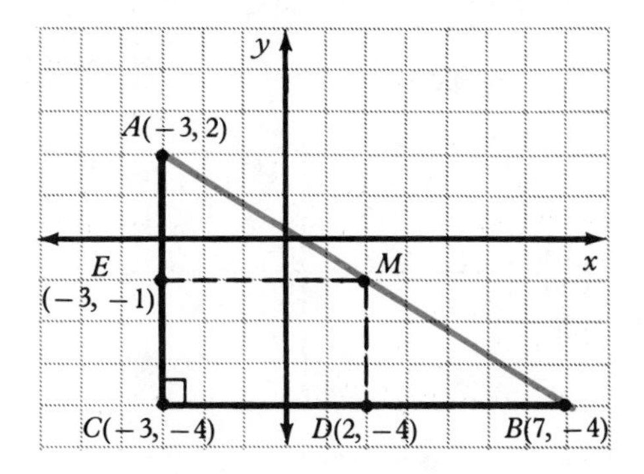

1. Why are the coordinates of C $(-3, -4)$?
2. Why are the coordinates of E, the midpoint of $\overline{AC}$, $(-3, -1)$?
3. Why are the coordinates of D, the midpoint of $\overline{BC}$, $(2, -4)$?
4. Using questions 2 and 3, why are the coordinates of M, the midpoint of $\overline{AB}$, $(2, -1)$?

Note that if the coordinates of A are (x_1, y_1) or $(-3, 2)$ and the coordinates of B are (x_2, y_2) or $(7, -4)$, then $\frac{x_1 + x_2}{2} = \frac{-3 + 7}{2} = 2$ and $\frac{y_1 + y_2}{2} = \frac{2 + (-4)}{2} = -1$. Therefore, the coordinates of M are $(2, -1)$.

Example

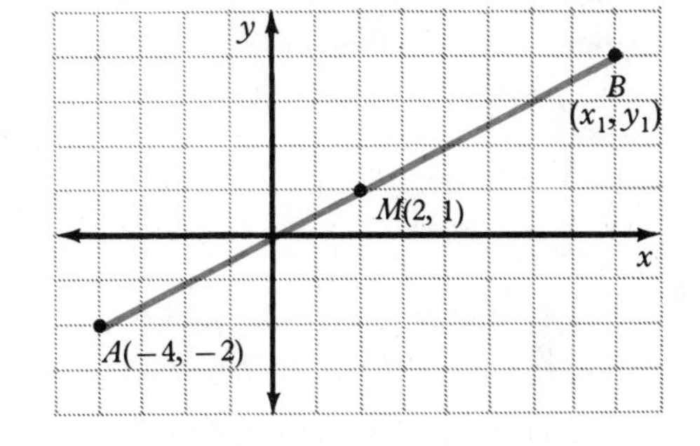

If M is the midpoint of $\overline{AB}$, where $(-4, -2)$ are the coordinates of A and $(2, 1)$ are the coordinates of M, find the coordinates of B.

Let (x_1, y_1) be the coordinates of B. By Theorem 14–1,

$$2 = \frac{-4 + x_1}{2} \quad \text{and} \quad 1 = \frac{-2 + y_1}{2}$$

Solving for x_1 and y_1, we obtain $x_1 = 8$ and $y_1 = 4$. The coordinates of B are $(8, 4)$.

APPLICATION

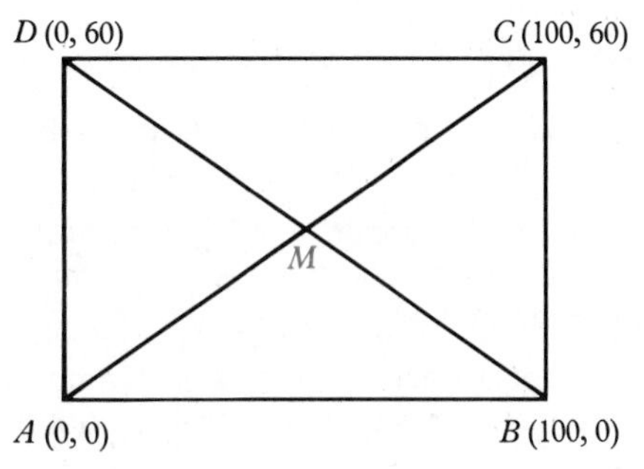

To find the coordinates of the center of the soccer field we must find the midpoint of $\overline{AC}$.

$$\left(\frac{x_1 + x_2}{2}, \frac{y_1 + y_2}{2}\right) = \left(\frac{0 + 100}{2}, \frac{0 + 60}{2}\right)$$

The coordinates of M are $(50, 30)$.

Would M have the same coordinates if we had found the midpoint of $\overline{BD}$?

EXERCISES

A.

1. Determine the midpoints of the following segments.

a.

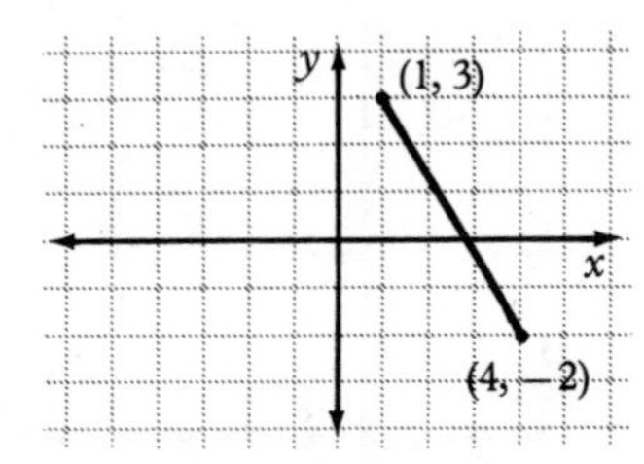

b.

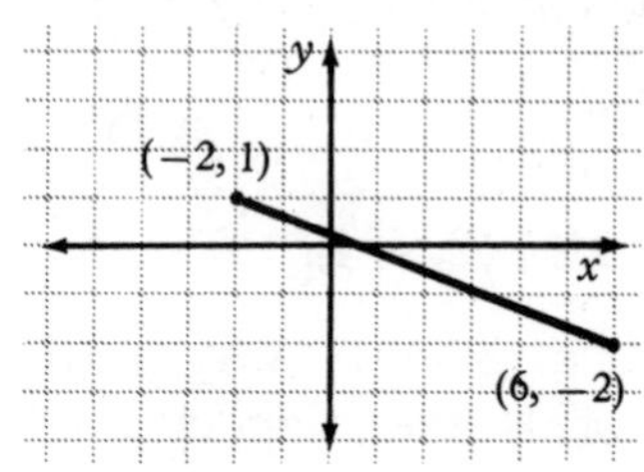

c.

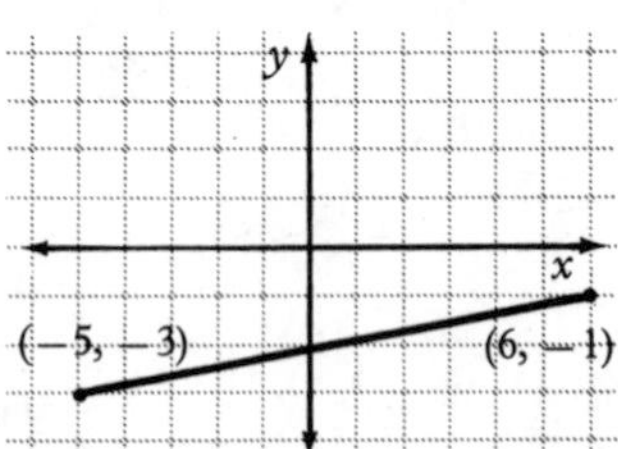

d.

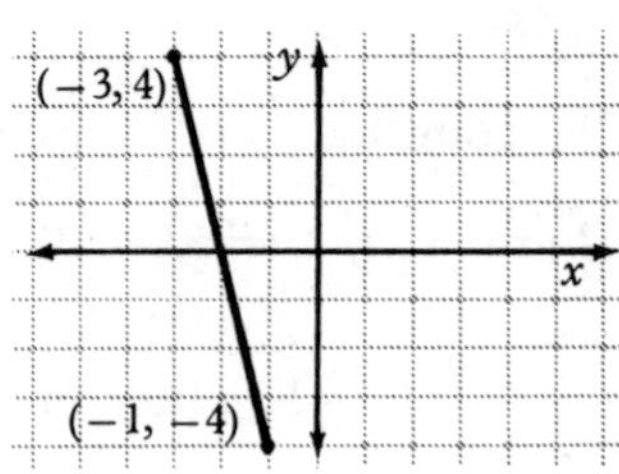

In exercises 2–7, determine the midpoints of segments whose endpoints have the following coordinates.

2. $(-3, 2)$ and $(7, 10)$
3. $(-7, 4)$ and $(9, -4)$
4. $(-1, -2)$ and $(5, 4)$
5. $(-3, -5)$ and $(-7, -2)$
6. $(-4, 2)$ and $(5, -3)$
7. $(7, -3)$ and $(0, 0)$
8. Graph the points $A(-2, 5)$, $B(6, 1)$, and $C(-4, -3)$ and draw $\triangle ABC$. Find the midpoints of $\overline{AB}$, $\overline{BC}$, and $\overline{AC}$.
9. Graph the points $A(1, 6)$, $B(6, 2)$, $C(8, -3)$, and $D(-5, 2)$. Find the midpoints of $\overline{AB}$, $\overline{BC}$, $\overline{CD}$, and $\overline{DA}$. Draw a quadrilateral by connecting the midpoints. What kind of quadrilateral is it?

Activity

Suppose the coordinates of A are $(-2, 6)$ and the coordinates of B are $(-4, 2)$. By Theorem 14–1 the coordinates of midpoint M are $(-3, 4)$.

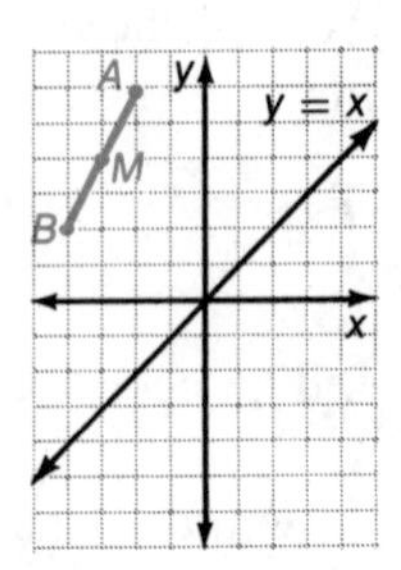

a. Use tracing paper or a MIRA to find the reflection of $\overline{AB}$ across the y-axis. Compare the coordinates of the midpoint of the reflected segment with the coordinates of M.

b. Reflect $\overline{AB}$ across the x-axis. Compare the coordinates of the midpoint of the reflected segment with the coordinates of M.

c. Make the same comparison when the line $y = x$ is used as a line of reflection.

B.

In exercises 10–14, M is the midpoint of $\overline{AB}$. The coordinates of two of the points are given. Find the coordinates of the third point.

10. $A(1, 1)$, $M(5, 1)$, find B.

11. $A(-2, -6)$, $M(-2, 1)$, find B.

12. $A(-5, -3)$, $M(2, 1)$, find B.

13. $M(0, 0)$, $B(-4, 3)$, find A.

14. $M(0, 0)$, $B(1, 6)$, find A.

15. Given the triangle ABC with vertices $A(-4, -3)$, $B(8, 0)$, and $C(6, 12)$. A line is drawn parallel to base $\overline{AB}$ and bisecting $\overline{AC}$. Find the coordinates of the point where the line intersects $\overline{BC}$.

16. Suppose the coordinates of A and B are $(-4, 6)$ and $(6, -2)$. Find the coordinates of X such that $AX = \frac{1}{4}AB$.

17. Suppose the coordinates of A and B are $(-7, -2)$ and $(5, -1)$. Find the coordinates of a point C on $\overleftrightarrow{AB}$ such that $AC = \frac{1}{2}AB$.

C.

18. Prove Theorem 14–1 using the following information.
Given: $P_1(x_1, y_1)$, $P_2(x_2, y_2)$, $P_1M = MP_2$
Prove: The coordinates of M are $\left(\frac{x_1 + x_2}{2}, \frac{y_1 + y_2}{2}\right)$.
(*Hint:* Draw the auxiliary lines that are indicated in the diagram.)

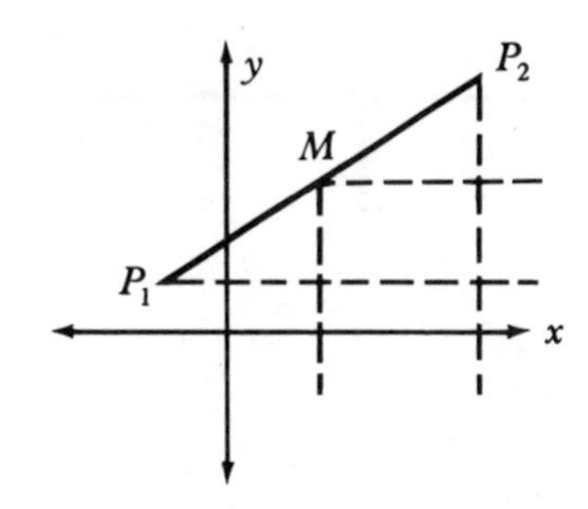

19. Consider the points $P_1(x_1, y_1)$ and $P_2(x_2, y_2)$. Find the coordinates of the points that trisect $\overline{P_1P_2}$.

PROBLEM SOLVING

Consider a three-dimensional coordinate system with an *x*-axis, *y*-axis, and a *z*-axis. A cube with each edge of 4 units is placed as shown in the diagram.

What are the coordinates (x, y, z) of the center of the cube?

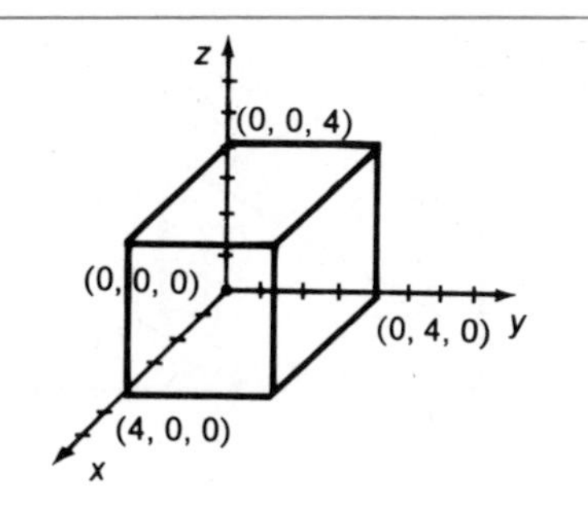

14–3 Slope of a Line

What is the slope or pitch of the roofs?

The slope of a line or a segment can be thought of as the ratio $\frac{\text{rise}}{\text{run}}$ as shown.

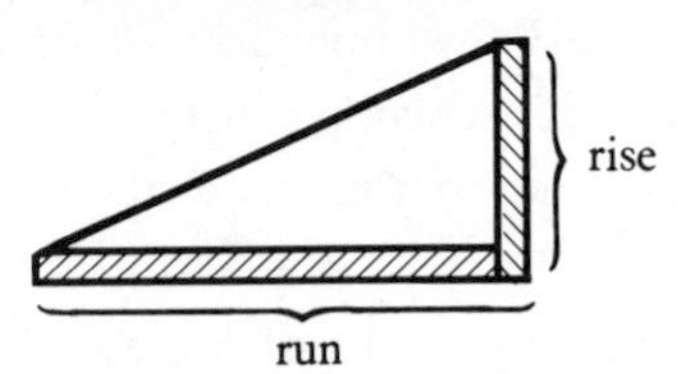

The letter m is used to designate slope. Study the following examples.

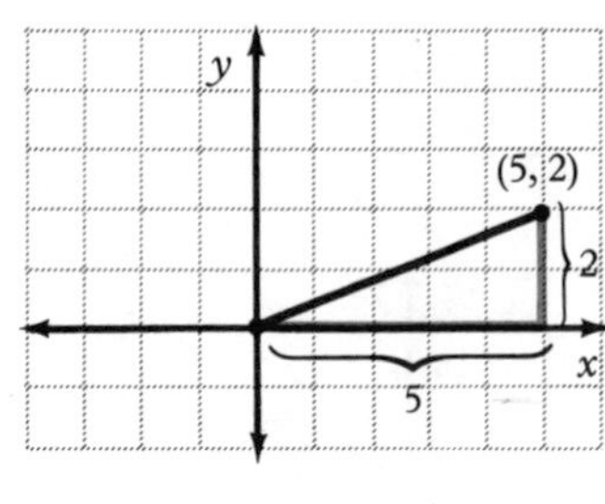

$m = \frac{2}{5}$

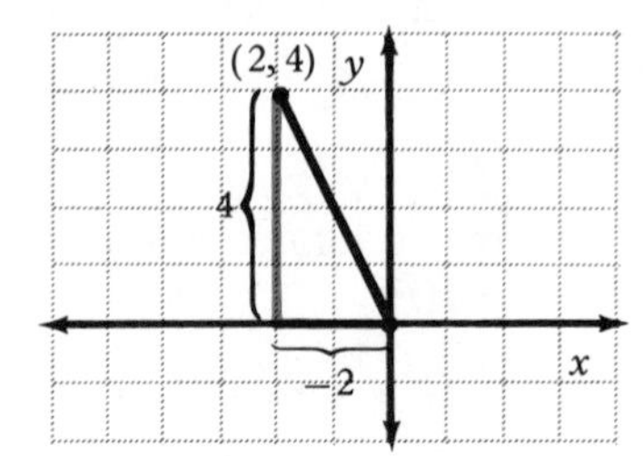

$m = \frac{4}{-2} = -\frac{2}{1}$

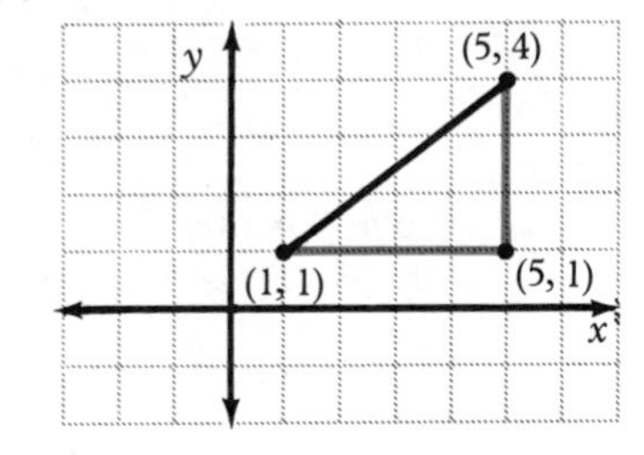

$m = \frac{3}{4}$

The definition of slope given below involves the Cartesian coordinate system.

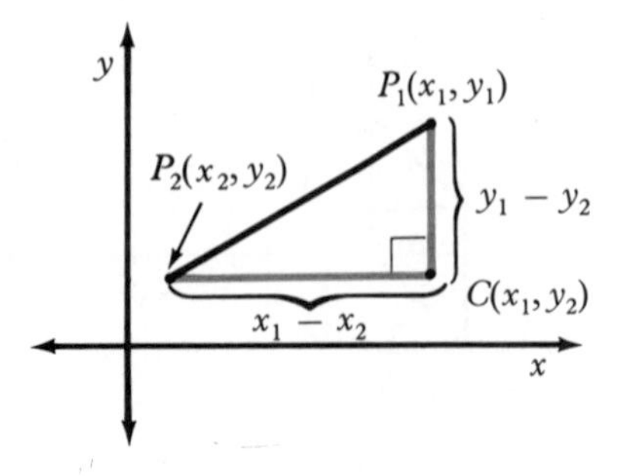

The slope of a line is determined by the change in the vertical distance $(y_1 - y_2)$ divided by the change in the horizontal distance $(x_1 - x_2)$.

Definition 14–1

If P_1 and P_2 have coordinates (x_1, y_1) and (x_2, y_2) respectively, then the **slope** m of $\overline{P_1P_2}$ is:

$$m = \frac{y_1 - y_2}{x_1 - x_2}$$

provided $x_1 - x_2 \neq 0$.

The examples below show that the slope of a line can be positive, negative, zero, or undefined.

Example 1 Positive slope

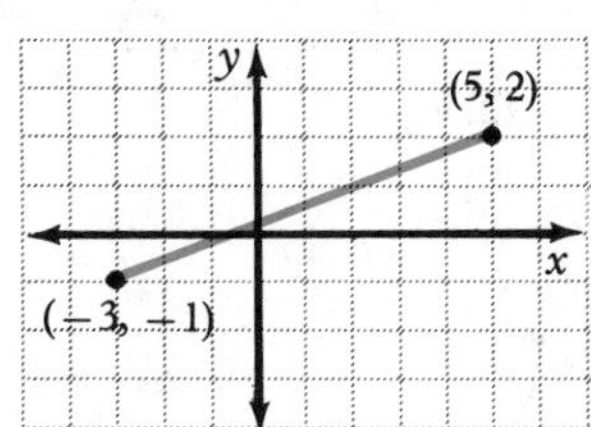

$$m = \frac{2 - (-1)}{5 - (-3)} = \frac{3}{8}$$

Example 2 Negative slope

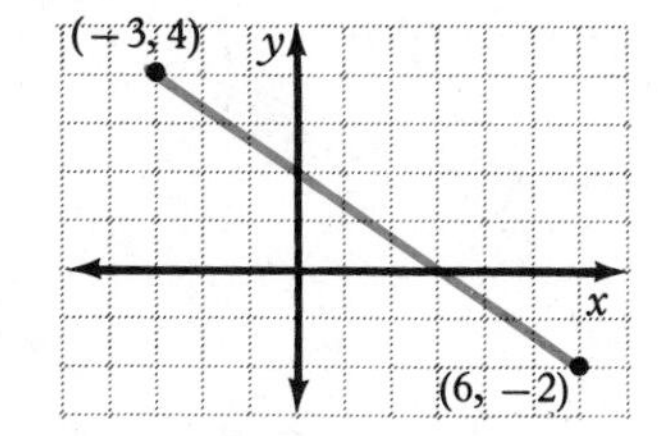

$$m = \frac{4 - (-2)}{-3 - 6} = -\frac{2}{3}$$

Example 3 Zero slope

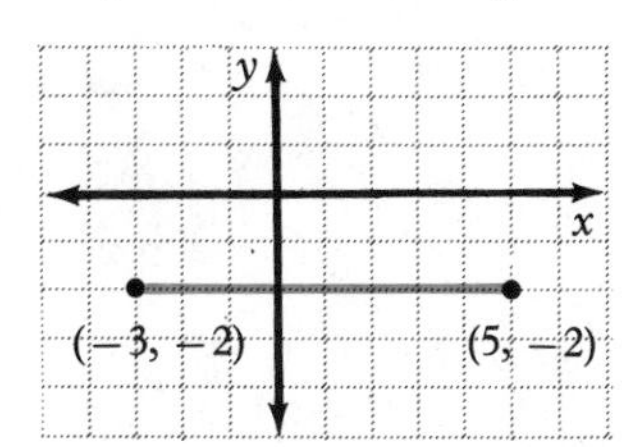

$$m = \frac{-2 - (-2)}{5 - (-3)} = \frac{0}{8} = 0$$

The slope of a line parallel to the x-axis is zero.

Example 4 Undefined slope

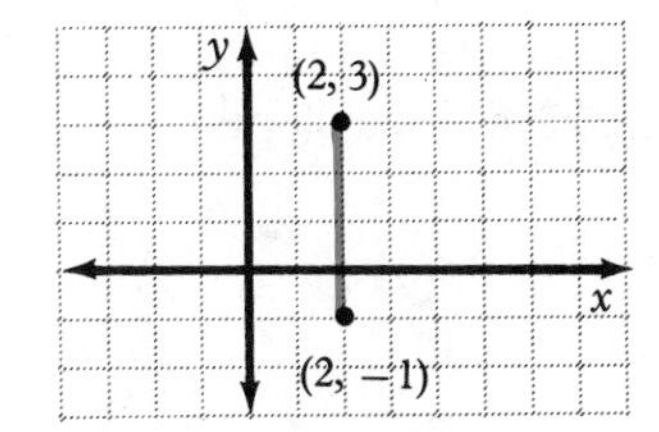

$$m = \frac{3 - (-1)}{2 - 2} = \frac{4}{0}$$

Thus, the slope is undefined. Why? The slope of a line parallel to the y-axis is undefined.

APPLICATION

If this house is 30 feet wide and the rise on the roof is 6 feet, what is the slope of the roof?

If $AB = 30$, then $AC = 15$.
Since $DC = 6$, then the

$$\text{slope} = \frac{\text{rise}}{\text{run}} = \frac{6}{15}.$$

Hence, the slope $= \frac{2}{5}$.

EXERCISES

A.

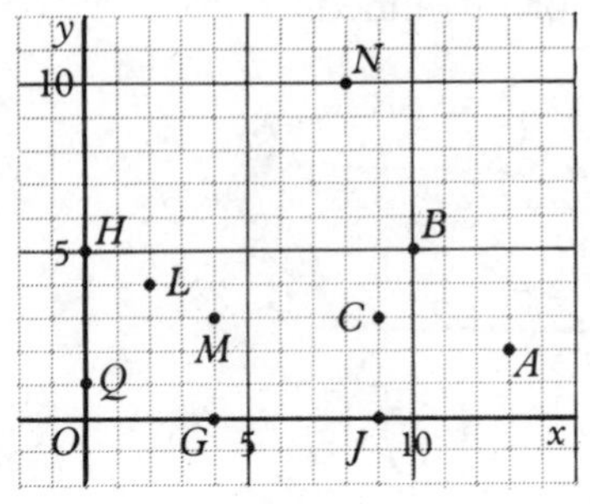

1. Determine the coordinates of each point and find the slope of the following segments.

a. $\overline{AB}$ **b.** $\overline{HN}$ **c.** $\overline{AC}$

d. $\overline{MC}$ **e.** $\overline{GJ}$ **f.** $\overline{LQ}$

g. $\overline{HG}$ **h.** $\overline{MB}$ **i.** $\overline{MG}$

In exercises 2–7, find the slope of a line that contains the given points.

2. $(0, 0), (4, 6)$ **3.** $(3, 5), (9, 2)$

4. $(-2, 5), (6, -3)$ **5.** $(-2, 10), (-6, -4)$

6. $(10, 2), (-2, 2)$ **7.** $(5, 0), (0, -5)$

8. The vertices of a parallelogram are $R(1, 4)$, $S(3, 2)$, $T(4, 6)$, and $U(2, 8)$. Graph the points and find the slopes of each of the sides. Which sides have equal slopes?

9. The vertices of a rectangle are $E(-2, 3)$, $F(4, 3)$, $G(4, -1)$, and $H(-2, -1)$. Find the slopes of each side. For which two sides are the slopes undefined?

B.

10. What is the slope of a line if it crosses the x-axis at 6 and the y-axis at -2?

11. The vertices of a triangle are $A(4, 6)$, $B(-1, 2)$, and $C(2, -4)$. Find the slope of each side.

Activity

Suppose the coordinates of A are $(-2, 4)$ and B are $(-6, 2)$.

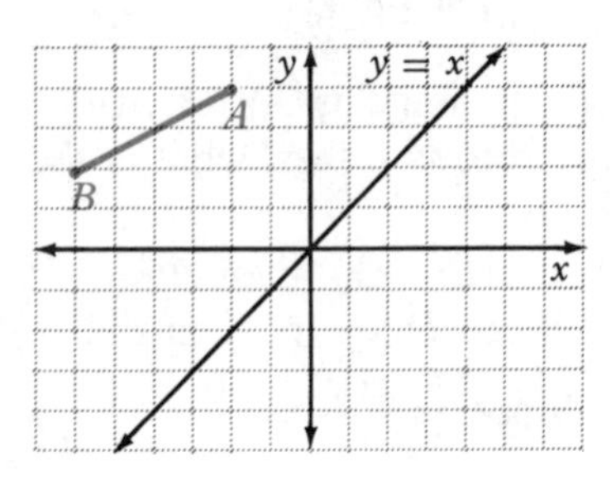

a. Use tracing paper or a MIRA to find the reflection of $\overline{AB}$ about the y-axis. Compare the slope of $\overline{AB}$ with the slope of the reflected segment.

b. Reflect $\overline{AB}$ about the x-axis and compare the slope of $\overline{AB}$ with the slope of the reflected segment.

c. Make the same comparison when the line $y = x$ is used as the line of reflection.

12. Given $\triangle ABC$ with $A(-2, 4)$, $B(6, 2)$, and $C(0, -4)$.

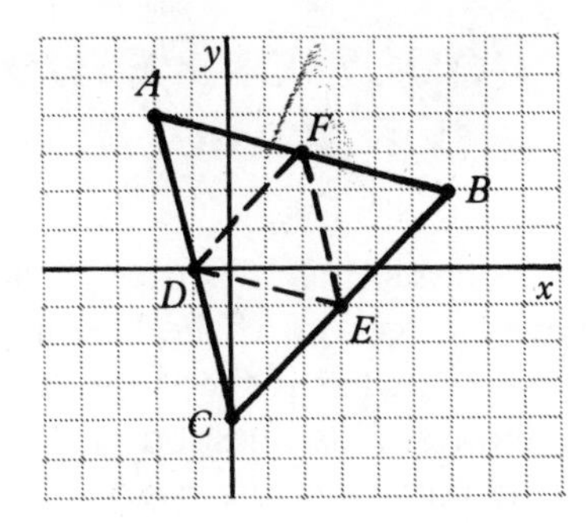

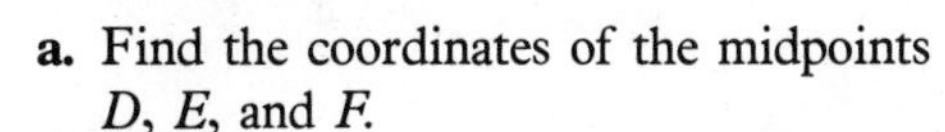

   a. Find the coordinates of the midpoints D, E, and F.
   b. Determine the slopes of $\overline{AB}$, $\overline{BC}$, and $\overline{AC}$.
   c. Determine the slopes of $\overline{DE}$, $\overline{DF}$, and $\overline{FE}$.
   d. What do you observe about the slopes you found in **b** and **c** above?

13. The vertices of a triangle are $X(11, 0)$, $Y(-5, 4)$, and $Z(3, 4)$.
   a. Find the slopes of its sides.
   b. Find the slopes of its medians. (Use Theorem 14–1 to find the midpoints of the sides.)

14. A line with a slope of -3 crosses the x-axis at $(8, 0)$. At what point does it cross the y-axis?

15. What is the slope of a line if the x-coordinate is always twice the y-coordinate?

C.

16. $ABCD$ is a quadrilateral with vertices $A(a, b)$, $B(c, b)$, $C(c + d, e)$ and $D(a + d, e)$. Find the slope of each side.

17. $\triangle ABC$ has vertices $B(-6, -3)$ and $C(8, -4)$. Slope of $\overline{AB} = \frac{1}{2}$ and slope of $\overline{AC} = -2$. Find the coordinates of point A.

18. A line with a slope of -1 contains the point $(5, -2)$. Solve for x, if the line also contains the point $(x, 8)$.

PROBLEM SOLVING

Three points A, B, and C are collinear if the slope of $\overline{AB}$ equals the slope of $\overline{BC}$. Use this fact to solve the following problem.

Given: $\triangle AXY$ with $A(0, 0)$, slope of $\overline{AY} = \frac{1}{2}$. $DEFG$, $HIJK$, and $LMNP$ are squares with these coordinates: $D(4, 0)$, $H(10, 0)$, and $L(18, 0)$.

Prove: F, J, and N are collinear.

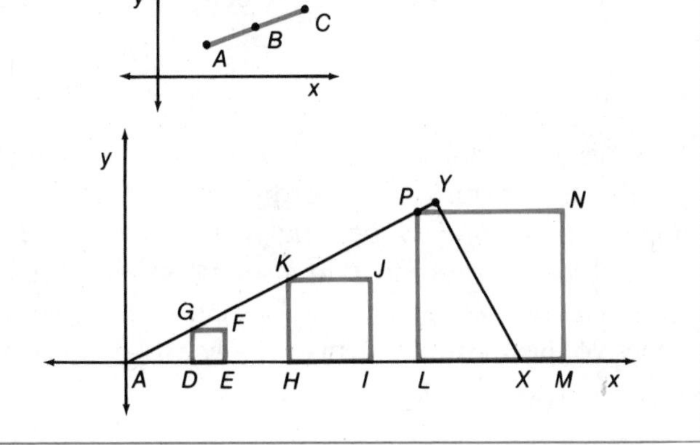

14–4 Slopes of Perpendicular and Parallel Lines

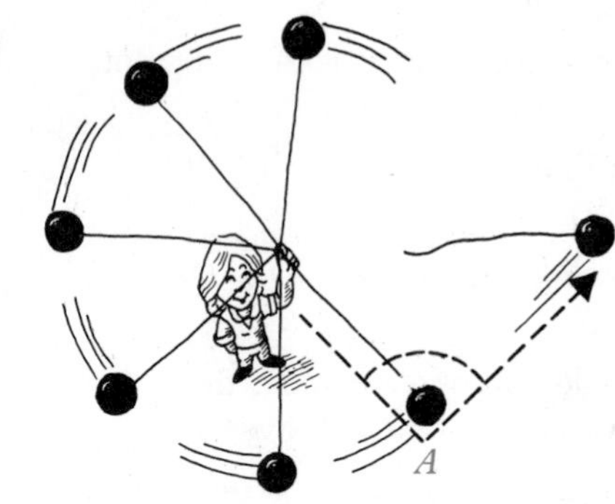

Suppose a ball on a string is twirled in a counterclockwise direction. If the ball is released at point A, what is the slope of the path that it follows? This question is examined at the bottom of the page.

First we shall consider the slopes of perpendicular lines. The lines shown are perpendicular. Determine the slope of each pair of lines.

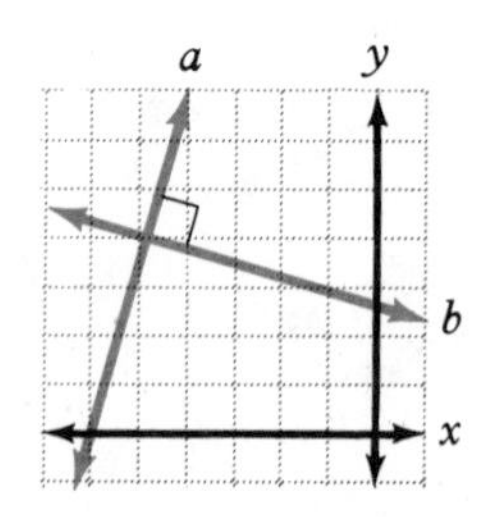

Observe that the slope of $a = 4$, slope of $b = -\frac{1}{4}$, and $4 \cdot -\frac{1}{4} = -1$.

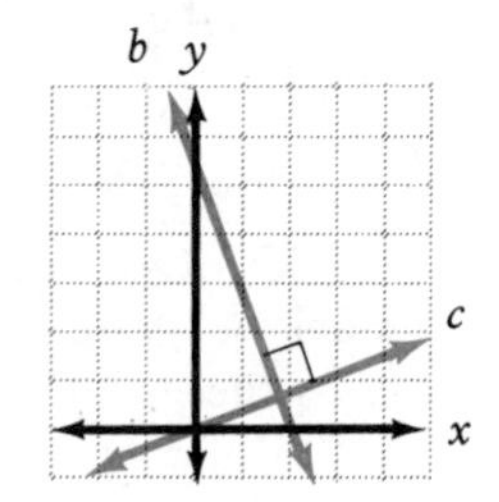

Observe that the slope of $b = -\frac{5}{2}$, slope of $c = \frac{2}{5}$, and $-\frac{5}{2} \cdot \frac{2}{5} = -1$.

These observations suggest the following theorem.

Theorem 14–2 The product of the slopes of two perpendicular lines is -1.

Theorem 14–2 is true only if neither line is parallel to the y-axis. Why?

APPLICATION

To solve the problem at the top of the page, assign a coordinate system. If the coordinates of A are $(3, -2)$, the slope of $\overline{OA}$ is $-\frac{2}{3}$. Surprisingly, the laws of science show that the ball will always move in a direction $\overrightarrow{AB}$ that is tangent to the circle. So $\overline{OA} \perp \overline{AB}$. By Theorem 14–2, the product of the slopes of these two segments is -1. So $-\frac{2}{3} \cdot$ slope of $\overline{AB} = -1$, or the slope of $\overline{AB} = \frac{3}{2}$.

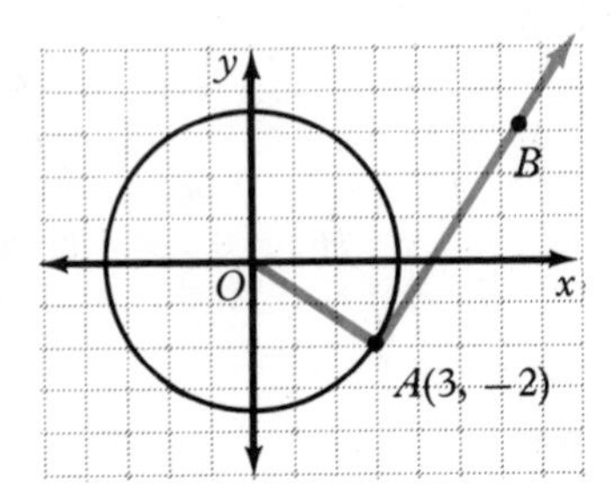

Consider the slopes of the roofs at the right. If the slope of $\overline{AB}$ is $\frac{2}{3}$ and $\overline{AB} \parallel \overline{CD}$, what is the slope of $\overline{CD}$? This question is answered at the bottom of the page.

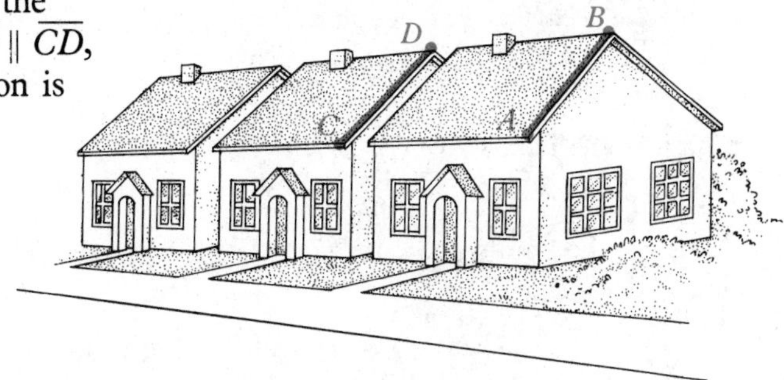

Now consider the slopes of parallel lines. The lines below are parallel. Determine the slopes of each pair of lines.

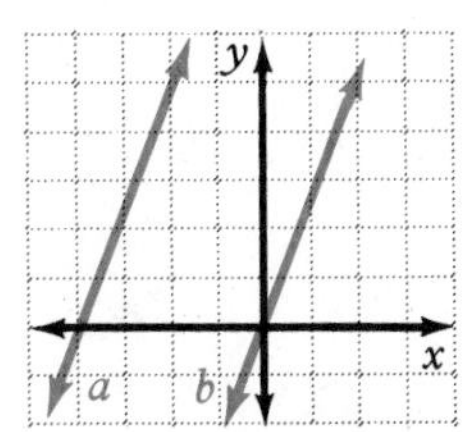

Observe that the slope of $a = \frac{3}{1}$, slope of $b = \frac{3}{1}$, and slope of $a =$ slope of b.

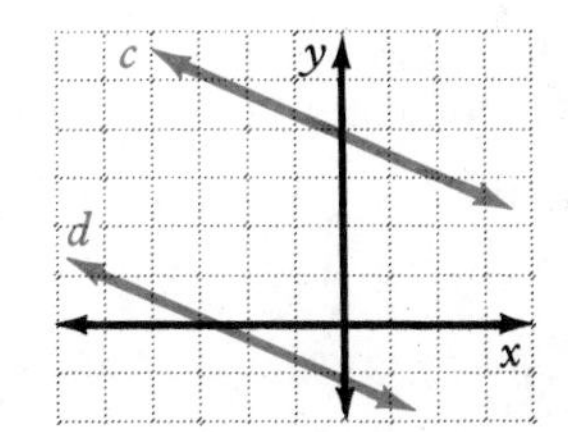

Observe that the slope of $c = -\frac{2}{5}$, slope of $d = -\frac{2}{5}$, and slope of $c =$ slope of d.

These observations suggest the following theorem.

Theorem 14–3 The slopes of two parallel lines are equal.

Theorem 14–3 is true only if neither line is parallel to the y-axis. Why?

APPLICATION

To answer the question at the top of the page assign a coordinate system. Then the slope of $\overline{AB} = \frac{2}{3}$. Theorem 14–3 tells us that the slope of $\overline{AB}$ equals the slope of $\overline{CD}$. Hence, the slope of $\overline{CD}$ equals $\frac{2}{3}$.

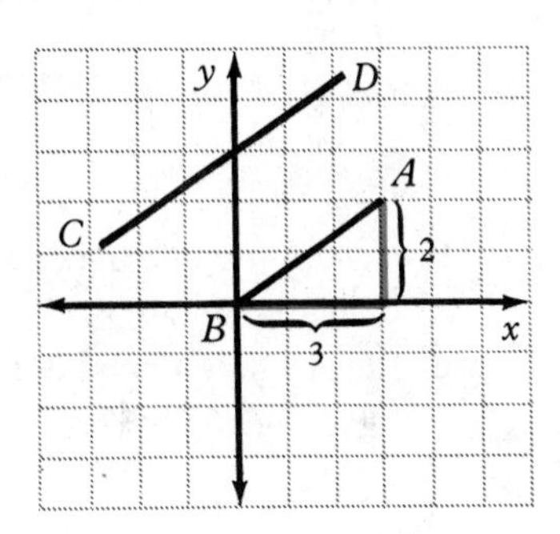

EXERCISES

A.

1. Consider the points $A(3, 5)$, $B(7, -1)$, $C(-4, 4)$, and $D(0, -2)$. Is $\overline{AB} \parallel \overline{CD}$?
2. Consider the points $A(3, 5)$, $B(7, -1)$, $C(0, 0)$, and $D(12, 8)$. Is $\overline{AB} \perp \overline{CD}$?
3. Show that $(3, 9)$, $(7, 5)$, $(4, -1)$, and $(0, 3)$ are the coordinates of the vertices of a parallelogram. (Use Theorem 14-3).
4. Show that $(1, 2)$, $(3, 1)$, $(0, -4)$, $(-2, -3)$ are the coordinates of the vertices of a parallelogram.
5. Show that $(1, -3)$, $(4, 5)$, $(-3, 7)$, and$(-6, -1)$ are the coordinates of the vertices of a parallelogram.
6. Show that $(4, 6)$, $(5, 1)$, and $(2, 4)$ are the coordinates of the vertices of a right triangle. (Use Theorem 14-2).
7. Show that $(7, 9)$, $(10, -3)$, and $(2, -5)$ are the coordinates of the vertices of a right triangle.
8. Show that $(1, 4)$, $(3, 5)$, $(-3, 12)$, and $(-1, 13)$ are the coordinates of the vertices of a rectangle.
9. Show that $(-3, -3)$, $(-1, -2)$, $(1, -6)$, and $(-1, -7)$ are the coordinates of the vertices of a rectangle.
10. Show that $(10, 2)$, $(8, 8)$, $(-1, 5)$, and $(1, -1)$ are the coordinates of the vertices of a rectangle.

Activity

Suppose $\overline{AB} \parallel \overline{CD}$, $\overline{EF} \perp \overline{AB}$, and $\overleftrightarrow{EF} \perp \overleftrightarrow{CD}$ with coordinates as shown.

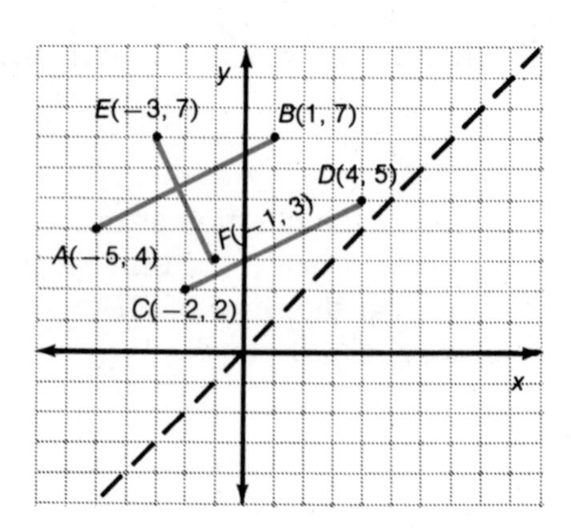

a. Using tracing paper or a MIRA, reflect $\overline{AB}$, $\overline{CD}$, and $\overline{EF}$ about the x-axis. Do the same relationships hold true with the reflected segments?

b. Reflect the segments about the y-axis. Do the same relationships hold true for these reflected segments?

c. Reflect the segments about the line $y = x$. Do the same relationships hold true for these reflected segments?

11. The vertices of a triangle have coordinates $(5, 1)$, $(-1, 7)$, and $(1, -3)$. Find the slopes of the three sides. Find the slopes of the three altitudes.

B.

12. Find y so that the line through $(-4, -3)$ and $(8, y)$ will be parallel to the line through $(4, -4)$ and $(3, 5)$.

13. Find y so that the line through $(-2, -1)$ and $(10, y)$ will be perpendicular to the line through $(6, -2)$ and $(5, 7)$.

14. Determine a so that the line through $(7, 1)$ and $(4, 8)$ will be parallel to the line through $(2, a)$ and $(a, -2)$.

15. Determine b so that the line through $(2, 3)$ and $(4, -5)$ is perpendicular to the line through $(4, -5)$ and (b, b).

16. The coordinates of A, B, and C are $(-3, 2)$, $(4, -2)$ and $(0, 6)$, respectively. Find D such that $\overline{AB} \parallel \overline{CD}$ and D is on the x-axis.

17. If the coordinates of A and B are $(0, 4)$ and $(-5, 1)$, and $\overleftrightarrow{AB} \perp \overleftrightarrow{AC}$, find the point at which $\overleftrightarrow{AC}$ crosses the x-axis.

C.

18. $ABCD$ is a rhombus with vertices $A(-3, 6)$, $B(5, 7)$, and $C(9, 0)$. Find the coordinates of D.

19. $ABCD$ is a parallelogram with vertices $A(3, 6)$, $B(5, 9)$, and $C(8, 2)$. Find the coordinates of D.

20. A circle with radius a and center at the origin contains the point with coordinates (c, d). Find the slope of the tangent to the circle at the point (c, d).

PROBLEM SOLVING

Consider the points $A(-2, 0)$, $B(6, 4)$, and $C(x, 0)$. If $\overline{AB} \perp \overline{BC}$, find the area of $\triangle ABC$. (*Hint:* First find the coordinates of point C.)

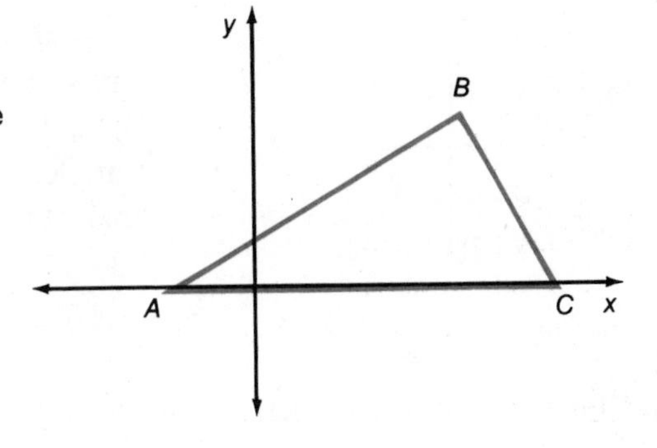

14–5 The Distance Formula

In this section we will study one of the most important formulas in analytic geometry—the *Distance Formula.* We can use the Distance Formula to find the distance the ball was thrown (see the picture on the right).

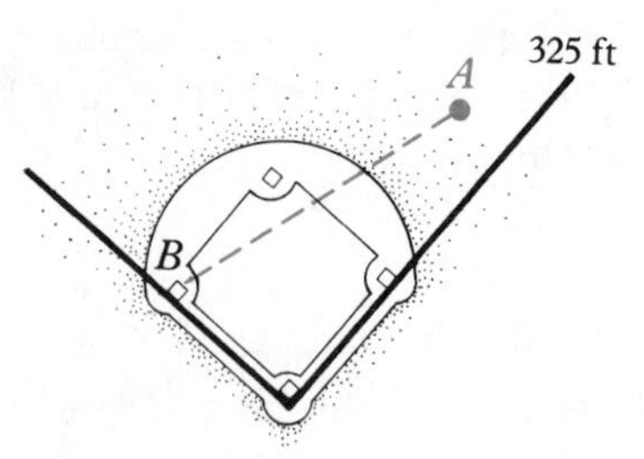

If a right fielder throws the ball from point A to third base (point B), how far did the ball travel?

Example 1 To find the length of a segment parallel to the x-axis.

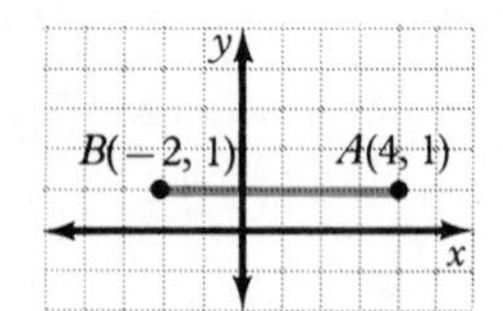

$AB = |4 - (-2)|$
$AB = |6|$
$AB = 6$

If $\overline{AB}$ is parallel to the x-axis, and the coordinates of A and B are (x_1, y_1) and (x_2, y_1), then $AB = |x_1 - x_2|$.

Example 2 To find the length of a segment parallel to the y-axis.

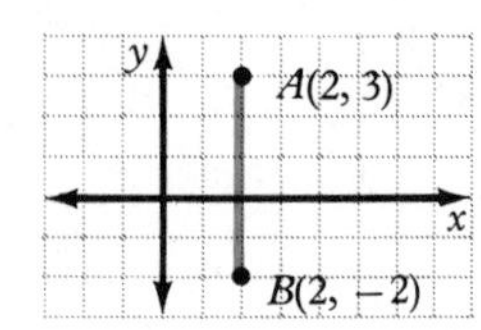

$AB = |3 - (-2)|$
$AB = |5|$
$AB = 5$

If $\overline{AB}$ is parallel to the y-axis, and the coordinates of A and B are (x_1, y_1) and (x_1, y_2), then $AB = |y_1 - y_2|$.

Example 3 To find the length of a segment not parallel to either axis.

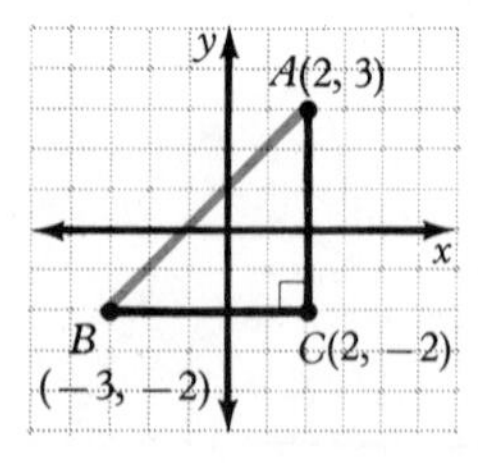

We wish to find the length of $\overline{AB}$. Let $\overline{BC}$ be parallel to the x-axis and $\overline{AC}$ be parallel to the y-axis. Then $BC = |2 - (-3)|$ and $AC = |3 - (-2)|$. $\triangle ABC$ is a right triangle. So by the Pythagorean Theorem, $AB^2 = BC^2 + AC^2$. Therefore, $AB^2 = (2 - (-3))^2 + (3 - (-2))^2$
or $AB = \sqrt{(2 + 3)^2 + (3 + 2)^2}$
$AB = \sqrt{25 + 25} = 5\sqrt{2}$

These examples suggest the following theorem.

Theorem 14-4 **The Distance Formula.** If A has coordinates (x_1, y_1) and B has coordinates (x_2, y_2) then $AB = \sqrt{(x_1 - x_2)^2 + (y_1 - y_2)^2}$.

Example

Use the Distance Formula to decide whether $\triangle ABC$ is isosceles.

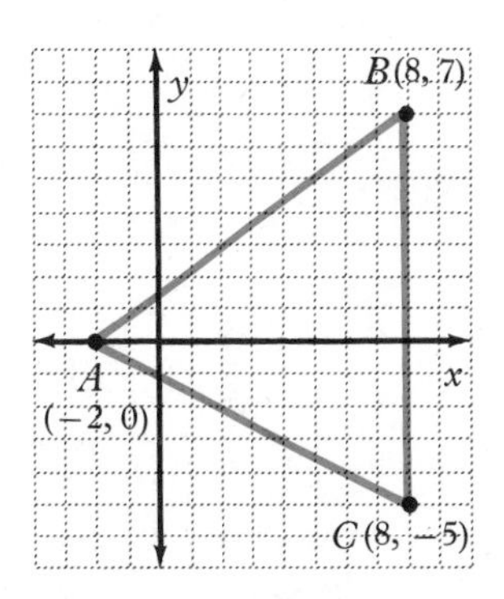

We begin by finding the lengths of the three sides.

$$AB = \sqrt{(8 - (-2))^2 + (7 - 0)^2} = \sqrt{149}$$
$$BC = \sqrt{0^2 + (7 - (-5))^2} = \sqrt{144}$$
$$AC = \sqrt{(8 - (-2))^2 + (-5 - 0)^2} = \sqrt{125}$$

No two sides are the same length, so $\triangle ABC$ is not isosceles.

APPLICATION

Now we return to the question posed at the beginning of this section: "How far did the fielder throw the ball?" Assign a coordinate system as shown on the right with home plate as the origin. The player will be assigned a position of (280, 20). Using the Distance Formula, we obtain:

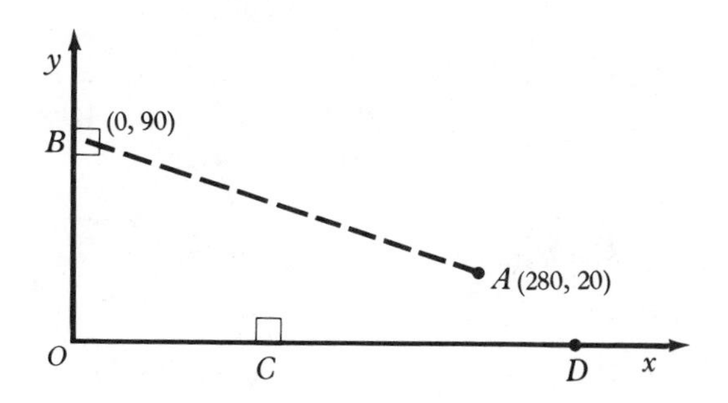

$$AB = \sqrt{(280 - 0)^2 + (20 - 90)^2}$$
$$AB = \sqrt{(280)^2 + (-70)^2}$$
$$AB = \sqrt{78{,}400 + 4900}$$
$$AB = \sqrt{83{,}300}$$
$$AB \doteq 288.62 \text{ feet}$$

The ball traveled about 289 feet.

B (0, 90)—third base
C (90, 0)—first base
D (325, 0)—right field fence
A (280, 20)—position of player

EXERCISES

A.

In exercises 1–8, find the distances between the given points.

1. $(-4, 5)$ and $(6, 5)$

2. $(3, 2)$ and $(3, -8)$

3. $(4, 5)$ and $(-3, -2)$

4. $(-2, 5)$ and $(5, -2)$

5. $(4, 0)$ and $(0, -6)$

6. $(1, 2)$ and $(-7, 3)$

7. $(-5, 3)$ and $(0, -4)$

8. $(6, -2)$ and $(7, 3)$

In exercises 9–12, use the Distance Formula to classify the triangle as scalene, isosceles, or equilateral.

9. $A(4, 5)$, $B(5, -2)$, and $C(1, 1)$.

10. $A(1, 1)$, $B(-3, 5)$, and $C(2\sqrt{3} - 1, 2\sqrt{3} + 3)$

11. $A(-6, 2)$, $B(1, 7)$, and $C(6, 3)$.

12. $A(10, -5)$, $B(-2, 1)$, and $C(7, 4)$.

In exercises 13 and 14, use the Distance Formula to determine whether or not the triangle is a right triangle.

13. $A(1, 4)$, $B(-2, -2)$, and $C(10, -8)$

14. $A(5, 7)$, $B(8, -5)$, and $C(-4, -4)$

15. Is it easier to use Definition 14-1 or Theorem 14-4 to show that a triangle is a right triangle?

16. Use the Distance Formula to show that $ABCD$ is a parallelogram if the vertices are $A(1, -5)$, $B(7, -1)$, $C(2, 0)$, and $D(-4, -4)$.

Activity

There is another way to determine points in a plane besides using Cartesian coordinates. For example, to locate P you could say,

"Travel at a 45° angle for 4 units."

The notation for this is represented by the ordered pair (4, 45°) or in general (r, θ) where θ represents the angle and r represents the distance from O to the given point.

Draw a ray $\overrightarrow{OM}$ (with O the origin) and then use your protractor to graph the following points:

1. (2, 30°)

2. (3, 90°)

3. (5, 90°)

4. (2.5, 120°)

5. (4, 42°)

6. (1, 180°)

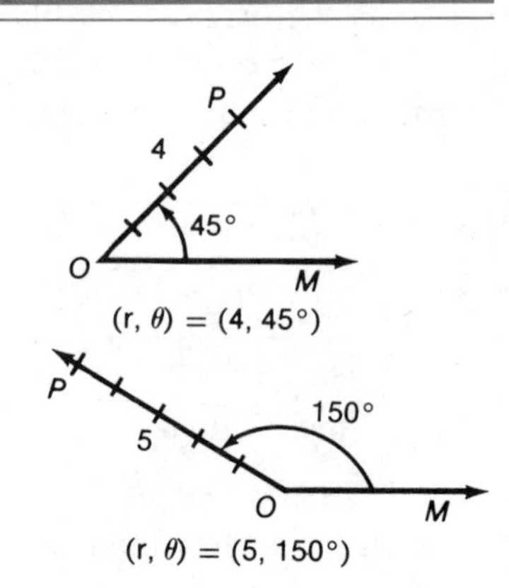

17. Find the length of the median $\overline{AD}$ in $\triangle ABC$ with vertices $A(2, 6)$, $B(3, -5)$, and $C(-1, 7)$.

In exercises 18–20, use the Distance Formula to determine if B is between A and C. (If B is between A and C, then $AB + BC = AC$.)

18. $A(-3, -7)$, $B(0, -2)$, $C(6, 8)$

19. $A(1, -2)$, $B(4, 3)$, $C(10, 12)$

20. $A(1, 4)$, $B(2, 3)$, $C(4, 1)$

B.

21. Find x if the distance between $(1, 2)$ and $(x, 8)$ is 10.

22. $ABCD$ is a rectangle inscribed in a circle with vertices $A(0, 0)$, $B(2, 1)$, $C(4, -3)$, and $D(2, -4)$. Find the length of the diameter of the circle.

23. Find the area of $\triangle ABC$ with vertices $A(-3, -4)$, $B(3, 4)$, and $C(-5, 0)$.

24. Find the area of $ABCD$ with vertices $A(-2, 3)$, $B(3, 8)$, $C(8, 3)$ and $D(3, -2)$.

C.

25. Find the coordinates of the point equidistant from $(3, 11)$, $(9, 5)$, and $(7, -1)$.

26. Find the coordinates of the point that is equidistant from $(0, 6)$ and $(10, 0)$ and lies on the line $y = x$.

27. Graph at least four points that satisfy the condition that the distance from the point $(1, 2)$ is always 5 units.

PROBLEM SOLVING

Consider a three-dimensional coordinate system with an x-axis, a y-axis, and a z-axis. A cube with each edge of 4 units is placed as shown in the diagram.

1. Find the length of $\overline{OP}$.

2. Find a formula for the length of $\overline{OP}$ in a cube of any size. (*Hint:* Let P have coordinates (x_1, y_1, z_1).)

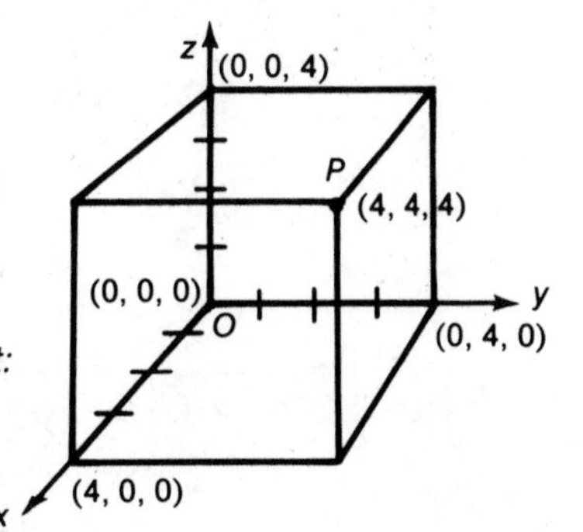

14–6 The Equation of a Line

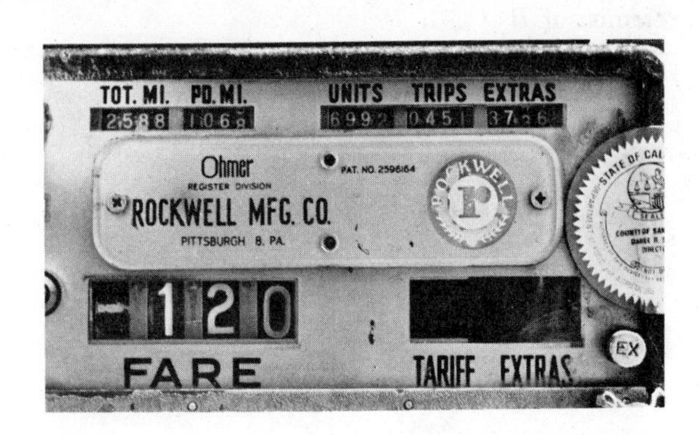

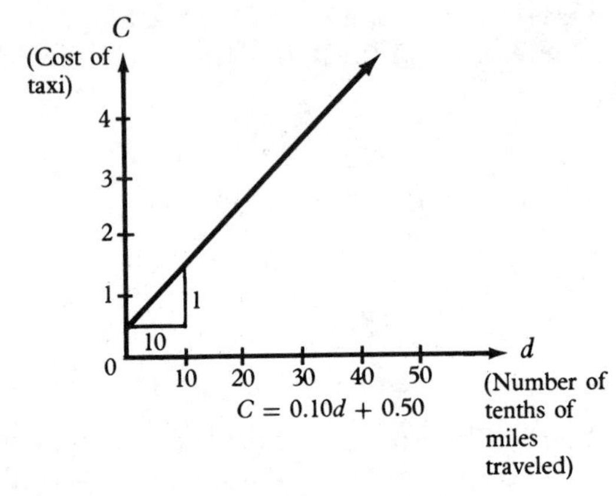

Relationships in our world can often be represented by a straight line graph. These relationships, such as the taxi fares shown above, are called *linear relationships.* Every linear relationship can be represented by an equation of the form $y = mx + b$ where the line cuts the y-axis at b and has slope m.

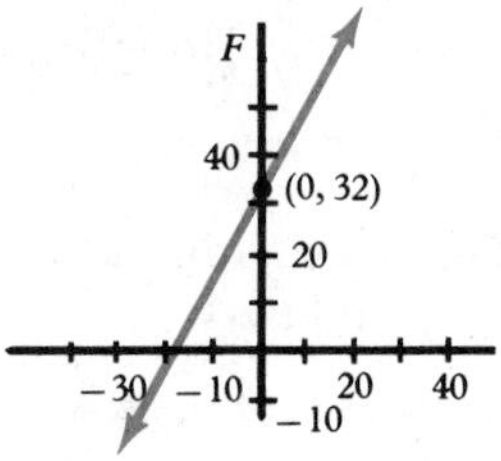

Example 1 The relationship between the Fahrenheit and the Celsius scales is given by the equation

$$F = \frac{9}{5}C + 32.$$

The slope is $\frac{9}{5}$. The F-intercept is 32.

Example 2 Suppose for every ounce of weight added to a spring it stretches an additional 0.5 inches. The relationship between the weight (x) and the length of the stretch (y) is given by the equation

$$y = 0.5x.$$

The slope is 0.5. The y-intercept is 0.

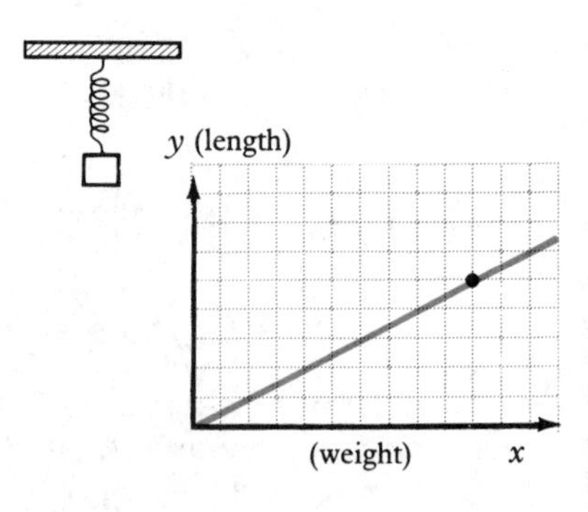

Theorem 14–5 Any straight line in the coordinate plane that is not parallel to the y-axis can be represented by the equation $y = mx + b$, where m is the slope and b is the y-intercept.

Example 1 Determine the slope and y-intercept of a line given an equation of the form $ax + by = c$.

Consider the equation $3x + 4y = 12$.
Solve for y. $3x + 4y = 12$

$$4y = -3x + 12$$
$$y = -\tfrac{3}{4}x + 3$$

Now read the slope and y-intercept. By Theorem 14–5

$$m = -\tfrac{3}{4} \text{ (the slope) and}$$
$$b = 3 \text{ (}y\text{-intercept).}$$

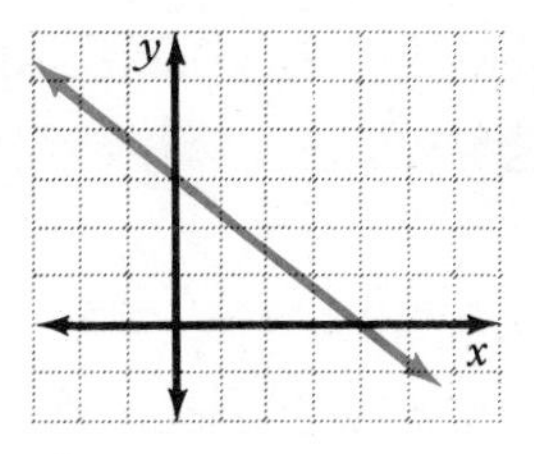

$3x + 4y = 12$

The following two examples illustrate how Theorem 14–5 can be used to find the equation of a line given certain conditions.

Example 2 Find the equation of a line given the slope of the line and a point on the line.

Consider a line with slope $\frac{2}{3}$ and a point $(-3, -4)$.

Step 1 The slope is determined by the equation $m = \dfrac{y_1 - y_2}{x_1 - x_2}$.
Consider the two points (x, y) and $(-3, -4)$ and obtain the equation

$$\frac{2}{3} = \frac{y - (-4)}{x - (-3)}.$$

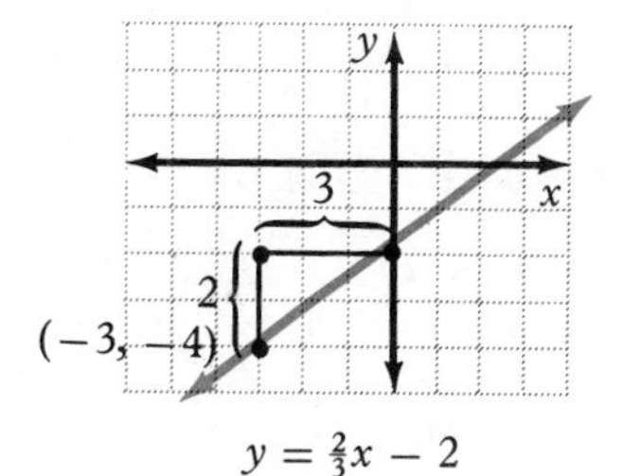

$y = \frac{2}{3}x - 2$

Step 2 Simplify the equation.

$$2(x - (-3)) = 3(y - (-4))$$
or $y = \frac{2}{3}x - 2$

Example 3 Find the equation of a line given two points on the line.

Consider a line which contains the points $(-3, 6)$ and $(1, 2)$.

Step 1 The slope $m = \dfrac{6 - 2}{-3 - 1} = \dfrac{4}{-4} = -1$

Step 2 Since the slope and a point are known, follow Example 2 using the points (x, y) and $(-3, 6)$.

$$-1 = \frac{y - 6}{x - (-3)} \text{ or } y = -x + 3$$

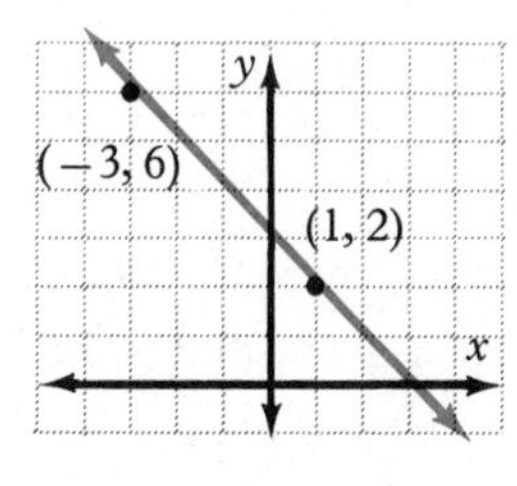

$y = -x + 3$

EXERCISES

A.

In exercises 1–6, write the equation of a line in the form $y = mx + b$.

1. $m = 2, b = 3$ **2.** $m = \frac{2}{3}, b = -2$ **3.** $m = -\frac{3}{4}, b = 5$

4. $m = -0.2, b = -2.5$ **5.** $m = 10, b = -4$ **6.** $m = 0, b = 2$

In exercises 7–10, graph the equation.

7. $y = x + 4$ **8.** $y = -2x - 3$

9. $y = \frac{3}{4}x - 5$ **10.** $y = -\frac{3}{2}x + 3$

In exercises 11–16, find the slope and y-intercept of each line and then graph the equation.

11. $y + 2x = 4$ **12.** $2y - x = 5$ **13.** $3x - 2y = 4$

14. $\frac{1}{2}y + \frac{1}{3}x = 1$ **15.** $5 - 3x = 2y$ **16.** $3x - 4y = 12$

In exercises 17-22, find the equation of the line given the slope and a point.

17. $m = 2, (1, -3)$ **18.** $m = -3, (-2, 1)$ **19.** $m = \frac{2}{3}, (0, 0)$

20. $m = -\frac{1}{2}, (4, 3)$ **21.** $m = \frac{3}{2}, (-3, -4)$ **22.** $m = -\frac{5}{2}, (0, 4)$

In exercises 23-28, find the equation of the line that contains the given points.

23. $(0, 0), (4, 3)$ **24.** $(-2, 1), (5, -3)$ **25.** $(0, 0), (-3, -3)$

26. $(0, -4), (6, 0)$ **27.** $(5, 2), (-3, 2)$ **28.** $(1, 3), (-4, -2)$

Activity

Identify two variables that you think have some relationship. For example:

a. a person's height and weight

b. the number of "at bats" and the number of "hits" for a baseball player

c. the circumference of various circles and corresponding diameters.

Then,

1. Graph the ordered pairs.

2. Draw a line that is the closest fit to the data.

3. Determine the slope and the intercept of the line.

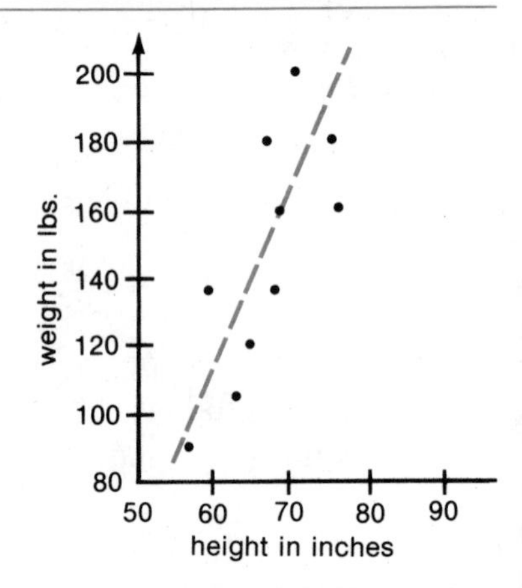

B.

In exercises 29–31, find the slope of a line that is perpendicular to the given line.

29. $y = -2x + 3$

30. $2x - 3y = 6$

31. $12x + 30y = 18$

32. The vertices of a triangle have coordinates $(0, 0)$, $(2, 4)$, and $(-4, 2)$. Find the equations of the sides of the triangle.

33. Find the point of intersection of the line $x - 3y = 1$ and the line containing the points $(1, 7)$ and $(6, -3)$.

34. If the x- and y-intercepts of a line are $(4, 0)$ and $(0, -3)$, what is the equation of the line?

35. Find the area of a triangle formed by the x-axis, the y-axis, and the line $y = x - 5$.

36. Find the equation of the median $\overline{AD}$ of $\triangle ABC$ with vertices $A(4, 4)$, $B(6, 2)$, and $C(-2, -4)$.

37. Find the equations of the diagonals of rectangle $ABCD$ with vertices $A(-6, -4)$, $B(-6, 2)$, $C(3, 2)$, and $D(3, -4)$.

38. Find the equation of the altitude $\overline{AD}$ of $\triangle ABC$ with vertices $A(-1, 5)$, $B(-7, -3)$, and $C(5, 1)$.

39. Find the equation of the line that is the perpendicular bisector of the segment $\overline{AB}$ with endpoints $A(10, 2)$ and $B(2, -6)$.

40. Find the equation of the line that contains the point $(4, 2)$ and is perpendicular to the line $y = -2x - 4$.

C.

41. A diagonal of a square lies on the line $3x - 5y = 14$. One vertex is at $(0, 4)$. Find the equation of the other diagonal.

42. The equations of two adjacent sides of a parallelogram are $x + 2y - 4 = 0$ and $3x + y + 3 = 0$. One vertex has coordinates $(8, -7)$. Find the equations of the other two sides.

43. Find the distance between the parallel lines with equations $y = -1x + 10$ and $y = -1x + 15$. (*Hint:* Draw an accurate diagram.)

44. The coordinates of $\triangle ABC$ are $A(0, 0)$, $B(6, 0)$, and $C(4, 6)$. $\overline{AD}$ is an altitude to $\overline{BC}$. Find the coordinates of D.

45. The coordinates of the vertices of a triangle are $(0, 0)$, $(18, 0)$, and $(6, 12)$. Find the coordinates of the centroid (the point of intersection of the medians).

PROBLEM SOLVING

Find the distance between the point $(2, 1)$ and the line $3x - 4y = 0$. (*Hint:* Draw an accurate figure and label the distance you are asked to find.)

14–7 The Equation of a Circle

Suppose a coordinate system is assigned so that the girl is at the origin. How could the path of the model airplane be described mathematically? The theorem in this lesson will help to answer this question.

In the examples below, show that the points are on the circle. This can be done by showing that the coordinates of the points satisfy the equation given for the circle.

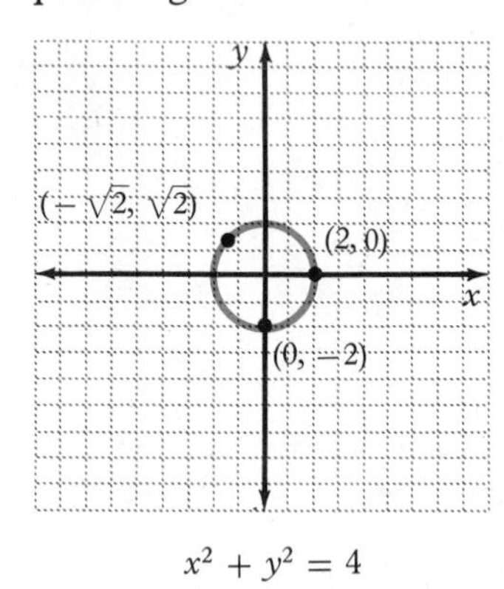

$x^2 + y^2 = 4$

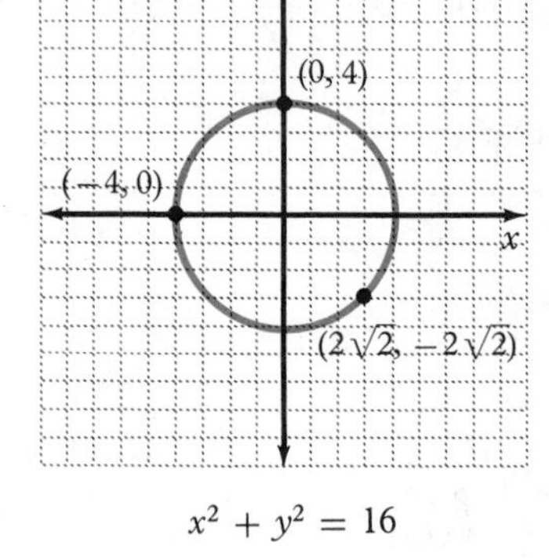

$x^2 + y^2 = 16$

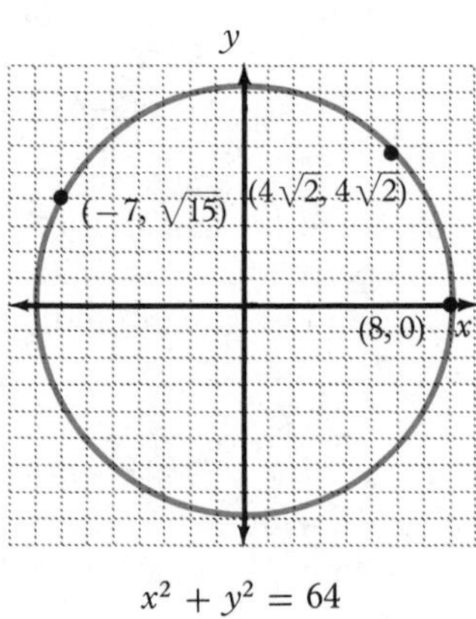

$x^2 + y^2 = 64$

Consider the circle on the right with its center at the origin and a radius of 5 units. Suppose (x, y) is a point on the circle. The Distance Formula tells us that

$$\sqrt{(x - 0)^2 + (y - 0)^2} = 5.$$

Hence $x^2 + y^2 = 25$, which is the equation of the circle.

This suggests the following theorem.

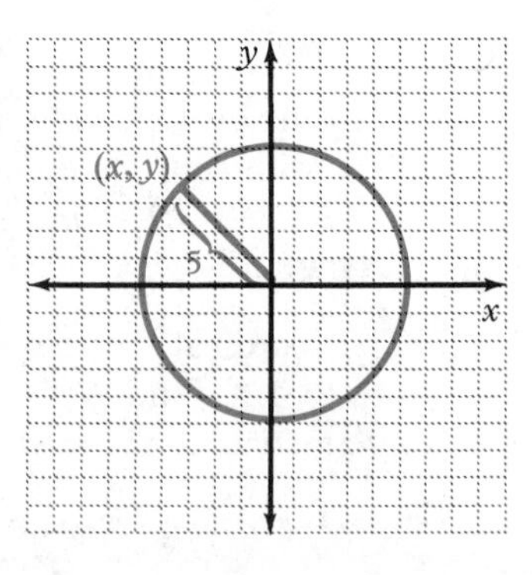

Theorem 14–6 The graph of the equation $x^2 + y^2 = r^2$ is a circle with radius r and center at the origin.

APPLICATION

Consider the girl flying the model airplane as described at the beginning of this section. If the girl is at the origin and if the string is 15 feet long, then by Theorem 14–6, the path of the plane is described by the equation

$$x^2 + y^2 = 225.$$

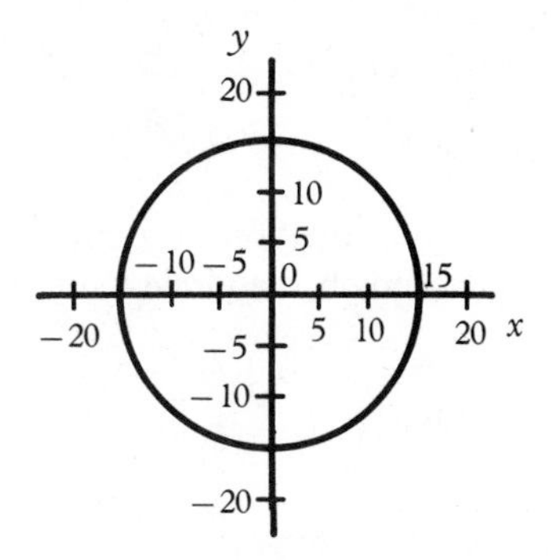

In the examples below, show that the points are on the circles. The coordinates of the center of the circle are given in red.

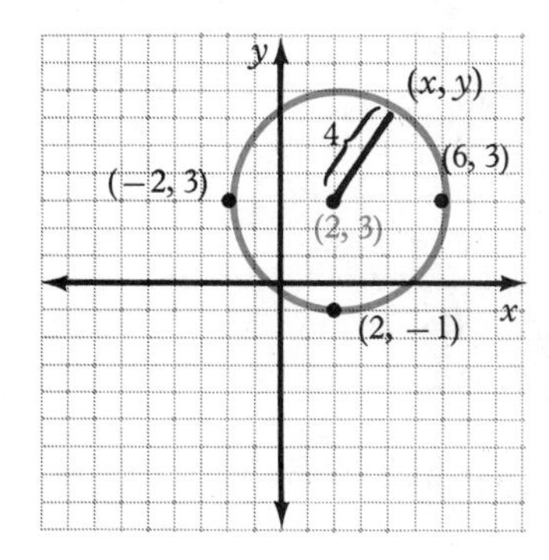

$(x - 2)^2 + (y - 3)^2 = 16$

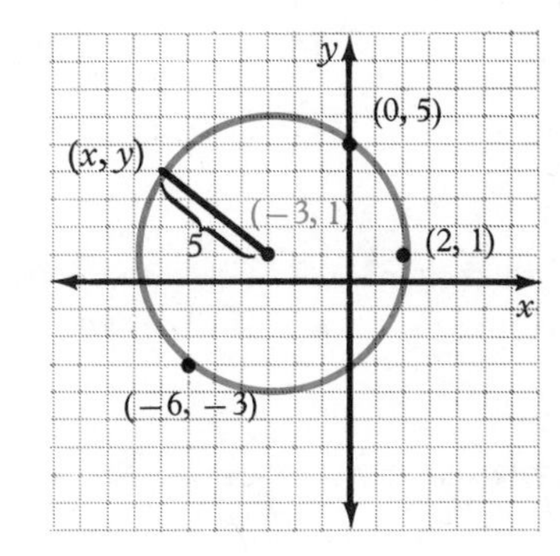

$(x - (-3))^2 + (y - 1)^2 = 25$
or $(x + 3)^2 + (y - 1)^2 = 25$

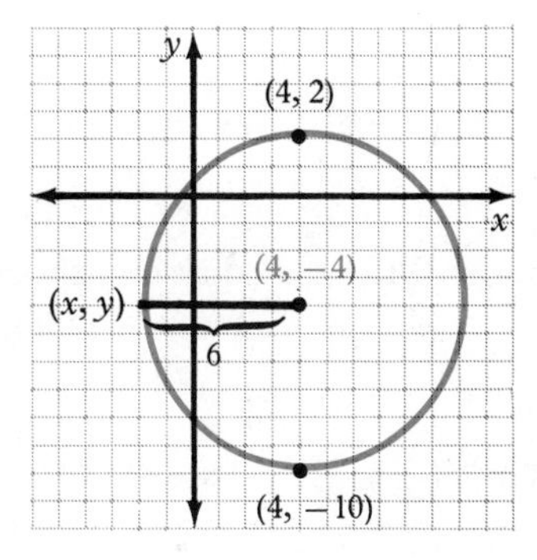

$(x - 4)^2 + (y - (-4))^2 = 36$
or $(x - 4)^2 + (y + 4)^2 = 36$

Suppose the circle on the right has a center at the point (h, k) and has a radius of r units. The Distance Formula tells us that

$$\sqrt{(x - h)^2 + (y - k)^2} = r.$$

Hence, the equation of the circle is

$$(x - h)^2 + (y - k)^2 = r^2.$$

We now state the following theorem.

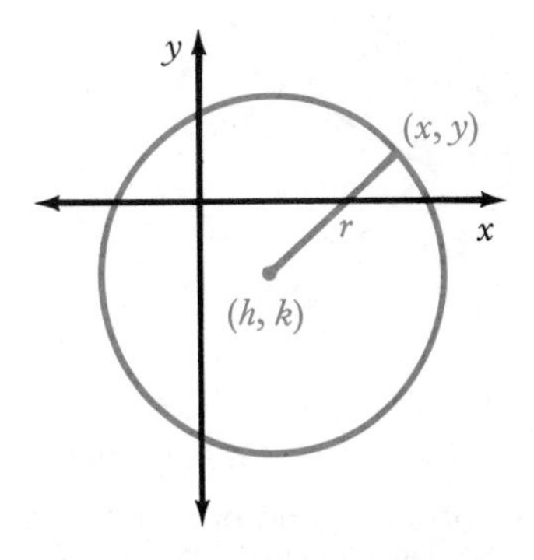

Theorem 14–7 The graph of the equation $(x - h)^2 + (y - k)^2 = r^2$ is a circle with radius r and center at the point (h, k).

EXERCISES

A.

In exercises 1–9, write the equation of a circle with the given center and radius. Then graph the circle using your compass.

1. (0, 0); 5
2. (0, 0); 2
3. (0, 0); 6
4. (0, 0); 4
5. (2, 3); 6
6. (−3, −4); 4
7. (5, 2); $\sqrt{2}$
8. (−4, 6); 2.5
9. (0, −4); 5

In exercises 10–17, find the center and the radius of the circle.

10. $x^2 + y^2 = 25$
11. $x^2 + y^2 = 36$
12. $x^2 + y^2 = 20$
13. $(x - (-3))^2 + (y - 4)^2 = 25$
14. $(x + 4)^2 + (y - 2)^2 = 10$
15. $x^2 + (y - 3)^2 = 12$
16. $(x + 2)^2 + y^2 = 9$
17. $(x + 2)^2 + (y + 4)^2 = 36$

B.

18. Write the equation of a circle with center at (−4, 0) and containing the origin.

19. Write the equation of a circle with center at (3, 4) and containing the origin.

Activity

An ellipse is a figure closely related to a circle. Study the definition below.

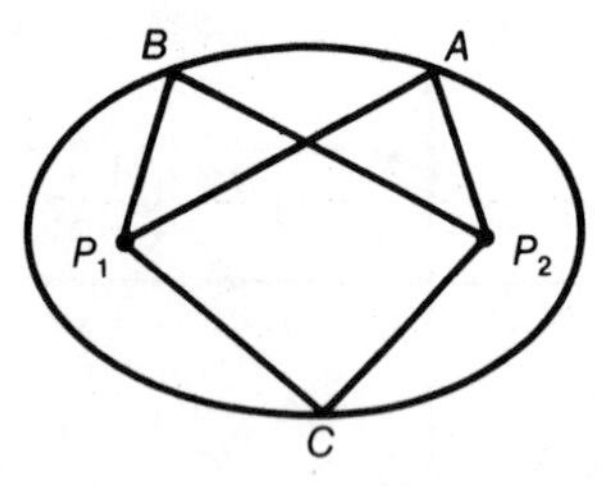

P_1 and P_2 are fixed points. The sum of the distances from any point on the curve to P_1 and P_2 is always the same. That is, $P_1B + BP_2 = P_1A + AP_2 = P_1C + CP_2$.

An *ellipse* is the set of points in which the sum of the distances from two fixed points (P_1 and P_2) to a point on the curve is a constant.

Here is how you can draw an ellipse.

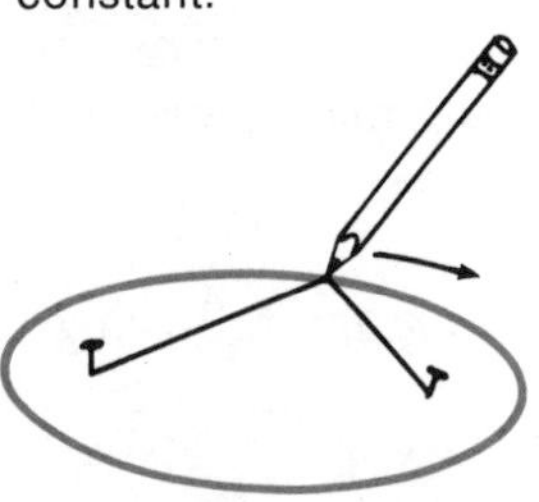

1. Fix two points with tacks.
2. Tie one end of a string to one tack and the other end to the second tack.
3. Move the pencil as suggested in the picture.

Draw several ellipses by changing the distance between the tacks and by changing the length of the string. When does the ellipse look more like a circle?

20. Write the equation of a circle with center at $(-2, 3)$ and containing the point $(3, 3)$.

21. Write the equation of a circle with a diameter whose endpoints are $(-4, 0)$ and $(2, 0)$.

22. Write the equation of a circle with a diameter whose endpoints are $(3, 6)$ and $(3, -2)$.

23. Write the equation of a circle with a diameter whose endpoints are $(-4, 8)$ and $(6, 2)$.

24. Write the equation of a line that is tangent to the circle $x^2 + y^2 = 25$ at the point $(-3, 4)$. (Remember that the tangent is perpendicular to the radius.)

25. Write the equation of the line of centers for the circles $(x + 4)^2 + (y - 2)^2 = 36$ and $(x - 5)^2 + (y + 3)^2 = 17$.

26. Write the equation of the circle with center at $(-5, -5)$ and tangent to both the x- and y-axis.

27. Write the equation of a circle that has the same center as the circle $(x + 4)^2 + (y - 3)^2 = 9$ and is tangent to the y-axis.

C.

28. Find the equation of the circle whose center is on the line $y = \frac{1}{2}x$ and that contains the points $(0, 6)$ and $(0, -2)$.

29. Write the equation of the circle with center at $(1, 7)$ and tangent to the line $x + 3y = 12$.

30. Find the length of a tangent from $(6, 4)$ to the circle $x^2 + y^2 = 36$.

PROBLEM SOLVING

Suppose a sphere with center at (0, 0, 0) contains the point $P(4, 4, 4)$ in a three-dimensional coordinate system. Write the equation that represents the sphere.

Write the equation of the sphere with center at (1, 3, 2) and containing the point (4, −2, 3).

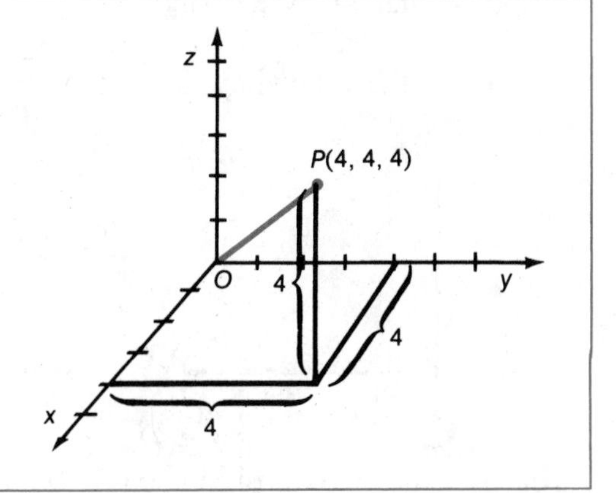

14–8 Using Coordinates to Prove Theorems

Some theorems can be easily proved using coordinates; however, it is very important to choose the coordinates carefully. Study the following two examples.

Example 1

Consider the theorem:

The diagonals of a rectangle are congruent.

Which of the following placements of the rectangles seems the best?

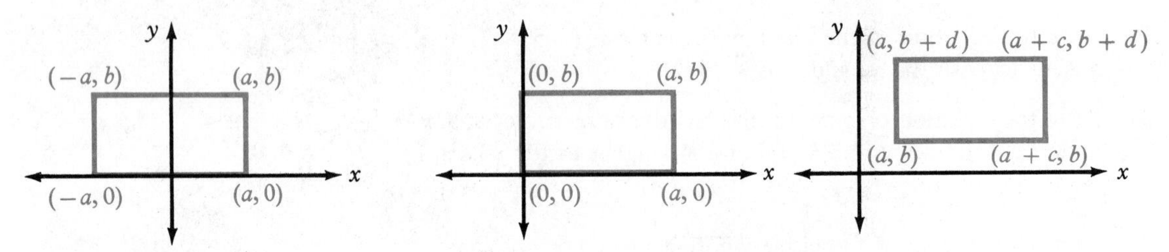

The theorem could be proved using the Distance Formula with any of the three positions. However, the middle figure may be the easiest to use since the coordinates needed have more zeroes.

Example 2

Consider this theorem:

The median to the base of an isosceles right triangle is perpendicular to the base.

Which of the following placements of an isosceles right triangle seems best to you?

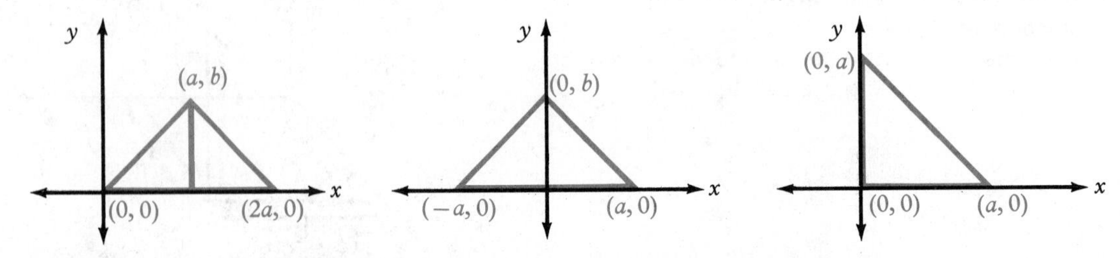

Each of the three positions could be used to prove the theorem. However, we will use the position on the right in the proof on the next page.

Example 3 Theorem: The diagonals of a rectangle are congruent.

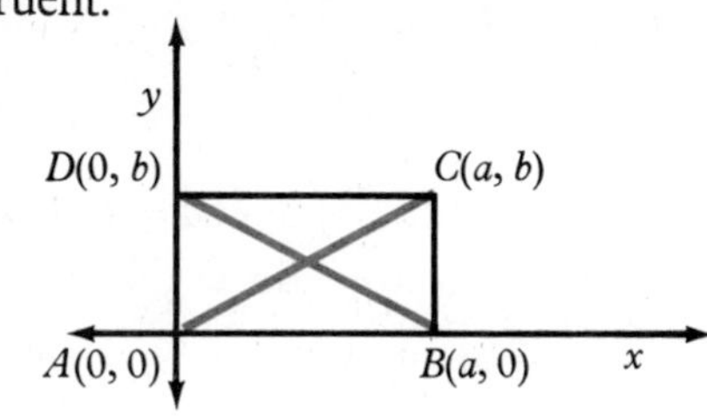

PROOF

Given: $ABCD$ is a rectangle with coordinates $A(0, 0)$, $B(a, 0)$, $C(a, b)$, $D(0, b)$ and diagonals $\overline{AC}$ and $\overline{BD}$.

Prove: $AC = BD$

Statements	Reasons
1. $ABCD$ is a rectangle with $A(0, 0)$, $B(a, 0)$, $C(a, b)$, $D(0, b)$.	1. Given
2. $AC = \sqrt{(a - 0)^2 + (b - 0)^2}$	2. Distance Formula
3. $AC = \sqrt{a^2 + b^2}$	3. Properties of numbers
4. $BD = \sqrt{(a - 0)^2 + (0 - b)^2}$	4. Why?
5. $BD = \sqrt{a^2 + b^2}$	5. Properties of numbers
6. $AC = BD$	6. Why?

Example 4 Theorem: The median to the base of an isosceles right triangle is perpendicular to the base.

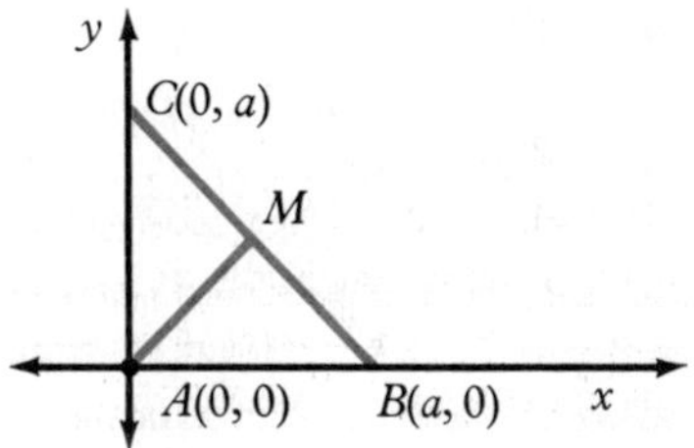

PROOF

Given: Isosceles right triangle ABC with $A(0, 0)$, $B(a, 0)$, $C(0, a)$ and $BM = MC$.

Prove: $\overline{AM} \perp \overline{BC}$

Statements	Reasons
1. Isosceles right triangle ABC with $A(0, 0)$, $B(a, 0)$, $C(0, a)$	1. Given
2. The coordinates of M are $\left(\frac{a}{2}, \frac{a}{2}\right)$.	2. Midpoint Formula (Theorem 14–1)
3. Slope of $\overline{AM} = \dfrac{\frac{a}{2} - 0}{\frac{a}{2} - 0} = 1$	3. Definition of slope
4. Slope of $\overline{BC} = \dfrac{a - 0}{0 - a} = -1$	4. Definition of slope
5. Slope of $\overline{AM}$ · slope of $\overline{BC} = (1)(-1) = -1$	5. Properties of numbers
6. $\overline{AM} \perp \overline{BC}$	6. Why?

EXERCISES

A.

In exercises 1–5, draw a coordinate system and position the figure. Give a statement about the figure that could be proved.

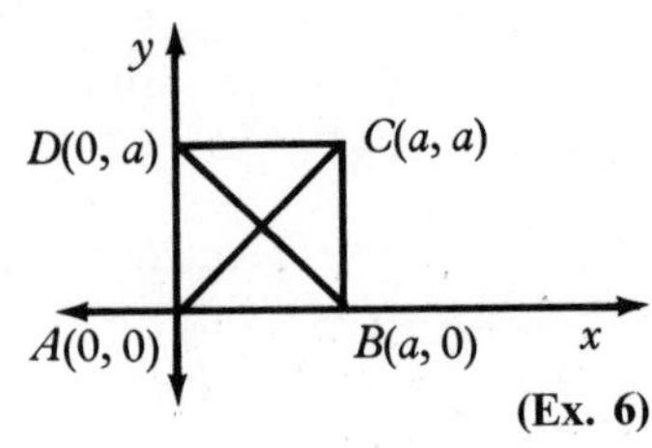

1. square
2. equilateral triangle
3. parallelogram
4. isosceles trapezoid
5. a trapezoid $ABCD$ with $\overline{AB} \parallel \overline{CD}$ and $m\angle A = m\angle D = 90$
6. **Given:** $ABCD$ is a square with $A(0,0)$, $B(a,0)$, $C(a,a)$, and $D(0,a)$.
   Prove: $AC = BD$

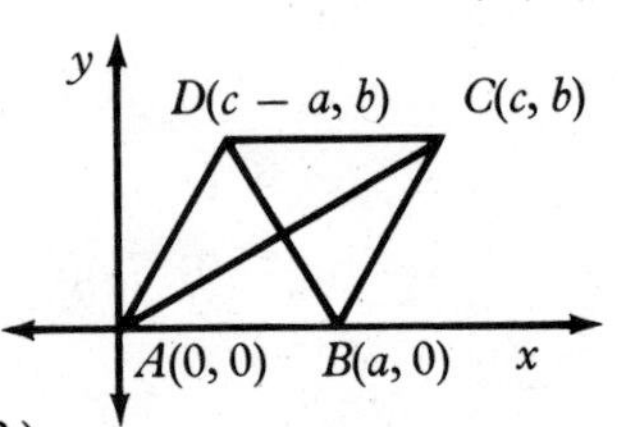

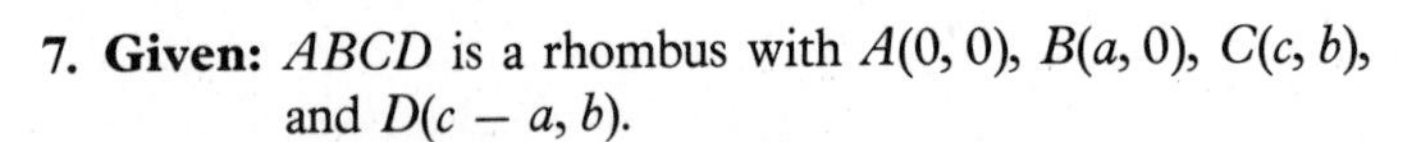

7. **Given:** $ABCD$ is a rhombus with $A(0,0)$, $B(a,0)$, $C(c,b)$, and $D(c-a,b)$.
   Prove: $\overline{AC} \perp \overline{BD}$
   (*Hint:* Show slope of $\overline{AC}$ · slope of $\overline{BD} = -1$. Remember $AD = AB$.)

Activity

Obtain styrofoam cones (or cones made of some other material). Slice the cones in various ways as suggested below. Note the type of figure formed.

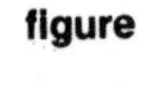

1. Slice a section parallel to the base. The figure formed is a *circle.*

circle

2. Slice a section that is not parallel to the base and does not intersect the base. The figure formed is called an *ellipse.* (See previous activity.)

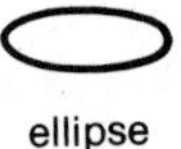

ellipse

3. Slice a section parallel to the slant edge of the cone. The figure formed is called a *parabola.*

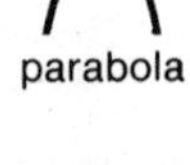

parabola

4. Slice a section perpendicular to the base. The figure formed is called a *hyperbola.*

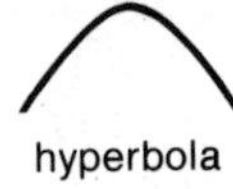

hyperbola

Can you see why these figures are called conics?

8. Given: $ABCD$ is a parallelogram with $A(0, 0)$, $B(a, 0)$, $C(c, b)$, and $D(c - a, b)$.

Prove: $\overline{AC}$ and $\overline{BD}$ bisect each other.

9. Given: Circle with center at the origin and chord $\overline{AB}$ with coordinates $(0, a)$ and $(a, 0)$

Prove: The perpendicular bisector of a chord of a circle contains the center.

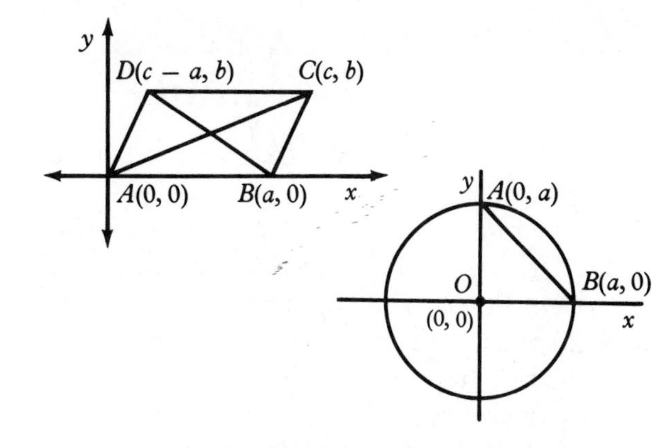

B.

10. Prove: The diagonals of a square are perpendicular. (Assign your coordinate system as shown in exercise 6.)

11. Prove: The diagonals of an isosceles trapezoid $ABCD$ are congruent. (Assign the vertices $A(0, 0)$, $B(a, 0)$, $C(c, b)$, and $D(a - c, b)$.)

12. Prove: The midpoint of the hypotenuse of a right triangle ABC is equidistant from the vertices. (Assign the vertices $A(0, 0)$, $B(a, 0)$, and $C(0, b)$.)

13. Prove: If the diagonals of parallelogram $ABCD$ are congruent, the parallelogram is a rectangle. (Assign the vertices $A(0, 0)$, $B(a, 0)$, $C(c, b)$ and $D(c - a, b)$.)

C.

14. Prove: If the diagonals of a trapezoid $ABCD$ are congruent, then the legs of the trapezoid are congruent.

15. Prove: The line segment joining the midpoints of two sides of a triangle is equal to one half of the third side and is parallel to it.

PROBLEM SOLVING

The following problem appeared on a college entrance examination. The intended answer was 7 faces. However, a high school student argued that 7 faces was not the correct answer. Was he right? If so, what is the correct answer?

In pyramids *ABCD* and *EFGHI* all faces except base *FGHI* are congruent equilateral triangles. If face *ABC* were placed on face *EFG* so that the vertices of the triangle coincide, how many exposed faces would the resulting solid have?

a. 5 b. 6 c. 7 d. 8 e. 9

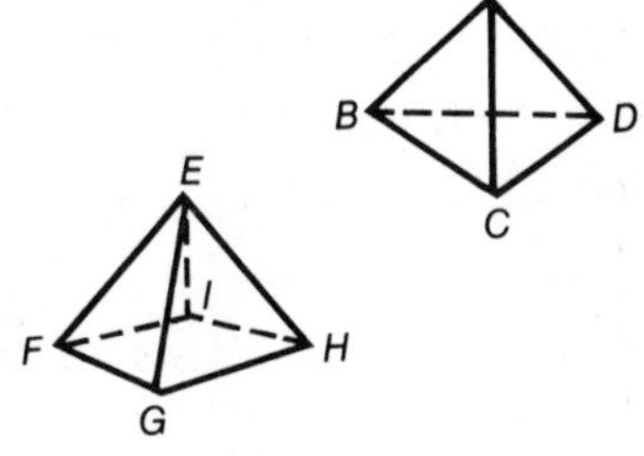

14–9 Transformations and Coordinate Geometry

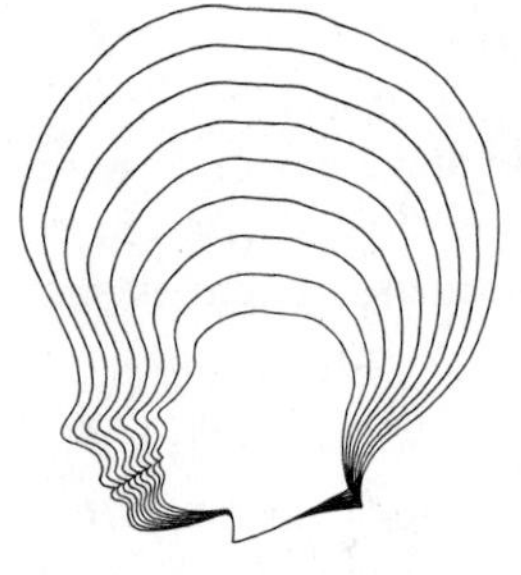

These pictures were generated by a computer at the University of Connecticut (see *Scientific American*, February 1980). The computer used a special type of transformation to show the sequence (top picture) that proceeds from infancy (inside profile) to adulthood (outside profile). A different type of transformation was used to produce the sequence (bottom picture) that proceeds from a "Neanderthal Man" (inside profile) to a futuristic being (outside profile). Transformations help simulate growth and changes in the body characteristics of people so they may be studied by scientists.

The effects of simple transformations, such as translations, reflections, rotations, and others, can be shown on a coordinate axis. Study this example.

Example: To graph a figure and its image after a transformation, when the transformation rule is $(x, y) \rightarrow (x + 4, y + 5)$.

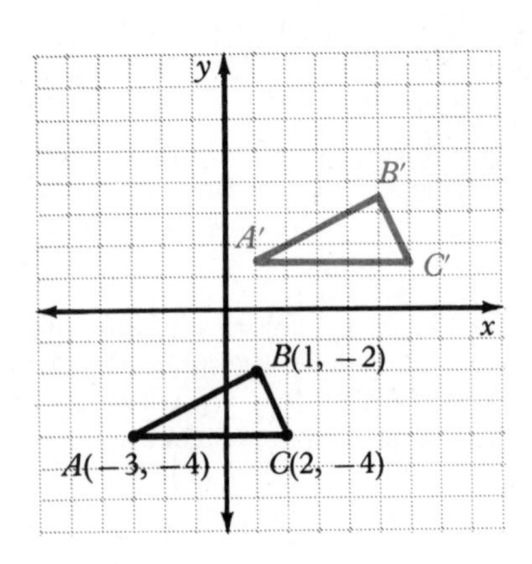

Step 1 Graph a figure, for example $\triangle ABC$.
$A(-3, -4)$ $B(1, -2)$ $C(2, -4)$

Step 2 Apply the transformation rule to points A, B, and C to get image points A', B', and C'.

$(x, y) \longrightarrow (x + 4, y + 5)$

$(-3, -4) \longrightarrow (1, 1)$

$(1, -2) \longrightarrow (5, 3)$

$(2, -4) \longrightarrow (6, 1)$

Step 3 Graph the image of $\triangle ABC$, that is, $\triangle A'B'C'$.

This transformation is a translation.

EXERCISES

A.

Graph each figure and its image using the transformation rule given in exercises 1-3.

1. Figure: Triangle ABC, $A(-6, 3)$, $B(-4, 5)$, $C(-3, 4)$
Transformation Rule: $(x, y) \rightarrow (x + 4, y + 3)$

2. Figure: Triangle DEF, $D(2, 1)$, $E(3, 4)$, $F(1, 5)$
Transformation Rule: $(x, y) \rightarrow (-x, y)$

3. Figure: Triangle PQR, $P(7, 1)$, $Q(7, 4)$, $R(5, 2)$
Transformation Rule: $(x, y) \rightarrow (-y, x)$

4. For exercises 1-3, tell whether the transformation is a translation, a rotation, or a reflection. If it is a translation, give the distance the figure is translated. If it is a reflection, specify the line of reflection. If it is a rotation, specify the center and the number of degrees.

B.

For exercises 5-7, graph the quadrilateral and its image. Then answer the questions.

5. Quadrilateral: $A(1, 1)$, $B(1, 2)$, $C(2, 1)$, $D(2, 2)$.
Transformation Rule: $(x, y) \rightarrow (3x, 3y)$
This transformation is called a *magnification*. How do the lengths of the sides of the figure compare with the lengths of the sides of the image? How do the areas compare?

6. Quadrilateral: $P(1, 2)$, $Q(1, 3)$, $R(3, 3)$, $S(3, 2)$
Transformation Rule: $(x, y) \rightarrow (x + 3y, y)$
This transformation is called a *shear*. How does the area of the image compare with the area of the quadrilateral?

7. Quadrilateral: $W(4, -1)$, $X(3, 2)$, $Y(-3, 2)$, $Z(-2, 1)$
Transformation Rule: $(x, y) \rightarrow (\frac{1}{2}x, 2y)$
This transformation is called a *stretch*. How does it change a figure? How do the areas compare?

C.

8. Make up some transformation rules and graph the figure and its image to see how the figure is transformed. Can you make a rule that "shrinks" a figure?

Important Ideas—Chapter 14

Terms

Cartesian coordinate system (p. 505)
Slope of a line (p. 512)

Theorems

14-1 If the coordinates of the segment $\overline{P_1P_2}$ are (x_1, y_1) and (x_2, y_2), then the coordinates of the midpoint of $\overline{P_1P_2}$ are $\left(\frac{x_1 + x_2}{2}, \frac{y_1 + y_2}{2}\right)$.

14-2 The product of the slopes of two perpendicular lines is -1. (Assuming neither line is parallel to the y-axis.)

14-3 The slopes of two parallel lines are equal. (Assuming neither line is parallel to the y-axis.)

14-4 **The Distance Formula.** If A has coordinates (x_1, y_1) and B has coordinates (x_2, y_2), then $AB = \sqrt{(x_1 - x_2)^2 + (y_1 - y_2)^2}$.

14-5 Any straight line in the coordinate plane that is not parallel to the y-axis can be represented by the equation $y = mx + b$, where m is the slope and b is the y-intercept.

14-6 The graph of the equation $x^2 + y^2 = r^2$ is a circle with radius r and center at the origin.

14-7 The graph of the equation $(x - h)^2 + (y - k)^2 = r^2$ is a circle with radius r and center at the point (h, k).

Chapter 14—Review

1. Find the distances between the coordinates.

   a. $(1, 2)$ and $(5, 8)$ **b.** $(-3, 4)$ and $(5, -2)$

   c. $(-4, -2)$ and $(2, -2)$

2. Find the slopes of the lines containing the coordinates in exercise 1.

3. Find the midpoints of the segments determined by the coordinates in exercise 1.

4. Find the equation of a line that contains the point $(2, -4)$ with a slope of -3.

5. Find the equation of a line that contains the point $(4, 1)$ and is parallel to the line $3x + 4y = 2$.

6. Show that $(8, -5)$, $(0, -7)$, and $(5, 7)$ are the vertices of a right triangle.

7. Find the missing coordinate so that $\overleftrightarrow{AB} \parallel \overleftrightarrow{CD}$ for $A(2, 5)$, $B(4, -2)$, $C(-3, -4)$ and $D(6, x)$.

8. Find the missing coordinate so that $\overleftrightarrow{AB} \perp \overleftrightarrow{CD}$ for $A(-4, -5)$, $B(7, -2)$, $C(-4, 6)$ and $D(x, 0)$.

9. Give the center and radius of the circle with equation $(x - 2)^2 + (y + 3)^2 = 24$.

10. Write the equation of a circle with center at the origin which passes through the point $(4, 3)$.

11. **Given:** $ABCD$ is a square with vertices $A(0, 0)$, $B(a, 0)$, $C(a, a)$, and $D(0, a)$.

    Prove: $\overline{AC} \perp \overline{BD}$

12. **Given:** Figure $WXYZ$ with vertices $W(0, 0)$, $X(a, 0)$, $Y(a + b, c)$, and $Z(b, c)$

    Prove: $WXYZ$ is a parallelogram.

Chapter 14—Test

1. Find the distances between the coordinates.

   a. $(3, 6)$ and $(-6, -3)$ b. $(-4, 0)$ and $(0, -4)$ c. $(-2, 5)$ and $(-2, -1)$

2. Find the slopes of the lines containing the coordinates in exercise 1.

3. Find the midpoints of the segments determined by the coordinates in exercise 1.

4. Find the equation of a line that contains the points $(-3, 5)$ and $(2, -4)$.

5. Find the equation of a line that contains the point $(3, 5)$ and is perpendicular to the line $2x + 6y = -3$.

6. Show that $(4, 5)$, $(6, 4)$, $(3, -1)$, and $(1, 0)$ are the coordinates of the vertices of a parallelogram.

7. Find the missing coordinate so that $\overleftrightarrow{AB} \parallel \overleftrightarrow{CD}$ for $A(-4, 2)$, $B(-1, -3)$, $C(6, 2)$, and $D(x, -4)$.

8. Find the missing coordinate so that $\overleftrightarrow{AB} \perp \overleftrightarrow{CD}$ for $A(5, -3)$, $B(-2, 4)$, $C(3, 3)$, and $D(-7, x)$.

9. Write an equation of a circle with center at $(2, 3)$ and radius 6.

10. Write the equation of a circle with center at the origin which passes through the point $(-5, 12)$.

11. **Given:** Isosceles triangle ABC with vertices $C(b, c)$, $A(0, 0)$, $B(2b, 0)$ and midpoints E and D of $\overline{AC}$ and $\overline{BC}$ respectively.

    Prove: $AD = BE$

12. **Given:** Figure $ABCD$ with vertices $A(-b, 0)$, $B(0, a)$, $C(b, 0)$, and $D(0, -a)$

    Prove: $ABCD$ is a rhombus.

Cumulative Review (Chapters 11–14)

1. Find the area of a square inscribed in a circle with a diameter of 10 cm.
2. Find the area of an isosceles triangle with a base of 8 cm and each of the equal sides being 5 cm.
3. Find the area of an equilateral triangle if its perimeter is 12 cm.
4. If the ratio of the perimeter of two similar triangles is 2:1, what is the ratio of their areas?
5. Find the area of a regular hexagon inscribed in a circle with a radius of 6 cm.
6. If a prism has an altitude of 6 m and a base with an area of 12 m^2, what is its volume?
7. If a pyramid has a base that is a square 3 m on a side and an altitude of 7 m, what is the volume of the pyramid?
8. Find the surface area of a right circular cylinder if its height is 10 cm and its base has a diameter of 4 cm. (Use $\pi = 3.14$.)
9. Find the volume of the cylinder given in exercise 8.
10. If a triangle ABC with vertices $A(3, 5)$, $B(5, -2)$, and $C(-4, 3)$ were reflected about the y-axis, what would be the coordinates of its image?
11. If a triangle ABC with vertices $A(4, -2)$, $B(-3, -7)$, and $C(1, 6)$ were reflected about the x-axis, what would be the coordinates of its image?
12. Give the equations of the lines of symmetry of the square with vertices (1, 1), (5, 1), (5, 5), and (1, 5).
13. If the point (2, 6) is rotated 180° about the origin, what would be the coordinates of its image?
14. Find the length of the hypotenuse of the right triangle with vertices at (6, 8), (9, −4), and (1, −6).
15. Find the equation of a line that contains the points (2, −6) and (−4, 3).

Symbols

$\overleftrightarrow{AB}$	line AB (page 12)
$\parallel$	is parallel to (page 13)
$\overline{AB}$	segment AB (page 16)
$\overrightarrow{AB}$	ray AB (page 16)
$\angle ABC$	angle ABC (page 17)
$\triangle ABC$	triangle ABC (page 17)
$\odot O$	circle O (page 17)
AB	length of segment AB (page 20)
$\cong$	is congruent to (page 20)
$m\angle ABC$	measure of $\angle ABC$ (page 20)
$\ncong$	is not congruent to (page 22)
$\perp$	is perpendicular to (page 28)
$p \rightarrow q$	p implies q (page 56)
$\sim p$	not p (page 60)
$p \leftrightarrow q$	p if and only if q (page 61)
$\nparallel$	is not parallel to (page 175)
$\not\perp$	is not perpendicular to (page 160)
$\neq$	is not equal to (page 161)
$\sqrt{}$	square root (page 227)
$\sim$	is similar to (page 313)
$\doteq$	is approximately equal to (page 331)
$\widehat{AB}$	minor arc determined by A and B (page 346)
$\widehat{ACB}$	major arc determined by A and B (page 346)
$m\widehat{AB}$	measure of $\widehat{AB}$ (page 346)
$A(R)$	area of region R (page 394)
$P(x, y)$	point P with coordinates x and y (page 505)

Table of Squares and Square Roots

N	N^2	$\sqrt{N}$	N	N^2	$\sqrt{N}$	N	N^2	$\sqrt{N}$	N	N^2	$\sqrt{N}$
1	1	1.000	26	676	5.099	51	2,601	7.141	76	5,776	8.718
2	4	1.414	27	729	5.196	52	2,704	7.211	77	5,929	8.775
3	9	1.732	28	784	5.292	53	2,809	7.280	78	6,084	8.832
4	16	2.000	29	841	5.385	54	2,916	7.348	79	6,241	8.888
5	25	2.236	30	900	5.477	55	3,025	7.416	80	6,400	8.944
6	36	2.449	31	961	5.568	56	3,136	7.483	81	6,561	9.000
7	49	2.646	32	1,024	5.657	57	3,249	7.550	82	6,724	9.055
8	64	2.828	33	1,089	5.745	58	3,364	7.616	83	6,889	9.110
9	81	3.000	34	1,156	5.831	59	3,481	7.681	84	7,056	9.165
10	100	3.162	35	1,225	5.916	60	3,600	7.746	85	7,225	9.220
11	121	3.317	36	1,296	6.000	61	3,721	7.810	86	7,396	9.274
12	144	3.464	37	1,369	6.083	62	3,844	7.874	87	7,569	9.327
13	169	3.606	38	1,444	6.164	63	3,969	7.937	88	7,744	9.381
14	196	3.742	39	1,521	6.245	64	4,096	8.000	89	7,921	9.434
15	225	3.873	40	1,600	6.325	65	4,225	8.062	90	8,100	9.487
16	256	4.000	41	1,681	6.403	66	4,356	8.124	91	8,281	9.539
17	289	4.123	42	1,764	6.481	67	4,489	8.185	92	8,464	9.592
18	324	4.243	43	1,849	6.557	68	4,624	8.246	93	8,649	9.644
19	361	4.359	44	1,936	6.633	69	4,761	8.307	94	8,836	9.695
20	400	4.472	45	2,025	6.708	70	4,900	8.367	95	9,025	9.747
21	441	4.583	46	2,116	6.782	71	5,041	8.426	96	9,216	9.798
22	484	4.690	47	2,209	6.856	72	5,184	8.485	97	9,409	9.849
23	529	4.796	48	2,304	6.928	73	5,329	8.544	98	9,604	9.899
24	576	4.899	49	2,401	7.000	74	5,476	8.602	99	9,801	9.950
25	625	5.000	50	2,500	7.071	75	5,625	8.660	100	10,000	10.000

Postulates and Theorems

Postulates

Points Existence Postulate. Space exists and contains at least four noncoplanar, noncollinear points. A plane contains at least three noncollinear points. A line contains at least two points. (page 68)

Point-Line Postulate. Two points are contained in one and only one line. (page 68)

Point-Plane Postulate. Three noncollinear points are contained in one and only one plane. (page 68)

Plane Intersection Postulate. If two planes intersect, then they intersect in exactly one line. (page 68)

Two Points, Line, Plane Postulate. If two points are in a plane, then the line containing them is in the plane. (page 69)

Plane Separation Postulate. Let N be a plane and ℓ a line in N. The points of the plane not on ℓ form two half-planes such that
a. each half-plane is a convex set.
b. if P is in one half-plane and Q is in the other, then $\overline{PQ}$ intersects ℓ. (page 69)

Space Separation Postulate. Let N be a plane in space. The points of space not on N form two half-spaces such that
a. each half-space is a convex set.
b. if a point A is in one half-space and B is in the other, $\overline{AB}$ intersects N. (page 69)

Perpendicular Postulate. Given a point and a line in a plane, there is exactly one line through the point perpendicular to the given line. Given a plane in space and a point not in that plane, there is exactly one line through the point perpendicular to the given plane. (page 69)

Ruler Postulate. a. To every pair of points there corresponds a unique positive number called the *distance* between the points. b. The points on a line can be matched one-to-one with the real numbers so that the distance between any two points is the absolute value of the difference of their associated numbers. (page 72)

Protractor Postulate. a. To each angle there corresponds a unique real number between 0 and 180 called the measure of the angle. b. Let P be a point on the edge of half-plane H. Each ray in the half-plane or its edge with vertex P can be matched one-to-one with the real numbers n, $0 < n < 180$, so that the measure of an angle formed by a pair of noncollinear rays with vertex P is the absolute value of the difference of their associated numbers. (page 73)

SAS Congruence Postulate. If two sides and the included angle of one triangle are congruent respectively to two sides and the included angle of another triangle, then the two triangles are congruent. (page 91)

ASA Congruence Postulate. If two angles and the included side of one triangle are congruent respectively to two angles and the included side of another triangle, then the two triangles are congruent. (page 91)

SSS Congruence Postulate. If all three sides of one triangle are congruent respectively to all three sides of another triangle, then the two triangles are congruent. (page 91)

Linear Pair Postulate. If two angles form a linear pair, the angles are supplementary. (page 146)

Parallel Postulate. Given a line ℓ and a point P not on ℓ, there exists only one line through P parallel to ℓ. (page 180)

Triangle Inequality Postulate. The sum of the lengths of two sides of a triangle is greater than the length of the third side. (page 244)

AAA Similarity Postulate. If three angles of one triangle are congruent to three angles of another triangle, then the triangles are similar. (page 316)

Arc Addition Postulate. If C is on $\widehat{AB}$, then $m\widehat{AC} + m\widehat{CB} = m\widehat{AB}$. (page 346)

Area Postulate. A unique positive number called the area can be assigned to each polygonal region. The area of region R is denoted by $A(R)$. (page 394)

Area of Congruent Regions Postulate. If two rectangles or two triangles are congruent, then the regions they bound have the same area. (page 395)

Area Addition Postulate. If a polygonal region is the union of n non-overlapping polygonal regions, then its area is the sum of the areas of these n regions. (page 395)

Rectangle Area Postulate. The area of a rectangle with length ℓ and width w is given by the formula ℓw. (page 395)

Volume Postulate. Each solid is assigned a unique positive number called its volume. (page 444)

Rectangular Solid Volume Postulate. The volume of a rectangular solid is equal to the product of its length, ℓ, width, w, and height, h. (page 444)

Volume Addition Postulate. If a solid is the union of two solids that have no common interior points, then its volume is the sum of the volumes of the two solids. (page 444)

Cavalieri's Postulate. Let S and T be two solids and X be a plane. If every plane parallel to X that intersects S or T intersects both S and T in a cross section having the same area, then Volume S = Volume T. (page 445)

Theorems

Proving Theorems Using Basic Properties

4–1 The reflexive, symmetric, and transitive properties hold for angle and segment congruence.

4–2 In an isosceles triangle the segment from the vertex angle to the midpoint of the opposite side forms a pair of congruent triangles.

4–3 **Addition of Equal Angles.** If $m\angle APB = m\angle DQE$, $m\angle BPC = m\angle EQF$, $\overrightarrow{PB}$ is between $\overrightarrow{PA}$ and $\overrightarrow{PC}$, and $\overrightarrow{QE}$ is between $\overrightarrow{QD}$ and $\overrightarrow{QF}$, then $m\angle APC = m\angle DQF$.

4–4 **Subtraction of Equal Segments.** If $AC = DF$, $BC = EF$, B is between A and C, and E is between D and F, then $AB = DE$.

4–5 **Addition of Equal Segments.** If $AB = DE$, $BC = EF$, B is between A and C, and E is between D and F, then $AC = DF$.

4–6 **Subtraction of Equal Angles.** If $m\angle APC = m\angle DQF$, $m\angle BPC = m\angle EQF$, $\overrightarrow{PB}$ is between $\overrightarrow{PA}$ and $\overrightarrow{PC}$, and $\overrightarrow{QE}$ is between $\overrightarrow{QD}$ and $\overrightarrow{QF}$, then $m\angle APB = m\angle DQE$.

4–7 **Congruent Complements Theorem.** Two angles that are complementary to the same angle (or congruent angles) are congruent.

4–8 **Congruent Supplements Theorem.** Two angles that are supplementary to the same angle (or to congruent angles) are congruent.

4–9 **Vertical Angles Theorem.** If two lines intersect, the vertical angles are congruent.

4–10 If one angle of a linear pair is a right angle, then the other is also a right angle.

4–11 **Exterior Angle Theorem.** The measure of an exterior angle of a triangle is greater than the measure of either remote interior angle.

Parallel Lines and Planes

5–1 If two lines are cut by a transversal and a pair of corresponding angles are congruent, then the lines are parallel.

5–2 If two lines are cut by a transversal and a pair of alternate interior angles are congruent, then the lines are parallel.

5–3 If two lines are cut by a transversal and a pair of alternate exterior angles are congruent, then the lines are parallel.

5–4 If two lines are cut by a transversal and a pair of interior angles on the same side of the transversal are supplementary, then the lines are parallel.

5–5 Given lines p, q, and r, if $p \parallel q$ and $q \parallel r$, then $p \parallel r$.

5–6 If two parallel lines are cut by a transversal, then alternate interior angles are congruent.

5-7 If two parallel lines are cut by a transversal, then alternate exterior angles are congruent.

5-8 If two parallel lines are cut by a transversal, then corresponding angles are congruent.

5-9 If two parallel lines are cut by a transversal, then the interior angles on the same side of the transversal are supplementary.

Triangles

6-1 If a triangle is isosceles, then its base angles are congruent.

6-2 If a triangle is equilateral, then it is equiangular.

6-3 If two angles of a triangle are congruent, then the sides opposite these angles are congruent.

6-4 The sum of the measures of the angles of a triangle is 180°.

6-5 The angles of an equilateral triangle each have a measure of 60°.

6-6 The measure of an exterior angle of a triangle is equal to the sum of the measures of its two remote interior angles.

6-7 **AAS Theorem.** If two angles and a side opposite one angle in a triangle are congruent to two angles and the corresponding side of a second triangle, then the two triangles are congruent.

6-8 **HA Theorem.** If the hypotenuse and an acute angle of one right triangle are congruent to the hypotenuse and an acute angle of another right triangle, then the triangles are congruent.

6-9 **HL Theorem.** If the hypotenuse and a leg of one right triangle are congruent to the hypotenuse and a leg of a second right triangle, then the triangles are congruent.

6-10 If a point P is equidistant from a pair of points A and B, then P lies on the perpendicular bisector of $\overline{AB}$. Conversely, a point on the perpendicular bisector of $\overline{AB}$ is equidistant from A and B.

More On Triangles

7-1 **Pythagorean Theorem.** If ΔABC is a right triangle, then the square of the length of the hypotenuse equals the sum of the squares of the lengths of the legs.

7-2 If ΔABC has side lengths a, b, and c and $c^2 = a^2 + b^2$, then ΔABC is a right triangle.

7-3 The length of the hypotenuse of a 45°-45°-90° triangle is $\sqrt{2}$ times the length of a leg.

7-4 The length of the longer leg of a 30°-60°-90° triangle is $\frac{\sqrt{3}}{2}$ times the length of the hypotenuse or $\sqrt{3}$ times the length of the shorter side.

7–5 The perpendicular bisectors of the sides of a triangle intersect in a point O that is equidistant from the three vertices of the triangle.

7–6 The angle bisectors of the angles of a triangle are concurrent in a point I that is equidistant from the three sides of the triangle.

7–7 The lines that contain the altitudes of a triangle intersect in a point.

7–8 The medians of a triangle intersect in a point that is two thirds of the way from each vertex to the opposite side.

7–9 If the measures of two angles of a triangle are unequal, then the length of the side opposite the smaller angle is less than the length of the side opposite the larger angle.

7–10 If the lengths of two sides of a triangle are unequal, then the measure of the angle opposite the shorter side is less than the measure of the angle opposite the longer side.

Quadrilaterals and Polygons

8–1 The opposite angles of a parallelogram are congruent.

8–2 The opposite sides of a parallelogram are congruent.

8–3 Each pair of adjacent angles of a parallelogram are supplementary angles.

8–4 If the opposite sides of a quadrilateral are congruent, then the quadrilateral is a parallelogram.

8–5 If a quadrilateral has one pair of opposite sides parallel and congruent, then it is a parallelogram.

8–6 If the opposite angles of a quadrilateral are congruent, then the quadrilateral is a parallelogram.

8–7 **Midsegment Theorem.** A segment joining the midpoints of two sides of a triangle is parallel to the third side and half its length.

8–8 The midpoints of the sides of a quadrilateral are the vertices of a parallelogram.

8–9 A parallelogram is a rectangle if and only if its diagonals are congruent.

8–10 A parallelogram is a rhombus if and only if its diagonals are perpendicular to each other.

8–11 A parallelogram is a rhombus if and only if each diagonal bisects a pair of opposite angles.

8–12 The segment joining the midpoints of the two nonparallel sides of a trapezoid is parallel to the two bases and has a length equal to one half the sum of the lengths of the bases.

8–13 In an isosceles trapezoid, base angles are congruent and the diagonals are congruent.

8–14 The sum of the measures of the angles of a convex polygon of n sides is $(n - 2)180°$.

8-15 The measure of an angle of a regular polygon of n sides is $\frac{(n-2)}{n}180°$.

8-16 The sum of the measures of the exterior angles of a polygon, one at each vertex, is 360°.

Similarity

9-1 If $\frac{a}{b} = \frac{c}{d}$, then $a \times d = b \times c$.

9-2 If $\frac{a}{b} = \frac{c}{d}$, then $\frac{a+b}{b} = \frac{c+d}{d}$.

9-3 If $\frac{a}{b} = \frac{c}{d}$, then $\frac{a-b}{b} = \frac{c-d}{d}$.

9-4 If $\frac{a}{b} = \frac{c}{d}$, then $\frac{a}{c} = \frac{b}{d}$.

9-5 If $a \times d = b \times c$, then $\frac{a}{b} = \frac{c}{d}$.

9-6 **Side-Splitting Theorem.** If a line is parallel to one side of a triangle and intersects the other two sides, then it divides the two sides proportionally.

9-7 If a line intersects two sides of a triangle and divides them proportionally, then the line is parallel to the third side.

9-8 **AA Similarity Theorem.** If two angles of one triangle are congruent to two angles of another triangle, then the two triangles are similar.

9-9 Two right triangles are similar if an acute angle of one triangle is congruent to an acute angle of the other triangle.

9-10 In a right triangle, the length of the altitude to the hypotenuse is the geometric mean between the lengths of the two segments of the hypotenuse.

9-11 Given a right triangle and the altitude to the hypotenuse, each leg is the geometric mean between the length of the hypotenuse and the length of the segment of the hypotenuse adjacent to the leg.

9-12 **SSS Similarity Theorem.** If three sides of one triangle are proportional to the three sides of another triangle, then the triangles are similar.

9-13 **SAS Similarity Theorem.** If two triangles have an angle of one triangle congruent to an angle of the other triangle, and if the corresponding sides including the angle are proportional, then the triangles are similar.

Circles

10-1 In a circle or in congruent circles, congruent chords have congruent minor arcs.

10-2 In a circle or in congruent circles, congruent minor arcs have congruent chords.

10-3 In a circle or in congruent circles, congruent chords are equidistant from the center.

10-4 In a circle or in congruent circles, chords equidistant from the center are congruent.

10-5 The perpendicular bisector of a chord contains the center of the circle.

10-6 If a line through the center of a circle is perpendicular to a chord that is not a diameter, then it bisects the chord and its minor arc.

10-7 If a line through the center of a circle bisects a chord, then it is perpendicular to the chord.

10-8 If a line is perpendicular to a radius at a point on the circle, then the line is tangent to the circle.

10-9 If a line is tangent to a circle, then the radius drawn to the point of contact is perpendicular to the tangent.

10-10 If a line is perpendicular to a tangent at a point on the circle, then the line contains the center of the circle.

10-11 The tangent segments to a circle from a point outside the circle are congruent and form congruent angles with the line joining the center and the point.

10-12 The measure of an inscribed angle is one half the measure of its intercepted arc.

10-13 An angle inscribed in a semicircle is a right angle.

10-14 An angle formed by two chords intersecting inside a circle has a measure equal to one half the sum of the intercepted arcs.

10-15 The measure of an angle formed by a tangent and a chord drawn to the point of contact is one half the intercepted arc.

10-16 The measure of an angle formed by two intersecting tangents to a circle is one half the difference of the measures of the intercepted arcs.

10-17 The measure of an angle formed by a tangent and a secant or two secants from a point exterior to a circle is one half the difference of the measures of the intercepted arcs.

10-18 If a tangent segment and a secant segment are drawn to a circle from an exterior point, then the square of the length of the tangent segment equals the product of the lengths of the secant segment and its external secant segment.

10-19 If two chords intersect in a circle, then the product of the lengths of the segments of one chord equals the product of the lengths of the second chord.

10-20 If two secant segments are drawn to a circle from an exterior point, then the product of the lengths of one secant segment and its external secant segment equals the product of the lengths of the other secant segment and its external secant segment.

Area and Perimeter

11-1 Given a parallelogram with base b and corresponding height h, the area A is given by the formula $A = bh$.

11-2 Given a triangle with base b and corresponding altitude h, the area A is given by the formula $A = \frac{1}{2}bh$.

11-3 **Heron's Formula.** If ΔABC has sides of length a, b, and c, then $A(\Delta ABC) = \sqrt{s(s - a)(s - b)(s - c)}$ where $s = \frac{1}{2}(a + b + c)$.

11-4 Given a trapezoid with bases b_1 and b_2 and altitude h, the area A is given by the formula $A = \frac{1}{2}h(b_1 + b_2)$.

11-5 Given a regular n-gon with sides of length s and apothem a, the area A is given by the formula $A = \frac{1}{2}ans = \frac{1}{2}ap$ where perimeter $p = ns$.

11-6 The ratio of the perimeters of two similar polygons is equal to the ratio of the lengths of any pair of corresponding sides.

11-7 The ratio of the areas of two similar polygons is equal to the square of the ratio of the lengths of any pair of corresponding sides.

11-8 The ratio of the circumference to the diameter is the same for all circles.

11-9 Given a circle with radius r and diameter d, the circumference C is given by the formula $C = \pi d = 2\pi r$.

11-10 Given a circle with radius r, the area A is given by the formula $A = \pi r^2$.

Solids

12-1 The lateral edges of a prism are parallel and congruent.

12-2 Given a prism with rectangular lateral faces. If the altitude of the prism is h and the bases have area B and perimeter p, then the surface area S is found by the formula $S = hp + 2B$.

12-3 Given a regular pyramid with slant height ℓ and a base with area B and perimeter p, the surface area S is found by the formula $S = \frac{1}{2}\ell p + B$.

12-4 The volume of any prism is the product of the length of an altitude and the area of the base.

12-5 Given a pyramid with base B and altitude h. If A is a cross section parallel to the base and the distance from the vertex to the cross section is K, then $\frac{\text{area } A}{\text{area } B} = \left(\frac{K}{h}\right)^2$.

12-6 Two pyramids with equal altitudes and bases of equal area have the same volume.

12–7 Given a pyramid with altitude h and base area B, the volume is found by the formula $V = \frac{1}{3}hB$.

12–8 Given a right circular cylinder with altitude h. If the circumference of the base is C, and the area of the base is B, then the surface area S is found by the formula $S = Ch + 2B = 2\pi rh + 2\pi r^2$.

12–9 Given a right circular cylinder with base area B and height h, the volume is found by the formula $V = Bh = \pi r^2 h$.

12–10 Given a right circular cone with slant height ℓ. If the circumference of the base is C, and the area of the base is B, then the surface area S is given by the formula $S = \frac{1}{2}\ell C + B = \pi r\ell + \pi r^2$.

12–11 Given a right circular cone with height h and base area B, the volume is found by the formula $V = \frac{1}{3}Bh = \frac{1}{3}\pi r^2 h$.

12–12 Given a sphere of radius r, the volume is found by the formula $V = \frac{4}{3}\pi r^3$.

12–13 Given a sphere of radius r, the surface area S is found by the formula $S = 4\pi r^2$.

12–14 There are exactly five regular polyhedra that are convex solids.

Transformations and Symmetry

13–1 Given a line reflection:
a. the reflection image of a segment is a segment of equal length;
b. the reflection image of an angle is an angle of equal measure.

13–2 If lines r and s are parallel, then a reflection over line r followed by a reflection over line s is a translation. Furthermore, if A'' is the image of A, then
a. $\overline{AA''} \perp r$,
b. $AA'' = 2d$ where d is the distance between the lines r and s.

13–3 If lines r and s intersect in point O, then a reflection over r followed by a reflection over s is a rotation. Point O is the center of the rotation and the angle of rotation is 2α, where α is the measure of the acute or right angle between lines r and s.

Coordinate Geometry

14–1 If the coordinates of the endpoints of the segment $\overline{P_1P_2}$ are (x_1, y_1) and (x_2, y_2), then the coordinates of the midpoint of $\overline{P_1P_2}$ are $\left(\frac{x_1 + x_2}{2}, \frac{y_1 + y_2}{2}\right)$.

14–2 The product of the slopes of two perpendicular lines is -1.

14-3 The slopes of two parallel lines are equal.

14-4 **The Distance Formula.** If A has coordinates (x_1, y_1) and B has coordinates (x_2, y_2) then $AB = \sqrt{(x_1 - x_2)^2 + (y_1 - y_2)^2}$.

14-5 Any straight line in the coordinate plane that is not parallel to the y-axis can be represented by the equation $y = mx + b$, where m is the slope and b is the y-intercept.

14-6 The graph of the equation $x^2 + y^2 = r^2$ is a circle with radius r and center at the origin.

14-7 The graph of the equation $(x - h)^2 + (y - k)^2 = r^2$ is a circle with radius r and center at the point (h, k).

Glossary

acute angle An angle with measure less than $90°$. (page 21)

acute triangle A triangle with three acute angles. (page 198)

affirming the hypothesis A pattern of reasoning represented as follows: Whenever $p \rightarrow q$ is true and p is true, we can conclude q is true. (page 64)

alternate exterior angles Two exterior angles with different vertices on opposite sides of a transversal. (page 171)

alternate interior angles Two interior angles with different vertices on opposite sides of a transversal. (page 171)

altitude of a parallelogram A segment perpendicular to a pair of parallel sides with endpoints on those parallel sides. (page 399)

altitude of a prism A segment between and perpendicular to the bases. (page 435)

altitude of a pyramid A segment from the vertex to the base perpendicular to the base. (page 435)

altitude of a trapezoid A segment perpendicular to the parallel sides. (page 403)

altitude of a triangle A segment from a vertex to a point on the opposite side (perhaps extended) that is perpendicular to that opposite side. (page 199)

angle The union of two noncollinear rays which have the same endpoint. (page 17)

apothem of a regular polygon The distance from its center to a side. (page 408)

arc A continuous part of a circle. (page 343)

area of a circle The number approached by the areas of the inscribed regular n-gons as n gets larger and larger. (page 420)

auxiliary line A line introduced to a figure to help solve a problem. (page 157)

axis of a cone The segment joining the vertex to the center of the base. (page 456)

axis of a cylinder A segment joining the center of the two bases. (page 452)

betweenness of a point Point B is between A and C if and only if A, B, and C are collinear and $AB + BC = AC$. (page 72)

betweenness of a ray $\overrightarrow{BC}$ is between $\overrightarrow{BA}$ and $\overrightarrow{BD}$ if and only if $\overrightarrow{BC}$, $\overrightarrow{BA}$, and $\overrightarrow{BD}$ are coplanar and $m\angle ABC + m\angle CBD = m\angle ABD$. (page 73)

bisector of an angle The bisector of $\angle ABC$ is a ray BD in the interior of $\angle ABC$ such that $\angle ABD \cong \angle DBC$. (page 24)

bisector of a segment Any point, segment, ray, line, or plane that contains the midpoint of the segment. (page 24)

central angle An angle with vertex at the center of a circle. (page 343)

chain rule A pattern of reasoning represented as follows: Whenever $p \rightarrow q$ is true and $q \rightarrow r$ is true, we conclude $p \rightarrow r$ is true. (page 65)

chord of a circle A segment with endpoints on the circle. (page 342)

circle The set of all points in a plane that are a fixed distance from a given point in the plane. (page 17)

circular cone A solid with a circular base and a vertex not on the plane containing the base. (page 456)

circular cylinder A solid with two congruent bases in parallel planes. The bases are congruent circular regions. (page 452)

circumference of a circle The number approached by the perimeters of the inscribed regular polygons as the number of sides of the regular polygons increases. (page 416)

circumscribed circle A circle that contains the three vertices of a triangle. The center of the circle is the point of intersection of the perpendicular bisectors of the sides of the triangle. (page 238)

collinear points Points that lie on the same line. (page 13)

complementary angles Two angles whose measures have a sum of $90°$. (page 144)

concurrent lines Three or more coplanar lines that have a point in common. (page 13)

congruent angles Angles that have the same measure. (page 20)

congruent arcs Two arcs of a circle that have the same measure. (page 347)

congruent circles Circles with radii of equal length. (page 347)

congruent segments Segments that have the same length. (page 20)

congruent triangles Two triangles are congruent if there is a correspondence between the vertices such that each pair of corresponding sides and angles are congruent. (page 85)

contrapositive of a statement The contrapositive of a statement $p \rightarrow q$ is the statement $\sim q \rightarrow \sim p$. (page 60)

converse of a statement The converse of a statement $p \rightarrow q$ is the statement $q \rightarrow p$. (page 60)

convex polygon A polygon is convex if all of the diagonals of the polygon are in the interior of the polygon. (page 32)

coordinate of a point on a line A real number associated with the point. (page 74)

coordinates of a point in a plane A pair of numbers (x, y) that name the location of the point. The first number is the x-coordinate and the second is the y-coordinate. (page 505)

coplanar points Points that all lie in one plane. (page 13)

corresponding angles Two angles on the same side of a transversal. One of the angles is an exterior angle, one is an interior angle. (page 171)

cosine ratio The cosine of an acute angle of a right triangle is the ratio

$$\frac{\text{length of adjacent side}}{\text{length of hypotenuse}}.$$

(page 330)

counterexample A single example that shows a generalization to be false. (page 49)

cross section of a solid A region common to the solid and a plane that intersects the solid. (page 445)

deductive reasoning Starting with a hypothesis and using logic and definitions, postulates, or previously proved theorems to justify a series of statements or steps which lead to the desired conclusion. (page 53)

degree measure The real number between 0 and 180 that is assigned to an angle. (page 20)

denying the conclusion A pattern of reasoning represented as follows: Whenever $p \rightarrow q$ is true and q is false, we conclude that p is false. (page 65)

diagonal of a polygon A segment joining any two nonconsecutive vertices of the polygon. (page 32)

diameter of a circle A chord that contains the center of the circle. (page 342)

distance formula If A has coordinates (x_1, y_1) and B has coordinates (x_2, y_2), then

$AB = \sqrt{(x_1 - x_2)^2 + (y_1 - y_2)^2}$. (page 520)

distance from a point to a line The length of the segment drawn from the point perpendicular to the line. (page 29)

distance between two points The points on a line can be matched one-to-one with the real numbers so that the distance between any two points is the absolute value of the difference of their associated numbers. (page 72)

edge of a polyhedron *See* Polyhedron

equation of a circle The graph of the equation $x^2 + y^2 = r^2$ is a circle with radius r and center at the origin. The graph of the equation $(x - h)^2 + (y - k)^2 = r^2$ is a circle with radius r and center at the point (h, k). (pages 528–529)

equation of a line Any straight line in the coordinate plane that is not parallel to the y-axis can be represented by the equation $y = mx + b$, where m is the slope and b is the y-intercept. (page 524)

equiangular triangle A triangle with three congruent angles. (page 199)

equilateral triangle A triangle with all sides congruent to one another. (page 33)

exterior angle of a triangle An angle that forms a linear pair with one of the angles of the triangle. (page 154)

face of a polyhedron *See* Polyhedron

generalization A conclusion arrived at through inductive reasoning. (page 44)

geometric mean A number x is a geometric mean between two numbers a and b if

$\frac{a}{x} = \frac{x}{b}$, $x \neq 0$, $b \neq 0$. (page 322)

great circle The intersection of a sphere and a plane containing the center of the sphere. (page 460)

half-plane For a line in a plane, the points of the plane not on the line form two half-planes. Each half-plane is a convex set. (page 69)

heptagon A polygon with seven sides. (page 32)

hexagon A polygon with six sides. (page 32)

hypotenuse The side opposite the right angle of a right triangle. (page 199)

if-then statement A statement of the form—if p, then q—where p and q are simple statements. p is called the *hypothesis*. q is called the *conclusion*. The symbol $p \rightarrow q$ (read p *implies* q) is used to represent an if-then statement. (page 56)

image A figure resulting from a transformation. (page 476)

indirect proof Assuming the negation of what is to be proved, then showing that this assumption leads to a contradiction. (page 158)

inductive reasoning Observing that an event gives the same result several times in succession, then concluding that the event will always have the same outcome. (page 44)

inscribed angle An angle with vertex on a circle and with sides that contain chords of the circle. (page 343)

inscribed circle A circle that touches each side of a triangle in exactly one point. The center of the circle is the point of intersection of the angle bisectors of the triangle. (page 238)

intercepted arc An arc with endpoints on the sides of inscribed or central angles. (page 343)

interior of an angle The interior of $\angle ABC$ is the intersection of the points on A's side of $\overleftrightarrow{BC}$ with the points on C's side of $\overleftrightarrow{AB}$. (page 17)

intersecting lines Two lines with a point in common. (page 13)

inverse of a statement The inverse of a statement $p \rightarrow q$ is the statement $\sim p \rightarrow \sim q$. (page 60)

isosceles triangle A triangle with two sides congruent to one another. (page 33)

legs of a right triangle The sides including the right angle of a right triangle. (page 199)

line of reflection *See* Reflection

line of symmetry *See* Reflection symmetry

linear pair of angles A pair of angles with a common side such that the union of the other two sides is a line. (page 144)

major arc An arc that does not lie in the interior of a central angle. The measure of a major arc is 360 minus the measure of its associated minor arc. (page 346)

median of a triangle A segment joining a vertex to the midpoint of the opposite side. (page 239)

midpoint of a segment The midpoint of segment AB is a point C between A and B such that $\overline{AC} \cong \overline{CB}$. (pages 24, 508)

minor arc An arc that lies in the interior of a central angle. The measure of a minor arc is the measure of its associated central angle. (page 346)

***n*-gon** A polygon with n sides. (page 32)

obtuse angle An angle with measure greater than 90°. (page 21)

obtuse triangle A triangle with an obtuse angle. (page 199)

octagon A polygon with eight sides. (page 32)

origin The intersection of the x- and y-axes in a coordinate plane. (page 504)

parallel line and plane A line and a plane that have no points in common. (page 170)

parallel lines Lines in the same plane that do not intersect. (page 13)

parallelogram A quadrilateral with both pairs of opposite sides parallel. (page 261)

parallel planes Planes that have no points in common. (page 170)

pentagon A polygon with five sides. (page 32)

perimeter of a polygon The sum of the lengths of the sides of the polygon. (page 408)

perpendicular bisector of a segment A line perpendicular to the segment and which contains its midpoint. (page 29)

perpendicular lines Two lines that intersect to form congruent right angles. (page 28)

perpendicular to a plane A line is perpendicular to a plane if it is perpendicular to each line in the plane that intersects the line. (page 28)

perpendicular planes Two planes are perpendicular if there is a line in one plane that is perpendicular to the other plane. (page 28)

pi (π) The ratio $\frac{C}{d}$, which is the same real number for any circle. (page 417)

plane figure A figure with all points in one plane, but not all on one line. (page 16)

polygon The union of segments meeting only at endpoints such that (1) at most two segments meet at one point, and (2) each segment meets exactly two other segments. (page 32)

polygonal region A subset of a plane bounded by a polygon (or polygons). (page 394)

polyhedron A finite number of polygonal regions called faces. Each edge of a region is the edge of exactly one other region. If two regions intersect, then they intersect in an edge or vertex. (page 434)

postulate A basic generalization accepted without proof. (page 52)

prism A polyhedron such that 1) there is a pair of congruent faces that lie in parallel planes and 2) all other faces are parallelograms. (page 435)

proportion An equality between two ratios. The ratios $\frac{a}{b}$ and $\frac{c}{d}$ are proportional if $\frac{a}{b} = \frac{c}{d}$, $b \neq 0$, $d \neq 0$. (page 304)

pyramid A polyhedron in which all faces but one have a vertex in common. (page 434)

Pythagorean Theorem If $\triangle ABC$ is a right triangle, then the square of the length of the hypotenuse equals the sum of the squares of the lengths of the legs. (page 226)

quadrilateral The union of four segments determined by four points, no three of which are collinear. The segments intersect only at their endpoints. (page 17)

radius of a circle A segment whose endpoints are the center and a point on the circle. (page 342)

ray A ray, $\overrightarrow{AB}$, is a subset of a line. It contains a given point A and all points on the same side of A as B. (page 16)

rectangle A parallelogram with four right angles. (page 261)

rectangular solid A prism with rectangular bases whose lateral edges are perpendicular to the bases. (page 444)

reflection A transformation, in a plane, over line ℓ that maps each point P of the plane onto the point P' as follows:

a. If P is on ℓ, $P' = P$.

b. If P is not on ℓ, then ℓ is the perpendicular bisector of $\overline{PP'}$.

P' is called the *image* of P and P is the *preimage* of P'. (page 476)

reflectional symmetry A figure F has reflectional symmetry if there is a line ℓ such that the reflection image over ℓ of each point P of F is also a point of F. The line ℓ is called the *line of symmetry*. (page 494)

regular polygon A polygon with all sides congruent to each other and all angles congruent to each other. (page 33)

regular polyhedron A polyhedron whose faces are all regular polygons with the same number of edges and whose vertices are each surrounded by the same number of faces. (page 464)

regular pyramid A pyramid with a regular polygon for its base and lateral edges of the same length. (page 435)

remote interior angles The two angles of a triangle, with respect to an exterior angle, that are not adjacent to the exterior angle. (page 154)

rhombus A parallelogram with four congruent sides. (page 261)

right angle An angle with measure of 90°. (page 21)

right cone A cone with its axis perpendicular to its base. (page 456)

right cylinder A cylinder with its axis perpendicular to both bases. (page 452)

right prism A prism having its lateral faces perpendicular to the bases. (page 435)

right triangle A triangle with a right angle. (page 199)

rotation A transformation with center O and angle α that maps each point P of the plane onto a point P' as follows:

a. If P is the center point O, $P' = P$.

b. If $P \neq O$, then $P'O = PO$ and $m\angle POP' = \alpha$.

P' is called the *rotation image* of point P. (page 488)

rotational symmetry A figure F has rotational symmetry if there is a rotation about a center A such that the rotation image of each point P of figure F is also a point of F. The center, A, of the rotation is called the *center of symmetry* for F. (page 495)

scalene triangle A triangle with no congruent sides. (page 198)

secant of a circle A line that intersects the circle in exactly two points. (page 343)

sector of a circle A region bounded by a central angle and its intercepted arc. (page 421)

segment A segment, $\overline{AB}$, is the set of points A and B and all the points between A and B. (page 16)

similar polygons Two polygons are similar if there is a correspondence between vertices such that corresponding angles are congruent and corresponding sides are proportional. (page 313)

sine ratio The sine of an acute angle of a right triangle is the ratio

$$\frac{\text{length of opposite side}}{\text{length of hypotenuse}}.$$

(page 330)

skew lines Two nonintersecting lines that do not lie in the same plane. (page 170)

slant height of a cone A segment joining the vertex to a point of the circumference of the base. (page 456)

slant height of a pyramid The altitude of one of the lateral faces from the vertex. (page 435)

slope of a line If P_1 and P_2 have coordinates (x_1, y_1) and (x_2, y_2), respectively, then the slope m of $\overline{P_1P_2}$ is

$$m = \frac{y_1 - y_2}{x_1 - x_2}$$

provided $x_1 - x_2 \neq 0$. (page 512)

space The set of all points. (page 11)

space figure A figure that has points not all in a single plane. (page 16)

sphere The set of all points that are a given distance from a given point. (page 460)

square A rectangle with four congruent sides. (page 261)

square unit A square region in which the length of a side is one unit of length. (page 398)

supplementary angles Two angles whose measures have a sum of 180°. (page 144)

surface area The surface area of prisms and pyramids is the sum of the areas of the lateral faces plus the area of the bases. (page 440)

symmetry *See* Reflectional symmetry and Rotational symmetry

tangent to a circle A line that intersects the circle in exactly one point. (page 343)

tangent ratio The tangent of an acute angle of a right triangle is the ratio

$$\frac{\text{length of opposite side}}{\text{length of adjacent side}}.$$

(page 300)

theorem A generalization that can be proved to be true using definitions, postulates, and the logic of deductive reasoning. (page 52)

transformation A rule or operation that changes a figure. The figure prior to the change is called the *preimage* and the figure after the change is called the *image*. (page 476)

translation Given an arrow AA', the translation image of a point P for the arrow AA' is the point P' where:

a. $AA' = PP'$, and
b. arrows AA' and PP' have the same direction.
(page 484)

transversal A line that intersects two coplanar lines in two different points. (page 171)

trapezoid A quadrilateral with exactly one pair of parallel sides. (page 261)

triangle The union of three segments determined by three noncollinear points. (page 17)

vertex of an angle The endpoint of the two noncollinear rays forming the angle. (page 17)

vertex of a polygon The endpoint of a side of the polygon. (page 32)

vertical angles Two angles that are formed by two intersecting lines but which are not a linear pair of angles. (page 150)

volume A measure of the amount of space occupied by a solid. Each solid is assigned a unique positive number called its volume. (page 444)

***x*-intercept** A line cutting the x-axis at the point $(a, 0)$ has x-intercept a. (page 527)

***y*-intercept** A line cutting the y-axis at the point $(0, b)$ has y-intercept b. (page 524)

Selected Answers

Answers are given for most odd-numbered problems and all Problem Solving exercises. Chapter Review and Cumulative Review answers include both even and odd. Answers are not given for Chapter Tests.

CHAPTER 1

pages 14-15

3. A, F, C; A, E, D; B, F, E; B, C, D
5. Example: A, F, D, B **7.** r, t, q
11. $\overleftrightarrow{AE}$, $\overleftrightarrow{BG}$, or $\overleftrightarrow{BF}$ **13.** $\overleftrightarrow{AB}, \overleftrightarrow{HC}, \overleftrightarrow{GD}$
15. 12; *ABCD, ADHE, CDHG, ABFE, BCGF, EFGH, ADFG, BCEH, ABGH, CDEF, BFHD, AEGC*
17. all possible except 2; maximum 6

pages 18-19

13. $\angle ABC, \angle CBA$ **15.** $\angle ACB, \angle BCA$
19. $\overleftrightarrow{AB}, \overleftrightarrow{AC}, \overleftrightarrow{AD}, \overleftrightarrow{BD}, \overleftrightarrow{BE}$ **21.** $\overleftrightarrow{AB}, p$ **23.** $\overrightarrow{BC}, \overrightarrow{BD}$
25. $\angle ABC, \angle ACB, \angle ACD, \angle ADC, \angle CAD, \angle CAB$
27. Yes, the segments have the same endpoints.
29. Three lines; no; the sides of a triangle are segments.
31. Draw segment *EI*.
Problem Solving Form a pyramid with a triangular base.

pages 22-23

1. 4 cm
3. $\overline{PQ} \cong \overline{RS}, \overline{MN} \ncong \overline{XY}, \overline{JK} \cong \overline{EF}$ **5.** 140° **7.** 90°
11. $\angle EOF, \angle FOM, \angle LOJ, \angle JOD$ **19.** $67\frac{1}{2}°$
Problem Solving

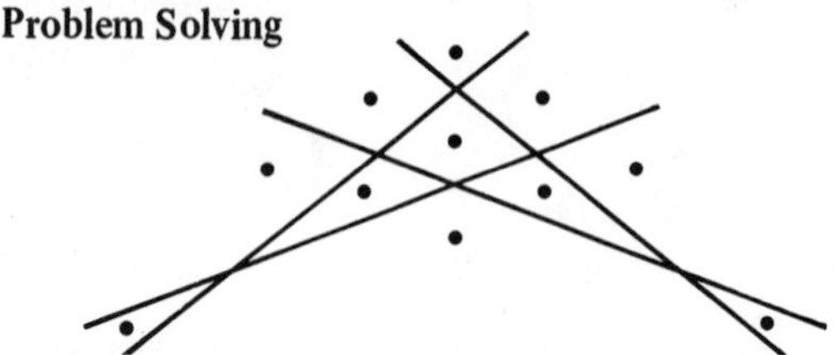

pages 26-27

5. yes **17.** 43

pages 30-31

1. $j \perp k$
7. *ABCD, ABFE*; *ABCD, BCGF*; *ABCD, CDHG*; *ABCD, ADHE*
13. A line contained in one plane must be perpendicular to the second plane.
15. Construct a perpendicular from *A* to a point *C* so that the riverbank is the midpoint of $\overline{AC}$. Let *M* be the intersection of $\overline{CB}$ and the riverbank. Then $AM + MB$ is the minimum.
Problem Solving *A* and *D*

pages 34-35

1b. Each segment does not meet exactly two other segments.
3a. same as ex. 1 **5.** $2c, 3c$ **9a.** regular
9d. regular
11. $\triangle AFB, \triangle CGB, \triangle AJE, \triangle EID, \triangle DHC, \triangle FBG, \triangle GCH, \triangle HDI, \triangle JIE, \triangle AFJ$
13. Even number of edges
15. *HIJ, ACEG, JIDEF, CEGJHA, BHIJFGA, CIDEGJHA, ABHICEFJG, AHBCIDEFJG*
Problem Solving $\frac{7\frac{1}{5}}{360} = \frac{500}{x}$; 25,000 miles

page 37 Chapter 1 Review

2a. false **2b.** false **2c.** false **2d.** true
2e. false **2f.** true **3.** none; one; two
4. Yes, both segments have the same endpoints.
11. planes: *ABCD, GHFE*; *BCFH, ADEG*; or *CDEF, BAGH*
12. line: *DE, CF, AG*, or *BH*
13. line: *AB* or *GH, AH* or *BG* **14.** line *CB*

page 39 Problem Solving Techniques

1. 10 **2.** 9 or 21 **3.** 20 **4.** 26 **5.** 19 ft
6. 1 block south

CHAPTER 2

pages 46-47

1. $\overline{CB}, \overline{GF}, \overline{XZ}$; the longest 3. three equal
5. $h = a + b + c$

Problem Solving

1. Slide #2 to the right.
2. Move #1 to the bottom right.

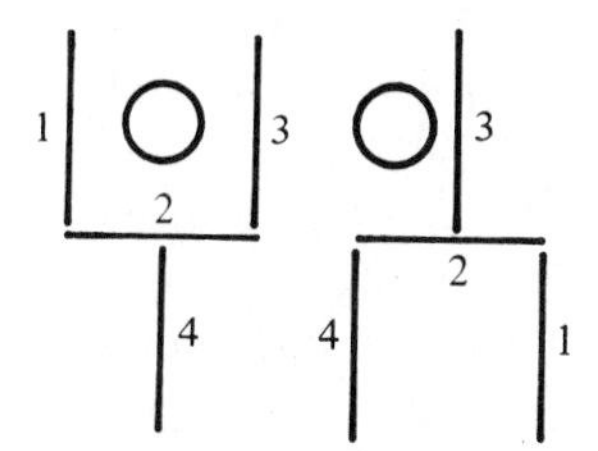

pages 50-51

1. false 3. a 5. False; use obtuse triangle.

Problem Solving

1.

		1		6		15		20		15		6		1		
	1		7		21		35		35		21		7		1	
1		8		28		56		70		56		28		8		1

2. 1, 2, 4, 8, 16, 32, 64, 128, 256, . . . , 2^{n-1}, where n is row number
3. $a^2 + 2ab + b^2$, $a^3 + 3a^2b + 3ab^2 + b^3$, $a^4 + 4a^3b + 6a^2b^2 + 4ab^3 + b^4$. Coefficients are the same as numbers in each row of Pascal's triangle.

pages 54-55

1. flat, level, surface
3. Yes. The definition of plane requires more basic terms.
7. Vertical angles are congruent.
9. The line segment joining the midpoints of two sides of a triangle is parallel to the third side.

Problem Solving $(30-3)-2=25$ or $25+2+3=30$ is correct. $(30-3)+2$ is not correct.

pages 58-59

1. (p) Jana is 15 years old (q) Jana is too young to vote in U.S. elections. True
3. (p) some apples are red (q) horses have four legs. True
5. (p) two lines intersect (q) those two lines are not parallel. True
7. (p) $\triangle ABC$ is isosceles (q) $\triangle ABC$ is equilateral. False
9. If a man lives in Denver, then he lives in Colorado.
11. If two lines are perpendicular, then they intersect to form congruent right angles.
13. If two lines are parallel, then they do not intersect.
15. (p) it ends in 2 (q) the number is even. If a number ends in 2, then the number is even.
17. (p) an equiangular triangle (q) must be equilateral. If a figure is an equiangular triangle, then it must be equilateral.
19. (p) do as I say (q) you will be rich. If you do as I say, then you will be rich.
21. (p) two of its angles are congruent (q) a triangle is isosceles. If two angles of a triangle are congruent, then the triangle is isosceles.
23. (p) $\overline{AB} \cong \overline{BC}$ (q) B is the midpoint of $\overline{AC}$. If $\overline{AB} \cong \overline{BC}$, then B is the midpoint of $\overline{AC}$.

Problem Solving nine trips across, eight return trips

pages 62-63

1. If a person is wet, then that person is swimming.
3. If a person doesn't have much money, then the person is poor.
5. If a person does not steal, then the person is not dishonest.
7. If a team does not win four World Series games, then it does not win the Series.
9. If you are not 16 years old or older, then you do not drive a car legally.
11. If we do not win the game tonight, then we will not win the championship.
13. If a triangle is equilateral, then it is equiangular. If a triangle is equiangular, then it is equilateral.
15. If two lines in a plane are parallel, then they have no points in common. If two lines in a plane have no points in common, then they are parallel.
17. If a quadrilateral is a parallelogram, then it has two pairs of parallel sides. If a quadrilateral has two pairs of parallel sides, then it is a parallelogram.

Problem Solving Alice

pages 66-67

1. She voted for Fred Friendly.
3. It does not snow. **5.** They are not parallel.
7. Point C is on the perpendicular bisector.
9. An angle with measure greater than 90° is an obtuse angle.
11. 1. If $\triangle ABC$ is a right triangle with $\angle C$ a right angle, then $m\angle A + m\angle B + m\angle C = 180$ and $m\angle C = 90$. 3. If $m\angle A + m\angle B = 90$, then $\angle A$ and $\angle B$ are complementary.
Problem Solving Lee is the clerk, Martinelli is the cashier, and Nielsen is the accountant.

pages 70-71

1. line, Two Points, Line, Plane Postulate
3. line, Point-Line Postulate
5. line, Perpendicular Postulate
7. line, Perpendicular Postulate
9. Plane Intersection Postulate
11. Perpendicular Postulate
13. Point-Plane Postulate
15. Perpendicular Postulate
17. Point-Plane Postulate **19.** 4
Problem Solving

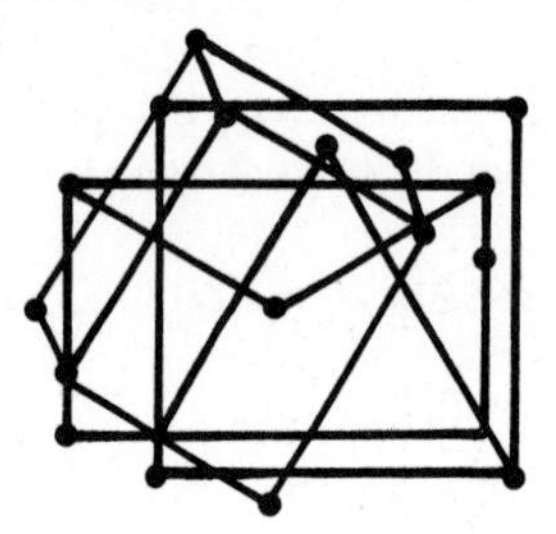

pages 74-75

1. 3 **3.** 9 **5.** 8 **7.** 11 **9.** 19 **11.** 8 **13.** 40
15. 155 **17.** 80 **19.** C **21.** B
23. Definition of between, Ruler Post. **25.** 28, 35
27. $BC = 14, CA = 42$ or 14 **29.** 4 or 24 **31.** 96
33. 20
Problem Solving $A = 0.010, B = 0.540, C = 0.249, D = 0.882, E = 1.1555$

page 77 Chapter 2 Review

1. equilateral triangle; equilateral triangle
2a. A kite, or a rhombus with no right angle
2b. A rectangle with adjacent sides not congruent
3. A postulate is a statement that is accepted as true without proof. A theorem is a statement that can be proved.
4a. false **4b.** true **4c.** false **4d.** false
5. 16 **6.** 30
7a. (hyp) they do not intersect (con) two lines are parallel
7b. (hyp) all squares (con) are rectangles
8a. If a figure has four right angles, then it is a square.
8b. If a figure is not a square, then it does not have four right angles.
8c. If a figure does not have four right angles, then it is not a square.
8d. rectangle (a and b)
9. the diagonals of figure $ABCD$ are congruent.
10. $\overleftrightarrow{AB}$ and $\overleftrightarrow{CD}$ are in the same plane.

page 79 Algebra Review

1. A **3.** D **5.** C **7.** F **9.** 32 **11.** 26 **13.** 1
15. -32 **17.** 12 **21.** $x \geq -18$ **23.** $x > 22$
25. $x > 20$ **27.** $-9, 9$ **29.** $3, -5$ **31.** $37, -37$
33. $6, -7$ **35.** $8, -8$ **37.** 11 **39.** 20 **41.** -12

CHAPTER 3

pages 86-89

1. not congruent **3.** congruent **5.** b **7.** b
9a. $\overline{BC} \cong \overline{DE}$ **9b.** $\overline{AB} \cong \overline{EF}$ **9c.** $\angle C \cong \angle D$
11. $\angle C \cong \angle D, \angle A \cong \angle O, \angle T \cong \angle G, \overline{CA} \cong \overline{DO}, \overline{AT} \cong \overline{OG}, \overline{CT} \cong \overline{DG}$
13. a, c **15.** APR, BTJ **17.** $\triangle ABC \cong \triangle A'B'C'$
19. $\triangle ABC \cong \triangle BAC, \triangle ABC \cong \triangle ACB, \triangle ABC \cong \triangle ABC, \triangle ABC \cong \triangle CAB, \triangle ABC \cong \triangle CBA$.
21. $\triangle ABD \cong \triangle DCA, \triangle BAE \cong \triangle CDE$
23. $\triangle AEB \cong \triangle ADC, \triangle DBC \cong \triangle ECB$
Problem Solving b, e; c, g; d, f
Congruent triangles: ADI, BCI; ADB, BCA; ADH, BCJ; AFC, BDG; AHI, BJI; AEI, BEI

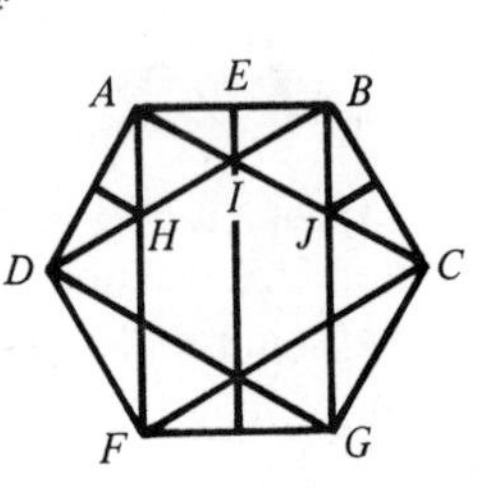

pages 92-95

1. $\triangle LMN$ 5. $\angle DBC$ 7. $\overline{BD}$ 9. $\angle BDC$
11. SAS 13. ASA 15. SSS
17. not enough information
19. not enough information
21. not enough information 23. SSS
25. not congruent 27. not congruent
31. $\overline{AC} \cong \overline{AC}$, $\triangle ACD \cong \triangle ACB$, SAS, definition of congruent triangles
33. $\triangle ABC \cong \triangle CDA$, ASA
35. $\triangle ABE \cong \triangle CBD$, SAS
37. $\triangle DBA \cong \triangle EBC$, ASA

Problem Solving 8, 27, 64

pages 98-99

1. SAS 3. ASA
5. $\overline{BD} \cong \overline{DB}$, a segment congruent to itself; ASA
7. SAS 9. ASA 11. $\angle B \cong \angle B$; ASA

Problem Solving All except middle pattern

pages 102-103

1. $\angle ZXM \cong \angle YXM$ 3. $\overline{AN} \cong \overline{BN}$
5. $\overline{PV} \cong \overline{QV}$, $\overline{SV} \perp \overline{PQ}$, $\angle PVS$ and $\angle QVS$ are right angles.
7. $\overline{QT} \cong \overline{ST}$ 9. Definition of angle bisector
11. Definition of midpoint
13. Definition of perpendicular bisector

Problem Solving

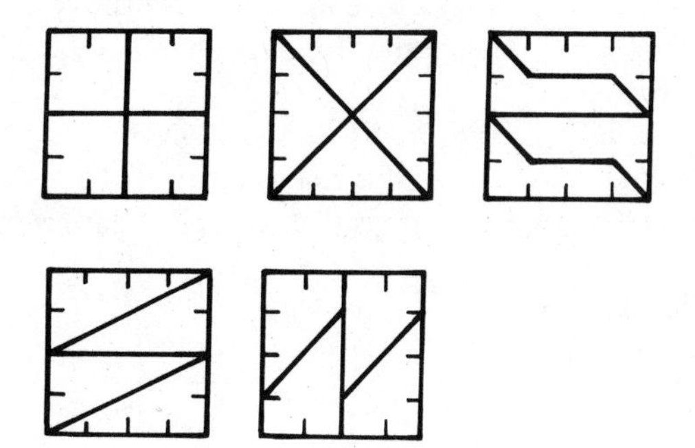

pages 106-109

1. SSS 3. ASA
5. 2. Given 3. Definition of perpendicular lines 4. $\overline{CD} \cong \overline{CD}$ 5. SAS
7. 2. $\angle 3 \cong \angle 4$ 3. Given 4. Def. of angle bisector 5. A segment is congruent to itself. 6. ASA
9. $\overline{XM} \cong \overline{XM}$; SAS 11. $\overline{NQ} \cong \overline{NQ}$; SSS
13. $\angle RAD \cong \angle EAH$; ASA
15. $\overline{AN} \cong \overline{EN}$, def. of midpoint; ASA
17. $\overline{ES} \cong \overline{NS}$, def. of segment bisector; SAS
19. $\angle ABF \cong \angle CBF$, def. of angle bisector; $\overline{AB} \cong \overline{CB}$, def. of regular pentagon; $\overline{BF} \cong \overline{BF}$; SAS
21. $\overline{AM} \cong \overline{CM}$, def. of midpoint; $\overline{MB} \cong \overline{MB}$, $\triangle AMB \cong \triangle CMB$, SSS; def. of congruent triangles

Problem Solving No unique solution; 7, 8, and 9 is one solution.

pages 112-115

1. $\triangle ABD$, $\triangle ACD$
3. $\triangle EFG$, $\triangle EIH$, $\triangle EFH$, $\triangle EIG$
5. $\triangle JNK$, $\triangle LNK$; $\triangle JNM$, $\triangle LNM$
7. 1. Given 2. $\overline{MO} \cong \overline{MO}$; A segment is congruent to itself. 3. SSS 4. $\angle PMO \cong \angle NMO$ 5. Def. of angle bisector
9. $\overline{AC} \cong \overline{AC}$; $\triangle ACB \cong \triangle ACD$, ASA; $CPCTC$
11. $\angle E \cong \angle B$, $\overline{AE} \cong \overline{AB} \cong \overline{ED} \cong \overline{BC}$; def. of regular polygon; $\triangle AED \cong \triangle ABC$, SAS; $\overline{AD} \cong \overline{AC}$, $CPCTC$; def. of isosceles
13. $\overline{CD} \cong \overline{ED}$, def. of segment bisector; $\triangle BCD \cong \triangle FED$, ASA; $CPCTC$
15. $AP = BP$ and $AN = BN$, since points P and N in the plane of the net are each an equal distance from base lines; $\overline{PN} \cong \overline{PN}$; $\triangle APN \cong \triangle BPN$, SSS; $\angle PNA \cong \angle PNB$, $CPCTC$; $\angle PNA$ and $\angle PNB$ are supplements with measure sum of 180°; each has a measure of 90° since the angles are equal; $\angle PNA$ and $\angle PNB$ are right angles and $\overleftrightarrow{PM}$ is perpendicular to $\overline{AB}$.
17. $\triangle AFE \cong \triangle BCD$, SAS; $\overline{AE} \cong \overline{BD}$, $CPCTC$; $\triangle AEB \cong \triangle DBE$, SSS; $CPCTC$
19. $\triangle DFG \cong \triangle CFG$, SAS; $\overline{FD} \cong \overline{FC}$, $CPCTC$; $\triangle AEF \cong \triangle ABF$, SAS; $\overline{EF} \cong \overline{BF}$, $CPCTC$; SSS

Problem Solving

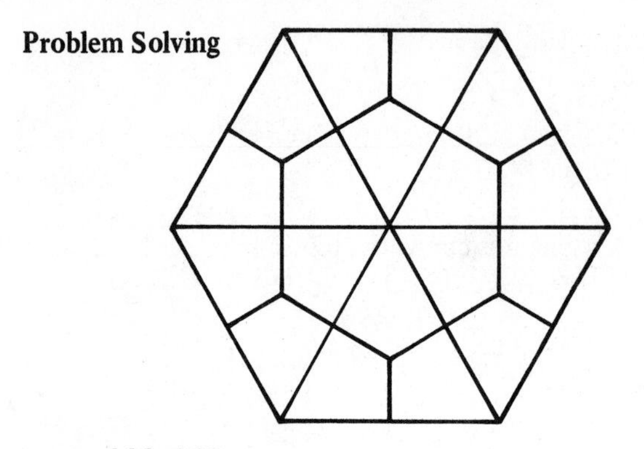

pages 118-119

1. $\Delta ABC, \Delta CDA$; $\Delta ABE, \Delta CDE$
3. $\angle 1 \cong \angle 2$; $\overline{AC} \cong \overline{DF}, \angle 3 \cong \angle 4$, given; $\Delta EFD \cong \Delta BCA, ASA$; $\overline{EF} \cong \overline{BC}$, $CPCTC$
5. $\overline{CB} \cong \overline{BC}$; $\Delta ECB \cong \Delta DBC, SAS$; $CPCTC$
7. $\Delta ACE \cong \Delta BDF, ASA$; $CPCTC$
9. $\Delta QPV \cong \Delta QRT, SAS$; $CPCTC$
11. $\angle AHG \cong \angle DHF$; $\Delta AHG \cong \Delta DHF, ASA$; $CPCTC$

Problem Solving A-36, B-36, C-24, D-8

page 121

1. $\Delta PUQ \cong \Delta TUS, ASA$; $\overline{QU} \cong \overline{SU}$, $CPCTC$; $\overline{QR} \cong \overline{SR}$, def. of segment bisector; $\overline{UR} \cong \overline{UR}$; SSS
3. $\Delta GFE \cong \Delta DEF, SAS$; $\overline{GE} \cong \overline{DF}$, $CPCTC$; $\Delta HGE \cong \Delta CDF, SAS$; $CPCTC$
5. $\Delta AHB \cong \Delta DHE, SAS$; $\angle 4 \cong \angle 3$, $CPCTC$; $\Delta ACB \cong \Delta DFE, ASA$; $CPCTC$

Problem Solving 255; let n = number of letters, $2^n - 1$

page 123 Chapter 3 Review

1. $\angle B \cong \angle Q, \angle A \cong \angle R, \angle C \cong \angle P, \overline{BA} \cong \overline{QR}, \overline{AC} \cong \overline{RP}, \overline{BC} \cong \overline{QP}$

2a. ASA 2b. SSS 2c. SAS 2d. SAS

3a. $\angle ABC$ and $\angle ABD$ are right angles.

3b. $\overline{FE} \cong \overline{GE}$ 3c. $\angle ABD \cong \angle CBD$; $\angle ADB \cong \angle CDB$

3d. All angles and sides are congruent.

4. $\angle QPM \cong \angle NPM, \angle QMP \cong \angle NMP$, def. of angle bisector; $\overline{MP} \cong \overline{MP}$, $\Delta MQP \cong \Delta MNP, ASA$; $CPCTC$
5. $\angle DBA \cong \angle EBC$, perpendicular lines form congruent right angles; $\Delta DBA \cong \Delta EBC, SAS$; $CPCTC$
6. $\Delta ZQX \cong \Delta PYX, SAS$; $CPCTC$

page 125 Cumulative Review Chapters 1-3

1a. false 1b. false 1c. true 3. deductive

4. inductive 5. no conclusion 6. $\overline{AB} \parallel \overline{CD}$

7a. If two lines are not perpendicular, then they are parallel.

7b. If two lines are not parallel, then they are perpendicular.

7c. If two lines are perpendicular, then they are not parallel.

7d. 7a, b; show nonperpendicular intersecting lines.

8. $\overline{AC} \cong \overline{AC}$; SSS
9. $\angle BAD \cong \angle CAD$; $\Delta BAD \cong \Delta CAD, SAS$; $CPCTC$

CHAPTER 4

pages 134-137

5. If two lines intersect, then they form two pairs of congruent angles.
7. If a segment is the angle bisector of a vertex angle of an equilateral triangle, then the segment is the perpendicular bisector of a side.
9. reflexive
11. If a triangle is isosceles, then the angles opposite the congruent sides are congruent.
13. If a triangle is equilateral, then all angles are congruent.
15. transitive property
17. $AB = AC$, transitive; three congruent sides
19. $BE = BD, AD = BD, BE = AD$, transitive; substitution
21. $\overline{DB} \cong \overline{BD}$, reflexive; ASA
23. $\angle AOB \cong \angle BOC$; $\angle BOC \cong \angle COD$; transitive
25. $\overline{AB} \cong \overline{CD}$, Theorem p. 132; $\angle A \cong \angle D, \overline{AE} \cong \overline{DF}$, $CPCTC$; SAS
27. $\Delta ABC \cong \Delta DEF, \Delta DEF \cong \Delta GHI$, given; $\angle A \cong \angle D, \angle D \cong \angle G$; $\angle A \cong \angle G$, transitive; $\overline{AB} \cong \overline{DE}$, $\overline{DE} \cong \overline{GH}$; $\overline{AB} \cong \overline{GH}$, transitive; complete pattern for four more pairs.

Problem Solving

a. 45, 66

b. yes

pages 140-143

1. transitive **3.** subtraction of equal angles
5. transitive
7. Subtraction of equal segments
9. $BE = AC$, transitive; subtraction of equal segments
11. 2. Reflexive property 3. Addition of equal segments
13. 3. Reflexive property 4. Addition of equal segments 5. Transitive property
15a. 29.73 cm **15b.** 6.045 cm
15c. Addition and subtraction of equal segments
17. Addition of equal angles
19. $\triangle ABE \cong \triangle DCE, ASA$; $AB = DC$, $CPCTC$; $AC = DB$, addition of equal segments
21. $AB = BC$; $m\angle ABF = m\angle CBG$, addition of equal angles; $\triangle FBA \cong \triangle GBC, SAS$; $\angle F \cong \angle G$, $\triangle FBD \cong \triangle GBE, ASA$; $CPCTC$
23. $\overline{AC} \cong \overline{CD}$; $m\angle ACB = m\angle DCE$, addition of equal angles; $\triangle ACB \cong \triangle DCE, ASA$; $\angle E \cong \angle B, \overline{EC} \cong \overline{BC}$, $CPCTC$; ASA
25. $\overline{AE} \cong \overline{DF}, \angle A \cong \angle D, \overline{AC} \cong \overline{DB}$, $CPCTC$; $AC - BC = DB - CB$; SAS
27. $\triangle ABE \cong \triangle DCE, SAS$; $\angle AEB \cong \angle DEC$, $CPCTC$; $m\angle EAF = m\angle EDG$, subtraction of equal angles; $\triangle AEF \cong \triangle DEG, ASA$; $\overline{FE} \cong \overline{GE}$, $CPCTC$
Problem Solving Note that 9 triangles can be arranged to form a triangle with 6 symbols at the center.

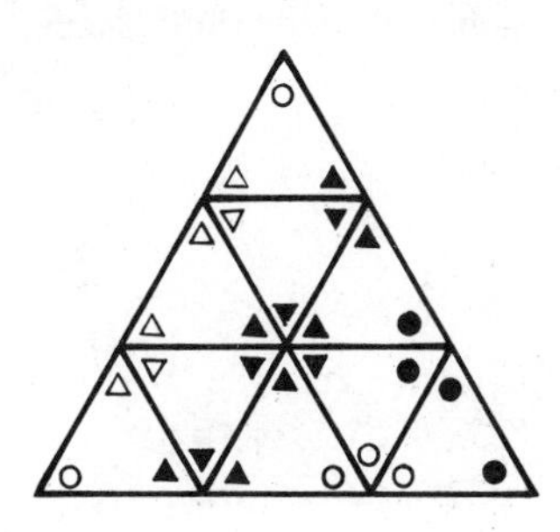

pages 148-149

1. $\angle COB$ **3.** $\angle 1$ or $\angle 2$
5. Complements of congruent angles
7. $\angle COF, \angle EOD$ **9.** $\angle HOA, \angle FOD$
11. Complements of same angle, $\angle AOC$
13. Complements of same angle, $\angle COE$ **15.** $90 - x$
17. $x + 4x = 180$; 36, 144
19. $\angle BAD \cong \angle BCD$, congruent supplements; ASA
21. $BW = BX = YD = DZ$; $\angle WBX \cong \angle ZDY$, congruent supplements; SAS
23. $\angle EBC \cong \angle EDC$, congruent complements; $\angle BEC \cong \angle DEC$, congruent supplements; ASA
25. Use the diagram on p. 146 with $\angle D \cong \angle C$, $\angle A$ complementary to $\angle C$, $\angle B$ complementary to $\angle D$; $m\angle A + m\angle C = 90$, $m\angle B + m\angle D = 90$; $m\angle A + m\angle C = m\angle B + m\angle D$, substitution; $m\angle A = m\angle B$, subtraction; $\angle A \cong \angle B$.
Problem Solving $x \doteq 1.618$; $y \doteq 0.618$; $\frac{x}{1} = \frac{1}{x-1}$; $x^2 - x - 1 = 0$; $x = \frac{1 \pm \sqrt{5}}{2}$; $x \doteq 1.618$

pages 152-153

1. $\angle COE, \angle BOF$; $\angle BOC, \angle FOE$
3. ex. $\angle AOC, \angle FOD$
5. 145 **7.** 145 **9.** 40 **11.** 50
13. $CO = DO$, $\angle COA \cong \angle DOB$, vertical angles; ASA
15. $\angle AEB \cong \angle DEC$; $\triangle AEB \cong \triangle DEC, SAS$
17. $\angle AEB \cong \angle DEC$; $\triangle AEB \cong \triangle DEC, SAS$; $\angle A \cong \angle D, \overline{AB} \cong \overline{DC}$, $CPCTC$; $AE + EC = DE + EB$; SAS
19. $\angle 1 \cong \angle 2$, $\angle 1$ and $\angle 2$ are supplements, given; $m\angle 1 + m\angle 2 = 180$; $2m\angle 1 = 180$, substitution, addition; $m\angle 1 = 90$.
Problem Solving Draw $\overline{AM}$ and $\overline{DM}$. $AB = 2a$; $m\angle AMD = 90$; $AM = DM = a\sqrt{5}$

pages 156-157

1. six; angles $ICB, FCA, CAD, HAB, ABG, EBC$
3. $\angle ACB, \angle ABC$
5. No, does not form linear pair with $\angle CAB$
7. Vertical angle **9.** Exterior angle
11. $m\angle 3 > m\angle 1$; $m\angle 1 > m\angle 4$, exterior angle; transitive
13. $m\angle ABD > m\angle BDC$; $m\angle BDC = m\angle EDF$
15. $m\angle RCB > m\angle B$; $m\angle RCB > 90$

17. In $\triangle XYZ$, $\angle 2$ is an obtuse angle, given; $m\angle 2 > 90$, def. of obtuse; $m\angle 1 + m\angle 2 = 180$; $90 > m\angle 1$; $m\angle 1 > m\angle Z$, $m\angle 1 > m\angle Y$, Ext. Angle Thm.; $90 > m\angle Z$, $90 > m\angle Y$, transitive.

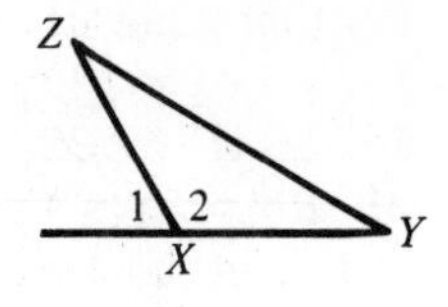

19. Use diagram for ex. 17; in $\triangle XYZ$, let $\angle 2$ be a right angle, given; $m\angle 1 > m\angle Z$, $m\angle 1 > m\angle Y$, Ext. Angle Thm.; $\angle 1$ is a right angle, subtraction; $90 > m\angle Z$, $90 > m\angle Y$, def. of right angle, substitution; neither $\angle Z$ nor $\angle Y$ are obtuse angles (ex. 16); in $\triangle XYZ$ let $\angle 2$ be an obtuse angle, given; $90 > m\angle Z$, $90 > m\angle Y$ (ex. 17); neither $\angle Z$ nor $\angle Y$ are right angles.

Problem Solving If the triangle is not isosceles, the midpoint of $\overline{BC}$ and the foot of the perpendicular are two distinct points.

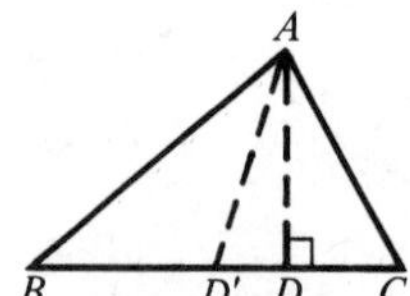

pages 160-163

1. $l \not\perp m$; The angles formed are not right angles.
3. The adjacent sides are parallel. The adjacent sides do not intersect.
5. $\overline{AB} \not\cong \overline{CD}$; $AB \neq CD$
7. $\angle A$ is not an acute angle. $m\angle A \geq 90$
9. $\triangle ABC$ is not an isosceles triangle. $AB \neq BC \neq AC$
11. not a contradiction **13.** form a contradiction
15. form a contradiction **17.** *c*
19. $m\angle A + m\angle B \neq 90$ (Exs. 19-27, answers may vary.)
21. $\triangle ABC \not\cong \triangle XYZ$ **23.** $m\angle A \neq 117$
25. $AB + EF = CD + EF$
27. $m\angle 1 + m\angle 2 \neq 180$
29. 1. Indirect Proof Assumption 2. Given 4. Reflexive Property 5. *SAS* Postulate 6. $\overline{AB} \cong \overline{AC}$, *CPCTC* 7. $\overline{AB} \not\cong \overline{AC}$, Given 8. $\overline{BD} \not\cong \overline{DC}$, Logic of Indirect Proof
31. A TV lawyer discovers that a client in a Denver crime was in Salt Lake City when the crime was committed. The lawyer makes the following statement. If my client was in Salt Lake City, then she did not commit the crime. The lawyer uses this reasoning. Suppose my client did commit the crime. The crime was committed in Denver. My client was in Salt Lake City. She could not be in Denver and Salt Lake City at the same time. Therefore, my client did not commit the crime.

33.

1. Suppose $\angle A$ and $\angle B$ are vertical angles.	1. Indirect Proof Assumption
2. $\angle A \cong \angle B$	2. Def. of vertical angles
3. $\angle A \not\cong \angle B$ (contradiction)	3. Given
4. $\angle A$ and $\angle B$ are not vertical angles.	4. Logic of Indirect Proof

35.

1. Suppose $BC = QR$	1. Indirect Proof Assumption
2. $\triangle ABC \cong \triangle PQR$	2. *SSS*
3. $\angle A \cong \angle P$	3. *CPCTC*
4. $\angle A \not\cong \angle P$ (contradiction)	4. Given
5. $BC \neq QR$	5. Logic of Indirect Proof

Problem Solving If you assume Ann is telling the truth, you reach a contradiction. If you assume Cal or Dee is telling the truth, you also reach a contradiction. If you assume Bob is telling the truth, you do not reach a contradiction. Hence, Ann is the guilty person.

page 165 Chapter 4 Review

1a. true **1b.** false **1c.** true
4a. $x = 22.5°$, $3x = 67.5°$ **4b.** 56 **4c.** 100, 80
5. 45 **6.** $\angle BCA \cong \angle DCE$; use *ASA*.
7. Use addition of equal angles.
8. $\triangle ABC \cong \triangle AED$, *ASA*; $\angle 3 \cong \angle 4$, *CPCTC*; use supplements of congruent angles.
9a. $\overline{AB} \parallel \overline{CD}$ **9b.** $\angle A$ and $\angle B$ are not supplements.

page 167 Problem Solving Techniques

1. 1296 **2.** 35 **3.** 45

CHAPTER 5

pages 172-173

1. ex. $\overleftrightarrow{EH}$, $\overleftrightarrow{FG}$, $\overleftrightarrow{CG}$, $\overleftrightarrow{DH}$
3. *EFGH* and *ABCD*, *BCGF* and *ADHE*, *ABFE* and *DCGH*
5. $\angle 2$ and $\angle 7$, $\angle 1$ and $\angle 8$
7. *ABG* and *DJK*, *AGL* and *CDJ*, *ABC* and *JKL*
9. $\overleftrightarrow{CD}$ and $\overleftrightarrow{EF}$; $\overleftrightarrow{AE}$
11. $\angle 14$ and $\angle 17$, $\angle 14$ and $\angle 11$

Problem Solving

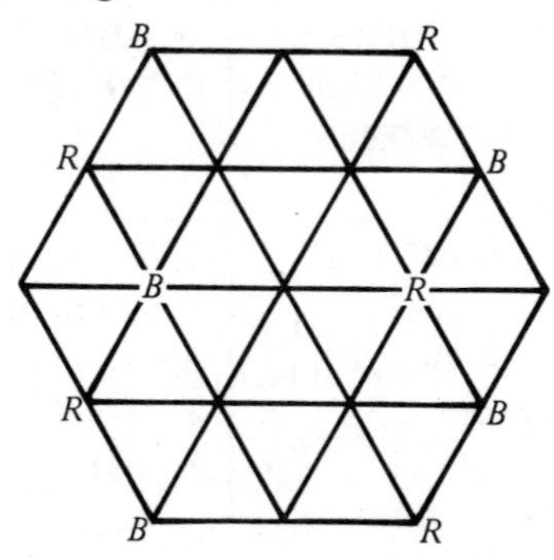

Problem Solving

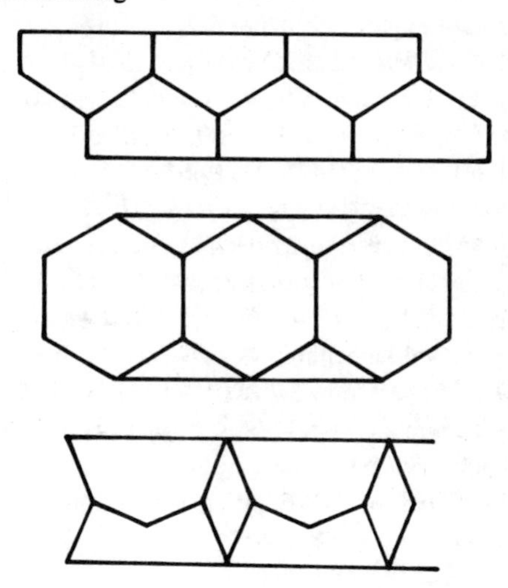

pages 176-179

1a. *a* and *c*, 5-1 1b. *a* and *b*, 5-2 1c. *b* and *c*, 5-4 1d. *a* and *c*, 5-2 1e. *b* and *c*, 5-1 1f. *a* and *b*, 5-3
3. Theorems 5-1, 5-2, 5-3, 5-4 5. $\angle 2$ and $\angle 3$
7. $\angle 8$ and ($\angle 4$ and $\angle 5$); $\angle 7$ and ($\angle 5$ and $\angle 6$)
9. *SSS*; $\angle 3 \cong \angle 2$, *CPCTC*; Theorem 5-2
11. $AF + FC = DC + CF$; $\triangle ABC \cong \triangle DEF$, *SSS*; $\angle ACB \cong \angle DFE$; Theorem 5-2
13. Use Theorem 5-4.
15. $\angle 2$ is supplementary to $\angle 3$, given; $\angle 2$ is supplementary to $\angle 1$, linear pair; $\angle 1 \cong \angle 3$, congruent supplements; $\ell \parallel m$, Thm. 5-1.
17. $\frac{1}{2}m\angle ABC = \frac{1}{2}m\angle BCD$, $\angle 2 \cong \angle 3$; Theorem 5-2
19. $(m\angle 2 + m\angle 3) + m\angle 1 = 180$; $m\angle 1 = m\angle 5$; $m\angle 1 = m\angle 4$; Thm. 5-1
21. Draw $\overline{DM}$ and $\overline{CM}$. Prove $\triangle AMD \cong \triangle BMC$, *SAS*; $\overline{DM} \cong \overline{CM}$, $\angle DMA \cong \angle CMB$, *CPCTC*; $\angle DMP \cong \angle CMP$; $\triangle DMP \cong \triangle CMP$, *SAS*; $\angle DPM \cong \angle CPM$. Use Thm. 5-4.
23. The plumb line is parallel to the doors, windows, and corners of the walls.

pages 182-183

3a. true 3b. true 3c. true 3d. true
5. not parallel
7. $q \parallel p$, Thm. 5-4; $q \parallel r$, Thm. 5-4; Thm. 5-5.
9. Use Thm. 5-1 or Thm. 5-2.
11. $\overline{BA} \perp \overline{BG}$, $\overline{HG} \perp \overline{BG}$; $\overline{BA} \parallel \overline{HG}$; $\overline{EF} \parallel \overline{HG}$; use Thm. 5-5.

Problem Solving Let *E* be the intersection of $\overline{AB}$ and $\overline{CD}$; $AE = BE$, $CE = DE$; $\angle AEC \cong \angle BED$; $\triangle AEC \cong \triangle BED$, *SAS*; $\angle EDB \cong \angle ECA$, *CPCTC*; alternate interior angles.

pages 186-189

1. 125 3. 125 5. 55 7. 125 9. 37 11. 37
13. 110 15. 28 17. 70 19. 70 21. 42
23. $m\angle ABC = m\angle CDA = 110$; $m\angle DAB = 70$
25. $m\angle 1 = m\angle 5 = 78$; $m\angle 2 = 102$
27. $\ell \parallel m$; $\angle 1 \cong \angle 3$, Thm. 5-8; $\angle 2$ is supplementary to $\angle 3$, linear pair; $\angle 2$ is supplementary to $\angle 1$; substitution.
29. An interior angle formed by *r* and *t* is 90°, Thm. 5-6; def. of perpendicular
31. $m\angle 1 = m\angle 11$, $m\angle 11 = m\angle 7$, $m\angle 1 = m\angle 7$, transitive; $m\angle 2 = m\angle 4$, $m\angle 4 = m\angle 9$, $m\angle 2 = m\angle 9$, transitive

33. $\angle 9$ is sup. to $\angle 6$, Thm. 5-9; $\angle 1 \cong \angle 6$, sup. of congruent angles; use Thm. 5-2.
35. $\angle B \cong \angle DEF, \triangle ABC \cong \triangle DEF, ASA$
37. $\angle 4 \cong \angle 2$, Thm. 5-8; $m\angle 1 + m\angle 2 = 180$, Thm. 5-9; $m\angle 1 + m\angle 4 = 180$, substitution
39. $\angle B$ is sup. to $\angle A$, $\angle D$ is sup. to $\angle A$, Thm. 5-9; sup. of congruent angles.
41. The edges of the striped wallpaper should be parallel so that $\angle A \cong \angle C$; since the floor is parallel to the ceiling, $\angle B \cong \angle C$. Therefore, $\angle A \cong \angle B$.

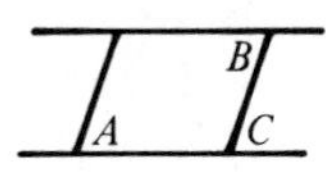

Problem Solving
1. Since $\overrightarrow{AB}$ is bent the same amount entering and exiting, a pair of congruent corresponding angles are formed making $\overleftrightarrow{AB} \parallel \overleftrightarrow{CD}$.
2. Use Thm. 5-5.

page 191 Chapter 5 Review

1a. $\angle 3$ and $\angle 6$, $\angle 4$ and $\angle 5$
1b. $\angle 2$ and $\angle 7$, $\angle 1$ and $\angle 8$
1c. $\angle 2$ and $\angle 6$, $\angle 1$ and $\angle 5$, $\angle 3$ and $\angle 7$, $\angle 4$ and $\angle 8$
2a. true **2b.** false **2c.** true **3a.** ABE and DCF
3b. $\overleftrightarrow{BC}$ and $\overleftrightarrow{FD}$, $\overleftrightarrow{AD}$ and $\overleftrightarrow{FC}$ **4.** no **5.** 55 **6.** 78
7. $\angle 8 \cong \angle 11$, Thm. 5-6. $\angle 10$ and $\angle 11$ are supplementary. Use Thm. 5-4.
8. $\overline{BA} \parallel \overline{DC}$, Thm. 5-1. Use Thm. 5-8.

page 193 Algebra Review

1. 4 **3.** $-\frac{5}{2}$ **5.** -8 **7.** 2 **9.** $\frac{4}{5}$ **11.** $x < 5$
13. $x < \frac{14}{3}$ **15.** $x > 36$ **17.** $-5 < x < 5$
19. $2\sqrt{2}$ **21.** $4\sqrt{3}$ **23.** $3\sqrt{3}$ **25.** $\frac{7}{8}$ **27.** $\frac{11\sqrt{2}}{4}$
29. $(-10, 34)$ **31.** $(4, 2)$ **33.** $(14, -4)$
35. $(7, 14)$ **37.** 3, 9

CHAPTER 6

pages 200-201

1a. scalene **1b.** equilateral **1c.** isosceles
1d. scalene **3a.** $\angle N$ **3b.** $\overline{MN}, \overline{PN}$ **3c.** $\overline{MP}$
3d. $\overline{MN}, \overline{PN}$
9. An equilateral triangle must be an acute triangle.
11. $\triangle XYZ$, altitudes $\overline{XZ}, \overline{YZ}, \overline{ZP}$; $\triangle ZPY, \overline{ZP}, \overline{PQ}, \overline{YP}$; $\triangle PQY, \overline{PQ}, \overline{QW}, \overline{YQ}$; $\triangle WQY, \overline{QW}, \overline{YW}$; $\triangle XPZ, \overline{XP}, \overline{ZP}$; $\triangle PQZ, \overline{PQ}, \overline{ZQ}$
13. $\triangle HAB, \triangle CBA$
15. Equilateral triangles ABC, DEF; scalene triangles DEA, FDC, EFB
17. $\overline{CD} \perp \overline{AB}, \overline{AE} \perp \overline{BC}$; $\angle CDB \cong \angle AEB$; $\angle B \cong \angle B$; $AB - AD = CB - CE, DB = EB$; $\triangle BAE \cong \triangle BCD$, ASA.
Problem Solving 16 triangles like $\triangle MON$; also triangles $AJC, BKD, CLE, FMH, GNI, JOL, AMD, BNE, FOI, JLC, AOE$

pages 204-207

1. $\angle B \cong \angle E$; $\angle ACD \cong \angle ADC$
3. $\angle MNL, \angle MLN$; $\angle KNL, \angle KLN$
5. $\triangle AEB, \triangle DEC, \triangle DEA, \triangle CEB$ **7.** 50 **9.** 31
11. 14 **13.** 30 **15.** $m\angle X = m\angle Z = 72$; $m\angle Y = 36$
17. $m\angle ABC - m\angle 3 = m\angle ACB - m\angle 4$
19. $\angle ACD \cong \angle ADC$; $\angle ACB \cong \angle ADE$, sup. of congruent angles; $\triangle ACB \cong \triangle ADE, SAS$; $\overline{AB} \cong \overline{AE}$
21. $\angle ABC \cong \angle ACB$; $m\angle EBC = m\angle DCB$; $\overline{BC} \cong \overline{CB}$; $\triangle DBC \cong \triangle ECB, ASA$
23. $\angle ACB \cong \angle ABC$; $m\angle 3 = m\angle 4$; $\overline{DC} \cong \overline{DB}$
25. $\angle D$ and $\angle ABD$ are each supplements of $\angle ABC$; $\angle D \cong \angle ABD$; $\overline{AD} \cong \overline{AB}$
27. $\triangle ABC \cong \triangle BAE, SAS$; $\angle CAB \cong \angle EBA, CPCTC$
29. In equilateral $\triangle ABC$, $\angle A \cong \angle C$, $\angle B \cong \angle C$, Thm. 6-1; $\angle A \cong \angle B \cong \angle C$; transitive
31. $\triangle ABC$ is isosceles with $\overline{AB} \cong \overline{AC}$; call the intersection of $\overline{BC}$ and the bisector of $\angle A$ point D; $\angle BAD \cong \angle CAD$; $\triangle BAD \cong \triangle CAD, SAS$; $\overline{BD} \cong \overline{CD}$, $\angle ADB \cong \angle ADC, CPCTC$; $\angle ADB$ and $\angle ADC$ are right angles, $\overline{AD} \perp \overline{BC}$.
33. $\triangle ABC$ is isosceles with $\overline{AB} \cong \overline{AC}$, $\overrightarrow{BD}$ bisects $\angle ABC$, $\overrightarrow{CE}$ bisects $\angle ACB$, given; $\angle ABC \cong \angle ACB$, base angles; $m\angle DBC = m\angle ECB$, halves of equals; $\triangle DBC \cong \triangle ECB, ASA$; $\overline{EC} \cong \overline{DB}$, $CPCTC$.
35. $\overline{XB} \cong \overline{YC}$; $\angle BXW \cong \angle CYZ$; $\angle ABC \cong \angle ACB$; $\triangle XBW \cong \triangle YCZ, ASA$
37. $m\angle EAP = m\angle DBP$, subtraction; $\overline{AP} \cong \overline{BP}$; $\angle EPA \cong \angle DPB$; $\triangle EPA \cong \triangle DPB, ASA$; $\overline{EP} \cong \overline{DP}$
Problem Solving 29, 16

pages 210-211

1. 54 **3.** 110 **5.** 55 **7.** 60 **9.** 110
11. 55, 40, 85 **13.** $180 - 90 = 90$; $\frac{90}{2} = 45$
15. In isosceles ΔXYZ, $m\angle X = m\angle Y$;
$m\angle X + m\angle Y + m\angle Z = 180$; $2m\angle X + m\angle Z = 180$;
$m\angle X + \frac{1}{2}m\angle Z = 90$; $m\angle X < 90$; use def. of acute angle.
17. In right triangle ABC with right $\angle B$,
$m\angle A + m\angle B + m\angle C = 180$; $m\angle B = 90$;
$m\angle A + m\angle C = 90$, subtraction; use definition of complementary angles.
19. $\angle DCE \cong \angle ECB$; $\angle A \cong \angle B$; use Thm 6-6;
$\angle ECB \cong \angle B$.
21. Draw $\overline{AC}$. $m\angle 1 + m\angle DAC = m\angle B + m\angle ACB$.
$m\angle 2 = m\angle DAC + m\angle DCA$. Add.
23.

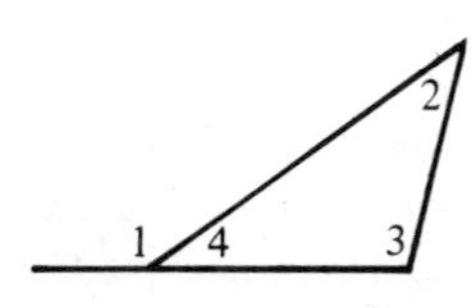

1. $m\angle 2 + m\angle 3 + m\angle 4 = 180$	1. Thm. 6-4
2. $m\angle 1 + m\angle 4 = 180$	2. Linear pair; def. of sup.
3. $m\angle 2 + m\angle 3 + (180 - m\angle 1) = 180$	3. Substitution
4. $m\angle 2 + m\angle 3 = m\angle 1$	4. Algebra

Problem Solving

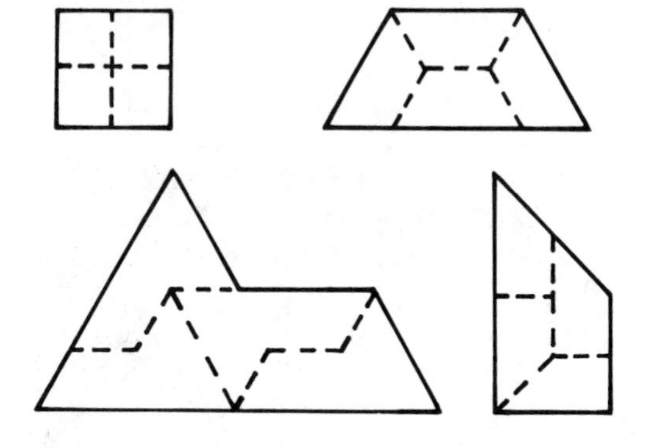

pages 214-215

1. HA **3.** ASA **4.** HA
7. $\angle CDA \cong \angle CDB$; $\overline{AC} \cong \overline{BC}$; HA **9.** AAS
11. $BE + EC = FC + CE$; AAS
13.

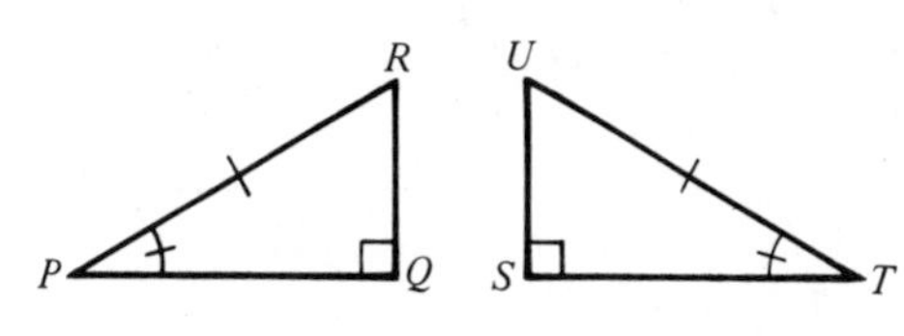

Use AAS Theorem.
15. $\Delta EAB \cong \Delta CBA$, SAS; $\angle AEB \cong \angle BCA$, $CPCTC$; $\angle EFA \cong \angle CFB$; AAS
17. Isosceles ΔABC with $\angle A \cong \angle B$, $\overline{FD} \perp \overline{AC}$, $\overline{FE} \perp \overline{BC}$, given; $m\angle ADF = m\angle BEF = 90$, defs. of perpendicular lines and right angles;

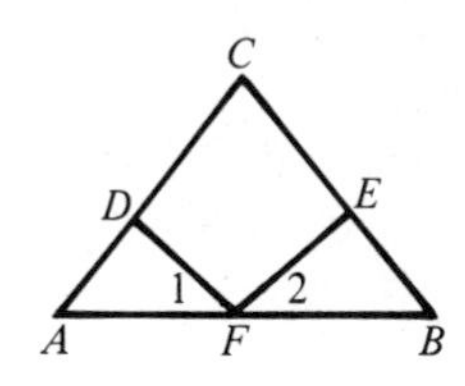

$m\angle A + m\angle ADF + m\angle 1 = m\angle B + m\angle BEF + m\angle 2$, Thm. 6-4, transitive; $m\angle 1 = m\angle 2$, subtraction.
Problem Solving 4

pages 218-219

1. HL **3.** HA **5.** ASA
7. not congruent; make $PQ = 2ST$, $PR = 2SU$, $QR = 2TU$
9. SSS **11.** 35
13. $\Delta ECB \cong \Delta DBC$, HA; $\angle DBC \cong \angle ECB$, $CPCTC$
15. $\Delta EFB \cong \Delta DFC$ (Ex. 14); $\overline{EF} \cong \overline{DF}$;
$\angle DEF \cong \angle FDE$; $\angle DEA \cong \angle EDA$, angle addition
17.

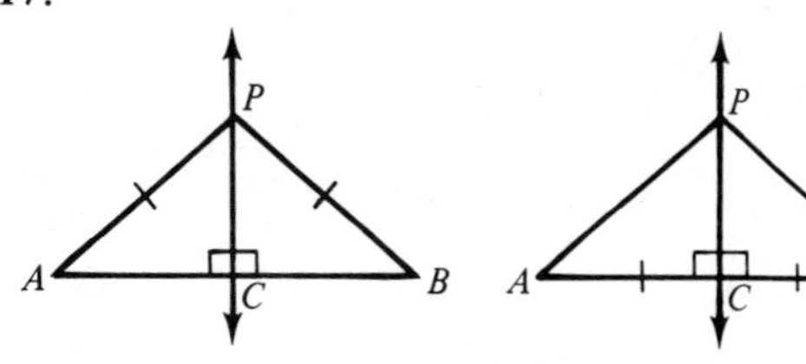

If P does not lie on $\overline{AB}$, then construct the perpendicular from P to $\overline{AB}$; $\Delta ACP \cong \Delta BCP$, HL; $\overline{AC} \cong \overline{BC}$, $CPCTC$. (If P lies on $\overline{AB}$, then P is the midpoint.) If P is on the perpendicular bisector, then $\Delta ACP \cong \Delta BCP$ by SAS, $\overline{PA} \cong \overline{PB}$, $CPCTC$.
Problem Solving A, yes; B, no; C, yes; D, no

page 221 Chapter 6 Review

1a. false **1b.** true **1c.** false **1d.** false
2. 70 **3.** 80
4. $m\angle CAB - m\angle DAB = m\angle CBA - m\angle DBA$
5. $\overline{AB} \cong \overline{BA}$; $\triangle ADB \cong \triangle BCA, AAS$
6. $\triangle ACD \cong \triangle ABD, HA$
7. $\triangle CYA \cong \triangle AXC, HL$; $\angle YCA \cong \angle XAC, CPCTC$; $\overline{BC} \cong \overline{BA}$
8a. Exterior angle equals the sum of two remote interior angles.
8b. 45
9. $\overline{KM} \cong \overline{KN}$; $\angle KMN \cong \angle KNM$; $\angle KMG \cong \angle KNH$, sup. of congruent angles; $\triangle KGM \cong \triangle KHN, ASA$; $\overline{KG} \cong \overline{KH}$

page 223 Problem Solving Techniques

1. 37 **2.** 28 **3.** $T_5 = 15, T_6 = 21, T_{10} = 55$
4. $P_5 = 35, P_6 = 51, P_{10} = 145$
5. $H_3 = 18, H_4 = 34, H_{10} = 235$

CHAPTER 7

pages 228-231

1. correct **3.** incorrect **5.** correct **7.** 5 **9.** 8
11. $\sqrt{19}$ **13.** 10 **15.** $2\sqrt{2}$ **17.** $\sqrt{5}$ **19.** yes
21. yes **23.** no **25.** $\sqrt{424} = 2\sqrt{106} \doteq 20.6$
27. $4\sqrt{2}$ ft
31. Area of square 1 = area of square 2; $4(\frac{1}{2}ab) + c^2 = 4(\frac{1}{2}ab) + a^2 + b^2$; $c^2 = a^2 + b^2$
33. $\frac{\sqrt{1440}}{0.5} \doteq 19$ rows **35.** 26.96 meters

Problem Solving
1a. 4 **1b.** 3 **1c.** 1 **1d.** 2
2a. $\sqrt{521}$ **2b.** $23 = \sqrt{529}$ **2c.** $\sqrt{545}$ **2d.** $\sqrt{565}$

pages 234-235

1. $2, 2\sqrt{2}$ **3.** 5, 5 **5.** $2, \sqrt{3}$ **7.** $2\sqrt{3}, 2$
9. $8\sqrt{7}, 8\sqrt{21}$ **11.** $38, 19\sqrt{3}$ **13.** $\frac{10\sqrt{3}}{3}$
15. $3\sqrt{3}$ m
17. In 30-60-90 triangle the side across from 30° angle is $\frac{s}{2}$; the side across from 60° angle is $\sqrt{3}$ times the length of the shorter leg or $\frac{s\sqrt{3}}{2}$.
19. $\frac{s\sqrt{3}}{3}$

Problem Solving
1. $AB^2 + 1^2 = 2^2, AB = \sqrt{3}$
2. $AD^2 + BD^2 = AB^2$; $AD = \sqrt{2}$
3. no

pages 240-243

1. $\overrightarrow{BX}, \overrightarrow{BY}, \overrightarrow{BZ}$ **3.** 3 **5.** 4 **13.** sometimes
15. sometimes **17.** sometimes
19. obtuse, outside; right, on; or acute, inside
23. $AD = DC$, def. of median and midpoint; $BA = BC$, def. of isosceles; $\angle A \cong \angle C$; $\triangle ABD \cong \triangle CBD, SAS$; $\angle ABD \cong \angle CBD, CPCTC$; $\overrightarrow{BD}$ is angle bisector.
25. In equilateral $\triangle XYZ$, M is midpoint of $\overline{XZ}$; $\triangle XYM \cong \triangle ZYM, SSS$; $\angle XMY$ and $\angle ZMY$ are congruent and sup. therefore, right angles; $\overline{YM}$ is altitude.
27. $\triangle NCB \cong \triangle MBC, ASA$; $\overline{MB} \cong \overline{NC}, \overline{MC} \cong \overline{NB}$, $CPCTC$; $\triangle MCN \cong \triangle NBM, SAS$; $\angle NMC \cong \angle MNB$, $\overline{OM} \cong \overline{ON}$
29. $\frac{3\sqrt{2}}{2}$
31. In equilateral $\triangle ABC, \overline{AD}$, $\overline{BE}$, and $\overline{CF}$ are medians; $AF = BF$, defs. of median, midpoint; $\triangle AFC \cong \triangle BFC$, SSS; $\angle AFC$ and $\angle BFC$ are congruent and sup. and therefore, right angles; $\triangle AFX \cong \triangle BFX, SAS$; since $\triangle ACF \cong \triangle BCF$, $\angle XCE \cong \angle XCD$; $CE = CD$, halves of equals; $\triangle ECX \cong \triangle DCX, SAS$; repeat pattern for $\overline{AD}$ and $\overline{BE}$.

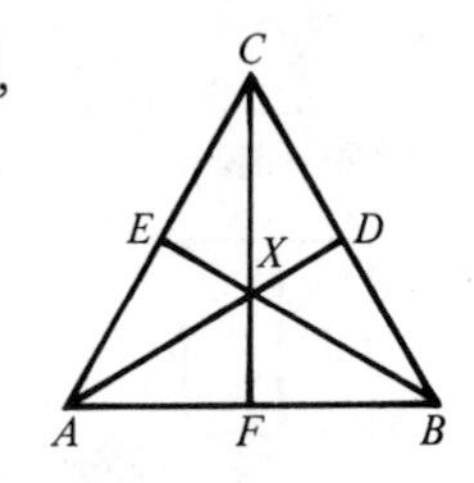

33. Isosceles $\triangle ABC, AC = BC$ with altitudes $\overline{BE}$ and $\overline{AD}$; $\angle CEB \cong \angle CDA$, defs. of altitude and right angle; $\triangle CEB \cong \triangle CDA, AAS$; $\overline{BE} \cong \overline{AD}, CPCTC$.

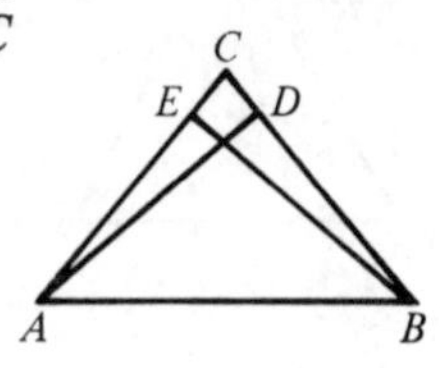

Problem Solving
1. $A'B = 5 = PR$; use AAS.
2. In $\triangle PRQ, y^2 = RQ^2 + 5^2$; $y + RQ = x$; substitute.

pages 246-247

1. yes 3. no 5. yes 7. yes
9. greater than 2 and less than 16
11. Choose C not on $\overline{AB}$; $AC + CB > AB$.
13. $AD + AB > BD$ and $CD + BC > BD$. Add.
15. H is at intersection of diagonals. $DH + HB = 4$. Form right triangle with AC as hypotenuse. $2^2 + (4 + 2\sqrt{3})^2 = AC^2$; $AC \doteq 7.7$; $DB = 4$; minimum $\doteq 11.7$

Problem Solving Find the length of the perpendicular from the top of the picture to point O (left diagram), $\sqrt{2}$; find AO, $(\frac{1}{2}AB)^2 + \sqrt{2}^2 = AO^2$; $AO = \frac{\sqrt{17}}{2}$; since the length of the wire is twice AO, length $= \sqrt{17}$.

pages 250-251

1. $\overline{AB}, \overline{AC}$ 3. $\overline{GH}, \overline{GI}$ 5. $AC < BC < AB$
7. $BC < AC < AB$ 9. $m\angle C < m\angle B < m\angle A$
11. $CD < BC < BD < AB$ $(AD = AB)$
13. In $\triangle ABD$, $BD < AB$; $CD = BD$; substitute.
15. Use ex. 14. 17a. possible, no
17b. possible, no 17c. possible, yes
17d. not possible 17e. not possible

Problem Solving

$\sqrt{3^2 - (\frac{3}{2})^2} - \sqrt{2^2 - (\frac{3}{2})^2} = \sqrt{\frac{27}{4}} - \sqrt{\frac{7}{4}}$;
$\frac{3\sqrt{3}}{2} - \frac{\sqrt{7}}{2} \doteq 1.3$ m

page 253 Chapter 7 Review

1a. false 1b. true 1c. true 1d. true
2. $\overline{CD}$ 3. $2\sqrt{2}$
4. In 30°-60°-90° $\triangle ABE$, $\overline{AE}$ is opposite 60° angle. $AE = \sqrt{3}$; $AC = 2\sqrt{3}$
6. Form triangle. Construct any two perpendicular bisectors.
7. 16 8. 12
9. Draw $\overline{XZ}$. In $\triangle XYZ$, $m\angle YXZ > m\angle YZX$. In $\triangle XWZ$, $m\angle ZXW > m\angle XZW$. Add.

page 255 Cumulative Review Chapters 4-7

1a. ex. $\overleftrightarrow{DF}$ 1b. ex. $\overleftrightarrow{FE}$ 1c. ex. $ABEH$ 1d. $\overleftrightarrow{HB}$
1e. $DGHA$ 2a. 75 2b. $113\frac{1}{3}, 66\frac{2}{3}$
2c. $123\frac{1}{3}, 56\frac{2}{3}$ 3. $\overline{AB} \cong \overline{AE}$; use ASA.
4. $BC + CD = ED + DC$; $\angle 5 \cong \angle 6$; use SAS.
5. 140 6. 70 7. $6, 3\sqrt{3}, 3\sqrt{2}$ 8. 13 9. yes
10a. 88 10b. 75 10c. 163
11. $\overline{CD}, \overline{BC}, \overline{BD}, \overline{AD}, \overline{AB}$

CHAPTER 8

pages 262-263

1. $\overline{DC}$ 3. $\overline{DC}, \overline{AB}$ 5. true 7. false 9. true
11. true 19. rhombus 21. 5.4 cm, 10.6 cm
23. c

Problem Solving $ABGI, DEGJ, HCID$; $HEGB, BJDH, JIEF, HFGC, CEDA, AJGC$

pages 266-269

1. $\overline{AB}, \overline{DC}$; $\overline{AD}, \overline{BC}$
3. $\angle A, \angle D$; $\angle D, \angle C$; $\angle C, \angle B$; $\angle B, \angle A$ 5. 132
7. 90 9. 132 11. 4 cm 13. 122 15. 58
17. If the opposite sides of a quadrilateral are not congruent, then the quadrilateral is not a parallelogram.
19. rhombus or trapezoid with 3 congruent sides
21. not a parallelogram, contrapositive of Thm. 8-1
23. not a parallelogram, contrapositive of Thm. 8-1
25. 17°, 163° 27. 17 29. 85
31. $\overline{CD} \parallel \overline{BA}$; $\angle CDB \cong \angle ABD$; vertical angles; $\triangle BEG \cong \triangle DEF$, ASA; $\overline{FE} \cong \overline{GE}$
33. $\overline{DC} \cong \overline{BA}$, $\angle D \cong \angle B$, $\overline{AD} \cong \overline{CB}$; $AD - AE = CB - CF$; $\triangle DEC \cong \triangle BFA$, SAS; $CPCTC$
35. Parallelogram $ABCD$ with right angle at A, given; $m\angle A = m\angle C = 90$, opp. angles; $\angle D$ is sup. to $\angle A$; $m\angle D = 90$; $m\angle D = m\angle B = 90$; use def. of rectangle.

37. $\angle A \cong \angle CBF$, Thm. 5-8; $\overline{AD} \cong \overline{BD}$, use HA; $\overline{DE} \parallel \overline{CF}$; use ex. 35.
39. Use def. of parallelogram and Thm. 5-9.
41. 90 43. 30
45. $\overline{KJ} \cong \overline{XY}$; $\overline{AB} \cong \overline{KJ}$; transitive
47. $\overline{BC} \cong \overline{PQ}$, Thm. 8-2; $\overline{BC} \cong \overline{KJ}$, def. of regular polygon; $\overline{KJ} \cong \overline{XY} \cong \overline{PS}$, Thm. 8-2; $\overline{PQ} \cong \overline{PS}$, substitution

Problem Solving

1. The cross section cuts at least one pair of parallel planes.

2. Any set of five faces of the cube must contain two pairs of parallel edges.

Problem Solving a, b, c, d, e

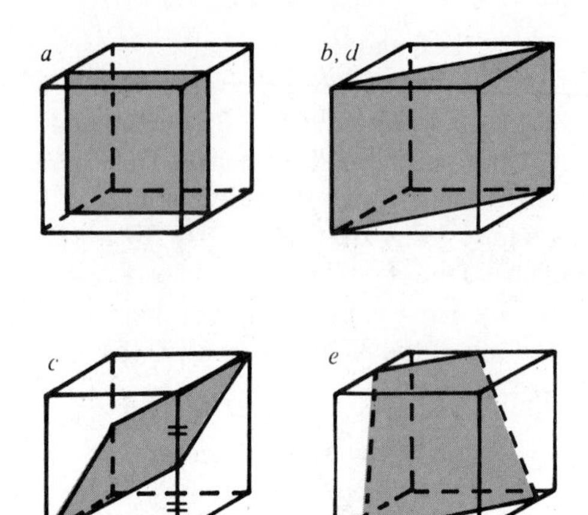

pages 272-275

1. yes 3. yes 5. no 7. 14 mm 9. 60°
11. $81\frac{2}{3}$, 8
13. $\overline{X_1X_2}$ and $\overline{Y_1Y_2}$ are congruent and parallel. $X_1X_2Y_2Y_1$ is a parallelogram. $\overline{X_1Y_1} \parallel \overline{X_2Y_2}$
15. $\overline{AD} \parallel \overline{BC}, \overline{EF} \parallel \overline{BC}, \overline{AD} \parallel \overline{FE}$; $\overline{AD} \cong \overline{BC}$, $\overline{FE} \cong \overline{BC}, \overline{AD} \cong \overline{FE}$; use Thm. 8-5.
17. $\Delta HAE \cong \Delta FCG, \Delta DHG \cong \Delta BFE, SAS$; $\overline{HE} \cong \overline{FG}, \overline{HG} \cong \overline{FE}, CPCTC$; use Thm. 8-4.
19. $\frac{1}{2}DC = \frac{1}{2}AB$; $\overline{DF} \parallel \overline{AE}$; use Thm. 8-5.
21. $AE = EC, DE = EB$, given; $\Delta AEB \cong \Delta CED$, $\Delta DEA \cong \Delta BEC, SAS$; $\overline{AB} \cong \overline{CD}, \overline{AD} \cong \overline{CB}$, $CPCTC$; Thm. 8-4

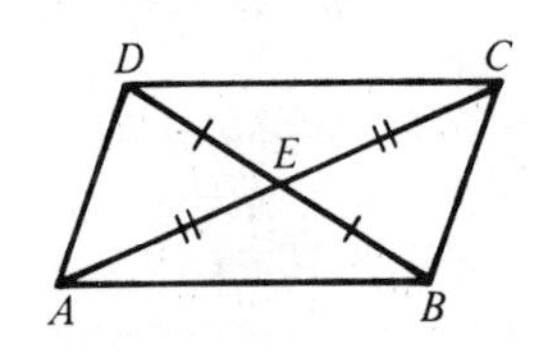

23. $AEGD$ and $ABFH$ are parallelograms, Thm. 8-5; $\overline{GE} \parallel \overline{DA}, \overline{HF} \parallel \overline{AB}$; use def. of parallelogram.
25. $\Delta AED \cong \Delta CDE, SAS$; $\angle CED \cong \angle ADE$; ΔAED and ΔCDE are isosceles; $m\angle EAD = 36$, triangle sum of 180; $m\angle EFD = 108$, triangle sum of 180; $m\angle BAF = m\angle BCF = 72$; $ABCF$ is a parallelogram, Thm. 8-6; $\overline{AB} \cong \overline{BC}$.
27. Draw $\overline{FB}$; $\Delta EBF \cong \Delta CBF, HL$; $EF = FC$; $\angle BDC \cong \angle DBC$, base angles; $\angle DFE \cong \angle DBC$, $180 - m\angle EFC$; $\angle BDC \cong \angle DFE$
29. $\overline{AC} \parallel \overline{BD}$, corresponding angles; use Thm. 8-5.

pages 278-281

1. 4 3. 10 5. 34 7. 5 9. 7.5 11. 8, 16
13. cannot determine 15. $b = 7$ 17. $a = 31.5$
19. 5, 10 21. no
23. Use Thm. 8-7, $\overline{FD} \parallel \overline{AE}, \overline{DE} \parallel \overline{AF}$
25. $ABDE$ is parallelogram; $\overline{AE} \cong \overline{BD}, \overline{AE} \parallel \overline{BD}$; get $YX = ZW, \overline{YX} \parallel \overline{ZW}$.
27. $WZYX$ is a parallelogram, Thm. 8-8; diagonals of parallelogram bisect each other.
29. $\overline{WZ} \parallel \overline{AB}, \overline{XY} \parallel \overline{AB}$, Thm. 8-7
31. $WG = GY, XG = GZ$, diagonals of parallelogram; use transitive property.
33. $YX = \frac{1}{2}DB, ZW = \frac{1}{2}DB, YX = ZW$; $\overline{YX} \parallel \overline{DB}$, $\overline{ZW} \parallel \overline{DB}, \overline{YX} \parallel \overline{ZW}$; use Thm. 8-5.
35. In $\Delta AOB, A'$ and B' are midpoints of sides, in $\Delta DOC, D'$ and C' are also midpoints; use Thms. 8-7 and 8-5.

Problem Solving

1. Prove congruent right triangles with $\overline{AB}, \overline{BC}, \overline{CD}$, and $\overline{AD}$ as corresponding parts.

2. $1^2 + (\frac{1}{2})^2 = \text{length}^2$; length $= \frac{\sqrt{5}}{2}$

3. $\frac{\sqrt{10}}{2}$

pages 284-287

1. $\overline{AD} \cong \overline{BC}, \overline{DC} \cong \overline{AB}, \overline{DB} \cong \overline{AC}, \overline{DE} \cong \overline{EB}, \overline{AE} \cong \overline{EC}, \overline{DE} \cong \overline{EC}, \overline{DE} \cong \overline{AE}, \overline{AE} \cong \overline{EB}, \overline{CE} \cong \overline{BE}$
3. $\angle DEA, \angle DEC, \angle CEB, \angle BEA$ 5. no 7. yes
9. no 11. yes 13. no 15. false 17. true
19. false 21. rectangle 23. not possible
25. square 27. $4x + 10 = 90$; $x = 20$; 116
29. $DB = AC$, $BE = AC$; $DB = BE$, transitive
31. Prove four triangles are congruent with EF, FG, GH, and HE as $CPCTC$;
$m\angle DHG + m\angle GHE + m\angle AHE = 180$;
$\angle DHG \cong \angle AEH$, $CPCTC$; $\angle AEH$ and $\angle AHE$ are complements, $\angle DHG$ and $\angle AHE$ are complements, substitution; $\angle GHE$ is a right angle.
33. $ZV = XV$, $WV = YV$; $\overline{ZX} \perp \overline{WY}$; use SAS
35a. If diagonals are congruent, then figure is a rectangle.
37. Draw $GFEH$; $\triangle DGH \cong \triangle CFG \cong \triangle BEF \cong \triangle AHE$, SAS; $\overline{GF} \cong \overline{FE} \cong \overline{EH} \cong \overline{HG}$; Thm. 8-10.
39. 1. If each diagonal bisects a pair of opposite angles, then a parallelogram is a rhombus; $\angle DAB \cong \angle DCB$, $\angle DCA \cong \angle DAC$, given, halves of equal angles; $\overline{AD} \cong \overline{DC}$;

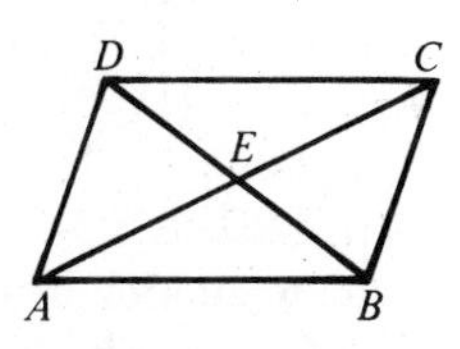

since opposite sides are also congruent, then all sides are congruent. 2. If a parallelogram is a rhombus, then each diagonal bisects a pair of opposite angles; $\triangle DCE \cong \triangle BCE$, HL; $\angle DCE \cong \angle BCE$, $CPCTC$; get $\angle DAE \cong \angle BAE$.

Problem Solving

1. $\frac{1}{2}$ 2. $\frac{\sqrt{2}}{2}$ 3. 12

pages 290-291

1. 33.5 3. 36 5. 17.15 7. 21 9. 18
11. $\angle DAP \cong \angle PAB$, angle bisector; $\angle DPA \cong \angle PAB$, alternate interior angles
13. Draw perpendiculars from D to $\overleftrightarrow{AB}$ intersecting at E and from C to $\overleftrightarrow{AB}$ intersecting at F; $\triangle DEA \cong \triangle CFB$, HL; $\angle DAB \cong \angle CBA$, congruent sup.; $\triangle DAB \cong \triangle CBA$, SAS.
15. Draw $\overline{DE} \parallel \overline{CB}$ with E on $\overline{AB}$; $DEBC$ is a parallelogram; $\overline{DE} \cong \overline{CB}$; $\overline{DE} \cong \overline{DA}$; $\angle A \cong \angle DEA$; $\angle DEA \cong \angle B$, corresponding angles; $\angle A \cong \angle B$, transitive.

Problem Solving

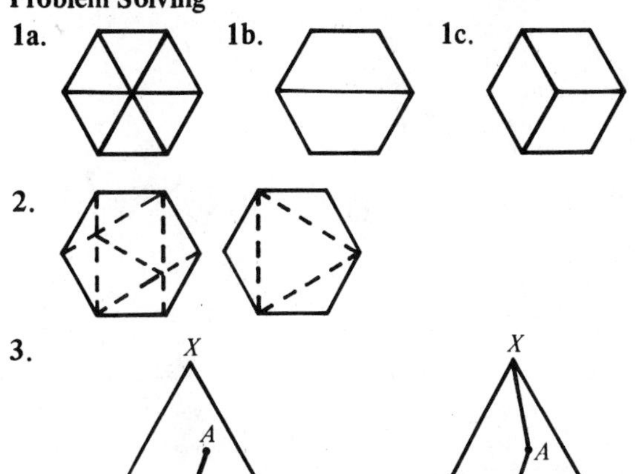

3. X A G C B Z Y X A G C B Z Y

Draw the Y-shaped figure centered at the centroid of the triangle so that: (1) $AG = BG = CG$, (2) $m\angle AGB = m\angle BGC = m\angle AGC = 120$, (3) $\overline{AG}$ does not lie on an altitude. Complete the figure by drawing $\overline{AX}$, $\overline{BY}$, and $\overline{CZ}$. $XAGCZ$, $YBGAX$, and $ZCGBY$ are congruent pentagons.

pages 294-295

1. 8 3. $x - 2$ 5. 1800° 7. 6120°
9. $(p-2)180°$ 11. 13 13. 12 15. 21
17. 140° 19. 156° 21. 176.4° 23. 45°, 30°
25. 5, 10 27. $60° + 128\frac{4}{7}° + 171\frac{3}{7}° = 360°$
29. Draw $\overline{XA}$ and $\overline{YB}$ intersecting at T; $\triangle XYB \cong \triangle YXA$, SAS; $\overline{XA} \cong \overline{YB}$, $CPCTC$; $\triangle XAB \cong \triangle YBA$, SSS; $\angle XAB \cong \angle YBA$, $CPCTC$; $\overline{TB} \cong \overline{TA}$, sides opposite congruent angles; $TX = TY$, subtraction; $\triangle BTA$ and $\triangle XTY$ are isosceles; $\angle TXY \cong \angle TYX$, $\angle TBA \cong \angle TAB$, base angles; $\angle XTY \cong \angle ATB$, vertical angles; $\angle TXY \cong \angle TAB$, sum of angles of triangle, subtraction; $\overline{XY} \parallel \overline{BA}$; $\angle XBA$ is sup. to $\angle BXY$, Thm. 5-9; $m\angle BXY = 135$, regular octagon; $m\angle XBA = 45$; $m\angle EBC = 45$ (same as above pattern); $m\angle ABC = 135 - 2(45) = 45$.

Y X A T B D E C Z

Problem Solving
1. 56 **2.** 50

page 297 Chapter 8 Review

1a. false **1b.** false **1c.** true **1d.** false **2.** 40
3. $\overline{DA} \cong \overline{CB}$; $\overline{EF} \cong \overline{CB}$; $\overline{DA} \parallel \overline{CB}$; $\overline{EF} \parallel \overline{CB}$; use Thm. 8-5.
4. $m\angle 3 = m\angle 1 = 60$; $\angle 4 \cong \angle ADE$; $m\angle 4 = \frac{(180-60)}{2} = 60$; $\angle A \cong \angle B$
5. $\angle 3 \cong \angle 1$, corresponding angles; $\angle 4 \cong \angle 3$, transitive
6. $EFGH$ is parallelogram using Thm. 8-7; $m\angle EHG = 100$; $m\angle EFG = 100$.
7. 20 **8.** 150 **9.** 100° **10.** 6.5

page 299 Algebra Review

1. 4 **3.** 7 **5.** 12 **7.** 9 **9.** ±3
11. $(0, -5)$ **13.** $(-\frac{3}{2}, 2)$ **15.** $(-3, 3)$
17. $(\frac{2}{3}, \frac{3}{4})$ **19.** 81 **21.** 7 **23.** -2 **25.** $-2, 5$
27. 5 **29.** $4, -3$ **31.** 36°, 54°, 90°

CHAPTER 9

pages 306-307

1a. Thm. 9-4 **1b.** Thm. 9-2 **1c.** Thm. 9-3
3a. $\frac{3}{2} = \frac{6}{4}$ **3b.** $\frac{\sqrt{2}}{1} = \frac{\sqrt{6}}{\sqrt{3}}$ **3c.** $\frac{2}{3} = \frac{XY}{MN}$
3d. $\frac{AB}{EF} = \frac{GH}{CD}$ **5a.** If $ad \neq bc$, then $\frac{a}{b} \neq \frac{c}{d}$
7. \$70 **9.** 67.5, 112.5 **11.** $12\frac{1}{2} \times 17\frac{1}{2}$ **13.** 3, 5
Problem Solving
1. 128 ft NS, 133 ft EW
2. NS: $\frac{32 \text{ ft}}{19 \text{ mm}} = \frac{x \text{ ft}}{76 \text{ mm}}$; EW: $\frac{32 \text{ ft}}{19 \text{ mm}} = \frac{y \text{ ft}}{79 \text{ mm}}$
3. approximately \$7000

pages 310-311

1a. true **1b.** true **1c.** true **1d.** false **1e.** true
1f. false **3.** $2\frac{2}{3}$ **5.** 2.4 **7.** 10 **9.** Thm. 9-6
11. 6, 24 **13.** 42 cm **15.** $7\frac{1}{5}, 10\frac{4}{5}$
Problem Solving $\frac{12}{5}, \frac{18}{5}$

pages 314-315

1. yes **3.** no **5.** $\angle I \cong \angle I'$, $\angle J \cong \angle J'$, $\angle H \cong \angle H'$
7. $6\frac{6}{7}, 10\frac{2}{7}$
9. $\angle A \cong \angle A$, $\angle ADE \cong \angle B$, $\angle AED \cong \angle C$; use definition of similar polygons.
11. $\frac{AD}{AB} = \frac{AE}{AC} = \frac{DE}{BC} = \frac{1}{3}$; $\angle ADE \cong \angle ABC$, $\angle AED \cong \angle ACB$, $\angle A \cong \angle A$
13. Make hypotenuse 2 units long.
15. $\triangle ADE \sim \triangle ABC$, AA; $\frac{AD}{AB} = \frac{AE}{AC}$; $\frac{AB}{AD} = \frac{AC}{AE}$; $\frac{AD + DB}{AD} = \frac{AE + EC}{AE}$; $1 + \frac{DB}{AD} = 1 + \frac{EC}{AE}$; $\frac{DB}{AD} = \frac{EC}{AE}$
Problem Solving 13, $4s + 1$, 41

pages 318-321

1. $\triangle XYZ$ **3.** $\triangle YZX$
5. Each contains two pairs of congruent angles.
7. 10 **9.** $3\frac{3}{8}$ **11.** no, different acute angles
13. yes, AAA **15.** $\angle ALB \cong \angle A'LB'$, $\angle B' \cong \angle B$
17. $\angle 3 \cong \angle 4$, vertical angles; $\triangle ABC \sim \triangle EDC$, Thm. 9-8
19. $\angle AED \cong \angle CEB$, vertical angles; $\angle EBC \cong \angle EDA$, alternate interior angles; AA
21. $\angle B \cong \angle E$, $m\angle BGA = m\angle EHD = 90$, $\angle BGA \cong \angle EHD$; $\triangle BGA \sim \triangle EHD$, AA; use def. of similar triangles.
23. Form parallelograms; $\angle E \cong \angle EHY$, opposite angles; $\angle A \cong \angle HNY$, AA.
25a. $\angle R \cong \angle R$; $\angle S \cong \angle RUS$; AA
25b. $\overline{RS} \parallel \overline{UV}$, $\angle R \cong \angle VUT$, $\angle 1 \cong \angle 2$; AA
27. $m\angle BAD = m\angle FEH$, halves of equal angles; $\triangle ABD \sim \triangle EFH$, AA
29. Draw $\overline{BG}$ intersecting $\overline{CF}$ at H; use Side-splitting Theorem; $\frac{BC}{CD} = \frac{BH}{HG}$ and $\frac{BH}{HG} = \frac{EF}{FG}$; use transitive property.
31. $\triangle AFC \sim \triangle AEB$, $\triangle BDA \sim \triangle BFC$, $\triangle CDA \sim \triangle CEB$; $\frac{AF}{AE} = \frac{FC}{EB}$, $\frac{BD}{BF} = \frac{DA}{FC}$, and $\frac{CE}{CD} = \frac{EB}{DA}$; $\frac{AF}{AE} \cdot \frac{BD}{BF} \cdot \frac{CE}{CD} = \frac{FC}{EB} \cdot \frac{DA}{FC} \cdot \frac{EB}{DA} = 1$
33. $\triangle ACB \sim \triangle ABD$, AA; $\frac{AC}{AB} = \frac{AB}{AD}$.
Problem Solving
1. $\frac{x}{20} = \frac{AB}{A'B'}$; $A'B' = \frac{20AB}{x}$
2. $A'B'$ is doubled.

pages 324-325

1. 6 **3.** $2\sqrt{5}$ **5.** AD and DB **7.** AB and AD
9. 6 **11.** 16 **13.** 15 **15.** $\frac{60}{13}$ **17.** 2
19. $EG = 12$; $HE = 6\sqrt{5}$; $72\sqrt{5}$ **21.** $\frac{7}{5}$
23. In $\triangle CDA$, $BD^2 = BC \cdot BA$, $BD = \sqrt{BC \cdot BA}$.
In $\triangle ADE$, $DF^2 = AF \cdot FE$, $DF = \sqrt{AF \cdot FE}$;
$BD \cdot DF = \sqrt{BC \cdot BA \cdot AF \cdot FE}$.
25. $\frac{BC}{AB} = \frac{AB}{AC}$; $\frac{BC + AB}{AB} = \frac{AB + AC}{AC}$; $\frac{AC}{AB} = \frac{AC + CD}{AC}$
Problem Solving $\frac{AF + CX}{AF} = \frac{AF}{CX}$, $\frac{CX + XB}{CX} = \frac{CX}{XB}$;
$AF^2 = AF \cdot CX + CX^2$; $CX^2 = CX \cdot XB + XB^2$,
$CX^2 = AF - AF \cdot CX$, add; $2CX^2 = 2AF \cdot XB$. Use Pyth. Thm., $2CX^2 = EX^2$, $2AF^2 = AE^2$, $2XS^2 = XY^2$, $AE^2 \cdot XY^2 = 2AF^2 \cdot 2XB^2 = 4AF^2 \cdot XB^2$ or $AE \cdot XY = 2AF \cdot XB$. $EX^2 = AE \cdot XY$, substitution

pages 328-329

1. yes, SSS **3.** no **5.** $\frac{4}{7}$
7. $\angle DOC \cong \angle AOB$, vertical angles; $\angle CAB \cong \angle DCA$, alternate interior angles; AA
9. $\frac{JK}{NM} = \frac{KL}{MP} = \frac{\frac{1}{2}KL}{\frac{1}{2}MP} = \frac{KI}{MO}$, $\angle K \cong \angle M$;
$\triangle KJI \sim \triangle MNO$, SAS sim; proportional parts
11.

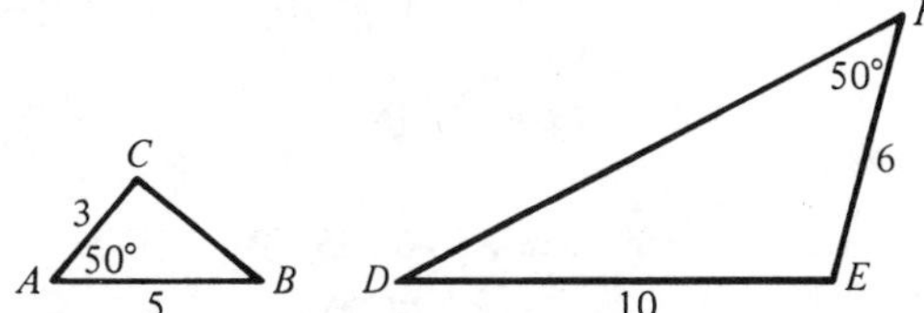

$\frac{AB}{DE} = \frac{5}{10}$; $\frac{AC}{EF} = \frac{3}{6}$; $\angle A \cong \angle F$; no similar triangles
13.

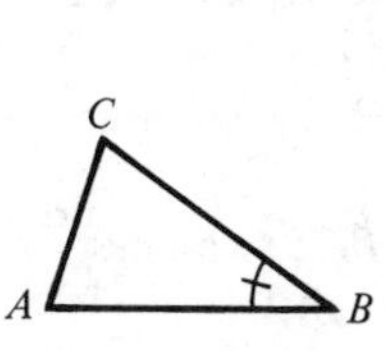

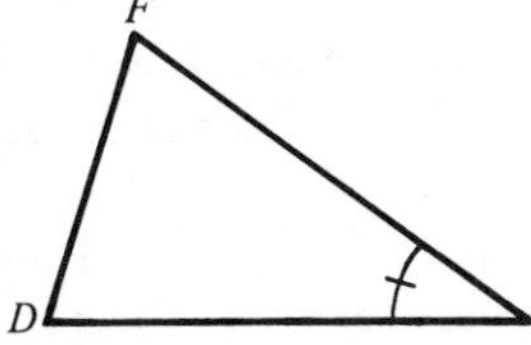

$\triangle ABC$ and $\triangle DEF$ are isosceles triangles with $\angle B \cong \angle E$; $\frac{(180 - m\angle B)}{2} = m\angle A$; $\frac{(180 - m\angle E)}{2} = m\angle D$;
$\triangle ABC \sim \triangle DEF$, AA.
Problem Solving Some possible answers are:
pentagon, $ABCDE \sim A'B'C'D'E'$;
star with pts. $ABCDE \sim$ star with pts. $A'B'C'D'E'$;
obtuse triangle, $AA'B \sim A'B''B'$; acute triangle, $AE'B \sim A'A''B'$; isosceles triangle, $AE'A' \sim A'A''B''$, $AEB \sim A'E'B'$, $C'CD \sim C'D''D'$; rhombus, $ABC'E \sim E'A'C''D'$; isosceles trapezoid, $ABC'D' \sim E'A'C''D''$, $ABCE \sim A'B'C'E'$

pages 332-333

1. $\frac{4}{3}, \frac{4}{5}, \frac{3}{5}$ **3.** 0.2924 **5.** 0.3839 **7.** 0.7002
9. 37° **11.** 17° **13.** 4° **15.** $10 \sin 40° = 6.4$
17. 25, 24, $\frac{24}{7}$ **19.** 53°, 37° **21.** 35.7 m
23. 0.42 cm
Problem Solving $\tan 40° = \frac{DC}{200 + BC}$, $\tan 60° = \frac{DC}{BC}$; 325.5 m

page 335

1. $\frac{\sqrt{2}}{2}$ **3.** $\sqrt{3}$ **5.** $\frac{1}{2}$ **7.** $\frac{1}{2}$ **9.** $\frac{1}{\sqrt{3}}$ or $\frac{\sqrt{3}}{3}$
11. $\sqrt{3}$ **13.** 30°
15. $2 \sin 30° = 2(\frac{1}{2}) = 1$;
$2 \sin 30° \cos 30° = 2(\frac{1}{2})(\frac{\sqrt{3}}{2}) = \frac{\sqrt{3}}{2}$;
$\sin(2 \cdot 30°) = \sin 60° = \frac{\sqrt{3}}{2}$; $2 \sin A \cos A = \sin 2A$
17. $\tan 2(30°) = \tan 60° = \sqrt{3}$; $2 \tan 30° = \frac{2\sqrt{3}}{3}$;

$$\frac{2 \tan 30}{1 - (\tan 30)^2} = \frac{2\frac{\sqrt{3}}{3}}{1 - \left(\frac{\sqrt{3}}{3}\right)^2} = \frac{\frac{2\sqrt{3}}{3}}{\frac{2}{3}} = \sqrt{3};$$

$$\tan 2A = \frac{2 \tan A}{1 - (\tan A)^2}$$

19. $\frac{50\sqrt{3}}{3}$ **21.** $4\sqrt{3}$

page 337 Chapter 9 Review

1a. true **1b.** true **1c.** false **1d.** true **1e.** true
2a. $12\frac{1}{2}$ **2b.** $3\frac{3}{5}$ **2c.** $2\frac{4}{7}$ **2d.** 6
3. $\triangle ABC \sim \triangle DCE$, AA; $\frac{AB}{DC} = \frac{BC}{CE}$ **4a.** $\frac{16}{3}$ **4b.** 9
4c. 9 **5a.** $\frac{8}{15}$ **5b.** $\frac{40}{41}$ **5c.** $\frac{4}{5}$ **6.** 67.5 ft
7a. $\angle EDF \cong \angle ECB$, Thm. 5-8; AA
7b. $\angle EFD \cong \angle BFA$, vertical angles; $\angle DEF \cong \angle ABF$, Thm. 5-7; AA
7c. $\angle A \cong \angle C$, opposite angles; $\angle CEB \cong \angle ABF$; AA

page 339 Problem Solving Techniques

1a. right **1b.** yes **1c.** DF **1d.** $EF = CF, AF = 6$
2. $EF = 4.2$ **3b.** 90
3c. $m\angle C = 90, m\angle 2 + m\angle 4 = 90, m\angle 1 + m\angle 3 = 90$;
$m\angle 1 + m\angle 2 + m\angle 3 + m\angle 4 = 180$;
$m\angle 1 + m\angle 2 + m\angle DEF = 180$,
$m\angle 3 + m\angle 4 + m\angle GFE = 180$, add;
$180 + m\angle DEF + m\angle GFE = 360$; $\angle DEF$ and $\angle GFE$ are supplements.

CHAPTER 10

pages 344-345

1. $\overline{AE}, \overline{AD}, \overline{BC}, \overline{BE}$ **3.** $\widehat{AE}, \widehat{BC}, \widehat{CD}, \widehat{AB}$
11. $\angle CAD, \angle ACD, \angle CDA, \angle CDB, \angle ADB$
13. $\angle AOB, \angle BOF, \angle FOE, \angle EOB, \angle AOF$
21. Shortest arc is a great circle.
Problem Solving
3. They are the same as the list on number 1.

pages 348-349

1. yes, no **3a.** 90 **3b.** 150 **3c.** 270 **3d.** 210
5a. 70 **5b.** 50 **5c.** 310
7. $\widehat{AB} \cong \widehat{EF}, \widehat{BC} \cong \widehat{FG}, \widehat{CD} \cong \widehat{DE}$
9. $\overline{AB} \cong \overline{CD}, \overline{AC} \cong \overline{BD}$ **11.** yes
13. Form congruent triangles, SSS; central angles congruent; def. of minor arc
15. $m\widehat{EA} + m\widehat{AS} = m\widehat{AS} + m\widehat{SY}$; $m\widehat{EA} = m\widehat{SY}$.
17. $m\widehat{ACB} = m\widehat{DAC}$; $m\widehat{DA} + m\widehat{AC} = m\widehat{BC} + m\widehat{AC}$;
$m\widehat{DA} = m\widehat{BC}$; $DA = BC$, Thm. 10-2;
$m\widehat{ACB} = m\widehat{DBC}$; $m\widehat{AC} + m\widehat{CB} = m\widehat{DB} + m\widehat{BC}$;
$m\widehat{AC} = m\widehat{DB}$; $AC = DB$, Thm. 10-2; use Thm. 8-4.
19. ΔSOR is isosceles, $\angle 1 \cong \angle 3$; $\angle 3 \cong \angle 4$; $\angle 1 \cong \angle 2$; $\angle 4 \cong \angle 2$, transitive
Problem Solving
2. four

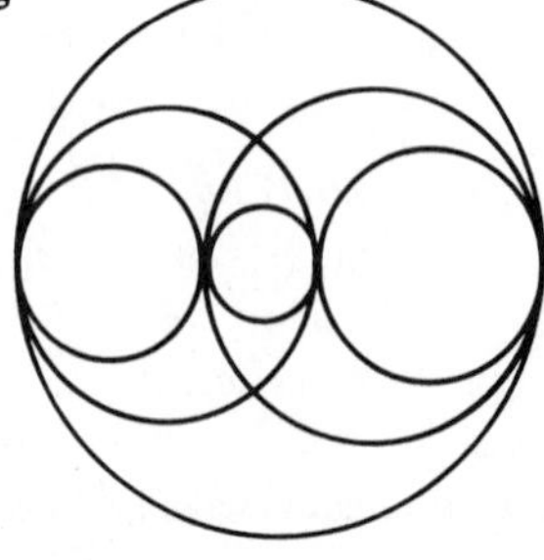

3. Extend segment connecting centers of C_1 and C_2 to outermost points of each circle. Bisect segment. Use center as a new radius.

pages 352-353

1. 3, Thm. 10-3
3. $\overline{OM} \cong \overline{ON}$, Thm. 10-3; $\frac{(180 - 150)}{2} = 15$
5. Thm. 10-4
7. $\overline{OX} \cong \overline{OY}$, sides opposite congruent angles; Thm. 10-4
9. Thm. 10-3
11. $\Delta XOZ \cong \Delta YOZ, HA$; $\overline{OX} \cong \overline{OY}$, $CPCTC$; Thm. 10-4
Problem Solving Use the figure at the bottom of page 350; equal chords are equidistant from the center; draw a perpendicular segment from the center to each chord; the perpendicular segment intersects the chord at its midpoint; use congruent triangles to prove the perpendicular segments are equal radii; equal radii determine a circle.

pages 356-359

3. $m\widehat{AC} = m\widehat{CB}$, Thm. 10-6 **5.** Thm. 10-6
7. Thm. 10-5 **9.** 5 **11.** 3 cm
13. $\overline{OM} \perp \overline{AB}$, Thm. 10-7; $AO^2 = AM^2 + OM^2$; 8
15. 2
17. $OB = 4$; $x =$ distance; $4 = x\sqrt{2}$; $x = 2\sqrt{2}$
19. Draw two chords of the arc; construct perpendicular bisectors of each chord; intersection gives center.
21. $\overline{AB} \perp \overline{XY}, \overline{CD} \perp \overline{XY}$, Thm. 10-7; two lines perpendicular to same line are parallel.
23. Find distance from O to $\overline{AB}$, $x^2 = 10^2 - 8^2$, $x = 6$; distance from F to midpoint of $\overline{CD}$ is also 6; 15.
25. $\angle MOQ \cong \angle MOP$; congruent arcs have congruent central angles; $\Delta XOM \cong \Delta YOM, HA$; $CPCTC$
27. $\overline{AC} \cong \overline{BC}$, Thm. 10-2; $\overline{OA} \cong \overline{OB}$; use Thm. 6-10.
Problem Solving $DC = AC, DB = AB$; SSS

pages 362-363

3. 39
5. $\overline{PB} \perp \overline{OB}, \overline{PA} \perp \overline{OA}$, Thm. 10-9; $\overline{PA} \parallel \overline{BO}, \overline{PB} \parallel \overline{AO}$, Thm. 5-4; $AOBP$ is parallelogram; $OA = OB = 4$; opposite sides congruent; $\angle P$ is right angle.
7. $\overline{OA} \perp \overline{AP}, \overline{OB} \perp \overline{BP}$, Thm. 10-9; $\triangle OAP \cong \triangle OBP$, HL; $CPCTC$
9. $\triangle PAO \cong \triangle PBO, HL$; $\overline{PA} \cong \overline{PB}$; $\overline{AO} \cong \overline{OB}$; Thm. 6-10
11. Draw $\overline{OB}$; $2m\angle OCB + m\angle COB = 180$, $2m\angle AOP + m\angle COB = 180$; $\angle AOP \cong \angle OCB$; Thm. 5-1
13. $\ell \perp m$ at P, given; assume ℓ does not contain center of circle; draw radius from center O to point P; $\overline{OP} \perp m$, Thm. 10-9; there is exactly one line through P perpendicular to m; line ℓ contains the center of the circle.

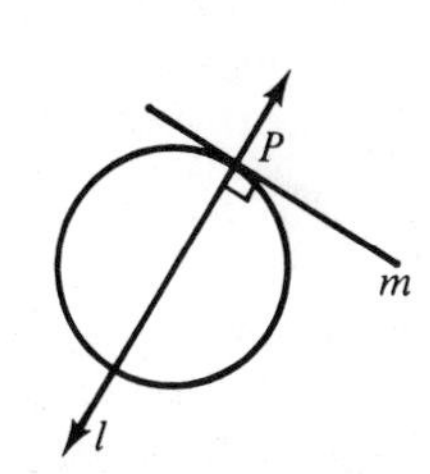

Problem Solving Connect D with point of tangency on $\overrightarrow{BC}$; show all three triangles are congruent by HL.

pages 366-367

1. 5 cm **3.** 10 cm **5.** 20
7. Call distance from A to circle, x; distance from B to circle, y; distance from C to circle, z; $x + y = 6$; $x + z = 10$; $y + z = 8$; $y = 2, OX = 2$.
9. E is point of intersection of $\overline{AB}$ and $\overline{CD}$; $\overline{AE} \cong \overline{ED}$ and $\overline{BE} \cong \overline{CE}, AE + BE = ED + CE$
11. $Y = \frac{3}{8}\sqrt{3} + \frac{3}{8} \doteq 1.025$
$X = 2Y + 3$
$X \doteq 5.05$

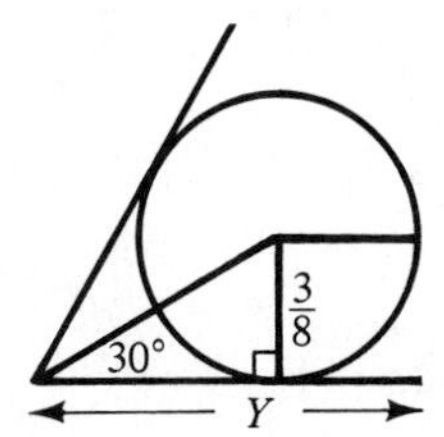

Problem Solving Draw perpendicular line from A to ℓ intersecting ℓ at D; $\triangle ADB$ is 30-60-90 triangle with $AB = \frac{d}{2}\sqrt{3}$.

pages 370-373

1. 25 **3.** 65
5. $m\angle A = 80, m\angle B = 55, m\angle C = 45$
7. 100, 120, 140 **9.** 80 **11.** 80 **13.** 40
15. 10 **17.** 120 **19.** 87 **21a.** 50 **21b.** 40
21c. 50 **21d.** 80
23. $\angle AEB$ and $\angle CED$, vertical; $\angle ABE$ and $\angle ECD$ intercept same arc; $\angle BAE$ and $\angle EDC$ intercept same arc.
25. $m\angle E = m\angle D = 90$; $\angle ABE \cong \angle CBD$, vertical angles.
27. Draw segment from P to center of given circle; bisect segment; use half of this segment as radius, use center as midpoint of segment, construct circle; points of intersection with given circle are points of tangency.
29. Sum of arcs intercepted by opposite vertices is $360°$; $\frac{1}{2} \cdot 360 = 180$.
31. Opposite angles are congruent and supplementary.
33. $\angle CAD \cong \angle ADB$, alternate interior angles; congruent inscribed angles intercept congruent arcs.
35. $\widehat{AD} \cong \widehat{BC}$; $m\widehat{DA} + m\widehat{AB} + m\widehat{BC} + m\widehat{CD} = 360$; $\angle ADC$ intercepts $\widehat{AB}$ plus $\widehat{BC}$, $\angle DAB$ intercepts $\widehat{BC}$ plus $\widehat{CD}$; $m\angle ADC + m\angle DAB = \frac{1}{2}(m\widehat{AB} + m\widehat{BC} + m\widehat{BC} + m\widehat{CD}) = 180$; $\angle ADC$ and $\angle DAB$ are supplementary; $\overline{AB} \parallel \overline{DC}$.
Problem Solving $\widehat{MP}$ of circle Q is congruent to $\widehat{MN}$ of circle O; $m\widehat{MP} = m\widehat{MN} = t$; $\angle MAP$ is an inscribed angle so $m\angle MAP = \frac{t}{2}$, Thm. 10-12.

pages 376-377

1. 25 **3.** 60 **5.** 55, 110 **7.** 55, 55, 75, 50, 20
9. O is the intersection of $\overline{AB}$ and $\overline{CD}$;
$m\angle AOD = \frac{1}{2}(m\widehat{AD} + m\widehat{BC})$;
$m\angle AOC = \frac{1}{2}(m\widehat{AC} + m\widehat{BD})$
11. $90 = \frac{1}{2}(m\widehat{AE} + m\widehat{CD}), 90 = \frac{1}{2}(m\widehat{AE} + m\widehat{BC})$;
$m\widehat{AE} + m\widehat{CD} = m\widehat{AE} + m\widehat{BC}$
Problem Solving 36, 60, 84, 108, 132

pages 382-385

1. 120 **3.** $22\frac{1}{2}$ **5.** 20 **7.** 3 **9.** 8 **11.** 23
13. 30 **15.** 85 **17.** 30 **19.** 110, 100
21. $6^2 = x(x+9)$; $x = 3$; $6^2 = 4(4+y)$; $y = 5$
23. 40 **25.** 20 **27.** 70
29. No, $\angle 1$ and $\angle 2$ are not supplementary. **31.** 7, 8
33. Call intersection of $\overline{AB}$ and ℓ_2 point X; vertical angles at X are congruent; major arcs are congruent; congruent alternate interior angles.
35. $m\angle 3 = \frac{1}{2}y$; $m\angle 2 = \frac{1}{2}x$; $m\angle P + m\angle 2 = m\angle 3$, exterior angle; $m\angle P = \frac{1}{2}(y - x)$
37. $\angle PCB \cong \angle PDA$; inscribed angles intercepting $\widehat{AB}$;
$\triangle PCB \sim \triangle PDA, AA; \frac{PA}{PB} = \frac{PD}{PC}$;
$PA \cdot PC = PB \cdot PD$.

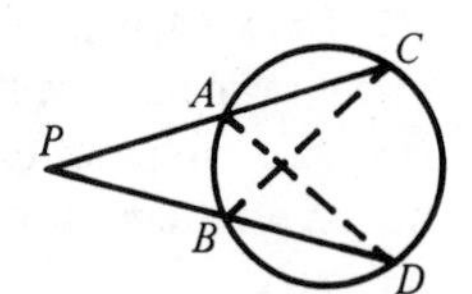

Problem Solving

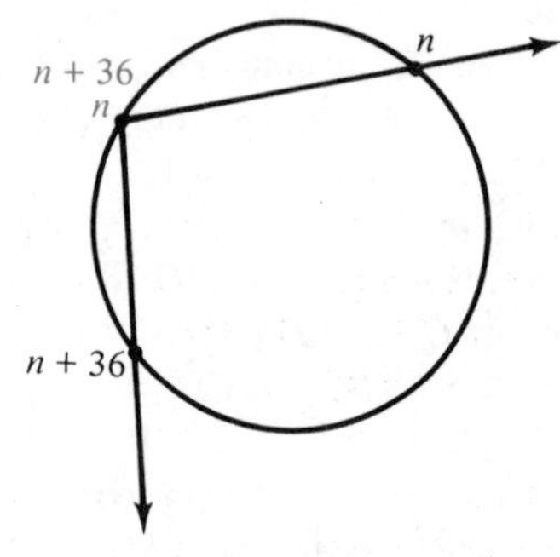

A ray is drawn from each red n through the black n for each integer 0, 1, 2, . . . , 71. Since the red numerals are spaced 10° apart, a red numeral n, $0 \leq n \leq 35$, and a red $n + 36$ name the same point. How do the points labeled with a black n and $n + 36$ compare? The point with a black $n + 36$ is 180° around the circle from point n. The result follows from Thm. 10-13.

page 387 Chapter 10 Review

1. true **2.** false **3.** false **4.** true **5a.** 60
5b. 30 **5c.** 75 **5d.** 90
6. Draw $\overline{AC}$; $\angle BAC \cong \angle DCA$, congruent minor arcs; alternate interior angles.
7a. 20 **7b.** 110 **7c.** 40 **7d.** 70 **7e.** 20
8a. 4 **8b.** 24 **9.** 17 cm **10.** $\sqrt{51}$, 12

page 389 Cumulative Review Chapters 8-10

1a. true **1b.** false **1c.** true **1d.** false
2a. $4\sqrt{2}$ **2b.** 4 or 9 **2c.** $\frac{144}{13}$ **2d.** AA **3.** 144
4a. 100 **4b.** 50 **4c.** 30 **4d.** 80
5. $\triangle ANB \sim \triangle CND, AA; \frac{NA}{NC} = \frac{NB}{ND}$ **6.** 40
7. $AB = \frac{1}{2}MP, DC = \frac{1}{2}MP, BC = \frac{1}{2}QN, AD = \frac{1}{2}QN$, Midsegment Thm.; $DC = AB$, $AD = BC$; $ABCD$ is a parallelogram, opposite sides congruent; $AB = AD = DC = BC$ since $MP = QN$.

CHAPTER 11

pages 396-397

3. no **5.** Area Postulate
7. Triangle with base 20, height 7; rectangle with length 10, width 7
9. 630 **11.** 6 **13.** 3 **15.** $3\frac{1}{2}$ **17.** 720
19. $2(32 \cdot 10\sqrt{2}/32) \cdot 1.1 = 31.1$; 32 sheets
21. $A(\triangle ACE) = A(\triangle AGE)$;
$A(\triangle AHI) + A(HIFG) + A(\triangle FIE) = A(\triangle ABI) + A(BCDI) + A(\triangle IDE)$; $A(\triangle AHI) = A(\triangle ABI)$, $A(\triangle FIE) = A(\triangle IDE)$; subtract.
Problem Solving $\frac{9}{4}$, no

pages 400-401

1. 147 **3.** $90\frac{3}{4}$ **5.** 12 **7.** $14 \cdot \frac{5}{2}\sqrt{3} = 35\sqrt{3}$
9. $12 \cdot \frac{5\sqrt{3}}{3} = 20\sqrt{3}$ **11.** $\frac{8}{3}$ **13.** quadrupled
15. equal **17.** 13
Problem Solving
1. yes
2. no

pages 404-407

1. 429 3. 264 5. 425 7. 198 9. $512\frac{1}{2}$
11. 8.75 13. 5 ft 15. 12.5 17. 30
19. Let h = distance between $\overline{AB}$ and $\overline{CD}$;
$A(AECD) = \frac{1}{2}h(AE + DC)$;
$A(EBCD) = \frac{1}{2}h(EB + DC)$; $AE = EB$
21. $\triangle ABD$ and $\triangle BDC$ have the same height and equal bases, $\overline{AD}$ and $\overline{CD}$.
23. $A(ABCD) = (h_1 + h_2)AB$; $A(\triangle CDX) = \frac{1}{2}h_1AB$;
$A(\triangle ABX) = \frac{1}{2}h_2AB$; $A(\triangle CDX + \triangle ABX) =$
$\frac{1}{2}h_1AB + \frac{1}{2}h_2AB = \frac{1}{2}AB(h_1 + h_2)$
25. $A(\triangle BAA') = A(\triangle CAA')$, same altitude and equal bases; let H be centroid of $\triangle ABC$;
$A(\triangle BHA') = A(\triangle CHA')$; $A(\triangle AHB) = A(\triangle AHC)$, subtraction;
$A(\triangle BHC') = A(\triangle AHC') = A(\triangle AHB') = A(\triangle CHB')$;
repeat procedure using $A(\triangle BAB') = A(\triangle CBB')$ as first step.
27. $A(ABCD) = \frac{1}{2}h(AB + DC)$;
$A(\triangle ADE) = A(ABCD) + (A(\triangle DCE) + A(\triangle ABE))$;
draw perpendiculars from E to $\overleftrightarrow{DC}$ and from E to $\overleftrightarrow{AB}$;
length of these altitudes $= \frac{1}{2}h$;
$A(\triangle ADE) = \frac{1}{2}h(AB + DC) - (\frac{1}{2} \cdot \frac{1}{2}hDC + \frac{1}{2} \cdot \frac{1}{2}hAB)$
$= \frac{1}{4}h(AB + DC)$; $\frac{1}{2}A(ABCD)$.
29. Use ex. 25; area addition.
31. $x\sqrt{2} = 3 - 2x$; $x = \dfrac{3}{2 + \sqrt{2}}$
33. In 30-60-90 triangle, $CG = \frac{\sqrt{3}}{3}$;
$A(\triangle CFG) = \frac{1}{2} \cdot \frac{\sqrt{3}}{3} \cdot 1 = \frac{\sqrt{3}}{6}$
Problem Solving
1. $\sqrt{2}$ 2. $\sqrt{3}$ 3. $\frac{\sqrt{3}}{2}$ 4. $\sqrt{2}$ 5. $\frac{\sqrt{2}}{4}$

pages 410-411

1. 102 3. 104 5. 72 7. $\frac{5\sqrt{3}}{3}, 25\sqrt{3}$
9. 11, 484 11. $20k$ 13. $20\sqrt{3}$ m, $50\sqrt{3}$ m^2
15. $20\sqrt{3}$ ft, 5 ft
17. 2, 96; 5, 225; 10, 400; 15, 525; 20, 600; 25, 625; enclose a square.
Problem Solving $10 + 2\sqrt{5} + \sqrt{2}$; $4 + 3\sqrt{5} + \sqrt{17}$; $3\sqrt{2} + 2\sqrt{10} + 2\sqrt{5} + 2\sqrt{13}$

pages 414-415

1. 1:2 3. 13:20 5. 3:4
7. 200, 72; $25x + 9x = 272$ 9. $\frac{YZ}{BC} = \frac{1}{2}; (\frac{1}{2})^2 = \frac{1}{4}$
11. 2:1 13. $\sqrt{288} \doteq 17$
Problem Solving 1:16

pages 418-419

1. circumference 3. $3\frac{1}{7}$, 3.14, 3.1416 5. 3, 6π
7. 4, 8 9. diameter 11. 36π in.^{2}
13. $(32 + 4\pi)$ ft 15. $(10 + 4\pi)$ m 17. 6 ft
Problem Solving $AD^2 + OD^2 = AO^2$; $OD^2 = 1 - \frac{s^2}{4}$;
$OD^2 = \frac{4}{4} - \frac{s^2}{4}$, $OD = \frac{\sqrt{4 - s^2}}{2}$; $CD = 1 - \frac{\sqrt{4 - s^2}}{2}$;
$x^2 = CD^2 + AD^2$; $x^2 = \left(1 - \frac{\sqrt{4 - s^2}}{2}\right)^2 + \left(\frac{s}{2}\right)^2$;
$x^2 = 2 - \sqrt{4 - s^2}$

pages 422-425

1. $4\pi, \frac{121}{4}\pi, \pi^3, 3\pi$ 3. $\pi, 9\pi, \frac{3}{2}\pi, \frac{25}{\pi}$ 5. 18π cm^2
7. $\frac{25\pi}{24}$ cm^2 9a. 3.93 cm^2 9b. 5.89 m^2
9c. 13.08 in.^{2} 11. 16:25 13. $2\sqrt{2}:\sqrt{5}$
15. $9 - \frac{9}{4}\pi$ 17. $9 - \frac{9}{4}\pi$ 19. $12\pi - 9\sqrt{3}$
21. 21.5%; $\dfrac{(9 - \frac{9}{4}\pi)}{9}$
23. $\frac{1}{2}\pi(\frac{3}{2}AB)^2 - \frac{1}{2}\pi AB^2 + \frac{1}{2}(\pi(\frac{1}{2}AB)^2) = \frac{3}{4}\pi AB^2$ shaded; fraction of circle is $\frac{1}{3}$.
25. Pythagorean Theorem,
$\frac{1}{2}\pi(\frac{a}{2})^2 + \frac{1}{2}\pi(\frac{b}{2})^2 = \frac{\pi}{8}(a^2 + b^2) = \frac{\pi}{8}(c^2) = \frac{1}{2}\pi(\frac{c}{2})^2$
27. $A_1 = \frac{\pi}{2}(\frac{AB}{2})^2 - \frac{\pi}{2}(\frac{AC}{2})^2 - \frac{\pi}{2}(\frac{BC}{2})^2$,
$A_1 = \frac{\pi((AC + BC)^2 - AC^2 - BC^2)}{8}$, $A_1 = \frac{\pi AC \cdot BC}{4}$;
$A_2 = \pi(\frac{CD}{2})^2$, $CD^2 = AC \cdot BC$, $A_2 = \frac{\pi AC \cdot BC}{4}$
29. Area of square − area of four quarter circles − area of small circle = shaded area; let $2x$ = length of side of square; draw 30-60-90 triangle with vertex at center and lengths $x, x, x\sqrt{2}$; radius of small circle is $x\sqrt{2} - x$; $(2x)^2 - \pi x^2 - \pi(x\sqrt{2} - x)^2 =$
$4x^2 - 4\pi x^2 + 2\pi x^2\sqrt{2}$; ratio of shaded area to circle area is $\frac{4}{\pi} - 4 + 2\sqrt{2}$ or 10%.
Problem Solving $\frac{1}{7}$

page 427 Chapter 11 Review

1a. $5\sqrt{2}$ **1b.** 40 **1c.** $5\sqrt{119}$ **1d.** 50 **2a.** 3
2b. $\frac{27}{4}$ **3.** 2:1 **4.** $\frac{27\sqrt{3}}{2}$ **5.** $\overline{AD}$
6. 30-60-90 triangle, $OB = 2$, $OA = 1$, $BA = \sqrt{3}$;
$\pi \cdot 2^2 - \frac{1}{2} \cdot 3 \cdot 2\sqrt{3} = 4\pi - 3\sqrt{3}$
7. 1:4 **8.** 4π

page 429 Algebra Review

1. 24 cm² **3.** 87.92 cm
5. 3658.7π cm³ or 11,488.2 cm³ **7.** $h = 3.6$ cm
9. $A = 58.5\pi$ in.² or 183.69 in.² **11.** $-2, 3$
13. -2 **15.** $-3, -2$ **17.** $10, -9$ **19.** $\frac{1}{5}, \frac{1}{3}$
21. 2, 3 **23.** 7900 yd² **25.** 93.75 cm²
27. 486 mm² **29.** 2 m

pages 442-443

1. c **3.** 24 **5.** 120 **7.** $12 + 2\sqrt{3}$
9. $72\sqrt{3} + \frac{81}{2}\sqrt{3} = 112.5\sqrt{3}$ **11.** 6 cm, 12 cm
13. Determine edge, $x^2 + (\frac{x}{2})^2 = c^2$, $c^2 = \frac{5}{4}x^2$;
$\frac{5}{4}x^2 + (2\sqrt{2})^2 = \text{height}^2$; height $= 2\sqrt{3}$ cm.
15. Each pan needs 880 cm²;
$880 \text{ cm}^2 \times \frac{1 \text{ m}^2}{10{,}000 \text{ cm}^2} = 0.088 \text{ m}^2$,
$100 \text{ m}^2 \cdot \frac{x \text{ pans}}{0.088 \text{ m}^2} = 1136$ pans

Problem Solving
1. Move upper right-of-center block inward one space.
2. Move lower front-corner block up and straight back.

CHAPTER 12

pages 436-439

1. *b* **3.** $\overline{AB}, \overline{BC}, \overline{CD}, \overline{DE}, \overline{AE}$
5. $\triangle FBC, \triangle FAB, \triangle FAE, \triangle FDE, \triangle FDC$
7. $\overline{EF}, \overline{HG}, \overline{IJ}, \overline{LK}, \overline{AB}, \overline{DC}$ **9.** same
11. $EFGH, \overline{AE}, \overline{BF}, \overline{CG}, \overline{DH}$ **13.** $ADHE$ **15.** 5
17. 6 **19.** $\overline{BH}, \overline{AG}, \overline{CE}, \overline{DF}$
23. $15^2 + 8^2 = 289 = 17^2$ **25.** $2\sqrt{33}$ **27.** $5\sqrt{3}$
29. 6
31. $\overline{AF}, \overline{FC}$, and $\overline{AC}$ are congruent diagonals and form equilateral triangular base; $\overline{FB}, \overline{CB}$, and $\overline{AB}$ are congruent edges and form equal lateral edges.
33. 8; *BDEA, ACFB, BDGC, ACHD, AFHE, BEGF, CFHG, DEGH*
35. Diagonals of parallelogram *AHGB* bisect each other.
37. In parallelogram *ABGH*, *O* is the midpoint of $\overline{AG}$ and $\overline{BH}$ (ex. 35); in parallelogram *ACGE* the diagonals $\overline{AG}$ and $\overline{CE}$ intersect at the midpoint; midpoint of $\overline{AG}$ is *O*.
39. Call inside corner *E*; *CABE* and *ABDE* are parallelograms, definition; $CE = ED = 9\sqrt{2}$, congruent opposite sides; add.
Problem Solving Method 1, 32; Method 2, $\sqrt{544} \doteq 23.3$

pages 446-447

1. 24 cm³ **3.** 64.6 cm³ **5.** 2 cubes **7.** 42 cubes
9. 60 **11.** $432\sqrt{3}$ **13.** eight times
15. 102 cm³ **17.** 5 ft
19. $\frac{1}{2}(8 \text{ ft})(30 \text{ ft} + 14 \text{ ft}) \times 620 \text{ ft} \times \frac{1 \text{ yd}^3}{27 \text{ ft}^3} \times \frac{\$1.50}{\text{yd}^3} =$
\$6062.22; \$6062.22 × 1.1 = \$6668.44

Problem Solving

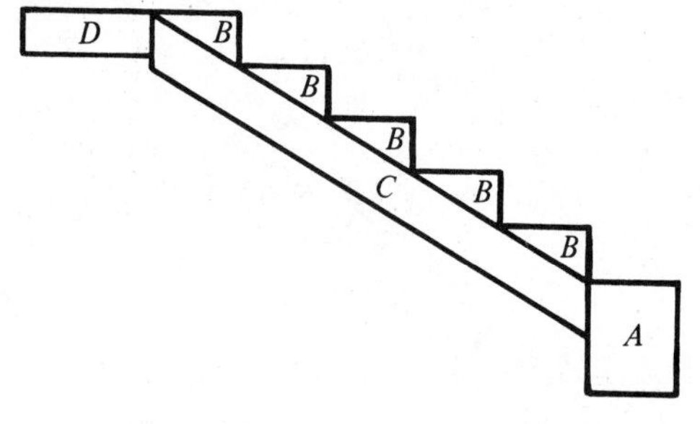

A. $1' \times 4'7\frac{1}{2}'' \times 4\frac{1}{2}' = 1 \times \frac{37}{8} \times \frac{9}{2} = \frac{333}{16} = 20.81 \text{ ft}^3$
B. $\frac{1}{2} \times 5 \times 1' \times \frac{9}{2}' \times \frac{15}{24}' = \frac{225}{32} = 7.03 \text{ ft}^3$
C. $5\frac{11}{12}' \times \frac{1}{2}' \times \frac{9}{2}' = \frac{71}{12} \times \frac{1}{2} \times \frac{9}{2} = \frac{213}{16} = 13.31 \text{ ft}^3$
D. $\frac{1}{3}' \times \frac{5}{2}' \times \frac{9}{2}' = \frac{45}{12} = 3.75 \text{ ft}^3$
$20.81 + 7.03 + 13.31 + 3.75 = 44.90 \text{ ft}^3$
$44.90 \div 27 = 1.66 \text{ yd}^3$

pages 450-451

1. true **3.** false **5.** false **7.** $26\frac{2}{3}$ **9.** $4583\frac{1}{3}$
11. $3456\sqrt{3}$ **13.** 9:4
15. $\frac{1}{3}\cdot 64\cdot 8-\frac{1}{3}\cdot 25\cdot 5=129$
17. $40^2=8^2+h^2$; $h=\sqrt{1536}$; $V=2\sqrt{1536}$;
$2\sqrt{1536}\text{ m}^3\times\frac{1000\ \ell}{1\text{ m}^3}\times\frac{1\text{ min}}{50\ \ell}\times\frac{1\text{ hr}}{60\text{ min}}\doteq 26.1\text{ hr}$
Problem Solving

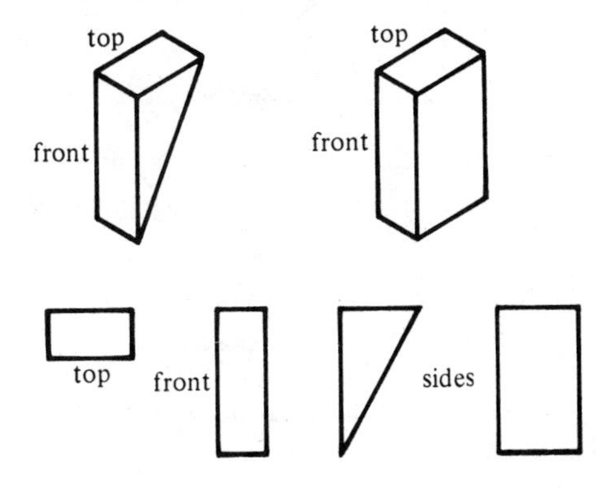

pages 454-455

1. 768π square units, 2880π cubic units
3. 300π square units, 625π cubic units
5. $\frac{1700\pi}{27}\doteq 197.8\text{ yd}^3$ **7.** 5.1 cm
9. $512-128\pi\text{ in.}^3$; $384-32\pi+64\pi\text{ in.}^2$
11. $r=$ radius of can; $h=$ depth of box; volume of cans $=6\pi r^2h$; volume of box $=24r^2h$; ratio $4:\pi$
Problem Solving $\frac{54\pi}{16}+\frac{27}{32}\text{ in.}^3$; $\frac{228\pi}{16}+\frac{9}{8}+\frac{9\sqrt{5}}{8}\text{ in.}^2$

pages 458-459

1. 320π; 200π **3.** $\frac{25\pi\sqrt{119}}{3}$; 85π **5.** 6
7. $36\pi+4\pi\sqrt{10}\text{ cm}^3$
9. $8\pi\sqrt{113}+16\pi\sqrt{165}$ **11.** 0.001 in.^3
13. 3:2; $\frac{3\sqrt{13}+9}{2\sqrt{13}+4}$
Problem Solving 1-4, 2-5, 3-3, 4-6, 5-1, 6-2

pages 462-463

1. $972\pi\text{ cm}^3$ **3.** $\frac{32\pi^4}{3}$ **5.** 3 **7.** $\sqrt{2}$
9. $1800\pi+\frac{4000}{3}\pi$ **11.** 228π cubic units **13.** 3 ft
15. Let $r=$ radius of sphere; let $h=2r$; lateral surface area $=2\pi rh=2\pi r(2r)=4\pi r^2$
17. 1:2
Problem Solving Volume of sphere $=972\pi$; determine altitude of cylinder, $9^2=3^2+h_1^{\,2}$,
$h_1=6\sqrt{2}$, alt $=12\sqrt{2}$;
cyl vol $=\pi\cdot 9\cdot 12\sqrt{2}=108\pi\sqrt{2}$;
$h=9-6\sqrt{2}\doteq 0.515$;
cap vol $=\frac{1}{2}\pi\cdot 9(0.515)+\frac{1}{6}\pi(0.515)^3\doteq 7.35$; vol of solid $=972\pi-108\pi\sqrt{2}-2(7.35)\doteq 2559\text{ cm}^2$

pages 466-467

1. regular tetrahedron; regular octahedron, regular icosahedron
3. "Roofs" don't join. **5.** tetrahedron **13.** yes
15. yes
Problem Solving
1. 12 **2.** 30 **3.** 30 **4.** 20

page 469 Chapter 12 Review

1. 96 cm^2; 64 cm^3 **2a.** 156 cm^2
2b. $72+12\sqrt{3}\text{ cm}^2$ **3a.** $\frac{200}{3}\text{ cm}^3$ **3b.** $32\sqrt{3}\text{ cm}^3$
4. $60\pi\text{ cm}^2$ **5.** $90\pi\text{ cm}^3$ **6.** 8 **7.** $36\pi\text{ cm}^3$
8. Volume is doubled. **9.** 3 cm **10.** $400\pi\text{ cm}^2$

page 471 Problem Solving Techniques

1. 7 times **2.** 5 times **3.** $\frac{1}{3}$ **4.** 23 minutes

CHAPTER 13

pages 478-479

1a. *A* **1b.** *D* **1c.** *I* **1d.** *G*
15. Diagonals of a rhombus are perpendicular bisectors of each other.

17.

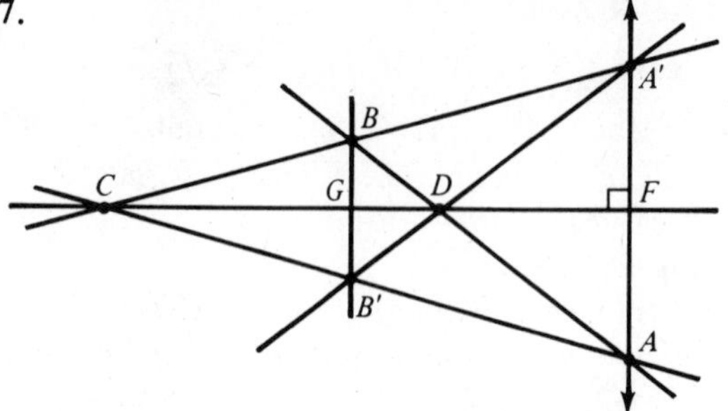

Draw $\overleftrightarrow{A'A}$, $\overleftrightarrow{AB}$ intersecting base line at D, $\overleftrightarrow{A'B}$ intersecting base line at C; the intersection of $\overrightarrow{A'D}$ and $\overrightarrow{AC}$ is B'; need to show that B' is the reflection of B over the base line; $\triangle A'FD \cong \triangle AFD$, SAS; $\overline{A'D} \cong \overline{AD}$, $\angle FA'D \cong \angle FAD$, $\angle A'DF \cong \angle ADF$, $CPCTC$; $\angle BDF \cong \angle B'DF$, vertical angles and addition; $\triangle A'FC \cong \triangle AFC$, SAS; $\overline{A'C} \cong \overline{AC}$, $CPCTC$; $\angle FA'C \cong \angle FAC$, $CPCTC$; $\angle CA'D \cong \angle CAD$, angle subtraction; $\triangle CA'D \cong \triangle CAD$, SAS; $\angle A'CD \cong \angle ACD$, $CPCTC$; $\triangle BDA' \cong \triangle B'DA$, ASA; $\overline{BD} \cong \overline{B'D}$, $CPCTC$; since $\angle BDF \cong \angle B'DF$, $\angle BDC \cong \angle B'DC$, congruent sup.; $\triangle BDG \cong \triangle B'DG$, SAS; $\overline{BG} \cong \overline{B'G}$, $CPCTC$; $\angle BGD$ and $\angle B'GD$ are right angles, congruent and sup. angles; $\overline{BG} \perp \overline{CF}$; B' is the reflection of B over $\overleftrightarrow{CF}$.

19. Thm. 13-1a

Problem Solving

1. The reason this looks so strange is that it was written using a mirror.

2. Nine + one + eight = eighteen

pages 482-483

1.

31	103	134
44	78	122
61	59	120
78	40	118
99	22	121

3.

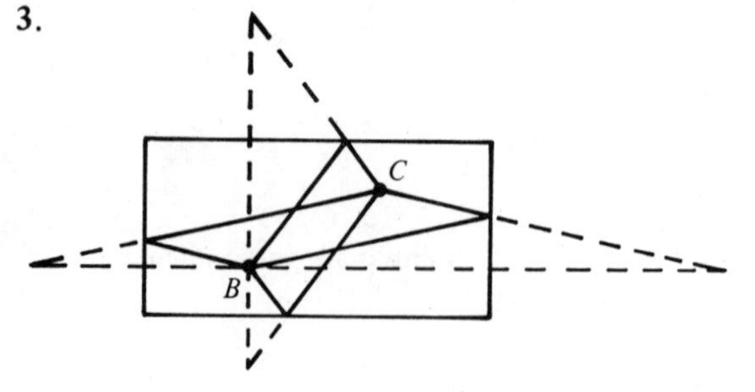

5.

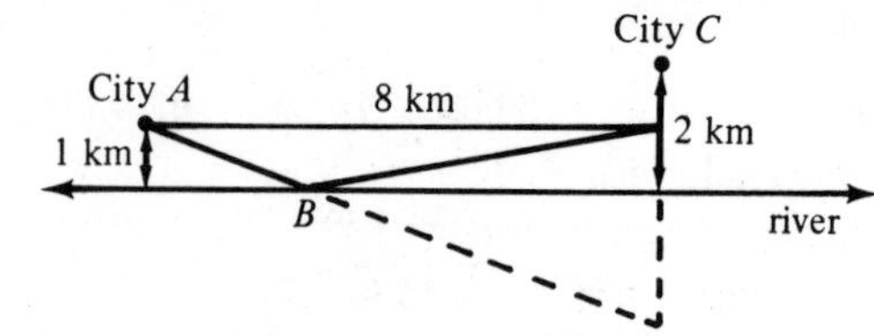

7.

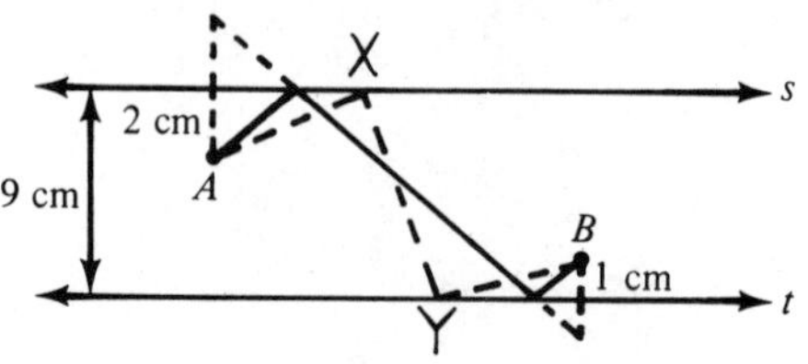

9.

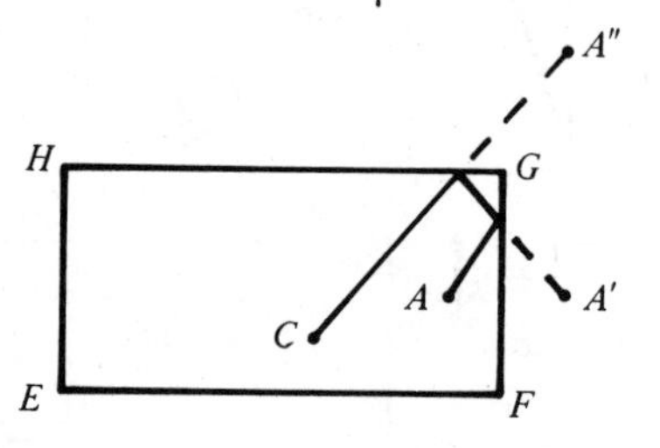

pages 486-487

1a. *F* **1b.** *H* **1c.** *G* **1d.** *E*

3.

X
Y

5.

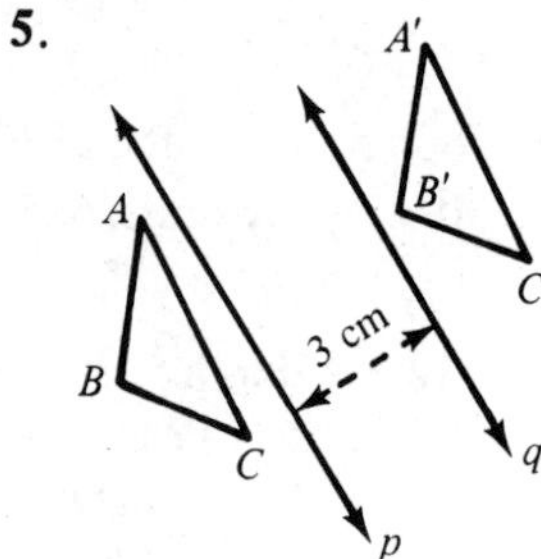

7.

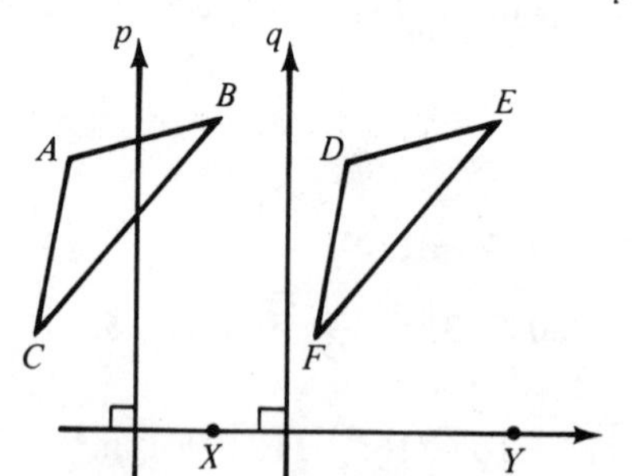

Problem Solving The region consisting of squares 1, 2, and 3 is $\frac{1}{3}$ shaded. The region consisting of squares 4, 5, and 6 is $\frac{1}{3}$ shaded, etc. Therefore, $\frac{1}{3}$ of the entire region is shaded.

pages 490-493

1. E 3. H
7.

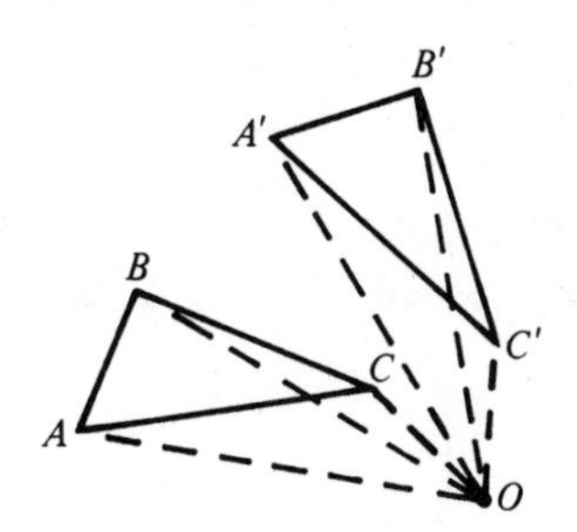

9. d
11.

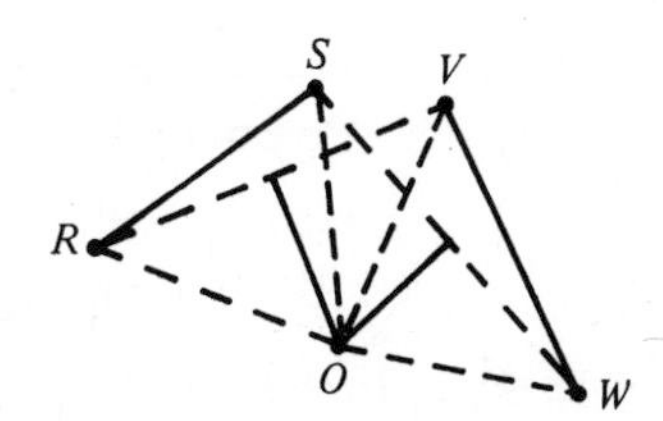

Find the intersection of the perpendicular bisectors of $\overline{RV}$ and $\overline{SW}$; $m\angle ROV = 95$.
13.

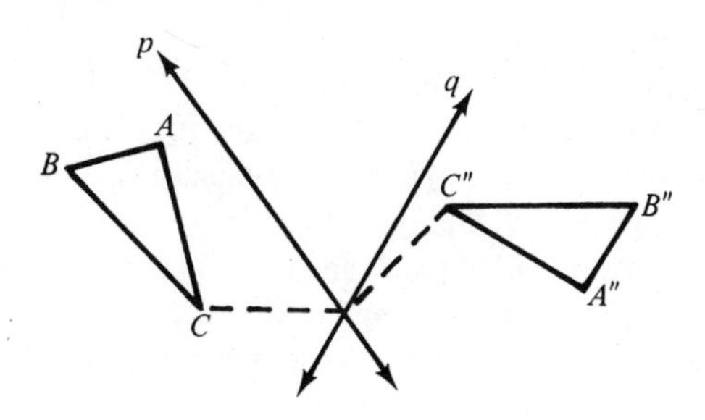

15. One half the angle of rotation
17a.

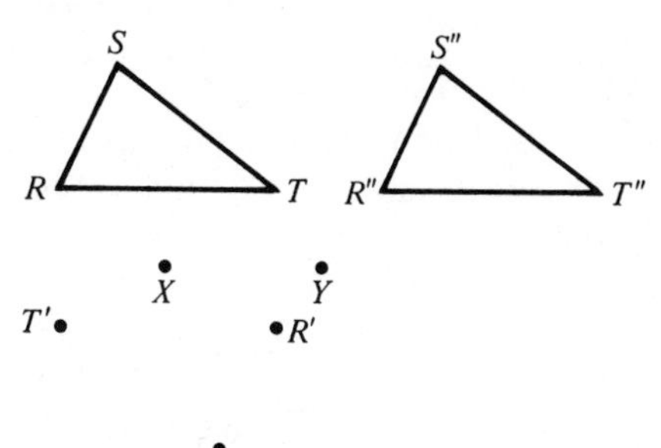

17b. A translation along $\overrightarrow{XY}$ twice the length of $\overline{XY}$.

Problem Solving
1. 120°, 180°, 240°, 300°
2. 120°, 240°; 90°, 180°, 270°

pages 496-497

1. yes 3. yes 5. yes
7.

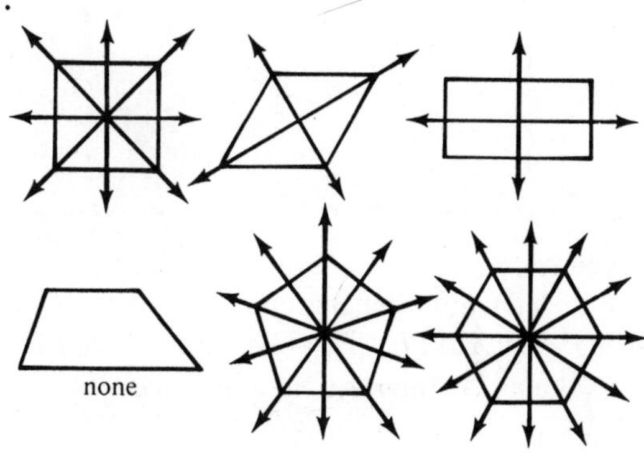

9. false
11.

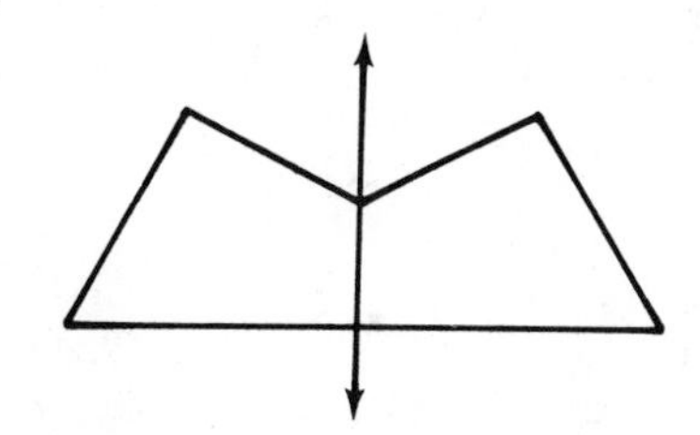

13. not possible 15. circle
17. ex. regular pentagon 19. p and r
Problem Solving Turn each card 180°.

page 499 Chapter 13 Review

1a. true 1b. true 1c. true 1d. false 1e. false
2. H, X, I 3. N, S, and Z 4. 8
5.

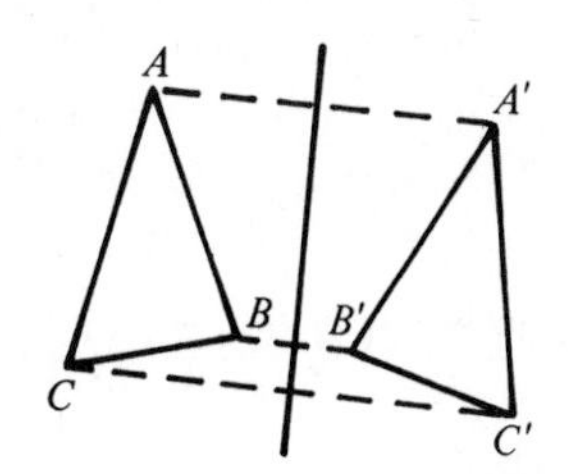

6.

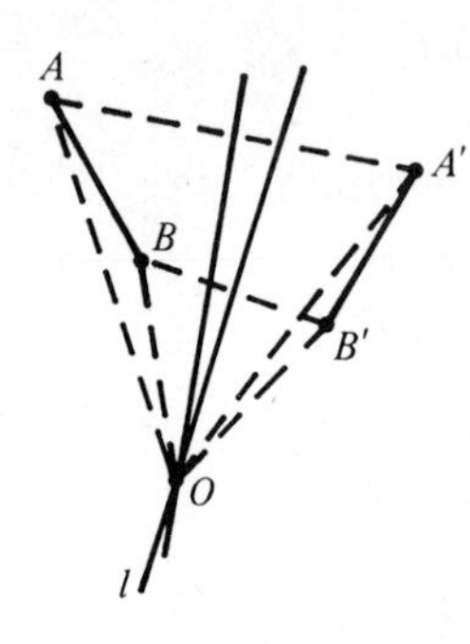

$m\angle BOB' = m\angle AOA' = 57$, clockwise rotation

page 501 Problem Solving Techniques

1. yes
2. $PA + PC = PB$ when P is on $\widehat{AC}$. $PA + PB = PC$ when P is on $\widehat{AB}$. $PB + PC = PA$ when P is on $\widehat{BC}$.
3. $2\sqrt{3}$ cm 4. Intersection of diagonals

CHAPTER 14

pages 506-507

9. obtuse **11.** right **17.** $(5, 3)$ **19.** $(3, -3)$ **21.** $(0, 2)$ **23.** $(3, -1), (-3, -1), (5, 3)$ **27.** -6

Problem Solving

1. $(3, 3\sqrt{3})$; $(3, -3\sqrt{3})$
2. $(0, 6), (6, 6)$; $(0, -6), (6, -6)$; $(3, 3), (3, -3)$
3. ex. $(1, 4), (7, 4)$

pages 510-511

1a. $(\frac{5}{2}, \frac{1}{2})$ **1b.** $(2, -\frac{1}{2})$ **1c.** $(\frac{1}{2}, -2)$ **1d.** $(-2, 0)$ **3.** $(1, 0)$ **5.** $(-5, -\frac{7}{2})$ **7.** $(\frac{7}{2}, -\frac{3}{2})$
9. $(\frac{7}{2}, 4), (7, -\frac{1}{2}), (\frac{3}{2}, -\frac{1}{2}), (-2, 4)$, parallelogram
11. $(-2, 8)$ **13.** $(4, -3)$ **15.** $(7, 6)$
17. $(-1, -\frac{3}{2})$
19. $\left(\frac{x_1 + x_2}{3}, \frac{y_1 + y_2}{3}\right), \left(\frac{2(x_1 + x_2)}{3}, \frac{2(y_1 + y_2)}{3}\right)$

Problem Solving $(2, 2, 2)$

pages 514-515

1a. $(13, 2), (10, 5)$; -1 **1b.** $(0, 5), (8, 10)$; $\frac{5}{8}$
1c. $(13, 2), (9, 3)$; $-\frac{1}{4}$ **1d.** $(4, 3), (9, 3)$; 0
1e. $(4, 0), (9, 0)$; 0 **1f.** $(2, 4), (0, 1)$; $\frac{3}{2}$
1g. $(0, 5), (4, 0)$; $-\frac{5}{4}$ **1h.** $(4, 3), (10, 5)$; $\frac{1}{3}$
1i. $(4, 3), (4, 0)$; undefined **3.** $-\frac{1}{2}$ **5.** $\frac{7}{2}$ **7.** 1
9. $\overline{EF}$, 0; $\overline{FG}$, undefined; $\overline{GH}$, 0; $\overline{HE}$, undefined
11. $\overline{AB}$, $\frac{4}{5}$; $\overline{BC}$, -2; $\overline{CA}$, 5
13a. $\overline{XY}$, $-\frac{1}{4}$; $\overline{YZ}$, 0; $\overline{XZ}$, $-\frac{1}{2}$
13b. Median of $\overline{XY}$, undefined; median of $\overline{ZX}$, $-\frac{1}{6}$; median of $\overline{YZ}$, $-\frac{1}{3}$
15. $\frac{1}{2}$ **17.** $\frac{1}{2} = \frac{y + 3}{x + 6}$, $-2 = \frac{y + 4}{x - 8}$; $A(\frac{24}{5}, \frac{12}{5})$

Problem Solving Determine coordinates of G, $\frac{1}{2} = \frac{y - 0}{4 - 0}$, $G(4, 2), F(6, 2)$; determine coordinates of K, $\frac{1}{2} = \frac{y - 0}{10 - 0}$, $K(10, 5), J(15, 5)$; determine coordinates of P, $\frac{1}{2} = \frac{y - 0}{18 - 0}$, $P(18, 9), N(27, 9)$; slope of $\overline{FJ}$ is $\frac{1}{3}$; slope of $\overline{JN}$ is $\frac{1}{3}$.

pages 518-519

1. yes
3. Slope of line formed by $(3, 9)$ and $(7, 5)$ equals slope of line formed by $(4, -1)$ and $(0, 3)$, slope of line formed by $(3, 9)$ and $(0, 3)$ equals slope of line formed by $(7, 5)$ and $(4, -1)$.
5. Line containing $(4, 5)$ and $(1, -3)$ is parallel to line containing $(-3, 7)$ and $(-6, -1)$; line containing $(4, 5)$ and $(-3, 7)$ is parallel to line containing $(1, -3)$ and $(-6, -1)$.
7. The product of the slopes of the line containing $(7, 9)$ and $(10, -3)$ and the line containing $(2, -5)$ and $(10, -3)$ is -1.
9. Parallelogram, line containing $(-3, -3)$ and $(-1, -7)$ is parallel to line containing $(-1, -2)$ and $(1, -6)$, line containing $(-3, -3)$ and $(-1, -2)$ is parallel to line containing $(-1, -7)$ and $(1, -6)$; use Thm. 14-2.

11. $-1, -5, 1$; $1, \frac{1}{5}, -1$ **13.** $\frac{1}{3}$ **15.** -8
17. $C(\frac{12}{5}, 0)$
19. Find slope of $\overline{AD}$ and $\overline{CD}$; use $D(x, y)$; use def. of slope twice to form two equations; solve; $D(6, -1)$.

Problem Solving $C(8, 0)$; alt $= 4$; $A = \frac{1}{2} \cdot 10 \cdot 4 = 20$.

pages 522-523

1. 10 3. $7\sqrt{2}$ 5. $2\sqrt{13}$ 7. $\sqrt{74}$
9. $BC = AC = 5$, isosceles 11. scalene
13. $\sqrt{225^2} = \sqrt{45^2} + \sqrt{180^2}$; yes
15. Definition of slope 17. midpoint (1, 1); $\sqrt{26}$
19. $\sqrt{34} + \sqrt{117} \neq \sqrt{277}$, no
21. $10 = \sqrt{(1-x)^2 + (2-8)^2}$; $100 = x^2 - 2x + 37$; $x = 9$ or -7
23. Slope of $\overline{BC} = \frac{1}{2}$, slope of $\overline{AC} = -2$, $\overline{BC} \perp \overline{AC}$; $BC = 4\sqrt{5}$, $AC = 2\sqrt{5}$; 20.
25. Find perpendicular bisectors of two segments; point of intersection is (2, 4).
27. Twice distance from $(-3, 7)$ to $(0, y)$ equals distance from (6, 1) to $(0, y)$; $2\sqrt{(-3)^2 + (7-y)^2} = \sqrt{6^2 + (1-y)^2}$; $y = 5$ or 13; (0, 5), (0, 13).

Problem Solving
1. $4\sqrt{3}$
2. $OP = \sqrt{x_1{}^2 + y_1{}^2 + z_1{}^2}$

pages 526-527

1. $y = 2x + 3$ 3. $y = -\frac{3}{4}x + 5$ 5. $y = 10x - 4$
7.

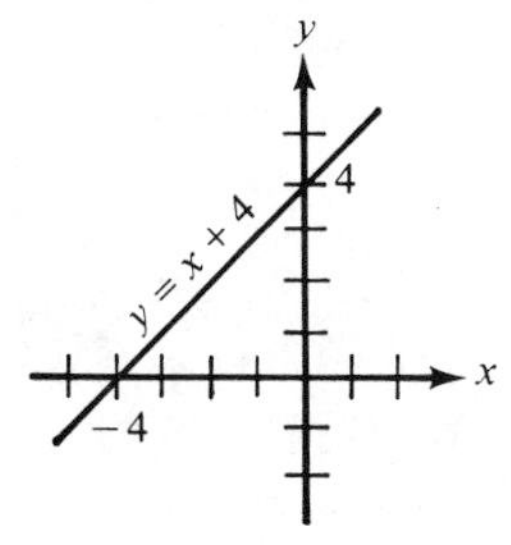

9.

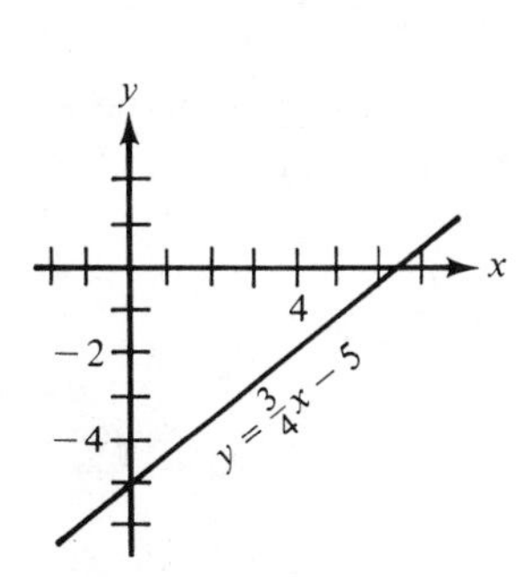

11. $m = -2, b = 4$ 13. $m = \frac{3}{2}, b = -2$
15. $m = -\frac{3}{2}, b = \frac{5}{2}$ 17. $y = 2x - 5$ 19. $y = \frac{2}{3}x$
21. $y = \frac{3}{2}x + \frac{1}{2}$ 23. $= \frac{3}{4}x$ 25. $y = x$
27. $y = 2$ 29. $m = \frac{1}{2}$ 31. $m = \frac{5}{2}$ 33 (4, 1)
35. $\frac{25}{2}$ 37. $y = \frac{2}{3}x, y = -\frac{2}{3}x - 2$ 39. $y = -x + 4$
41. $y = -\frac{5}{3}x + 4$ 43. Form 45-45-90 triangle; $\frac{5}{2}\sqrt{2}$
45. Graph; $\frac{2}{3}$ of distance between (0, 0) and midpoint (12, 6) is (8, 4).

Problem Solving Find intersection of given line with equation $4y = 3x$ and altitude with equation $3y = -4x + 11$ giving $(\frac{44}{25}, \frac{33}{25})$; use distance formula, $\frac{2}{5}$.

pages 530-531

1. $x^2 + y^2 = 25$ 3. $x^2 + y^2 = 36$
5. $(x-2)^2 + (y-3)^2 = 36$
7. $(x-5)^2 + (y-2)^2 = 2$ 9. $x^2 + (y+4)^2 = 25$
11. (0, 0); 6 13. $(-3, 4)$; 5 15. (0, 3); $2\sqrt{3}$
17. $(-2, -4)$; 6 19. $(x-3)^2 + (y-4)^2 = 25$
21. $(x+1)^2 + y^2 = 9$
23. $(x-1)^2 + (y-5)^2 = 34$
25. $y = -\frac{5}{2}x - \frac{2}{9}$ 27. $(x+4)^2 + (y-3)^2 = 16$
29. Graph; find equation of radius perpendicular to tangent line; solve system of two equation for point of intersection; (0, 4); $r = \sqrt{10}$; $(x-1)^2 + (y-7)^2 = 10$

Problem Solving $x^2 + y^2 + z^2 = 48$; $(x-1)^2 + (y-3)^2 + (z-2)^2 = 35$

pages 534-535

1-5. Answers will vary.
7. Slope of $\overline{AC} = \frac{b}{c}$; slope of $\overline{BD} = \frac{b}{c-2a}$; $AD = \sqrt{(c-a)^2 + b^2}$, $AB = \sqrt{a^2}$, $\sqrt{(c-a)^2 + b^2} = \sqrt{a^2}$, solve for a, $a = \frac{c^2 - b^2}{2c}$; substitute in slope of $\overline{BD}$; $-\frac{c}{b}$
9. Midpoint of $\overline{AB}$ is $(\frac{a}{2}, \frac{a}{2})$; slope of $\overline{AB} = -1$; $y = x$ contains (0, 0).
11. $AC = \sqrt{c^2 + b^2}$; $BD = \sqrt{(-c)^2 + b^2}$
13. $AC = \sqrt{c^2 + b^2}$; $BD = \sqrt{(c-2a)^2 + b^2}$; $\sqrt{c^2 + b^2} = \sqrt{c^2 - 4ac + 4a^2 + b^2}$, solve for c, $c = a$; rename $D(0, b)$, $C(a, b)$.

15. In $\triangle ABC$, $A(0, 0)$, $B(2a, 0)$, $C(2b, 2c)$; $D(b, c)$ is midpoint of $\overline{AC}$; $E(b + a, c)$ is midpoint of $\overline{BC}$; $DE = \sqrt{a^2} = a$; $DE = \frac{1}{2}AB$; slope of $\overline{DE}$ is 0, $\overline{DE} \parallel \overline{AB}$.

Problem Solving 5 faces

page 537

1.

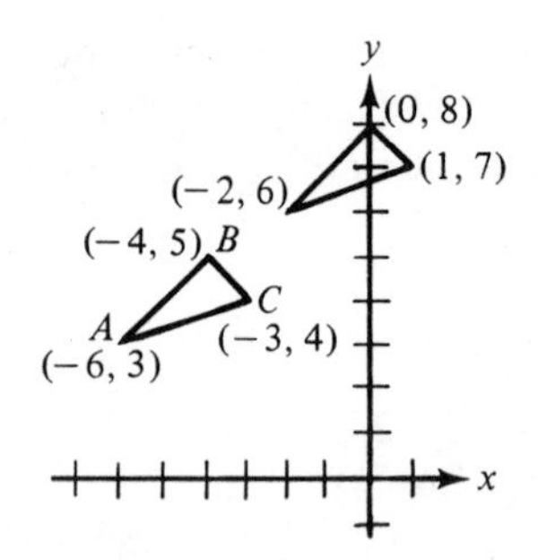

3.

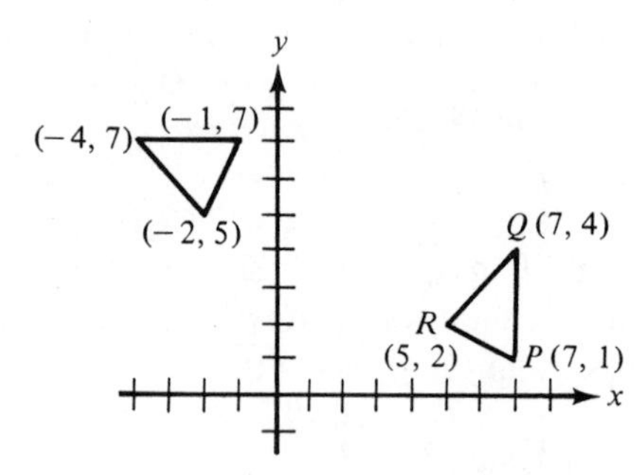

5.

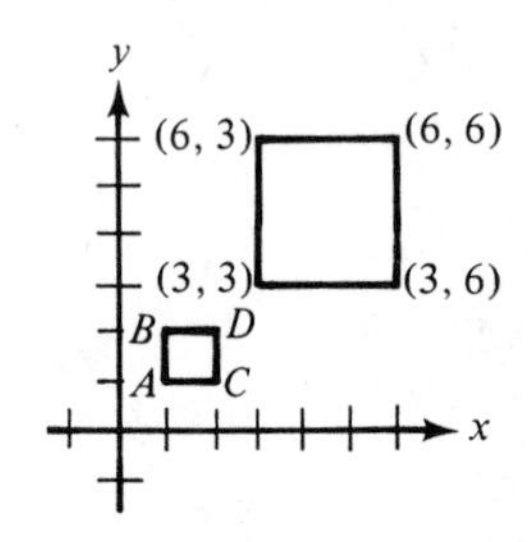

Lengths of sides of $\square ABDC$ are $\frac{1}{3}$ length of magnification.

7. Shrinks horizontally and stretches vertically; equal

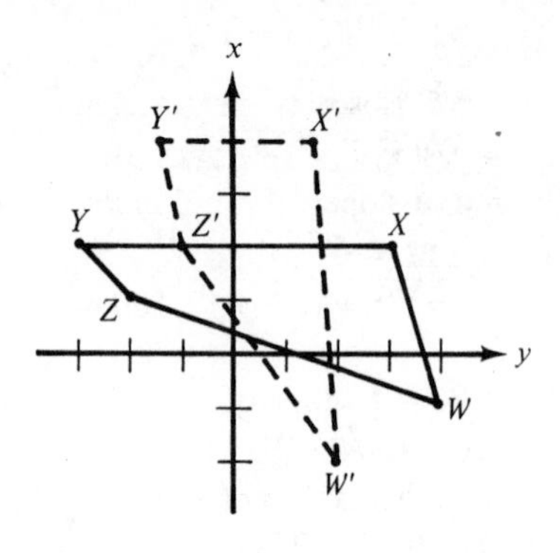

page 539 Chapter 14 Review

1a. $2\sqrt{13}$ **1b.** 10 **1c.** 6 **2a.** $\frac{3}{2}$ **2b.** $-\frac{3}{4}$
2c. 0 **3a.** $(3, 5)$ **3b.** $(1, 1)$ **3c.** $(-1, -2)$
4. $y = -3x + 2$ **5.** $y = -\frac{3}{4}x + 4$
6. Line containing $(5, 7)$ and $(8, -5)$ is perpendicular to line containing $(0, -7)$ and $(8, -5)$.
7. $x = -\frac{71}{2}$ **8.** $x = -26$ **9.** $(2, -3)$; $2\sqrt{6}$
10. $x^2 + y^2 = 25$
11. Slope of $\overline{AC}$ is 1; slope of $\overline{BD}$ is -1; product of slopes is -1.
12. $WX = a$; $YZ = a$; slope of WX is 0; slope of YZ is 0; $\overline{WX} \parallel \overline{YZ}$; Thm. 5-8.

page 541 Cumulative Review Chapters 11-14

1. 50 cm² **2.** 12 cm² **3.** $4\sqrt{3}$ cm² **4.** 4:1
5. $54\sqrt{3}$ cm² **6.** 72 m³ **7.** 21 m³
8. 150.72 cm² **9.** 125.60 cm²
10. $(-3, 5), (-5, -2), (4, 3)$
11. $(4, 2), (-3, 7), (1, -6)$
12. $y = x$; $y = -x + 6$; $y = 3, x = 3$ **13.** $(-2, -6)$
14. $\sqrt{221}$ **15.** $y = -\frac{3}{2}x - 3$

Index

Acknowledgments

Page	Credit
2 TL	Lick Observatory/University of California
TC	Grant Heilman Photography
BL	Grant Heilman Photography
3 TL	George B. Fry III*
TR	Jim Goldberg*
BL	George B. Fry III*
BR	Rene Burri/Magnum Photos
9	Robert A. Isaacs
14	George B. Fry III*
17 TC, B	George B. Fry III*
33 BR	George B. Fry III*
43	George B. Fry III*
44	B. C. by permission of Johnny Hart and Field Enterprises
48	© copyright, 1980, Universal Press Syndicate. All Rights Reserved.
50	Hale Observatories
53	© 1961 United Feature Syndicate, Inc.
56	© 1961 United Feature Syndicate, Inc.
64	© 1961 United Feature Syndicate, Inc.
65 T, B	© 1971 United Feature Syndicate, Inc.
83	Rene Burri/Magnum Photos
84	Courtesy General Motors
104	© 1980 United Feature Syndicate, Inc.
118	Baron Wolman*
126 T	Tom Stack/Tom Stack & Associates
B	Roger B. Smith/Editorial Photocolor Archives, Inc.
129	Robert A. Isaacs
130	© 1958 United Feature Syndicate
143	*Games and Puzzles,* No. 46 (March 1976), by permission of EduGames (U.K.) Ltd.
150	Samuel Chamberlain
158	B. C. by permission of Johnny Hart and Field Enterprises
162	Copyright © 1969 by Martin Gardner, Reprinted by permission of SIMON & SCHUSTER, a Division of Gulf & Western Corporation.
169	Robert A. Isaacs
170	© 1979 Steve Finberg
181	Culver Pictures
194 T	© Lester V. Bergman & Associates
197	Jim Goldberg*
202	Rene Burri/Magnum Photos
225	Robert A. Isaacs
236	© Leonard Freed/Magnum Photos
244	Robert A. Isaacs
256 T	Courtesy of The Perkin-Elmer Corporation
BL	Courtesy of Applicon, Inc.
BR	Lockheed Missiles and Space Company, Inc.
259	Joseph W. Molitor
290	Bureau of Reclamation
300	Michos Tzovoras/Editorial Photocolor Archives, Inc.
301, 303	Joseph W. Molitor
304 T	Bill Plummer*
307 B	Courtesy of LeRoy Troyer and Associates
312 L	Chevrolet Motors Division, General Motors Corporation
R	Lockheed-California Company
322, 325	Grant Heilman Photography
330	Julian E. Caraballo/Tom Stack & Associates
341	Robert A. Isaacs
350, 351	Illinois State University Photo Services
369	Phiz Mezey*
390 TL	Phiz Mezey*
393	© 1979 Barrie Rokeach
403	U.S. Department of Interior
408	U.S. Air Force
416	Photo courtesy of Hewlett-Packard Company
433	Robert A. Isaacs
434 T	Scala/Editorial Photocolor Archives, Inc.
444	Baron Wolman*
460	NASA
464 TL	David Scharf/Peter Arnold Inc.
TR	Lester V. Bergman & Associates
475	Robert A. Isaacs
476	Drawing by W. Miller; © 1962, The New Yorker Magazine, Inc.
479 BR	From Martin Gardner, *The Ambidextrous Universe.* Copyright © 1979 by Martin Gardner (New York: Charles Scribner's Sons, 1979) Reprinted with the permission of Charles Scribner's Sons.
484	Drawing by Charles Addams; © 1957 The New Yorker Magazine, Inc.
494 T, C	George B. Fry III*
503	Robert A. Isaacs
536	Robert E. Shaw/University of Connecticut

* Photographs provided expressly for the publisher. All other photographs by Wayland Lee, Addison-Wesley staff.